CANADA

SCALE 1:15,840,000 OR ONE INCH TO 250 MILES

MILES 100 50 0 100 200 300 400 500 MILES

KILOMETRES 100 0 100 200 300 400 500 600 700 800 KILOMETRES

Federal Capital...⊛
Provincial Capital...⊛
Railways, Main..――――
Railways to Resources..― ― ― ―
Special Geographical Locations..............................⊙

1965

The Birds of Canada

The Birds of Canada

By W. Earl Godfrey

Colour Illustrations by John A. Crosby
Line Drawings by S. D. MacDonald

Ottawa 1966

Canada

National Museum of Canada
Bulletin No. 203
Biological Series No. 73

Issued under the authority of
The Honourable Judy LaMarsh, P.C., Q.C., M.P.
Secretary of State

Contents

Topography of a Bird

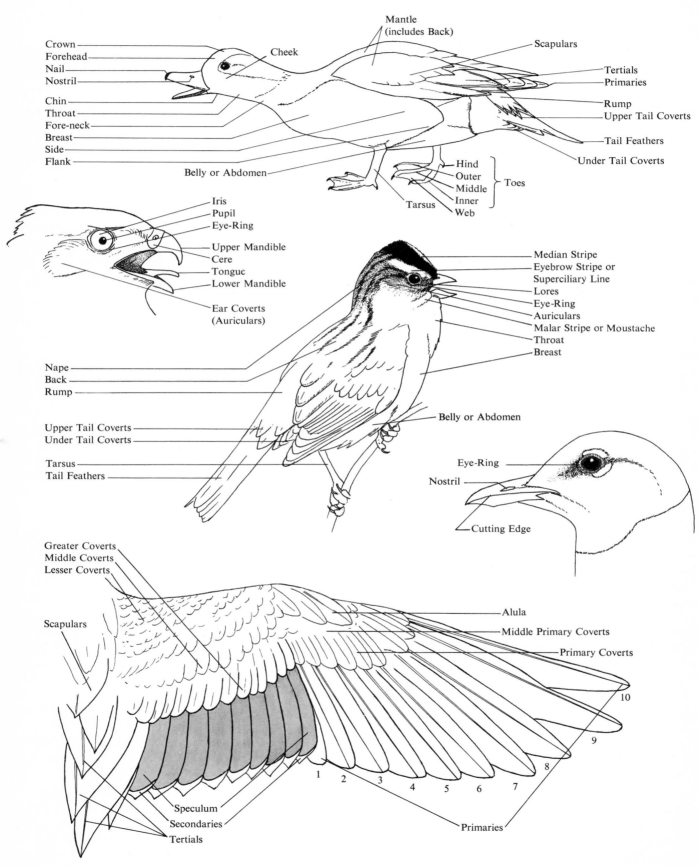

Crown
Forehead
Nail
Nostril
Chin
Throat
Fore-neck
Breast
Side
Flank
Cheek
Mantle (includes Back)
Scapulars
Tertials
Primaries
Rump
Upper Tail Coverts
Tail Feathers
Under Tail Coverts
Belly or Abdomen
Hind
Outer
Middle
Inner
Web
Toes
Tarsus

Iris
Pupil
Eye-Ring
Upper Mandible
Cere
Tongue
Lower Mandible
Ear Coverts (Auriculars)
Nape
Back
Rump
Upper Tail Coverts
Under Tail Coverts
Tarsus
Tail Feathers

Median Stripe
Eyebrow Stripe or Superciliary Line
Lores
Eye-Ring
Auriculars
Malar Stripe or Moustache
Throat
Breast
Belly or Abdomen

Eye-Ring
Nostril
Cutting Edge

Greater Coverts
Middle Coverts
Lesser Coverts
Scapulars
Alula
Middle Primary Coverts
Primary Coverts
10
9
8
7
6
5
4
3
2
1
Speculum
Secondaries
Tertials
Primaries

Introduction

The Value of Birds

There is no way of estimating in dollars and cents the total value of our bird life, but we do know that it is immense. Vast numbers of birds wage continuous warfare on the insect hordes that strive to devour our crops, devastate our forests, and annoy us generally. Other kinds destroy countless tons of weed seeds annually. The hawks during the day and the owls by night maintain a round-the-clock check on the numbers of rodent pests. Gulls and other birds perform a useful service as scavengers.

The hunting of game birds in season provides healthful sport to many thousands of Canadians. This is the nucleus of an industry involving guns, ammunition, hostelries, special apparel, and transportation. The Canadian Wildlife Service has estimated that in 1961 some 344,900 hunters of waterfowl in Canada spent $27,258,470 on that aspect of game bird hunting alone.

The study of birds as a hobby is an absorbing recreation that is enjoyed regularly by thousands of Canadians in all seasons and in all types of terrain. Their numbers are mushrooming. They use binoculars, spotting scopes, cameras, a large variety of bird books, outdoor apparel, and various forms of transportation. Many enthusiasts plan their vacation itineraries in the hope of satisfying their particular interest in birds. At least one province, Nova Scotia, is aware of this and has included a bird list in its tourist literature. Years ago it was said that the Gannets of Bonaventure Island, Quebec, through the tourists they attract, brought $100,000 a year to the nearby village of Percé. This figure is doubtless much greater today.

Birds add immeasurably to the enjoyment of everyday life and contribute to a sense of well-being. Although one cannot put a price tag on the sight of the first spring Robin, the plunge of an Osprey, or the vesper carillon of a Hermit Thrush, these and the countless other aesthetic aspects of our birds are as real as the economic ones and fully as great.

Needless to say, most birds as well as their nests and eggs are protected by law, and it is illegal to kill or molest them. Open seasons are provided, however, for many game birds. A few species considered harmful to man's interests are not protected at all. An increasing number of provinces now make it illegal to destroy our valuable birds of prey.

Bird Study as a Hobby

Estimates of the numbers of birdwatchers on this continent vary between two million and ten million people. Probably the former is fairly accurate. The study of birds is a fascinating hobby that can be pursued almost anywhere by men and women of all ages and in all walks of life. It may be carried on in one's backyard or in neighbouring fields and woods or be taken to distant lands. It is inexpensive, and one can put as much or as little energy into it as desired. Even the sick can watch birds at the backyard feeder or from a car. It is an avocation in which interest grows the more one pursues it. Regardless of where the bird student may be, he is never at a loss for something interesting to do in his leisure time.

Although man has an inherent interest in all animals, it is in birds that the greatest interest lies for the greatest number of people. The average person cannot, under ordinary circumstances, see an adequate daily variety of mammals, snakes, frogs, and fishes to sustain interest. The reverse is true for insects, whose overwhelming numbers and variety discourage all but the serious student.

Birds are sufficiently numerous, varied, and elusive to challenge our ability to identify them, and yet they do not overwhelm us with difficulties. Their seasonal coming and going add interest to the changing year. Their colours, songs, graceful motions, intriguing habits, varied personalities, and mysterious migrations are additional reasons for the great popularity of bird study as a hobby.

The ability to identify birds accurately and efficiently in the field improves with practice and experience. Many people watch birds purely for recreation and do not want to go beyond this stage. They regard identification as a kind of game, the idea being to run up as high a score as possible in number of species identified in a day, a year, or in total experience. It is true that this activity adds little to the science of ornithology, but, like other outdoor sports, it does provide a great deal of healthful exercise and enjoyment for large numbers of people.

Although the science of ornithology is a well-advanced one that keeps professionals continuously employed on a wide variety of problems, there always has been plenty of room for serious, competent amateurs. In fact, one of the reasons why ornithology is so well advanced today is that many amateurs have contributed high-quality research toward a better understanding of birds and their biology. Some of the very best work in ornithology has been done by medical doctors, lawyers, dentists, business executives, and housewives, to mention only a few. A glance at the list of acknowledgments in this book will show some of the many amateurs who contributed valuable information.

The Classification of Birds

Often people speak of 'birds and animals' as though birds were something apart, different from animals. Birds, of course, are animals. All living things are either animals or plants—and birds certainly are not plants! Birds differ in many ways from other animals, but the most obvious difference is that birds—and only birds—possess feathers. Birds may be thought of, then, as feathered animals. All birds belong to the animal class Aves, which comprises only birds.

For the classification of all living things, biologists have devised an ingenious system which is in use throughout the world. By this system the seemingly overwhelming variety of living things is broken down into an orderly arrangement.

Living things are first divided into two major categories called kingdoms, the animal (Animalia) and the plant (Plantae). These categories are subdivided into successively smaller groups according to relationships. In this way each unit is ultimately grouped with its nearest relative. A specimen of the Song Sparrow from Saskatchewan, *Melospiza melodia juddi*, for example, would be classified as follows:

Kingdom – **Animalia**

Phylum – **Chordata**

Subphylum – **Vertebrata**

Class – **Aves**

Order – **Passeriformes**

Family – **Fringillidae**

Genus – *Melospiza*

Species – *melodia*

Subspecies – *juddi*

Scientific Names

Scientific names are composed of Latin words or latinized words derived from Greek or, less often, other languages. One of the main advantages of scientific names is that they are understood in all countries of the world regardless of language. They are made up of either two or three parts, and all are printed in italics.

The first part of the scientific name is the name of the genus (plural genera). It *always* begins with a capital letter. The second part is the name of the species, and the third (when present) is that of the subspecies. The species and subspecies parts of the scientific name *never* begin with a capital letter.

The genus contains from one to a number of closely related species which have certain characters in common that separate them from species in other genera. Generic names therefore help us to recognize closely related species. We know at once, for instance, that *Dendroica auduboni* (Audubon's Warbler) is more closely related to *Dendroica coronata* (Myrtle Warbler) than it is to *Mniotilta varia* (Black-and-white Warbler), because both *auduboni* and *coronata* belong to the same genus, *Dendroica*.

Breeding populations of some (not all) species have evolved differences in colour or size within geographically limited parts of the breeding range that distinguish the populations of those particular areas from other populations of that species. When this is the case, the scientific name has a third part, the name of the subspecies. For instance, Myrtle Warblers breeding in the northwestern part of the range of that species average larger and have their dark breast markings slightly less solidly black than those nesting in the Prairie Provinces and eastern North America. The species is, therefore, divisible into two subspecies, *Dendroica coronata hooveri* McGregor of the Northwest and *Dendroica coronata coronata* (Linnaeus) of the remainder of its breeding range.

It will be noted that the surname of the author of a species or subspecies name follows that name without intervening punctuation and is not italicized. In cases where the species or subspecies is now placed in a genus other than that in which it was originally described, the surname of the author of the name is placed within parentheses.

Scope of the Book

The book includes all the bird species known by the writer to occur, or to have occurred, in Canada up to January 1, 1964, a total of 518 species. Three forms regarded as full species by the A.O.U. *Check-list of North American Birds* (Fifth Edition) are here combined with other species. One form, regarded by the Check-list as a subspecies, is here treated as a full species. Strict adherence to the Check-list, then, would add two more species to the total.

The occurrence of almost all of these 518 species in Canada is documented by at least one specimen taken in this country. In the case of one well-marked species, the Smew, no specimen is known to have been taken in Canada, but excellent coloured photographs are available.

Twenty additional species, which have been recorded in this country on the basis of sight records alone or on otherwise inconclusive evidence, are mentioned but are given hypothetical status and are enclosed in parentheses. A few other species have been mentioned in the literature as occurring in Canada but are here disregarded. Two species, the Red-faced Cormorant and the Storm Petrel, have been recorded erroneously in conspicuous places and are here mentioned in order to obviate further confusion concerning their status in Canada.

Names of Birds

The English, French, and scientific names for species are provided from the most authoritative and up-to-date sources. The scientific and English names are, in most cases, those advocated by that standard authority on the taxonomy and nomenclature of birds on this continent, the American Ornithologists' Union's *Check-list of North American Birds* (Fifth Edition, 1957). In accordance with the policy of the A.O.U. Check-list (Fifth Edition) and other recent authoritative works in other parts of the world, the use of English and French names for subspecies has been discontinued. Species sequence is that of the A.O.U. Check-list (Fifth Edition).

In this latest edition the A.O.U. Committee thought it advisable to change a few of the English names. In such cases the new names have been adopted here and should be adopted by all North Americans. The old names are shown in parentheses, but their use is not recommended.

In a very few cases, the English name used here differs slightly from that of the A.O.U. Check-list, but the difference is so small that this will cause no confusion. For instance, 'Robin' of the Check-list is here called 'American Robin' to distinguish it from other robins of the world.

Branta nigricans, Chen hyperborea, and *Buteo harlani,* treated as full species by the A.O.U. Check-list, are treated here as being conspecific with, respectively, *Branta bernicla, Chen caerulescens,* and *Buteo jamaicensis. Larus argentatus thayeri* of the A.O.U. Check-list is regarded here as a separate species, *Larus thayeri.*

The standard English names of bird species are capitalized. This helps to avoid ambiguity. For example, someone writes, "I saw a yellow warbler this morning; also a solitary vireo." One cannot be *sure* whether this correspondent had identified the particular species, the Yellow Warbler, or intended to say that he saw one of the several warblers that are yellow in colour but was not able to identify the particular species. Similarly any unaccompanied vireo is a solitary vireo, but not necessarily a 'Solitary Vireo.' Only the names of species are capitalized, not such general terms as 'warblers' or 'ducks.' For example, "The Black Duck was the only duck identified."

The French vernacular names used are those recommended in *Noms des oiseaux du Canada—Noms français, anglais, et scientifiques* (Second Edition, 1961, Canadian Wildlife Service, Ottawa, 20 p.). In one or two cases concerning species of accidental occurrence in Canada, where that authority provided no French name, the writer adopted the best name available from other reliable sources. In the case of *Aethia pusilla* a new French name was coined.

Coloured Plates

Four hundred and thirty-one species of regular occurrence in Canada are depicted in colour by artist J. A. Crosby. Not all plumages could, of course, be shown, but use of the plates in conjunction with the species descriptions in the text should eliminate difficulty in making species identification. The number of the plate on which each illustrated species is shown is given at the beginning of the description of that species. The plates and descriptions supplement each other and should be used together in identifying unfamiliar species.

Descriptions of Species

Total length (abbreviated to L.) is given in inches at the beginning of each species description. This is measured from the tip of the bill to the tip of the tail, with the bird flat on its back, its bill parallel with the ruler, its neck extended but not unduly stretched. This particular measurement should never be made from a dried skin. Although this measurement is not of great scientific value, it is useful in indicating relative size.

The majority of birds show variation in their plumages which is correlated with age, sex, season, or colour phases. In a few species there is very little variation (e.g., Black-capped Chickadee), but in some, variation is very great (e.g., Herring Gull, Snow Goose). Since not all plumages or plumage variations could be described in a book of this size, only those most frequently encountered are dealt with. Although simple descriptive terms are used as often as possible, technical words could not, and probably should not, be avoided. They are defined in the glossary or are otherwise identified in the topography of a bird (p. 2).

Beginners should keep in mind a few fundamentals concerning the plumages and molts of birds. In adults, the plumages of the male and female of some species, such as the Black-capped Chickadee and the Song Sparrow, look almost identical; in many others, the female is similar but perceptibly duller, as in the American Robin or Slate-colored Junco; in others, the female is strikingly different and decidedly less colourful as in the Red-winged Blackbird, Brown-headed Cowbird, Williamson's Sapsucker, and White-winged Crossbill. In most species in which the male and female differ, it is usually the female that is duller coloured and smaller. Rarely is the female more brightly coloured and larger, but this is the case in the phalaropes. In our hawks and owls the female is usually larger than the male.

In some species, such as the Bobolink, Scarlet Tanager, and Lark Bunting, the adult male is far more brightly coloured in the nesting season, but in late summer he molts into an inconspicuous plumage similar to that of the female.

In most birds the first plumage is a natal down, worn at hatching or acquired shortly thereafter. The young individual then passes through a series of molts and plumages (the duration varying among species) until it attains fully adult (or definitive) plumage. Reference is frequently made in the descriptions in this book to juvenal plumage. This is the first plumage acquired after the natal down. The juvenal plumage is usually worn but a short time, and it is not to be confused with the term 'juvenile,' which is applied to any *immature* bird and its plumage at any stage.

Some birds, like the Horned Lark, acquire adult (or definitive) plumage in about three months, in their first late summer or early autumn; others, like the Bobolink, in their first late winter or early spring; many passerine birds such as the Rose-breasted Grosbeak acquire it late in their second summer. The Herring Gull requires about 3½ years, and the

Bald Eagle takes five or more years to acquire full adult plumage.

Most adult birds completely renew their plumage at least once a year in late summer or early autumn by molting (this includes both the shedding and replacement of feathers). Many others have an additional partial molt in late winter or early spring, before the breeding season. In a very few species, of which the Sharp-tailed Sparrow and Bobolink are examples, there are two complete molts a year.

Abnormalities sometimes alter the appearance of birds. Albinism, the absence of colour in feathers that are normally coloured, is due to the failure of pigment to develop, and the result is white feathers. This may be complete or only partial. The opposite condition, caused by an excess development of dark pigment, results in abnormally dark plumage; this is called melanism. It is much less common than albinism.

Measurements

Measurements *in millimetres* of the wing, tail, exposed culmen, and tarsus are given for adult males; of only the wing for adult females. In most cases ten males and ten females were measured. Small and large extremes of the series measured are given, with averages in parentheses. These measurements are useful as an aid to identification of the species. Unless otherwise credited, measurements were made from Canadian material in the National Museum of Canada. In cases where more than one subspecies is found in Canada, the particular subspecies measured is indicated.

Methods used in taking these measurements are those advocated by Baldwin, Oberholser, and Worley (1931, *Sci. Pub.*, Cleveland Mus. Nat. Hist., Vol. 2, p. i–ix, 1–165).

Fig. 1 Length of wing

Wing: The length of the closed wing is the distance on the closed wing from the most anterior point of the wrist joint to the tip of the longest primary, unflattened (Fig. 1).

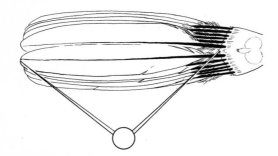

Fig. 2 Length of tail

Tail: The length of the tail is measured from that point between the two middle feathers where they emerge from the skin to the tip of the longest tail feather (Fig. 2).

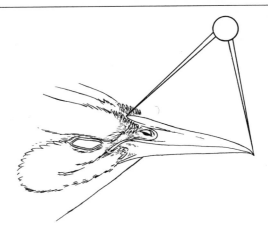

Fig. 3 Length of exposed culmen

Exposed Culmen: This measurement is the distance from that point on the culmen where the feathers of the forehead cease to hide the culmen, forward in a straight line to the tip of the bill. It is really the chord of the exposed culmen. It is best taken with dividers (Fig. 3).

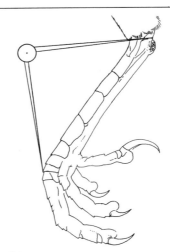

Fig. 4 Length of tarsus

Tarsus: This measurement, taken with dividers, is the distance from the middle point in the heel joint *behind* to the lower edge of the lowest undivided scute or to the junction with the base of the middle toe, in *front*. (Fig. 4).

Field Marks

Field marks are the points to look for, which distinguish quickly and accurately in the field each species from those species most closely resembling it; for instance, how to tell a Common Loon from a Yellow-billed Loon, or a Double-crested Cormorant from a Pelagic Cormorant. It is assumed that the reader can tell a loon from a cormorant or a duck. The beginner should learn to distinguish members of one family from those of other families. By studying the coloured plates and the short accounts of each family, he will soon be able to tell at a glance loons from grebes, cormorants, or waterfowl (ducks, geese, and swans); or warblers from vireos or sparrows.

Voice

Voice is here included under 'Field Marks' because the sounds of birds are an extremely useful aid to locating and identifying in the field. In fact, for an experienced observer with good ears, most (not all) bird species are readily identifiable by voice alone. Needless to say, familiarity with bird sounds should be developed as rapidly as possible.

Here in print it is impossible to represent with any degree of accuracy the songs of birds. The best that can be done is to suggest rhythms and syllables that may convey some idea of what to listen for. Only the commonest and most characteristic of bird sounds are given, mainly as an aid to identification.

Excellent recordings of the songs of most of our birds are available at reasonable prices from several sources. There is no quicker way to learn the songs. Regardless of how it is done, learning them is important, for familiarity with bird sounds vastly increases the efficiency and enjoyment of the observer.

Habitat

Birds are by no means evenly distributed across their ranges. Each species has its particular likes concerning the type of surroundings it prefers, an ecological complex that best suits the requirements of that species as an environment in which to live. This environmental complex is its habitat. Particular habitat preferences are characteristic of each species and are inherited by each individual of that species. Thus all Horned Larks seek open areas and shun woodlands, while Brown Creepers inhabit woodlands and shun treeless areas. Distribution patterns within the range, then, are often intricate, and population densities vary according to the availability of suitable habitat.

In this book the habitat preferences of each species of regular occurrence in Canada are outlined. Of necessity, this is done in broad terms in such a vast and ecologically varied area as Canada. Such broad terms as 'mature coniferous forest' or 'second-growth deciduous woodland' also have an additional advantage of being readily understood by everyone.

Nesting

In most cases, nesting data are given only for the species known to nest in this country. Incubation periods are credited to the author who published them or to persons who kindly furnished the writer with their unpublished data.

Range

A succinct outline of the extralimital range of the species has been given to indicate the extent of the breeding range in the world and the winter range in the Western Hemisphere. It ties the Canadian part of the breeding range in with the range in other parts of the world and indicates where the birds that leave this country in autumn spend the winter.

Range in Canada

This is a summary of the known distribution in this country. The extent of the breeding range in the larger provinces and in the territories is indicated by citing breeding localities with emphasis on peripheral ones. From sections of the range where the species is common, only one or two sample localities could be cited. It will be understood, therefore, that no attempt could be made to cite all known breeding localities.

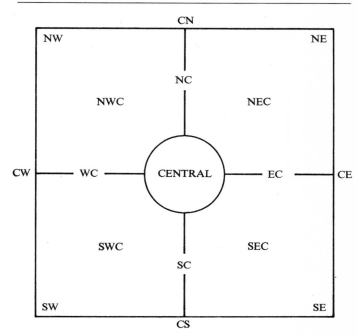

Fig. 5 Explanation of directional terms used in range summaries

Data used in delimiting these ranges were taken from a great many sources, most (but by no means all) of them published. All data were carefully considered before being used, and all are thought to be reliable. At the beginning, documentation of all the data was visualized, but it soon became apparent that this was not practicable in a one-volume book. The writer can furnish, upon request, the source of any particular distributional or other data.

Range maps show the breeding range in Canada of most of the birds that nest in the country. Areas in which breeding might occur but is not definitely known are indicated by question marks. For the species with a very restricted breeding range in this country no map is provided.

Subspecies

In accordance with recent practice, vernacular names for subspecies have been abolished.

In all species divisible into subspecies, which occur in Canada regularly, a paragraph is given dealing briefly with

7

the subspecies found in this country. In the case of casual or accidental species, the subspecies is given under 'Status in Canada.' When no subspecies is mentioned anywhere in the account of a species, it can be assumed that no subspecies are recognized.

Bird-Banding

Bird-banding, the marking of the individual bird by placing a numbered band on its leg, is directed in Canada by the Canadian Wildlife Service in cooperation with the United States Fish and Wildlife Service. By thus marking birds, a great mass of valuable information is being accumulated that could be secured in no other way.

If you find a *dead* wild bird with a band on its leg, remove the band and send it to the Canadian Wildlife Service, Ottawa, Ontario. Should the bird be uninjured, do *not* remove the band; merely record the complete band number and release the bird. In all cases give the date and place of capture, the manner in which it was secured, and the name of the person who secured it. You will be notified in due course as to where, when, and by whom the bird was banded.

Bands or band numbers on Rock Doves or Domestic Pigeons are not wanted.

Acknowledgments

The coloured illustrations are the work of John A. Crosby. Stewart D. MacDonald is responsible for the black-and-white drawings and for the art work on the range maps. Henri Ouellet made all the measurements (except total length) not credited otherwise, gathered together much useful distributional information concerning the southern and central half of Quebec from various sources, many unpublished, and assisted in many other ways. Miss V. M. Humphreys processed preliminarily a great deal of distributional information and checked many data.

As is usual in preparing a book of this nature, the literature has been freely drawn upon for general information. Measurements of species not adequately represented in the National Museum of Canada were taken from Ridgway (1901–1946) and Friedmann (1950). For distributional data outside Canada, the A.O.U. *Check-list of North American Birds* (1957, Fifth Edition) was invaluable.

The writer wishes to thank the many people who so kindly furnished data of various kinds, manuscripts, local lists, photographs, or specimens: John W. Aldrich, A. E. Allin, James L. Baillie, Jr., A. W. F. Banfield, Fred G. Bard, C. O. Bartlett, Jean Bedard, A. E. Bourguignon, P. W. P. Browne, E. W. Calvert, Austin W. Cameron, J. Mitchell Campbell, Raymond Cayouette, Roland C. Clement, F. Graham Cooch, Fred N. Cowell, I. McT. Cowan, Albert R. Davidson, Alex. Dzubin, R. Y. Edwards, A. J. Erskine, Richard Fyfe, J. B. Gollop, J. E. V. Goodwill, Charles J. Guiguet, Donald R. Gunn, Joseph A. Hagar, Francis Harper, R. D. Harris. E. O. Höhn, Captain Eric Holdway, Harold V. Hosford. C. Stuart Houston, Miss Mary F. Jackson, Hamilton M. Laing, the late A. G. Lawrence, Mrs. Louise de K. Lawrence, Harrison F. Lewis, Hoyes Lloyd, T. M. Lothian, James K. Lowther, Harry G. Lumsden, R. H. MacKay, Andrew H. Macpherson, Lloyd B. Macpherson, S. D. MacDonald, C. D. MacInnes, T. H. Manning, Patrick W. Martin, Mrs. Hettie Miller, Willett J. Mills, Hugh C. Monahan, David A. Munro, Robert W. Nero, Jacques Normandin, Harry C. Oberholser, Henri Ouellet, Réginald Ouellet, Ralph S. Palmer, David F. Parmelee, Theed Pearse, Harold S. Peters, Stuart S. Peters, Miss Hazel Petty, Bruce C. Pigot, G. A. Poynter, Mrs. Helen Quilliam, A. L. Rand, Chandler S. Robbins, J. F. Roy, L. S. Russell, W. Ray Salt, Douglas C. Sadler, D. B. O. Savile, F. H. Schultz, Donald A. Smith, Neal G. Smith, W. John Smith, L. L. Snyder, J. D. Soper, W. Austin Squires, George M. Stirrett, Richard W. Sutton, Rev. René Tanguay, John S. Tener, Lewis McI. Terrill, Leslie M. Tuck, Robie W. Tufts, Stanley E. Vass, Lawrence H. Walkinshaw, Sam Waller, Alexander Wetmore, A. L. Wilk, Miss Audrey E. Wilson, V. C. Wynne-Edwards, and many others.

I am grateful to Mr. Ed. M. Harrison of the Western Society of Vertebrate Zoology, Los Angeles, California, for the privilege of examining the late John R. Cruttenden's field notes.

Order **Gaviiformes**–Loons
Family **Gaviidae**–Loons

Number of Species in North America 4; in Canada 4

Large swimming birds usually seen on open water comprise this Order. They are frequent divers and have larger and longer bodies than grebes and most ducks, and shorter necks than geese. They fly with feet extended beyond the stubby tail, the neck slanted slightly downward giving a somewhat hump-backed appearance. The bill is *sharply pointed*, very different from ducks and geese, and is never hooked at tip as in cormorants and mergansers. The head is never crested, and the plumage is hard and glossy, velvety about head and neck. The short and very stiff tail is much better developed than in grebes. Toes are four in number, the front three completely connected by webs (in cormorants, all four are connected by webs; in grebes, toes are lobed, not webbed).

Loons are excellent swimmers and divers, diving from the water surface with head lowered in a plunging motion accompanied by a forward thrust of the body. Progress under water is very rapid; the body is propelled usually by the feet only, but the wings sometimes are used, especially in spurts and turns. As in other diving birds, certain physiological adaptations of blood and muscle chemistry enable loons to remain submerged for considerable periods. They can ride low in water or sink slowly out of sight by changing their specific gravity through compression of plumage and forcing of air from lungs. Fish, which make up a large part of their food, are caught by underwater pursuit.

Because the legs are attached far back on the body, loons move awkwardly on land, usually by either pushing along on the breast in frog-like leaps or assuming a semi-erect posture, shuffling forward with tarsi flat on the ground. They seldom come ashore except for nesting purposes. The nest is placed near the water's edge to permit return to water with minimum of time and effort. Three of the four species cannot fly from land; and even from water, take-off is laboured and space-consuming. Once in the air, however, they fly swiftly and directly. During the molting of the flight feathers, the primaries and secondaries being shed simultaneously, loons are flightless. In adults of the Common, Yellow-billed, and Arctic loons, the flightless period is usually in late winter; in the Red-throated this takes place in autumn. This awkward period occurs away from the nesting grounds. On broad expanses of open water they can secure food and escape potential enemies with ease.

COMMON LOON
Le Huart à collier. *Gavia immer* (Brünnich)
Plate 1. L. 28 to 35 in.

Sexes alike. A large loon with straight, evenly tapered bill. *Summer adults:* Head and neck black with greenish gloss, an incomplete white collar, white bar across throat, and black bill; back, boldly checkered black-and-white; belly white. *Winter adults:* Upper parts dark grey, feathers of back tipped with pale grey; lower cheeks, throat, fore-neck, breast, and belly, white; bill greyish with blackish ridge (adults sometimes retaining some summer plumage which produces blotched black-and-white areas on head and neck). *Young in first winter:* Like winter adult but throat and fore-neck more or less speckled with browns; bill shorter, horn colour blackish on ridge.

Measurements. *Adult male:* wing, 339.0–381.0 (360.9); tarsus, 87.0–96.2 (92.9); exposed culmen, 72.5–90.1 (81.5) mm. *Adult female:* wing, 315.8–360.0 (337.9); tarsus, 80.0–91.0 (86.3); exposed culmen, 73.0–86.0 (79.9) mm.

Field Marks. A large, heavy-headed loon. *Summer adult:* All-black head separates it from the Red-throat and Arctic, which have conspicuous areas of grey on the head. Very much like the Yellow-billed but has a *straight black* bill, *Winter adults and young:* All are similarly coloured dark grey above, white below. The Common Loon is a larger bird with noticeably heavier bill than the Arctic and Red-throated. Bill straight and robust, not slightly upturned as in Red-throated and Yellow-billed.

Habitat. Adults in spring, summer, and fall inhabit fresh-water lakes and sometimes larger rivers while these are open; in winter, inshore sea coasts or larger bodies of fresh water near the coast. Immatures frequent coastal inshore salt water at all seasons, less often fresh water.

Nesting. Usually only one pair to a lake, but large lakes may have two or more pairs. Nest near water's edge, preferably on islands, also on shores of fresh water. It is usually a mass of decaying vegetation, sometimes a mere depression on a muskrat house; occasionally the eggs are laid on bare ground. *Eggs*, usually 2; vary in colour from olive green to olive brown with blackish or brownish spots. Incubation 29 days (Olson and Marshall), by both sexes. Chicks abandon the nest soon after natal down is dry.

Range. Breeds from northern Alaska, western and southern Mackenzie, southern Keewatin, northern Manitoba, northern Ontario, central Baffin Island, Greenland, and Iceland south to northeastern California, northwestern Montana, North Dakota, northern Illinois, northern Ohio, northern New York, New Hampshire, and Maine. Winters mainly on the coasts from southern Alaska south to Baja California and from Newfoundland to Florida and Texas; also uncommonly on the lower Great Lakes; and from the British Isles to the western Mediterranean Sea.

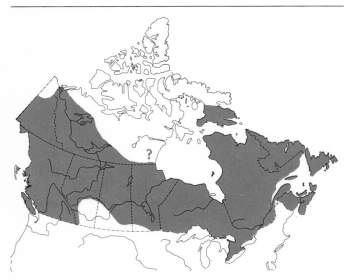

Breeding Distribution of Common Loon

Range in Canada. Breeds from northern Yukon, western and southern Mackenzie (Mackenzie Delta, Great Bear Lake, Great Slave Lake), northern Saskatchewan, northern Manitoba, northern Ontario, central Baffin Island (Cumberland Sound), southward through southern British Columbia (but scarce on coastal islands north of Queen Charlotte Sound), southwestern and central-eastern Alberta (absent from southeastern corner), south-central Saskatchewan (Moose Mountain, Crescent Lake, but absent from most of the southern plains), southern Manitoba, southern Ontario (but now absent from many lakes in thickly settled southern parts), southern Quebec, New Brunswick, Prince Edward Island, Nova Scotia, and Newfoundland. Recorded in summer on the barrens and coast of eastern Mackenzie and Keewatin, but proof of breeding is lacking. Alleged nesting in northern Baffin Island requires confirmation. More definite data are needed to delimit the respective breeding ranges of this and the Yellow-billed Loon, where the ranges come together or overlap.

Migrates through most of southern Canada and across northern Yukon (Porcupine River). Winters on the coast of British Columbia and on the Atlantic coast of Newfoundland, New Brunswick, Prince Edward Island, and Nova Scotia; uncommonly lower Great Lakes (Toronto).

Remarks. Soon after the winter ice breaks up on the interior lakes, the Common Loon returns to nest. Although it breeds over vast areas of Canada, it is now generally restricted to more remote waters where it is sparsely dis-

tributed. Usually there is only one pair to a lake, although larger lakes may have two or more pairs. On the breeding lakes, courtship and vocalizing are spectacular performances. Loons are devoted parents, and at least one of the pair remains with the young most of the time. Ten or eleven weeks elapse after hatching before the young can fly from their natal lake. Freeze-up forces both adults and young to the sea-coasts where they winter. The following spring the young remain on inshore salt water and do not return to the breeding waters until mature.

The voice is loud, resonant, and greatly varied. It has been variously described as maniacal, blood-curdling, horrible, beautiful, and thrilling. Three basic calls are (1) a laughing tremolo, (2) a weird yodel, (3) a wolf-like wail.

Like other loons, it is an excellent swimmer and diver. Fish are caught by underwater pursuit, the bird propelling itself usually by the feet only; but sometimes the wings also are used in spurts and turns. Ordinarily it does not stay under water more than a minute, but, under stress, submergences of three minutes or more have been recorded. Smaller fishes are eaten under water; larger, spiny ones may be brought to the surface before being swallowed. By compressing the plumage and forcing air from the lungs it can ride low in the water and can even sink slowly out of sight. Because the legs are attached far back on the body, it moves awkwardly on land and therefore spends most of its time afloat. When undisturbed, loons often roll over on one side and preen vigorously, one foot waving slowly in the air. At such times the gleaming white under parts are visible for long distances. Often loons rear up on the water, flap wings, stretch neck, shake head, then settle back on the water.

Take-off for flight, which cannot be accomplished from land, is laboured. The bird half-flies, half-runs across the water for from twenty yards to a quarter-mile. A breeze is a help but is not necessary. Flight is rapid, direct, and steady. Ground speeds up to 62 m.p.h. have been recorded. Landing, at the end of a flat, low glide, is an impressive sight, the body impact leaving a long trail of spray on the water.

Away from the breeding grounds this loon is found in singles, pairs, small loose groups, occasionally considerable flocks. Sometimes they swim and dive in well-spaced single file. Adults are flightless for a short time in late winter when all the flight feathers are molted simultaneously. Subadults molt these feathers at other times depending on age.

Fishes are their primary food, but their diet also includes crustaceans, molluscs, frogs, and vegetation. The fishes eaten are mainly ones of little economic importance, and some of the fishes taken compete with useful fishes for food and habitat. Loons are not frequenters of swift trout streams; usually they are so sparsely distributed that they do no real harm. Occasionally, however, they concentrate about fishermen's nets and setlines, in which they get caught, and damage them in their efforts to escape. Much persecuted in the past, they no longer nest in most of their former haunts in thickly settled country. Even on remoter waterways this loon is losing out to the summer cottager, the outboard motor, and the rifle. Wise laws now protect this picturesque bird at all seasons, but it is too late to restore it to many of its former lakes.

YELLOW-BILLED LOON

Le Huart à bec jaune. *Gavia adamsii* (Gray)
Plate 1. L. 30 to 35 in.

Like the Common Loon but differs as follows. *Summer adults:* Bill whitish yellow, appears slightly uptilted (culmen almost straight, but lower edge of bill in profile has an abruptly upward angle; commissural line of upper mandible slightly convex, curving a little below a straight line between gape and bill tip); head with purplish gloss, that of chin, throat, and lower neck sharply but not conspicuously defined against the rest of head, which is duller with a suggestion of green; white patches of throat and sides of neck made up of fewer, coarser, vertical white streaks; white spots on back larger, especially on scapulars, and fewer, with those on rump sparser and not extending up lower back; shafts of primaries paler (pale brown above, becoming darker at tips; below, almost white to tips). *Winter adults:* Like the Common Loon in winter but differs in bill colour and bill shape and in paler primary shafts. *First autumn and winter young:* Like the Common Loon of similar age but upper parts slightly paler, more greyish; white areas of cheek more extensive, usually reaching to or above eye; primary shafts paler; lesser wing coverts more conspicuously margined with grey. When the bill is fully developed, the shape differs as in adults of the two species, but this is slow developing and in the first autumn the shape is not very different. In available specimens examined, a small protuberance, lacking in the Common Loon, is present at the angle of gonys, but disappears when the bill is fully developed.

Measurements. *Adult male:* wing, 366.0–388.0 (376.4); tarsus, 90.0–99.0 (95.1); exposed culmen, 89.0–97.0 (91.3) mm. *Adult female:* wing, 361.0–387.0 (368.7); tarsus, 88.0–96.0 (91.1); exposed culmen, 86.5–96.0 (89.5) mm.

Field Marks. Summer and winter adults of the species are easily separated from the Common Loon by their whitish yellow, slightly upturned bill. Since juvenals in the first fall are very difficult to determine, caution should be taken in identifying them. Before the bill is fully developed, it is not very different from the Common Loon, but on direct comparison under exceptional conditions the paler upper parts and neck mottling and slightly more extensive white of cheeks of the Yellow-billed might be discerned.

Habitat. Adults in summer inhabit tundra freshwater lakes, ponds, and rivers, especially those with ice-push islands, on which the nest is sometimes placed. Coastal bays and inlets are visited for feeding purposes. In winter both adults and immatures inhabit saltwater bays, inlets, and open ocean along the coast. Immatures apparently remain on salt water until mature.

Nesting. On shore or islands of tundra ponds, lakes, and rivers and not far from water's edge; nest varies from little or no material to a heap or mound of mud and marsh vegetation, or sometimes a considerable heap of vegetation. *Eggs,* 2; similar to those of the Common Loon, but in the small sample examined the ground colour averages more brownish, less olive. Incubation period unknown.

Range. Breeds in northern Finland, Novaya Zemlya, northern Siberia, northern Alaska, and northwestern

Breeding Distribution of Yellow-billed Loon

Canada. In North America it winters in southeastern Alaska and uncommonly off the coast of British Columbia.

Range in Canada. Breeds from northern Banks Island, Victoria Island, Prince of Wales Island, and Melville Peninsula (probably) south to northern Yukon (Herschel Island) and the barren grounds of northern and central eastern Mackenzie (Hanbury River, Thelon River, but not in Mackenzie Valley) and south-central Keewatin (Angikuni Lake, Yathkyed Lake).

Migration to and from the wintering grounds apparently is mostly coastwise around northern Alaska, but some migrants occur as far south as Great Slave Lake. Casual in northwestern British Columbia (Atlin), northwestern Saskatchewan (Fond du Lac), and northeast to Devon Island and Jens Munk Island, N.W.T.

Winters in small numbers in coastal British Columbia (Comox, Hardy Bay).

Remarks. This loon replaces its near relative, the Common Loon, in northwestern North America north of treeline. Because of the similarity of the two species and consequent confusion by observers, range details for this species are not too clear, but the ranges of the two species appear to be mainly allopatric. Some authors have treated these loons as mere races of the same species, but there seems to be no justification for this. The respective characters separating the two appear to be trenchant, and there is little or no evidence of intergradation shown in the considerable number of specimens seen by the writer. One case of presumed hybridization is known: a Common x Yellow-billed Loon taken at Port Credit, Ontario, December 7, 1956, is in the Royal Ontario Museum.

ARCTIC LOON

Le Huart arctique. *Gavia arctica* (Linnaeus)
Plate 1. L. 23 to 29 in.

Bill straight, evenly tapered. *Summer adults* somewhat like the Common Loon but *crown and hind-neck grey;* long white streaks down sides of neck; size smaller. *Winter adults* like the Common Loon, dark grey above, white below; but the back is plain black without light tips to the feathers, size smaller. *Juvenals in first autumn and winter* are like winter adults, but feathers of back are brownish instead of blackish and are narrowly tipped with light grey (Fig. 6).

PLATE 1

A   B

Fig. 6 Feathers from mantle of
(A) juvenal Arctic Loon   (B) juvenal Red-throated Loon

Measurements. (*G. a. pacifica*): *Adult male:* wing, 281–303.5 (293.7); tarsus, 70.2–78.5 (74.3); exposed culmen, 49.5–55.0 (51.9). *Adult female:* wing, 277–304 (290.7); tarsus, 67.2–75.0 (71.9); exposed culmen, 49.0–54.0 (50.8) mm.

Field Marks. A small loon with a straight bill. In *summer adults* the grey hind-neck and black throat are a combination that readily identifies it. In *winter adults*, the plain blackish back (no grey feather tips) is diagnostic at close range. *Fall and winter juvenals* have faintly 'scaly' backs like those of the Common and Yellow-billed, but in any plumage the Arctic is a smaller bird with less robust bill. Its straight bill separates it from the Red-throated and Yellow-billed, both of which have slightly uptilted bills.

Habitat. In summer, adults frequent freshwater lakes (usually larger, deeper ones than the Red-throat), in terrain varying from flat to mountainous in either treeless or wooded country, both near the coast and far inland; in winter, coastal salt water, tending to favour more offshore waters than the Red-throat.

Nesting. Nest near water's edge varies from a lined depression in the ground to a mass of vegetation and mud, sometimes built up in shallow water. *Eggs*, usually 2; varying from greenish olive to dark umber, with blackish spots and blotches. Incubation period averages 29 days for each egg (Zedlitz).

Range. Circumpolar. Breeds from Scotland, the Scandinavian countries, northern Russia, and Siberia south to between latitudes 50° and 55° N; and from Alaska east across northern Canada to Baffin Island. In North America winters mainly along the Pacific Coast from southeastern Alaska south to southern Baja California.

Range in Canada. Breeds from Banks, Victoria, and Prince of Wales islands, Boothia Peninsula, northern Melville Peninsula, Prince Charles and North Spicer islands, and central Baffin Island (Nettilling Lake, Cumberland Sound) south to southern Yukon (probably), southern Mackenzie (Great Slave Lake), northern Manitoba (Herchmer, possibly Reindeer Lake), northern Ontario (Little Cape, Cape Henrietta Maria), northwestern Quebec (locally: 25 miles

north of Port Harrison), and southern Baffin Island (Big Island). Recorded in summer in northwestern British Columbia, northern Alberta, and northern Saskatchewan, but breeding evidence unsatisfactory.

Winters on the coast of British Columbia. Scarce transient in southern interior British Columbia (Okanagan Lake, Arrow Lake), southern Alberta (Brooks), southern Saskatchewan (Regina), and central Manitoba (Cormorant Lake). Accidental in southeastern Quebec (Whale Head, October 1923; between Ste. Flavie and Rimouski, July 1934) and in southern Ontario (sight records only: Toronto).

Breeding Distribution of Arctic Loon

Subspecies. Varies geographically in colour of adult summer plumage only and in size. (1) *Gavia arctica pacifica* (Lawrence), with purplish throat sheen, paler grey nape, shorter bill and wing, is the only race that breeds in Canada. (2) *G. a. viridigularis* Dwight, with greenish throat sheen, darker grey nape, longer bill and wing, breeds in e. Siberia and intergrades with *pacifica* in the Prince of Wales region, Alaska, and is reported to have been taken at Victoria and Comox, B.C. A third race is found in Europe. Individuals with greenish throat sheen but otherwise typical of *pacifica* occur sporadically in N.A. populations.

Remarks. Because of its remote summer home, few Canadians have a chance to know this attractive loon. The Alaska Highway provides easy access to a few lakes in southern Yukon where its interesting courtship and distraction displays may be seen. Its voice is varied. Raven-like croaks and growls are frequent. A prolonged, mournful wail is often given, particularly at dawn or evening. Under stress it has a habit of emitting a dog-like yelp just before it dives. A guttural *kwuk-kwuk-kwuk* is uttered during flight.

RED-THROATED LOON
Le Huart à gorge rousse. *Gavia stellata* (Pontoppidan)
Plate 1. L. 24 to 27 in.

A small loon with a slender bill which appears uptilted because of the abrupt upward angle of its lower edge.

13

Summer adults with dark grey head, red throat patch, and plain (not checkered black-and-white) back are unmistakable. *Winter adults and immatures* are, like other loons, dark grey above and white below, but in the hand the Red-throat is easily separable by its speckled back (other winter loons have either 'scaly' or plain backs) (*see* Fig. 6). *Juvenals in first fall and winter* differ from winter adults in the pattern of the back feathers: the white spots are longer, narrower, forming V-marks, especially on scapulars and wing coverts; the spots are more greyish, less pure white.

Measurements. *Adult male:* wing, 272.5–292.5 (280.2) mm; tarsus, 68.5–78.1 (73.9); exposed culmen, 48.2–57.1 (52.4). *Adult female:* wing, 259.0–281.0 (270.4); tarsus, 65.5–73.1 (69.9); exposed culmen, 46.4–54.6 (51.0) mm.

Field Marks. A smallish loon with slightly uptilted bill. *Summer adults* with dark grey head, red throat patch, and plain brown back (not checkered black-and-white) are easily distinguished from other loons. *Winter adults and immatures* are more difficult, but the uptilted bill will usually separate them from Common and Arctic loons. Its much smaller size and much slenderer bill distinguish it from the Yellow-billed. At close range the back is speckled with white (instead of 'scaly' or all black); thus it differs from other winter loons.

Habitat. Adults in summer frequent freshwater ponds and lakes, generally smaller and shallower than those used by the Arctic Loon, mainly on tundra but to some extent in forested country as well. They often visit larger lakes, rivers, and salt water to feed. In winter, adults and young frequent the seacoast. On the west coast it tends to favour more inshore ocean areas than the Arctic Loon. Most immatures at all seasons remain on salt water until mature.

Nesting. Nest, a depression in the ground or in a heap of moss or other vegetation on the shores or islands of ponds and lakes; very close to water's edge or in shallow water. *Eggs*, usually 2; varying in colour between olive and dark brown with spots and blotches of blackish brown. Incubation 27 days (W. H. Drury), 29 days (G. M. Sutton), by both sexes, begins with laying of first egg. Only one brood a season.

Range. Circumpolar. Breeds from northern Alaska across northern Canada and Greenland, south to coastal British Columbia, southern Mackenzie, James Bay, and Newfoundland (probably) and Miquelon Island; also across northern Eurasia. Winter range in North America extends mainly from the Aleutian Islands south along the Pacific Coast to northwestern Mexico; and from southern Newfoundland south to southern Florida and the Gulf of Mexico coast.

Range in Canada. Breeds from Prince Patrick and northern Ellesmere Island (Alert) south to northern Yukon (north coast), southern Mackenzie (Great Slave Lake), northwestern Saskatchewan (Little Gull Lake), Keewatin, northern Manitoba, James Bay (South Twin Island), coastal northern and southeastern Quebec (north shore of the Gulf of St.

Lawrence and Anticosti Island; perhaps Gaspé Peninsula), coast of Labrador; also on coastal British Columbia (Queen Charlotte Islands, Swanson Bay; also isolated nesting near Courtenay, Vancouver Island); isolated nesting also on north shore of Lake Superior (Thunder Cape, Rossport). Recorded in summer in Newfoundland (but evidence of breeding is needed). Summer records also for northeastern Alberta.

Winters on the coast of British Columbia, Newfoundland, New Brunswick, and Nova Scotia; small numbers on the lower Great Lakes. Migration is mostly coastal. A rare transient in the southern interior of the country but has been recorded in all provinces.

Breeding Distribution of Red-throated Loon

Remarks. Although the Red-throated Loon is similar to other loons, it differs from them in several respects. The red throat patch and plain uncheckered back are unique among adult summer plumages of loons. The flightless period of adults occurs in the autumn instead of late winter or early spring. Its take-off from water, which is much quicker and less laboured than other loons, enables it to inhabit much smaller ponds, and it is the only loon known to be able to fly directly from land. It is inclined to be more sociable than most loons. Although seen usually in small loose flocks, ones, or twos, it sometimes gathers into larger groups on favourite feeding waters; migration flocks of up to 500 have been observed.

On the breeding grounds it has spectacular courtship and distraction displays. In summer its repertoire is weird and varied, in keeping with the wildness of the arctic tundra ponds it frequents. A prolonged mournful wail is common, an impressive far-carrying *gayorworrk;* and in flight a rapid guttural *kwuk-kwuk-kwuk-kwuk*, much like that of the Arctic Loon.

Order **Podicipediformes**–Grebes
Family **Podicipedidae**–Grebes

Number of Species in North America 6; in Canada 5

Grebes are 'tailless' water birds with smaller and shorter bodies than loons and usually straighter necks. They are excellent swimmers and divers. By altering their specific gravity they can lower themselves in the water until only the head or bill shows. In the breeding season adults of all but the Pied-billed have crests or ruffs which loons never have. The bill is slender (except the Pied-billed with its stubby chicken-like bill) and pointed, very different from that of ducks and geese. In flight all Canadian species, except the Pied-billed, show a patch of white (absent in loons) in the wing. Grebes have lobed toes (Fig. 7), not fully webbed ones.

Fig. 7 Foot of a grebe

The tail feathers are vestigial, almost invisible. There is a narrow, bare strip in front of the eye. The feathers of the under parts have a peculiar silvery sheen. As in loons, the legs are attached far back on the body, and grebes therefore move awkwardly on land. Grebes have a habit of swallowing their own feathers, and the stomach often contains large numbers of them. The Prairie Provinces and southeastern British Columbia are richest in grebes, both in species and numbers, during the nesting season.

RED-NECKED GREBE (Holboell's Grebe)
Le Grèbe jougris. *Podiceps grisegena* (Boddaert)
Plate 2. A large grebe (L. 18 to 20.5 in.)

Bill straight or slightly downcurved, tapering to a point, rather long (1.6 to 2.4 in.) and slender, yellowish in colour. In *summer adults* the conspicuous whitish cheeks and throat and chestnut-red neck are a combination that instantly separates it from other grebes. The much smaller Horned Grebe also has a reddish neck in summer, but the cheeks and throat are black. *Winter plumage* is very different, and like most grebes the Red-necked has grey upper parts and white under parts. Its larger size and longer *yellowish* bill distinguish it from the Horned, Eared, and Pied-billed grebes. It is about the size of the Western Grebe, but it lacks the strong contrast of black and white on head and neck; it has grey instead of white on sides of neck, and the ridge of the bill is slightly downcurved instead of straight or slightly upcurved. In flight the wing shows *two* patches of white, one in front near where it joins the body, the other along the hind edge.

Measurements (*P. g. holböllii*). *Adult male:* wing, 187–203 (196.2); tail, 33.5–41 (37.5); exposed culmen, 43–58 (50.6); tarsus, 59.5–70 (64.4). *Adult female:* wing, 180.5–195 (188.7) mm.

Habitat. In summer, freshwater lakes, marshes, and sluggish rivers usually, but not necessarily, with margins or islands of emergent vegetation such as *Scirpus* or *Phragmites*. In winter, inshore coastal salt water, occasionally several miles from shore; sometimes freshwater lakes while they remain open.

Nesting. Either in single pairs or colonially. Nest, a low damp mass of aquatic vegetation often on a bed of broken-down marsh plants, often floating and attached to surrounding vegetation; occasionally on a muskrat house. *Eggs*, 3 to 8 (usually 4 or 5); plain bluish white, generally nest-stained. Incubation 23 days (Heinroth and Heinroth), by both sexes. One brood annually.

Range. Breeds in Alaska, western and central-southern Canada and northwestern United States (Washington east to Minnesota); also in Europe and northern Asia. In North America it winters mainly along the coasts from the Aleutian Islands and southeastern Alaska south to central California and on the Atlantic Coast from Newfoundland south to central Florida.

Range in Canada. Breeds from northern Yukon (Old Crow), northwestern and southern Mackenzie (Mackenzie Delta; 50 miles south of Fort Anderson; Great Slave Lake), northern Saskatchewan (Fond du Lac, Churchill River), central Manitoba (Thicket Portage), western and central Ontario (Sioux Lookout, Whitefish Lake, Favourable Lake,

Lillabelle Lake) south through interior British Columbia (rarely also on Vancouver Island), southern Alberta (Brooks), southern Saskatchewan (Cypress Hills, Moose Mountain), southern Manitoba, and southern Ontario (locally: Burlington; Lorne Park; and Luther Marsh, 22 miles west of Orangeville).

Winters along the coast of British Columbia and on the Atlantic Coast north to Newfoundland, more rarely on the Great Lakes and interior British Columbia. Migrates through much of the southern interior of the country but is rare in Labrador (Makkovik, Spotted Island). Not uncommon sometimes on the inner north shore of the Gulf of St. Lawrence (Moisie Bay) and is probably regular along the St. Lawrence River drainage. Casual on Southampton Island.

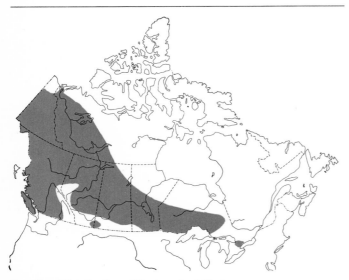

Breeding Distribution of Red-necked Grebe

Subspecies. *Podiceps grisegena holböllii* Reinhardt is the only subspecies known in Canada. It is slightly larger than the nominate race of the Old World.

Remarks. On its breeding grounds this large, handsome grebe is a noisy bird. Sometimes it breeds in small colonies, and when several call at the same time the result is a cacophony of wails, brays, and cackles. On the lakes of Manitoba its food is largely crayfish, salamanders, and aquatic insects. It also eats minnows and other small fishes, small crustaceans, molluscs, tadpoles, and some vegetation.

In autumn migration, concentrations build up at certain points along Lake Ontario. At Willow Beach, near Port Britain, some three miles west of Port Hope, several hundred, more or less, may be seen in September and October.

HORNED GREBE
Le Grèbe cornu. *Podiceps auritus* (Linnaeus)
Plate 2. L. 12.5 to 15 in.

A small grebe with short straight bill. Sexes alike. In flight shows a *single* white patch in wing. *Summer adults* with their broad *buffy ear tufts*, conspicuous against black head, are likely to be mistaken only for the Eared Grebe. Its *chestnut*

Fig. 8 Bill details of
Horned Grebe (A) lateral view; (B) dorsal view
Eared Grebe (C) lateral view; (D) dorsal view

neck readily separates it from the Eared Grebe, which has a black neck, and it lacks the helmet head-shape of the Eared. *Winter plumages* are very different, and all grebes are more plainly and somewhat similarly attired. Smaller size, shorter neck, and much shorter bill distinguish it from the Red-necked and Western grebes, and the slender bill is very different from that of the Pied-billed. It closely resembles the Eared Grebe, but the blackish of the crown extends down only to the lower side of the eye where it gives way abruptly to white; in the Eared Grebe the transition from black to white is gradual, and the ear coverts are grey, not white. The sides of the neck are whiter (less greyish) in the Horned Grebe. In the hand, the two may be separated in any plumage by the bill. In the Horned, the height of the bill at the base is greater than its width; in the Eared, its width equals or exceeds its height (Fig. 8).

Measurements (*P. a. cornutus*). *Adult male:* wing, 135.5–146.5 (141.3); tail, 33.5–38.5 (36.1); exposed culmen, 23.3–25.6 (24.4); tarsus, 43.5–48.5 (46.6). *Adult female:* wing, 131–141 (136.9) mm.

Habitat. In summer, freshwater ponds, sloughs, and protected shallow bays of lakes, especially those with some emergent vegetation, in both the plains and wooded country. In winter, mainly inshore salt water, occasionally well off shore, sometimes larger freshwater lakes.

Nesting. Not colonial. Usually one pair to a pond; larger water bodies may have several pairs. Nest of soft or decayed emergent or aquatic vegetation, floating and anchored or on broken-down marsh vegetation, either in the open or sheltered by emergent vegetation. *Eggs*, 4 or 5, sometimes 3, rarely up to 10; the last perhaps a product of more than one female; dull bluish white, usually nest-stained. Incubation 24 to 25 days (A. D. DuBois), by both sexes.

Range. Breeds from central and southern Alaska and Canada (*see* Range in Canada) south to Idaho, northern South Dakota, northern Iowa, and central Wisconsin (sporadically farther east); also in Iceland, the Faroes, and Eurasia. In North America, it winters mainly on the coasts from the Aleutian Islands to southern California, and from Nova Scotia to Florida; less commonly in the interior from the Great Lakes southward. In the Old World it winters south to the Mediterranean Sea, Iran, Turkestan, and Japan.

16

Range in Canada. Breeds from northern Yukon (Old Crow), northwestern and southern Mackenzie (Anderson River, Great Slave Lake; recorded in summer on Mackenzie Delta and Smart Lake), southern Keewatin (Simons Lake) southward through interior British Columbia, Alberta, Saskatchewan, and Manitoba; sporadically and very locally eastward to eastern Ontario (Algonquin Park; formerly east to Leeds County); also in southeastern Quebec (Anticosti and Magdalen islands); formerly New Brunswick (near Milltown).

Migrates through much of southern Canada but very rare in Newfoundland. Winters in British Columbia (mainly the coast, but small numbers occasionally in southern interior); also on the coasts of Nova Scotia, Prince Edward Island, and New Brunswick; occasionally on the lower Great Lakes.

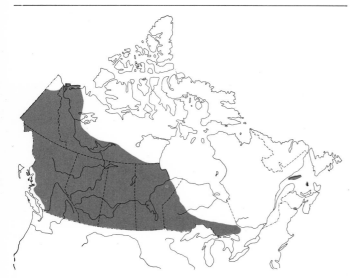

Breeding Distribution of Horned Grebe

Subspecies. *Podiceps auritus cornutus* (Gmelin) is the North American race. It averages paler than the nominate race of the Old World.

Remarks. In early June, in full nuptial plumage, this little grebe is a handsome bird. Its rich chestnut neck and flanks look their best in bright sunshine, and the buffy ear tufts glow against the jet black head. By July, molt and fading have greatly dulled its beauty. Unlike the Eared Grebe it does not nest in large colonies, but it has a wide distribution in the West, and many a small slough has its pair in summer. A small body of water is adequate; and if the water does not dry up, the birds will not often leave it. When the striped-headed young emerge from the egg, they soon take to water, and both parents care for them. The family spends the long summer days feeding, preening, dozing, or just floating. As with other grebes the young often ride on the backs of their parents as they swim about.

J. A. Munro has studied the food eaten in British Columbia. In the interior in summer, aquatic insects, particularly Odonata nymphs, water boatmen (corixidae), and Coleoptera are the chief food of both adults and young. In winter on the coast, crustaceans are the most important food with small fishes second in importance.

EARED GREBE
Le Grèbe à cou noir. *Podiceps caspicus* (Hablizl)
Plate 2. L. 12 to 14 in.

A small grebe with short slender bill which appears slightly uptilted. Sexes alike. *Summer adults* with their buffy ear tufts are likely to be confused only with the Horned Grebe from which they differ in having a *black neck* and a helmet-shaped head. In *winter*, its smaller size and shorter, weaker bill separate it from the Red-necked and the differently-marked Western Grebe. The slender bill is quite unlike that of the Pied-billed. Though very much like the Horned Grebe, the dark colour of the top of head is slightly more extensive, particularly behind the eye and on the ear region; the neck is more extensively greyish, and the shape of the head (J. A. Munro) is more triangular and the carriage more upright. In the hand, the bill dimensions (*see* Fig. 8, Horned Grebe) are diagnostic.

Measurements (*P. c. californicus*). *Adult male:* wing, 122.5–132 (128.1); tail, 26–39 (31.8); exposed culmen, 22.8–27.8 (25.8); tarsus, 40–44 (42.9). *Adult female:* wing, 119–127.5 (122.9) mm.

Habitat. In the breeding season, marshy, shallower parts of freshwater lakes and ponds in both wooded and treeless country. In winter, mostly coastal salt water in Canada but also fresh water in the United States.

Nesting. Usually colonial, nesting in large or small colonies, small groups, or single pairs. Nest, a soggy heap of vegetation usually floating or built up from the bottom or on a dense bed of vegetation. It may be hidden in marsh vegetation or be completely exposed. *Eggs*, usually 3 or 4, but clutches variable 1 to 6; bluish or greenish white, generally nest-stained. Incubation period 20½ to 21½ days (Nancy McAllister), by both sexes.

Range. Breeds from southwestern Canada (east to Manitoba) south to northern Baja California, central Arizona, northern New Mexico, and southern Texas; also widely in Eurasia and Africa. In North America winters mainly from southern British Columbia to Colombia.

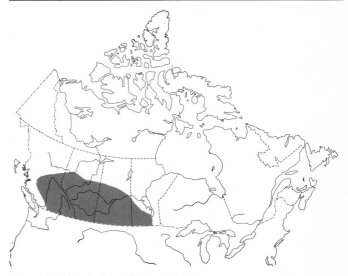

Breeding Distribution of Eared Grebe

Range in Canada. Breeds in central and southern interior British Columbia (Tachick Lake, Kleena Kleene, Okanagan Valley), Alberta (Cardinal and Fairmont lakes, probably Birch River delta, southward), north-central and southern Saskatchewan (Kazan Lake, Nipawin southward), and southern Manitoba (Shoal Lake).

Winters regularly on the coast of southern British Columbia.

Casual in southern Mackenzie (Great Slave Lake) and southern Ontario (Niagara Falls, Lorne Park).

Subspecies. *Podiceps caspicus californicus* Heermann is the race that inhabits North America. Two additional races are found in the Old World.

Remarks. Marshy lakes in the western provinces are the summer home of this attractive grebe. Its commonest call-note is *co-eeeek*, given with a rising inflection and suggesting a contralto swamp tree frog. It often nests in large communities, which are busy places in nest-building time. Usually only the female carries nesting material. This is secured either on the water surface or by diving. The bird swims with a beakful to the nest, drops it unceremoniously, then swims away for more. Occasionally the working bird hops awkwardly onto the flimsy nest and shapes it with her body. Although nests are often close together, relationships between the nesting pairs are mostly harmonious. Sometimes an intruder is driven off by a charge with lowered head. Aquatic insects appear to be the chief summer food of both adults and young in interior British Columbia, with amphipods and terrestrial beetles eaten also in some numbers. On the coast in winter, mysids and amphipods are much relished (J. A. Munro).

WESTERN GREBE

Le Grèbe de l'Ouest. *Aechmophorus occidentalis* (Lawrence)
Plate 2. L. 22 to 29 in.

A large grebe with long, very slender neck, sharply contrasted black-and-white coloration, and a slender, sharp, slightly uptilted yellowish bill.

Measurements. *Adult male:* wing, 190–205 (199.3); tail, 36.5–52.5 (41.8); exposed culmen, 65.3–80.5 (74.7); tarsus, 72–80 (77.2). *Adult female:* wing, 179–196.5 (186.6) mm.

Habitat. In the breeding season, freshwater lakes with some emergent vegetation. In winter coastal saltwater bays and lagoons, sometimes open freshwater lakes.

Nesting. In colonies on borders of freshwater lakes. Nest, a mass of vegetation, floating and attached to nearby vegetation, or stationary; rarely on dry shore. *Eggs,* 3 to 5 or more; dull, plain bluish white, usually nest-stained. Incubation about 23 days (A. C. Bent), by both sexes.

Range. Breeds from western Canada (east to Manitoba) south to California, northern Utah, North Dakota, Nebraska (locally), and southwestern Minnesota. Winters mainly along the Pacific Coast from southeastern Alaska and British Columbia south to northwestern Mexico.

Range in Canada. Breeds in south-central and southern interior British Columbia (locally: Williams Lake, Swan Lake in Okanagan Valley, Salmon Arm), north-central and southern Alberta (Peace River district, Christina Lake

southward east of the mountains), central and southern Saskatchewan (Kazan Lake, Emma Lake southward), and southwestern Manitoba (north probably to northern Lake Winnipegosis, Lake St. Martin, Shoal Lake).

Winters commonly on the coast of British Columbia, occasionally in the southern interior (Okanagan Lake). A common spring and autumn migrant on lakes of southern interior British Columbia. Casual in southern Yukon (Teslin Lake), northeastern Alberta (Lake Athabasca), and southern Ontario.

Breeding Distribution of Western Grebe

Remarks. On certain western lakes, this graceful grebe nests in colonies of various sizes, although the summer cottager with his outboard motor has driven it from some of the lakes it formerly favoured. Its plaintive, far-carrying, high-pitched *creek-creek*, given in twos, is easily recognizable. Some of its displays are spectacular, particularly when two birds rear up vertically and race side-by-side over the water's surface. This grebe is often more gregarious than other species both in summer and winter. Its diet is similar to that of other grebes but probably includes more small fishes.

PIED-BILLED GREBE

Le Grèbe à bec bigarré. *Podilymbus podiceps* (Linnaeus)
Plate 2. L. 12 to 15 in.

A small grebe with a *very stout bill*, its ridge decidedly down-curved. In breeding plumage, adults have a black throat-patch and a blackish band-like spot on the bill. In winter the black areas on throat and bill are lacking, but the stubby hen-like bill-shape is always diagnostic. In flight it shows *no well-defined white patches* in the wing.

Measurements. *Adult male:* wing, 126–136 (129.3); tail, 35.5–43.5 (39.2); exposed culmen, 20–24.5 (22.8); tarsus, 40.5–43.5 (41.9). *Adult female:* wing, 112.5–127.5 (118.5) mm.

Habitat. In summer, freshwater ponds, sloughs, sluggish streams, shallow bays of lakes, all with margins or islands of emergent and aquatic vegetation. In winter, it inhabits fresh water where open; saltwater tidal creeks, estuaries, and bays.

Nesting. Not colonial. Nest, a substantial structure of soft decayed marsh vegetation, either floating or built up from shallow water bottom. *Eggs*, usually 5 to 7; dull bluish white or greenish white, usually nest-stained with buffy. Incubation, 21 to 24 days, probably averages 23 days, by both sexes. The young, like those of other grebes, leave the nest and take to the water soon after hatching.

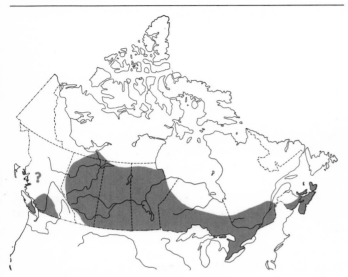

Breeding Distribution of Pied-billed Grebe

Range. Western Hemisphere from southern Canada, south through Central America, the West Indies, and South America to Chile and southern Argentina. Winters from southwestern British Columbia and the Great Lakes (rarely) southward.

Range in Canada. Breeds in central and southern British Columbia (Williams Lake, perhaps Tachick and Ootsa lakes, southward including Vancouver Island), central southern Mackenzie (Slave River Delta), Alberta, Saskatchewan (Lake Athabasca southward), Manitoba (Churchill southward), central Ontario (Matheson, Lillabelle Lake southward), southwestern Quebec (Saguenay River Valley at St. Fulgence; Quebec City; Lac aux Loutres; Montreal), southern New Brunswick, Prince Edward Island, and Nova Scotia (Falls Lake, Aylesford, Cape Breton Island).

Winters regularly in southwestern British Columbia (mainly on the coast; rarely in the southern interior: Okanagan Lake), rarely in southern Ontario (lower Great Lakes). Casual in southern Yukon (Dezadeash Lake, Marsh Lake), James Bay (Moose Factory, Charlton Island), the north shore of the Gulf of St. Lawrence (Bonne Espérance, Moisie River), and Newfoundland (various records, mostly in autumn). Accidental in northern Labrador (Ramah) and southern Baffin Island (Fair Ness).

Subspecies. *Podilymbus podiceps podiceps* (Linnaeus) is the only race inhabiting Canada. Other races are found in the West Indies and in South America.

Remarks. This is the grebe most often seen in most parts of eastern Canada. Soon after the ice leaves our freshwater ponds and marshes, this grebe puts in an appearance, and here it remains until ice begins to form again in the autumn. Alert and rather shy, it often keeps out of sight in the marsh vegetation. It is noisy in spring, and its presence is frequently made known by its surprisingly far-carrying voice. The commonest call is a hollow *kow-kow-kow*, repeated perhaps a dozen times, speeding up and becoming *kow-uh* toward the end.

Order **Procellariiformes** – Albatrosses, Shearwaters, Petrels, and Allies

Birds of this Order spend most of their lives at sea and ordinarily come ashore only to nest. In size they range from great albatrosses to swallow-like petrels. The wings are long and pointed and have ten primaries and usually many secondaries. The tail is short or moderate in length. The bill covering is formed of horny plates, more or less clearly separated by sutures (Fig. 9). The external nostrils are encased in well-formed tubes. The front toes are rather long and fully webbed; the hind toe is small and is not connected to the front toes by a web. A distinctive feature of birds of this Order is a peculiar stomach oil which can be ejected when the bird is disturbed. This has a strong, musky odour which persists on museum specimens for decades.

Family **Diomedeidae** – Albatrosses

Number of Species in North America 6; in Canada 3

Large ocean birds, effortless flyers, possessing very long, very narrow wings, which are stiffly held in flight. The bill is strongly hooked at the tip and strongly plated (*see* Fig. 9). There are *two nostril tubes*, one on each side of the bill near its base. Hind toe is rudimentary or absent. The seas of the Southern Hemisphere are richest in albatrosses. Thirteen species are known in the world. Only three have been recorded in Canada, and none of them nests in this country.

SHORT-TAILED ALBATROSS

L'Albatros à queue courte. *Diomedea albatrus* Pallas
L. about 37 in.

Adults: Head, body (including back), and bases of wings, white. Rest of wings and tail, dark brown. *Immature:* All sooty. Like the Black-footed Albatross but lacks any pale area around the base of the bill; the bill is pale pinkish, the feet bluish white, not black.
Range. Bred, formerly at least, on Torishima, the Perry group, the Bonins, and other islands in the Pacific Ocean. Although now greatly reduced and near extinction, there has been a recent small increase in its numbers.
Status in Canada. Formerly of regular occurrence off British Columbia (reportedly common off Cape Beale in April 1894. A specimen taken at Esquimalt on June 4, 1893. Two specimens taken on Juan de Fuca Strait in 1889).
Remarks. All white-bodied albatrosses off British Columbia should be examined carefully, since the Laysan Albatross, *Diomedea immutabilis*, has been reported some 200 miles off the Queen Charlotte Islands. Superficially it looks like the adult Short-tailed, but the back is dark like the wings.

BLACK-FOOTED ALBATROSS

L'Albatros à pattes noires. *Diomedea nigripes* Audubon
Plate 3. L. 28.5 to 36.0 in.

Wingspread about 7 feet. A dark-bodied albatross, blackish above and slightly lighter below, with a whitish area near the base of the dark bill. Adults have white tail coverts. In immature birds the whitish area at the base of the bill is often absent or poorly indicated, and there is no white in the tail coverts. The black feet and dark bill separate it in any plumage from immatures of the Short-tailed Albatross.

Fig. 9 Bill of Black-footed Albatross

Measurements. *Adult male:* wing, 427–519 (474.9); tail, 146–153 (149.5); exposed culmen, 106–109 (107.4); tarsus, 95–99 (96.7). *Adult female:* wing, 413–454.5 (429) mm.
Habitat. The open ocean, usually well off shore.
Range. Bred, formerly at least, on Torishima, Bonin, Iwo Jima, Marshall, and Hawaiian islands in the Pacific Ocean, but no longer does so on some of these islands. The majority now nest on the Leeward chain of Hawaiian Islands. Ranges over the Pacific north to southern Bering Sea.
Status in Canada. A fairly common non-breeding visitor to offshore waters of British Columbia from March to autumn.
Remarks. Like other albatrosses, this is a wanderer over

the trackless ocean. Since the decline of the Short-tailed Albatross it is the only albatross that comes regularly into Canadian waters, but ordinarily it does not venture close to shore. To see it, one usually must travel some miles out to sea. Its effortless gliding flight, low over the wave troughs, is a source of wonder for the few who have a chance to observe it. P. W. Martin (MS.) has found it in the pelagic waters off British Columbia as early seasonally as March 18 and increasing in numbers as the spring progresses. He found a growing tendency toward flocking in summer, and by mid-August he not infrequently saw groups of up to twenty individuals. This albatross feeds mainly on squid and fish but often follows fishing boats for scraps of offal. It nests in late fall and winter on islands in the Pacific and is only a non-breeding visitor to Canadian waters.

YELLOW-NOSED ALBATROSS
L'Albatros à nez jaune. *Diomedea chlororhynchos* Gmelin
L. 32 in.

Head and neck white, back of neck and cheeks tinged with grey. A blackish or greyish line from eye to base of bill. Back, upper side of wings, and tail, slaty brown. Under side of wings white with dark border. Rump, upper tail coverts, and under parts, white. Bill of adults black *with a yellow ridge;* of immatures all black.

Status in Canada. Accidental in Quebec (Moisie River, August 20, 1885) and New Brunswick (between Machias Seal Island and Grand Manan, August 1, 1913).

This monotypic species is primarily a bird of the South Atlantic and Indian oceans.

Family **Procellariidae** – Shearwaters and Fulmars

Number of Species in North America 20; in Canada 10

Shearwaters (subfamily Puffininae) are smaller than albatrosses and, like them, are strictly marine. In flight they alternate rather rapid wing strokes with lengthy glides, the long narrow wings held stiffly at right angles to the body. Both the upper and lower mandibles are hooked. The two nostril tubes are situated on top of the bill (*see* Fig. 10).

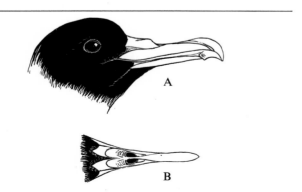

Fig. 10 Bill of Sooty Shearwater
    (A) lateral view   (B) dorsal view

Fulmars (subfamily Fulmarinae) are more robust in form and more gull-like than shearwaters, and they have a relatively stubby bill, of which only the upper mandible is hooked. The nostrils, which are enclosed in a conspicuous tube on top of the bill, are separated from each other by a narrow septum.

NORTHERN FULMAR
Le Fulmar boréal. *Fulmarus glacialis* (Linnaeus)
Plate 3. L. 18 to 20 in.

Bill relatively much chunkier than that of any gull or shearwater. Conspicuous nostril tube over posterior part. Upper mandible strongly hooked. Neck short. Tail slightly rounded. Two colour phases. LIGHT PHASE: Head, neck, and under parts white. Back and upper surface of wings (tail paler) slaty grey, flight feathers darkest. Bill usually yellowish. DARK PHASE: Entire plumage smoky grey; bill dark, becoming yellowish at tip. Many stages of intermediacy between the dark and light phases are common. Fulmars are somewhat gull-like in shape, but the wings, which are narrow, are stiffly held in flight. Wing beats differ from those of gulls, being more rapid and alternating with long glides. Dark phase resembles the Sooty Shearwater, but the Fulmar's bill is much chunkier, neck thicker.

Measurements (*F. g. minor*). *Adult male:* wing, 305–328 (319.2); tail, 119–128 (124.8); exposed culmen, 35–38.5 (36.8); tarsus, 50–58.5 (53.6). *Adult female:* wing, 258–310.5 (283.6) mm.

Habitat. The open ocean. At nesting time frequents cliffs at or near salt water.

Nesting. In colonies, sometimes immense, on steep cliffs usually at salt water. The Cape Searle colony, Baffin Island, in 1950 was conservatively estimated at 200,000 birds (Wynne-Edwards). No actual nest is made, the egg being laid on bare rock or in a shallow hollow in soil, or in vegetation on cliff ledges. *Egg,* one only; white. Incubation about 53 to 57 days (varies considerably), by both parents. The young fly six to seven weeks after hatching.

Range. Discontinuously circumpolar, breeding in the north Atlantic, north Pacific, and Arctic oceans. In North America it breeds in colonies along the coasts of Alaska, the Canadian Arctic, and in Greenland.

Range in Canada. Breeds in colonies, mostly very large, in the Arctic: Baffin Island (Cape Searle, Coutt's Inlet, Admiralty Inlet), Devon Island (Cape Vera), Prince Leopold Island, and probably northern Somerset Island, N.W.T. Found in summer in many other parts of the Canadian Arctic west to Banks Island (rarely), north to Ellesmere Island, and commonly southward to waters off Newfoundland, but not Hudson Bay. Probably the commonest bird at sea in the eastern Canadian Arctic where it is found from late April to late September or early October. Winters off both the Pacific and Atlantic provinces, the majority well at sea. Rare in summer in the Gulf of St. Lawrence but small numbers regularly in November. Casual or accidental in Ontario (Arnprior, May 3, 1924; Ottawa River opposite Pointe Fortune, Quebec, November 15, 1928; Meaford, November 20, 1936), and southwestern Quebec (Beauport).

Breeding Distribution of Northern Fulmar

Subspecies. Three races occur in Canada. (1) *Fulmarus glacialis minor* (Kjaerbølling) is the only race known to breed in this country. (2) *F. glacialis glacialis* (Linnaeus), an Old World and east Greenland race, is a non-breeding wanderer to eastern Canadian waters (taken off Lab., Nfld., and N. S.), distinguishable only in the hand by its more robust bill. It doubtless occurs more often than the records indicate. (3) *F. g. rodgersii* Cassin, nesting locally from Siberia to Alaska, is a regular non-breeding wanderer to offshore waters of B. C., but there is no record of it in the Canadian Arctic.

CORY'S SHEARWATER
Le Puffin cendré. *Puffinus diomedea* (Scopoli)
L. 19 to 21 in.

A large, white-bellied shearwater of the Atlantic. Most like the slightly smaller, somewhat darker Greater Shearwater (Plate 3), but the grey on the top of the head extends farther down the sides of the face, blending into (not sharply contrasting with) the white of the throat; it usually has no well-defined white rump patch, and the bill (in *P. d. borealis*) is yellowish not blackish.
Habitat. The open ocean well off shore.
Range. The eastern Atlantic and western Indian oceans, the Mediterranean and Adriatic seas to Asia Minor.
Status in Canada. A non-breeding wanderer to waters off the Atlantic Coast. A specimen was collected about 40 miles off Dover, Nova Scotia, July 27, 1916. That it is commoner than generally realized off southern Nova Scotia is indicated by J. E. V. Goodwill's field notes, in which he recorded it at sea off various southern Nova Scotia localities on twenty-nine dates, July to October, 1960 and 1961. Hypothetical off western Newfoundland where one was reported on August 11, 1920 (Griscom and Janvrin, *The Auk* 39:103–104).
Subspecies. *Puffinus diomedea borealis* Cory, which breeds on the Azores, Madeira, Salvages, and the Canary is., is the only subspecies known to occur in Canada.

PINK-FOOTED SHEARWATER
Le Puffin à pattes roses. *Puffinus creatopus* Coues
L. 19 in.

Upper parts, including sides of face and sides of neck, greyish brown. Under parts, mostly white but chin and throat, sides of body, and wing linings with varying amounts of grey mottling. Under tail coverts greyish brown, more or less mottled with white. Bill mainly pale-yellowish flesh. Legs and feet, pale flesh.
Field Marks. A white-bellied shearwater of the Pacific, slightly larger than the Manx Shearwater, with grey and white wing linings (giving them a greyer appearance) and with a *pale* instead of dark bill. The light under parts separate it from the Sooty and Pale-footed shearwaters.
Habitat. The ocean.
Range. Breeds on islands off the coast of Chile, wandering northward in the Pacific to southeastern Alaska.
Status in Canada. A scarce but regular, non-breeding visitor to offshore waters of British Columbia from late April to early September. Flocks of up to 20 individuals in August 1949 off Ucluelet (P. W. Martin, MS.). Four specimens collected on Swiftsure Banks, off Cape Flattery, August 14, 1946 (Munro and Cowan, 1947).

PALE-FOOTED SHEARWATER
Le Puffin à pattes pâles. *Puffinus carneipes* Gould
L. 19.5 in.

Entire plumage sooty, including wing linings. Bill, flesh coloured with dark tip. Legs and feet, flesh coloured: In the field an all-dark shearwater resembling the Sooty but with flesh-coloured bill, legs, and feet.
Habitat. The open ocean.
Range. Breeds on islands in Australian and New Zealand seas. Wanders northward to waters off Japan and British Columbia.
Status in Canada. Patrick W. Martin first recognized the occurrence of this species off British Columbia on July 31, 1937, on the Goose Island Banks. He secured specimens there on July 8 and 18, 1939, and found the species locally rather numerous. He again visited the area on July 14, 1946, and secured two more specimens. Additional ones were taken there in 1947 and 1948. Martin observed two on La Pérouse Bank on July 14, 1946, and collected one there on August 22, 1949. He noted at least eight off Triangle Island on June 28 and 29, 1949.

GREATER SHEARWATER
Le Grand Puffin. *Puffinus gravis* (O'Reilly)
Plate 3. L. 18 to 20 in.

Head with sooty brown cap extending somewhat below eyes and sharply marked off from white cheeks. Upper parts sooty brown, darkest on wings and tail, many feathers of back and wing coverts with pale greyish margins. Posterior upper tail coverts white, forming a narrow white band across base of tail. Under parts white, the white extending up sides of neck to form an incomplete collar. Belly with small ashy patches. Under tail coverts ashy grey. Bill blackish. Legs and feet flesh coloured, outer side of legs and outer toe blackish.

Measurements. *Adult male:* wing, 305.5–328 (318.2); tail, 105.5–120 (113.3); exposed culmen, 45.5–51 (47.7); tarsus, 56.5–62 (59.5) mm.

Field Marks. An Atlantic white-bellied shearwater. The white under parts readily separate it from the Sooty Shearwater, the only other common shearwater in Canadian Atlantic waters. Differs from the rarer Cory's Shearwater, also white-bellied, by a white band at the base of the tail, black bill, and by the black cap being sharply defined against white cheeks. Manx Shearwater, of accidental occurrence in eastern Canadian waters, is smaller, more contrastingly marked with black and white, and lacks the white band at the base of the tail.

Habitat. The open ocean.

Range. Known to breed only in the south Atlantic Ocean on islands in the Tristan da Cunha group. Wanders northward as far as Greenland and northern Europe; also to Africa and South America.

Status in Canada. Non-breeding summer visitant (May–October) to pelagic and offshore waters, rarely near shore, of Nova Scotia, southern New Brunswick, Newfoundland, north to northern Labrador and eastern Hudson Strait (Resolution Island). Scarce in the Gulf of St. Lawrence (Whale Head, Quebec).

Remarks. To see shearwaters one usually must go some ten or more miles out on the ocean, for ordinarily they do not come close to our shores. They are wonderful flyers, the long stiffly-held wings carrying them in effortless rapid glides over surprisingly long distances, especially when the wind is blowing. They fly low, often so close to the heaving water surface that one of the wing tips almost seems to drag as the bird banks gracefully. Shearwaters dive to pursue food but usually alight on the water before doing so. In dead calm they experience great difficulty in taking off, flapping awkwardly for considerable distances with alternately paddling feet.

These greedy feeders flock to fishing boats for the offal thrown overboard when fish cleaning is going on. They fight vigorously among themselves for possession of choice morsels, with squeals of delight or frustration. They feed on squids, caplin and other small fishes, offal, and similar sea food.

[Wedge-tailed Shearwater. *Puffinus pacificus* (Gmelin). Hypothetical. Jewett (1929, *The Auk* 46: 224) recorded a skin of this species labelled "Vancouver, B.C." with no other data, and the authority for the record is unknown.]

[New Zealand Shearwater. *Puffinus bulleri* Salvin. Hypothetical. Two observed by Nichols (1927, *The Auk* 44: 326–327) off the British Columbia coast on August 7, 1926. No specimen has been collected in Canada.]

SOOTY SHEARWATER
Le Puffin fuligineux. *Puffinus griseus* (Gmelin)
Plate 3. L. 16 to 18 in.

Upper and under parts sooty brown, becoming blackish on wings and tail. *Wing linings greyish white. Bill dusky.* Legs and feet blackish, purplish on inner sides of legs and webs.

Measurements. *Adult male:* wing, 255–298.5 (285.9); tail, 83.5–93 (88.8); exposed culmen, 39–43 (41.8); tarsus, 53.5–60.5 (56.8). *Adult female:* wing, 243.5–294 (270.8) mm.

Field Marks. An all-dark shearwater (including bill and feet) with whitish wing linings. The only dark-bellied shearwater likely to be seen on the Atlantic Coast of Canada. On the Pacific, the Pale-footed Shearwater is similar but has flesh-coloured bill, legs, and feet, and dark wing linings. The Slender-billed Shearwater has darker grey wing linings and a shorter tail, and it is smaller.

Habitat. The open ocean but tending to approach shore more often than most shearwaters.

Range. Breeds on islands near Cape Horn, near New Zealand, and off the coast of Chile. Wanders widely over the great oceans: north to the Aleutian Islands in the Pacific, to northern Labrador and (casually) southern Greenland in the Atlantic.

Status in Canada. A non-breeding summer visitant to pelagic and offshore waters of both the Atlantic and Pacific coasts. Fairly common off the Atlantic Coast from June to October off New Brunswick, Nova Scotia, Newfoundland, and Labrador north to eastern Hudson Strait; rare in the Gulf of St. Lawrence (Prince Edward Island; southeastern Quebec: Bonne Espérance; Anticosti Island). Common to abundant off the British Columbia coast (occasionally common in Strait of Georgia), occurring from early March to October. In winter recorded twice near Victoria.

SLENDER-BILLED SHEARWATER
Le Puffin à bec mince. *Puffinus tenuirostris* (Temminck)
Plate 3. L. 14 in.

Upper parts sooty or blackish. Under parts slightly paler. Wing linings usually greyish (sometimes whitish). Bill and feet dusky.

Field Marks. An all-dark shearwater of the Pacific. Its dark bill and legs distinguish it from the Pale-footed Shearwater. Very difficult to distinguish from Sooty Shearwater; its smaller size usually not apparent; the under side of the wings is usually more greyish, less whitish than in the Sooty, but there is much overlapping.

Habitat. The open ocean.

Range. Breeds on islands off southeastern Australia. After the breeding season it wanders widely over the Pacific Ocean and northward to the Aleutians.

Status in Canada. A common late summer and autumn visitant to the pelagic waters off British Columbia, occasionally entering waters of the coast littoral.

MANX SHEARWATER (Black-vented Shearwater)
Le Puffin manx. *Puffinus puffinus* (Brünnich)
L. 12.25 to 15.00 in.

P. p. opisthomelas: Upper parts sooty brown, becoming blackish on rump. Under parts mainly white with brownish grey wash on sides of neck, variable in extent, sometimes meeting across upper breast. Under tail coverts dark brown with paler tips. Wing linings mainly white. *P. p. puffinus:* Similar to *P. p. opisthomelas,* but upper parts black, under tail coverts mostly white (only outer webs of outermost black), and extensive brownish wash on sides of neck and upper breast lacking.

Field Marks. On the Pacific most likely to be confused with Pink-footed Shearwater but is a much smaller bird with a dark bill and with white instead of grey wing linings. It is a much smaller bird than the Greater and Cory's shearwaters of the Atlantic and lacks the white band at the base of the tail shown by the Greater; the bill is dark, not yellowish as in Cory's.

Habitat. The ocean.

Range. *P. p. opisthomelas* breeds on islands off Baja California. *P. p. puffinus* breeds in Bermuda, Salvages Islands, Madeira, the Azores, locally northward to the British Isles, the Faroes, and Iceland. Additional races are found in other parts of the world.

Status in Canada. Of casual occurrence on both coasts. (1) *Puffinus puffinus opisthomelas* Coues has been recorded off Vancouver Island: off Albert Head, October 24, 1891, November 1891; sight records of single birds off Cape Scott on July 15, 1940 (P. W. Martin) and Goose Islands Banks, August 14, 1948 (C. J. Guiguet). (2) *Puffinus puffinus puffinus* (Brünnich) has been taken off our Atlantic Coast. Newfoundland: a specimen at St. Anthony, May 24, 1947, and a sight record by V. C. Wynne-Edwards, 60 miles east of Cape Race (Peters and Burleigh, 1951); specimen off Cape Spear, July 10, 1958 (L. M. Tuck). New Brunswick: specimen labelled 'St. John,' no further data (Squires, 1952).

Subspecies (*see* Status in Canada). Until recently *opisthomelas* was considered a distinct species, the Black-vented Shearwater.

LITTLE SHEARWATER (Allied Shearwater)
Le Puffin obscur. *Puffinus assimilis* Gould
L. 11 in.

A small shearwater with contrasting black upper parts and white under parts. Very similar to the nominate race of the Manx Shearwater, *Puffinus puffinus puffinus*, but much smaller. Wing, 7 inches instead of 9 inches.

Range. Breeds on islands in the Atlantic (Tristan da Cunha, Gough, Canary, Salvages islands; Madeira and the Azores) and in the south Pacific (off southwestern Australia, Chatham, Norfolk, Lord Howe, and Kermadec islands).

Status in Canada. Accidental. One specimen taken on Sable Island, Nova Scotia, on September 1, 1896.

Subspecies. The above specimen is referable to *Puffinus assimilis baroli* Bonaparte.

BLACK-CAPPED PETREL
Le Diablotin errant. *Pterodroma hasitata* (Kuhl)
L. 14 to 16 in.

A rather heavy-bodied, stout-billed petrel with a dark cap, accentuated usually by a white collar and with white tail coverts and white at base of tail. Upper parts sooty becoming brown or greyish brown on back (feathers often with paler margins), darker on wings. End of tail similar to wings. *Base of tail and tail coverts, white.* Forehead, sides of head, and neck, white; with usually a white collar behind the dark cap. Under parts and wing linings, white. Bill black, stout (fulmar-like but with tip of lower mandible downcurved). There is a dark colour phase, which, however, retains the white upper tail coverts.

Status in Canada. Accidental. Three records, all for Ontario: a male found dead on Toronto Island, October 30, 1893; a specimen taken some 17 miles west of Toronto about 1893; one found dead at Morgan's Point, Welland County, Ontario, on August 21, 1955. Canadian specimens of this species, which breeds in much reduced numbers in the West Indies, are hurricane victims.

Family **Hydrobatidae** – Storm Petrels

Number of Species in North America 11; in Canada 4

Small (length 7 to 9 in.) ocean birds, somewhat swallow-like in flight. Of the four species known to occur in Canada three are dark sooty brown (appearing blackish at a distance) with a white rump patch; the fourth is ashy grey. They spend most of their lives on the ocean coming to land ordinarily only for nesting purposes. Flitting close to the surface of the ocean, often pattering up and down the waves as though walking on them, they are easily recognized as petrels. The upper mandible is decidedly hooked, the lower slightly so (*see* Fig. 11). The single nostril tube is situated on top of the bill at its base. They are the 'Mother Carey's Chickens' of the sailors.

FORK-TAILED PETREL
Le Pétrel à queue fourchue. *Oceanodroma furcata* (Gmelin)
Plate 3. L. 8 to 9 in.

A bluish grey petrel, palest on throat and under tail coverts. Area about eye blackish. Wings with more or less dusky or blackish on coverts, tips, and linings. Tail forked, bluish grey except whitish outer web of outermost feathers. Bill and legs black.

Measurements (*O. f. plumbea*). *Adult male:* wing, 145.3–155.9 (151.4); tail, 82.4–91.3 (86.5); exposed culmen, 13.9–15.2 (14.6); tarsus, 25.4–27 (26.2). *Adult female:* wing, 149.9–156.1 (153.2); tail 82.6–96.5 (88.5); exposed culmen, 13.9–15.3 (14.6); tarsus, 24.4–27.5 (25.7) mm (Grinnell and Test).

Field Marks. A pearl grey petrel of the west coast with a decidedly forked tail and no white rump patch.

Habitat. Open sea. In breeding season comes to land, usually coastal islands, for nesting.

Nesting. In colonies. Nest usually at end of a shallow burrow in soil; occasionally in rock crevices. *Egg*, one only; dull white, usually with a faint circle of tiny dark dots around the larger end. Incubation by both sexes.

Range. Breeds on the Kurile, Komandorskie, and Aleutian islands and southward along the North American Pacific Coast to northern California.

Range in Canada. Common throughout the year on coastal waters off British Columbia. It nests in scattered

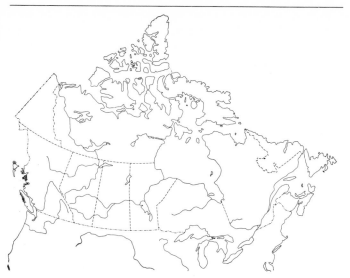

Breeding Distribution of Fork-tailed Petrel

colonies along the British Columbia coast (west coast of Vancouver Island; in Queen Charlotte Sound, and the Queen Charlotte Islands at Cox Island).

Subspecies. *Oceanodroma furcata plumbea* (Peale) is the only subspecies known to occur in Canada, although the slightly larger, slightly paler more northern nominate race might eventually be found as a visitant.

Remarks. Because of its colour, size, and habitat, this pretty petrel of the Pacific is not likely to be mistaken for any other bird. It is rather confiding and can readily be 'chummed up' to a boat with small scraps of fish liver and occasionally even be caught in the hand. Vocally it has a variety of soft twitterings and high-pitched squeaks.

LEACH'S PETREL

Le Pétrel cul-blanc. *Oceanodroma leucorhoa* (Vieillot)
Plate 3. L. 7.5 to 8.9 in.

Tail forked. Plumage including wing linings mainly sooty blackish brown. Wing coverts greyish brown. Upper tail coverts white (some middle ones greyish brown), creating a white rump patch. Bill, legs, and feet (including webs) blackish.

Fig. 11 Bill of Leach's Petrel

Measurements (*O. l. leucorhoa*). *Adult male:* wing, 145.5–159.5 (153.1); tail, 78.5–89.5 (84.2); exposed culmen, 15.5–17.5 (16.4); tarsus, 23.5–25.5 (24.3). *Adult female:* wing, 149.5–162 (154.3) mm.

Field Marks. A blackish petrel of both the east and west coasts with a white rump patch and a forked tail. Does not usually follow ships. On the east coast it is likely to be con-

fused with the similar Wilson's Petrel, but Wilson's has a square tail and (at very close range) yellow webs between the toes, and longer legs which project slightly beyond the tail. The Fork-tailed Petrel of the west coast is entirely different.

Habitat. The ocean. At nesting time, coastal islands, or rarely mainland headlands, either wooded or grassy and treeless.

Nesting. In colonies, often dense. Nest in a chamber (sometimes with a few grasses or similar soft material) at the end of a shallow burrow in the ground excavated mainly by the male. *Egg*, one only; dull white, usually with a faint wreath of lilac dots about the larger end. Incubation, by both sexes, is long, variously given 41 to 50 days, probably 41 to 42 days. Each bird may incubate for about 96 consecutive hours without food (at least up to 144 hours, according to W. A. O. Gross) and is relieved by its mate at night.

Range. Breeds locally in the north Pacific (northern Japan, the Kurile and Aleutian islands, and southeast along the Pacific Coast of North America to Baja California) and the north Atlantic (southern Labrador, Greenland, Iceland, and the Faroes south to Massachusetts and the British Isles).

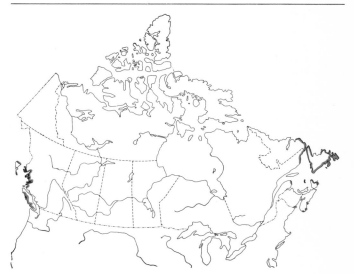

Breeding Distribution of Leach's Petrel

Range in Canada. Found on both the Pacific and Atlantic coasts. Breeds on the coastal islands of British Columbia where it is locally common but generally less numerous than the Fork-tailed Petrel. Occurs off the British Columbia coast throughout the year. On the Atlantic it nests on coastal islands (rarely the coastal mainland) from southern Labrador (Gannet Islands, St. Peter's Island), Newfoundland, Quebec (outer north shore of the Gulf of St. Lawrence at Boat Islands and off Romaine; Bonaventure Island; Bird Rocks), New Brunswick (Grand Manan Island), and Nova Scotia (Seal, Mud, Pearl, Ciboux, and St. Paul islands, and near Louisburg on the mainland of Cape Breton Island). Recorded in Nova Scotia from April 11 to November 13; in New Brunswick, April 23 to December. Accidental in Ontario (Cornwall, July 19, 1939; near Kingston, August 16, 1955). Casual in northern Quebec (near Fort Chimo, July 12, 1882) and probably eastern Baffin Island (Cape Mercy).

Subspecies. (1) *Oceanodroma leucorhoa leucorhoa* (Vieillot) is the breeding form of the Atlantic; also on the coast of Japan and the Aleutian Islands. (2) *Oceanodroma leucorhoa beali* Emerson, slightly smaller in size, breeds from se. Alaska south along the coast of B. C. to n. Calif.

Remarks. One could be standing in the middle of a petrel colony without knowing it. Although the ground below may be honeycombed with their burrows, the entrances are made inconspicuous by growing vegetation. During the daylight hours the incubating birds do not stir, and their mates remain far out at sea. Even the faint musky odour exuded by these birds is recognizable only to the few who are familiar with it. When darkness comes on, however, the colony bustles with activity as these ocean foragers return to relieve their incubating mates. The air comes alive with sounds of flitting wings, eerie voices, and ghost-like forms. When daylight returns, the colony again appears deserted.

Like other petrels, this one spends most of its life on the trackless ocean coming ashore only for nesting. Its food includes molluscs, crustaceans, small fishes, and oily materials gleaned from the ocean. It also takes refuse matter left by whales. This petrel can be attracted to a boat by throwing bits of fish liver overboard. As in other petrels, the stomach contains an oily, orange-coloured liquid, which is ejected by the birds apparently as a protection. Its strong musky smell persists on museum specimens indefinitely.

This harmless, gentle bird has many enemies. Cats, dogs, and rats introduced onto islands where it nests can soon wipe out whole colonies. Perhaps before the coming of the white man, it nested more frequently on the mainland, but it rarely does so today. It is probably significant that the nearest thing to a mainland colony ever seen by the writer (a small one near Louisburg, Cape Breton Island, Nova Scotia, where near-mainland conditions prevail) was made conspicuous by the wings of dead petrels left lying about by some predator. Larger gulls take a heavy toll by pursuing and capturing petrels, especially on moonlit nights. Lights at lighthouses lure others to their deaths.

HARCOURT'S PETREL (Madeira Petrel)

Le Pétrel de Harcourt. *Oceanodroma castro* (Harcourt)
L. 7.75 to 8.10 in.

Like Leach's Petrel but tail less-deeply forked, white rump patch not divided by a dark grey median area, but the feathers of the rump patch have blackish tips, and the white of rump extends to and across the under parts near the base of the tail (not merely as a few white feathers).

Status in Canada. Accidental. One record. A female, *Oceanodroma castro castro* (Harcourt) was found alive on the Rideau River, near Ottawa, Ontario, on August 28, 1933. This race of the species breeds on islands in the Atlantic Ocean from the Azores south to Ascension and St. Helena islands.

WILSON'S PETREL

Le Pétrel océanique. *Oceanites oceanicus* (Kuhl)
Plate 3. L. 7 to 7.5 in.

Tail not forked. General colour blackish brown, the secondary wing coverts greyish with narrow whitish margins. Upper tail coverts white, under tail coverts mainly white basally. Base of tail with more or less (concealed) white. Bill, legs, and toes black, webs yellowish.

Field Marks. In Canada an Atlantic species. It resembles the Leach's Petrel but has a square instead of a forked tail. The toes extend beyond the tip of the tail when the bird is flying. The yellow webs between the toes are diagnostic, if they can be seen. Often follow ships.

Habitat. The ocean.

Range. Ranges widely over the oceans except the north Pacific. Breeds on the South Orkneys, South Shetlands, Antarctica, and on islands near Cape Horn.

Status in Canada. A fairly common to common non-breeding summer visitant, mainly to pelagic and offshore waters (but sometimes coming close to shore) of Nova Scotia, New Brunswick, Newfoundland, and perhaps southern Labrador (sight records only). Sometimes found in the Gulf of St. Lawrence (near Bonne Espérance, P.Q.; Miscou Island, N.B.). Accidental in southwestern Quebec (Lake Deschênes, Sept. 23, 1938) and southern Ontario (Long Beach, August 14, 1955; Lake Muskoka, 1897).

Subspecies. *Oceanites oceanicus oceanicus* (Kuhl).

Remarks. The Wilson's Petrel, like the Greater and Sooty shearwaters, nests and raises its young during our winters (its summers) in the Southern Hemisphere. It 'winters' during our summers in the Northern Hemisphere on pelagic and offshore waters to the Atlantic Ocean, regularly from June to September.

[Storm Petrel. *Hydrobates pelagicus* (Linnaeus). Erroneously recorded. Records for Canada prove to be based on misidentifications of other species.]

Order **Pelecaniformes**–Tropicbirds, Pelicans, Cormorants, Frigatebirds, and Allies

This Order comprises fish-eating birds with all four toes connected by webs, a pouch extending from bottom of bill to throat, nostrils either small or absent, and the bill, except in tropicbirds, boobies, and gannets, with a hook at the tip.

Family **Phaëthontidae**–Tropicbirds

Number of Species in North America 3; in Canada 1

Medium-sized marine birds, boldly marked in white and black, the adults with greatly elongated central tail feathers and with a bill gently tapered and pointed, not hooked (*see* Fig. 12). Unlike gulls, they fly with quick wing beats. Their streaming tail feathers separate them readily from both gulls and terns. They are birds of the tropical and subtropical seas and of accidental occurrence in Canada.

[**Red-billed Tropicbird.** Le Paille-en-queue à bec rouge. *Phaëthon aethereus* Linnaeus. Hypothetical. References by authors to the occurrence of this species on the Newfoundland banks seem to be based on P. E. Freke's assertion that he 'noticed' this bird there in August 1876 (*see* Peters and Burleigh, 1951).]

WHITE-TAILED TROPICBIRD
(Yellow-billed Tropicbird)
   Le Paille-en-queue à bec jaune. *Phaëthon lepturus* Daudin
   L. 28 to 32 in.

Adults: Central tail feathers extremely elongated and slender (19 or 20 inches long). Plumage mainly white, often with a suggestion of pink. A broad black stripe through the eye. Outer webs of primaries, median wing coverts, and tertials, black. Flanks with greyish black streaks. Bill gently tapering, pointed, *orange. Immatures:* Similar but central tail feathers only slightly elongated, back barred with black, and bill yellow.
   Habitat. Salt water, normally tropical.
   Range. Breeds in Bermuda, the Bahamas, the West Indies, the south Atlantic, southwest Pacific, and Indian oceans.
   Status in Canada. Accidental. Four specimens, *Phaëthon lepturus catesbyi* Brandt, for Nova Scotia (Shubenacadie, September 6, 1870; Wolfville, August 27, 1927; Brier Island, October 7, 1962; Cape Sable, October 9, 1962).

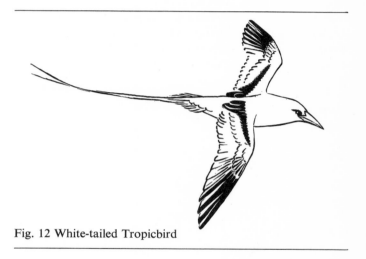

Fig. 12 White-tailed Tropicbird

Family **Pelecanidae**–Pelicans

Number of Species in North America 2; in Canada 2

Very large water birds with long, flattened bill, conspicuous gular pouch, long wings, short tail, robust legs, and fully-webbed toes. Upper mandible is hooked at tip; lower mandible has a large naked pouch, which is connected with the throat and is capable of great distension.

WHITE PELICAN
   Le Pélican blanc. *Pelecanus erythrorhynchos* Gmelin
   Plate 4. L. 55 to 70 in.

Wingspread 8 to nearly 10 feet. *Adults:* Bill long, flattened, with very conspicuous pouch, and in the breeding season an upright horny process on the culmen. Plumage mostly white with wing tips (primaries and many secondaries) black. Breast and lesser wing coverts with narrow lanceolate feathers tinged yellow. Bill and pouch yellow with reddish tinge. Bare skin around eyes, orange; eyelids red. Feet orange-red. *Immatures:* Similar, but feathers on back of head ashy grey, bill and feet duller.
   Measurements. *Adult male:* wing, 586–614(602.5); tail, 157–162 (158.5); exposed culmen, 332–365 (347.3); tarsus, 119.5–124.5 (121.8). *Adult female:* wing, 533.5–543 (538.3) mm.

Field Marks. Unmistakable pelican outline. A very large white water bird with black wing tips and a conspicuous yellow throat pouch. Flies with neck doubled back against the shoulders. The Whooping Crane, Snow Goose, and Gannet are also large white birds with black wing tips, but they fly with outstretched neck. North American swans are all-white with no black in the wings; they fly with outstretched neck.

Habitat. In breeding season, interior lakes in both treeless and forested country. In winter, the sea-coast and freshwater lakes.

Nesting. In colonies, on islands of interior lakes. Nest, a depression on the ground usually with various kinds of debris scraped up about the rim; sometimes on matted-down vegetation. *Eggs*, usually 2; white, usually nest-stained. Incubation is by both sexes.

Range. Breeds locally from southwestern Canada south to southern California, northern Utah, southern Montana, and South Dakota. Winters from southern United States to Guatemala.

Breeding Distribution of White Pelican

Range in Canada. Local summer resident in the western provinces. Breeds locally from southern interior British Columbia (Stum Lake), northern Alberta (near Fort Smith, N.W.T., but just south of the Mackenzie boundary), northern Saskatchewan (Preston Lake), central Manitoba (Talbot Lake), and western Ontario (Lake of the Woods), south through the International Boundary. Recorded in summer on Great Slave Lake, Mackenzie District. A common and fairly regular transient through the Nicola and Kamloops regions of British Columbia. One winter record (Cowichan Bay, British Columbia, February 28, 1947). Stragglers recorded from northern Mackenzie (Liverpool Bay, June or July, 1900); northern Ontario (Hannah Bay, June 1943); southern Ontario and southern Quebec (various records); New Brunswick (Grand Manan; Pointe du Chêne; Cape Spencer; and near St. Stephen); and Nova Scotia (Kings County, about fifty between September 27 and October 15, 1948).

PLATE 3

1 Sooty Shearwater

2 Slender-billed Shearwater

3 Black-footed Albatross

4 Greater Shearwater

5 Fork-tailed Petrel

6 Leach's Petrel

7 Wilson's Petrel

8 Northern Fulmar, light phase

1a

2

1b

3a

3b

4a

4b

5a

5b

6a

6b

Crosby

PLATE 4

1 Gannet,
    (a) adult
    (b) first-year immature

2 White Pelican, adult

3 Pelagic Cormorant,
    (a) immature
    (b) adult in fresh
        breeding plumage

4 Brandt's Cormorant,
    (a) immature
    (b) adult in fresh
        breeding plumage

5 Double-crested
  Cormorant,
    (a) immature
    (b) adult in fresh
        breeding plumage

6 Great Cormorant,
    (a) adult in fresh
        breeding plumage
    (b) immature

Remarks. Canadian bird life offers few more spectacular sights than a long line or V of precisely spaced White Pelicans flying majestically across the prairie sky. The snowy whiteness of the great birds, enhanced by the jet black wing tips and enriched by the yellow bill and feet, stands out oddly, even far in the distance. They flap in unison half a dozen times, glide, flap again, then glide. Every motion is easy, unhurried, graceful, even in the strongest prairie gales. They are excellent gliders and often spend considerable time high in the air. In an amazingly short time after take-off, these ponderous birds, with wingspreads up to nearly ten feet, can become mere tiny white specks in the sky overhead. Occasionally their descent is highly spectacular, for sometimes they drop down like meteors, the wind rushing like thunder through their half-closed wings. They are highly gregarious; feeding, roosting, flying, and nesting in flocks.

On the water they float with surprising buoyancy. Take-off, while briefly laboured, is rapid for such large birds. Unlike Brown Pelicans, they do not often dive from the air but catch their food on or near the water surface while swimming or wading. They eat fishes, frogs, and salamanders. Competent studies show that the fishes taken include vast numbers of minnows and that most of the larger species captured by them are slow-moving non-game fish of little interest to man. Judging by the number of inquiries received from prospective visitors to the Prairie Provinces as to where pelicans may be seen, they are one of the attractions the Prairies have for Easterners. Although its numbers have decreased in many of its prairie haunts, the White Pelican is one of few large birds that still can be seen in something resembling former numbers. This magnificent bird should not be destroyed for petty or imaginary reasons.

BROWN PELICAN
Le Pélican brun. *Pelecanus occidentalis* Linnaeus
L. 44 to 54 in.

Bill and pouch shape similar to that of White Pelican. *Adults in summer:* Head mainly white (yellowish on top), this extending down neck framing the pouch; rest of neck and hind head dark chestnut brown. Upper parts grey, somewhat streaked with brown. Under parts dark brown. *Adults in winter:* Similar to adults in summer but hind head and hind-neck white. *Immature:* Head and neck dark brown. Under parts whitish, the sides tinged with brownish grey.

Field Marks. Great pouched bill, large size, pelican outline. Brown and grey coloration is very different from that of the White Pelican. Unlike the White Pelican, it dives from the air.

Range. Breeds from South Carolina and California southward along the coasts to Central and South America; also the Greater and Lesser Antilles.

Status in Canada. Casual visitant to the coast of British Columbia (Queen Charlotte Straits, July 18, 1913; Race Rocks, January 1898, August 1939; Burrard Inlet, November 1880; Esquimalt Harbour, November 24, 1904; Victoria, December 19, 1932, November 7–16, 1935). Accidental in Nova Scotia (Prospect, December 1896; Three Fathom Harbour, June 1899; Clark's Harbour, June 1924; Louis-

29

burg, May 19, 1904; River John, May 31, 1885; Pictou Island, May 15, 1892).

Subspecies. British Columbia specimens are referred to *P. o. californicus* Ridgway. I have not been able to examine N. S. specimens which probably are *P. o. carolinensis* Gmelin, but there is a possibility of the occurrence of the West Indian race, *P. o. occidentalis*, there also.

Family **Sulidae** – Boobies and Gannets

Number of Species in North America 5; in Canada 2

Large, long-winged marine birds with a small inconspicuous throat pouch. On the wing, they frequently interrupt their flapping with short glides and often dive from the air. Their bills are rather long, tapered, straight (but more or less decurved at tip, not hooked). Although marine, they are not usually found far at sea, preferring the vicinity of the coast. Only the Gannet is boreal in distribution.

BROWN BOOBY (White-bellied Booby)
Le Fou brun. *Sula leucogaster* (Boddaert)
L. 30 in.

Adults: Head, neck, chest, and upper parts brown. Lower breast and belly white, contrasting sharply with brown of chest. Bill and feet yellowish. Juvenals are greyish brown, palest on the belly.

Range. Breeds in the West Indies and widely in tropical and sub-tropical parts of the Atlantic, Pacific, and Indian oceans.

Status in Canada. Accidental. One record only. A specimen was found alive near Blanche, Shelburne Co., Nova Scotia, on July 28, 1941, by A. D. Simmons. It was very tame, permitting handling. Mr. Simmons's photograph and description of it are readily identifiable. The subspecies could not be determined, but it probably was *Sula leucogaster leucogaster* (Boddaert).

GANNET
Le Fou de Bassan. *Morus bassanus* (Linnaeus)
Plate 4. L. 34 to 40 in.

Bill somewhat longer than head, tapering, sharp-pointed (upper mandible slightly decurved near tip, but not hooked). *Adults:* Mainly white, the head and neck with a yellowish suffusion. Wing tips and bare skin about eye, black. Bill greyish. Iris pale grey. *Immature in first year:* Head, neck, and upper parts, dark greyish brown or slate with white triangular spots, particularly numerous on head and neck. Belly white with grey feather margins. Various stages of immaturity occur between the first-year birds, just described, and the adults, one stage presenting a rather striking piebald appearance.

Measurements. *Adult male:* wing (flattened), 487–511.5 (501.1); tail, 189.5–225.5 (214.5); exposed culmen, 93.5–107 (99.1); tarsus, 59–65 (62.5). *Adult female:* wing (flattened), 485–503 (495.9) mm.

Field Marks. A large marine bird. Adults might be confused with gulls, but the black of the wing tips is more extensive and is more sharply cut off from the white than in large gulls. Even at considerable distances Gannets are whiter-backed than the gulls that usually associate with them. In any plumage the longer bill, head, and neck of Gannets project farther ahead of the body than in gulls. This silhouette in flight, as well as the pointed tail, gives Gannets a characteristic 'pointed at both ends look.'

Habitat. Coastal salt water, but not often far at sea. Accidental inland. In the breeding season, for nesting, rocky islands usually with steep cliffs; sometimes mainland cliffs.

Nesting. In colonies, sometimes very large, on coastal islands. Nest is placed on ledges of cliffs and sometimes on the flat top of coastal islands above the cliffs. Nest is mainly of seaweed (sometimes sticks and other debris are added), nest material varying from bulky to little or none. Nests usually close together. *Egg*, one only; white with pale bluish tinge, generally nest-stained. Incubation variously given 42 to 46 days, one instance of 46 days (W. Duval); by both sexes. One brood annually.

Range. Breeds very locally along the North Atlantic coast from Nova Scotia (formerly) north to Newfoundland; also in Iceland, the Faroes, and the British Isles. Winters along the coasts from Virginia to Florida and from the British Isles to the Azores.

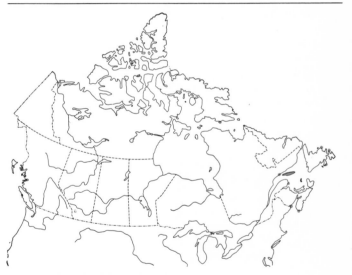

Breeding Distribution of Gannet

Range in Canada. Fairly common in spring, summer, and autumn on the Atlantic Coast (recorded March to December). Breeds in southeastern Quebec (Anticosti Island, Bonaventure Island, Magdalen Islands; formerly Perroquet Island, Mingan group, until about 1887), Newfoundland (Funk Island, Baccalieu Island, Cape St. Mary's); formerly in New Brunswick (Gannet Rock, south of Grand Manan, until about 1866), and Nova Scotia (Gannet Rock, until about 1880). Recorded in summer along the Atlantic Coast at points far distant from the actual breeding colonies, regularly in small numbers off Prince Edward Island, and north to southern Labrador (Ramah Bay). Accidental inland at various localities in the upper St. Lawrence River Valley, Ottawa River, Lake Ontario, and Lake Erie (e.g., Montreal, Ottawa, Kingston, Toronto, Niagara River).

Remarks. Some three miles off the picturesque village of Percé, P.Q., the famous Bonaventure Island Gannet colony provides thousands of visitors each year with one of the most spectacular and readily accessible ornithological sights on this continent. As the boat rounds a projecting corner of the island, the great Gannet ledges come into view, all snowy white with birds. In passing slowly along the base of the 400-foot cliffs the motor boat disturbs the birds, and they leave the ledges like snow before a wind. Thousands of glistening white Gannets scale and wheel in every direction, and all the while a dull roar persists, the united voices of the additional thousands still on the ledges.

In recent years, since the island became a sanctuary, the colony has flourished (D. B. Peakall recently estimated 13,250 nests there) and has overflowed to the flat top of the island above the cliffs, a veritable snowfield of birds. There they can be studied at close range, for they are extremely tame. Within a short time their fighting, courting, nest building, incubation, displays, feeding of the young, and weird flight take-offs may be seen.

Although Gannets are usually silent elsewhere, the breeding grounds are a bedlam of harsh, loud *kar-úck, kar-úck, kar-úck*, which often sounds like 'get out, get out, get out.' The nests are placed close together, and there is a good deal of quarrelling. Although the bill is powerful, with serrated sharp cutting edges that can easily cut to the bone a human hand or finger, the birds do not often injure one another seriously in these encounters.

Take-off from a crowded colony is a strange procedure. The bird wanting to leave for a flight solemnly raises the head and points the bill tip skyward, partly spreads the wings and depresses the tail. With weird moans it waddles and hops its way toward the cliff edge or a less crowded part of the colony. Each time it passes too close to a neighbour, a furore is created with many a bill thrust and vocal threat received. Using both legs and wings, it rushes ahead and becomes airborne. Once in the air its flight is easy and graceful, alternating flaps and glides.

In midsummer some nests contain young of various sizes; others have eggs still being incubated. During incubation the two large webbed feet are placed over the single egg. Gannets have no incubation patch. The newly hatched young are greyish black, almost naked, and very ugly. Later they grow a woolly white covering of down.

Earliest spring arrival date at Bonaventure Island noted by William Duval, for many years the warden, is March 22, 1952. Earliest egg date is April 26, 1951; average May 2 to 4.

Gannets secure their fish food by diving from heights up to 100 feet in the air. When a fish is sighted, the bird checks its speed momentarily, half closes its wings, and drops head-first like an arrow, vertically or on a slight plane. As it hits the water it sends the spray high into the air. A flock of diving Gannets is a fascinating sight. They are useful to fishermen in providing the location of fish schools. Gannets do not remain long under water but almost invariably they manage to swallow their prey before emerging. Bonaventure

Gannets in the breeding season eat herring, mackerel, capelin, and squid.

This picturesque bird is now protected by law, and Bonaventure Island is a sanctuary. This was not always so. Taverner (1918, *Ottawa Nat.* 32: 21–26) gives a graphic account of the senseless slaughter of the Bonaventure Gannets that used to take place. At the same time he predicted that the time would come when the people would realize that the Bonaventure colony would be a source of attraction to strangers and an asset too valuable to be wantonly destroyed. Not long ago it was estimated, doubtless very conservatively, that the Gannets of Bonaventure bring $100,000 annually to the village of Percé in tourist trade.

Family **Phalacrocoracidae** – Cormorants

Number of Species in North America 6; in Canada 4

Large water birds, 25 to 36 inches long, the adults shiny black. Bill slender, upper mandible strongly hooked. Adults have no external nostrils and therefore breathe through the mouth. They have a small naked throat pouch, a bare space about the eyes, and a stiff and rather long tail. All four toes are connected by webs. They inhabit both salt and fresh water. Their food is mainly fishes, which are taken by underwater pursuit; sometimes amphibians and crustaceans.

Field Marks. Adults are big black water birds, generally larger and longer than ducks. Cormorants often fly in lines or V-formation, like geese, but the all-blackness of adults distinguishes them, and the longer, slenderer tail of cormorants is diagnostic in any plumage. Loons lack the long tail and have gleaming white under parts. When cormorants perch, they sit very upright, sometimes with half-spread wings. On the water they hold the bill higher than loons or geese.

GREAT CORMORANT (European Cormorant)
Le Grand Cormoran. *Phalacrocorax carbo* (Linnaeus)
Plate 4. L. 34 to 40 in.

Bill slender, rather long, hooked. Feathers of throat impinge in a point on the throat pouch. Tail feathers, fourteen in number. *Spring and summer adults:* Mainly shiny bluish black or greenish black, but feathers of upper back, scapulars, and wing coverts bronzy brown with broad black margins. In spring, white hairlike feathers (lost by early summer) are scattered over head and neck, and there is a white patch on the flanks (also lost by early summer). Throat pouch dull yellow, bare, bordered behind by white feathers. Iris green. *Winter adults:* Similar but white feathers on head, neck, and flanks wanting. *Immatures:* Mainly brownish black with more or less white on belly and breast, the light areas of under parts thus usually more extensive than in the Double-crested.

Measurements. *Adult male:* wing, 340–366 (355.7); tail, 150–169.5 (156.9); exposed culmen, 70–82.2 (77.8); tarsus, 67–74 (71.7). *Adult female:* wing, 326–346.5 (341.9) mm.

Field Marks. As this cormorant is confined in Canada to the Atlantic Coast, the slightly smaller Double-crested Cormorant is the only other cormorant likely to be seen with it. Adult Greats in summer have a white hind border to the throat pouch, and in late winter and in spring a small white patch on the flanks. The adult Double-crest, on the Atlantic Coast, has no white patch. The Great has a yellowish throat pouch, not *orange*-yellow, as in the Double-crest. Immature Greats usually (not always) have white bellies, white extending to the base of the tail; thus the pale areas of under parts are usually more extensive than in Double-crests of similar age. *Voice:* Usually silent, but on nesting ledges adults have a variety of growls, croaks, and chucks. Downy young have high-pitched whining notes, a little like a Semipalmated Plover.

Habitat. Frequents coastal salt water, usually not venturing seaward beyond sight of land. Sometimes visits fresh waters near the coast. Rests on coastal islands, rocks, shore cliffs, piling, and sand bars. Nests on coastal cliffs, sometimes trees.

Nesting. In colonies often mixed with Double-crested Cormorants on coastal cliffs and islands, preferring the higher ledges. Nest, a rather bulky pile of seaweed and sticks usually on cliff ledges or flat cliff tops, rarely (McKinnon Point and Durrell Point, P. E. I.) in low trees. *Eggs*, usually 3 or 4; bluish green or bluish white with chalky covering. Incubation, about 28 days (Witherby) by both sexes. One brood annually.

Range. Breeds in Europe, Asia, Africa, and Australia, southern Greenland, and the southern Atlantic Coast of Canada.

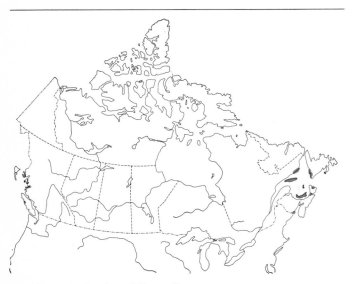

Breeding Distribution of Great Cormorant

Range in Canada. Breeds locally along the Atlantic Coast in Newfoundland (Port au Port Peninsula, Guernsey Island, Coal River); Quebec (Anticosti Island; Magdalen Islands; Lake Island, St. Mary Islands, Outer Wapitagun Islands); Prince Edward Island (Cape Tryon, East Point, McKinnon Point, Durrell Point); Nova Scotia (Hertford Island; Crystal Farm, Antigonish County); and formerly on Grand Manan

Island, New Brunswick. Anticosti Island has the largest breeding population (sixteen known colonies). Winters in southern Canadian waters north to Newfoundland and the outer north shore of the Gulf of St. Lawrence, but many individuals move somewhat farther south into United States waters. Accidental far inland (Toronto, Ontario, November 21, 1896).

Subspecies. *Phalacrocorax carbo carbo* (Linnaeus) is the race inhabiting Canada, Iceland, and n. Europe. Seven additional races are found in other parts of the World.

Remarks. In 1940, the known breeding population of the Great Cormorant in Canada was 2,172 birds (H. F. Lewis, *The Auk* 58: 360–363). This, however, did not include 360 individuals in Newfoundland nor 242 individuals found later in Prince Edward Island. Probably the total Canadian breeding population was then close to 3,000 birds.

DOUBLE-CRESTED CORMORANT
Le Cormoran à aigrettes. *Phalacrocorax auritus* (Lesson) Plate 4. L. 29 to 35 in.

Bill rather long (2.0 to 2.5 in.), slender, hooked. Tail feathers, twelve. Feathers of hind edge of throat pouch not impinging in a point on its bare skin. *Adults:* Mainly shiny greenish black, the feathers of upper back and wing coverts bronzy with black margins. Naked throat pouch and skin around and in front of eye, orange-yellow. Spring adults have an inconspicuous tuft of feathers on either side of head (shed early in nesting season), which is black in eastern race, largely white in western races. Bill dusky, sometimes mixed with yellow; iris green; legs and feet black. *First-year immatures:* Mostly dark sooty brown, paler below with much buff streaked with brown, the belly darker than the breast. Feathers of back and wing coverts with dark margins.

Measurements (*P. a. auritus*). *Adult male:* wing, 301–321 (309.2); tail, 132–154.5 (140.2); exposed culmen, 59–64.5 (61.2); tarsus, 62–69 (66.3). *Adult female:* wing, 273–313 (292.5) mm.

Field Marks. The only cormorant likely to be seen in the interior. On the Atlantic Coast likely to be confused with only one species (*see* Great Cormorant). On the Pacific Coast, the Double-crest's orange-yellow throat pouch separates it from the other cormorants found there. *Voice:* Usually silent except on nesting grounds. In courtship a series of *oak, oak, oak* sometimes dwindling to *tick, tick, tick;* a loud *hawk;* a louder *r-r-r-o-o-o-p;* a variety of croaks; young during and shortly after hatching *weet-weet-weet;* more mature young have a variety of high-pitched squeaking notes.

Habitat. Freshwater lakes and rivers, estuaries, coastal salt water but usually not far at sea. Nests on cliff ledges and their flat tops, and in trees near water. Rests on cliffs, rocks, gravel bars, and piling near water.

Nesting. In colonies, sometimes in association with other cormorants, gulls, etc. near either fresh or salt water. Nests placed on bare rock or soil on rocks, islets, cliff ledges and tops, or in trees near water. Nest is moderately bulky; composed usually of sticks, weed stalks, seaweed and other available materials. *Eggs*, usually 3 or 4 (2 to 7 recorded);

Breeding Distribution of Double-crested Cormorant

pale greenish blue with chalky covering, soon becoming nest-stained. Incubation averages about 28 days (van Tets *in* Drent and Guiguet), 24½ to 29 days (various authors), by both parents.

Range. Breeds from southwestern Alaska, central Alberta, James Bay, and Newfoundland south to Mexico and the Bahamas.

Range in Canada and Subspecies. (1) *Phalacrocorax auritus auritus* (Lesson) is a locally distributed spring, summer, and autumn resident breeding locally from Alberta east to the Atlantic Coast, north to central Alberta (very locally: probably Lac la Biche), central Saskatchewan (Peter Pond Lake), central Manitoba (Talbot Lake), southern James Bay (Way Rock), the north shore of the Gulf of St. Lawrence, and Newfoundland southward; formerly southern Labrador. Accidental on southern Baffin Island (Frobisher Bay). (2) *Phalacrocorax auritus albociliatus* Ridgway breeds on the coast of southern British Columbia (Bare Island, near Sidney, Vancouver Island; Ballingall Island) and winters in the same general region. (3) *Phalacrocorax auritus cincinatus* (Brandt) winters commonly about Vancouver Island but is not known to breed in Canada. The species (subspecies not determined) has been recorded in summer in interior British Columbia and is of casual occurrence in southern Yukon (Dawson).

Remarks. On the water, cormorants ride low with the tail submerged. They are excellent swimmers and divers. Dives are made from the water's surface and are usually of 20 to 30 seconds' duration but sometimes longer. Ordinarily underwater propulsion is by the feet alone, but sometimes the wings are used also. Take-off from water requires considerable paddling, flapping, and splashing. Once in the air they fly well with steady flaps. Occasionally there are glides over short distances. Often they fly low over the water, but occasionally, particularly when in flocks, they fly at considerable heights. Flying flocks may be in single-line formation, in more or less asymmetrical V's, or without obvious formation. On land they walk rather awkwardly. When perched, they have a characteristic habit of often partly extending both wings, holding them stationary in that position or sometimes waving them gently.

Cormorants are fish-eaters. Extensive studies of the food of this species made by H. F. Lewis in eastern Canada revealed that it usually does little economic harm.

BRANDT'S CORMORANT
Le Cormoran de Brandt
Phalacrocorax penicillatus (Brandt)
Plate 4. L. 28 to 35 in.

Throat pouch with a narrow finger of feathers extending forward from mid-throat onto throat pouch. Head never crested. *Adults:* Black with greenish or bluish iridescence. Throat pouch dull blue. Small patch behind throat pouch pale brown contrasting with rest of head and on shoulders. In nuptial plumage with long white hair-like feathers on sides of head. *Immatures:* Mainly dark brown (blackish on top of head, hind-neck, rump, and tail) and with a very pale patch behind throat pouch.

Measurements. *Adult male:* wing, 272.5–284 (279.9); tail, 106.5–129 (116.2); exposed culmen, 68–71.5 (69.9); tarsus, 62.5–67 (65). *Adult female:* wing, 257.5–267.5 (262.8) mm.

Field Marks. A Pacific Coast species. The dull blue throat pouch is often not discernible but is very different from the yellow one of the Double-crested Cormorant in all plumages. The small pale brown area at the base of the bill is lacking in the Pelagic, a slightly smaller species with less heavy head and bill. In spring Pelagics show a white flank patch when flying which Brandt's never have.

Habitat. Coastal salt water, nesting and roosting on rocky islands.

Nesting. In colonies, usually on rocky islands. Nest of seaweed, moss, and grass. *Eggs*, usually 4; pale bluish white.

Range. Breeds along the Pacific Coast from southern British Columbia to Baja California. Some winter in southern coastal British Columbia.

Range in Canada. Rather common winter visitant and local breeder on the coast of British Columbia. Breeds on small islands on west side of Vancouver Island, between Tofino and Ucluelet.

PELAGIC CORMORANT
Le Cormoran pélagique. *Phalacrocorax pelagicus* Pallas
Plate 4. L. 25 to 26 in.

Throat pouch small, the bare part much restricted. Bare skin on face and throat dull red. Head crested in nesting season. *Adults:* Mainly black with purplish iridescence on head and neck, greenish and purplish gloss on back. In nuptial plumage with a crest on forehead, another on crown; narrow white feathers on sides of neck; a white patch on each flank, but these are lost by early summer. *Immatures:* Pale sooty brown, slightly paler below.

Measurements (*P. p. pelagicus*). *Adult male:* wing, 271–290 (276.5); exposed culmen, 45–55 (50.2). *Adult female:* wing, 247–274 (260.7) mm (Palmer, 1962).

Field Marks. In spring (February to July) shows white flank patches in flight, lacking in other Pacific Coast species.

Its dull red throat pouch is difficult to see but is very different from the yellow one of the Double-crested. It lacks the pale area behind the throat pouch shown by Brandt's and is smaller (with slenderer neck and bill) and glossier. *Voice:* On the breeding cliffs various groans, but usually the bird is silent.

Habitat. Coastal salt water. Reported to dive more deeply than other cormorants. Rests on sand bars, rocky islands, cliffs, logs, piling, etc. For nesting it tends to use the narrow ledges of precipitous cliffs more extensively than other cormorants.

Nesting. In colonies often with other bird species. Nests on narrow ledges of steep cliffs facing the sea, on islands, and sometimes even on lighthouses; nest rather bulky, composed of seaweed, grass, sticks, and moss. *Eggs*, usually 3 or 4; pale bluish with chalky deposit, often nest-stained. Incubation averages 31 days, by both parents (G. F. van Tets *in* Drent and Guiguet).

Range. The north Pacific from northeastern Siberia to Japan and southern China; Bering Sea; and from Alaska to Baja California.

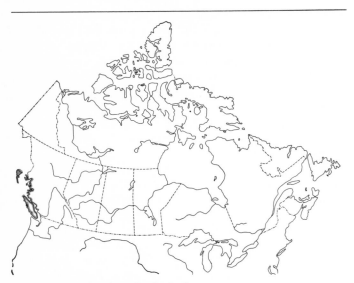

Breeding Distribution of Pelagic Cormorant

Range in Canada. Common permanent resident along the British Columbia coast.

Subspecies. (1) *Phalacrocorax pelagicus resplendens* Audubon breeds commonly along the s. coast of B. C. (near Victoria and for an undetermined distance northward). (2) *P. p. pelagicus* Pallas averages larger with a comparatively heavier bill, breeds on Queen Charlotte Is., and visits the coast of s. B. C. in winter.

[Red-faced Cormorant. Le Cormoran à face rouge. *Phalacrocorax urile* (Gmelin). Erroneously recorded (*Birds of Canada*, p. 59; *The Auk*, 1927, Vol. 44, p. 219–220). The writer has examined the specimen (NMC 4066, Departure Bay, B.C., April 7, 1910) on which rests the supposed evidence of occurrence in Canada of this Siberian and Alaskan species. It is unquestionably *P. auritus*. The feathers of the throat impinge abnormally on the gular sac. This condition is due to damage to the skin, which is so cleverly repaired that it escaped the notice of several authorities who examined it previously.]

Family **Anhingidae** – Darters

Number of Species in North America 1; in Canada 1

ANHINGA
L'Anhinga. *Anhinga anhinga* (Linnaeus)
Fig. 13. L. 34 to 36 in.

Cormorant-like but much slenderer, with snakier neck, much longer tail, and unhooked, heron-like, sharply pointed bill. In adults the outer webs of the two middle tail feathers are decidedly crimped. *Adult male:* Mainly black with greenish iridescence. Back and scapulars streaked and spotted with silvery grey; wing coverts white. Tail with brownish grey tip. *Adult female:* Similar but head, neck, and breast brownish. *Immature:* Mainly brownish.

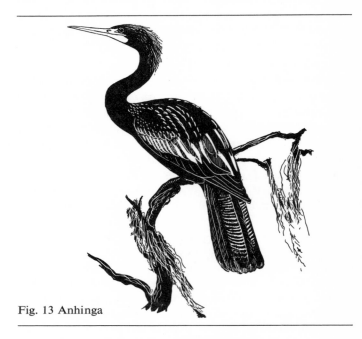

Fig. 13 Anhinga

Range. Tropical and sub-tropical Americas.
Status in Canada. Accidental in Ontario (Wellington, September 7, 1904; Garden River, about 1881).
Subspecies. *Anhinga anhinga leucogaster* (Vieillot).

Family **Fregatidae** – Frigatebirds

Number of Species in North America 1; in Canada 1

Frigatebirds are found throughout the tropical seas. With a greater wingspread in proportion to their body weight than probably any other bird, they are marvellous flyers. Facing the wind they can remain in the air for long periods, as motionless as a boy's kite. When feeding, they perform swift, ineffably graceful darts as they catch fish near the water surface or pursue gulls and terns, forcing them to give up their prey. They have extremely long forked tails, tiny feet, and rather long bills, both mandibles of which are decidedly hooked at the tip. They have a small throat pouch which is capable of great distention.

MAGNIFICENT FRIGATEBIRD (Man-o'-war-bird)

La Frégate marine. *Fregata magnificens* Mathews
Fig. 14. L. 37.5 to 45.0 in., wingspread 84 to 96 in.

Bill rather long with both mandibles hooked. Tail very long, deeply forked. Feet and throat pouch small. *Adult male:* Black, with bronzy or purplish gloss on upper parts, scapulars lanceolate. *Adult female:* Similar but breast and upper belly white, lesser wing coverts greyish brown; rest of plumage duller and more brownish. *Immature:* Like adult female but head and neck white.

Field Marks. Large size combined with long narrow wings, long deeply forked tail (tail is often closed in gliding flight), and coloration, described above. Sometimes glides for long periods on motionless wings. Does not swim or sit on the water.

Range. In the Atlantic from the Bahamas to coastal Brazil, the Cape Verde Islands and coast of Gambia; in the eastern Pacific from Baja California south to the Galápagos Islands, coastal Ecuador and Peru. Wanders to the coasts of southern United States.

Status in Canada. Accidental in Nova Scotia (Halifax Harbour, October 16, 1876; off Devil's Island, June 1891; Pennant Bay, December 5, 1932; Lower Wedgeport, July 14, 1949, and for several succeeding days; Freeport, August 4, 1949); Newfoundland (Bonavista Bay, about 1932); Quebec (Godbout, sight record August 13, 1884).

Subspecies. *F. m. rothschildi* Mathews.

Fig. 14 Magnificent Frigatebird

Order **Ciconiiformes**—Herons, Storks, Ibises, Flamingoes, and Allies

The long-legged, long-necked, short-tailed wading birds comprising this Order feed in the shallow water of marshes, swamps, and shores. They have long, rather broad wings with rounded tips; rather long bills, straight in most species, curved in some; long, slender toes which are never completely webbed.

Family **Ardeidae**—Herons and Bitterns

Number of Species in North America 15; in Canada 12

Wading birds with long legs, long necks, and short tails; rather long straight bills which taper to a point; and long, broad, round-tipped wings. Plumage rather long and loose. Crests and plumes are usually present in the breeding season. Small area in front of eyes (lores) is always bare. Toes are long and slender, with a small web connecting the base of the outer and middle ones, hind toes on same level as the others (not elevated); middle toenail pectinate (comb-like) on inner border (*see* Fig. 15). They fly with the neck doubled back against the shoulders and thus are easily separable in flight from cranes.

Fig. 15 Middle toenail of Great Blue Heron

GREAT BLUE HERON (Incorrectly 'Crane')
Le Grand Héron. *Ardea herodias* Linnaeus
Plate 5. L. 43 to 52 in.

Bill about 5 inches, rather stout at base tapering to a sharp tip. *Adults* (*breeding plumage*): Head white with a broad black stripe on either side, extending from above the eye to the nape and projecting behind the head in a slender black crest. Neck, greyish brown with a double row of black down the fore-neck. Lower neck and back with long slender plumes. Upper parts mainly greyish blue. Under parts, variously streaked and marked with black and white. Bill yellowish (to almost orange in breeding period), sometimes with a dusky ridge. Legs brownish green, often with reddish hue in mating season. *Immatures*: Similar but with entire crown dark slate and with no crest or plumes.

Measurements (*A. h. herodias*). *Adult male:* wing, 444–475.5 (463.1); tail, 171–188.5 (180); exposed culmen, 125–152 (143.1); tarsus, 171–186 (179.3). *Adult female:* wing, 444–459 (450) mm.

Field Marks. Our largest heron. Its colour and large size separate it from other Canadian herons. In the West the Sandhill Crane is of similar size, but its plumage is plain grey without streaks, and adult cranes have a red bare area on the forehead. In flight, herons carry the neck doubled back with head against the shoulders; cranes carry the neck straight out. *Voice:* Under stress, various squawks and croaks; also a slightly goose-like *onk* but harsher.

Habitat. Feeds in and about open shallow water, either fresh or salt; edges of bays, streams, river margins, sloughs, lakes, ponds, ditches, mud flats, and marshes. Nests in deciduous, coniferous, and mixed woodland sometimes at considerable distances from water.

Nesting. Nests in various-sized colonies. Nest, a flattish structure of sticks usually in the upper strata of tall trees; sometimes in bushes or even on the ground where trees are wanting. Nests are repaired and used in successive years. *Eggs*, commonly 3 to 5, usually 4; pale greenish blue. Incubation by both sexes lasts about 28 days (A. C. Bent). One brood annually.

Range. Southeastern Alaska east to the Gaspé Peninsula and Nova Scotia and south to Mexico, the West Indies, and Galápagos Islands. Winters from southern British Columbia and the northern United States south to Panama, Colombia, and Venezuela.

Range in Canada. Breeds in British Columbia (along the coast from Vancouver Island to Queen Charlotte Islands; and very locally in the interior at Enderby and along Kootenay River); central and southern Alberta (Lesser Slave Lake southward); central and southern Saskatchewan (Prince Albert National Park southward); southern Manitoba; central and southern Ontario (Lake of the Woods, Dryden, Lake Abitibi southward); southern Quebec (Basque Island, Gaspé), New Brunswick, Prince Edward Island, and Nova Scotia. Wanders farther northward in summer to southern Yukon (Carcross), southern Keewatin (Nueltin Lake), northern Ontario (James Bay), northern Quebec (Fort Chimo), and Newfoundland (several records). Winters commonly on the British Columbia coast, occasionally in the Maritimes and southern Ontario.

Breeding Distribution of Great Blue Heron

Subspecies. (1) *Ardea herodias herodias* Linnaeus breeds in e. Canada and westward at least to Alta. (2) *Ardea herodias fannini* Chapman, a darker race, breeds on the Pacific Coast. In the interior of B. C. few breeding records are known, but Munro and Cowan (1947) suggest that specimens from Okanagan Valley and Edgewood, perhaps wanderers from areas farther south, are referable to *A. herodias treganzai* Court, a subspecies which has the neck and upper parts paler than in the two races known in Canada.

Remarks. This is the largest, most widely distributed, and most numerous heron in most parts of Canada. It is often mistakenly known as 'crane,' but it is not related to the cranes. Whether standing motionless or in stately slow-measured flight, this is among the most picturesque of birds. It is particularly numerous, especially in late summer, about the tidal bays and mud flats in parts of the Maritimes.

Its stilt-like legs enable it to wade well out in the water shallows. There, motionless and with infinite patience, it waits until a fish or frog ventures close by. A quick thrust of the long neck and spear-like bill captures the prey. When this is eaten, the bird again assumes its motionless posture. Often food is secured by slow stalking.

This heron eats fishes, frogs, salamanders, water snakes, large insects, including grasshoppers, and mice and other small rodents. Most of the fishes it takes are of little interest to man. Ordinarily it does not frequent trout streams, except where the occasional stream crosses an open meadow. At open pools of fish hatcheries it can be destructive, and where herons are common, such pools are best screened in. Otherwise it does little harm and indeed considerable good as a destroyer of water snakes, small rodents, and insects. Although alert and wary, it formerly was much persecuted by the thoughtless and uninformed. Today the federal Migratory Birds Convention Act makes it illegal to destroy this picturesque bird.

GREEN HERON

Le Héron vert. *Butorides virescens* (Linnaeus)
Plate 5. L. 16 to 22 in.

Adults: Top of head and crest, black with greenish gloss. Sides of head and whole neck, rich chestnut. Throat and stripe down front of neck, white with brown streaks. Back, glossy green with elongated bluish-grey plumes. Wing coverts glossy green, finely edged with buff. Belly bluish grey. Eye yellow. Bill greenish black, paler on lower mandible, yellowish at base. Legs and feet yellow. *Immatures:* Similar but plumes wanting; under parts are whitish, heavily streaked with brown. Bill and legs duller and paler than in adults.

Measurements (*B. v. virescens*). *Adult male:* wing, 176.5–186.5 (181.9); tail, 60.5–70 (65.4); exposed culmen, 56.5–64 (60.5); tarsus, 51–53.5 (52). *Adult female:* wing, 171.5–178 (175.7) mm.

Field Marks. Small size, dark colour (looks blackish at a distance), and yellow legs combine to distinguish it. Back looks bluish in certain lights, sometimes causing confusion with adult Little Blue Heron, which, however, has dark legs. When nervous, it raises crest and twitches tail. *Voice:* A harsh, loud *keow*. Various clucks, squawks, and grunts.

Habitat. Edges of water, such as sluggish streams, ponds, and marshes sheltered by bushes and trees; alder thickets on drowned land.

Nesting. Usually nests are solitary but sometimes are in small colonies. Nest, a rather flimsy structure of sticks, generally 10 to 20 feet up in a tree; sometimes on the ground. *Eggs*, usually 4 or 5; greenish or greenish blue. Incubation about 20 days (E. G. Cooley), by both parents.

Breeding Distribution of Green Heron

Range. Western Washington, Nevada, Texas, central Minnesota, southern Ontario, and southern New Brunswick south to the West Indies, Central America, and Colombia. Winters from southern United States southward.

Range in Canada. Local summer resident from late April to October. Breeds in southern Ontario (north to Wellington, York, and Carleton Counties), southern Quebec (Ste. Rose), and southern New Brunswick (rare, but eggs collected on Washademoak River). Has been recorded, north of its known breeding range, in southern Manitoba (Brandon, sight record), southern Ontario (Muskoka District; Pimisi Bay), Quebec (Upper Razade, Quebec City); Newfoundland (Haricot, St. John's, Port au Port), and Nova Scotia (Lawrencetown, Westport, Prospect). There are sight records for southern British Columbia (near Chilliwack and Pitt Meadows), and a specimen from Vancouver Island (Duncan, June 9, 1963).

Subspecies. *Butorides virescens virescens* (Linnaeus) is the only race known to occur in Canada. Probably, however, the B. C. sight records refer to the western race *B. v. anthonyi* (Mearns).

LITTLE BLUE HERON
Le Petit Héron bleu. *Florida caerulea* (Linnaeus)
Plate 6. L. 20 to 29 in.

Adults: Head (crested with a few long feathers from nape) and neck dark purplish red. Body dark slaty blue. Numerous plumes extend down back and beyond tail. Lower neck with a tuft of elongated feathers. Eye yellow or greyish. Bill black at tip, bluish at base. Legs and feet bluish black. *Immatures:* Mainly white in first year but with variable small amounts of slate colour on wing tips. Bill black-tipped, pale bluish basally. Legs dark greenish. Immatures eventually acquire a patchy white-and-blue aspect. They wear this during much of their second year.

Field Marks. The blackish-looking adults might be confused with the somewhat smaller Green Heron, but the latter has yellow legs. The white immatures somewhat resemble egrets, but the bill is different from the yellow bill of the large Common Egret or the Cattle Egret, and the greenish legs are unlike those of the Snowy Egret. Older immatures have a patchy white-and-blue aspect that is unmistakable.

Habitat. Margins of lakes and ponds, marshes. More often on fresh than on salt water.

Range. Breeds in the southern Atlantic and Gulf states, north along the coast to Massachusetts (casually), and south through Central America, the West Indies, and in South America to Peru and Uruguay. Wanders northward occasionally to southeastern Canada.

Status in Canada. Rare non-breeding spring, summer, and autumn wanderer to eastern Canada, most records being for late summer and fall. Recorded north to southern Ontario (north to French River, Sudbury District, where one was found dead with feet frozen in ice on December 16, 1947; also to Manitoulin Island); Quebec (Moisie Bay, August 1928); southern Labrador (L'Anse au Loup, May 23, 1900); Newfoundland (ten or more records June to December 5); Nova Scotia (specimens taken as early as March 18, as late as October 23); New Brunswick (recorded rarely from April 17 to October); and Prince Edward Island (Ellerslie, August

20, 1958; Brackley, April 29, 1962). Sight records for Saskatchewan (*see* Houston, 1957, *Blue Jay* 15: 52).

Subspecies. *Florida caerulea caerulea* (Linnaeus).

CATTLE EGRET
Le Héron garde-boeuf. *Bubulcus ibis* (Linnaeus)
Plate 5. L. 19 to 20 in.

Adults: In breeding plumage mainly white with elongated pinkish buff feathers on crown, back, and lower neck. Bill yellow, orange, or reddish. Legs, greenish yellow to dull reddish. In winter, similar but buffy areas much paler, less extensive, and elongated feathers much shorter. Bill yellow; legs greenish dark brown or blackish. *Immatures:* Plumage all white, the feathers of crown, back, and lower neck not elongated. Bill yellow, legs greenish dark brown or blackish.

Measurements. *Adult male:* wing, 231–251 (241.7); tail, 86–94.5 (91); exposed culmen, 53–63 (57); tarsus, 72–87 (77.2). *Adult female:* wing, 230–247 (239.5); tail, 81–93 (87.9); exposed culmen, 50–60 (55.2); tarsus, 70–78 (73.1) mm (adapted from Friedmann).

Field Marks. A small, stocky, mainly white heron with short neck and heavy chin. The buffy areas of adults, when visible, distinguish the species from other white herons ordinarily found in Canada. The Cattle Egret's yellow bill separates it from the slightly larger Snowy Egret and immature Little Blue Herons. Our only other white heron with a yellow bill is the Common Egret, an obviously very much larger bird with long neck and legs. Cattle Egrets often associate with grazing cows in pastures, but this habit is sometimes shared by the Snowy Egret.

Habitat. Forages frequently on grassland often associating with cattle, whose grazing activities stir up insects, which form a large proportion of its food; also marshes.

Nesting. Usually in bushy shrubbery or low in a tree. Nest is of twigs, grasses, and leaves. *Eggs,* 4 to 6; pale blue.

Range. Widely distributed in the Old World, but only recently became established in the New World (noted in Surinam between 1877 and 1882 and in British Guiana in 1911–12). It was first collected in North America on April 23, 1952, at Wayland, Massachusetts, but evidence suggests it appeared in Florida in the early 1940's. In 1957 it was breeding in Florida, Louisiana, and North Carolina. By 1962, it was nesting in Canada (southern Ontario).

Range in Canada. A very recent arrival, first known to breed in 1962; first occurrence 1952. Has been recorded in Newfoundland (Grand Banks, about October 31, 1952); Nova Scotia (Cape Sable Island, December 3, 1957; East Sable River, November 23, 1957; Brooklyn, November 1957; Bon Portage Island, one found dead, 1962); New Brunswick (Charlotte County, April 1961: one shot out of a flock of 20); Quebec (Lake St. Peter: two, of flock of five, shot on August 15, 1960; about 20 seen there August 25, 1960); Ontario (Port Rowan, May 4–6, 1956; Lake St. Clair, May 26, 1956; Port Dover, May 1, 1959; Angus, May 23, 1960; Toronto, May 24, 1960. In spring of 1962 it appeared at numerous southern localities including Ottawa and bred at two localities); and Manitoba (near Brandon, May 27 and on several succeeding days, 1961).

First nested in Canada in 1962: Ontario (Presqu'ile Provincial Park and at Luther Marsh, 22 miles west of Orangeville).

Subspecies. *Bubulcus ibis ibis* (Linnaeus).

COMMON EGRET (American Egret)

La Grande Aigrette. *Casmerodius albus* (Linnaeus)
Plate 5. L. 34.75 to 42.00 in.

No crest. *Adults:* Plumage all white. In the breeding season a cascade of slender plumes sweeps down from the back and beyond the tail. Bill orange-yellow. Legs and feet black. *Immatures:* Similar but without plumes.

Field Marks. A very large white heron, almost as big as the Great Blue Heron, with *yellow* bill, black legs and feet. Snowy Egrets and immature Little Blue Herons are also white but have dark bills and are much smaller. The Cattle Egret is also a white heron with a yellow bill, but it is very much smaller and its stockier build is obvious. *Voice:* A harsh rattling croak.

Nesting. Nests usually in colonies, sometimes with other species. Nest, of sticks, usually in a tree at various heights. *Eggs,* 3 to 5; pale bluish green.

Range. Inhabits all continents. In the New World breeds from Oregon, southern Idaho, southern Saskatchewan, southern Manitoba, southern Minnesota, extreme southern Ontario, and New Jersey south through the West Indies, Mexico, Central and South America.

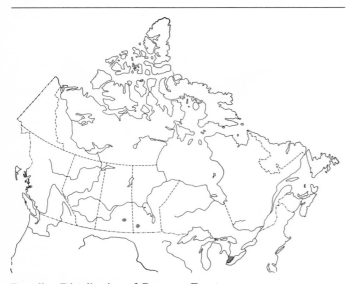

Breeding Distribution of Common Egret

Range in Canada. Nesting has been recorded from southeastern Saskatchewan (Qu'appelle Valley, north of Regina); Manitoba (Pipestone); and in southern Ontario (East Sister Island, western Lake Erie; perhaps near Amherstburg). An irregular visitant, especially in late summer, to southern parts of Ontario, Quebec, New Brunswick, and Nova Scotia. Recorded west to Alberta (Cowley, Big Lake) and north to southern Saskatchewan (Davidson); southern Manitoba (Duck Bay, Lake Winnipegosis); southern Ontario (Orillia and Lake Nipissing); southern Quebec (Godbout River;

Little Mecatina River, Nicolet); and Newfoundland (Harbour Main, Pass Island, Bell Island).

Subspecies. *Casmerodius albus egretta* (Gmelin).

Remarks. In the southern United States this graceful large heron is common. In the early 1900's it was sadly reduced in numbers by hunters who killed them for their long plumes for the millinery trade. Wise laws now make it illegal in both the United States and Canada to destroy it. Under this protection it has regained much of its original numbers and range.

SNOWY EGRET

L'Aigrette neigeuse. *Leucophoyx thula* (Molina)
Plate 6. L. 20 to 27 in.

Adults in breeding plumage: White, with crest of loosely-webbed feathers and long filamentous plumes (shed later) growing from back and forming a train over back and tail. Bill black. Lores yellow. Legs black, toes yellow. *Immatures:* Similar but without plumes and more or less yellowish up the back of the legs.

Measurements (*L. t. thula*). *Adult male:* wing, 240–289 (259.9); culmen, 74–89 (83.3); tarsus, 83–106 (97.1). *Adult female:* wing, 233–273 (251.2) mm (A. M. Bailey).

Field Marks. A small white heron with *black bill* and *yellow feet.* The black bill separates it from the similar-sized Cattle Egret and the much larger Common Egret. The uniformly coloured bill differs from the two-coloured bill of immature Little Blue Herons.

Habitat. Margins of both fresh and salt water of marshes, ponds, bays, wet meadows; sometimes fields and beaches.

Range. Breeds from southern United States (along the Atlantic Coast north to New Jersey) south through the West Indies and Central America to South America (Chile and Argentina). Wanders farther northward, especially in late summer. Winters from southern United States southward.

Status in Canada. Rare non-breeding wanderer to Alberta (Pincher Creek, May 11, 1901; Sandy Lake, May 1909); New Brunswick (near mouth of Bay of Fundy); Nova Scotia (Lower Clark's Harbour, September 18, 1944; at Halifax, 1868; and Windsor, 1872); Newfoundland (Trepassey, August 18, 1948; near St. John's, November 5, 1955). There are sight records for Ontario, Saskatchewan, and British Columbia.

Subspecies. Records for e. Canada are referred to *Leucophoyx thula thula* (Molina). Possibly the Alta. specimens, not examined by the writer, are referable to the larger western race *L. t. brewsteri* (Thayer and Bangs).

LITTLE EGRET

L'Aigrette garzette. *Egretta garzetta* (Linnaeus)

Adults in breeding plumage: Plumage all white. Head with two very long (140–160 mm), extremely narrow, pointed crest feathers. Upper breast with a number of longer feathers very narrow at end but broad and loose at base. Back with numerous loose plumes. Bill and lores black, base of lower mandible greenish grey. Legs black, toes (in nominate race) yellow. *Adults in fall and winter:* Similar, but lack head plumes, and the plumes of the back are fewer and shorter.

This Old World species resembles the Snowy Egret. It lacks the yellow lores of the Snowy Egret and in the breeding season possesses two very long, narrow crest feathers, which are quite unlike any crest feathers of the Snowy.

Range. Southern Europe and Asia, Africa, Sumatra, Java, and Australia. One record for North America.

Status in Canada. Accidental. A female was collected at Flatrock, Conception Bay, Newfoundland, on May 8, 1954, by Robert Emerson and was donated to the National Museum of Canada by L. M. Tuck.

Subspecies. *Egretta garzetta garzetta* (Linnaeus).

LOUISIANA HERON
Le Héron à ventre blanc. *Hydranassa tricolor* (Müller)
L. 25 in.

Adults: Upper parts mainly dark blue. Nape and hind-neck feathers longer with a purplish sheen (in breeding plumage with a white occipital crest). Throat whitish, more or less tinged with chestnut, this continuing in a narrow line down front of neck. Lower back and rump whitish, but in the breeding season this is obscured by brownish-grey plumes which reach to or beyond the tail. Neck and breast bluish slate, on the breast mixed with purplish feathers. Abdomen and under wing coverts white. *Immatures:* Mainly dull brown or bluish above, with chestnut neck, white throat and abdomen. In the field the white abdomen contrasting with dark breast and upper parts makes recognition rather easy.

Range. Baja California, the Gulf coast of United States, and southern Maryland south to the West Indies and northern South America.

Status in Canada. Accidental. Two records for New Brunswick (a specimen found dead on Hammond River, near Nauwigewauk, in April 1895; another taken at Little River in April, about 1920). Sight records only for Ontario.

Subspecies. *Hydranassa tricolor ruficollis* (Gosse).

BLACK-CROWNED NIGHT HERON
Le Bihoreau à couronne noire
Nycticorax nycticorax (Linnaeus)
Plate 5. L. 23 to 28 in.

Bill, neck, and legs stout. No long plumes on back. *Adults:* Crown and back, black with greenish gloss. Forehead white. Two to four slender long white feathers extending back from hind head. Neck, wings, rump, and tail, grey. Under parts white, tinged (except throat) with grey. Bill blackish. Legs and feet yellow to reddish. *Immatures:* Upper parts greyish brown with streaks of buffy white, and with spots of white on wings. Outer edge of primaries often tinged with rusty. Neck and under parts white, heavily streaked with brown.

Measurements (*N. n. hoactli*). *Adult male:* wing, 295–324 (308.5); tail, 118–125 (122.8); exposed culmen, 75.5–79.5 (78.1); tarsus, 81–84 (82.8). *Adult female:* wing, 289–307.5 (297.5) mm.

Field Marks. Rather stout with relatively heavy neck and short legs. The contrasting black back and all-white under

parts identify the adult. Immatures look somewhat like the American Bittern but lack its yellowish tendency in general colour and the black streak down side of neck; the wing tip of this heron is not more blackish than the rest of the wing. This heron often alights in trees; the bittern very rarely does so. Immatures are very difficult to distinguish in the field from young Yellow-crowned Night Herons (*see* following species). *Voice:* In flight a single characteristic *kwok*. In breeding colonies various squawks.

Habitat. Salt and freshwater marshes, tidal estuaries, mud flats, edges of lakes, ponds, and sluggish streams, sometimes fields. Roosts and nests in trees.

Nesting. In colonies. Nest of sticks, usually in trees, occasionally in bushes, rarely on the ground. *Eggs,* usually 3 to 5; pale bluish green. Incubation by both sexes, 24 to 26 days (A. O. Gross). One brood yearly.

Range. Widely distributed in both New and Old World. In New World from Washington, southern Idaho, and southern Canada south through the West Indies, Central and South America to northern Chile and central Argentina.

Breeding Distribution of Black-crowned Night Heron

Range in Canada. Locally distributed spring, summer, and autumn resident, breeding locally in Alberta (Beaverhill Lake), southern Saskatchewan (Prince Albert, Yorkton, Moose Mountain, Qu'Appelle Valley, Deep Lake, and near Davidson), southern Manitoba (Oak Lake, Shoal Lake), southern Ontario (Pelee Island, Port Weller, Luther Marsh, probably Ottawa), southern Quebec (Montreal, Lake St. Peter, Basque Island, Ste. Anne de la Pocatière; probably near Gaspé), and New Brunswick (Tracadie, Woodstock, Nantucket Island, Long Island). Uncommon visitant to Nova Scotia, Prince Edward Island, and rarely to British Columbia (Summerland). Has wandered north to central Quebec (Lake Mistassini, August 6, 1885) and Newfoundland (Come-by-Chance, March 17, 1947).

Subspecies. *Nycticorax nycticorax hoactli* (Gmelin).

Remarks. As its name implies, this stocky, short-legged heron is active at night. During the daylight hours it is more inclined to roost in trees. About sunset and in the gathering dusk it makes its steady way on broad wings to its feeding marshes. Often the characteristic flight calls, a throaty *qwock*, serve to direct one's eyes to its dim silhouette. It is not entirely nocturnal and crepuscular, however, for in areas where it is common it not infrequently is active during the daylight hours, particularly when the weather is dull. It feeds largely on fishes but takes also frogs, crayfish and other crustacea, and small rodents.

YELLOW-CROWNED NIGHT HERON

Le Bihoreau violacé. *Nyctanassa violacea* (Linnaeus)
Plate 5. L. 22 to 28 in.

Adults: Top of head, two long crest feathers, and white patch on side of face tinged with yellow. Feathers of back, black broadly margined with grey. Flight feathers slate. Breast and belly grey. Bill black. Legs and feet yellow. *Immatures:* Very similar to immature Black-crowned Night Heron but darker (more slaty, less brownish). Crown slightly darker than back. Flight feathers slate with no traces of rust, which is often present in the Black-crown. In the Yellow-crowns the tarsus is longer than the combined length of middle toe and nail (about equal in the Black-crown).

Measurements. *Adult male:* wing, 281–300 (294); tail, 102.0–118.7 (109.2); culmen from base, 64.5–75.6 (70.9); tarsus, 93.6–106.2 (99.4). *Adult female:* wing, 271–305 (290) mm (A. Wetmore).

Field Marks. Stocky build, white cheek patch, and streaked back characterize the adults. Immatures very difficult to separate from young Black-crowns in the field. In flight the longer legs of the Yellow-crown extend the feet well beyond the tail. Under excellent close-range conditions the somewhat darker general colour and the slightly stouter bill may be discerned. Immatures might be confused with the American Bittern, but they lack its rich brown colouring and its black line down the side of the neck. Voice quite similar to that of the Black-Crown.

Nesting. Usually in small to large colonies; sometimes single pairs. Nest is of sticks, in trees or bushes. *Eggs*, 2 to 6, usually 3 to 5; pale bluish green.

Range. Breeds from southern United States (and north along the Atlantic seaboard to Massachusetts and sporadically north to Indiana, Ohio, and perhaps extreme southern Ontario), south through the West Indies, Central America, and northern South America.

Status in Canada. Reported to breed at East Sister Island, west end of Lake Erie, Ontario, where apparently a nest was discovered on May 23, 1954 (Baillie, 1954, *Audubon Field-Notes* 8: 310). Otherwise a rare wanderer to southern Manitoba (St. François Xavier, May 7, 1959; R. W. Sutton, in litt.), southern Ontario (Toronto, August 15, 1898; near Kitchener, April 26, 1954); southern New Brunswick (Grand Manan, April 2, 1931); Nova Scotia (Cape Island, late March 1902; near Wolfville, September 13, 1932, and July 28 and August 12, 1937; Cole Harbour, September 14, 1925; McNab's Island, September 28, 1919); and Newfoundland (Petites about March 26, 1940; also a specimen with no data other than Newfoundland).

Subspecies. *Nyctanassa violacea violacea* (Linnaeus).

LEAST BITTER

Le Petit Butor. *Ixobrychus exilis* (Gmelin)
Plate 6. L. 11 to 14 in.

Adult male: Top of head, back, and tail, black. Back of neck, larger wing coverts, and outer webs of inner secondaries, chestnut. Rest of wing coverts brownish yellow. Primaries slaty. Throat whitish. Sides of head, sides of neck, and under parts, pale buff with a blackish brown patch on either side of breast. Wing lining yellowish white. Bill mostly yellow with dark ridge. Legs greenish. *Adult female:* Similar, but the blacks of the upper parts are mostly replaced by dark chestnut. Two buffy lines down back. Throat and under parts streaked with brown. *Immatures:* Similar to adult female, but feathers of back have buffy tips.

Colour Phase. An uncommon, local colour phase in which the creams and whites are replaced by chestnut. It was formerly thought to be a different species and was called Cory's Least Bittern, *Ixobrychus neoxena*.

Measurements. *Adult male:* wing, 111.5–115.3 (113.5); tail, 38.5–44 (43.9); exposed culmen, 39.5–47.5 (44.7); tarsus, 39–41 (40). *Adult female:* wing, 110–116 (113.2) mm.

Field Marks. Tiny size separates it from other herons. Its contrasting colour pattern is very different from that of the rails. *Voice:* A series of five or six low cooing sounds. When disturbed, a cackling *ca-ca-ca*.

Habitat. Cattail marshes and marshy vegetation of ponds or sluggish streams.

Nesting. In freshwater marshes. Nest, a rather frail structure built in and supported by a clump of marsh vegetation usually from 6 inches to 2½ feet above water. *Eggs*, usually 4 or 5; bluish white or greenish white. Incubation 17 to 18 days (M. W. Weller), by both sexes.

Range. From southern Canada and northern United States, south to the West Indies and through Mexico and Central America to Brazil and Paraguay. Winters from southern United States southward.

Range in Canada. Breeds locally in southern Manitoba (Delta: nest with four eggs collected on June 7, 1949, by

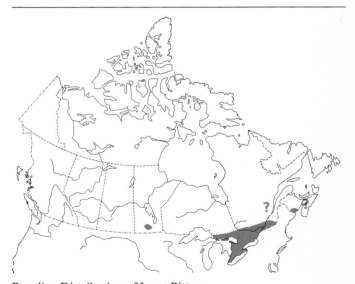

Breeding Distribution of Least Bittern

R. W. Sutton, in litt.), southern Ontario (north to near Sault Ste. Marie; Lake Nipissing; Ottawa), southern Quebec (Montreal, St. Lambert, Magog, possibly Quebec), and southern New Brunswick (Little River). In Nova Scotia specimens have been taken at Upper Prospect, March 16, 1896; Cape Island, April 25, 1907; Little Hope Light, September 1, 1935; and the species has been reliably reported in summer near the Nova Scotia border (Squires, 1952), but no proof of nesting in Nova Scotia is yet known. In Newfoundland three autumn records: St. John's, early October 1882, and September 8, 1953; off Cape St. Francis, August 5, 1933. Casual in southern Saskatchewan where an undated specimen was taken at Moon Lake (*Blue Jay*, 16(2): 64–65); there is a sight record from Crane Lake. The one record for British Columbia (J. A. Munro, *Murrelet* 36: 44) is for Vernon, July 30, 1955. Old reports of a specimen taken at York Factory, northern Manitoba, cannot now be verified.

This diminutive heron remains pretty much within the dense vegetation of the marshes. It is rather quiet and secretive. Consequently, for some parts of its range where it is thought to be rare or absent, it may be commoner than the records show.

Subspecies. *Ixobrychus exilis exilis* (Gmelin). There is a possibility that the B.C. record might be referable to the race *hesperis*, which has not been identified in Canada.

AMERICAN BITTERN

Le Butor américain. *Botaurus lentiginosus* (Rackett)
Plate 6. L. 24 to 34 in.

Adults: Upper parts yellowish brown with irregular small spots, bars, streaks, and freckles of darker browns and buffs. Yellowish streak over eye. Throat whitish with a brown stripe down its centre. Black streak down sides of neck. Breast, sides, and abdomen, yellowish white broadly streaked with brown. Primaries brownish slate. Bill yellowish with blackish ridge. Legs and feet greenish yellow. *Immatures:* Similar to adults but without black stripe on sides of neck and more lightly marked generally.

Measurements. *Adult male:* wing, 259–275 (268.9); tail, 76.5–101 (90.2); exposed culmen, 70–86 (75.2); tarsus, 84.5–98 (89.5). *Adult female:* wing, 236–275 (244.8) mm.

Field Marks. Most likely to be confused with immature Night Heron, but it is a generally more yellowish bird. In flight its wing tips are darker than the rest of the wing. Its black neck stripe when seen is diagnostic, but it is sometimes hard to see and is lacking in immatures; consequently its absence is not diagnostic. Its remarkable voice, once learned, is unmistakable. Rarely alights in trees. Night Herons do so regularly. *Voice:* A hollow deep *pump-er-lunk*, repeated several times and heard most often in the evening or dawn of spring and early summer. At the height of the breeding season often heard any time of day, particularly in cloudy weather. It is audible for considerable distances. In flight, especially when startled, a croaking *ok-ok-ok-ok*; also a single harsh croak.

Habitat. Fresh and salt marshes, swamps, moist meadows, wet alder or willow thickets, less often drier fields.

Nesting. Nest, a platform of marsh vegetation in cattails, bulrushes, and similar marsh vegetation; occasionally in dry fields. *Eggs*, 4 to 6; olive brown or olive buff. Incubation period about 24 days (Mousley), by the female.

Range. Breeds from southern Canada south to southern California, southern Colorado, Missouri, western and central Texas, Pennsylvania, and Maryland. Winters from the middle and southern United States and southwestern British Columbia southward.

Breeding Distribution of American Bittern

Range in Canada. Breeds in central and southern interior British Columbia (probably north to Kispioux Valley and Swan Lake), southwestern Mackenzie (Great Slave Lake), Alberta, Saskatchewan, Manitoba (north to Churchill), Ontario (north to Moose Factory and Hudson Bay coast), Quebec (north to Fort George and the inner north shore of the Gulf of St. Lawrence, Anticosti and Magdalen islands), Newfoundland, New Brunswick, Prince Edward Island, and Nova Scotia. Recorded north to near Fort Norman, Mackenzie; Nueltin Lake, Keewatin; Great Whale River, Quebec; and Hamilton Inlet, Labrador.

Winters in southwestern British Columbia (Lulu Island, Ladner, Courtenay; rarely Queen Charlotte Islands), and occasionally in extreme southern Ontario.

Remarks. In the evenings of late spring and early summer the deep hollow vocalizing of the American Bittern adds a pleasant mysteriousness to the marshlands of most parts of southern Canada. The 'song' to some ears resembles the sucking sounds made by an old-fashioned water pump or those of a stake being driven into the mud by a wooden hammer; hence the bird's local names 'Thunder Pump' and 'Stake Driver.'

The streaked breast and general coloration of this bittern blend perfectly with the marsh vegetation it inhabits. When alarmed it draws its plumage in tight, points the bill straight up in the air, and 'freezes.' Thus, motionless, it is very difficult to see—an excellent example of protective coloration. If approached too closely, however, it springs awkwardly into the air with a rush of wings, dangling legs, and harsh croaks. Once in the air, it is a good flyer.

Most of this bittern's motions are deliberate. In capturing prey, however, the javelin-like beak is thrust out with flashlike speed. When used in self-defence, the beak also is a vicious weapon, capable of destroying a human eye. One jab has been known to repel a large steer (Tufts, 1961).

This bittern does little harm and probably considerable good. In the marshes it feeds on frogs, snakes, small fishes, crayfish, and other water animals. Sometimes it visits open fields to catch grasshoppers and mice.

Family **Ciconiidae** – Storks and Wood Ibises

Number of Species in North America 1; in Canada 1

Long-legged heron-like birds, their bills stout at the base tapering to the tip. In the Wood Ibis (really a stork), the bill is decurved near the tip (*see* Fig. 16). The family is widely distributed in the world, and the Common Stork, *Ciconia ciconia*, of the Old World is probably the most familiar species.

WOOD IBIS

La Cigogne américaine. *Mycteria americana* Linnaeus
Fig. 16. L. 35 to 45 in.

Bill very stout at base, tapered, downcurved near tip. *Adults:* Head and part of neck bare, dark grey or blackish grey. Plumage mainly white. Flight feathers greenish black. Tail bluish black. Legs blackish. *Immatures:* Similar but head and neck more or less feathered. Plumage greyish, with less green in the black of the flight feathers.

Field Marks. A larger white heron-like bird, with black flight feathers and tail and long stout bill, downcurved at tip. Flies with neck outstretched like a crane, showing a large amount of black along entire hind edge of spread wing. The long, trailing legs separate it from the White Pelican. On the ground the combination of the colour pattern, the heavy downcurved bill, and the dark bare head and neck make it unmistakable.

Fig. 16 Head of Wood Ibis

Range. Southern United States to South America.
Status in Canada. Casual or accidental visitant. Southern Ontario (near Simcoe, November 1892; Glengarry County, August 2, 1948; Kingston, September 1954; Hamilton, November 9, 1950). New Brunswick (near East Saint John, June 3, 1911).

Family **Threskiornithidae** – Ibises and Spoonbills

Number of Species in North America 4; in Canada 3

Heron-like birds with slender, long, downcurved bill. Upper mandible has a deep groove extending along both sides almost to the tip. The family is distributed widely in the warmer parts of the world.

GLOSSY IBIS

L'Ibis luisant. *Plegadis falcinellus* (Linnaeus)
L. 22 to 25 in.

Bill slender, long, downcurved with a groove along either side. Skin around and in front of eye, bare. *Adults:* Mainly rich chestnut with greenish and purplish iridescence on crown, back, rump, tail, and wings. Bare skin in front of eye bluish. *Immatures:* Head and neck greyish brown or brownish black streaked with white. Upper parts with greenish gloss. Under parts dull brownish grey.

Measurements. *Adult male:* wing, 256.5–278 (268.6); tail, 93.5–104.5 (99.9); exposed culmen, 128.5–148 (134.3); tarsus, 103.5–112.5 (107.2). *Adult female:* wing, 240.5–249 (244.8) mm.

Field Marks. The long evenly downcurved bill obviates confusion with all but the curlews and other ibises. The Glossy Ibis is obviously darker (looks black at a distance) and larger than any curlew. It closely resembles the White-faced Ibis, but adults of the latter in breeding plumage have a narrow white margin at the front of the face. In immature plumages the two cannot be safely separated in the field.

Range. In the New World from southeastern United States (north to New Jersey and Virginia) to Cuba and Hispaniola. Found also in southern Europe, southern Asia, Africa, and Australia.

Status in Canada. Casual wanderer to Ontario (Hamilton, two specimens collected, May 1857; Lake Simcoe, two collected, fall, 1828; Lake St. Clair, sight record, May 23, 1954); Quebec (Montreal, specimen taken May 27, 1900; Ile aux Grues, September 17, 1956; Missisquoi Bay, sight record of two, May 14, 1956); Prince Edward Island (several reported, August 1878); Nova Scotia (Pictou County, specimen taken about 1865; Pictou, two taken from small flock about 1910; White Point Beach, one collected from flock of seven, May 10, 1946); New Brunswick (Maugerville, sight record of two by George Boyer and Bruce Wright, May 7, 1952); and Newfoundland (Cape Broyle, sight record of six by Stuart Peters, April 25, 1956; Torbay, flock of seven, May 24 and 26, ·1958, by L. M. Tuck; specimen taken at Cappahayden, October 10, 1958).

Subspecies. *Plegadis falcinellus falcinellus* (Linnaeus).

WHITE-FACED IBIS (White-faced Glossy Ibis)

L'Ibis à face blanche. *Plegadis chihi* (Vieillot)
Plate 6. L. 22 to 25 in.

Adults in breeding plumage: Like the Glossy Ibis but with a narrow whitish area extending from forehead to behind eye and down along base of bill to the throat (absent in fall and winter). Bare skin in front of eye, reddish. *Immatures:* Very similar to the immature Glossy Ibis, but head and neck average slightly paler brown.

Range. From central California, eastern Oregon, Colorado, Nebraska, southwestern Louisiana, and Florida (locally), south to Argentina and Chile.

Status in Canada. Casual straggler to British Columbia: an immature collected in summer, 1902, at Sardis, on Luckakuck River. Macoun and Macoun (1909, *Catalogue of Canadian Birds*) mention a specimen from Salt Spring Island and one from the mouth of Fraser River, but Munro and Cowan (1947) assert that these specimens, no longer extant, were never examined by a competent authority.

WHITE IBIS

L'Ibis blanc. *Eudocimus albus* (Linnaeus)
L. 24 to 27 in.

Bill long, slender, downcurved. *Adults:* White except the tips of four wing primaries, which are black. Bill, legs, and bare skin in front of eye, orange to red. *Immatures:* Head, neck, and back, brownish streaked with white. Rump, breast, and abdomen, white.

Field Marks. Adults are white heron-like birds with narrowly-black wing tips, a long downcurved red or orange bill, and a reddish face. Wood Ibises also are white but with a black tail, a black area along the hind part of the spread wing, and dark bill. Immature White Ibises differ from young Glossy and White-faced ibises in having a white rump and white under parts.

Range. From southern United States south to the West Indies, Peru, and Venezuela.

Status in Canada. Accidental in Ontario (Clayton, one of two collected, October 13, 1955, is in the collection of A. E. Bourguignon); Quebec (Nicolet, specimen taken, September 1934); and Nova Scotia (Bon Portage Island, specimen collected July 15, 1959).

[**Scarlet Ibis.** *Eudocimus ruber* (Linnaeus). Hypothetical. One competently observed in Point Pelee National Park, Ontario, September 11 to October 2, 1937, by G. M. Stirrett (1941, *Can. Field–Nat.* 55: 13) and others, may have escaped from captivity.]

PLATE 5

1 Cattle Egret, adult in breeding plumage

2 Common Egret, adult in breeding plumage

3 Green Heron,
    (a) immature
    (b) adult

4 Black-crowned Night Heron,
    (a) immature
    (b) adult in breeding plumage

5 Yellow-crowned Night Heron, immature

6 Great Blue Heron, adult in breeding plumage

1a

1b

2

3a

3b

4

5

Crosby

PLATE 6

1 Least Bittern,
    (a) adult female
    (b) adult male

2 Snowy Egret, adult

3 Little Blue Heron,
    (a) first-year immature
    (b) adult

4 American Bittern, adult

5 White-faced Ibis, adult

Order **Anseriformes** – Screamers, Swans, Geese, and Ducks

Family **Anatidae** – Swans, Geese, and Ducks

Number of Species in North America 62; in Canada 46

Water birds with lamellate, flattened (except in mergansers), round-tipped bill; narrow pointed wings; usually short tail; short to medium legs set rather far apart; four toes, the front ones webbed, the hind one slightly elevated and free.

Subfamily **Cygninae** – Swans

Large waterfowl, the adults of which have all-white plumage (in North American species), very long necks, and a narrow patch of bare skin in front of the eye.

MUTE SWAN
Le Cygne muet. *Cygnus olor* (Gmelin)
L. 58 in.

Adults: Plumage white. Bill orange or pinkish with black base and a *black knob on forehead* (larger in male). *Immatures:* Whitish, mottled and tinged with greyish brown, darkest on crown, lightest on breast; bill dusky flesh or pinkish, dark at base, no knob on forehead of first-year birds.

Status in Canada. This native of temperate Eurasia is kept in captivity in various parts of North America. Some have escaped and exist in a wild or semi-wild state. Ontario specimens (Long Point Bay, October 1934; also sight records at Hamilton) probably wandered there from New York state, where some Mute Swans exist in a feral state. Recently Mute Swans have been reported nesting and wintering in Regina, Saskatchewan.

WHISTLING SWAN
Le Cygne siffleur. *Olor columbianus* (Ord)
Plate 7. L. 48 to 55 in.

Adults: Plumage all white, usually more or less rust-stained about head and neck. Bill, legs, and feet, black. Bare skin in front of eye, black, usually (not always) with a yellow or orange spot of variable size. *Immatures:* Pale ashy grey, darkest on head and neck. In first autumn, bill is purplish flesh, becoming black toward tip, cutting edges, nostrils, and base. Space in front of eye lacks yellow spot and is more or less covered with fine feathers. In spring, the bill has become mostly black but sometimes with some ruddy flesh colours and the loral spot indicated in pale flesh.

Measurements. *Adult male:* wing, 517–552 (539.4); tail, 138–187 (168.3); exposed culmen, 85.5–97 (91.0); tarsus, 114–121 (116.8). *Adult female:* wing, 510–558 (533) mm.

Distinctions. Very similar to the larger Trumpeter Swan. Any native swan with a wing length under 22 inches (560 mm) and weight, unless very thin, under 20 pounds is probably a Whistling Swan. Trumpeter Swans sometimes in winter become very thin and may weigh less than 20 pounds. Positive identification of these two similar swans is provided by differences in convolutions of the windpipe in the breast bone (*see* Fig. 17).

Fig. 17 Longitudinal section through sternum of Whistling Swan. Identification is provided by the windpipe which does not make a high vertical loop over a bony hump. Compare Trumpeter Swan, Fig 18.

Field Marks. Because of large size and all-white plumage (no black wing tips), it is likely to be mistaken only for the even larger, locally distributed Trumpeter Swan. When the yellow spot in front of the eye is observed, this marks it as a Whistling Swan, but not all Whistling Swans possess this spot. *Voice:* In chorus suggests a flock of Canada Geese but is more musical and often has a quavering quality. A common three-note call is strongly accented in the middle. The voice is less deep and far-carrying than that of the Trumpeter Swan, and the differences when learned make one of the best field marks.

Habitat. In spring and fall migration it frequents lakes, sloughs, rivers, and sometimes fields. In summer, marshy lakes and ponds on low tundra of the North are popular, but the immediate vicinity of water is not necessary; large lakes for molting.

Nesting. Nest, a mound of moss or grass on the ground,

frequently near water. *Eggs*, 3 to 5; creamy white. Incubation period said to be 35 to 40 days (A. C. Bent).

Range. Breeds in Alaska and the Canadian low Arctic. Winters mainly on the Pacific and Atlantic coasts of the United States from Washington to California and from Maryland to North Carolina.

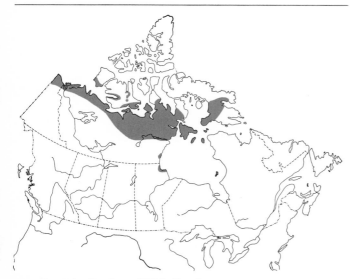

Breeding Distribution of Whistling Swan

Range in Canada. Breeds in the low and middle Arctic from southern Banks Island (near Sachs Harbour), southern Victoria Island (Cambridge Bay), King William Island, and central-western Baffin Island (Nuwata), south to Mackenzie (Mackenzie Delta, Mason River, Thelon Sanctuary), Southampton Island, Hudson Bay (Mansel Island, Belcher Islands, and Nottingham Island), and northeastern Manitoba (Churchill—H. C. Hanson, pers. comm.). Spring and autumn migrant through both coastal and interior British Columbia, the Prairie Provinces, and Ontario (but scarce east of the Great Lakes). Scarce transient in extreme eastern Ontario and southwestern Quebec. Casual in New Brunswick, Nova Scotia, Prince Edward Island, and Newfoundland. Occasionally has wintered in southern British Columbia (South Thompson River near Chase).

Remarks. This fine bird may be observed in numbers at Long Point, Lake Erie, Ontario, on spring migration between March 20 and April 10.

TRUMPETER SWAN
Le Cygne trompette. *Olor buccinator* (Richardson)
Plate 7. L. 54 to 66 in.; wingspread, 74 to 114 in. or more

Similar to Whistling Swan but larger, heavier, with relatively longer bill and slightly straighter culmen. Any native swan with a total length of 55 inches or more, a weight of 22 pounds or more, and a folded wing of 23 inches or more is probably this species. *Adults (sexes similar)*: Similar to Whistling Swan but larger, bare skin in front of eye plain black, never with a yellow spot (*see also* Fig. 18). *Immatures*: Similar to Whistling Swan but larger. In first autumn plumage grey above, darkest on crown and back of neck;

bill pinkish, blackish at tip, base, and about nostrils; legs and feet olive buff, webs yellowish to greyish becoming dusky with age (Whistling Swan does not have yellow in the feet).

Measurements. *Adult male* (5 measured): wing, 564–628 (596.5); tail, 182.5–200 (189.3); exposed culmen, 93–111.5 (104.0); tarsus, 118–128.5 (123.1). *Adult female* (4 measured): wing, 565–636 (592.8) mm.

Field Marks. Swans are very large, long-necked, all-white birds with no black in the wing tips. They fly with straight neck. Under most circumstances, the Trumpeter and the Whistling Swan are difficult to distinguish in the field because the larger size of the Trumpeter is rarely obvious. Adults never have a yellow spot in front of the eye, *usually* shown by the Whistling Swan, but mere absence of it does not necessarily indicate a Trumpeter Swan because some Whistling Swans lack it. *Voice:* When learned by the observer, it is probably the best way to distinguish the two at a distance. Deeper and more far-carrying than that of the Whistling Swan; a loud, trumpet-like, slightly guttural *ko-hoh* uttered from one to a number of times.

Habitat. Lakes, large sloughs, rivers; sometimes feeds in fields and grain stubbles. In winter, the mouths of rivers on the coast also are frequented.

Nesting. On a small island or muskrat house in a marshy freshwater lake or pond. Nest is a bulky platform of aquatic vegetation lined with down. *Eggs*, usually 5 to 8; dull white, often nest-stained. Incubation period about 32 days (R. H. Mackay), by the female alone.

Fig. 18 Longitudinal section through sternum of Trumpeter Swan showing the high vertical loop made by the windpipe over a bony hump

Range. Breeds locally in southern Alaska, northern British Columbia (probably), central-western Alberta, Oregon, eastern Idaho, southwestern Montana, and Wyoming; formerly over a wider area. Winters in southeastern Alaska, western British Columbia, Idaho, Montana, and Wyoming.

Range in Canada. Breeds locally in northern British Columbia (probably), central-western Alberta (Grande Prairie Region), and in very small numbers in southeastern Alberta (Brooks, Cypress Hills), and extreme southwestern Saskatchewan (Cypress Hills). It is being reintroduced at Swan Lake, near Vernon, British Columbia (D. A. Munro).

Winters in western British Columbia (coastal islands including Queen Charlotte and Vancouver islands; and on lakes in the interior: Lonesome Lake, formerly Vaseaux Lake).

Formerly ranged much more widely, breeding in northern

Mackenzie (Franklin Bay, lower Anderson River, Fort Rae), Manitoba (Norway House), and perhaps east to Eastmain, Quebec.

Formerly occurred sparingly in migration in southern Ontario (St. Clair Flats, November 20, 1875; November 1884; also Toronto and Long Point), and southwestern Quebec (Longueuil).

Subfamily **Anserinae**–Geese

Geese inhabiting Canada are intermediate in size and neck length between swans and ducks. Compared with swans, they are smaller, have shorter necks, and have no bare patch in front of the eye. Unlike, most ducks, the sexes are coloured alike; there is no iridescent wing patch or speculum, and they have no 'eclipse' plumage. They are better walkers than ducks and feed more frequently on land. Tarsi are reticulate, not scutellate (*see* Fig. 19).

Fig. 19 Reticulate tarsus of a goose

CANADA GOOSE

La Bernache canadienne. *Branta canadensis* (Linnaeus)
Plate 7. L. 22 to 40 in.

Varies greatly geographically, the subspecies *minima* being the smallest goose in Canada, *maxima* the largest. Although there is considerable geographic variation in colour also, all the subspecies have similar colour patterns. *Adults* (*B.c. interior*): Head and neck black, with a large white patch on each cheek, the two cheek patches meeting under the throat; upper parts of body and wings greyish brown, the feathers narrowly tipped with brownish white; rump blackish; upper tail coverts white; tail black; under body brownish grey with paler feather tips, the sides and flanks usually darkest, lower belly and under tail coverts white; feathers of breast broad and square-tipped; bill and legs black; eye brown. *Immatures* (*first autumn and winter*): Similar to adults but breast feathers are narrower, softer, less conspicuously tipped; outer primaries with more pointed, less rounded tips.

Measurements (*B. c. interior*, one of the larger races). *Adult male:* wing, 430–473 (456.8); tail, 131–149 (143.9); exposed culmen, 46–55.5 (50.7); tarsus, 81–91.5 (89.1). *Adult female:* wing, 427–467 (445.5) mm (J. W. Aldrich).

Field Marks. Varies geographically from near Mallard size to large but is always readily recognizable as a Canada

Goose by the combination of long black neck and black head with large *white cheek patches*. Brant are similar in appearance but have a narrow white collar on the black neck and no white cheek patch on the all-black head. High-flying flocks in migration travel in a V-formation. *Voice:* the 'honk' is a sonorous, two-syllabled nasal *ka-ronk* slightly up-slurred at the end and with a break in the voice between the two syllables. The small races have higher-pitched voices.

Habitat. Breeds over vast, ecologically varied areas in both treeless and forested country which varies from prairies and plains in the West and coastal plains in the Arctic to mountains. Nests in the vicinity of water near lakes, ponds, and larger streams, marshes, muskegs, and hummocky coastal plains in the Arctic. Often forages on berry-bearing tundra, feeding especially on fruit of *Vaccinium* and *Empetrum*. In migration, lakes, rivers, coastal and freshwater marshes, bays, grassy fields, and grain stubbles.

Nesting. Usually on the ground near water, favouring particularly islets or muskrat or beaver houses. Occasionally in a tree nest of a hawk or other large bird or on a cliff ledge. Nest is a depression lined, sometimes bulkily sometimes scantily, with sticks and various vegetal materials obtainable in the vicinity, and with an inner lining of down. *Eggs*, most often 4 to 6; white but often nest-stained. Incubation period 24 to 25 days (C. D. MacInnes), 25 to 28 days (C. W. Kossack), 28 to 33 days (J. S. Dow). Incubation by the female, the male guarding.

Range. Breeds from the Komandorskie and Kurile islands (formerly) and from western Alaska eastward to Labrador and Newfoundland and south to northeastern California, Utah, Kansas, and rarely to Maine and Massachusetts. Winters from southern Canada (locally) south to northern Mexico and the Gulf Coast of United States.

Breeding Distribution of Canada Goose

Range in Canada. Breeds from northern Yukon (Herschel Island), northern Mackenzie (Richards Island, lower Anderson River), Victoria Island (Walker Bay, Cambridge Bay), King William Island, Boothia Peninsula (Felix Harbour), Melville Peninsula, Southampton Island, and southern

Baffin Island (Foxe Peninsula, probably Cumberland Peninsula), south through Yukon, Mackenzie, and Keewatin, and south through southern British Columbia (including Queen Charlotte and Vancouver islands), southern Alberta, southern Saskatchewan, southern Manitoba, north-central Ontario (coast of Hudson Bay and inland 60 or more miles; Mattagami River; locally farther south); southern James Bay (Twin and Charlton islands), central and southeastern Quebec (Lake Albanel, Natashquan, Anticosti Island, Blanc Sablon, locally farther south), southern Labrador (Sawbill, L'Anse au Clair), and Newfoundland.

Winters on the coast of British Columbia, southern Alberta (small numbers: Bow River), southern Saskatchewan (small numbers: Regina), extreme southern Ontario, Prince Edward Island, Nova Scotia (Port Joli, Port Hebert, Sable River estuary, Barrington Bay, Cole Harbour), and Newfoundland (Stephenville. About 1,000 winter in the province—L. M. Tuck).

Casual on Banks Island and Bylot Island, N.W.T.

Subspecies. The subspecies of this goose are at present imperfectly understood. (1) *B. c. canadensis* (Linnaeus), a large palish form: e. Que., Lab., Nfld. (2) *B. c. interior* Todd, a large form but darker and browner than *canadensis:* ne. Man. (Churchill), Ont., w. Que., s. Baffin I. (not typical). (3) *B. c. maxima* Delacour, the largest form and slightly paler than *canadensis:* s. Man., its area of intergradation westward with *moffiti* not yet clearly understood, but probably including s. Alta. and s. Sask. (4) *B. c. moffiti* Aldrich, coloured like *maxima* but somewhat smaller, especially bill and tarsus: interior s. and c. B.C. (Lac la Hache). (5) *B. c. parvipes* (Cassin), colour similar to *moffiti* but size much smaller: interior Yukon, Mack., Keewatin, n. B.C. (Tuya Lake). (6) *B. c. fulva* Delacour, a large form much darker above and below than any of the above-mentioned races: coastal B.C. (7) *B. c. hutchinsii* (Richardson), a very small short-billed form similar in coloration to *parvipes:* Victoria I., Adelaide Pen., Melville Pen., Southampton I., and coast w. Baffin I., N.W.T. (8) *B. c. minima* Ridgway, even smaller than *hutchinsii* and very much darker: migrant to coastal B.C. (9) *B. c. leucopareia* (Brandt), of the Aleutian I., now greatly reduced in numbers, formerly occurred in winter in coastal B.C. (10) *B. c. taverneri* Delacour is postulated to be the breeding form of coastal northern Yukon and nw. Mack. (Mack. Delta).

Remarks. The Canada Goose is *the* wild goose to most Canadians. The majority of people see it in its spring or autumn migration flying high overhead. This is a thrilling and inspiring sight. When the geese are on the move and their resonant honking drifts down to us, there are few who do not pause and gaze upward as the big birds in V-formation move majestically across the sky. Despite their size they fly swiftly and soon pass out of sight.

This splendid goose is extremely popular as a game bird, but despite heavy hunting pressure it has managed to maintain quite good numbers. It is wary and sagacious, but courageous and formidable in defence of its nest or young. Family ties are very strong. Pairs usually mate for life, but when one of the pair dies, the other may take another mate. The young fly south in autumn with their parents and do not separate from them until they return in spring to the nesting grounds. Migrating flocks often comprise several families.

BRANT (includes Black Brant)
La Bernache cravant. *Branta bernicla* (Linnaeus)
Plate 7. L. 23 to 30 in.

(*Branta bernicla hrota*). *Adults:* Head, neck, chest, and foreneck black, contrasting with belly. Narrow white crescent on either side of neck. Back and upper sides of wings brown, the margins of the feathers paler. Wing tips blackish. Rump and tail, black. Tail coverts white, the upper ones producing a broad white band at base of tail. Belly and sides, brownish grey with paler feather tips, giving a barred effect to the flanks. Bill and legs, black. *Young in first autumn:* Like adults but white crescent on sides of neck wanting or poorly indicated; no barring on flanks; breast feathers narrower, softer, not square-tipped. Wing coverts, tail feathers (usually), and secondaries tipped with white. *Branta bernicla nigricans* (Black Brant). *Adults:* Similar to *hrota*, but belly dark slaty brown or blackish brown with little or no contrast with chest. White crescents usually meet in front of neck but not on hind-neck. Young similar to young *hrota* but belly much darker.

Measurements (*B. b. hrota*). *Adult male:* wing, 321–351 (333.9); tail, 96–105 (99.7); exposed culmen, 32–34 (32.9); tarsus, 60–69 (63.2). *Adult female:* wing, 296–336 (314)mm.

Field Marks. Like the Canada Goose, it has a black head and neck but lacks its white cheeks. Black of neck extends down to include breast (breast is pale in Canada Goose). Adult has narrow white patch on sides of neck which the Canada lacks. On the water hind parts ride higher. *Voice:* A hoarse *r-r-r-ronk*, *car-r-rup*, or *ruk-ruk;* when feeding, chattering sounds.

Habitat. In winter and migration, mainly along salt water bays, rocky shores, and tidal flats, particularly where eel grass (*Zostera*) is present. When occasionally it stops at inland points, it frequents lake and river shores, sometimes cultivated fields. In summer arctic coastal islands, deltas, broad river valleys, well-vegetated uplands, and tundra lakes, usually near the coast.

Nesting. Nests in loose colonies or singly. Nest on the ground, well lined with down, the foundation varying from a mere hollow in the ground to a mound of mosses and lichens. *Eggs*, usually 3 to 5, often more; creamy white. Incubation by female while male stands guard, usually 23 to 24 days but varying between 22 and 26 days (T. W. Barry).

Range. Circumpolar, breeding in arctic North America and Eurasia. In North America winters along the Pacific Coast from Queen Charlotte Islands to Baja California and along the Atlantic Coast from Massachusetts to North Carolina.

Range in Canada. Breeds locally in maritime areas throughout the Arctic Archipelago north to Prince Patrick, Ellef Ringnes, and northern Ellesmere islands and south to the arctic mainland of Mackenzie (Mackenzie Delta, Perry River); Keewatin (Cape Fullerton), Southampton Island; and Baffin Island (Cape Alberta, West Foxe Islands). An isolated breeding record has been reported from Copper

Cliff, Ontario (Baillie, 1955, *Audubon Field Notes* 9: 23). Migrates along the British Columbia coast, the east coast of Hudson and James bays, also overland between Ungava Bay and the lower St. Lawrence River and inner north shore of the Gulf of St. Lawrence, and is a locally common transient on the coasts of New Brunswick, Prince Edward Island, Nova Scotia (particularly Cumberland, Colchester, and Pictou counties), and the Magdalens. In recent years transients in southern Ontario (Ottawa River; lower Great Lakes) have become more or less regular. Otherwise scarce in the interior but recorded from southern Keewatin, Alberta (Grande Prairie, Jasper, Cooking Lake), Saskatchewan, Manitoba, and interior Quebec.(Although it migrates regularly across the interior of Ungava, flight appears to be usually non-stop between Ungava Bay and the lower St. Lawrence River; *see* Lewis, *The Auk* 54: 73–95.) Scarce and irregular on Labrador coast (Nain, Jack Lane's Bay). Casual in Newfoundland. In Canada, winters only on the coast of British Columbia (mostly southern Georgia Strait and adjacent waters).

Breeding Distribution of Brant

Subspecies. Two well-marked subspecies (described above) are found in Canada, and a third, intermediate in colour between them, occurs in the Old World. (1) *B. b. nigricans* (Lawrence) breeds in the w. Arctic along the coast of Mack. and northward on Banks and Prince Patrick is., intergrading on the latter with *hrota;* winters along the Pacific Coast; casual in migration in s. Yukon and s. Sask. (2) *B. b. hrota* (Müller) breeds in the e. Arctic and westward to Adelaide Pen., probably Prince of Wales I.; intergrades with *nigricans* on Melville and Prince Patrick is. and in the Perry R. region. No specimens are available from Victoria I. The validity of another alleged North American race (Delacour and Zimmer, 1952, *The Auk*, 69: 83-84) is not established.

There is considerable controversy about the forms of this species. The A.O.U. *Check-list of North American Birds* (1957) and some authors treat *nigricans* as a separate species, apparently because it and *hrota* do not seem to interbreed to a great extent in areas where they breed sympatrically. If pair formation occurs on the widely separated wintering grounds or on the migration routes of the two forms, this would account for their segregation on the breeding grounds, and the two should be considered subspecies. Interbreeding has been indicated by Manning, *et al.* (1956) by intermediate specimens, and a mixed pair on Prince Patrick I. has been observed by S. D. MacDonald.

Remarks. This small goose is primarily a saltwater bird and is a favourite with gunners along the coasts. It does not ordinarily fly in the familiar V-pattern of its near relative, the Canada Goose, but in long wavering lines or formationless flocks. Brant like company and usually are seen in groups. Spring migration is late, and in the Maritimes many Brant linger at favourite feeding places until the first week of June. In migration and on the wintering grounds Brant feed mainly on eel grass (*Zostera*), uncovered by the receding tide, or in shallow water by tipping up, like ducks.

BARNACLE GOOSE
La Bernache nonnette. *Branta leucopsis* (Bechstein)
Fig. 20. L. 25 to 28 in.

Adults: Head mainly white with a black bar extending from eye to base of bill, the black of neck reaching up over nape and hind crown (leaving broad white forehead). Neck and breast black. Back bluish grey, the feathers with broad blackish subterminal bars and brownish white tips. Rump and tail black. Upper and under tail coverts white. Belly greyish white, contrasting sharply with black breast. Flanks bluish grey, barred with brownish white. Bill, legs, and feet black. *Immatures:* Similar but duller, the neck more greyish, the back more brownish.

Fig. 20 Barnacle Goose

Field Marks. Suggests a small Canada Goose but with a conspicuous white forehead.

Range. Breeds in eastern Greenland, Spitsbergen, and Novaya Zemlya.

Status in Canada. Casual visitant to Baffin Island, N.W.T. (Boas Lake, August 1924); Quebec (Cap Tourmente, October 26, 1925, and October 1953; Rupert House; Lake St. Peter, autumn, 1926). There are only sight records for Labrador (Okak) and Ontario (Kingsville, October 27 to December 15, 1955).

EMPEROR GOOSE

L'Oie empereur. *Philacte canagica* (Sewastianov)
Fig. 21. L. ca. 36 in.

Adults: Head and back of neck white; throat and fore-neck black. Back, breast, and sides bluish grey, each feather with a blackish subterminal bar and a white tip, creating a barred effect. Secondaries and tertials with wide white margins. Tail white. Belly grey, each feather with a whitish tip. Bill pinkish or purplish with whitish tip. Legs and feet orange-yellow. *Immatures:* Somewhat like adults but entire head mottled with grey and body plumage duller. The white head is attained at the first autumn molt. It is more or less flecked with black.

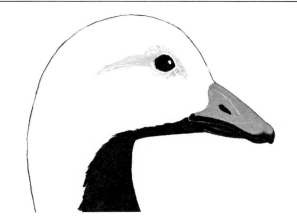

Fig. 21 Emperor Goose, adult

Field Marks. Most closely resembles the 'blue goose' phase of the Snow Goose but has a black throat and fore-neck and a dark rump. At close range the barred upper parts are obvious.

Range. Breeds on the coast of northeastern Siberia, St. Lawrence Island, and coastal northwestern Alaska. Winters mainly in the Aleutian Islands but wanders also down the North American coast casually as far as California.

Status in Canada. Rare winter visitant to the coast of British Columbia. Most frequently recorded from Masset, Queen Charlotte Islands, but has occurred also at Chemainus, Tlell, Cape Scott, Discovery Island, and Triple Island.

WHITE-FRONTED GOOSE

L'Oie à front blanc. *Anser albifrons* (Scopoli)
Plate 7. L. ca. 26 to 30 in.

Adults: Head, neck, back, rump, and wings, greyish brown. Forehead and narrow area behind base of bill, white. Tail, dark brown edged with white. Upper tail coverts mostly white, creating white band across base of tail. Breast and belly greyish, heavily and irregularly blotched with blackish brown. Bill mostly pinkish (yellowish in one race). Legs and feet, orange. *Immatures:* Similar to adults but lack white face patch (which begins to develop late in first fall) and are without black blotches on under parts. Legs yellowish grey, becoming orange with age.

Measurements (*A. a. frontalis*). *Adult male:* wing, 378–445 (412); tail, 117–127 (121); exposed culmen, 48–53 (51.2); tarsus, 73–77 (74.9) mm. *Adult female:* wing, 388–421 (403.9) mm.

Field Marks. A brownish goose with no black on head or neck. Adults with narrow, white face patch, black blotches on under parts, and yellow or orange feet. Immatures lack the diagnostic markings about face and under parts; they thus resemble immature blue phase Snow Geese, but the under parts are whiter and there is a narrow *white* band at base of tail which contrasts with dark rump. In young 'blues' the rump and upper tail coverts are uniform pale *grey*. The White-front's yellow legs are diagnostic, as, in Canada, only the otherwise very different Emperor Goose has yellow legs. The blue phase of the Snow Goose at close range shows a 'grinning patch' (*see* Fig. 22), lacking in White-fronted. *Voice:* Rapidly repeated, usually in pairs, clanging laughlike *wah-wah*, *wah-wah*, or *kow-yow*. When feeding, a conversational gabbling.

Habitat. In breeding season the arctic tundra: edges of lakes; grassy flats; valleys, islands and deltas of streams. In migration, marshes, lakes and ponds, grassy fields, and grain fields.

Nesting. Often nests gregariously. Nest on ground, of mosses, grasses, tundra rubbish, lined with down and feathers. *Eggs*, usually 4 to 6; creamy white, often nest-stained. Incubation, by female while male stands guard, 27 to 28 days (Laidlay *in* Witherby, *et al.*).

Range. Circumpolar (but absent as a breeder in eastern North America), Alaska, western Canada, eastern Greenland, Iceland, Scandinavia, and Spitsbergen. Winters in western North America (from southern British Columbia and southern Illinois south to Mexico), North Africa, India, China, and Japan.

Breeding Distribution of White-fronted Goose

Range in Canada. Breeds from northern Yukon (Old Crow flats), northern Mackenzie (Mackenzie Delta, Franklin Bay, Anderson River, Coronation Gulf, mouth of Perry River), southern Victoria Island (Cambridge Bay), northern Kee-

51

watin (Sherman Basin), south to middle-eastern Mackenzie (Mackay Lake, Outram River, and headwaters of the Hanbury), and Keewatin (Angikuni Lake, Thelon River, McConnell River). A spring and fall transient in Manitoba, Saskatchewan, Alberta, and British Columbia (common along coast). Of rare or casual occurrence in migration east of the Prairie Provinces in Ontario, Quebec, New Brunswick, Prince Edward Island, Nova Scotia, Newfoundland, and Labrador (near Hopedale). Winters occasionally in south-western British Columbia (Vancouver Island).

Subspecies. (1) *Anser albifrons frontalis* Baird is by far the commonest race and breeds in most, if not all of the Canadian breeding range outlined above. (2) *A. a. gambelli* Hartlaub is a larger, slightly darker form, the status of which is uncertain. Its breeding range is unknown, but specimens have been recorded from Mackenzie Delta, Repulse Bay, and the arctic coast e. of Fort Anderson. If it is a valid race or, as some think, a full species, its breeding range remains to be found. (3) *A. a. flavirostris* Dalgety and Scott, similar to *frontalis* but with a yellow bill, breeds in w. Greenland and winters in the British Isles. Just how many specimens of this species that have been taken in the past in e. Canada are referable to *flavirostris* cannot now be determined. Its occurrence in Canada, however, is shown by two records from Que. (near Matane, late September 1946; also a sight record near Rimouski, June 20, 1959); and one from P.E.I. (Black Banks, October 21, 1961); N.S. (Debert, November 12, 1949); and Nfld. (St. Brides, October 10, 1952).

SNOW GOOSE (including 'Blue Goose')
L'Oie blanche. *Chen caerulescens* (Linnaeus)
Plate 8. L. 25 to 30 in.

Sides of mandibles with blackish 'grinning patch' (Fig. 22). WHITE PHASE: *Adults:* Mainly white but often rust-stained on head, neck, and under parts. Wing tips black, the primaries grey at their bases. Bill pinkish, blackish at cutting edges. Legs and feet reddish. *Immatures:* Head and hind-neck more or less greyish, chin and throat whitish (often rust-stained). Back, scapulars, and wing coverts grey with paler feather edges. Secondaries dusky with whitish edges.

Fig. 22 Bill of Snow Goose showing 'grinning patch'

Primaries blackish becoming grey at their bases. Rump and upper tail coverts, white. Tail variable grey and white. Under parts white, the sides sometimes lightly washed with grey. Bill brownish or blackish. Legs and feet purplish grey. BLUE PHASE: *Adults:* Head and neck white (often rust-

stained), frequently with variable blotches of blackish brown on hind-neck. Upper back and scapulars dark brown, feather tips pale brown. Upper wing coverts bluish grey. Primaries and secondaries, blackish with greyish bases. Tertials blackish with white edges, grey basally. Lower back, rump, and upper tail coverts vary from bluish grey to whitish. Tail feathers greyish brown with pale edges. Breast, belly, and sides usually dark greyish brown but often variable, occasionally almost all white. Abdomen and under tail coverts usually grey or whitish. Bill and legs as in white phase. *Immatures:* Somewhat variable but usually head, neck, back, and under parts slaty grey; chin white; otherwise similar to adults. Bill and legs dark grey during first fall. They become like adults during their second summer.

Measurements (*C. c. atlantica*). *Adult male:* wing, 430–485 (450); tail, 135–160 (140); exposed culmen, 59–73 (67); tarsus, 86–97 (92). *Adult female:* wing, 425–475 (445) mm (Kennard).

(*C. c. hyperborea*). *Adult male:* wing, 395–460 (430); tail, 115–165 (130); exposed culmen, 51–62 (58); tarsus, 78–91 (84); *Adult female:* wing, 380–440 (420) mm (Kennard).

Field Marks. Both phases have pink feet and a dark 'grinning patch' on side of bill. BLUE PHASE: Adult would be confused only with the rare Emperor Goose of the Pacific Coast, but the latter has black fore-neck and throat, and orange legs. WHITE PHASE: White or greyish-white geese with black wing tips, they are likely to be confused with Ross's Goose (*see* Ross's Goose). *Immatures* of the blue phase resemble immature White-fronted but have dark legs and bill, grey instead of white upper tail coverts. *Voice:* A rather high-pitched falsetto monosyllabic *kowk*, somewhat musical in chorus, which is given both in flight and on the ground. While feeding, gabbling and groaning sounds. In nesting season, a sheep-like *kha-ah* is an alarm call.

Habitat. In migration (mostly avoids forested habitat) stops on fresh or saltwater marshes, lakes, wet fields, grain fields, sandbars. In summer frequents low, hummocky coastal plains with ponds, shallow lakes, or streams, less often higher, drier terrain as well; also more rarely far in the interior as at Beverly Lake. The race *atlantica* on Bylot Island breeds also on protected slopes of ravines.

Nesting. Nests mainly in loose colonies (occasionally in single pairs) sometimes associated with Brant. Nest, on the ground, a mass of mosses or other tundra vegetation lined with down. *Eggs,* usually 3 to 5, most often 4; white to creamy but usually nest-stained. Incubation 20 to 25 days, usually 22 to 23 days (F. G. Cooch); in *atlantica* 23 to 25 days (L. Lemieux), by female only, male standing guard.

Range. Northeastern Siberia, northern Alaska, arctic Canada, and northern Greenland. Winters mainly from southern British Columbia south to California; along the Gulf coast from Mexico (Veracruz) and Texas to western Florida; on the Atlantic coast, New Jersey to South Carolina.

Range in Canada. Breeds in colonies of various sizes in the Arctic from Banks Island, Victoria Island, Prince of Wales Island, and northern Ellesmere Island (Hilgard Bay) south to northern Mackenzie (Mackenzie Delta, Anderson River, Perry River), Keewatin (Beverly Lake, Southampton Island, Coats Island, McConnell and Tha-Anne rivers), northeastern

Breeding Distribution of Snow Goose

Manitoba (25 miles east of Churchill), northern Ontario (Cape Henrietta Maria), James Bay (Akimiski Island), and southern Baffin Island. Reported without confirmation to have bred formerly on Twin Islands, James Bay. Migrates spring and fall through British Columbia (white phase), Alberta (mainly white phase), Saskatchewan (mainly white phase), and Manitoba (in early spring dark phase common with percentage of whites increasing as season advances; autumn, 75 per cent whites; F. G. Cooch). Large autumn concentrations build up in southern James Bay. Fall migration southwestwardly across Ontario is usually made nonstop in late October, although in rare years large numbers sometimes stop for a short time in settled parts. Usually a few stop regularly on the south shore of Georgian Bay. In spring there is a considerable migration northeastward over northwestern Ontario (Rat Rapids) toward James and Hudson bays. In Quebec, large numbers, mostly *atlantica*, converge in spring and fall on Cap Tourmente (near St. Joachim, 30 miles below Quebec City on the St. Lawrence River). East of central Quebec and in Labrador and the Maritime Provinces the species is of casual occurrence in migration. Winters in Canada only in southwestern British Columbia (mouth of Fraser River).

Subspecies. (1) *Chen caerulescens atlantica* Kennard (Greater Snow Goose), a larger race not known to have a blue colour phase, is a high-arctic form which breeds on Ellesmere, Axel Heiberg, Devon, Somerset, Prince of Wales, and extreme northern Baffin is., intergrading apparently with the nominate race in the Clyde River region of Baffin I. In spring and fall migration most individuals of this race converge on Cap Tourmente, Quebec, and spend some time there. (2) *Chen caerulescens caerulescens* (Linnaeus), smaller in size and with two colour phases (described above). It breeds in the low Arctic of the East and apparently all of the breeding range west of Prince of Wales I. In migration it is the only race likely to be encountered in settled country w. of Que. Prov. On its breeding grounds, the proportion of blue phase individuals diminishes east to west but is said (F. G. Cooch, MS.) to be increasing.

Remarks. Although the Snow Goose is a common migrant in parts of western Canada, there is one place in eastern Canada south of James Bay where it stops regularly and in large numbers. This is at Cap Tourmente, some 30 miles east of Quebec City. There, especially in fall, against a background of 1,800-foot Cap Tourmente, resplendent in autumn colours, the swirling thousands of snow-white geese are a beautiful sight.

Apparently the whole population of the subspecies *atlantica* stops at Cap Tourmente, and this provides a ready means of censusing its numbers. In 1900 the number of birds stopping there was estimated at 2,000 to 3,000; in 1921 at 5,000 to 6,000; in 1937 at 10,000; in 1941 at 20,000; in 1951 at 30,000; in 1958 at 47,500. These estimates thus reveal a very substantial increase in numbers since the turn of the century. In autumn the first geese arrive there usually in early September, and there is a gradual build-up of numbers until about mid-October. They remain until the marshes freeze up, usually in late November. Spring arrival is, as a rule, in the latter part of March, and the geese spend about one and one-half months there before resuming their northward flight toward their high-arctic breeding grounds. Lemieux (*Can. Field-Nat.* 73: 117–128) provides additional detailed information on the breeding history of this subspecies on Bylot Island, N.W.T.

ROSS'S GOOSE
L'Oie de Ross. *Chen rossii* (Cassin)
Plate 8. L. 21 to 23 in.

No 'grinning patch' on side of bill. *Adults:* Mainly white. Wing tips black, greyish at base. Bill pinkish with greenish or bluish area near base; has *warty protuberances between base and nostrils* (*see* Fig. 23) which are lacking in young birds and in some females. Legs and feet pink. *Immatures:* Similar to immature Snow Goose but much smaller and with shorter bill, the upper parts more whitish.

Fig. 23 Ross's Goose

Measurements. *Adult male:* wing, 355–386 (372.4); tail, 106–129 (118.3); exposed culmen, 37.5–42 (40.3); tarsus, 68–73 (69.7). *Adult female:* wing, 338–385 (359.7) mm.

Field Marks. The smallest mainly-white goose. A diminutive edition of the Snow Goose, scarcely larger than a large duck. Lacks black 'grinning patch.' At very close range warty protuberances at base of bill may be discerned. *Voice:* A double-noted *luk-luk*, different from that of the Snow Goose, higher pitched, almost squeaky.

Habitat. On breeding grounds, tundra and low islands of freshwater lakes, floodplain marshes of rivers. In migration across eastern Alberta frequents large lakes, ponds, and stubble fields.

Nesting. In colonies. Nest varies from a scrape in the ground, lined with down, to a considerable mound of moss and other material. *Eggs,* most often 4 but varying from 2 to 9; dull white. Incubation period 24 days (J. Delacour); in captivity 21 days (Blaauw).

Range. Breeds very locally in the Canadian low Arctic. Winters mainly in the Sacramento and San Joachim valleys of California and rarely elsewhere in southern United States (Louisiana, eastern Texas).

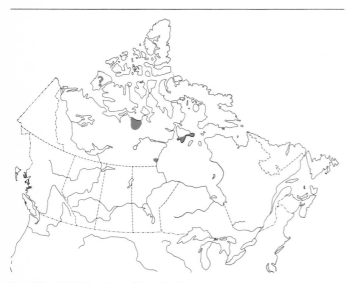

Breeding Distribution of Ross's Goose

Range in Canada. Breeds in northeastern Mackenzie (on Perry River and on adjoining Queen Maud Gulf); southeastern Keewatin (McConnell River); and Southampton Island (Boas River Delta, probably East Bay). Recorded in summer also from Banks Island.

Main migration is in a southwest-northeast direction with spring and autumn concentrations on the Peace-Athabasca deltas of western Lake Athabasca. Most pass through eastern Alberta (Stetler, Sullivan Lake, Coronation, and Hanna vicinities), and western Saskatchewan (Kindersley, Kerrobert, Macklin, Alsask vicinities). Scarce transient in central-southern and southeastern Saskatchewan (Caron, Regina, Imperial Beach); Manitoba (The Pas, Killarney, Portage la Prairie, Winnipeg; probably Churchill), northern Ontario (Fort Severn; foot of James Bay), and British Columbia (Stuart Lake, Comox, Kuper Island, Rawling's Lake). In western Mackenzie it is a scarce visitor to Great Slave Lake, and there are unconfirmed old reports from the mouth of Horton River and Fort Anderson.

Remarks. The breeding grounds of this small goose remained a complete mystery until discovered in 1938 by

Angus Gavin on Perry River along the Mackenzie-Keewatin boundary. Its total numbers were for some time thought to be about 2,000. More recent estimates, based on censuses on the wintering grounds in California, are decidedly more optimistic and in 1965 placed its total numbers at about 31,880. Even this figure may prove to be too low.

Subfamily **Dendrocygninae**–Tree Ducks

FULVOUS TREE DUCK
Le Dendrocygne fauve. *Dendrocygna bicolor* (Vieillot)
L. 20.5 in.

Adults (sexes alike): Legs long for a duck, reaching beyond tail. Hind toe much elongated. Tarsus reticulated in front. Mainly plain cinnamon or fulvous in coloration with reddish brown crown; blackish line down back of neck; front and sides of neck, dull white streaked with brown; wing coverts mainly chestnut; flanks with creamy white stripes; back and wings dark brown with many rust-tipped feathers; upper tail coverts creamy white. Bill slaty grey. Legs bluish grey. *Immatures:* Similar but with little chestnut on wings.

Range. Southern United States south to Mexico; from Panama to the Guianas, and central Brazil to northern Argentina; also eastern Africa, India, and Ceylon.

Status in Canada. Casual visitant to British Columbia (near Alberni in September 1905, five were shot from a flock of eleven); Ontario (specimen taken at Frenchman Bay, west of Toronto, November 27, 1962); and New Brunswick (Grand Manan Island, November 4, 1961, flock of 21, one shot. Near Evansdale, November 21, 1961, five of a flock of six were shot by hunters. Perhaps these were remnants of the flock seen earlier on Grand Manan Island).

Subspecies. *Dendrocygna bicolor helva* Wetmore and Peters.

Subfamily **Anatinae**–Surface-feeding Ducks

Ducks of this large subfamily do not ordinarily dive. Food is commonly secured under shallow water by submerging perpendicularly the head, neck, and most of the body, leaving the tail above water, sticking straight up in the air. They feed also on the water surface or on land. Unlike that of the diving ducks, the hind toe has no lobe (*see* Fig. 24). In most species the speculum (wing patch) is more or less brightly coloured and iridescent.

Fig. 24 Foot of surface-feeding duck

MALLARD

Le Canard malard. *Anas platyrhynchos* Linnaeus
Plate 9. L. 19.5 to 27.0 in.

Adult male in breeding plumage, with green head and neck, narrow white collar, chestnut lower neck and breast, and violet wing patch (speculum) bordered *both in front and behind* by a white bar; needs no further description. Bill greenish yellow. Legs orange. In summer an eclipse plumage similar to the female is assumed, and molt into breeding plumage requires most of the autumn. *Adult female:* Top and sides of head, buff streaked with dark brown. Throat usually unmarked, sometimes spotted or streaked. Upper parts dark brown, the feathers broadly edged with buffy. Wing patch as in male but more greenish. Wing linings white. Breast and abdomen, buff marked with blackish brown and with U-shaped markings on breast feathers. Sides and flanks darker with buffy feather edges. Tail dark greyish brown, much paler (whitish) on outer edges. Bill yellowish or greenish, more or less mixed with black. Legs and feet reddish orange. *Juvenal:* Similar to adult female but slightly duller and without U-shaped markings on breast feathers.

Measurements. *Adult male:* wing, 273–290 (282); tail, 78–94 (86.3); exposed culmen, 52.5–59.5 (56.1); tarsus, 44–49 (46.3). *Adult female:* wing, 230–276 (259) mm.

Field Marks. *Adult male:* Green head, narrow white collar, chestnut breast. Male Shoveler has chestnut sides and under parts but white breast. *Female and Immatures:* Resemble Black Duck but general colour lighter. Wing with *two* white bars, one in front and one behind wing patch, which are visible for considerable distances in flight. Whitish outer sides of Mallard's tail are visible over some distance in flight. In the Black Duck, the tail is uniformly dark. *Voice:* A rather loud *quack* is given by the female. The male's voice is similar but softer and higher pitched.

Habitat. One of the most adaptable of ducks, frequenting marshes, sloughs, ponds, small and large lakes, quiet waters of rivers, and flooded land in both treeless and wooded country. Also forages on land, especially grainfields, and can get along with very little water. Prefers fresh to salt water, but does frequent coastal salt water, especially in winter.

Nesting. Nest, usually on ground, generally near water but sometimes far from it; rarely in a tree. Nest of grasses, reeds, leaves, well lined with down. *Eggs,* 5 to 15 (usually 8 to 12); dull greenish or greyish buff to nearly white. Incubation, 28±3 days (Girard), by the female, begins after laying of last egg.

Range. North America, Europe, and Asia.

Range in Canada. Common breeder in the western provinces, progressively scarcer farther east. Breeds in Yukon (across the southern part, and north to Old Crow flats); Mackenzie (near Aklavik, Fort Anderson, near Fort Norman, Fort Simpson, and at various points on Great Slave Lake; recorded in summer on Great Bear Lake and various points south of it), southern Keewatin (Windy River; recorded in summer off Tavani); through British Columbia, Alberta, Saskatchewan, and Manitoba; Ontario (locally in southern and eastern parts, commonest in western part near Manitoba boundary; recorded in summer on coasts of James and Hudson bays, probably breeding on Sandy Island, James Bay); Quebec (breeds in southwestern part: Hudson Heights, Laprairie, Lake St. Peter, Valcartier, St. Bruno de Kamouraska; recorded in summer near Amos, at Lake Abitibi, and on eastern James Bay). Scarce transient in eastern Quebec, New Brunswick, Nova Scotia, Prince Edward Island, and Newfoundland. Recorded (race unknown) in migration on the coast of Labrador and on Ungava Bay. Casual on Victoria Island, N.W.T.

Winters commonly in southern British Columbia (north to Stuart Lake); locally in southern Alberta (Calgary), southern Saskatchewan (Regina, rarely elsewhere), southern Ontario (north to Ottawa), southwestern Quebec (Montreal), and rarely Newfoundland and Nova Scotia.

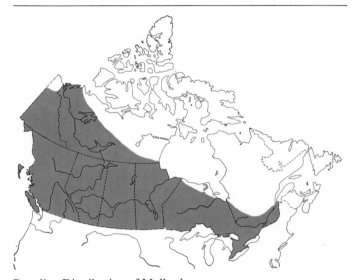

Breeding Distribution of Mallard

Subspecies. *Anas platyrhynchos platyrhynchos* Linnaeus. As Austin (1932) and Todd (1963) have suggested for Labrador, some east coast visitors may be of the Greenland race, *A. p. conboschas* Brehm.

Remarks. Doubtless no other duck in the world is so widely known as the Mallard. In the wild it is found in much of the earth's north temperate zone. In captivity it is the ancestor of most varieties of domestic ducks, several of which still resemble it closely. Handsome and swift, this good table bird is a favourite with sportsmen, particularly in the West. In the Atlantic Provinces and Ungava its place is taken by a close relative, the Black Duck. Its food is varied, consisting of succulent aquatic vegetation, seeds, insects, and small aquatic animals. It is very fond of grains, wild rice, and corn. It is said to perform a useful function in devouring large numbers of mosquito larvae.

BLACK DUCK

Le Canard noir. *Anas rubripes* Brewster
Plate 9. L. 21 to 24 in.

Adults: Crown, nape, and line through eye, dark brown. Rest of head brownish grey, finely streaked with a dusky hue, the chin and throat usually immaculate. Body mainly dark brown, the feathers with buffy borders. Wing patch purple, bordered in front and behind by black, the hind bar often with a very narrow white edge. Wing linings white. Feathers of sides of breast of male and female usually differ (Fig. 25), the buffy interior markings U-shaped in male, V-shaped in female. Bill greenish yellow in male,

Fig. 25 Feathers from sides of breast of Black Duck
(A) adult female   (B) adult male

more olive in female and often blotched with dusky (but variable). Legs reddish, orange, or greenish. *Juvenal:* Similar to adults, but bill and feet duller, under parts more streaky, breast feathers lack U- or V-shaped markings.

Measurements. *Adult male:* wing, 243–290 (267.9); tail, 81.5–94.5 (90.7); exposed culmen, 49.5–60 (53.8); tarsus, 45–48.5 (46.7). *Adult female:* wing, 244–280 (265.9) mm.

Field Marks. Dark brown above and below (in flight, white wing-linings flash contrastingly), darker than Mallard and lacking Mallard's whitish outer tail feathers and wing bars. *Voice:* A *quack* or series of them, that of male lower, softer, and shorter.

Habitat. Shallow margins of lakes, ponds, pools, quiet streams, coves, bays, mud flats, marshes, wet fields, grain fields, and open water. Frequents both salt and fresh water. During nesting, both dry and wet woodland.

Nesting. Usually on ground often in wooded areas (sometimes some distance from water), in bushy or grassy fields, on islands, or along brooks. Sometimes in a hole or fork in a tree, occasionally in an abandoned crow or hawk nest. Nest of twigs, stalks, grasses, leaves, with down lining. *Eggs,* 6 to 12, average 9; greenish buff to creamy white, unspotted. Incubation 26 to 28 days by female (A. C. Bent); 28 days (B. S. Wright).

Range. Breeds from northern Manitoba east to Labrador and Newfoundland and south to northern Minnesota, Wisconsin, Ohio, Pennsylvania, Maryland, and eastern Virginia. In winter from southeastern Canada to Texas, the Gulf states, Florida, and Bermuda.

Range in Canada. Commonest breeding duck in most of southeastern Canada. Breeds in Manitoba (common summer resident at Churchill, probably breeding, although apparently many are post-breeding males; scarce local summer resident in southern Manitoba at Lake St. Martin, Seven Sisters dam; three observations of pairing with Mallard in

Delta regions noted by H. A. Hochbaum), Ontario (commonly throughout eastern half and northward to James and Hudson bays, scarcer westward, rare and local near Manitoba border), Quebec (common throughout south and central parts, including Anticosti and Magdalen islands, and northward to about treeline, occurring farther north coastwise after breeding), Labrador (mostly away from the outer coast, near Sandwich Bay, upper Hamilton River, Okak, Rigolet, Davis Inlet, Alleuk Bight), and throughout Newfoundland, New Brunswick, Nova Scotia, and Prince Edward Island.

Rare visitant to Alberta (specimens collected at Athabasca Delta, September 23, 1940; Lac la Nonne in the late 1920's; another near Kelsey, fall, 1950; recently reported breeding near Kelsey and Hanna), Saskatchewan (occurs sparingly but not known to breed). Mackenzie (a few in summer on Thelon and Finnie rivers; recorded, perhaps erroneously, from Anderson River), Keewatin (summer records from Windy River; Chesterfield Inlet), Franklin (Cape Dorset, Baffin Island, three collected on June 8, 1934).

Winters in southern Ontario (north to Sault Ste. Marie and Ottawa), southern Quebec (Montreal), and on the coasts of Nova Scotia, Prince Edward Island, New Brunswick, and southern Newfoundland. Recorded in winter at Cartwright, Labrador (L. M. Tuck, MS.).

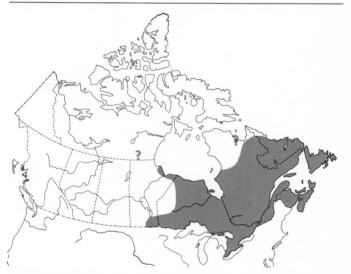

Breeding Distribution of Black Duck

Subspecies. None recognized. For years the large red-legged winter adults were thought to belong to a separate subspecies, supposedly breeding in the northern part of the range and migrating southward with the advent of cold weather. These characters have been shown by Shortt (1943, *Wilson Bull.* 55: 3–7) to be a product of age, sex, and season. That they are not peculiar to birds of any one geographical area has been well demonstrated by bird banding. The myth of a 'northern' race of Black Duck is still prevalent, however, among sportsmen.

Remarks. The Black is *the* wild duck to the sportsmen of eastern Canada, where it takes the place of the equally-famous Mallard of the West. Wary and swift on the wing, it taxes the marksmanship of even the most experienced gunner. As a table bird it is a favourite on account of its good size and usually excellent flavour. In coastal areas, when much-hunted, Blacks spend most of the daylight hours on salt water or on remote mud flats exposed by the tide. In the evening or after dark they fly in to the grain stubbles or freshwater marshes and leave them again at dawn. Even when undisturbed in late summer they are inclined to be more active in the evening than at other times, and they then regularly build up considerable assemblages in certain favourite feeding places.

GADWALL

Le Canard chipeau. *Anas strepera* Linnaeus
Plate 9. L. 18 to 22 in.

Adult male (*winter and spring*): Head and neck, grey, speckled with blackish, paler on chin and throat. Back dark grey, vermiculated with white, some scapulars broadly edged with yellowish brown. Upper and under tail coverts black. Tail brownish grey, the feathers with paler margins. Folded wing greyish at bend, then chestnut (on middle coverts), then black (greater coverts). Wing patch (speculum) white, bordered in front by black. Breast brownish black with numerous white or buffy crescentic marks (feathers white at base). Sides dark grey, crossed by narrow wavy white lines. Belly and wing linings, white. Bill dark grey. Legs and toes, yellow or orange with blackish webs. In summer a complete molt produces a female-like eclipse plumage. This is gradually molted, and by November the adult nuptial plumage of winter and spring is again almost complete. *Adult female:* Head and neck similar to male. Back, scapulars, rump, upper tail coverts, breast, and sides, dusky with buffy edges and markings. Wing somewhat as in male's, but chestnut much reduced in extent or lacking. Lower breast, belly, and wing linings, white. Bill, dull orange with dusky culmen and spots. Legs dull yellow. *Young in first autumn:* Similar to female but belly streaked with dusky and general colour somewhat darker.

Measurements. *Adult male:* wing, 259–276 (266); tail, 78–91 (81.4); exposed culmen, 40.5–46.5 (43.5); tarsus, 40.5–43 (41.3). *Adult female:* wing, 241–251 (245.8) mm.

Field Marks. Adult male is a grey medium-sized duck showing (especially in flight) a small white wing patch and a black rump. The white wing patch, when it can be seen, separates females and immatures from similar-appearing Mallards and Pintails. American Widgeons also usually show a white area in the wing, but it is situated on the forewing. On the Gadwall it is a patch near the rear edge of the wing. *Voice:* Female's 'quack' is usually softer than that of Mallard and slightly higher pitched. Male has loud 'kack, kack,' a shrill whistled call (Wetmore), and a croaking note usually preceding a whistled note in display.

Habitat. In summer prefers sloughs and shallow margins of lakes bordered by good cover (*see also* Nesting). Sometimes feeds on grain stubble fields. It does not often occur on salt water.

Nesting. Nest on the ground usually near water (often on low islands) but on drier ground than most ducks and usually concealed by vegetation; sometimes on open prairie at some distance from water. Nest of grasses, weed stalks, and other vegetation and is lined with down. *Eggs* usually 10 to 12; dull creamy white. Incubation 25 to 28 days, by the female (various authors).

Range. Western North America, Europe, and Asia.

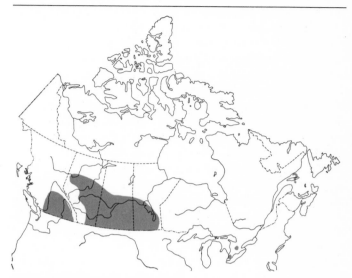

Breeding Distribution of Gadwall

Range in Canada. Breeds locally in southern interior British Columbia (Swan and Goose lakes, Okanagan Valley; 150-Mile House, Cariboo); southern and central Alberta (east of the mountains, and north to Peace River district); southern and central Saskatchewan; southern and central-western Manitoba (north to about Saskatchewan River Marshes), and in southern Ontario (very locally: Walpole Island in Lake St. Clair and at Luther Marsh). For Quebec, the only breeding evidence rests on a half-grown young, allegedly of this species, taken by Verrill (Lewis, *Can. Field-Nat.* 38: 72) on Anticosti Island.

Has been recorded north of its breeding range in British Columbia (Driftwood Valley), northern Saskatchewan (Fond du Lac); and northern Manitoba (Churchill).

In migration in southern British Columbia it is more common in fall than in spring, with a relatively large autumn population in Okanagan Valley. A more or less regular migrant in Ontario, this applying to southern parts; rare in extreme eastern Ontario (Ottawa). Rare migrant in southwestern Quebec (Senneville, Amos, Kamouraska). In Nova Scotia two specimen records, both on the Grand Pré meadows, November 14, 1931, and November 11, 1947. Occurrence in New Brunswick and Prince Edward Island is not satisfactorily established.

Winters regularly but not abundantly on the coast of British Columbia from Victoria to Masset, Queen Charlotte Islands, and sometimes in the southern interior (Okanagan Landing).

Remarks. Despite its wide distribution in the world, the Gadwall is not very numerous. A bird of temperate climates, it seems reluctant to venture very far north. Its flesh is not highly prized by most sportsmen.

PINTAIL

Le Canard pilet. *Anas acuta* Linnaeus
Plate 9. L. male 26 to 30 in.; female 20 to 24 in.

Adult male (winter, spring, early summer): Head and neck brown with a white line extending up either side of neck to near ear region. Back with fine vermiculations of a blackish hue and white producing a grey effect. Scapulars long, pointed, black with contrasting whitish margins. Fore-wing grey. Speculum varying between metallic green and bronze-purple, preceded in front by a band of chestnut and bordered behind by black, then white. Two long, black central tail feathers. Outer tail feathers dark brown, edged with white. Under parts mainly white, the sides finely barred with black giving grey effect. Under tail coverts with white outer margins. Bill bluish grey, blackish on ridge and nail. Legs and feet bluish grey to olive grey with dusky webs. A complete molt in summer produces a female-like eclipse plumage, and the breeding plumage is not assumed until mid or late fall. *Adult female:* Top of head buffy brown, heavily streaked with black. Sides of head and neck, buffy white streaked with dusky. Throat similar but only lightly streaked or immaculate. Upper back, dark brown with U-shaped buffy markings. Wing browner than in male, speculum duller, often speckled with black. Tail pointed, somewhat elongated, dark brown, marked with buffy white. Under parts dingy white, more or less mixed with dusky, about equally on breast; sides brownish with whitish V-shaped markings. Bill mainly dark greyish blue. Legs and feet greyish blue to greenish grey with dusky webs. *Immatures:* Resemble adult female but under parts are more heavily streaked.

Measurements. *Adult male:* wing, 262–279 (271); tail, 158–205.5 (180.7); exposed culmen, 48.5–54 (51.7); tarsus, 42–47 (44.1). *Adult female:* wing, 230–266 (251.3) mm.

Field Marks. Long very slender neck, pointed tail, and a narrow but conspicuous white line along the rear edge of the spread wing. *Voice:* Female, a low *quack*; male, a low two-syllable whistle, usually given in display.

Habitat. Shallow bodies of fresh water and marshes, large and small; also outside breeding season, salt and brackish waters of the coast. Frequently feeds on grain stubbles.

Nesting. Nest on the ground, frequently near water and often some distance from it. Nest sometimes well hidden in vegetation but is frequently placed in the exposed open prairie. *Eggs,* usually 7 to 10; vary in colour from pale olive green to pale buff. Incubation, by the female, requires 23 days (various authors).

Range. Inhabits both the New and Old worlds. In North America breeds in Alaska, Canada, western Greenland, and the western United States and winters from southern Canada southward.

Range in Canada. Breeds from Yukon (Old Crow flats, Dawson, and Lapierre House), northern Mackenzie (Mackenzie Delta, Anderson River, Bathurst Inlet, perhaps Perry River), southern Victoria Island (probably Cambridge Bay), southern Keewatin (Simon's Lake, Beverly Lake, Southampton Island), northern Ontario (Hudson and

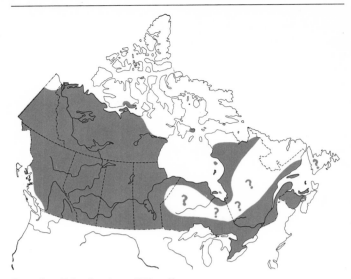

Breeding Distribution of Pintail

James Bay coasts and lowlands; e.g., Shagamu River, Cape Tatnum, Cape Henrietta Maria, Raft River), northern and central Quebec (Lake Aigneau and False River, probably Povungnituk; Roggan River, but rare or absent from much of the interior), south through interior British Columbia, southern Alberta, Saskatchewan, Manitoba, southern Ontario (locally, Port Arthur, Erieau, Kingston, Ramsayville), southern Quebec (locally: East Templeton; Pointe St. Denis; Nun's Island; Mal Bay, Gaspé Peninsula; Magdalen Islands; Anticosti Island; and north shore of the Gulf of St. Lawrence); New Brunswick (locally, Midgic, Saint John Valley); Prince Edward Island (Hillsborough River), and Nova Scotia (Amherst Bog).

Recorded in summer from Banks Island, Adelaide Peninsula, Chesterfield Inlet, Southampton Island, rarely Baffin Island (Aitken Lakes, Koukdjuak River, Cape Alberta), and Newfoundland (possibly breeds). Uncommon transient in Labrador and Newfoundland. Abundant transient on the coast of British Columbia and decidedly more common in migration in eastern Canada than at other times.

Winters on the coast of British Columbia (particularly southern parts but north to Queen Charlotte Islands), extreme southern Ontario, and uncommonly in the Maritimes; north rarely to southern Newfoundland.

[**Falcated Teal.** *Anas falcata* Georgi. Hypothetical. A full plumage male observed near Vernon, British Columbia, April 15, 1932, by Allan Brooks (1942, *Condor* 44: 33).]

COMMON TEAL (European Teal)

La Sarcelle européenne. *Anas crecca* Linnaeus
Plate 10. L. ca. 14.5 in.

Adult male in breeding plumage: Similar to Green-winged Teal but has no vertical white bar in front of wing; also the long pointed scapulars are white with black outer borders, vermiculations of back coarser, and the whitish border around the green area on side of head more extensive. *Female and Immature:* Like Green-winged Teal.

Field Marks. Male in breeding plumage separable from Green-winged Teal by the lack of a white vertical bar in front of wing and the presence of a narrow horizontal white stripe above the wing. Females are not separable from those of the Green-winged Teal in the field.

Range. Breeds from Iceland, northern Europe and Asia, and the Aleutian Islands south to Spain, northern Italy, southern Russia, and northwestern China.

Status in Canada. Casual visitant. Nova Scotia (specimen taken near Halifax, September 1, 1854; another taken near Mineville, February 14, 1913; sight record by George Boyer on Amherst Point Sanctuary, April 26, 1955; another sight record at Halifax, April 4, 1954). New Brunswick (specimen taken at St. Andrews about 1880 is still extant). Newfoundland (a female banded in England was shot at Barr'd Island, Fogo District, on December 5, 1952). Labrador (specimen taken by Elliott Coues on July 23, 1860, no further locality; another was received from a half-breed at Hamilton Inlet in 1891 by the Bowdoin Expedition). British Columbia (a male, taken at Masset, January 1, 1946, where also several were reliably observed in winter, 1939).

Subspecies. *Anas crecca crecca* Linnaeus.

GREEN-WINGED TEAL
La Sarcelle à ailes vertes. *Anas carolinensis* Gmelin
Plate 10. L. 14.5 in.

Our smallest duck. Size distinguishes it from all other ducks of regular occurrence in Canada except the Blue-winged and Cinnamon teals, the Bufflehead, and the Ruddy Duck. The bright green speculum separates it from the latter two, and a complete absence of blue on the fore-wing from the first two (*see also* Common Teal).

Measurements. *Adult male:* wing, 172–189 (180.7); tail, 61–74 (68); exposed culmen, 36–40.5 (38.1); tarsus, 30–33 (31.4). *Adult female:* wing, 164–176.5 (170.5) mm.

Field Marks. Adult male's small size and markings in winter and spring are unmistakable. In flight the lack of any large bluish patch on the fore-wing separates it from other North American teals (*see also* Common Teal). *Voice:* Female, a weak quack. Male, a short high-pitched whistle.

Habitat. Freshwater ponds, marshes, shallow edges of lakes; also in migration and winter, shallow salt and brackish water and shores.

Nesting. Nest on the ground, usually near fresh water but sometimes some distance from it, generally concealed by grass or shrubbery. *Eggs,* usually 10 to 12, sometimes more or less; white to pale olive buff. Incubation, 21 to 23 days, is by the female (A.C. Bent).

Range. Breeds from middle Alaska and the northwestern and middle Canadian mainland south to California, northern New Mexico, northern Nebraska, Minnesota, northern Ohio, western New York, Maine, and Nova Scotia. Winters mainly in the United States.

Range in Canada. Breeds from northern Yukon (Herschel Island), northwestern and western Mackenzie (Aklavik; Tuktoyaktuk; near Norman Wells; Great Slave Lake; Grassy Island marshes on Thelon River); southern Kee-watin (near Simon's Lake, Windy Bay, Eskimo Point),

northern Manitoba (Churchill); coast and lowlands of southern Hudson Bay, James Bay (Raft River, Roggan River), northern Quebec (Leaf Bay); north-central Labrador (Nain, Henley Harbour) and Newfoundland; south through interior British Columbia, Alberta, Saskatchewan, and Manitoba; middle and southern Ontario (very locally: near Orangeville; Rainy River district; Cochrane, Ottawa, and near Kingston); southern Quebec (Lake St. John, Pointe des Monts, Anticosti Island, near Sorel, Oka, Magdalen Islands); Labrador (Nain); New Brunswick (Maugerville; Grand Manan); Prince Edward Island; and Nova Scotia (including Cape Breton Island). In poorly known interior northern Quebec, actual breeding has not yet been discovered, but possibly a sparse local nesting population will eventually be found.

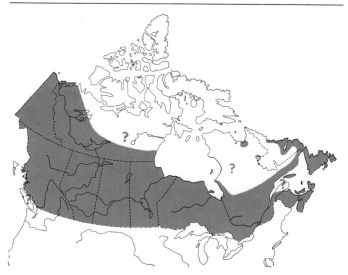

Breeding Distribution of Green-winged Teal

Has wandered north to Perry River, Repulse Bay, and Cape Dorset, N.W.T. Migrates through most of southern Canada.

Winters in British Columbia (commonly on the coast; in small numbers in Okanagan Valley), and sparingly in southern Ontario, Nova Scotia, and Newfoundland.

BAIKAL TEAL
La Sarcelle élégante. *Anas formosa* Georgi
L. 16 in.

Adult male: Crown, back of neck, throat, and stripe across the face from eye to throat, black; line along sides of crown and another bordering black of hind-neck, white; sides of face buffy; a broad metallic green patch extending from above eye, back to nape and down sides of neck. Body with a crescentic white line on side of breast and at base of tail. Wing with green speculum. *Adult female:* Similar to female Green-winged Teal but with round whitish patch at base of bill and with the dark colour of crown extending in a spur down to eye.

Range. Breeds in Siberia. Winters from China, Korea, and Japan to India. Casual or accidental in North America.

59

Status in Canada. One record. An immature male was collected by James Hatter at Ladner, B.C., on December 20, 1957. It was flying with a flock of Pintails.

BLUE-WINGED TEAL

La Sarcelle à ailes bleues. *Anas discors* Linnaeus
Plate 10. L. 14.5 to 16.0 in.

Adult male (*breeding plumage*): Head and upper neck, lead grey with purplish tinge and with large white crescent in front of eye. Chin blackish. Back, rump, and tail, dark brown; the feathers margined and otherwise marked with buff. Fore-wing chalky blue, a narrow white border separating the blue area from a bright green speculum. Breast, abdomen, and sides brown, thickly crossed and spotted with black. On either side of base of tail a conspicuous white patch. Under tail coverts black. Eye brown. Bill bluish black or bluish grey, blackish on ridge. Legs and feet, dull yellow. *Adult female:* Head and neck, greyish white streaked with dusky, darkest on crown and with dusky line through eye. Chin and throat, whitish. Back, rump, and tail, dark brown; the feathers marked with buff. Wings as in male but speculum dull blackish with greenish gloss. Breast and sides brown, feathers edged with buff. Abdomen whitish mottled with brown. *Immature* (*first autumn*): Resembles adult female, but richer green speculum distinguishes young males from young females. Later, further changes toward maturity occur.

Measurements (*A. d. discors*). Adult male: wing, 176–193 (185.8); tail, 66–74 (70.4); exposed culmen, 40–42 (41.2); tarsus, 31–33.5 (32.1) mm. Adult female: wing, 160–182.5 (174.3) mm.

Field Marks. Small size. Large white crescent in front of eye and blue fore-wing easily distinguish adult male. In other plumages the blue fore-wing, conspicuous in flight, separates this teal from all other ducks but the Cinnamon Teal and Shoveler. The latter is larger and has a huge bill. Adult male Cinnamon Teal is cinnamon red. Females and young Blue-winged and Cinnamon Teal are not distinguishable in the field, but the latter is not likely to be seen in eastern Canada. When at rest the female resembles the female Green-winged Teal, and both have a green speculum in the wing, but the presence of blue in the wing, best seen in flight, distinguishes the Blue-winged. *Voice:* Female, a weak, high-pitched *quack;* male, a sibilant, high-pitched *seep-seep*.

Habitat. Freshwater ponds, lakes, sloughs, marshes, weedy margins of sluggish rivers, even tiny streams. Not often a bird of salt or brackish water.

Nesting. Nest, on the ground, usually concealed in grass or other vegetation (but sometimes exposed), generally near water. Nest of grasses and other soft vegetation, lined with down. *Eggs*, usually 9 to 12; buffy white. Incubation, by female alone, between 21 and 23 days (A.C. Bent); 23 to 24 days (J. Delacour).

Range. Breeds from southern Canada south to southern California, New Mexico, middle Texas, Louisiana, and North Carolina. Winters from southern United States south to Ecuador, Brazil, and the West Indies.

60

PLATE 7

1 Canada Goose

2 White-fronted Goose,
  (a) adult
  (b) immature

3 Brant, adult

4 Whistling Swan, adult

5 Trumpeter Swan,
  (a) immature
  (b) adult

Crosby

Range in Canada. Summer resident, scarcer on the Pacific and Atlantic coasts. Breeds across southern Canada from Vancouver Island (Victoria) east to Cape Breton and Magdalen Islands, and southwestern Newfoundland (Doyles, Grand Codroy River), and north to northern British Columbia (Atlin); southern Yukon (rarely: Whiskers Creek, possibly Pelly River); southwestern Mackenzie (Great Slave Lake); central Manitoba (The Pas); central Ontario (Lillabelle Lake; southern James Bay); southern Quebec (Lake St. John, Magdalen Islands). Recorded in summer at Fort Simpson and Fort Norman, N.W.T., Thicket Portage and Churchill, Manitoba; southern James Bay; Anticosti Island; rarely the north shore of the Gulf of St. Lawrence (Pointe des Monts; Moisie Bay; Gull Island, St. Augustin); and rarely in southern Labrador (male and female taken at Battle Harbour, May 13, 1937).

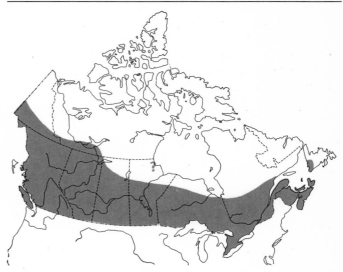

Breeding Distribution of Blue-winged Teal

Subspecies. (1) *Anas discors discors* Linnaeus is the breeding form of all of Canada except the Maritimes. (2) *Anas discors orphna* Stewart and Aldrich, a very slightly darker subspecies, breeds in N.S., probably N.B. and P.E.I., and perhaps the Magdalen Is. (only N.S. specimens examined).

CINNAMON TEAL

La Sarcelle cannelle. *Anas cyanoptera* Vieillot
Plate 10. L. ca. 16 in.

Adult male (*breeding plumage*): Head, neck, breast, sides, and flanks, dark cinnamon red. Crown and chin blackish. Back, rump, and tail, dark brown. Shorter scapulars cinnamon and black, longer scapulars brown with buffy medial stripes and blue outer vanes. Fore-wing blue, the ends of greater coverts white. Speculum iridescent green with black inner and outer borders. Abdomen usually dusky brown. Under tail coverts blackish. Eye orange. Bill blackish. Legs and feet, dull orange-yellow; webs dusky. *Adult female:* Like the female Blue-winged Teal, but with slightly longer bill. *Immature* (*first autumn*): Like adult female, but young male has much richer green speculum.

Measurements. *Adult male:* wing, 174–196 (186.3); tail, 64–75 (67.6); exposed culmen, 41.5–48 (46.1); tarsus, 31.5–35 (33.4). *Adult female:* wing, 169–189 (177.6) mm.

Field Marks. Small size, dark red colour, and blue fore-wing of adult male are unmistakable. Females and young can be distinguished from all but Blue-winged Teal and Shoveler by blue fore-wing. The huge bill of the Shoveler, a larger bird, is very different. Females of Cinnamon and Blue-winged teal cannot usually be separated in the field. *Voice:* Apparently much more silent than most ducks. I have never heard its voice. Male is said to have a "low, rattling, chattering note" (Wetmore). Female has a weak *quack.*

Habitat. Shallow fresh water: lakes, sloughs, sluggish streams, particularly those with margins of emergent vegetation and muddy shores.

Nesting. Nest on the ground. *Eggs*, 6 to 13, usually 10 to 12; whitish to pale pinkish buff. Incubation reportedly 24 to 25 days in a South American race, by the female.

Range. Breeds from southwestern Canada south to central Mexico; also in South America. North American birds winter from southwestern United States south to Costa Rica, Panama, and northern Colombia.

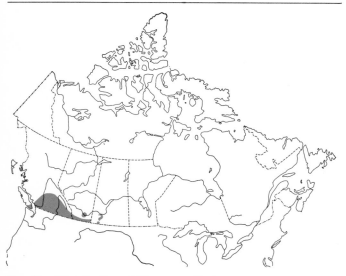

Breeding Distribution of Cinnamon Teal

Range in Canada. Uncommon local summer resident in southwestern Canada. Breeds locally in southern British Columbia (north to Williams Lake, west to Victoria); southern Alberta (Brooks; also observed regularly, probably breeds, south of a line through Stirling and Mountain View); and probably southwestern Saskatchewan (*see* summer records below).

Recorded in breeding season, but not known to breed, north to Quesnel, B.C.; Edmonton, Alberta; and in Saskatchewan (Crane Lake; Moose Jaw area; near Val Marie; Old Wives Lake, Leech Lake, Regina). Rare in southern Manitoba (Shoal Lake, Oak Lake). Casual in Ontario (Mitchell Bay, three males shot in October 1939; Big Point marsh: male shot on November 14, 1953). Sight records for Quebec (Laprairie, Nun's Island, and Lake St. Peter).

Subspecies. *Anas cyanoptera septentrionalium* Snyder and Lumsden.

EUROPEAN WIDGEON
Le Canard siffleur d'Europe. *Mareca penelope* (Linnaeus) Plate 9. L. 17.5 to 20.0 in.

Adult male: Similar to American Widgeon but head and neck rusty red; forehead and crown, creamy buff; flanks, vermiculated black-and-white. *Adult female and immatures* are very much like American Widgeon and are best distinguished by the colour of the axillars (Fig. 26), which are thickly but finely speckled or marbled with dark grey instead of being pure white (or mainly so).

Fig. 26 Axillars of
(A) European Widgeon   (B) American Widgeon

Field Marks. Adult male readily distinguished from American Widgeon by rusty red head and buffy crown. Females of the two species are very similar, but the head of the European female is often tinged reddish; that of the American is always grey.

Range. Breeds in Iceland and across northern Europe and northern Asia (mostly between latitudes 71° and 48° N). Winters south to northern Africa, Asia Minor, Indo-China, Formosa, and Japan. Straggles regularly to North America (southern Canada and the United States).

Status in Canada. Scarce autumn and spring transient; local winter resident. British Columbia (scarce but regular winter resident on coast, October 30 to March 30). Alberta (Valhalla Lake; Jasper). Ontario (specimen taken at Long Point, October 12, 1914. Sight records for London, April 4, 1937; Port Colborne, March 26, 1935; Port Credit, March 20, 1957; Hamilton, May 20, 1957; March 31, 1935; near Barrie, April 26, 1942; Humber Marsh, December 5 and 8, 1943; Simcoe County, April 1942). Quebec (two specimens taken at Lochaber, one in fall, 1926, one on October 27, 1934; a third near Johan Beetz Bay; a fourth at Bonne Espérance, November 1919, together with a sight record at Esquimaux Point, June 13, 1923; a fifth specimen was taken near Cap Tourmente, October 28, 1933). Labrador (specimen shot at Seal Cove, October 1900). Newfoundland (specimens from Stephenville Crossing, October 5, 1927, and near St. John's, October 20, 1935, and from Conception Bay, October 20, 1953). New Brunswick (specimen taken near Grand Manan Island on November 1, 1927). Prince Edward Island (specimen shot September 26, 1936). Nova Scotia (specimens taken at Cape Sable, December 1926; near Yarmouth, January 9, 1912; Grand Pré, October 28, 1929, and November 10, 1944; Wallace, November 4, 1953; West Lawrencetown, November 14, 1957; Masstown, early November 1947). Single individuals banded in Iceland have been taken in Newfoundland, Prince Edward Island, and Nova Scotia. Sight record only for Manitoba (a male, June 3, 1949, closely observed near Hartney by F.G. Cooch).

Although Hasbrouck (*The Auk* 61: 104) and others suspect the breeding of this species in North America, part of their suspicions are based on a young specimen allegedly of this species taken in late summer at Fort Rae, but Preble (1908, p. 280) has shown that this specimen was erroneously identified.

AMERICAN WIDGEON (Baldpate)
Le Canard siffleur d'Amérique
Mareca americana (Gmelin)
Plate 9. L. 18 to 22 in.

Adult male: Forehead and top of head, white; broad green patch from eye to nape; rest of head creamy, thickly speckled with black. Upper back pinkish brown, finely crossed with wavy black lines. Middle upper tail coverts greyish, finely barred with blackish; outer ones mainly black. Fore-wing with large white patch. Speculum greenish bordered by black. Breast and sides pinkish brown. Axillars white (sometimes lightly shaft-streaked). Belly white. Under tail coverts black. Bill, greyish blue with black tip. Feet, pale greyish blue with dusky webs. *Adult female:* Head and neck creamy, heavily streaked with dusky. Back greyish brown, feathers edged with yellowish brown. Speculum mostly black, often with traces of green. Fore-wing with poorly defined whitish area. Axillars white, occasionally shaft-streaked. Breast and sides reddish brown. Belly white. Under tail coverts, mixed brown and white. Bill and feet duller than in male.

Measurements. *Adult male:* wing, 252–280 (263); tail, 95–124 (107.8); exposed culmen, 36–39 (37.4); tarsus, 38–41 (39.3). *Adult female:* wing, 209–244 (233.3) mm.

Field Marks. Conspicuous white crown of adult male. In flight, white patch on front of wing of adult male and female (but much less noticeable in female). Immatures, before acquiring the white wing patch, otherwise generally resemble the adult female. In all plumages the white belly contrasts sharply with the dark breast in flight overhead (*see* European Widgeon). *Voice:* Male has pleasing mellow whistled notes usually grouped in threes. Female, a rather hoarse *quack*. On the water their appearance is often distinctive. They ride high and sometimes pivot lightly as they daintily peck at the surface for food.

Habitat. Breeds about freshwater sloughs, ponds, and marshy borders of lakes. In migration frequents also shallow coastal bays.

Nesting. Nest of grasses and weeds, lined with down,

placed in a hollow on dry ground not always near water. *Eggs,* 7 to 12 (usually 9 to 11); creamy white. Incubation 24 to 25 days (J. Delacour), by the female.

Range. Breeds mainly from Alaska east to Hudson Bay, and south (east of the coast ranges) to northeastern California, Colorado, and Nebraska. Winters from southern Alaska, southern Illinois, and southern New England south to Central America and the West Indies.

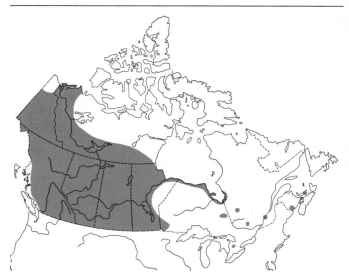

Breeding Distribution of American Widgeon

Range in Canada. Breeds from Yukon (north to Old Crow Flats), northwestern and middle Mackenzie (Mackenzie Delta, Anderson River, Great Slave Lake), southern Keewatin (Windy River, Old Post), northern Manitoba (occasionally, Churchill), south through interior British Columbia (Mile 85 Haines Road; Kleena Kleene; Swan Lake in Peace River area; Nulki Lake; Swan Lake in Okanagan), Alberta, Saskatchewan, and Manitoba; also locally in Ontario (Fort Severn, Cape Henrietta Maria, Nikip Lake, Leith, Luther Marsh, Toronto, Mud Lake), western Quebec (Moar Bay, Taschereau, Blue Sea Lake, Nicolet); and recently locally in Nova Scotia (Amherst Point), New Brunswick (Saint John valley), and Prince Edward Island (Deroche Pond). Migrates commonly through British Columbia, Alberta, Saskatchewan, and Manitoba; regularly but less commonly in most of Ontario and southwestern Quebec. Has been recorded along the outer north shore of the Gulf of St. Lawrence (Mecatina Island, Mingan, Parson Island). Casual or accidental in Newfoundland; also Banks Island (Raddi Lake), N.W.T. Winters regularly in southwestern British Columbia, rarely in southern Ontario, and casually in Nova Scotia.

SHOVELER
Le Canard souchet. *Spatula clypeata* (Linnaeus)
Plate 10. L. 17 to 21 in.

Bill longer than head, much wider at end than at base. *Adult male (breeding plumage):* Head and most of neck, dark green with purplish reflections. Breast and shoulders white.

Middle back, dark slaty brown, feathers tipped paler. Rump and upper tail coverts, blackish with greenish gloss. Most scapulars white, longer ones blue. Fore-wing blue; speculum green, bordered in front by a white line and above by black. Abdomen, sides, and flanks, chestnut. Patch on either side of tail, white. Under tail coverts black. Eye orange or yellow. Legs and feet, vermilion. *Adult female* (*breeding plumage*): Head and neck greyish buff, streaked with dusky, darkest on crown. Back, scapulars, rump, and upper tail coverts, dark brown; the feathers with buffy markings and margins. Wing similar to male but duller and with little or no black. Breast, abdomen, and under tail coverts buffy, streaked and mottled with dusky. Bill variable, greyish to brownish, tending to orange along cutting edges. Legs and feet orange. *Juvenals:* Similar to adult female, but breast and belly of young male tinged with chestnut. Young female like adult female, but fore-wing is slaty, green of speculum absent or much reduced.

Measurements. *Adult male:* wing, 231–252 (238.9); tail, 75.5–89 (83.9); exposed culmen, 63–66.5 (65.4); tarsus, 36–40.5 (38.2). *Adult female:* wing, 217–245 (225.7) mm.

Field Marks. The long bill is distinctive in both males and females at all seasons. The unique markings of the adult male can be seen in flight at long distances, the white breast contrasting markedly with dark head and abdomen. Blue-winged and Cinnamon teal also have blue fore-wings but are much smaller and have much shorter bills. *Voice:* A rather silent species. Male has deep *woh, woh, woh.* Female, weak *quacks.*

Habitat. In breeding season, shallow, often muddy fresh-water lakes, marshes, sloughs, and pot-holes, especially those providing good cover and food.

Nesting. Nest of grasses and similar material, lined with down; on the ground and usually not any great distance from water. *Eggs*, 6 to 14, usually 10 to 12, clutches tending to be smaller in re-nesting attempts; dull very pale olive buff to very pale greenish grey. Incubation variously recorded from 21 to 25 days, probably 23 to 25, by the female.

Range. Holarctic. In North America breeds mainly from Alaska east to Manitoba and south to California, New Mexico, Nebraska, and western Iowa, locally farther east. Winters from coastal southern British Columbia, Arizona, the Gulf coast, and coastal Georgia and South Carolina south to Costa Rica and the West Indies.

Range in Canada. Breeds from Yukon (locally, Old Crow flats, Pine Lake, Sulphur Lake, Sheldon Lake), western Mackenzie (Aklavik, Great Slave Lake), northern Saskatchewan (Lake Athabasca), northern Manitoba (rarely, Churchill), south through interior British Columbia, Alberta, Saskatchewan, and Manitoba; rarely in Ontario (Grand River, near Toronto; near Dunnville; Ottawa; Kingston; has been recorded in summer on James Bay), Quebec (Lake St. Peter, Lake St. Francis), New Brunswick (near Sackville), and Prince Edward Island (Mount Stewart). Spring and fall migrant through British Columbia (including coast), Alberta, Saskatchewan, and Manitoba; less commonly but regularly in southern Ontario and southeastern Quebec. Rare migrant in New Brunswick, Prince Edward Island, Nova Scotia, and Newfoundland (St. John's, October 5, 1957). Recorded rarely from Lake St. John; the north shore of the Gulf of St. Lawrence (Romaine, June 1, 1915); Anticosti Island (October 11, 1938); and Magdalen Islands (Grindstone Island, September 1906), Quebec. Some winter in southwestern British Columbia.

WOOD DUCK
Le Canard huppé. *Aix sponsa* (Linnaeus)
Plate 10. L. 17.0 to 20.5 in.

Head crested. *Adult male* (*breeding plumage*): Head, iridescent green and blue, deepening to purplish black below eye with a narrow white line above the eye and another extending back from it; chin, throat, and fore-neck, white with a conspicuous spur of white extending up onto cheek and another around side of neck. Back, rump, and upper tail coverts, bronze-green. Tail dark glossy green above. Fore-wing greyish brown, greater coverts metallic green and purple; speculum bluish green, bordered behind by a thin white line. Upper breast, reddish chestnut with small white markings. A vertical white bar on shoulder, bordered behind by a black one. Sides buffy, crossed by fine black wavy lines, bordered above and behind by black and white. Patch of purplish chestnut on either side near base of tail. Eye, orange-red to vermilion. Bill, nail, ridge, and lower mandible blackish, sides of bill pinkish, base red with narrow yellow border behind. Legs and feet dull yellow or orange with dusky webs. *Adult female:* Crest shorter. Head brownish grey with greenish gloss. Chin, throat, line at base of bill, and small patch around eye, white. Rest of upper parts greyish brown with bronzy gloss on upper tail coverts and tail. Wing similar to male but duller. Neck grey; breast and flanks, mottled grey, brown, and buff. Belly white, sparsely spotted with dusky. Eye blackish brown. Eyelids yellow. Legs and feet dull yellow. *Immature:* Somewhat like adult female but in male a spur of white extends up onto cheek as in adult male.

Measurements. *Adult male:* wing, 215–232 (223); tail, 91.5–110 (102.3); exposed culmen, 31–36 (33.1); tarsus,

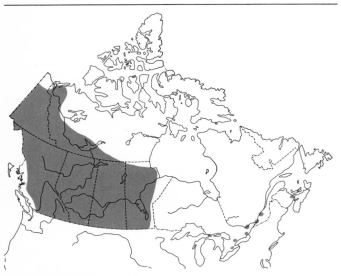

Breeding Distribution of Shoveler

34.5–37.5 (35.8). *Adult female:* wing, 203–225 (213.8) mm.

Field Marks. White face markings of male unmistakable. Crest and small white patch around the eye identify female. When swimming the head bobs with each foot stroke. In flight the large tail and down-pointed bill are noticeable. Often the narrow white line on hind edge of spread wing is visible. The Pintail also has such a wing marking, but the Pintail's very long neck is quite different from that of the Wood Duck. *Voice:* A squealing *oo-eek, oo-eek, oo-eek* is uttered when the bird is flushed from the water in alarm, a good means of field identification when, as so often happens, it cannot be seen in its woodland habitat.

Habitat. Woodland lakes, ponds, and streams.

Nesting. Nests in a hollow trunk or limb of a tree, sometimes in a hollow made by a large woodpecker or in a nesting box. Entrance may be anywhere from several to 50 feet above ground, often (but not necessarily) near water. *Eggs,* 8 to 15; pale buffy white. Incubation 28 to 30 days (A.C. Bent), by the female. One brood annually. Downies leave the nest by climbing (for which their very sharp claws are well adapted) to the nest hole and dropping lightly to the ground.

Range. Breeds from southern British Columbia and northwestern Montana, south to central California; and from southern Manitoba east to Nova Scotia and south to the eastern Dakotas, eastern Kansas, east-central Texas, the Gulf Coast, Florida, and Cuba. Winters south to central Mexico.

Breeding Distribution of Wood Duck

Range in Canada. Breeds in southern British Columbia (Vancouver Island, Graham Island, Sumas Prairie, Chilliwack, Okanagan Valley, East and West Kootenay valleys), southern Alberta (Midnapore), central Saskatchewan (Cumberland House, Emma Lake; reports of nesting at Hudson Bay Junction have been received by Sam Waller, in litt.), southern Manitoba (Delta; probably north to Pike Lake, near The Pas and Cedar Lake), southern Ontario (north to Pimisi Bay, Combermere, Westmeath), southwestern Quebec (north to Ile aux Coudres), New Brunswick,

the peninsula of Nova Scotia (locally), and Cape Breton Island (rarely: River Denys, Nyanza), and Prince Edward Island (locally: Schooner Pond). Has been recorded north in Ontario to Moose Factory; in Quebec to the north shore of the Gulf of St. Lawrence (one banded in early fall at Johan Beetz Bay; recorded at Long Point); Newfoundland (Burin, Spruce Brook, Bowring Park, Cape Broyle, Ferryland). A few winter in southwestern British Columbia and extreme southern Ontario (Lake Erie).

Subfamily **Aythyinae**–Diving Ducks

Ordinarily the birds of this subfamily feed by diving below the water surface. They have flat bills similar to those of surface-feeding ducks, but the hind toe is broadly lobed (Fig. 27).

Fig. 27 Foot of diving duck

REDHEAD

Le Morillon à tête rouge. *Aythya americana* (Eyton) Plate 11. L. 17 to 23 in.

Adult male (winter and breeding plumage): Head and upper neck, chestnut with slight purplish gloss. Breast, lower neck, fore-back, rump, upper and under tail coverts, black. Back and scapulars, sides and flanks, finely barred black-and-white, giving grey appearance. Wing coverts grey. Speculum paler grey with narrow white border. Fore part of abdomen white, hind part crossed by fine greyish lines. Eye yellow. Bill pale bluish with whitish ring behind black tip. Legs and feet bluish grey. *Adult female (winter and breeding plumage):* Head and neck brown, darkest on crown and back of neck, paling to whitish brown at base of bill and on chin. Faint pale streak behind eye. Back, scapulars, and rump, dark brown; feathers with paler edges. Tail and tail coverts brown. Wing similar to male's. Belly whitish. Fore-neck, breast, and sides brownish, feathers tipped with ashy. Eye brown. Bill and feet duller than male's.

Measurements. *Adult male:* wing, 223–242 (231.6); tail, 50.5–66 (58.5); exposed culmen, 46–52.5 (49.4); tarsus, 41–43 (41.8). *Adult female:* wing, 202–231 (219.2) mm.

Field Marks. Resembles the Canvasback, but head profile is very different; the Redhead has an abruptly rising forehead and slightly concave bill; the Canvasback has a long sloping forehead. The back of the male Redhead is decidedly more greyish, less whitish. Female Redheads resemble female scaups and Ringnecks. In flight the *grey* wing patch of the Redhead separates it from both species of scaups which have white areas in the wings, and the female Redhead has only a buffy suggestion of a lighter area at the base of the bill where female scaups have a well-marked white one. Female Ringnecks are darker and have a more definite eye-ring and ring on the bill. *Voice:* Male has a cat-like *mee-ow;* female a coarse *kurr-kurr-kurr;* also purring and growling notes.

Habitat. Freshwater lakes and their shallow edges. In migration often rafts well out on lakes coming in to shallower margins in the evening. Not usually a saltwater duck, it frequents fresh or brackish water even when near the sea-coast.

Nesting. Nest, a mass of vegetation, well cupped and lined with down (also very often lays eggs in nests of other ducks). Nest is usually placed among emergent vegetation of shallow water, but sometimes on dry land, in some areas commonly. *Eggs,* 10 to 16, are pale olive buff or creamy buff. Incubation 22 to 24 days, by female (A. C. Bent).

Range. Breeds from southern part of western Canada south to southern California, central Arizona, northwestern New Mexico, western Nebraska, northern Iowa, and southern Wisconsin. Winters in middle and southern United States and Mexico, in smaller numbers farther north.

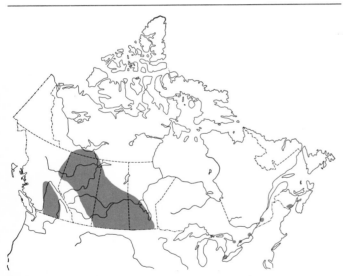

Breeding Distribution of Redhead

Range in Canada. Breeds in interior British Columbia (north at least to Nulki Lake; recorded in breeding season north to Peace River region), southwestern Mackenzie (Fort Resolution), Alberta (Wood Buffalo Park, Peace River, Lesser Slave Lake, Flat Lake, Buffalo Lake, Astotin Lake, Belvedere, Brooks; not southwestern corner), Saskatchewan (north at least to Kazan Lake), central-western and southern Manitoba (north to Cedar Lake, Lake St. Martin), southern Ontario (rarely and locally: Lake St. Clair; Charter Island, Lennox-Addington County; Luther Marsh; formerly

Toronto Island), southwestern Quebec (very locally: Lake St. Francis), and New Brunswick (very rarely: Middle Island, St. John River; formerly probably near St. Croix). Recorded in breeding season in southern Yukon (Teslin Lake). Migrates through southern parts of the western provinces including southwestern British Columbia; regularly (locally common but scarce in extreme east) in southern Ontario where formerly it was much commoner; uncommonly in southwestern Quebec; rarely in New Brunswick, Prince Edward Island, and Nova Scotia. Winters in southern British Columbia in small numbers (formerly abundantly in Okanagan Valley), southern Ontario (Lake Erie, Lake Ontario), and very rarely Nova Scotia.

RING-NECKED DUCK

Le Morillon à collier. *Aythya collaris* (Donovan)
Plate 11. L. 15.5 to 18.0 in.

Adult male (breeding plumage): Crown feathers rather long and erect, giving head a triangular shape. Head and neck, black glossed with purple and green; chin white; neck with narrow inconspicuous chestnut collar about lower neck. Back, scapulars, rump, upper and under tail coverts, tail, and breast, black. Belly white, hind part crossed by fine blackish lines. Sides and flanks white, crossed by fine blackish lines giving a grey effect. A spur of white extends upward in front of folded wing. Wing coverts sooty; speculum pearl grey; tertials slightly glossed greenish; under wing coverts white and brownish grey. Eye yellow. Bill, dark slate with bluish white band near end and a narrow whitish margin at base and edges. Legs and feet greyish blue to grey. *Adult female:* Head and neck greyish brown, darkest on crown; area behind base of bill, narrow eye-ring, and chin, whitish. No collar. Back, scapulars, rump, tail coverts, and tail, dark brown, the feathers with paler edges. Wing similar to male's but coverts duller. Breast and sides brownish with paler feather margins. Belly, mottled brown and white. Eye (variable) yellowish to brownish. Bill, dark lead colour with light band near tip less prominent than in male and lacking markings at base and edges. Legs and feet similar to male's. *Immatures:* In early autumn both sexes similar to adult females, but in September and October sexes begin to differentiate, the blackish feathers of males appearing among the brownish feathers of head and back. In any plumage the greenish gloss to the tertials distinguishes the Ring-necks from similar Redheads.

Measurements. *Adult male:* wing, 188.5–201 (195.6); tail, 53–62.5 (57.9); exposed culmen, 44.5–54 (48.2); tarsus, 34–37 (35.3). *Adult female:* wing, 176–191 (184.1) mm.

Field Marks. The triangular head shape is different from that of other species. Males somewhat resemble scaups but have *black* backs, a spur of white extending up in front of the folded wing, and a white ring near end of the bill. The female's whitish ring around the eye separates it from scaups and the Redhead, which it closely resembles. Its light area near base of bill is less well defined than in scaups. Back and head are somewhat darker than in the Redhead. The grey speculum, if visible, separates it from the scaups, which have a white one. *Voice:* Male is generally silent but in breeding season has a low-pitched hissing whistle which is not far-carrying. Female has scaup-like notes and growls.

Habitat. Mainly shallow fresh water (often acid) of marshes, sedge meadows, and bogs; occasionally tidal estuaries and bays. Unlike most diving ducks, it is not often found far out on large expanses of open water. In migration, also rivers and larger lakes, particularly those with marshy edges. Not often found on strictly salt water at any time.

Nesting. Nest, on low vegetated margins of open water of bogs, ponds, and sloughs, is of marsh vegetation found at the nest site and is lined with down. *Eggs*, 6 to 14 (average 9); olive grey, olive brown, or buffy brown. Incubation, 25 to 29 days, is by female (H. L. Mendall).

Range. Breeds from Canada south to northeastern Washington, Michigan, northeastern New York, northern Vermont, central New Hampshire, and southern Maine with isolated or sporadic breeding south to southern Oregon, northeastern Nevada, northwestern Montana, southern Colorado, central Nebraska, northwestern Indiana, northwestern Pennsylvania, and eastern Massachusetts. Winters mainly from southern United States (north on the coasts to southern British Columbia and Massachusetts) south through Mexico to Guatemala and in the West Indies.

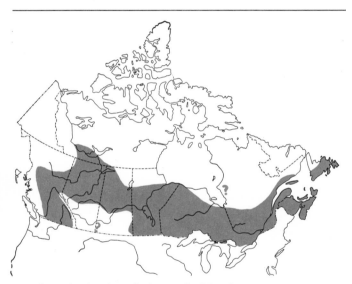

Breeding Distribution of Ring-necked Duck

Range in Canada. Breeds in central and southern interior British Columbia (north at least to Bulkley Valley; commonly in Cariboo parklands; locally in East Kootenay near Invermere; former breeding reported at Chilliwack); southwestern Mackenzie (Fort Simpson, lower Slave River); northern and middle Alberta (south to Edmonton and Elk Island Park); Saskatchewan (northwest to Lake Athabasca and south to about the southern edge of the aspen parklands, locally to Redvers area; and probably the Cypress Hills); middle and southern Manitoba (north at least to The Pas and Pikwitonei region); Ontario (locally; northward to near Hudson Bay in Severn area; Kenora, Port Arthur, Geraldton, and Cochrane districts; Manitoulin Island; and eastward in the area between Lake Ontario and the Ottawa River); Quebec (Messines, Lochaber Bay on the Ottawa

River, Lake Magog, Lake Edmond, Rush and Green lakes, Lake St. John, Anticosti Island, Piashti River near north shore of Gulf of St. Lawrence. Recorded in summer on east side of James Bay); New Brunswick (mainly southern part); Prince Edward Island; Nova Scotia (commonly Cape Breton Island, locally elsewhere); and Newfoundland (Gander, Codroy, and Upper Humber rivers, Goobies, Whitbourne). Recorded in summer in southern Yukon. Winters in southwestern British Columbia; occasionally southern Ontario (Great Lakes); rarely Nova Scotia (Lockeport, Port Hebert Harbour, Sable River). Has greatly extended its range in eastern Canada in recent years.

CANVASBACK
Le Morillon à dos blanc. *Aythya valisineria* (Wilson)
Plate 11. L. 15.5 to 18.0 in.

Bill long, forehead sloping. *Adult male* (*winter and breeding*): Head and neck chestnut, darkening to blackish on crown, base of bill, and throat. A broad, sharply defined black area extending completely around fore part of body in front of wings. Back, scapulars, and sides, white crossed by fine wavy dusky lines. Rump and tail coverts black. Tail blackish. Wing coverts grey, tertials white, all crossed by fine wavy lines; secondaries, including speculum, grey. Abdomen white, its hind part crossed by wavy fine lines. Eye red. Bill blackish. Legs and feet greyish blue. *Adult female* (*winter and breeding*): Head and neck, dark reddish brown to buffy brown, darkest on crown and back of neck, paling to nearly white on chin and throat and around eye. Upper breast and fore-back, dark brown with paler feather edges. Scapulars, rump, and upper tail coverts, brown crossed with whitish. Tail greyish brown. Wing coverts dusky brown, finely dotted and streaked with white. Primaries brownish, secondaries and speculum grey. Sides and flanks brown, with light feather edges producing barred effect. Belly whitish, more or less mottled with greyish brown. Eye brown. *Immature:* In early fall it resembles adult female, but the under parts are more decidedly mottled. Sexes differentiate in September and October.

Measurements. *Adult male:* wing, 222–231 (227.2); tail, 52–60 (57.6); exposed culmen, 59–65 (62.2); tarsus, 44–46 (45.5). *Adult female:* wing, 210-226 (217.4) mm.

Field Marks. Long bill combined with sloping forehead makes a profile unlike that of any other duck. The white back of the male separates it at some distance from the male Redhead, which has a grey one. *Voice:* Male (usually silent) has courtship notes rendered as *ick, ick, cooo* (A. A. Allen), first two parts quick and high pitched, not far-carrying; the last part is louder and at a distance may be the only part heard. Female has a coarse *kurr;* also a *quack.*

Habitat. Deeper waters of marshes, larger sloughs, deep water lakes with pondweed and vegetated margins. In migration and winter also salt and brackish bays; large lakes; and (where open) sluggish parts of larger rivers.

Nesting. Nest, a bulky structure of marsh vegetation, lined with down, usually in shallows near open water, sometimes on dry ground; occasionally at some distance from water. *Eggs* are greyish olive or greenish drab and average 10 to a clutch. Incubation 23 to 28 days usually 24 days (J. Delacour), by the female.

Range. Breeds from interior-central Alaska and western continental Canada south to northern California, western Nevada, Utah (locally), northern Colorado, and northern Minnesota. Winters mainly from northern and middle United States south to the Gulf States and Mexico.

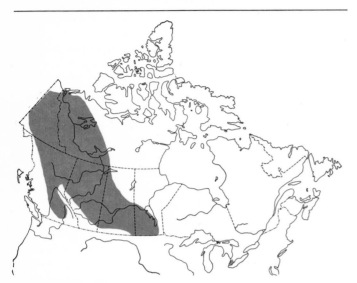

Breeding Distribution of Canvasback

Range in Canada. Common breeder, but much scarcer than formerly, in western Canada. Local winter resident. Breeds in interior British Columbia (Atlin, Cariboo, and Peace River parklands); Yukon (Old Crow, Sulphur Lake, Pelly Valley, Lake Marsh); western Mackenzie (Aklavik, Anderson River, and Fort Resolution); Alberta (except Rocky Mountains and southern prairies, south to Brooks); Saskatchewan (Kazan Lake, Candle Lake, and Nipawin, probably northwest to Lake Athabasca, and south to Crane Lake and Redvers); middle and southern Manitoba (The Pas, Lake St. Martin, Riding Mountain, southern Lake Winnipeg, Killarney); and extreme southern Ontario (very rarely and locally: Walpole Island).

Migrates through southern parts of western Canada including southwestern British Columbia; also regularly in southern Ontario (especially Lake Erie) but scarce in extreme eastern parts. Scarce and irregular in southwestern Quebec (Montreal, Quebec, Trois Rivières); casual in New Brunswick (French Lake, Grand Bay) and in Nova Scotia (Clark's Harbour, Little Harbour Lake, Voglers Cove). Winters in fluctuating numbers in southwestern British Columbia and extreme southern Ontario (mainly Lake Erie from Rondeau Park west; smaller numbers farther east: upper Niagara River; Toronto; Kingston).

GREATER SCAUP

Le Grand Morillon. *Aythya marila* (Linnaeus)
Plate 11. L. 17.00 to 20.75 in.

Adult male (*winter and breeding plumage*): Head, neck, breast, shoulders, fore-back, rump, tail coverts, and ventral area, black; head and neck with *greenish* gloss. Middle back and scapulars, white crossed by wavy black lines. Wing coverts, slaty brown, finely marked with white. Tail and primaries, dark brown. Speculum white, bordered in front, above, and behind with black. Belly white, sharply cut off from black breast, the hind part crossed by zig-zag narrow blackish lines; sides and flanks white, finely vermiculated with black. Eye yellow. Bill greyish blue with black nail. Legs and feet bluish grey. *Adult female* (*winter and breeding*): Head dark brown with well-defined whitish area at base of bill and chin. Back, rump, upper tail coverts, and tail, dark brown. Upper side of wing dark brown, speculum as in male. Upper breast, sides, and flanks, greyish brown with buffy feather tips. Belly white, mottled with dusky. Eye dark yellow. Bill dull bluish grey, nail black. *Immatures:* In September both sexes resemble the adult female, but the white face patch is more restricted. In October and November the sexes differentiate, and by February the head of the male closely resembles that of the adult.

Measurements. *Adult male:* wing, 213–229 (222.4); tail, 51.5–59 (56); exposed culmen, 41.5–48 (45.2); tarsus, 36.5–41.5 (39.5). *Adult female:* wing, 197–219 (209.9) mm.

Field Marks. Very difficult to separate in life from the slightly smaller Lesser Scaup. In good light and at close range the Greater has a greenish gloss to the head; that of the Lesser is dark purple. In flight the white wing stripe of the Greater extends farther toward the tip. There is, however, much overlapping, and only extremes can be recognized with certainty. This *white* wing stripe separates the scaups in all plumages from the similar Ringneck and Redhead, which have a grey one. The well-defined whitish patch

Breeding Distribution of Greater Scaup

at the base of the female's bill also is characteristic of the scaups, but *see* the Ringneck and the Redhead, which have less well-defined similar markings. Scaups have yellow eyes. *Voice:* Male, generally silent, is said to have a cooing note in courtship; also a low whistle. Female has a harsh *kerr* or *kerr-urr*.

Habitat. In breeding season, lakes, ponds, and more

sluggish rivers. In migration and winter, saltwater bays and coasts, large freshwater lakes. Generally it is less partial to smaller bodies of water than the Lesser Scaup.

Nesting. Nest on ground, usually near shore of lake or pond or on islands in lakes; sometimes covered by grasses. Nests may at times be relatively close together. Nest, a hollow in ground or tussock, lined with surrounding vegetation, down, and feathers. *Eggs*, usually 8 to 10; olive-grey to olive-buff. Incubation, by the female, lasts 23 to 27 days (J. Delacour).

Range. Holarctic. Breeds in Iceland, Orkneys, Hebrides, Norway, Sweden, Russia, and Siberia, mostly north of lat. 60°; on Bering Island; and in Alaska and Canada. In North America it winters on the Pacific Coast (southern Alaska to California); on the Atlantic Coast to the Gulf States and Mexico; and on lakes Erie and Ontario.

Range in Canada. Full extent of breeding range uncertain owing to confusion in literature with Lesser Scaup. Breeds in Yukon (Old Crow flats; widely recorded in summer also in southern parts), northwestern British Columbia (Haines Road); Mackenzie (Mackenzie Delta, Anderson River, Ptarmigan Lake); southern Keewatin (Windy River; probably McConnell River); northern Manitoba (Churchill); northern Ontario (inland from Hudson Bay coast); central-western, northern, and southeastern Quebec (Moar Bay, Great Whale River, Lead Bay – Chimo region, Anticosti Island, Magdalen Islands); and Newfoundland (Browsey Island). Perhaps also Labrador (Nain; south of Lake Melville).

Rare migrant in Alberta (La Saline) and Saskatchewan (Indian Head). Winters in British Columbia (regularly on the coast, sometimes on Okanagan Lake, South Thompson River); southern Ontario (commonly on Lake Ontario and Lake Erie); southern Quebec (occasionally Montreal), and the Maritime Provinces (north to Newfoundland).

Subspecies. *Aythya marila nearctica* Stejneger.

LESSER SCAUP
Le Petit Morillon. *Aythya affinis* (Eyton)
Plate 11. L. 15 to 18 in.

Very similar to Greater Scaup but slightly smaller. In the hand, the relatively smaller nail of the bill is usually diagnostic in any plumage. *Adult male* (*winter and breeding*): Like the Greater Scaup but head with mainly purple gloss (instead of mainly greenish). Sides and flanks more heavily vermiculated (less whitish). White in wings usually does not extend far into primaries. *Adult female:* Like Greater Scaup but smaller and with the white stripe in wing more restricted.

Measurements. *Adult male:* wing, 193–209 (199.8); tail, 48.5–57.5 (51.9); exposed culmen, 39.5–43.5 (41.7); tarsus, 35.5–37.5 (36.3). *Adult female:* wing, 187–200.5 (192.9) mm.

Field Marks. Separable from Greater Scaup only under good observation conditions. Although the present species is smaller, this is useless in the field. Adult male Lesser Scaups have a purplish (instead of greenish) gloss to the head and also more greyish (less whitish) sides. Females usually cannot be distinguished on the water. In flight both sexes can often be separated from the Greater Scaup by the shorter

white wing stripe (Plate 11), which in the Lesser does not extend far, if at all, onto the primaries. For separation from other ducks, *see* Greater Scaup. *Voice:* Similar to Greater Scaup.

Habitat. In the breeding season, the vicinity of interior lakes and ponds; low islands; moist sedge meadows. In migration and winter, it inhabits *smaller* interior lakes, ponds, and rivers to a greater extent than the Greater Scaup but, like it, frequents also coastal bays, estuaries, and large lakes.

Nesting. Nest is a hollow in dry ground lined with grass and feathers. It is often hidden by grass or bushes and usually is not very far from water. *Eggs*, 8 to 12; olive-buff. Incubation 23 to 26 days (R. D. Harris), by female.

Range. Breeds in interior northwestern North America from central Alaska and western Canada (north to about tree limit) south to northern Idaho, northeastern Colorado, Nebraska, and Iowa. Winters mainly from southern British Columbia, Colorado, Arkansas, southern Illinois, and eastern Maryland south to northern South America and the West Indies.

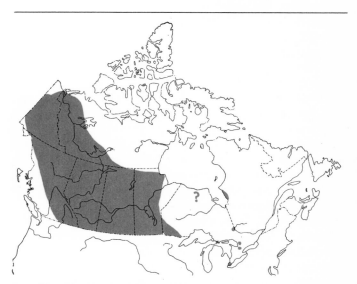

Breeding Distribution of Lesser Scaup

Range in Canada. Breeds in Yukon (north to Old Crow), western Mackenzie (Mackenzie Valley north to wooded parts of Mackenzie Delta, Anderson River, Great Slave Lake); interior British Columbia (south at least to Columbia Lake and Vernon; north to Atlin); Alberta (commonly in northern half; locally in south about larger lakes and irrigation projects); Saskatchewan; Manitoba (north to Churchill); Ontario (very locally: Kenora; Lake St. Clair; Luther Marsh; between Baptiste and Elephant lakes; Toronto Island; mouth of Nottawasaga River; Rebecca Lake, probably elsewhere); and central-western Quebec (Moar Bay region).

Migrates more or less commonly through the western provinces (including western British Columbia) and Ontario; fairly commonly in southwestern Quebec (St. Lawrence River; occasionally east to Johan Beetz Bay and Anticosti Island); uncommonly in New Brunswick and Nova

Scotia; rarely Newfoundland. Winters in small numbers in coastal British Columbia and southern Ontario (Lake Erie).

[**Tufted Duck.** *Aythya fuligula* (Linnaeus). Hypothetical. Sight record only. British Columbia (Vancouver, November 4–11, 1961).]

COMMON GOLDENEYE (American Golden-eye)
Le Garrot commun. *Bucephala clangula* (Linnaeus)
Plate 12. L. 16.5 to 20.0 in.

Adult male (*winter and breeding plumage*): Head and upper neck, black with green and purple reflections and a large *round* white spot behind base of bill. Back, rump, and upper tail coverts, black. Tail dark grey. Inner scapulars black, the outer ones white with black edges. Middle and greater wing coverts and most of secondaries, white. Lesser coverts near bend of wing, black. Primaries and wing linings, blackish brown. Lower neck (all round), breast, and sides, white. Flanks white with black feather edges. Eye yellow. Bill blackish. Legs and feet yellow or orange with dusky webs. *Adult female* (*winter and breeding*): Head brown. Neck with white collar incomplete behind. Back, scapulars, and upper tail coverts bluish grey, feathers edged with pale grey. Rump blackish. Upper tail coverts, dark brown tipped with grey. Tail greyish brown. White of wing less extensive than in male. Speculum white crossed by a dark bar. Upper breast grey with white feather tips. Belly white. Sides and flanks grey, feather tips whitish. Under tail coverts, white mixed with dark grey. Eye pale yellow. Feet yellowish or orange. Bill dusky with yellowish band near tip (sometimes more extensively yellow). *Immatures:* In early autumn resemble adult females but lack white collar.

Measurements. *Adult male:* wing, 215–235 (225.4); tail, 77–95 (87); exposed culmen, 35–43.5 (38.4); tarsus, 39–42 (40.1). *Adult female:* wing, 188–220 (204.2) mm.

Field Marks. A medium-sized chunky duck with large areas of white in wings. Male has large *round* white spot behind base of bill. In females the dark head colour extends only partly down neck, leaving white lower neck. Wings whistle more loudly in flight than in most ducks. For distinctions from Barrow's Goldeneye, *see* next species. *Voice:* Generally silent in fall and early winter. In courtship, male has a harsh vibrating double-noted *zzee-at*. Female has a variety of harsh, low-pitched *grrk* notes. The characteristic musical whistle heard in take-off or in flight is not vocal but is produced by the wings.

Habitat. In nesting season, woodland lakes and muskeg ponds. In other seasons it frequents the sea-coast, tidal estuaries, freshwater lakes and rivers. Wintering in numbers on rivers where current is adequate to keep water open, it is one of the characteristic winter ducks of the interior.

Nesting. Nests in natural cavities in trees, large woodpecker holes. Will use nest boxes, occasionally chimneys. Nest heights, from 5 to 60 feet above ground. Perhaps in local absence of suitable trees may resort to rock cavities. *Eggs*, 6 to 15 (average 10); pale bluish green. Incubation by the female, variably reported 26 to more than 30 days. Young flutter from nest to ground or water.

Range. Breeds north to or near tree limit in Europe, Asia, and North America. In North America from Alaska to Newfoundland and southward to southern Canada and northern United States (northwestern Montana, northern parts of Minnesota, Michigan, Vermont, and Maine). Winters from southeastern Alaska and southern Canada south to California, the Gulf Coast, and Florida.

Breeding Distribution of Common Goldeneye

Range in Canada. Breeds north to near tree limit in Yukon, western and southern Mackenzie (Mackenzie Delta, Mackenzie Valley, Great Slave Lake), southwestern Keewatin (Nueltin Lake), northern Manitoba, northern Ontario, northern Quebec (Indian House Lake), middle Labrador, and Newfoundland, south to southern British Columbia (locally: Swan Lake in Okanagan), Alberta and Saskatchewan (except southernmost parts where suitable trees are lacking), southern Manitoba, southern Ontario (at least to Orillia), southern Quebec, New Brunswick, Prince Edward Island, and Nova Scotia (mainly Cape Breton Island). Wanders in summer somewhat north of nesting grounds. Winters where open water permits, in coastal and southern British Columbia, middle and southern Alberta (small numbers at Edmonton, Banff, Calgary, Drumheller), southern Ontario, southern Quebec (north at least to Pointe des Monts), Newfoundland, New Brunswick, Prince Edward Island, and Nova Scotia.

Subspecies. *Bucephala clangula americana* (Bonaparte).

BARROW'S GOLDENEYE
Le Garrot de Barrow. *Bucephala islandica* (Gmelin)
Plate 12. L. 16.5 to 20.5 in.

Adult male (*winter and breeding*): Similar to Common Goldeneye, but the head is highly glossed with purple or violet and with large white *crescent* behind base of bill. Body similar to Common Goldeneye but with less white in wings and scapulars. White of scapulars a mere row of large dots over folded wings. White of fore-wing greatly reduced and completely separated from white speculum by a black bar. Eye yellow. Bill black. Legs and feet orange-yellow with dusky webs. *Adult female* (*winter and breeding*): Very similar to American Goldeneye, but head is usually slightly darker brown. Feathers of hind-neck usually longer, giving the head a more puffy appearance. Eye pale yellow. Bill usually more extensively yellow (especially from February to May) than in the Common Goldeneye.

Measurements. *Adult male:* wing, 225–243 (235.3); tail, 85–91 (88.8); exposed culmen, 31–38 (34.5); tarsus, 41–43 (46.3). *Adult female:* wing, 201–214 (207.2) mm.

Distinctions. Females and immatures closely resemble Common Goldeneyes but have shorter, stubbier bills, which taper more abruptly toward the tip (Fig. 28). Males have a more abrupt forehead which in immature males can readily be felt as a lump under the plumage by stroking the forehead with the finger. The windpipe of both young and old males (not females) of the Common Goldeneye has a conspicuous bulbous enlargement that is lacking in Barrow's Goldeneye.

Field Marks. A white *crescent* at the base of the bill, instead of a round white patch, separates adult males from those of the Common Goldeneye. The more extensive black of the body of Barrow's Goldeneye, which extends as a black spur close to the waterline in front of the wing, also is diagnostic. The vertically rising forehead of the present species is a useful character, too. Females of the two species are often extremely difficult to separate in life, but Barrow's has a stubbier, more extensively yellow bill (February to May).

Fig. 28 Bill of
(A) Common Goldeneye   (B) Barrow's Goldeneye

Habitat. In British Columbia in nesting season, lakes and ponds, either acid or alkaline, usually near the nesting tree but sometimes up to at least one-half mile from it. In spring, concentrations occur on large lakes, but most disperse to smaller lakes and ponds as the latter become ice-free. In winter, mostly coastal rivers, estuaries, and lakes. Usually does not favour highly saline water (J. A. Munro). Habitat of eastern populations poorly known, but winter habitat includes coastal freshwater rivers and estuaries and salt-water bays. Nesting in much of the eastern population is independent of trees.

Nesting. Nest when in timbered country usually in hollows in trees; otherwise mostly in holes in rocks; rarely in a Crow's nest. In British Columbia and Alberta mean *clutch* size is 9, range 4 to 15; incubation period averages 32.5 days, standard deviation ± 1.5 days, range 30 to 34 days, counted from time last egg is laid (Mary F. Jackson).

Range. Breeds in widely separated areas: from southern Alaska and southern Yukon south to eastern Washington and California (high central Sierra Nevada); also in Labrador, southwestern Greenland, and Iceland. In winter it is found somewhat farther south.

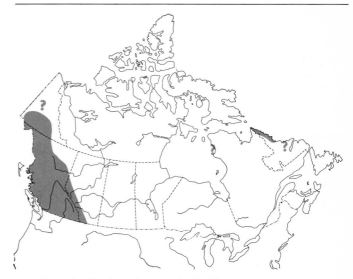

Breeding Distribution of Barrow's Goldeneye

Range in Canada. Breeds (in two widely separated areas): southern Yukon (Canol Road, Takhini River, Kathleen River, Burwash Landing); British Columbia (widely: Atlin, Peace River area, Alta Lake; densest population in dry belt of Okanagan, Nicola, Kamloops, Chilcotin, and Cariboo districts; alleged breeding on Vancouver Island not yet conclusive); and southwestern Alberta (mountains and foothills); also in Labrador (probably Killinek). Recorded in summer at McCormack Island, eastern Hudson Bay. Definite nesting records for eastern Canada are needed.

Winters in coastal British Columbia but rarely in the interior to Exshaw and Calgary, Alberta; and from the north shore of the Gulf of St. Lawrence (Bonne Espérance, Piashti Bay) southward coastally along Anticosti Island, Gaspé Peninsula, New Brunswick, Prince Edward Island, and Nova Scotia, and on lower St. Lawrence River; more rarely on the Great Lakes, upper St. Lawrence drainage (Ottawa; Sherbrooke), and Lake St. John.

Rarely reported from Newfoundland (specimen: Notre Dame Bay, March 9, 1956; sight records at Gander and Marysville by L. M. Tuck), western Mackenzie (old records at forts Anderson, Rae, Simpson, and Providence) and non-mountainous parts of Alberta (Camrose, Elk Island Park, Beaverhill Lake).

BUFFLEHEAD
Le Petit Garrot. *Bucephala albeola* (Linnaeus)
Plate 12. L. 12.5 to 15.0 in.

Adult male (*winter and breeding*): Head dark with strong green, purple, and bronze gloss and with a large triangle of white, starting below the eye and broadening upward over back of head. Neck white. Back and rump black, paling to

71

grey on upper tail coverts. Tail grey. Inner scapulars black, outer ones white with fine black outer edge. Wing coverts mainly white with black along front edge of wing. Primaries blackish. Secondaries mainly white. Tertials black. Wing linings dusky mixed with white. Breast and sides white, becoming pale greyish on abdomen. Eye brown. Bill leaden blue, usually yellowish along edge of upper mandible. Legs and feet, pinkish flesh. *Adult female (winter and breeding)*: Head and neck, dark greyish brown with a narrow white cheek patch extending backward from below the eye. Back, scapulars, rump, upper tail coverts, sooty brown. Tail sooty grey. Upper sides of wings similar to back but with white patch in secondaries. Sides grey. Breast and belly white. Eye brown. Bill dusky or dark lead grey. Legs grey with pinkish or bluish tinge. *Immatures:* In first autumn closely resemble female.

Measurements. *Adult male:* wing, 163–173 (167.7); tail, 67.5–78 (73.9); exposed culmen, 27–30.5 (28.9); tarsus, 33–35 (33.9). *Adult female:* wing, 141–167 (152.6) mm.

Field Marks. A small duck with a white patch in the wing which distinguishes it from the teals. Male in breeding plumage, with a large wedge of white on the head; looks a little like the male Hooded Merganser but may be distinguished even at long distances by its white flanks, and at closer range also by its stubbier bill. Females and immatures are small dark ducks with a small white patch on the side of the head and a small white area in the wing especially noticeable in flight. *Voice:* Male, a squeaky whistle; also a guttural rolling note. Female, a hoarse croak somewhat like the Goldeneye but weaker.

Habitat. In breeding season ponds and lakes in or near open woodland. At other seasons freshwater and alkali lakes, and rivers of the interior; and saltwater bays and estuaries on the coast.

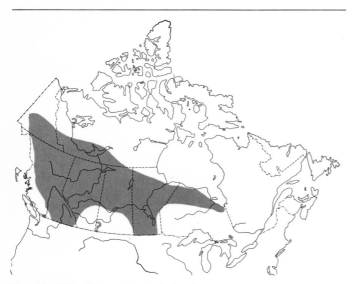

Breeding Distribution of Bufflehead

Nesting. Nests in holes in trees, preferably those made by large woodpeckers; will use nesting boxes. Nest cavity lined with down and feathers. *Eggs* buffy to creamy white. *Clutch size* in British Columbia 5 to 16 (perhaps those over 12 are a product of more than one bird), usually 7 to 10; incubation period 29 to 31 days (A. J. Erskine), by the female.

Range. Breeds from west-central and southern Alaska and forested parts of western Canada south to southern British Columbia, northern Montana, and central Manitoba; locally in Oregon and northeastern California. Winters from the Aleutian Islands, Alaska Peninsula, the Great Lakes, and the Maritime Provinces south to Mexico and the Gulf Coast.

Range in Canada. Breeds (in the vicinity of woodland) in southern Yukon, western Mackenzie (Little Buffalo River, Great Slave Lake, Fort Simpson, probably Fort Norman), British Columbia (widely east of the Cascades); Alberta; Saskatchewan; middle and southern Manitoba. Absent as a breeder in treeless southern parts of the Prairie Provinces but perhaps breeds in Cypress Hills region; sparsely and locally in northwestern Ontario and rarely in southern Ontario (Sudbury).

In migration found commonly also in western British Columbia, southern parts of the Prairie Provinces; fairly commonly in southern Ontario and southwestern Quebec, and less commonly in New Brunswick, Nova Scotia (including Cape Breton Island), Prince Edward Island, and Newfoundland. Winters in coastal and southern British Columbia (entire length of coast; Okanagan Lake); southern Alberta (very locally: Calgary); southern Ontario (Lake Erie, Lake Ontario); southern New Brunswick, Nova Scotia, and southern Newfoundland (regularly off Traytown and Gambo).

OLDSQUAW

Le Canard kakawi. *Clangula hyemalis* (Linnaeus)
Plate 13. L. 17.5 to 23.5 in.

Bill short, rather high at base. *Adult male (fall, winter, early spring)*: Head and neck mainly white with grey cheeks and a large dark brown patch extending from rear of cheek to side of upper neck. Back, rump, upper tail coverts, and breast, brownish black. Wing blackish with brown speculum. Scapulars slender, pointed, pearl grey. Wing linings greyish brown. Lower belly to tail, white becoming grey on sides and flanks. Tail with two central feathers very long, slender, pointed; rest of tail feathers dusky, edged with white, outermost with increasing extent of white. Eye variable, brown to reddish brown. Bill, basal half and nail blackish, pinkish near tip. Legs and feet bluish grey. *Adult male (late spring, early summer)*: Head and neck brown with large, sharply-defined patch of grey on sides of head and small white area behind and above eye. Back and scapulars brown with russet edges. *Adult female (fall, winter, early spring)*: Head and neck mainly white, but crown, throat, and patch on side of upper neck brownish black. Back, upper tail coverts, tail, and wings, blackish brown. Tail greyish brown, central tail feathers only slightly elongated. Breast mixed grey and brown. Belly white. *Adult female (summer plumage)*: Head and neck mostly brown with white distributed as follows: ring about eye, line extending back from eye, spot at base of bill, and area on side of neck. Rest of plumage similar to winter but more bleached and abraded. Bill greyish brown to greenish, darkening toward tip. Legs bluish grey. *Im-*

matures: Adult plumage not attained until second year. Young until late summer resemble adult female in summer, but head and neck are brownish grey and scapulars have no grey edges. In late fall, young male begins to resemble adult male about the head.

Measurements. *Adult male:* wing, 209–228 (220.4); tail, 165–237 (194.9); exposed culmen, 26–30 (27.5); tarsus, 34–38 (35.8). *Adult female:* wing, 152–219 (194.1) mm.

Field Marks. In winter plumage, the large dark patch on the sides of the white head makes recognition of both sexes easy. In summer, the adult male's large white patch on the sides of the otherwise dark brown head is unlike any other duck. The male's long tail could be confused only with that of the differently marked Pintail. In flight no other extensively white duck has all-dark wings. *Voice:* A noisy duck with a variety of calls of several syllables, often rather musical and easily recognized once learned. The voice is far-carrying and in chorus at a distance somewhat suggests the baying of hounds. Courting male calls a throaty *ah, ah, ungha.*

Habitat. In summer, tundra lakes and ponds; also coasts and islands. In other seasons, coastal waters and large fresh-water lakes and rivers.

Nesting. Nest in a depression in the ground often in grasses or dwarf willow near a tundra pond or lake, on an island, or near salt water. *Eggs,* usually 6 to 8; olive to yellowish buff. Incubation, probably about 24 days, by female.

Breeding Distribution of Oldsquaw

Range. Breeds in the Arctic of both the New and Old Worlds. In North America, winters mainly on the coasts from the Aleutians to Washington and from northern Greenland to South Carolina; in the interior mainly on the Great Lakes but also (irregularly, in smaller numbers) on other lakes and rivers of the United States.

Range in Canada. Breeds throughout the Arctic from Prince Patrick and northern Ellesmere islands south to southern parts of the tundra in northern Yukon (Old Crow), northwestern British Columbia (50 miles west of Atlin), northwestern and middle Mackenzie, southern Keewatin

(Windy River), northeastern Manitoba (Churchill), coast and islands of Hudson and James bays (Cape Henrietta Maria, Bear Island, Grey Goose Island, South Twin Island), northern Quebec (Payne Lake, Fort Chimo, Indian House Lake), and south along the coast of Labrador to southeastern Quebec (Bradore Bay). Winters along the coast of British Columbia, on open water of the Great Lakes, and along the Atlantic Coast from southern Labrador and northern Newfoundland (Hare Bay) southward through the Maritimes.

HARLEQUIN DUCK

Le Canard arlequin. *Histrionicus histrionicus* (Linnaeus)
Plate 13. L. 15.00 to 17.75 in.

Adult male (winter and breeding plumage): Head and neck mainly dark leaden blue. A crescentic white patch at base of bill, an oval white ear patch, and another white patch down side of neck. A black median stripe through centre of crown with chestnut on either side of it. Narrow white collar around neck, incomplete in front and behind. Back slaty blue. Tail black, slender and pointed. Long bar on side of breast, white bordered with black. Speculum metallic blue. Inner secondaries extensively white. Wing linings brown. Upper breast bluish. Belly dark brown often with bluish wash. Sides chestnut. Eye reddish brown. Bill bluish grey to bluish black. Legs and feet bluish grey. *Adult female:* Head and neck dark brown with three white areas, one behind eye, one below the eye, and one in front of eye reaching the forehead. Rest of plumage blackish brown, more greyish below and becoming whitish on abdomen. Bill, legs, and feet paler and duller than in male. *Immature:* In first autumn resembles adult female. Young male begins to resemble adult in late autumn but is not completely like adult until second year.

Measurements. *Adult male:* wing, 188–202 (196.4); tail, 77–101.5 (91.6); exposed culmen, 25–27 (25.8); tarsus, 36.5–38.5 (37.8). *Adult female:* wing, 179–201 (188.6) mm.

Field Marks. Pattern of adult male is unmistakable. Female might be confused with female Bufflehead or Surf Scoter. It has usually three (sometimes only two) whitish areas on the head, whereas the female Bufflehead has but one, and in flight lacks the Bufflehead's white wing patch. Its small size and short-bill profile separate it from the female Surf Scoter. When swimming it bobs its head slightly with each stroke. *Voice:* Usually rather silent. A low whistle beginning with two longer notes and ending in a trill, on a descending scale. A series of harsh croaks.

Habitat. In breeding season, swift rivers and streams. In other seasons, coasts and islands, often the roughest and rockiest of shores where the water is highly turbulent and the surf breaks constantly.

Nesting. Nest is placed on the ground, usually near fast streams, often in a clump of bushes or in recesses in rocks. Reports of nesting in hollow trees require confirmation. *Eggs,* usually 6 or 7; cream to pale buff. Incubation, probably 30 to 32 days, is by the female.

Range. Breeds in eastern Siberia, southern and middle Alaska (north probably to Anaktuvuk Pass) and southern

Yukon south in the mountains to central California and Colorado; and from southern Baffin Island, Greenland, and Iceland south to Newfoundland. Winters from breeding range south to Korea, southern Japan, central-western California, and Massachusetts; rarely farther south.

Breeding Distribution of Harlequin Duck

Range in Canada. Breeding range divided into two widely separated parts. Western part: Yukon, British Columbia (Atlin, McDonald Creek on Alaska Highway, Glacier National Park, Nicola, Likely, Penticton region, Wise Island), southwestern Alberta (Rocky Mountains: Valley of Ten Peaks). Eastern part: southeastern Baffin Island (Crook's Inlet to Cumberland Sound), Labrador, Quebec (Lake Minowean, Indian House Lake; probably Ungava Bay and outer north shore of the Gulf of St. Lawrence; Gaspé Peninsula: flightless young caught and photographed on Port Daniel River, early August 1959, Raymond Cayouette, in litt.); perhaps Newfoundland.

Recorded in summer in western Mackenzie (Mackenzie Valley, Great Slave Lake). Migrates mainly to and from the coasts. Rare transient in the interior east of the Rockies in Alberta (Lake Athabasca, Beaverhill Lake), Saskatchewan (Saskatchewan Landing), Manitoba (Pike Lake, north of The Pas; Shoal Lake), Ontario (Port Arthur, Hamilton, Niagara River, Toronto), southwestern Quebec (Lachine Rapids, Ste. Anne de Bellevue). Winters along the coast of British Columbia and on the Atlantic Coast in southern Labrador, Newfoundland, and the coast of the Maritimes.

LABRADOR DUCK

Le Canard du Labrador
Camptorhynchus labradorius (Gmelin)
Fig. 29. L. 19 to 23.5 in.

Bill rather long and broadened toward tip. Lamellae of lower mandible long. Feet large. Anterior part of cheek with stiff feathers. *Adult male:* Head and neck, white with black longitudinal stripe through crown and a narrow black collar around lower neck. Back, rump, tail and tail coverts, pri-

maries and under parts, black. Scapulars and wings (except primaries) mostly white. Basal part of bill and around nostrils, yellow; rest blackish. *Adult female:* Mostly brownish grey with paler area on cheeks. Chin and throat whitish. Upper breast mottled grey and whitish. Wings with white speculum.

Range. Extinct. Breeding range unknown but presumed to have been in Labrador. In winter occurred south probably to Chesapeake Bay. Last record of a living bird December 12, 1878, at Elmira, New York.

Status in Canada. Extinct. Presumed, on unsatisfactory evidence, to have bred in southern Labrador and in that part of Quebec formerly included under the name 'Labrador.' Three specimens mentioned by Dutcher (1891, *The Auk* 8: 203–204) from 'Labrador' may have come from either Quebec or Labrador. In migration and winter it occurred in Nova Scotia (Pictou, Halifax Harbour) and New Brunswick (Grand Manan). Recorded also from southwestern Quebec (Laprairie, spring, 1862: specimen) where its occurrence was probably rare or casual. The last specimen known to be taken in Canada was shot on Grand Manan, New Brunswick, in April 1871.

Remarks. The Labrador Duck became extinct before much was recorded about it. Details of its life history and even the reasons for its extinction are largely unknown and are likely to remain so. It does not seem to have been numerous anywhere within its restricted range. As it was not especially good to eat, hunters did not often seek it on its wintering grounds. Authors have suggested that its breeding grounds may have been restricted to a few islands

Fig. 29 Labrador Duck

in 'Labrador.' In that case it would have been more susceptible than other species of wider distribution to the havoc wrought on bird populations there by mid-eighteenth century plumage hunters and eggers. Others have suggested that its peculiarly specialized bill may have been correlated with feeding on particular food, which later became unavailable in adequate quantity. Its diet is known to have included mussels and small surf clams, however. The most plausible explanation of its passing seems to be that the already small numbers were singly unable to withstand persecution by man, particularly on its restricted breeding grounds.

STELLER'S EIDER
L'Eider de Steller. *Polysticta stelleri* (Pallas)
Fig. 30. L. 17 to 18 in.

Adult male (*winter and breeding*): Head and part of upper neck, shiny white with greenish tuft of feathers on forehead and back of head. Ring about eye, spot on back of head, and entire chin and throat, black. Collar about neck bluish black. Middle of back, entire rump, tail coverts, and tail, black. Long scapulars purplish with white inner webs. Wing coverts white. Speculum blue, bordered by white. Inner secondaries and tertials curved outward, inner webs white,

Fig. 30 Steller's Eider

outer webs mostly metallic blue. Middle of belly blackish brown, paling to cinnamon-buff on breast and sides. Black spot on sides near front of folded wing. Eye brown. Bill greyish blue. Legs and feet dark bluish grey. *Adult female:* Head and neck, brown mixed with buff, darkest on crown. Body blackish brown cross-marked with buff, becoming blackish on belly. Speculum blue, bordered in front and behind with white. Eye brown. Bill dusky bluish. Legs and feet dark bluish grey.

Measurements. *Adult male:* wing, 210–225; bill, 37–42; tarsus, 36–40. *Adult female:* wing, 210–218 mm (J. C. Phillips).

Field Marks. The smallest, trimmest, and most 'uneider-like' of the eiders. Markings of adult male are unmistakable. Female's dark, rich brown general coloration and *Mallard-like speculum* identify it.

Range. Breeds in northeastern coastal Siberia from the Lena Delta and New Siberian Islands east to Chukotski Peninsula and Anadyr Bay, and in Alaska east probably to Barter Island and Humphrey Point, and south to St. Lawrence Island and Hooper Bay, perhaps to the Aleutians and Alaska Peninsula. In winter it ranges somewhat farther south, in North America to the Aleutians, Alaska Peninsula, Kodiak Island, and rarely to Queen Charlotte Islands.

Status in Canada. Not known to nest in Canada but possibly might do so on the Yukon coast. Otherwise of casual or accidental occurrence: one specimen from British Columbia (Masset, October 15, 1948) and two from Quebec (near Pointe des Monts, February and March, 1898). Casual at Cumberland Sound, Baffin Island; and Cape Bathurst, Mackenzie.

COMMON EIDER (American Eider)
L'Eider commun. *Somateria mollissima* (Linnaeus)
Plate 13. L. 20 to 26 in.

Forehead profile rather flat. Feathering at base of bill extends forward to below nostril (Fig. 31). Southeastern subspecies *S. m. dresseri* (*see also* Subspecies): *Adult male* (*winter and breeding*): Two bare frontal processes with rounded ends extend backward on either side of forehead. Plumage mostly black and white. Top of head black, this cap divided almost in two by a median white streak; rest of head white with green wash on back of head, nape, and below border of cap. Neck, breast, back, fore-wing, scapulars, spot on either side of rump, white. Tertials curved outward. Middle of rump, tail coverts, greater wing coverts, belly, and sides, black. Eye brown. Bill in spring orange-yellow, otherwise varying from grey to green. Legs and feet yellowish or greenish. *Adult female:* A brownish duck. Bill processes narrower than in male. Head and neck, brown streaked with black, darkest on crown. Upper parts dark brown to blackish brown, the feathers barred or edged with buff. Breast and sides buffy, the feathers barred with blackish and tipped with greyish buff. Belly, sooty brown with vague dark bars. Greater wing coverts, greyish brown lightly tipped with white forming two narrow wing bars. Secondaries and tertials brown with buffy outer edges. Tertials curved outward. Eye brown. Bill duller and greener than in winter male, sometimes yellowish.

Measurements (*S. m. dresseri*). *Adult male:* wing, 262–291 (274); tail, 82.5–102 (92.4); exposed culmen, 52–58.5 (56.4); tarsus, 49–56 (53.4). *Adult female:* wing, 250–293 (271.5) mm.

Field Marks. Contrasting solid areas of black and white with a black belly mark the males as eiders. Adult male separable from King Eider by all-white back and flat forehead profile. Brown females and immatures separable from Black Duck by their flat forehead profile and barred flanks. Females closely resemble female King Eider, but Common Eider has barred flanks (flank markings crescent-shaped in King Eider), somewhat longer bill, and an extension of the feathering on side of bill, forward to below the nostril. In fresh plumage female Common Eider is slightly less rich brown. In flight this eider often alternates flapping with short glides. *Voice:* Male has drawn-out cooing *ah-hoo* or *ah-ee-oo* of various intensities, used especially in display; also moaning notes. Female: hoarse *kuk-kuk-kuk* notes, like other diving ducks.

Habitat. A marine species. Is fond of low-lying rocky coasts and large and small rocky islands but is found also along other types of shore, especially where mussel beds and reefs provide feeding grounds. Occasionally uses fresh water near the coast. Sometimes occurs well offshore on salt water.

Nesting. Often highly colonial. Nest, foundation of plant material. Sometimes, perhaps frequently, old nest sites are re-used (F. G. Cooch). Down lining is added as egg-laying progresses. Usually near salt water in rock-sheltered situations or in depressions in low vegetation. *Eggs*, usually 4 to 6; olive to olive-buff. Incubation, by the female, lasts 28 to 29 days (F. G. Cooch).

Range. Holarctic. Breeds from Iceland, Spitsbergen, Novaya Zemlya, south to the British Isles, Denmark, France, and the Baltics, also northern Siberia; and in North America from the Arctic south coastally to Kodiak Island and Maine. In winter somewhat farther south.

Breeding Distribution of Common Eider

Range in Canada. Breeds locally and commonly on the coastal islands and shores of Yukon, Banks Island, Victoria Island (Simpson Bay, Walker Bay, Finlayson Islands), Jenny Lind Island, and the coasts of Mackenzie (east at least to Bathurst Inlet); and from middle Ellesmere Island, Devon Island (Croker Bay), Somerset Island (Port Leopold), Cornwallis Island (Resolute Bay), Baffin Island, Southampton Island, Hudson and James bays, Hudson Strait (east of Cape Weggs), Ungava Bay, Labrador, Newfoundland, north shore of the Gulf of St. Lawrence, lower St. Lawrence River (Rivière Ouelle, Gaspé Peninsula, Ile aux Coudres), and the Maritime Provinces (but breeding on Prince Edward Island not established). It winters from southern Baffin Island and islands north of Hudson Bay southward along the Atlantic Coast to the Maritimes and in Hudson and James bays. Some inhabiting the western part of the arctic range move westward around northern Alaska to winter in Bering Sea; a few may remain (Taylor I., N.W.T.). Rare in British Columbia (two late fall records: Vancouver Island; Queen Charlotte Islands). Casual in southern Ontario (Niagara River); and in Manitoba (specimens: Giroux, November 1911; Lake Manitoba, October 23, 1911).

Subspecies. (1) *S. m. dresseri* Sharpe, described above, occupies the se. Atlantic part of Canada n. to the Hamilton Inlet area of Labrador. (2) *S. m. borealis* (Brehm) has the bill frontal processes narrower, terminating in sharp points instead of broad rounded ones, and the male has a less extensive greenish wash on head; breeds from about Hamilton Inlet, Lab., northward, and westward in the Arctic to Somerset, Cornwallis, and Southampton islands. Many winter farther south in the breeding range of *dresseri*. (3) *S. m. sedentaria* Snyder resembles *dresseri* and has similar bill frontal processes, but adult females and immatures are

PLATE 9

1 Pintail,
   (a) adult male in
      breeding plumage
   (b) adult female

2 Black Duck

3 Mallard,
   (a) female
   (b) adult male in
      breeding plumage

4 American Widgeon,
   (a) male in breeding
      plumage
   (b) female

5 European Widgeon,
   adult male in breeding
   plumage

6 Gadwall,
   (a) adult male in
      breeding plumage
   (b) female

1a

1b

3a

2

3b

4a

6a

4b

4b

5

6b

4a

6a

Crosley

noticeably paler and greyer; breeds and winters on Hudson and James bays (s. of Southampton, Coats, and Mansel islands). (4) *S. m. v. nigra* Bonaparte: male has large black V on throat (this occasionally occurs also in other races), and in both sexes anterior end of feathered area on side of bill is more rounded than in other races; the bare frontal processes average narrower and more sharply pointed than in even *borealis;* breeding range from Bathurst Inlet and Victoria I. westward, and apparently separated from the ranges of the eastern races by a hiatus.

KING EIDER

L'Eider remarquable. *Somateria spectabilis* (Linnaeus)
Plate 13. L. 20.75 to 24.00 in.

Feathers on side of bill do not extend forward as far as nostril (Fig. 31). *Adult male* (*winter and breeding*): Top of head, nape, and sides of upper neck, pale bluish grey. Bill processes broadened into a knoblike yellow frontal shield. Greenish patch on cheeks bordered above by narrow white line. Border about bill processes, small patch about eye, and large V on throat, black. Rest of head, neck, fore-back, upper breast, shoulders, patch on either side of base of tail, white. White of breast tinged pinkish. Lower back, scapulars, rump, tail coverts, lower breast, belly, and sides, black. Tail brownish black. Anterior lesser wing coverts and greater coverts blackish, rest white. Remainder of wing blackish. Some tertials (erectile in life) out-curved with purplish black outer webs. Legs and feet yellowish to orange with dusky webs. Eye brown. Bill processes rich yellow, bill red to orange with purplish nail. *Adult female:* Very similar to female Common Eider but has slightly warmer brown coloration, unstreaked chin, more decidedly *crescentic* black markings on sides. Feathers on *top* of bill extend forward to above nostrils, but those on *sides* of bill fall far short of nostril (reverse of Common Eider).

Fig. 31 Bill of
   (A) King Eider female
   (B) Common Eider female

Measurements. *Adult male:* wing, 264–283 (273); tail, 81–87.5 (83.7); exposed culmen, 26–30 (28.9); tarsus, 46.5–50 (48.1). *Adult female:* wing, 245–274 (263.4) mm.

Field Marks. Adult male is unmistakable. Female closely resembles female Common Eider, but at very close range differently shaped feathered areas of bill may be discerned (*see* above). Sides, and sides of breast, have more decidedly *crescentic* black markings in present species. King Eider is usually a more warmly brown bird, particularly compared with the Hudson Bay race of Common Eider, *sedentaria*, but this is not always reliable compared with other races of the Common Eider. *Voice:* Male, in courtship, a low musical *coo uur-aaa-oo* with emphasis on last syllable; female, coarse grunting croaks (S. D. MacDonald).

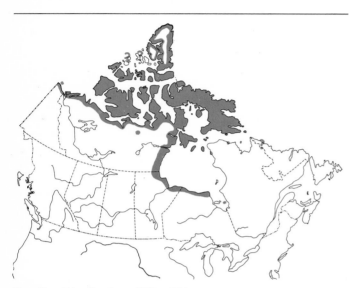

Breeding Distribution of King Eider

Habitat. In breeding season much less marine than Common Eider, preferring the vicinity of tundra freshwater ponds, lakes, and streams for nesting, usually not at any great distance from the coast which is frequently visited for feeding purposes. Rarely considerably inland (Garry Lake, Keewatin). At other seasons, the habitat is mainly marine, like the Common Eider's. Its more frequent occurrence on the Great Lakes probably reflects its greater tolerance for fresh water.

Nesting. Unlike the Common Eider, it is not colonial and the nest is usually near fresh water but sometimes on flat tundra at considerable distance from water. Nest, on the ground, often partly protected by sparse vegetation or rocks, is lined with down (noticeably darker than that of Common Eider). *Eggs*, usually 4 to 7; resemble those of Common Eider in colour but average smaller. Incubation by female; period 22 to 23 days (David F. Parmelee). Young are inclined to form packs with adult females in charge.

Range. Breeds on islands in Bering Sea, in arctic Alaska, across arctic Canada, Hudson and James bays, Greenland, and the northern coasts and islands of Europe and Asia, from the Kanin Peninsula of northern Russia, Spitsbergen and Novaya Zemlya, east to Anadyr. In western North America, it winters north to the limit of open water in Bering Sea, south to the Aleutian and Kodiak islands, with stragglers south to California (very rarely), and in eastern North America mainly from southern Greenland to New-foundland, with smaller numbers south to Massachusetts, New York, and New Jersey.

Range in Canada. Breeds along the arctic coast and islands from the high Arctic (Prince Patrick and northern Ellesmere islands; recorded rarely on Ellef Ringnes but not known to nest), south to the coast of northern Yukon, northern Mackenzie, and Keewatin (mainly coasts but also in interior at Garry Lake), Southampton Island, Hudson and James bays (Chesterfield Inlet, McConnell River, Cape Henrietta Maria, South Twin Island), northern Quebec (Stupart Bay, Kogaluk River), and probably northern Labrador (but evidence unsatisfactory).

Winters on open water off Labrador, the Gulf of St. Lawrence, and Newfoundland (regularly, especially southwest coast). Recorded rarely in New Brunswick and Nova Scotia. Apparently the western arctic population migrates westward to winter in the Bering Sea. Individuals, however, from as far west as King William and Southampton islands help swell large August migration concentrations off west Greenland. Casual in British Columbia (Victoria, January 11, 1942; Hardy Bay, October 18, 1938), and rare on the upper St. Lawrence River and tributaries and Great Lakes (Montreal, Ottawa, Toronto, Niagara River, etc.). Accidental in Alberta (Calgary, November 4, 1894) and at Lake Mistassini, Quebec.

[**Spectacled Eider.** L'Eider à lunettes. *Lampronetta fischeri* (Brandt)
Field Marks. Adult male has a large white area surrounding the eye. This is framed with a narrow black border (hence the name 'spectacled'). The black under parts extend forward across the breast almost to base of neck, thus differing from other eiders. Female resembles other eiders, but in good light one can discern a paler brown area, the counterpart of male's 'spectacles.'

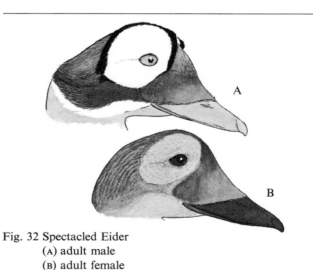

Fig. 32 Spectacled Eider
(A) adult male
(B) adult female

Status in Canada. Hypothetical. No specimen has yet been taken in Canada, but as the species is known to occur more or less regularly on Barter Island and Demarcation Point, Alaska, near the Yukon border, it probably occurs at least occasionally on the poorly known Yukon coast. Manning, Höhn, and Macpherson (1956) provide a convincing sight record of a male on Sachs River, Banks Island, on June 20, 1952. C. J. Guiguet (in litt.) observed a male "in full or near full plumage" at 60 to 70 feet off southern Vancouver Island (James Island) on September 22, 1962.]

WHITE-WINGED SCOTER
La Macreuse à ailes blanches
Melanitta deglandi (Bonaparte)
Plate 13. L. 19.5 to 23.0 in.

Feathers on sides of bill extend forward almost to nostril. *Adult male (winter and breeding plumage)*: Mainly black; a white spot extending backward and upward below the eye; and a wing patch formed by the white of the secondaries. Eye pale grey or whitish. Bill with black swollen base, red or purplish sides becoming orange near base, ridge white, edges black, nail reddish. Legs purplish pink on outer sides, tending to orange on inner sides. *Adult female:* Head and neck brownish black, often with two vague whitish patches, one on ear, one in front of eye. Rest of plumage sooty brown, some feathers with paler edges. Wing patch formed by white secondaries. Eye brown.

Measurements (*M. d. deglandi*). *Adult male:* wing, 262–285 (274.1); tail, 77.5–87 (81.6); exposed culmen, 37–44 (39.6); tarsus, 49.5–52.5 (51.1). *Adult female:* wing, 254–271 (259.9) mm.

Field Marks. Scoters are good-sized, thick-necked, heavy-headed ducks, the males mostly black, females dark sooty brown. They are often seen in rafts of various sizes or flying in groups low over the water. This is the only scoter with a white wing patch which is conspicuous in flight but usually is not visible while the birds are resting. Young and some adult females show two lighter patches on the sides of the head, similar to the female Surf Scoter but different from the Common Scoter.

Habitat. Salt water of coasts (usually not far from shore), freshwater lakes inland, and larger rivers. Rarely comes to land except for nesting. Nest, usually near fresh water in shrubby tangles and woodland, often on an island, more rarely at some distance from water. Many, perhaps mostly post-breeding males and non-breeders, are found on coastal salt water even during the nesting season.

Nesting. Nest, on the ground, usually well hidden in shrubbery, a depression lined with grasses, dark down, and a few feathers. *Eggs*, 8 to 14; pale ochraceous pink. Incubation by female.

Range. Breeds from northwestern Alaska and the interior of the western Canada mainland, mostly south of tree limit (summers commonly in eastern Canada, but definite evidence of breeding needed), south to northeastern Washington and central North Dakota. Winters on the Pacific Coast (Aleutian Islands and Alaska Peninsula to Lower California) and on the Atlantic Coast (Gulf of St. Lawrence to South Carolina) and sporadically in the interior to Colorado, Nebraska, Louisiana, and in small numbers on the Great Lakes.

Range in Canada. The commonest scoter in most areas. Breeds widely in Yukon, western Mackenzie (Mackenzie Delta, Stanton), southern Keewatin (Nueltin Lake), and southward in interior British Columbia (Atlin; François Lake; Nicola and Quesnel regions; Swan Lake, Peace River; Cariboo parklands), Alberta (on most larger lakes, except in mountainous southwestern part, commonest in central parts), Saskatchewan (Flotten Lake, Emma Lake, lakes

Breeding Distribution of White-winged Scoter

north of Nipawin, York Lake region, Cypress Lake, Last Mountain Lake, Quill Lake, Lake Athabasca), Manitoba (Churchill, Lake St. Martin, Shoal Lake), and extreme western Ontario (Ney Lake). Widely distributed in summer also on coasts of eastern Canada (James Bay, Labrador coast, Gulf of St. Lawrence, Newfoundland, and the Maritimes) and the coast of British Columbia, but without satisfactory evidence of breeding. Recorded in summer north to northeastern Mackenzie (Cape Bathurst and mouth of Coppermine River; sight records, Bathurst Inlet), Ungava Bay, and more rarely Hudson Strait and West Foxe Islands. Winters commonly along the coast of British Columbia and on the Atlantic Coast north to Newfoundland and the Gulf of St. Lawrence; and in irregular small numbers on the Great Lakes.

Subspecies. The breeding population of nw. Alaska has been separated as *M. d. dixoni* (Brooks) on the basis of shorter, relatively broader, blunter-tipped bill, but its validity is not too well established. *M. d. deglandi* (Bonaparte) is the breeding bird of most of Canada with the possible exception of Mackenzie Delta. Individuals of both races are found in winter on the B.C. coast.

SURF SCOTER
La Macreuse à front blanc
Melanitta perspicillata (Linnaeus)
Plate 13. L. 19.5 to 23.0 in.

Feathers extend forward on ridge of bill to form a blunt point, in male almost or quite to nostril; no feathers on side of bill. *Adult male:* Plumage black with white triangle on forehead and another on nape. Bill with base swollen and elevated along ridge abruptly descending over nostrils; a roundish or squarish black patch on sides of bill near base, bordered behind and above by orange or red and in front and below by white; ridge and nasal area reddish; nail yellowish. Eye white. Legs reddish on outer side, orange inner side with blackish blotches; webs blackish. *Adult female:* Crown to just below eye, brownish black; rest of head and neck, brown with two vague whitish areas, one in front of cheek, the other over ear; nape with vague greyish or whitish patch. Body blackish brown, paler below. Wings plain brown. Eye brown. Bill blackish with roundish black spot on sides near base faintly indicated. *Immatures:* In first autumn, they resemble adult females, but the two whitish areas on sides of head are better defined, under parts whiter, and the whitish patch on nape is lacking.

Measurements. *Adult male:* wing, 232–244 (236.3); tail, 79–86 (81.8); exposed culmen, 35–42 (37.7); tarsus, 43–47 (44.8). *Adult female:* wing, 203–230.5 (221.5) mm.

Field Marks. Male has solid black colour and contrasting white head markings. Female and immatures have two vaguely defined whitish areas on sides of head like the White-winged Scoter, but Surf Scoter has no white wing patch.

Habitat. Similar to White-winged Scoter.

Nesting. Nest similar to that of White-winged Scoter but said to use less grass in its construction. *Eggs,* 5 to 7; pinkish or buffy white. Incubation by the female.

Range. Breeds in Alaska and locally in northern continental Canada. Winters mainly on the salt water of coasts from the Aleutians and southeastern Alaska to the Gulf of California and from southern Newfoundland to Florida. Also in small numbers on the Great Lakes and more rarely at other interior points in the United States.

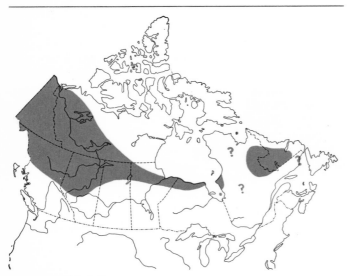

Breeding Distribution of Surf Scoter

Range in Canada. *Summers* regularly from northern Yukon, the arctic coast of western Mackenzie, and southern Keewatin south through the coast and middle interior of British Columbia, northern Alberta, northern Saskatchewan, and northern Manitoba, the coasts and islands of southern Hudson and James bays, the coast and interior of Labrador, and the coasts of the Atlantic provinces (scarce in Newfoundland). Casual north to Repulse Bay. Actual breeding data are few: Breeds in Yukon (probably: both sexes summer commonly), western Mackenzie (Mackenzie Delta, Anderson River, Great Bear Lake, Great Slave Lake), Alberta (Elk Island Park), northern Saskatchewan (Lake Athabasca), James Bay (Charlton and Sheppard islands),

Ontario (Lake at 55° 15′ N, 86° 35′ W), Labrador (Petitsikapau Lake, Grand Falls), and Quebec (Wakuach Lake and near Otelnuk Lake). According to Bent (1925), eggs and the parent female were collected on Akpatok Island, Ungava Bay. Audubon's account of a nest near little Mecatina, P.Q., is not completely satisfactory. Winters commonly on the coast of British Columbia (rarely in southern interior) and on the Atlantic Coast from Newfoundland and the Gulf of St. Lawrence southward; occasionally on lakes Erie and Ontario. Migration is mainly coastwise, but small irregular numbers are recorded in southern parts of the interior provinces. Common migrant at Lake Mistassini, interior Quebec, perhaps indicating an overland route between James Bay and the Atlantic Coast.

COMMON SCOTER (formerly American Scoter)
La Macreuse à bec jaune. *Oidemia nigra* (Linnaeus)
Plate 13. L. 17.0 to 21.5 in.

Feathers at base of bill do not extend nearly to nostrils either along the ridge or sides of bill. *Adult male:* Plumage entirely black except under surface of flight feathers, which is grey (contrasting with black under wing coverts). Eye brown. Bill black with swollen basal part yellow to orange. Legs brownish black. *Adult female:* Top of head and nape, dark brown; rest of head greyish with indistinct brown mottling. Rest of upper parts, sooty brown often with paler feather edges. Belly lighter brown. Eye and legs as in male. Bill (lacks basal swelling of male) blackish often with yellow streaks. Young in first autumn similar to adult female but paler, more whitish on abdomen and breast.

Measurements. *Adult male:* wing, 213–233 (225.4); tail, 83–97 (88.5); exposed culmen, 42–45.5 (43.7); tarsus, 45–48.5 (46.5). *Adult female:* wing, 210–230 (220.4) mm.

Field Marks. Adult male our only scoter without a patch of white either in wing or on head. Female has plain light cheeks (females of other scoters usually show two light patches on side of head), against which brown cap is well defined. Also female White-winged has white patch in wing (conspicuous in flight) which Common Scoter lacks.

Habitat. Similar to White-winged Scoter.

Nesting. Nest, a depression in the ground lined with grass and down, near freshwater pools, lakes, and rivers in either tundra or wooded country. *Eggs,* 6 to 10; light to pinkish buff. Incubation by female.

Range. Circumpolar. Breeds in Alaska and northern continental Canada; also from Iceland, Spitsbergen, northern parts of Norway, Russia, and Siberia, south to Scotland and north-central Siberia. In North America, winters on the Pacific Coast from the Aleutian Islands to southern California; the Atlantic Coast from Newfoundland to South Carolina; and in small numbers on the Great Lakes.

Range in Canada. Widely but locally distributed in summer. Definite breeding records are few: southern Keewatin (Windy River); northern Quebec (Leaf Bay); and Newfoundland (Avalon Peninsula; Missen Topsail; and near Grand Lake). Summers regularly on the British Columbia coast, Hudson and James bays (commonly), southern Hudson Strait and Ungava Bay, Labrador, Newfoundland, Gulf of St. Lawrence but is scarce off the southern Maritimes. Rarely recorded in Yukon, much of Mackenzie (recorded rarely on Great Slave Lake), interior British Columbia, Alberta, and Saskatchewan, southern Manitoba. Winters along the coast of British Columbia and on the Atlantic Coast from Newfoundland south; a few irregularly on the Great Lakes.

Subspecies. *Oidemia nigra americana* Swainson.

Subfamily **Oxyurinae**–Ruddy and Masked Ducks

Small freshwater ducks represented in Canada by only one species. They have broad flat bills, and the hind toe is lobed. However, the nail of the bill is decidedly hooked at the tip, and the stiff, spikelike tail feathers with very short tail coverts are different from those of other ducks.

RUDDY DUCK
Le Canard roux. *Oxyura jamaicensis* (Gmelin)
Plate 12. L. 13.5 to 17.0 in.

Bill broad, with concave ridge, the nail small and slightly turned back under end of bill (Fig. 33). Tail feathers stiff, narrow, rather long, their coverts short. *Adult male (breeding plumage)*: Top of head to below eye, and nape, black. Large cheek patch and chin, white. Neck, sides of breast, and all upper parts (except wings, rump, and tail), chestnut. Upper side of wing brown, secondaries tipped white. Rump and tail brown. Wing linings, mixed white and brown. Under tail coverts white. Abdomen, silvery white mixed with dusky. Eye brown or reddish brown. Bill blue. Legs and feet bluish grey with dusky webs. *Adult male (fall and winter)*: Crown duller and browner; chestnut areas replaced by dark brown and grey. *Adult female*: Top of head to below eye, and a poorly defined streak across cheeks, dark brown. Back, scapulars, rump, upper tail coverts, and upper side of wings, blackish brown irregularly crossed with buffy or greyish lines. Under parts silvery white mixed with dusky. Eye brown. Bill dusky. Legs bluish grey. Young in first autumn resemble adult female.

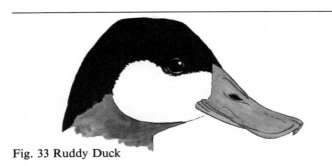

Fig. 33 Ruddy Duck

Measurements. *Adult male:* wing, 133–147.5 (141.4); tail, 67–79 (72.2); exposed culmen, 38.5–41 (40.3); tarsus, 33–38 (34.2). *Adult female:* wing, 134–145.5 (139.5) mm.

Field Marks. On the water often cocks tail up like a wren, but this is not unique as other ducks sometimes do it too. Adult male in breeding plumage has large white cheek patch,

black cap, and extensive reddish chestnut on upper parts and sides; in fall and winter, it lacks chestnut colouring, but black cap and white cheek patch are obvious. Female has dark cap and light cheek, the latter crossed by a poorly defined horizontal line; might be confused with female Common Scoter, but the Ruddy is much smaller with entirely different buzzy flight.

Habitat. Essentially a freshwater duck. In summer, freshwater lakes, ponds, sloughs, with margins of emergent vegetation. In migration prefers similar fresh or brackish water bodies, often extensive; but will frequent saltwater bays on occasion.

Nesting. Nest, a well-concealed woven mass of marsh vegetation attached to growing marsh plants, usually a few inches over water. *Eggs*, 5 to 10; extremely large for so small a duck, with thick, rough shell, dull white in colour. Incubation 27 days (T. E. Randall), 25 to 26 days (J. B. Low).

Range. Southern part of western (mainly) Canada south to Guatemala, the West Indies; also central and eastern Andes of Colombia. Winters mainly from southern British Columbia and Middle United States southward.

Breeding Distribution of Ruddy Duck

Range in Canada. Breeds in central and southern British Columbia (north at least to Nulki and Tachik lakes and Peace River parklands; mainly in the interior but locally also on Vancouver Island); Alberta (except southwestern part); southwestern Mackenzie (probably Canol Road near Norman Wells: female with young carefully observed by S. D. MacDonald and W. J. Smith; Great Slave Lake); central and southern Saskatchewan (north at least to Kazan and Emma lakes); and southwestern Manitoba (north to near Moose and Cedar lakes, east at least to Red River valley); very locally and sporadically farther east in southern Ontario (Lake St. Clair; Luther Marsh; Wainfleet Swamp; near Mitchell's Bay); and southern Quebec (Lake St. Peter — flightless juvenal taken from hunter's bag by D. A. Munro). Regular migrant in southern parts of western Canada, east to the Great Lakes, scarcer farther east, rare in the Maritimes and Newfoundland. Casual north to southern Yukon

81

(Alaska Highway at Takhini River; Sulphur Lake), north-eastern Manitoba (York Factory), and eastern Hudson Bay (Great Whale River). Winters in small numbers in southern British Columbia and southern Ontario (Lakes Erie and Ontario).

Subspecies. *Oxyura jamaicensis rubida* (Wilson).

Subfamily **Merginae**—Mergansers

Ducks with a slender cylindrical bill, hooked at the tip and equipped with well-developed, sharp, backward-directed lamellae, ideal for catching and holding fish (Fig. 34). As in the duck subfamilies Anatinae, Aythyinae, and Oxyurinae, the tarsi are scutellate. The hind toe is lobed as in the diving ducks.

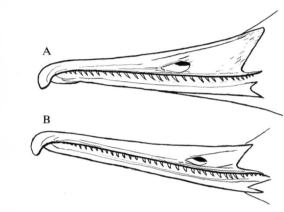

Fig 34 Bill of
(A) Common Merganser
(B) Red-breasted Merganser

HOODED MERGANSER

Le Bec-scie couronné. *Lophodytes cucullatus* (Linnaeus)
Plate 14. L. 16.5 to 23.0 in.

Head crested in both sexes. *Adult male* (*winter and breeding*): Head and neck black with large triangle of white extending backward from behind eye and with narrow black border along nape. Back, black becoming brownish on rump and tail. Two spurs of black reach down onto sides of breast. Fore-wing grey. Speculum white, divided by black bar. Inner secondaries and tertials, black striped with white. Sides and flanks, reddish brown crossed by fine blackish lines. Breast and belly white. Eye yellow. Bill blackish. Legs and feet, pale yellowish brown. *Adult female:* Head and neck greyish brown, throat much paler, crest brownish and shorter than in male. Back, scapulars, rump, and tail, dark brown. Wings brown with restricted white wing patch. Breast and sides brownish grey. Belly white. Eye brown. Bill dusky above, yellowish below. Legs brownish. *Young* resemble female, but they are paler, and the crest is poorly developed.

Measurements. *Adult male:* wing, 188–197 (192.8); tail, 87.5–99.5 (93.2); exposed culmen, 32–43 (39.3); tarsus, 31–39 (33). *Adult female:* wing, 172–188 (182.6) mm.

Field Marks. Adult male's large white head patch could be confused with that of the Bufflehead, but its slender merganser bill and coloured flanks are very different. The female Hooded Merganser is identified as a merganser by the slender bill. Its small size and darker coloration separate it from other mergansers.

Habitat. Primarily a freshwater duck. In nesting season, freshwater ponds, lakes, and rivers in or near woodland. In migration and winter, similar freshwater bodies. Sometimes frequents saltwater bays, but much less often than the Red-breasted and Common mergansers.

Nesting. Nests in a hole in a tree. *Eggs*, usually 5 to 12; larger numbers recorded, probably a product of more than one female. Incubation period said to be 31 days, but this requires confirmation.

Range. Breeds from southern Alaska and across southern Canada, south mainly to Oregon, Wyoming, Iowa, eastern Missouri, eastern Arkansas, and western Tennessee. Winters from southern British Columbia, the Great Lakes, and Massachusetts south to the Gulf Coast and Mexico.

Range in Canada. Northern limits of range poorly known. Breeds in British Columbia (north to Queen Charlotte Islands and in the interior at least to Vanderhoof and perhaps the Topley areas), Alberta (breeding records for the mountains at Banff, Crow's Nest Pass, and Waterton Lake; recorded in summer at Barrhead), Saskatchewan (reportedly at Quill Lake, but definite Saskatchewan data are needed; *probably* breeds sparingly but widely in wooded parts), Manitoba (southern and middle wooded parts recorded in summer north to Churchill and Misty Lake), central and southern Ontario (north to Kenora region, Lake Nipigon, Kapuskasing, Gogama), southern Quebec (Montreal, St. Cyrille in L'Islet County, perhaps north to Mistassini Post), southern New Brunswick (St. Croix and St. John

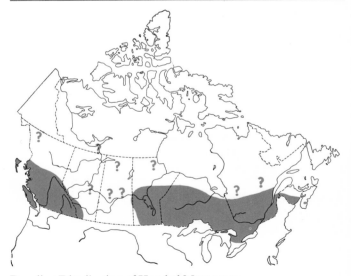

Breeding Distribution of Hooded Merganser

rivers), and Nova Scotia (rarely: Sand Lake Brook, Queens Co. — R. W. Tufts, in litt.). Occurrences north to southern Mackenzie (Great Slave Lake), southern Keewatin (Four-hill Lakes), northern Ontario, and northern Quebec (Clearwater Lake). Scarce visitor to Prince Edward Island; rare in Newfoundland (Trepassey; also sight records: Cape Broyle and La Manche). Winters in small numbers in southern British Columbia and occasionally on the southern Great Lakes.

COMMON MERGANSER (formerly American Merganser)
Le Bec-scie commun. *Mergus merganser* Linnaeus
Plate 14. L. 21 to 27 in.

Nostrils nearer to middle of bill than to base (thus different from Red-breasted Merganser). *Adult male:* Head and upper neck blackish, strongly glossed with green. Upper back and scapulars black. Rump, upper tail coverts, and tail, grey. Fore-wing mainly white, greater coverts crossed by a dark bar. Primaries and outermost secondaries blackish brown, others mainly white. Lower neck, breast, belly, sides, and under tail coverts, white faintly suffused with pinkish. Eye variable, red to brown. Bill red, dusky on ridge and tip. Legs and feet red. *Adult female:* Head conspicuously crested. Head and upper neck, tawny brown. Chin and throat, white. Lower hind-neck, back, scapulars, rump, tail, and sides, grey. Upper side of wings, grey with white speculum. Abdomen and under tail coverts, white. Eye reddish or yellowish. Bill dull reddish with dusky ridge and nail. Legs dull red. *Young in first winter:* Resemble adult female but have shorter crests.

Measurements. *Adult male:* wing, 267.5–281 (273.8); tail, 100.5–111.5 (104.1); exposed culmen, 54.5–59 (56.5); tarsus, 47.5–54.5 (51.9). *Adult female:* wing, 236–274 (249.9) mm.

Field Marks. Long slender bill marks it as a merganser. Adult male is likely to be confused only with the Red-breasted Merganser but lacks the conspicuous crest and reddish breast band of that species. Females of the two are more difficult, but in the Common Merganser the white throat is more sharply defined and the red of the neck is sharply cut off from (not blended into) the whitish breast.

Habitat. Primarily fresh water. In summer frequents freshwater lakes and rivers, usually in or near woodland. In winter mostly freshwater rivers and the open water, when available, of lakes; less often coastal salt water. Clear water is preferred and is probably necessary for feeding.

Nesting. Nest is usually in tree cavities but sometimes in holes in banks, in rock piles, and on the ground among bushes. *Eggs,* usually 8 to 12; creamy white. Incubation by the female, reportedly lasts 28 to 32 days (various authors).

Range. Holarctic: southern Alaska, and across southern Canada, Iceland, Scotland, Norway, Sweden, Russia, and Siberia, south to California, Arizona, South Dakota, Minnesota, Michigan, central New York, Maine, the Netherlands, Germany, and south-central Russia. In North America winters south to southern California, northern Mexico, the Gulf Coast, and Florida.

Range in Canada. Breeds in southern Yukon (north at least to Sheldon Lake and Dawson), southern Mackenzie (Great Slave Lake, Hill Island Lake), British Columbia, Alberta (mountainous southwest and Lake Athabasca regions; only a migrant in southern prairies), Saskatchewan (wooded parts: Athabasca Lake, Churchill River, Flotten

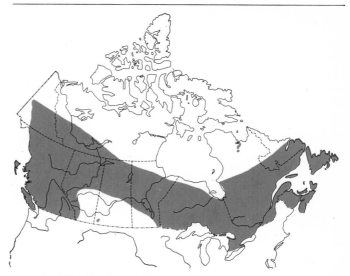

Breeding Distribution of Common Merganser

Lake, Torch River, Kingsmere Lake; probably Cypress Hills region), Manitoba (Cormorant Lake, Moose and Cedar lakes, Oxford Lake, northern Lake Winnipegosis, Waterhen Lake, Lake St. Martin, Riding Mountain. Reported as breeding on Nelson River), Ontario (Moose River and Sioux Lookout south to southern Lake Huron and Peterborough County), central and southern Quebec (north to Lake St. John and Lake Mistassini), Labrador (Grand Falls, Flatwaters Cove), Newfoundland, New Brunswick, Nova Scotia, probably Prince Edward Island. Recorded in summer, but not known to breed, north to central Mackenzie (Thelon River), southern Keewatin, and northern Quebec. Winters in British Columbia (coast; small numbers in southern interior), southern Alberta (a few regularly near Calgary), southern Ontario (Great Lakes, lower Ottawa and St. Lawrence valleys), southern Quebec (north to Lake St. John), Newfoundland, and the Maritime Provinces.

Subspecies. *Mergus merganser americanus* Cassin.

RED-BREASTED MERGANSER
Le Bec-scie à poitrine rousse. *Mergus serrator* Linnaeus
Plate 14. L. 20 to 25 in.

Head crested. Nostrils nearer base of bill than in Common Merganser. *Adult male* (*winter and spring*): Head and upper neck, black glossed with green; conspicuous crest. Back, most of scapulars, and tertials, black. Wing, black and white. Rump, upper tail coverts, and sides, grey finely crossed with wavy black lines. Breast pale cinnamon, streaked and mottled with black. Lower neck and abdomen white. Eye, legs, and feet, red. Bill red with dusky ridge. *Adult female:* Head and neck cinnamon brown, darkest on top of head, blending into whitish on throat. Rest of upper parts grey. Wing with white speculum crossed by black bar. Sides brownish grey. Abdomen white. Eye and bill red; legs dull reddish.

Measurements. *Adult male:* wing, 231–251 (244.1); tail, 78.5–87 (82.3); exposed culmen, 55–63.5 (58); tarsus, 45–50 (46.9). *Adult female:* wing, 205.5–246 (221.3) mm.

Field Marks. Adult male, with its greenish-black crested head and reddish breast band, is easy to recognize. Females and young similar to Common Merganser, but brown of head *blends* into whitish throat and into grey of lower neck (not sharply cut off as in Common Merganser).

Habitat. Generally more marine than Common Merganser; preferring coastal salt water in winter. In breeding season both salt and fresh water: bays, lagoons, estuaries; also freshwater lakes and rivers.

Nesting. Nest on ground, under bushes, sometimes in rock piles or under logs or tree roots, usually near water. It is a depression, often with some grasses or leaves, lined with down (down darker than that of Common Merganser). *Eggs,* 7 to 12, variable; greenish buff to buffy, more richly coloured than in Common Merganser. Incubation, 26 to 30 days, by female (various authors).

Range. Holarctic. Breeds from Alaska, Mackenzie, southern Baffin Island, Greenland, Iceland, Scandinavia (from 71° N), and Russia, south to British Columbia, southern Manitoba, central Michigan, eastern Maine, Scotland, Ireland, northern Germany, Poland, and middle Russia. In North America winters (especially along the coasts) from southern Canada to southern United States.

Breeding Distribution of Red-breasted Merganser

Range in Canada. Breeds from Yukon (north to arctic coast), Mackenzie (north to Mackenzie Delta and Fort Anderson, perhaps Perry River), southern Keewatin (Angikuni Lake, Thlewiaza River), and southern Baffin Island (Nettilling Lake; Cumberland Sound) south to northern British Columbia (Atlin region), northern Alberta (Lake Athabasca; reports of breeding farther south require confirmation), northern and central Saskatchewan (Reindeer, Kazan, Flotten, and Namew lakes), Manitoba (Churchill, Cochrane River, Lake St. Martin, Seven Sisters dam), southern Ontario (Bay of Quinte, Brothers Island, Kingston), central and, locally, southeastern Quebec (Lake Mistassini, Anticosti Island, Magdalen Islands), Labrador, Newfoundland, New Brunswick, Nova Scotia (including Sable Island), and Prince Edward Island. Winters in British Columbia (regularly all along coast; occasionally in southern interior), the Great Lakes (small numbers), St. Lawrence Valley (Ile aux Basques), Newfoundland, and the Maritimes.

Subspecies. *Mergus serrator serrator* Linnaeus.

SMEW

Le Harle piette. *Mergellus albellus* (Linnaeus)
L. ca. 16 in.

A small merganser with shorter, more 'duck-like' bill than other mergansers and a drooping, not conspicuous, crest. *Adult male:* Mainly white with dark patch from around eye to base of bill; at closer range its black middle back, small black-and-white crest, and two narrow dark lines up sides of breast can be seen. *Females and immatures:* Have conspicuous pure white cheeks and throat sharply contrasted against the chestnut-red rest of head; back, breast, and flanks, grey; belly white. Both sexes have white wing patches (female's smaller) conspicuous in flight.

Status in Canada. Accidental. One record: Four colour photographs taken by D. R. Gunn on Niagara River, southern Ontario, on February 26 and March 6, 1960, show so clearly the unmistakable markings and profile of a female or immature Smew that there can not be the slightest doubt concerning the identification of this stray from the Old World. Many competent observers, including some who are familiar with it in Europe, saw this individual during late February 1960.

Order **Falconiformes**–Diurnal Birds of Prey–
Vultures, Hawks, and Falcons

Family **Cathartidae**–American Vultures

Number of Species in North America 4, in Canada 2

Large, long-winged birds *with the head bare of feathers;* a strongly hooked bill with large open nostrils; toes rather long (the hind one elevated), but weakly hooked and unsuitable for grasping and holding prey. They feed on dead animals and thus serve a useful purpose as scavengers. Flight, on long, broad wings, with much protracted sailing and circling, is extremely graceful.

TURKEY VULTURE

Le Vautour à tête rouge. *Cathartes aura* (Linnaeus)
Plates 15, 20. L. 26.5 to 32.0 in.

Head and extreme upper neck bare except for sparse hair-like bristles. Bill rather long, hooked, with very large broad nostrils. Wings long. *Adults:* Naked head and upper neck, red. Upper body, wings, and tail black, the feathers of back and wing coverts edged with brown. Neck and under parts black. Eye brown. Bill whitish, red basally. Legs, flesh colour. *Juvenal:* Similar to adults but bare skin of head blackish.

Measurements (*C. a. septentrionalis*). *Adult male: wing,* 518–550 (535.9); tail, 252–298 (271); culmen from cere, 24–25 (24.4); tarsus, 65–71 (68.1). *Adult female:* wing, 527–559 (545.8) mm (Friedmann).

Field Marks. A large long-winged (wingspread to 6 feet) black bird with small red (blackish in young) head and longish hooked bill. In flight it soars effortlessly for long periods with wings held definitely above horizontal in a broad V; often tilts gracefully from side to side; black under wing coverts contrast with paler flight feathers.

Habitat. Inhabits various types of terrain, except heavy unbroken forest. Spends long periods on the wing, often at considerable heights.

Nesting. No nest. *Eggs* (usually 2) are laid on the ground among rocks, under logs, on cliffs, or in caves. They are yellowish white with bold irregular blotches of browns and often sparse spots of pale lavender. Incubation period variously reported: 30 to 41 days (*in* Bent, 1937).

Range. Southern Canada, south through the United States to the West Indies, Central America, and to southern South America.

Range in Canada. Breeds in small numbers in southern British Columbia (Comox, Pender Island, Harrison, Oliver),

central and southern Alberta (locally north to near Ashmont), southern Saskatchewan (Moose Jaw, Rush Lake, mouth of Old Wives Creek, Qu'Appelle Valley; possibly north to Saskatchewan River), southern Manitoba (Duck Mountain, Elk Island, Long Lake), western Ontario (Poplar Bay, Kenora), southern Ontario (north to Bruce Peninsula, Credit Forks, Georgetown). Rare visitor to southern Quebec (Lac Raymond, Wright, Barrington, Hatley, Pointe des Monts), New Brunswick (some eighteen records at various points), and Nova Scotia (well-spaced records at various points including Cape Breton Island). Casual in northern

Breeding Distribution of Turkey Vulture

Ontario (Fort Severn, Moose Factory). Accidental in Labrador (Nain, West St. Modeste) and Newfoundland (St. Anthony, Renews). Winters occasionally in southern British Columbia (Comox, Oyster River, Okanagan Landing).

Subspecies. (1) *Cathartes aura septentrionalis* Wied is the breeding subspecies of s. Ont. and e. U.S. Most wanderers to other parts of e. Canada are probably referable to it. (2) *C. a. teter* Friedmann, with an average shorter tail and wings, inhabits w. Canada including w. Ontario. (Wetmore, 1964, *Smithsonian Misc. Collections* 146 (6): 1–18, maintains that *meridionalis* is an older name for *teter* Friedmann.)

BLACK VULTURE
Le Vautour noir. *Coragyps atratus* (Bechstein)
L. 24 to 27 in.

Bare head and neck mark it as a vulture. Differs from Turkey Vulture in somewhat smaller size; black instead of red head, long narrow nostrils; relatively shorter wing (longest primaries little longer than largest secondaries); shorter tail (less than half the length of the folded wing instead of more than half); and square instead of rounded tail. In flight the Black Vulture shows a light area near end of each wing, a shorter square-tipped (not rounded) tail, and its flaps are more rapid.

Range. Southern United States south through Mexico and Central America to Argentina and Chile.

Status in Canada. Casual or accidental in southern Ontario (specimen: July 21, 1947, four miles north of Niagara Falls), southwestern Quebec (specimens: both from Beauport, October 28, 1897; March 20, 1932), New Brunswick (about 12 records: Spruce Lake, Grand Manan, Campobello Island, Escuminac), and Nova Scotia (specimens: Pugwash, January 12, 1896; Owl's Head, Halifax County, December 1, 1918). Additional sight records have been reported for eastern Canada and for Saskatchewan.

Family **Accipitridae**–Kites, Hawks, Eagles, Harriers

Number of Species in North America 25; in Canada 13

A large family widely distributed in the world and containing a great variety of both large and small species. The bill is strongly hooked (but has no toothlike projection as in the falcons) and has a membranous covering on its base called a *cere*. The strong feet are equipped with sharp, curved talons for catching and holding prey. The sexes are usually (not always) coloured similarly; the female is larger than the male.

The accipiters (Goshawk, Sharp-shinned, and Cooper's hawk) have short rounded wings and a long tail thus showing a characteristic silhouette (Plate 20). The buteos (Red-tailed, Red-shouldered, Broad-winged, Swainson's, Rough-legged, and ferruginous hawks) are heavily built hawks with broad round wings and broad rounded tails (Plate 19).

Most hawks perform an extremely useful service in curbing the numbers of harmful rodents. Because of the depredations of a small minority (Goshawk, Cooper's, and Sharp-shinned hawks), the tendency has been all too general to condemn the whole family, and consequently all hawks have been slaughtered indiscriminately, often by persons who should know better. An increasing number of Canadian provinces now protect by law these valuable, beautiful, and exciting birds.

Unfortunately, another period now confronts these birds. Several species, notably the Bald and Golden eagles and the Peregrine Falcon, have decreased abruptly in recent years over large parts of their ranges. The evidence indicates that pesticides are the primary responsible factor.

SWALLOW-TAILED KITE
Le Milan à queue fourchue
Elanoïdes forficatus (Linnaeus)
L. 24 in. (including very long tail)

Almost unmistakable. A medium-sized hawk, strikingly marked with contrasting black and white, with very long deeply forked tail (outer feathers project 8 inches beyond middle ones) and long pointed wings. Wings and tail, solid black except mainly-white tertials. Rest of plumage including head, shoulders, and under parts, white. Under wing coverts white, contrasting with black flight feathers.

Range. From South Carolina, Georgia, Florida, and the Gulf Coast southward through eastern Mexico and Central America to northern Argentina and Bolivia.

Status in Canada. Accidental. Single specimens support its occurrence in Ontario (specimen said to be "certainly an Ontario record," probably Toronto, taken many years prior to 1907, recorded by Fleming, *The Auk* 24: 87) and Nova Scotia (Lower East Pubnico, extant specimen, August 1905). There are unconfirmed additional (mostly old) sight records for Saskatchewan, Manitoba, and Ontario. Formerly when more numerous within its normal range it probably strayed to Canada more frequently than it does today. Canadian records are presumably referable to the nominate race *E. f. forficatus* (Linnaeus).

GOSHAWK
L'Autour. *Accipiter gentilis* (Linnaeus)
Plates 16, 20. L. 20 to 26 in.

A robust, long-tailed, relatively short-winged hawk. Feathers extend halfway down front and sides of tarsus. Tail somewhat rounded. *Adults:* Upper parts dark bluish slate becoming blackish on top of head and behind eye. A light stripe extends from base of bill backward over eye to back of head. Under parts grey to whitish with dusky shaft streaks and numerous grey vermiculations. Tail crossed by three or four poorly defined blackish bars and tipped greyish. Eye red; feet yellow. *First-year immatures:* Upper parts dusky brown mixed with buffy. Light streak over eye. Tail crossed by four or five dusky bars and tipped whitish. Under parts buffy to whitish, prominently streaked with dark brown. Eye, yellowish grey.

In any plumage, separable from other similar hawks, except the Cooper's Hawk, by five emarginate primaries; and from Cooper's Hawk by the extension of feathering halfway down the tarsus. Any Canadian accipiter over 20 inches in length is almost certainly a Goshawk.

Measurements (*A. g. atricapillus*). *Adult male:* wing, 308–330 (319.1); tail, 216.5–235.5 (226.3); culmen (from cere), 21–23 (21.6); tarsus, 70–82.5 (78.4). *Adult female:* wing, 324.5–356 (347.1) mm.

Field Marks. Long tail and short rounded wings, habit of flying with short rapid flaps then sailing briefly mark it as one of our three accipiters. Large size immediately separates it from the Sharp-shinned Hawk. The Cooper's Hawk more closely approaches it in size. Adults of both Cooper's and the Goshawk have blue backs, but the light *stripe over the* *eye* and *grey underparts* identify the Goshawk. Immatures of the two are similar in colour, but the Cooper's Hawk is always somewhat smaller and slenderer.

Habitat. Forests and woodlands, perhaps preferring mixedwood types; also forest edges and clearings; hunts at low levels.

Nesting. Nest, a bulky structure of sticks with bark lining and often a few fresh twigs of evergreen, is placed 20 to 75 feet up in a tree, either deciduous or coniferous, the former preferred. Often uses same nest in successive years. *Eggs* usually 2 to 4; pale bluish white. Incubation probably about 36 to 38 days.

Range. Breeds in forested parts of Europe and Asia; and in North America from forested parts of Canada south to northwestern Mexico, Colorado, Minnesota, and western Maryland. In winter, ranges somewhat farther south.

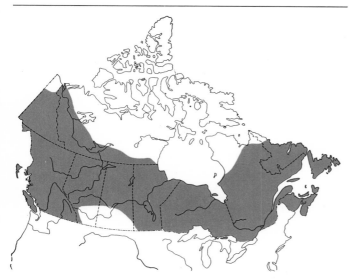

Breeding Distribution of Goshawk

Range in Canada. Breeds in wooded parts of Yukon (north to Old Crow Flats), western Mackenzie (Mackenzie Delta, Grandin River, Wood Buffalo Park), British Columbia (probably throughout, but definite breeding records are needed from the coast and coastal islands), Alberta (except southern prairies south of Rosedale), northern and middle Saskatchewan (south at least to Beaver, Spruce, and Carrot rivers), Manitoba (except extreme southwestern part; breeds south to Aweme), Ontario (south to Thunder Bay District; Mount Albert, north of Toronto; and Mallorytown Landing on St. Lawrence River); Quebec (near Chimo, Great Whale River, Pointe des Monts, Old Chelsea, Ile Jésus); Labrador (Hopedale; probably north to near tree limit); Newfoundland, New Brunswick, Prince Edward Island, and Nova Scotia; possibly southwestern Keewatin (Nueltin Lake). Stragglers (north of breeding range) to Horton River, and southeastern Baffin Island. Winters in the breeding range (north to Mackenzie Delta; and Chimo, P.Q.) and southward in varying numbers.

Subspecies. (1) *Accipiter gentilis atricapillus* (Wilson) is the form inhabiting all of Canada except w. B.C. (2) *A. g. laingi* (Taverner), a darker-coloured race, inhabits Van-

couver I. and Queen Charlotte Is. and is probably a permanent resident there, although breeding has not yet been conclusively shown.

A specimen taken at Red Bay, Lab., on November 11, 1925, has been provisionally identified as an example of the Old World race, *A. gentilis gentilis* (Linnaeus), according to Todd (1963). It has not been examined by the writer.

SHARP-SHINNED HAWK

L'Épervier brun. *Accipiter striatus* Vieillot
Plates 16, 20. L. male 10 to 12 in., female (larger than male) 12 to 14 in., therefore the smallest of the accipiters.

An accipiter less than 14 inches in total length is likely to be this species. Adults have upper parts dark blue; breast and abdomen, barred dull reddish brown and white. First-year birds have brown upper parts; whitish, heavily brown-streaked breast and abdomen. Thus very similar to Cooper's Hawk, but usually decidedly smaller, with relatively slenderer and longer legs and square-tipped tail and with cap not appreciably darker than back. Easily distinguished from the similar-sized Pigeon and Sparrow hawks by its lack of a tooth-like projection on the upper mandible and its short, rounded wings.

Measurements (*A. s. velox*). *Adult male:* wing, 152.5–173.5 (167.3); tail, 124.5–139.5 (132.5); culmen (from cere), 10–10.9 (10.5); tarsus, 47–53.5 (49.5). *Adult female:* wing, 188–206 (199.7) mm.

Field Marks. Short, rounded wings and long tail mark it as an accipiter. Almost identical with Cooper's Hawk but usually smaller; however, a large female Sharp-shin is of about the same size as a small male Cooper's Hawk. The Cooper's Hawk has the tip of the tail slightly rounded (that of the Sharp-shin is square), and the Cooper's cap is darker than the back. The similar-sized Sparrow and Pigeon hawks have longer, pointed wings of falcons, and the Sparrow Hawk, in addition, has a reddish back and tail.

Habitat. Woodland and wood edges; also, particularly in migration, hedges, bushy clearings, and shores frequented by other bird migrants.

Nesting. Nest is placed in a tree, preferably coniferous, 10 to 70 feet up. It is rather large (crow size), is made of small sticks and lined with twigs and bark. *Eggs,* usually 3 to 6; dull white or bluish white, irregularly and handsomely blotched with browns. Incubation 34 to 35 days (Nice), by both parents.

Range. Breeds from northwestern Alaska and forested parts of Canada south to northern Mexico, the Gulf Coast of United States, and Greater Antilles. Winters from extreme southern Canada to Costa Rica.

Range in Canada. Breeds in woodland in central and southern Yukon (presumably north to Old Crow), central western and southern Mackenzie (forts Resolution and Simpson; Grandin River near Mazenod Lake; occurs in summer northwest to Aklavik Range); British Columbia, Alberta (except treeless southeast); Saskatchewan (north to Stoney Rapids), central and southern Manitoba; central and southern Ontario (recorded in summer north to Moose Factory); southern and middle Quebec (north probably to

Lake Mistassini and Pointe des Monts; sight records in summer near Matamek and Natashquan; Anticosti Island), Labrador (Goose Bay), Newfoundland, New Brunswick, Prince Edward Island, and Nova Scotia. Migrates through most of southern Canada with large September concentrations passing through Point Pelee, Ontario. Winters in small numbers in coastal and southern British Columbia, southern Ontario, southern Newfoundland, and the Maritimes.

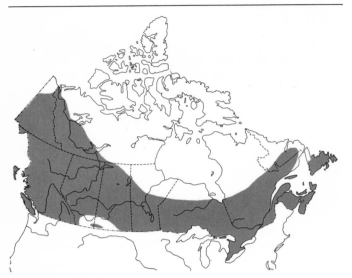
Breeding Distribution of Sharp-shinned Hawk

Subspecies. *Accipiter striatus velox* (Wilson) is the breeding subspecies of all of Canada, except the Queen Charlotte Is. (and perhaps other coastal parts of B.C.), where its place is taken by *A. s. perobscurus* Snyder, a somewhat darker subspecies.

Remarks. The Sharp-shinned and Cooper's hawks, as well as the Goshawk, feed largely on other birds and are among the few hawks that deserve the blame that unfortunately has been heaped on hawks in general. People should learn to distinguish these three species and avoid shooting by mistake the other beneficial kinds of hawks.

COOPER'S HAWK

L'Épervier de Cooper. *Accipiter cooperii* (Bonaparte)
Plates 16, 20. L. male 14 to 18; female 17 to 20 in.

Accipiter outline. Similar to the Sharp-shinned Hawk in all plumages but decidedly larger with relatively stouter legs and a rounded tail; in adults the blackish cap is more or less well defined against the colour of the back and lower neck. The Goshawk, which is decidedly larger and in adults differently coloured below, is separable by the tarsus, more than half of which is feathered, less than half in Cooper's. The Broad-winged Hawk is of about the same size as Cooper's, and immatures are similarly coloured, but the Broad-wing lacks the Cooper's heavy barring on the under side of the flight feathers and has only three outermost primaries emarginate (five in Cooper's).

Measurements. *Adult male:* wing, 217–258.5 (234.2); tail, 181–215.5 (191.5); culmen (from cere), 15–19.5 (16.9); tarsus, 60.5–70.5 (66.4). *Adult female:* wing, 241–268 (256.1) mm.

Field Marks. Accipiter outline. Intermediate in size between Sharp-shinned and Goshawk. Rounded tail and, in adults, usually somewhat darker cap separate it under good conditions from the usually smaller Sharp-shin. The Goshawk is larger and heavier, the bluish-backed adults with greyish (not reddish) under parts. Young Broad-wings have a buteo outline and lack heavy barring on under side of flight feathers.

Habitat. Similar to Sharp-shinned Hawk but, according to Palmer (1949), found more often in woodland and less in forest edges than its smaller relative.

Nesting. Nest, constructed of sticks and often lined with bark and sometimes a little moss or grass, is placed 20 to 60 feet up in a coniferous or deciduous tree. *Eggs,* generally 3 to 5; greenish white, either unmarked or slightly spotted with brown.

Range. Breeds from southern Canada south to northwestern Mexico, south-central Texas, central Alabama, and central Florida. Winters mainly from northern United States south to Costa Rica.

Range in Canada. Breeds in southern British Columbia (Quamichan Lake, Okanagan Landing, Burnaby, Nita Lake, Lac La Hache), southern Alberta (Seebe; probably Banff and Jasper parks), southern and central Saskatchewan (Spirit Lake, Yorkton, Fort Qu'Appelle, Armley, Carlton), southern Manitoba (Aweme, Hillside Beach, Deer Lodge, Fort Garry), southern Ontario (definite breeding records north to Ottawa, Port Sydney, Port Arthur, and Rainy River; recorded, but not known to breed, north to Casummit Lake and Timmins), southern Quebec (Lake St. Louis, Ile Jésus), rarely in New Brunswick (Bayswater), and very rarely Nova Scotia (Black River).

Winters in southern British Columbia and occasionally in southern Ontario, rarely north to Ottawa.

Remarks. Like the Sharp-shinned, this is one of the few hawk species considered detrimental to man's interests.

Breeding Distribution of Cooper's Hawk

RED-TAILED HAWK (includes Harlan's Hawk)
La Buse à queue rousse. *Buteo jamaicensis* (Gmelin)
Plates 17, 19. L. male 19 to 22; female 21 to 24 in.

In parts of western Canada highly variable in appearance. Breeding populations from Ontario east are relatively uniform, and the following description applies to eastern birds (*see also* Subspecies). *Adults* (*B. j. borealis*): Above dark brown variously intermixed with white and rufous. Upper surface of tail, chestnut with narrow black subterminal band and whitish tip. From corner of mouth down side of neck a dusky stripe. Under parts whitish with broad (often poorly defined) band across abdomen, formed by blackish longitudinal markings of varying density and extent. Under side of tail greyish, sometimes faintly barred. *Immatures:* Similar to adults but upper side of tail pale brownish (sometimes tinged reddish), crossed by ten or more narrow dusky bars; general coloration darker, contrasting more with whites.

In the hand, separable in all plumages from Rough-legged and Ferruginous hawks by its half-feathered (instead of fully-feathered) tarsus. Swainson's Hawk has three outermost primaries sharply emarginate, Red-tail four (Fig. 35).

Fig. 35 Four emarginate primaries of Red-tailed Hawk

Measurements (*B. j. borealis*). *Adult male:* wing, 340–390 (361.4); tail, 198.5–225.5 (208); culmen (from cere), 22–28 (24.5); tarsus, 81–86 (83.6). *Adult female:* wing, 354.5–384 (371.5) mm.

Field Marks. The buteo outline with broad, rounded wings and broad tail shows well in flight. Adults, with upper side of tail chestnut, are the only large hawk so marked. Both adults and immatures (except dark phase) show a more or less well-defined belt across the *abdomen*. Swainson's Hawk, of the West, also has a dark band on the under parts, but it is across the *breast*, and in soaring the wings tilt somewhat upward (held horizontal in Red-tail). Rough-legged Hawks with dark abdominal bands have a conspicuous black crescent on the under side of the spread wing near the wrist. Dark-phased individuals of the Red-tail are often difficult to distinguish in life from dark-phased Rough-legged, Ferruginous, and Swainson's hawks, but red in the tail of the adult (often absent in *harlani* and *kriderii*) marks

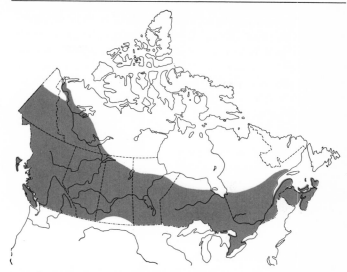

Breeding Distribution of Red-tailed Hawk

the Red-tail. Swainson's soars on slightly uptilted more-pointed wings.

Habitat. Both woodland and open country but usually in the vicinity of trees during the nesting season, although cliff ledges are used for nesting where trees are not available.

Nesting. Nest usually in trees, either deciduous or coniferous, and frequently well up. Will use low trees where large ones are not available; also cliff ledges. Nest a bulky structure of sticks, often lined with bark. *Eggs*, 2 to 4, occasionally more; whitish usually lightly spotted with browns. Incubation about 28 days (A. C. Bent).

Range. Central Alaska and Canada north to near limit of large forests (except Newfoundland), south through United States and Mexico to Panama and the West Indies.

Range in Canada (includes *harlani*). Breeds from central Yukon (commonly southwestern part, scarcer farther east, breeding north to Fortymile and Fort Selkirk), northwestern and southwestern Mackenzie (Aklavik; Fort Norman; Slave River; near Fort Smith), northern Saskatchewan, north-central Manitoba (Ilford), central Ontario, and southwestern Quebec (north to Mistassini Lake and Mingan) south through southern British Columbia, southern Alberta, southern Saskatchewan, southern Ontario, southern Quebec, New Brunswick, Prince Edward Island, and Nova Scotia. Winters in small numbers in southwestern British Columbia, southern Ontario, and occasionally in the Maritimes.

Subspecies. (1) *Buteo jamaicensis borealis* (Gmelin), which breeds from w. Ont. east, has a plain red tail usually with black subterminal bar, as described above. (2) *B. j. calurus* Cassin is generally more heavily coloured, sometimes with dark reds intermixed, especially on breast, and has both dark and light phases with various intermediate stages. It breeds from middle Manitoba w. to interior B.C. (3) *B. j. kriderii* Hoopes, of the southern prairies is characterized by variable, often substantial, amounts of white in the plumage including the tail, and a dilution of colour of dark parts. (4) *B. j. harlani* (Audubon), of Yukon and northern B.C., is a heavily pigmented form, characterized especially by the tail which is mottled and freckled with black, grey, white, and red in various proportions and with longitudinal streaks instead of transverse bars. Under parts vary from black to mainly white, and almost no two are coloured alike, there being also various admixtures of white in the upper plumage and tail. (5) *B. j. alascensis* Grinnell, of the Queen Charlotte Is., resembles *calurus* but is smaller. (I have not seen adequate material to appraise *B. j. abieticola* Todd, *Annals Carnegie Mus.* 31: 291.)

RED-SHOULDERED HAWK

La Buse à épaulettes rousses. *Buteo lineatus* (Gmelin)
Plates 17, 19. L. male 18 to 23; female 19 to 24 in.

Buteo outline. Intermediate in size between Red-tailed and Broad-winged hawks. Four outermost primaries emarginate (inner web abruptly cut away near tip) thus separating it from other buteos, except the Red-tailed Hawk. Separable from the Red-tail by the tarsus (half-feathered in the Red-tail, much less than half in Red-shoulder). *Adults:* Upper parts brown mixed with buffy and whitish, 'shoulder' of wing (lesser coverts) mainly reddish brown. Tail above, blackish crossed by five or more narrow white bars and tipped with white; below, whitish or greyish inconspicuously banded. Breast and abdomen barred and streaked with reddish brown and white, many feathers with black shaft streaks. *Immatures:* Upper parts darker brown than in adults and lacking most of the reddish brown colour (also much restricted on lesser coverts). Tail above, brown crossed by numerous inconspicuous lighter bands which are often mixed with rusty. Breast and abdomen, whitish striped with brown.

Measurements (*B. l. lineatus*). *Adult male:* wing, 311–326 (318.3); tail, 194–208.5 (201.2); culmen (from cere), 20–22 (21.1); tarsus, 72–80 (77.3). *Adult female:* wing, 331–346 (340.1) mm.

Field Marks. Often seen (like the Red-tail) soaring slowly in wide circles. Buteo outline but less stocky with relatively longer tail than in Red-tail and Broad-wing. Adults when perched usually show a distinctive checkered blackish and white area on the side of the folded wing. Adults are reddish-breasted, and the upper side of the tail is crossed by several narrow but conspicuous white bars, thus differing from the Red-tail. An adult of the smaller Broad-winged Hawk is similarly marked, but the white bars across the tail are much broader. Young Broad-wings are smaller and stockier with a shorter tail. In flight overhead, Red-shoulders show a whitish area near the ends of the spread wings (*see* plate), but this is not always a reliable diagnostic feature. The red 'shoulders' are diagnostic but are hard to see in life.

Habitat. Woodland, particularly in low country; woodlots and groves near open fields and farming country.

Nesting. The nest, a bulky structure of sticks lined with bark strips, leaves, lichens, often green twigs with leaves attached, is placed from 25 to 60 feet up in either a deciduous or coniferous tree. *Eggs*, 2 to 4; dull white, variously (sometimes boldly) marked with browns. Incubation variously reported 25 to 28 days, by both sexes.

Range. Northern California to northwestern Baja California; and from eastern Nebraska, Wisconsin, Michigan,

southern Ontario, and southern Quebec south to the Florida Keys, Gulf coast of United States, and eastern Mexico. In winter retreats from northernmost breeding grounds.

Range in Canada. Breeds in southern Ontario (north at least to Port Sydney, Lake Nipissing, and Ottawa region), southwestern Quebec (Hull region, Montreal, Lennoxville, Hatley, Quebec City), and rarely southern New Brunswick

Breeding Distribution of Red-shouldered Hawk

(Washademoak Lake). Sight records without breeding evidence north to Algoma district, Timmins, and Lowbush, Ontario; and Blue Sea Lake, Quebec. Occasional in winter in southern Ontario (Toronto, Hamilton, Point Pelee).

Subspecies. *Buteo lineatus lineatus* (Gmelin) is the only subspecies known to occur in Canada.

BROAD-WINGED HAWK

La Petite Buse. *Buteo platypterus* (Vieillot)
Plate 16, 19. L. male 13.5 to 16.5; female 15.0 to 18.5 in.

Shaped like a Red-tailed Hawk but much smaller, only three primaries emarginate, and tarsus less than half feathered. *Adults:* Dark brown above. Tail brownish black above with two visible light grey or whitish bands across it (the one farther to the rear broadest) and narrowly tipped whitish. Dark streak down lower jaw. Breast reddish brown, usually with some white (but sometimes almost solid brown). Flanks and abdomen barred brown and white. (*Note:* A melanistic colour phase is known in both adults and young, but it is very rare.) *First-year young:* Upper parts dark brown, head and neck streaked with buff, wing coverts and feathers of back edged with same. Upper tail coverts largely mixed with white. Tail above, greyish brown faintly crossed by five or six narrow dusky bars and narrowly tipped with white; tail underneath, pale grey narrowly barred with dusky, especially on inner webs. Under parts creamy white, streaked with dark brown, but brown streaks sparser or absent on mid-breast, mid-abdomen, and under tail coverts.

Measurements. *Adult male:* wing, 239–272.5 (263.4); tail, 149–162.5 (155.1); culmen (from cere), 17.5–20 (18.4);

tarsus, 59.5–67.5 (63.4). *Adult female:* wing, 279–291.5 (284) mm.

Field Marks. A small crow-sized buteo. Resembles Red-shouldered Hawk, but in any plumage its shorter tail distinguishes it. In adults the whitish rear tail band is much broader than in the Red-shoulder. The Broad-winged is a smaller hawk than the Red-tail. Its rather melancholy call, in a minor key, slightly suggestive of a Wood Pewee, is readily recognizable among woodland hawks.

Habitat. Forests and woodlands.

Nesting. The nest, usually rather small and often poorly constructed (sometimes uses nest of Crow or other large bird), is made of sticks and twigs, sparsely lined with bark and mosses; often twigs bearing green leaves are added. Generally 20 to 40 feet up in either deciduous or coniferous tree. *Eggs,* 2 to 4; variable in colour but usually whitish, blotched and spotted with reddish brown and purple. Incubation 23 to 25 days (F. L. Burns), by both sexes. One brood annually.

Range. Breeds in woodland from Alberta east across southern Canada and south to eastern Texas, the United States Gulf coast, southern Florida, and the West Indies. Winters mainly from southern Mexico to Colombia, Venezuela, Ecuador, northern Peru, and western Brazil. Occasionally farther north.

Range in Canada. Breeds in wooded parts of central Alberta (Miquelon Lakes north at least to Lesser Slave region and Cold Lake), central Saskatchewan (Niska Lake, Prince Albert, Nipawin), southern Manitoba (Red River valley, Carman, Portage la Prairie, Lake St. Martin; probably north to about The Pas), southern and central Ontario (Favourable Lake and Fraserdale southward), southern Quebec (Amos, Lake St. John, Montreal, Hull, Blue Sea Lake), New Brunswick (Grand Manan, Saint John, St. Leonard), and rarely in Nova Scotia (near Halifax). Reported without evidence of breeding north to Lake Athabasca, Alberta and Saskatchewan; Moose Factory, Ontario; and eastern Gaspé Peninsula (Mount St. Alban, Cap Bon Ami).

Breeding Distribution of Broad-winged Hawk

In autumn migration, spectacular numbers are sometimes observable at Hawk Cliff, just east of Port Stanley, Ontario, and smaller numbers at other points on the north shore of Lake Erie and western Lake Ontario, especially between September 18 and 23.

Subspecies. *Buteo platypterus platypterus* (Vieillot) is the only subspecies found in Canada.

SWAINSON'S HAWK

La Buse de Swainson. *Buteo swainsoni* Bonaparte
Plates 17, 19. L. male 18.75 to 20.60; female 18.9 to 22.0 in.

Slightly smaller than the Red-tailed Hawk, but separable from it and the Red-shouldered Hawk in any plumage by three (instead of four) emarginate outer primaries. The differently proportioned Goshawk has five emarginate primaries. Rough-legged and Ferruginous hawks have completely feathered legs; those of Swainson are less than half-feathered. Plumage of adult extremely variable. *Adult male* (pale phase): Upper parts dark brown usually with rusty feather margins; crown and back of neck generally with white showing through. Tail above, greyish crossed by numerous narrow bands of dusky and tipped whitish. Outer upper tail coverts, whitish barred with brown. Under parts with broad band of cinnamon or russet across breast; throat white; abdomen buffy white, its sides usually barred with brown. Feet yellow. *Adult female* (pale phase): Similar to adult male but breast band often (not always) darker, less rufous. *Adults* (dark phase): Upper and under parts brownish black, except under tail coverts, which are buffy white, barred with dark brown (many intermediate stages between these pale and dark extremes are common). A rufous phase occurs in which the under parts are heavily washed and barred with reddish brown. *Juvenal* (apparently worn through first winter): Upper parts, dark brown mixed with buff or white; forehead whitish; cheeks buffy with dusky streaks; crown, nape, and sides of neck, streaked blackish, buffy, and whitish; outer upper-tail coverts (except dark phase) with more or less white; tail similar to adult; under parts buffy, heavily spotted on breast and upper abdomen with blackish brown; throat whitish with sparse dusky streaks; thighs barred dusky. In dark phase the upper parts are darker, white of upper tail coverts much more restricted, and under parts blackish spotted with tawny.

Measurements. *Adult male:* wing, 360–396.5 (378.6); tail, 181–204.5 (189.5); culmen (from cere), 21.5–23 (22.4); tarsus, 62–73 (67.3). *Adult female:* wing, 390–418 (403.1) mm.

Field Marks. A large western open-country buteo, the commonest large hawk of the prairies. Similar to the Red-tailed Hawk in size but has narrower, more pointed wings and never a red tail. Extremely variable in appearance, but most (pale phase) adults show a broad *band across the breast* which is diagnostic (Red-tailed and Rough-legged hawks have band across *abdomen*). In flight a narrow whitish area is usually present on the sides of the rump (but very different from well-defined large white rump patch of Marsh Hawk); when gliding, wings are held slightly above horizontal (*see also* Marsh Hawk and Turkey Vulture). Dark-phased and immature Swainson's resemble

PLATE 11

other dark buteos, but the shape and angle of its wings and whitish rump area, when discernible, are helpful.

Habitat. Open dry country of the West: plains, prairies, dry mountain valleys and foothills; less commonly, tundra of the low Arctic. Sparse woods or even single small trees or bushes are adequate for nesting purposes.

Nesting. The bulky nest of sticks, lined with finer materials, is built in either a large or small tree, usually deciduous (sometimes bushes), at heights varying from ground level to considerable heights depending on local conditions. The same nest is often used in successive years. *Eggs*, usually 2, sometimes 3; pale bluish to dull white, most frequently sparingly and irregularly marked with brown, less often immaculate. Incubation about 28 days, by both sexes (A. C. Bent).

Range. Breeds from Alaska (locally) east to northwestern Mackenzie and Manitoba; east to Illinois (rarely); and south to northern Mexico. Winters mainly in Argentina.

Breeding Distribution of Swainson's Hawk

Range in Canada. Summer resident, spring and fall transient. Breeds in British Columbia (very locally: Okanagan Landing, Dog Creek. Recorded in summer at Swan Lake, Okanagan Valley; Chilcotin River; Telegraph Creek; Atlin), Yukon (no definite breeding record but occurs in summer sparsely near Whitehorse, Carcross, Morley River, Dawson, Porcupine River at Yukon-Alaska boundary), Mackenzie (range poorly known: old breeding record near Fort Anderson and on Onion River near Lockhart River), Alberta (commonly on prairies of southern part; occasionally Waterton Lake Park; observed in summer in Banff Park, Joussard, Grouard, High Prairie, Saskatoon Lake, and La Glace), southern Saskatchewan (Carlton, Prince Albert), and southwestern Manitoba (Treesbank, Carberry, Aweme). Recorded north to Bernard Harbour, Dolphin and Union Strait, Mackenzie, September 9, 1914. Casual on coast of British Columbia (Victoria, Union Bay) and in eastern Canada: Ontario (Moose Factory, Toronto, Ottawa) and southern Quebec (Montreal and Ste-Anne-de-la Pérade).

Remarks. This is the common hawk of the prairies. It is

1 Ring-necked Duck,
  (a) female
  (b) adult male in
      breeding plumage

2 Lesser Scaup,
  (a) immature male
  (b) adult male in
      breeding plumage
  (c) adult female

3 Greater Scaup,
  (a) adult male
  (b) adult female

4 Canvasback,
  (a) adult male in
      breeding plumage
  (b) female

5 Redhead,
  (a) adult male in
      breeding plumage
  (b) female

1a

1b

2a

2b

2b

2c

2b

3a

3a

3b

3a

4a

5a

5a

4b

5a

5b

4a

Crosby

frequently seen perched on a roadside fence post or quartering leisurely over the grasslands in search of rodents, which make up most of its food. It is an efficient and tireless destroyer of gophers, mice, and, to some extent, grasshoppers. Like all our buteos, it is an extremely valuable bird.

ROUGH-LEGGED HAWK
La Buse pattue. *Buteo lagopus* (Pontoppidan)
Plates 17, 19. L. male 19.5 to 22; female 21.5 to 23.5 in.

Legs feathered to toes. Plumage extremely variable, including pale and dark phases and various intermediates. Separable in all plumages from other Canadian hawks except the Ferruginous (and obviously distinctive Golden Eagle) by its *completely feathered legs* to the base of the toes. In all plumages it is distinguishable from the Ferruginous Hawk by bill shape, the bill being markedly narrower at the gape in the Rough-legged Hawk, broader in the Ferruginous Hawk when viewed from above (Fig. 36).

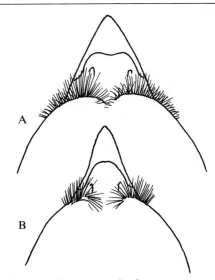

Fig. 36 Bill (viewed from above) of
    (A) Ferruginous Hawk
    (B) Rough-legged Hawk

In PALE PHASE (commoner in most localities) the adult male generally (not always) differs from the adult female in having abdomen barred rather than blotched or patched with dark brown, and his tail tends to have several narrow dark bands on the posterior half alternating with whitish (female one or more broad band). For detailed analysis of sexual dimorphism, *see* Cade (*Condor* 57: 313–346). Immatures of the *pale phase* resemble adults but lack bars on the tibiae; have the terminal half of tail unbarred dark brown; have a better-defined, more extensive abdominal band than even adult females; and the whitish of under parts is buffier. DARK PHASE: Uniform blackish brown above and below, but usually with some concealed white on basal third of tail and some light barring on rest of tail. Tail, tipped whitish. Primaries usually have some white on inner webs, and there is considerable and variable white on under wing surface.

Measurements. *Adult male:* wing, 380–412.5 (401.5); tail, 195–223 (208.9); culmen (from cere), 21.5–24.5 (22.3); tarsus, 64.5–71.5 (68.1). *Adult female:* wing, 412–434 (422.8) mm.

Field Marks. A large, long-winged buteo of the open country (*see also* Ferruginous Hawk) with a habit of hovering in the air over one spot like an Osprey or Sparrow Hawk. Light-phase (usually commoner) birds have a large dark wrist mark on under side of wing, white base to the tail, and (in immatures and most adult females) a conspicuous dark patch on the belly. Dark-phase birds are similar to other dark-phase buteos but show considerable white on the under side of wing and in spread wing tips; the habit of hovering is also helpful in recognition. Frequently when hovering the legs are dangled, showing *fully feathered legs.* The Ferruginous Hawk of the prairies is the only other hawk with legs feathered to toes (*see* Ferruginous Hawk). Dark-phase Swainson's lacks conspicuously white areas in the under surface of the wings.

Habitat. In summer inhabits the low Arctic and Subarctic, especially where escarpments, rocky outcrops, cliff ledges, ravines, steep river-banks, or low trees provide nesting places. In migration and winter, it prefers open country such as fields and marshes.

Nesting. Nest is made of sticks, grasses, and weed stalks (depending on availability of material) and is placed on cliff ledges, boulders, shelves in steep river-banks, and, when available, in trees at heights of 20 to 30 feet; occasionally on flat ground. Nest is used in successive years, resulting sometimes in large accumulations of debris. *Eggs,* 2 to 6 (usually 3 to 5); greenish white, variously blotched, streaked, smeared, or spotted with browns. Incubation period about 31 days (*in* Witherby).

Breeding Distribution of Rough-legged Hawk

Range. Panboreal. Breeds from Alaska eastward across low arctic and subarctic Canada; northern Scandinavia, northern Russia, and northern Siberia. In North America, it winters south to California, New Mexico, Oklahoma, Tennessee, and Virginia; casually farther south.

Range in Canada. Breeds in northern Yukon (Herschel Island, Old Crow); across the Arctic Archipelago; north rarely to Prince Patrick Island and Bylot Island, and east to southeastern Baffin Island (York Sound); northern and eastern Mackenzie (Mackenzie Delta, Anderson River, Coronation Gulf, Bathurst Inlet, Perry River, Dickson Canyon, Helen's Falls on Hanbury River, Artillery Lake); Keewatin (Back River, Baker Lake, Nueltin Lake, Beverly Lake); northern Manitoba (Churchill); Southampton Island; east coast of Hudson Bay (Long Island, Christie Island); northern and southeastern Quebec (Great Whale River, Chimo, Seal Lake, Lac Aulneau, Indian House Lake; outer north shore of Gulf of St. Lawrence; Wolf Bay eastward; reported formerly and doubtfully at Pointe des Monts); Labrador (Cape Chidley, Davis Inlet, near Hopedale, Ailik, and Red Bay), and Newfoundland (locally: Meagle Mountain, Partridgeberry Hills). Probably northern Ontario (Cape Henrietta Maria). Recorded in summer in southern Yukon, southern James Bay, northern Lake Superior, and Anticosti Island, but breeding data lacking.

Winters in irregular numbers in southern British Columbia, southern Prairie Provinces, southern Ontario, southern Quebec, Newfoundland, and the Maritime Provinces.

Subspecies. *Buteo lagopus s. johannis* (Gmelin) is the only subspecies of known occurrence in Canada.

FERRUGINOUS HAWK

La Buse rouilleuse. *Buteo regalis* (Gray)
Plates 17, 19. L. Male 22.3 to 23.0; female 23.8 to 24.8 in.

Tarsus feathered to toes, thus differing from other hawks except Rough-legged, from which it differs in its markedly wider bill and in plumage. Both pale and dark colour phases occur, the former commoner. *Adults* (pale phase): Upper parts, brown streaked with white on head and neck, much orange-cinnamon about shoulders, back, and on upper tail coverts. Tail, white to greyish often with ochraceous wash of variable extent, unbanded. Cheeks, brown streaked with white. Throat, breast, and abdomen white, usually with sparse brown markings on abdomen and sides. Thighs, ochraceous barred with dark brown. Wing lining, white mixed with ochraceous and dark brown. *Adults* (dark phase): Dark brown, some of the feathers edged with cinnamon. Tail similar to pale phase but often more heavily washed with dark brown. *First-year immatures* (light phase): Somewhat like adults but orange-cinnamon of upper parts greatly reduced and confined to feather edges. Under parts white but with dark brown streaks on breast (variable in extent, often absent) and brown spots, sometimes blotches on sides of abdomen. Thighs very different from adult: white, spotted with dark brown. Tail grey (white basally) and tipped whitish, the grey area indistinctly banded on upper side. *First-year immatures* (dark phase): Somewhat like dark-phase adults but tail crossed by indistinct bars and tipped whitish.

Measurements. *Adult male:* wing, 415.5–439.5 (426.8); tail, 224.5–229 (226.5); culmen (from cere), 26.5–27.5 (27); tarsus, 82.5–89.5 (86). *Adult female:* wing, 415–465 (437.5) mm.

Field Marks. A large buteo of the southern prairies. Pale-phased adults are separable from similar buteos by the reddish brown colour about the shoulders, back, and rump; extensively white under parts with *contrasting dark thighs;* and unbanded plain white or greyish tail. Dark-phase birds have uniformly dark bodies with whitish or greyish tail, usually definitely lighter than the back, and large areas of white on under side of the flight feathers. In flight often shows flash of white near ends of upper side of wing. The Rough-leg shows this but is otherwise differently marked and is not likely to be on the southern prairies in summer. Pale-phase immatures are extensively white below but lack the diagnostic contrasting thigh colour of the adults.

Habitat. Plains, prairies, and badlands.

Nesting. Nest is of sticks, twigs, and sometimes sagebrush roots and is placed in trees, on ledges of badlands and river cutbanks, and on hillsides. Nests are used in successive years, sometimes becoming immense. *Eggs*, most often 3 to 5; white with usually bold blotches and spots of brown. Incubation said to last 28 days (A. C. Bent).

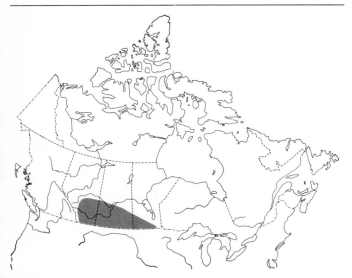

Breeding Distribution of Ferruginous Hawk

Range. Breeds from eastern Washington and southern parts of the Canadian Prairie Provinces south to Nevada, New Mexico, and northwestern Texas. Winters mainly from southwestern United States to central Mexico; casually farther north.

Range in Canada. Breeds (much scarcer than formerly) in southern Alberta (east of the Rocky Mountains, north to near Alliance), southern Saskatchewan (north, formerly at least, to vicinity of Carlton), and southwestern Manitoba (Spruce Woods Forest Reserve).

GOLDEN EAGLE

L'Aigle doré. *Aquila chrysaëtos* (Linnaeus)
Plates 15, 20. L. male 30 to 35; female 35 to 41 in.
Wingspread of male, 75 to 84; of female, 82 to 92 in.

Separable in all plumages from the Bald Eagle by the legs, which are *feathered to the toes* (Fig. 37). *Adults:* Mainly dark brown (fading paler), legs usually paler. Nape and hind-neck, tawny or golden brown. Tail dark brown, base paler and with several poorly defined ashy bands. Bill dusky. Cere and feet yellow. *Immatures:* Similar to adults but with more white in tail. Juvenal is darker and has basal two-thirds of tail white and considerable white in the secondaries. Older immatures as they approach maturity have decreasing amounts of white in tail and wing.

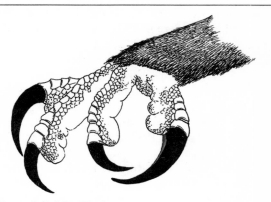

Fig. 37 Foot of Golden Eagle

Measurements. *Adult male:* wing, 555–610 (580.5); tail, 320–360 (337.4); culmen (from cere), 37–41 (39.5); tarsus, 101–122 (111.6) (one specimen 130). *Adult female:* wing, 620–666 (633.2) mm (Friedmann).

Field Marks. Great size and much more massive bill separate it from dark-phase buteos. In soaring the wings are held horizontal, thus differing from vultures, and the eagle's head is feathered. Ospreys always have white under parts. The adult Bald Eagle, with its white head and tail, is readily separable from the Golden. Many immature Golden Eagles have a white tail with a sharply contrasting dark terminal band and show a white area in the spread wing (Plate 20). Adults are a bit difficult to distinguish from young Bald Eagles, but often the 'golden' back of the neck of the Golden Eagle is visible. The fully feathered legs of the Golden are diagnostic but are hard to see in the field.

Habitat. Variable. Mountainous terrain, foothills with grassy areas inhabited by ground squirrels, the vicinity of cliffs in various situations from those on prairie river valleys to sea cliffs. In winter and migration, it hunts over various types of country, including plains.

Nesting. Nest, usually on a cliff, sometimes in a tree, is constructed of sticks and similar coarse material and lined with grasses, weeds, mosses, and leaves. When used for a number of years it may become very large. *Eggs*, usually 2; white or pale buffy, usually more or less spotted and blotched with brown. Incubation 43 days (Walker and Walker).

Range. Holarctic. Locally distributed in North America from Alaska and Canada south to southern United States and central Mexico; also found across Europe and Asia south to northern Africa.

Range in Canada. Scarce, local permanent resident. No longer occupies many of its former breeding localities in the East. Less rare in mountains of the West. *Breeds* locally in Yukon (Sheep Creek Canyon and elsewhere in Kluane

PLATE 13

Game Sanctuary; widely distributed in small numbers in southern half and north to the coast); Mackenzie (Mackenzie Delta; Anderson River; Horton River; near Fort Reliance); British Columbia (mostly east of coast range: Tank Creek, near Merritt; Langley Lake; McIntyre Creek; rarely on coast: Upper Campbell Lake); Alberta (mainly in mountains: Old Fort Point, Sheep Creek, Cascade Mountain, Lake Louise; also reported on Red Deer River in Brooks region; reported formerly from Edmonton region); Saskatchewan (Stone River, Beechy, Snakebite Coulee, Big Muddy Valley, Killdeer Badlands); Manitoba (Cochrane River 40 mi. north of Brochet; Hell Gate Gorge); Ontario (Sutton Lake, Cape Henrietta Maria; probably Pipestone Lake. Formerly Thunder Cape and near York branch of Madawaska River; Mazinaw Lake; Schooner Lake); Quebec (Sugluk Inlet; Finger Lake – Leaf Bay region; formerly Pointe des Monts, Anticosti Island, Baie St. Paul, Mont Notre Dame, Gaspé Peninsula); and Labrador (Lake Michikamau); probably Keewatin (recorded as occurring at Back River near Wolf Rapids; Repulse Bay; and inland from Eskimo Point). Very rare visitor to New Brunswick, Nova Scotia, and Prince Edward Island. Casual in Newfoundland (St. John's, January 31, 1951).

Winters in much of the breeding range.

Subspecies. *Aquila chrysaëtos canadensis* (Linnaeus), the only race known in North America.

[**Gray Sea Eagle.** L'Aigle gris. *Haliaeetus albicilla* (Linnaeus). Hypothetical. Sight records on Cumberland Sound, Baffin Island, October 1877; and in spring, 1878, when a pair allegedly nested there (Kumlien, *U.S. Nat. Mus. Bull.* 15: 82). Birds resembling this species at Pangnirtung, Baffin Island, described by policeman, no date, to Soper (1928). Said to have bred at Okak, Labrador, by Weiz (1866, *Proc. Boston Soc. Nat. Hist.* 10, p. 267). An immature male dated March 18, 1898, said by a taxidermist to have been taken on Vancouver Island, B.C. (Bishop, 1905, *The Auk* 22: 79–80). Although some of these records, particularly those from Cumberland Sound, seem convincing, unfortunately none is completely satisfactory.]

BALD EAGLE

L'Aigle à tête blanche
Haliaeetus leucocephalus (Linnaeus)
Plates 15, 20. L. male 30 to 34; wingspread 72 to 85 in.
L. female 35 to 37; wingspread 79 to 90 in.

Legs only partly feathered (Fig. 38). Bill relatively longer than in Golden Eagle. *Adults:* Dark brown with pure white head, neck, tail, and upper tail coverts. Bill and feet yellow. *Immature:* Requires about four years to attain pure white head and tail. In first year very dark brown all over, but white bases of feathers of under parts show through, giving mottled effect. White on head and tail increases with successive plumages until pure white head and tail are attained. Separable from Golden Eagle, in any plumage, by legs which are not feathered completely to toes.

Measurements (*H. l. alascanus*). *Adult male:* wing, 561–577 (568.4); tail, 277.5–283.5 (282.2); culmen (from cere), 48.5–53 (50.1); tarsus, 84–91 (88.5). *Adult female:* wing, 600–614.5 (605.6) mm.

Field Marks. Great size and markings of adult are un-

1 Oldsquaw,
   (a) male in summer
   (b) female in summer
   (c) male in winter
   (d) female in winter

2 Harlequin Duck,
   (a) adult male in breeding plumage
   (b) male in 'eclipse' plumage
   (c) female

3 Common Scoter,
   (a) adult male
   (b) female

4 Surf Scoter,
   (a) adult male
   (b) female

5 White-winged Scoter,
   (a) adult male
   (b) female

6 Common Eider,
   (a) female
   (b) adult male in breeding plumage

7 King Eider,
   (a) adult male in breeding plumage
   (b) female

1a
1b
1c
1d
2a
2b
2c
3b
4a
4b
5a
5b
6a
6b
7a
7b

Crosby

mistakable. Immatures are more difficult. Osprey has white under parts. Vultures have unfeathered head. Longer bill and superior size separate it from the dark buteos. Most likely to be confused with Golden Eagle (*see* Plates 15, 20).

Habitat. Usually the vicinity of water: larger rivers, lakes, sea-coasts, and the adjacent countryside.

Nesting. Mostly in trees, frequently near the top; more rarely on cliff ledges. Nest, a large structure of sticks and weeds with a wide variety of trash as lining material. As nests are used for many years, they may become huge. *Eggs*, usually 2 (sometimes 1 or 3); dull white and small for so large a bird. Incubation about 35 days (F. H. Herrick) by both sexes.

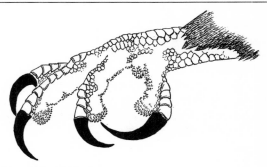

Fig. 38 Foot of Bald Eagle

Range. Breeds from northwestern Alaska and central Canada south to southern United States and Baja California. Winters from Alaska and southern Canada southward to, or beyond, southern limits of breeding range.

Range in Canada. Locally distributed breeder and, in southern parts, winter resident; commonest along the Pacific and (somewhat less so) Atlantic coasts. Breeds locally in Yukon (Aishihik Lake, Johnson's Crossing, probably north

Breeding Distribution of Bald Eagle

to Porcupine River); Mackenzie (Mackenzie Delta, Lockhart and Anderson rivers, Lake Hardisty, Great Bear River, Fort Rae, Hornby Channel); British Columbia (commonest on coast; locally but widely distributed in interior); Alberta (northern half and in southwestern mountains); Saskatchewan (mainly northern half: Lake Athabasca, Reindeer Lake, Candle Lake, Emma Lake, Grove Lake, Middle Lake; formerly at least in southwestern corner: Little Frenchman Creek); Manitoba (Eyrie Lake, Landing Lake, Churchill, Cedar Lake, Moose Lake); central and southern Ontario (north at least to Lake of the Woods; Gaherty Island, near Kenora; Lake Nipigon; Swastika; probably Little Abitibi Lake); southern and central Quebec (north at least to Anticosti Island, Mascanin or Jalobert Bay); southern Labrador (Petitsikapau Lake; adults in summer reported on Hamilton River below Grand Falls; Cartwright's mention of nesting eagles may refer to Osprey); Newfoundland; New Brunswick; Nova Scotia; and Prince Edward Island (Souris district).

Recorded in summer north to Old Crow, Yukon; Windy River, Keewatin; Cocos Lake and Moose Factory, Ontario; Lake Waswanipi, Lake Mistassini, Knob Lake, and near Ungava Bay, Quebec. Winters north to northern British Columbia, Alberta, southern Ontario, southern Quebec, southern Newfoundland (Baccalieu, Notre Dame Bay), and the Maritime Provinces.

Subspecies. (1) *Haliaeetus leucocephalus alascanus* Townsend is the breeding subspecies all across Canada. (2) *H. l. leucocephalus* (Linnaeus), a slightly smaller subspecies, is a non-breeding visitor to Que. (St. Germaine; Lac St. Jean Co.), N.B. (Leger Brook, Millbank, Chipman), N.S. (Halifax, East Jeddore), and P.E.I. (Kings Co.) between May 6 and October 18.

Remarks. The Bald Eagle is a large majestic bird which has declined alarmingly in recent years. It is a scavenger more than a predator, subsisting mainly on fish. It is commonest along the sea-coasts, where cast-ups from the sea supply most of its food requirements. Occasionally it makes its own kills and sometimes it robs the Osprey of its finny prey. On occasion, usually when fish food is not available, it may take a few birds.

MARSH HAWK

Le Busard des marais. *Circus cyaneus* (Linnaeus)
Plates 15, 20. L. male 17.5 to 20; female 19 to 24 in.

Head with partial facial disc slightly suggestive of an owl. Legs long and slender; wings and tail, long in proportion to body size. Well-defined white rump patch (upper tail coverts) present in all plumages except downy. *Adult male:* Head, neck, and upper parts, bluish grey becoming blackish on wing tips; contrasting *white rump patch* (upper tail coverts); tail grey with narrow dusky bands. Breast, abdomen, and thighs white, sparsely spotted with rusty. Under wing coverts mainly white, contrasting with blackish tips. Eye and legs yellow. *Adult female:* Upper parts dark brown with intermixture of cinnamon on scapulars and some wing coverts; neck streaked brown and buffy; conspicuous white rump patch; tail crossed by five to seven dusky bars. Under parts, buffy white streaked with brown, mainly on throat and breast. Under side of flight feathers with alternating light and dusky bars. Eye pale yellowish to greyish brown;

legs yellow. *Immature* (first fall and winter): Resembles adult female but darker and more richly coloured. Light markings on wing coverts, head, neck, and outer tail feathers, deeper cinnamon. Tail crossed by four or five bars. Under parts, rich rusty brown and less extensively, less heavily streaked. Eye dark brown.

Measurements. *Adult male:* wing, 329–351 (340.9); tail, 201–225 (213.7); culmen (from cere), 16.5–17.3 (16.9); tarsus, 71–79.5 (75.4). *Adult female:* wing, 355–398 (376.7) mm.

Field Marks. Readily recognizable. A slender, long-winged, long-tailed, medium-sized hawk (gull grey in adult male, reddish brown in female and young) with a conspicuous white rump patch in all plumages. Most often seen quartering low over open country with alternating flaps and glides. When gliding, wings are held a little above horizontal, somewhat like a vulture. It is widely distributed and not uncommon in southern Canada.

Habitat. Hunts over broader fields, meadows, marshes (both fresh and salt) and similar open country.

Nesting. Nest, composed of weeds, sticks, grasses, and rushes, is placed on the ground among low bushes or other low vegetation, usually in a moist meadow or marshy place but sometimes, especially on the prairies, in dry areas. *Eggs,* 4 to 6 (usually 5); bluish white sometimes sparsely spotted or smeared with pale brown. Incubation variously reported 21 to 31 days, probably about 29 to 31 days.

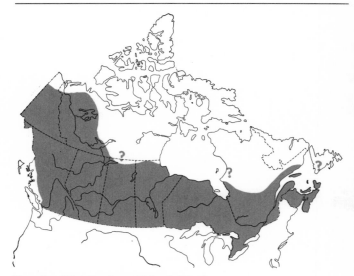

Breeding Distribution of Marsh Hawk

Range. Holarctic. Breeds from western Alaska east across central Canada and south to southwestern United States, western Oklahoma, southern Illinois, Ohio, and southeastern Virginia; also from Norway, Sweden, Russia, and Siberia, south to Portugal, Spain, and central Asia. In North America it winters from southern Canada south to Colombia and the West Indies.

Range in Canada. Breeds in Yukon (north at least to Lapierre House, probably Old Crow); Mackenzie (lower Anderson River, Fort Rae, Fort Resolution, Fort Providence, Fort Simpson); British Columbia (throughout interior but not on coast except perhaps on Lulu Island); Alberta; Saskatchewan (breeding records needed from northern part); Manitoba; Ontario (definite breeding records lacking from northern part); southern Quebec (north at least to Lake St. John and to Natashquan on north shore of Gulf of St. Lawrence; also Magdalen Islands); and the Maritime Provinces; probably Newfoundland (a few occur in summer but definite breeding evidence lacking).

Recorded north to northern Yukon (Blow River mouth), southern Keewatin (Windy River); Repulse Bay, N.W.T.; Great Whale River mouth, Quebec; and Dead Islands Harbour, Labrador.

Migrates through breeding range and along coast of British Columbia. Winters in small numbers in southern British Columbia, Alberta, southern Ontario, and Nova Scotia.

Subspecies. *Circus cyaneus hudsonius* (Linnaeus).

Family **Pandionidae** – Ospreys

Number of Species in North America 1; in Canada 1

This family contains only a single species, the Osprey. This bird subsists entirely on fishes which are captured in shallow water by diving from the air. Its bill is strongly hooked, and its feet are peculiarly adapted for catching and holding slippery fish. The talons are long and sharp, the outer toe is reversible, and the soles of the feet have sharp horny spicules (Fig. 39).

Fig. 39 Foot of Osprey showing spiny processes on soles

OSPREY

L'Aigle pêcheur. *Pandion haliaetus* (Linnaeus)
Plates 16, 20. L. 21 to 24.5 in.; wingspread 54 to 72 in.

A large, very long-winged hawk. Legs heavy and bare except for a short way down front; soles of feet equipped with sharp horny processes for holding slippery fish. Plumage rather stiff. *Adults:* Head mostly white, streaked brown on crown and with broad blackish brown stripe down side of neck from eye to back. Rest of upper parts dark brown. Under parts white, the breast more or less spotted with brown. *Young, first autumn:* Similar to adult but brown feathers of upper parts have whitish tips, and the crown is more heavily streaked.

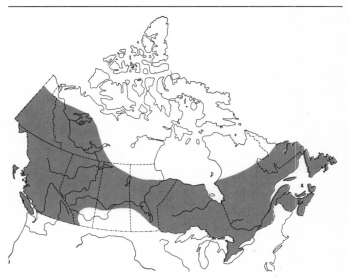

Breeding Distribution of Osprey

Measurements. *Adult male:* wing, 457–488 (469.7); tail, 197–215 (204.2); culmen (from cere), 31–33.5 (32.4); tarsus, 56.5–62.5 (61). *Adult female:* wing, 488–518 (493.3) mm.

Field Marks. Large size separates it from most hawks, and its white under parts distinguish it from eagles and vultures. Its facial markings and slight crest are also distinctive. Habitually hunts over water, often hovering in the air, and dives in spectacular manner into water for fish. In flight, the long slender wings are angled backward, noticeably at the bend, and a black wrist mark shows on their undersides.

Habitat. The vicinity of lakes, large rivers, and coastal bays.

Nesting. Nest, a massive structure of sticks, is placed at various heights usually in isolated trees, either dead or living; sometimes on telephone poles, cliff pinnacles, or on the ground. It is used and added to year after year. Sometimes nests in scattered colonies. *Eggs*, 2 to 4; buffy white, handsomely blotched very heavily to lightly with rich browns. Incubation 35 days (Witherby), 38 days (Siewert); mainly or solely by female.

Range. Cosmopolitan, occurring in tropical and temperate parts of all continents. In the Western Hemisphere breeds from Alaska and central Canada south to the Bahamas, Mexico, and British Honduras; winters from southern United States south to the West Indies, northern Argentina, Paraguay, and Peru.

Range in Canada. Breeds in Yukon (locally north to Kandik River); southern Mackenzie (Great Slave Lake; perhaps farther north, for it has been observed in summer north to Great Bear Lake and Fort Norman area); British Columbia; Alberta (except extreme southeastern part); northern and central Saskatchewan (Lake Athabasca; Ile-à-la-Crosse; Big River; Nipawin area); Manitoba (Overflowing River; Hayes River between Swampy Lake and Fox River; near York Factory; Lake St. Martin; Hillside Beach; Indian Bay); Ontario (Kenora, Moose Factory, and Lake Abitibi south to Simcoe County, and the east end of Lake Ontario); southern and central Quebec (north to near mouth of Great Whale River and Knob Lake region; probably Indian House Lake); southern and central Labrador (north to Jem Lane's Bay and inland along Hamilton River); Newfoundland; and New Brunswick, Prince Edward Island, and Nova Scotia. Migrates through all of southernmost Canada.

Subspecies. *Pandion haliaetus carolinensis* (Gmelin).

Remarks. Ospreys subsist entirely on fish, which they capture by spectacular dives from the air. They hit the water with a resounding splash and occasionally disappear momentarily below the surface. Then, with a few flaps of their powerful wings they clear the water, shrug off the excess water, and continue flying. If successful in catching a fair-sized or large fish, this is carried, in both claws, parallel with the bird's body, head first. Most of the fish it takes, such as tomcod and flounders on the coasts, and suckers, perch, and sunfish on freshwater lakes and rivers are of little economic importance.

Family **Falconidae** – Falcons and Caracaras

Number of Species in North America 9; in Canada 6

Falcons are among the swiftest and most picturesque of the diurnal birds of prey. Because of their spirit, power, and speed, they were the favourites of the old falconers for use in hunting. They have powerful taloned feet and a strong hooked bill with a membranous covering or cere at its base. On the cutting edge of the upper mandible toward the tip is a toothlike projection (absent in Caracaras) which distinguishes the falcons from other diurnal birds of prey (Fig. 40).

Fig. 40 Bill of
    (A) a falcon   (B) an accipiter

They fly with quick, powerful wing strokes. In silhouette they have long pointed wings and a medium to longish, somewhat tapered tail (Plate 20). As in most birds of prey, the female is larger than the male.

CRESTED CARACARA (Audubon's Caracara)
Le Caracara commun
Caracara cheriway audubonii (Cassin)
Fig. 41

Accidental. Specimen taken near Port Arthur, Ontario, on July 18, 1892 (Brown, 1893, *The Auk* 10: 364).

Fig. 41 Crested Caracara

GYRFALCON
Le Gerfaut. *Falco rusticolus* Linnaeus
Plates 18, 20. L. male 21 to 22.5; female 22 to 24.5 in.

Toothed upper mandible identifies it as a falcon. Large size, stout legs and feet, legs feathered in front more than halfway to toes, and markings, are all features that distinguish it from other falcons. Plumage variable. Pale phase mainly white, usually more or less barred, spotted and streaked with dark brown. Dark phase is mainly leaden blackish brown, above and below; the under parts are narrowly streaked with white. Many intermediate stages with barred or unbarred tails are common. White (pale phase) birds are commonest in the breeding season in the eastern high Arctic; darkest birds in the Ungava Peninsula. In adults the cere and feet are usually yellow; in immatures, bluish or greyish.

Measurements (*F. r. obsoletus*). *Adult male:* wing, 355–373 (364.1); tail, 190.5–206 (201.7); culmen (from cere), 21.5–23.5 (22.3); tarsus, 60.5–63 (61.2). *Adult female:* wing, 361.5–407 (384.4) mm.

Field Marks. Pale phase is unlike any other hawk. Easily separable from Snowy Owls by its smaller head, narrower pointed wings, and quicker wing beats. Darker birds are likely to be confused with the immature Peregrine Falcon, but are more uniformly coloured, and the moustache stripe is more obscure or lacking.

Habitat. In summer, arctic and subarctic open country near cliffs or mountains both inland and on rocky coasts; sometimes wooded country. In winter various types of open country, sometimes wooded.

Nesting. Nest usually placed on cliffs, often inaccessible. Usually no real nest is built beyond a few sticks, grasses, or moss, but as it is used in successive years, an accumulation of the remains of prey develops. Sometimes it nests also in trees. Nests of other birds, such as the Rough-legged Hawk, occasionally are used. *Eggs*, usually 3 or 4; creamy white with pale rufous suffusion and (not always) spots and blotches of reddish browns. Incubation period 28 to 29 days (A. L. V. Manniche).

Range. Holarctic. Breeds in Alaska, northern Canada, Greenland, Iceland, northern Scandinavia, northern Russia, and northern Siberia. In North America, it winters from the breeding grounds irregularly southward to southern Canada and rarely to Washington, Montana, Ohio, New York, and Massachusetts.

Breeding Distribution of Gyrfalcon

Range in Canada. Breeds sparsely across arctic Canada, but vast areas exist from which definite breeding records are wanting. Breeds from northern Banks Island (Mercy Bay); Ellesmere Island (Slidre Fiord, Bay Fiord, Cape Hayes); Bylot Island; Baffin Island (Admiralty Inlet, Abodyar Island, Clyde Inlet, Dorset); and Boothia Peninsula (Felix Harbour) south to southern Yukon, northern Mackenzie (Mackenzie Delta, Anderson River, Point Lake, Thelon River, Lynx Lake); southern Keewatin (Edehon Lake); northern Quebec (Digges Island, Wakeham Bay, Fort Chimo); and northern Labrador (Nachvak Bay, perhaps Paul Island). Records of breeding at Atlin, British Columbia; Fort Chipewyan, Alberta; and Bradore, Quebec, are unsatisfactory. Wanders south of breeding range in winter.

Subspecies. (1) *Falco rusticolus obsoletus* Gmelin is the breeding subspecies across arctic Canada. The fourth primary from the outside is usually shorter than the outermost. (2) *F. r. uralensis* (Severtzov and Menzbier) is known in Canada only as a visitor to B.C. Fourth primary from outside equal to or longer than outermost. The writer has examined (courtesy B.C. Prov. Museum) B.C. specimens from Alberni, January 30, 1917; Saanich, December 1904; Victoria, November 10, 1916.

PRAIRIE FALCON

Le Faucon des prairies. *Falco mexicanus* Schlegel
Plates 18, 20. L. male 16.8 to 18; female 18.5 to 20.0 in.

Toothed upper mandible marks it as a falcon. Inner toe (without claw) reaches to or beyond penultimate joint of middle toe (contrary in Peregrine Falcon). Resembles Pere-

grine Falcon, but see 'Field Marks.' *Adults:* Head with whitish line over eye and dark brown moustache (malar) streak. Upper parts brown, feathers margined and incompletely barred with tawny; paler band across hind-neck. Central tail feathers plain, rest barred buff and brown. Throat white, rest of under parts streaked and otherwise marked with dark brown, these markings coalescing to a brownish patch on flanks. Axillars mainly brown contrasting with whitish under wing coverts. *Juvenal:* Resembles adults but upper parts darker and under parts more buffy.

Measurements. *Adult male:* wing, 301–349.5 (317.2); tail, 163–191 (173.3); culmen (from cere), 20–21.5 (20.9); tarsus, 51.5–54 (52.9). *Adult female:* wing, 330–358 (346.6) mm.

Field Marks. A crow-sized falcon. Most like Peregrine Falcon but decidedly paler and sandy brown above (not dark slate or blackish). In flight shows *dark axillars and flank patches.* Pigeon and Sparrow hawks are obviously smaller.

Habitat. Typically dry open country of the West; in breeding season the vicinity of cliffs, canyons, coulees, badlands, and rock outcrops; hunts over adjacent grasslands and sometimes high mountains and wooded country.

Nesting. Eggs are laid on bare rock or in a scrape or in the nest of other large birds. Prefers shallow cavities or ledges protected by an overhang. *Eggs,* 3 to 6; resemble those of the Peregrine Falcon but are much lighter in colour.

Range. Breeds from dry parts of southwestern Canada south to Baja California, southern parts of Arizona and New Mexico, and northern Texas. Winters from southwestern Canada to central Mexico.

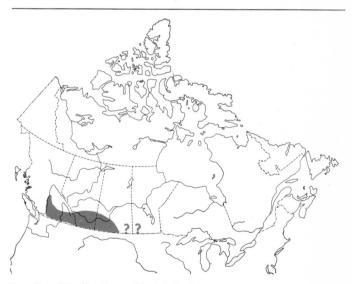

Breeding Distribution of Prairie Falcon

Range in Canada. Breeds in southern British Columbia (dry southern interior: Vaseaux Lake, Napier Lake, Doc English Gulch, Dog Creek); southern Alberta (Rosebud, Rumsey, Little Sandhill Creek, Brooks); and southern Saskatchewan (Battle Creek; Frenchman River, 15 miles east of Eastend; Big Muddy Valley; Beechy).

Species has been recorded north to Nulki Lake, B.C.; Battle River region, Alta.; and St. Louis, Sask.; and east to southern Manitoba (Whitewater Lake, Winnipeg). Winters in small numbers in southern British Columbia, Alberta, Saskatchewan, and Manitoba (rarely).

PEREGRINE FALCON (Duck Hawk)

Le Faucon pèlerin. *Falco peregrinus* Tunstall
Plate 18, 20. L. male 15 to 18; female 18 to 21.4 in.

Toothed upper mandible marks it as a falcon. Inner toe (without claw) does not quite reach penultimate joint of middle toe (extends to or beyond in Gyrfalcon and Prairie Falcon). Somewhat resembles Prairie Falcon, but see 'Field Marks.' *Adults:* Crown, hind-neck, face, and well-defined moustache mark, blackish; back, upper wings, and rump, ashy blue barred with dark slate; tail barred with blackish and tipped whitish. Under parts, buffy white to pinkish with blackish brown bars on sides and thighs, usually spots on abdomen. Under wing coverts and axillars, white barred with black. *Immatures:* Crown, face, and upper parts, blackish brown edged with buffy. Moustache marks blackish. Tail dark brown, crossed by narrow buffy bars (often obsolescent or indicated by spots) and tipped buffy white. Under parts buffy, heavily streaked (except throat) with blackish brown.

Measurements (*F. p. anatum*). *Adult male:* wing, 301.5–318 (311.1); tail, 137–146.5 (141.7); culmen (from cere), 18.5–20 (19.4); tarsus, 47–49.5 (48.2). *Adult female:* wing, 340–366 (356.2) mm.

Field Marks. A powerful crow-sized falcon. Conspicuous head-pattern visible for a considerable distance but resembles that of the Prairie Falcon. The Peregrine is much darker above (blackish or bluish instead of sandy brown) and lacks the contrasting axillars and flank patches shown in flight by the Prairie Falcon. Adult Peregrines are barred below, and the under parts of immatures are usually very much more heavily streaked than in Prairie Falcons.

Habitat. In breeding season the vicinity of cliffs and adjacent country, both coastal and inland; often about sea-bird colonies. At all seasons more open country is preferred, particularly shores and marshes frequented by shorebirds and waterfowl. Occasionally large cities.

Nesting. Little or no nest. Eggs laid on a cliff ledge (rarely cliff top); rarely in broken top of a great tree, or on a tall city building; occasionally on the ground. *Eggs*, usually 3 to 5; with creamy ground colour generally concealed by heavy markings of rich reddish browns. Incubation 33 to 35 days (J. A. Hagar), by both sexes,

Range. Practically cosmopolitan. Breeds from Alaska, northern Canada, and Greenland south through the Americas (not in West Indies) to southern South America; also from northern Norway, Novaya Zemlya, and northern Siberia south to South Africa, India, Ceylon, Malay States, Philippines, East Indies, Australia, and Tasmania (not New Zealand). In North America winters north to northern United States, southwestern British Columbia, and southern Ontario.

Range in Canada. Breeds locally, depending on availability of nest sites and food, on Banks Island (Cape Lambton, Russell Point, Cape Kellett, Nelson Head; probably Sachs Harbour); Victoria Island (Minto Inlet, Holman Island, and near Washburn Lake and Cape Isabella); Somerset Island (Fort Ross); Boothia Peninsula; and Baffin Island (Gibbs Fiord, Pangnirtung, head of Frobisher Bay, Dorset); and south through Yukon (below Fort Selkirk, Old Crow); Mackenzie (Arctic Red River, Fort Good Hope, Liard River, Grandin River, Great Bear and Great Slave lakes, Anderson River including mouth, Timber River, Helen Falls, Bathurst Inlet); Keewatin (Adelaide Peninsula, Repulse Bay, Back River, Beverly Lake, Windy River, Angikuni Lake, Carr Lake); Southampton Island; British Columbia (commonest on north coast: Langara Island, Moore Islands, Scott Island group; Okanagan Falls, Kalamalka Lake, Hanceville); Alberta (Athabasca Lake, Athabasca District, Rosebud, Red Deer River, Brooks region); Ontario (north shore of Lake Superior, Algonquin Park, and Bruce Peninsula south to Leeds and Grey counties; nesting not known in northern Ontario); Quebec (Chimo, False River mouth, Christie Island, Gaspé Peninsula, Bic, Kamouraska, Montreal, Aylwin); Labrador (Cape Chidley, Okak, Nain, Pamiarluk, Makkovik, Gannet Islands), New Brunswick (Grand Manan Island); and Nova Scotia (Diamond Island; Advocate).

Definite breeding records lacking, but probably breeds sparingly in Saskatchewan, Manitoba, and Newfoundland as species occurrence is recorded locally in summer. Migrates through all of southern Canada including Prince Edward Island. Winters in British Columbia (along coast), southern Ontario, and rarely Nova Scotia and New Brunswick. Very rarely elsewhere.

Subspecies. (1) *Falco peregrinus anatum* Bonaparte is the subspecific name currently applied to all Canadian breeding populations (except those of islands along the British Columbia coast). However, specimens from arctic Canada may prove separable from *anatum* because of paler coloration and less extensive black malar stripe. (2) *F.p. pealei* Ridgway, inhabiting the Queen Charlotte Is. and Moore Is., B.C., differs from *anatum* in its darker coloration and slightly larger size.

Remarks. The streamlined, powerful Peregrine Falcon is one of the swiftest birds in the world, capable of overtaking flying prey with ease. Its victim is often struck such a powerful blow by the large taloned feet that it is killed in the air instantly. In a dive pursuing prey the Peregrine has been timed at speeds up to 180 miles per hour. Although its food is almost entirely made up of other birds, it is nowhere sufficiently numerous to have any appreciable ill effect on any one species. Its numbers have declined sharply in recent years.

PIGEON HAWK

Le Faucon émerillon. *Falco columbarius* Linnaeus
Plates 18, 20. L. male 10 to 10.6; female 12 to 13 in.

Toothed bill separates it as a falcon. Obviously small size distinguishes it from all other Canadian falcons but the Sparrow Hawk. Very different coloration (always lacks any red in upper parts and never has conspicuous face markings found in all plumages of Sparrow Hawk) distinguishes it from that species. *Adult male* (*see* Subspecies): Upper parts, blue streaked with black; tail banded with black (subterminal band widest) and tipped with white. Throat white. Breast and abdomen, buffy streaked with dark brown, often forming bars on sides which sometimes have a bluish tinge. Narrow whitish line over eye. Under wing coverts crossed by alternating white and brown bands giving somewhat checkered appearance. *Adult female:* Similar to male but blue of upper parts replaced by dark brown (but often with a suggestion of bluish). *Immatures:* Resemble closely adult female but pure brown above with no suggestion of bluish; buffier below.

Measurements (*F. c. columbarius*). *Adult male:* wing, 173–192 (184.5); tail, 111.5–117 (114.5); culmen (from cere), 12–13.5 (12.7); tarsus, 35.5–37 (36.2). *Adult female:* wing, 201–215 (206.9) mm.

Field Marks. Small size eliminates confusion with all but Sharp-shinned and Sparrow hawks. Pointed, longish wings distinguish it from the similarly coloured Sharp-shinned Hawk (which has short, rounded wings). Complete lack of reddish coloration in the tail or of conspicuous black face markings separates it from the Sparrow Hawk.

Habitat. Variable. In breeding season open (sometimes denser) woodland, either coniferous or deciduous; and woodland openings; wooded prairie coulees. Hunts in almost any type of country, especially outside breeding season, including marshes, beaches, mud flats, and fields, often far removed from trees.

Breeding Distribution of Pigeon Hawk

Nesting. Nest is frequently an abandoned one of some other species, such as the Crow or Magpie, in either a coniferous or deciduous tree; occasionally in a tree cavity or on a cliff ledge; sometimes a hollow in the ground. *Eggs,* usually 4 or 5; the creamy white ground colour much hidden by profuse markings and blotches of browns. Incubation period 29 to 31 days (G. A. Fox).

Range. Breeds in wooded parts of Alaska and Canada south to South Dakota, Michigan, and northern New York; also in forests of northern Europe and Siberia. In North America, it winters mainly from southern British Columbia and southern United States (small numbers north to southern Canada) south to the West Indies, Venezuela, and Peru.

Range in Canada. Widely distributed in summer; scarce in winter. Breeds in Yukon (recorded north at least to Old Crow); Mackenzie (Reindeer Depot; forts Anderson, Rae, Providence, Resolution, McPherson; Soulier Lake); southwestern Keewatin (Ennadai Lake); British Columbia (widely distributed but not known on Queen Charlotte Islands); Alberta; Saskatchewan; Manitoba; Ontario (south at least to Haliburton District); Quebec (probably north to Indian House Lake and Chimo); Labrador (Makkovik; probably north to Cape Chidley); Newfoundland (commonly throughout); Nova Scotia (rarely: Pictou, Halifax); and probably New Brunswick and Prince Edward Island.

Winters in southern British Columbia (not uncommon on south coast; more rarely in interior); occasionally in southern Alberta (Calgary, Edmonton; Millet); southern Saskatchewan (Skull Creek, Dodsland, Saskatoon); southern Ontario; southwestern Quebec (Montreal, Quebec); New Brunswick; Nova Scotia; and Newfoundland.

Subspecies. In Canada, four. (1) *Falco columbarius columbarius* Linnaeus, a rather dark subspecies: e. Canada intergrading with *bendirei* in n. Man. and with *richardsonii* in sw. Man. (2) *F. c. suckleyi* Ridgway, very dark coloration; breeds in coastal B.C. (Owikeno Lake; Upper Campbell Lake); also apparently in interior (Redstone, Chilcotin — Munro and Cowan, 1947), but limits of range imperfectly known. (3) *F. c. richardsonii* Ridgway, a very pale subspecies: prairie and aspen grove belt of s. Alta. (n. at least to Lac la Nonne), s. Sask. and extreme sw. Man. (4) *F. c. bendirei* Swann, intermediate in colour between *columbarius* and *richardsonii;* n. Sask., n. Alta., Mack., Yukon, e. B.C. (area of intergradation with *suckleyi* poorly understood), and probably mountainous sw. Alta.

SPARROW HAWK

La Crécerelle américaine. *Falco sparverius* Linnaeus
Plates 18, 20. L. male 8.75 to 10.65; female 9 to 12 in.

Toothed upper mandible. The only Canadian hawk combining small size, much red in tail and upper parts, and conspicuous black face markings. *Adult male:* Top of head blue with (usually) large chestnut crown patch. Face with narrow black patch from front of eye down along side of throat and another down across ear. Back reddish, barred with black. Tail, chestnut with broad black subterminal bar. Upper wing coverts blue, more or less spotted with black. Breast and belly white to buffy, with large black spots. *Adult female:* Resembles male but back and tail duller and both heavily barred with black. Wing coverts similar to back. Breast and belly striped with brown. *Immatures* similar to adults of their respective sexes.

Measurements. *Adult male:* wing, 174.5–187 (181.9); tail, 113–122 (117.1); culmen (from cere), 11.5–13 (12); tarsus, 34.5–37.5 (36.3). *Adult female:* wing, 171.5–201 (186.3) mm.

Field Marks. Our only small hawk showing conspicuous red in the tail and back. At closer range the black face marks are visible. Often hovers over one spot. Often noisy, repeating *killy-killy-killy*. When perching frequently flicks its tail.

Habitat. Hunts more open country: fields, meadows, burntlands, prairies, woodland openings, cities, in both flat and hilly terrain. Often perches on dead-topped trees, fence posts, poles, and buildings. In breeding season availability of nesting sites (*see* Nesting) is, of course, necessary.

Nesting. Nests (little or no attempt at nest building) in a natural cavity or woodpecker hole in a tree; sometimes also in a cliff cavity, magpie nest, bank burrow, bird box, or suitable recess in a building. Incubation 29 days (A. Sherman).

Range. Central Alaska and much of forested Canada south through North, Central, and South America (including the West Indies) to Tierra del Fuego and San Fernandez Islands. Winters from northern United States and (locally in small numbers) southern Canada southward.

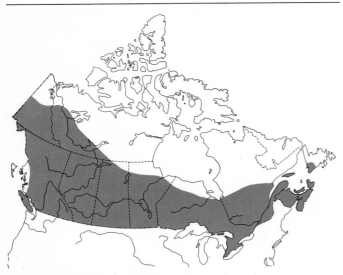

Breeding Distribution of Sparrow Hawk

Range in Canada. Common summer resident across southern Canada. Small numbers winter locally. *Breeds* in southern Yukon (fairly common north to Dawson area; birds recorded north to Lapierre House); western Mackenzie (forts Good Hope, Simpson, Providence, and Resolution, also Canol; birds recorded in breeding season along Mackenzie River north to Aklavik); British Columbia (except northern parts of heavily forested coast), Alberta, Saskatchewan (north to Lake Athabasca; perhaps absent from extreme northeast corner), Manitoba (north to Bird), Ontario, southern Quebec (north to Pointe des Monts and Lake St. John; possibly to Lake Mistassini and Lower Moisie River where recorded rarely), New Brunswick, Prince Edward Island, Nova Scotia, and southwestern Newfoundland.

Winters in small numbers in southern British Columbia, southern Ontario, southwestern Quebec, and Nova Scotia (occasionally).

Subspecies. *Falco sparverius sparverius* Linnaeus.

Remarks. Like other birds of prey, the Sparrow Hawk has

PLATE 15

1 Marsh Hawk,
   (a) adult male
   (b) adult female
   (c) first-year immature

2 Turkey Vulture, adult

3 Bald Eagle, adult

4 Golden Eagle, adult

Crosby

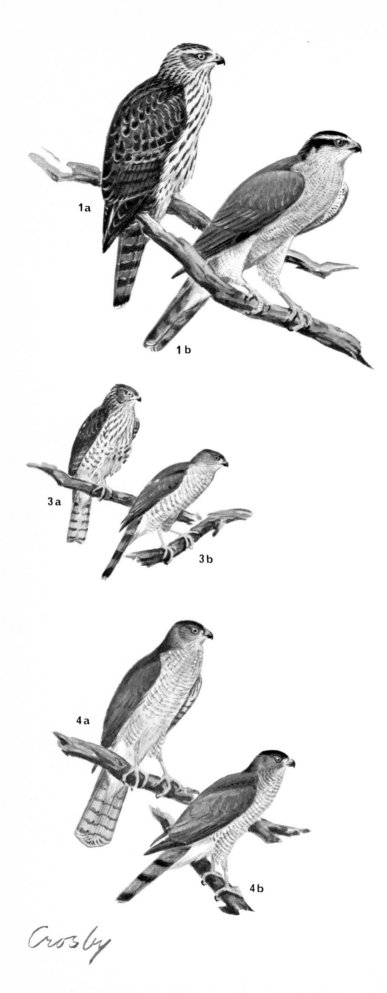

1a

1b

2a

2b

3a

3b

4a

4b

5

Crosby

remarkable eyesight. It spends much time searching for its prey from a vantage point of some tree-top, telephone pole, fence post, or even a television antenna on a city apartment building. It is inclined to be sociable; often several will be found foraging harmoniously for grasshoppers in the same field.

The name 'Sparrow Hawk' is unfair to this handsome and beneficial little falcon. In summer and early autumn, when grasshoppers, crickets, caterpillars, and dragonflies abound, it feeds on such large insects almost exclusively. In colder seasons, when insects can no longer be found, it must rely mainly on mice and some small birds for food.

Writers who dislike the inappropriate name 'Sparrow Hawk' for this little falcon have suggested 'Grasshopper Hawk' as a substitute. Although the latter is an excellent name, it has never caught on. Recently more and more people have been using the name 'American Kestrel' because of the close relationship between our bird and the Kestrel of the Old World.

Order **Galliformes**–Megapodes, Curassows, Pheasants, Grouse, and Hoatzins

Fowl-like, scratching ground birds make up this order which has a vast distribution in the world and contains many of the important game birds. The Jungle Fowl is the ancestor of our domestic hen, and this and the Turkey are important components of the poultry industry.

Family **Tetraonidae**–Grouse and Ptarmigan

Number of Species in North America 10, in Canada 9

These fowl-like birds have completely or partly feathered legs (in ptarmigan the toes also are feathered, Fig. 42); species with unfeathered toes have in winter a fringe of horny pectinations on either side of the toes (Fig. 43); feathers

Fig. 42 Feathered foot of Willow Ptarmigan

hide the nostrils; over the eye is a small bare stripe. On the sides of the neck in some species there are elongated feathers, and in others there is bare skin capable of distension.

BLUE GROUSE (Dusky and Sooty grouse)
Le Tétras sombre. *Dendragapus obscurus* (Say)
Plate 22. L. male 18.5 to 22.5; female 17.2 to 18.8 in.

Tail square or slightly rounded. Legs feathered to base of toes. Large size separates it from most Canadian grouse, and square or slightly rounded tail feathers from the equally large Sage Grouse (which has pointed tail feather tips).

Fig. 43 Foot of Ruffed Grouse
(A) in winter
(B) in summer

Coloration most similar to that of the much smaller Spruce Grouse, but the male's breast is uniformly slaty (no decidedly black patch); and adult female has the centre of abdomen plain slaty (barred in female Spruce Grouse). *Adult male:* Head and neck slaty, mixed on throat and sides of neck with white. Upper parts blackish, more or less finely mottled with grey or brown and with buffy brown on wings. Tail black with or without (*see* Subspecies) a well-defined terminal grey band. Under parts slaty with white markings on flanks and under tail coverts. *Adult female:* Similar to male but crown, scapulars, chest, and sides barred or otherwise marked with brown. Tail with indistinct tail band (individually variable regardless of subspecies).

Measurements. *Adult male:* wing, 223–239 (231.9); tail, 159–182 (169.9); exposed culmen, 18.5–21 (19.7); tarsus, 43–47.5 (45.5). *Adult female:* wing, 196–218 (206.1) mm.

Field Marks. Adult male a large, dark, slate-coloured grouse, most likely to be confused with the much smaller male Spruce Grouse. In Canada, coastal males have a well-defined grey terminal tail band, but this is lacking in interior males. Blue Grouse males have a uniformly slaty breast without the well-defined black patch of male Spruce Grouse (also a western race of the Spruce Grouse *franklinii* has white spots on upper tail coverts, always lacking in Blue Grouse). Females are similar to female Spruce Grouse but have a plain slaty patch in the middle of the abdomen, and the under parts are less extensively and less heavily barred.

Habitat. Varies seasonally. In breeding season many inhabit lowland burntlands, slashings, open mountainsides, meadows, forest edges and openings, although some, especially in northern British Columbia and Yukon, breed near treeline. After the breeding season and during winter it inhabits coniferous forests at higher altitudes. In winter it is largely arboreal, feeding mainly on needles of conifers.

Nesting. Nest, a depression on the ground lined with grasses, leaves (including conifers), and similar material available near the nesting site. Nest is often at foot of a tree or near a log or rock. *Eggs*, usually 7 to 10; creamy, finely dotted with browns. Incubation 24 to 25 days (J. F. Bendell).

Range. Southeastern Alaska, southern Yukon, and extreme southwestern Mackenzie south along the coast to northern California, and in the mountains south to southern California, northern Arizona, and central New Mexico; east to southwestern Alberta and the Black Hills, South Dakota.

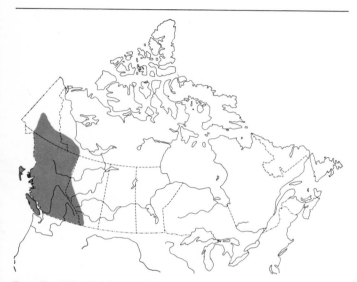

Breeding Distribution of Blue Grouse

Range in Canada. Permanent resident in western mountains: southern Yukon (locally north to Mayo Lake but apparently absent from the St. Elias range: west to about 30 miles west of Whitehorse), extreme southwestern Mackenzie (near mouth of Nahanni River; mountains west of Fort Simpson), British Columbia (including Queen Charlotte and Vancouver islands, islands in Georgia Strait, most of the interior but apparently absent locally from some quite large areas), and southwestern Alberta (Jasper, Banff, and Waterton National parks; Canmore, Coleman). Migrations local and vertical, many breeding in valleys and wooded plains and wintering at considerable altitudes in coniferous forests.

Subspecies. In Canada, four. (1) *Dendragapus obscurus sitkensis* Swarth (Queen Charlotte Islands; islands in Queen Charlotte Sound, B.C.): adult male with distinct terminal tail band; females more reddish brown, less blackish, than in *fuliginosus*. (2) *D. o. fuliginosus* (Ridgway) (mainland coast of British Columbia and Vancouver Island; inland to Lillooet) males with distinct grey terminal tail-band, like *sitkensis;* females duller brown with more black in upper parts. (3) *D. o. pallidus* Swarth (drier parts of southern interior British Columbia: habitat adjoining Okanagan and

Similkameen valleys and north at least to Chilcotin drainage); males without distinct tail-band, rectrices broader and more truncate than in *sitkensis* and *fuliginosus;* both sexes paler. (4) *D. o. richardsonii* (Douglas) (s. Yukon, sw. Mackenzie, interior B.C. except range of *pallidus*, and extreme sw. Alberta) adult males with tail similar to that of *pallidus*, both sexes darker than *pallidus*, paler than *fuliginosus*, females less reddish than *sitkensis*.

SPRUCE GROUSE (Franklin's Grouse)
Le Tétras des savanes. *Canachites canadensis* (Linnaeus)
Plate 22. L. 15 to 17 in.

Legs feathered to toes. *Adult male:* Upper parts, finely barred black and grey, often brownish especially on wings. Tail black, broadly tipped with pale brown (except in *franklinii* of the West which has all-black tail and white-tipped upper tail coverts). Forehead, cheeks, throat, and upper breast, black narrowly bordered with white. Lower breast black centrally, broadly barred with white laterally and on middle of abdomen. Sides mixed grey and black. Under tail coverts, black tipped with white. *Adult female:* Very different. Upper parts irregularly barred black, grey, and rusty. Tail irregularly barred black and rusty (in *franklinii* upper tail coverts tipped with white). Under parts barred black, white, and rusty, rustiest on breast. *Immatures* resemble adults of their respective sexes.

Measurements (*C. c. canadensis*). *Adult male:* wing, 168–186.3 (177.1); tail, 113–131.8 (120.9); exposed culmen, 13.6–17 (15.2); tarsus 34.9–39.8 (36.9). *Adult female:* wing, 161–178 (168.4) mm.

Field Marks. East of the Rocky Mountains, the black-breasted male is readily identifiable. In the western mountains, it might be confused with the Blue Grouse (q.v.). Females somewhat resemble Ruffed Grouse but have bars across the back and shorter tail without a black subterminal bar, and lack ruffs. Since Spruce Grouse are absurdly tame, they can be closely approached and studied.

Habitat. Usually coniferous and mixedwood forests, muskeg, forest edges, and openings; also older burntlands and blueberry barrens.

Nesting. Nest, a depression on the ground sparsely lined with grasses and leaves, often under a small isolated conifer sapling on dry ground near a wet bog. *Eggs* (usually 4 to 7, occasionally more) are buffy, handsomely marked with rich browns. Incubation (period uncertain) by female, probably about 24 days (R. S. Palmer).

Range. Permanent resident in coniferous woodland from about treeline in Canada and Alaska south to northeastern Oregon, western Montana, northwestern Wyoming, northern Minnesota, Michigan, northern New York, northern Vermont, northern New Hampshire, and Maine.

Range in Canada. Permanent resident, north to near treeline, in coniferous forests. Extirpated in vicinity of thickly settled parts of range in the south but still common in remoter suitable parts of the country. Breeds in Yukon (north to Rampart House, Old Crow), western and southern Mackenzie (southern Mackenzie Delta, Norman Wells, Fort Franklin, Lake Hardisty, Fort Simpson, Great Slave

PLATE 17

Lake), southern Keewatin (Windy River), British Columbia (mainland, but not known from coastal islands), Alberta (except southeastern prairies), northern and south-central Saskatchewan (south to Nipawin and Fishing Lake), Manitoba, Ontario (south to about Algonquin Park; formerly south to Peel and Leeds counties), northern, central, and southern Quebec (north to Richmond Gulf and Fort Chimo; extirpated from thickly settled southwestern parts; absent from Anticosti and Magdalen islands), Labrador, New Brunswick (but unknown from Grand Manan group), and Nova Scotia (including Cape Breton Island). Absent from Newfoundland. Absent also from Prince Edward Island, possibly occurred formerly and was extirpated

1 Ferruginous Hawk, adult, pale phase

2 Red-tailed Hawk, adult

3 Red-shouldered Hawk, adult

4 Swainson's Hawk, adult, pale phase

5 Rough-legged Hawk,
  (a) adult male, pale phase
  (b) adult female, pale phase

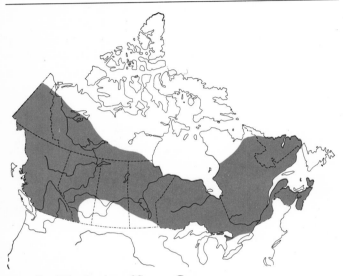

Breeding Distribution of Spruce Grouse

Subspecies. (1) *Canachites canadensis franklinii* (Douglas): inhabits southern two-thirds of mainland B.C. (except Peace River; north at least to Ingenika River, and Hudson Hope) and mountainous sw. Alberta. Male differs from other races in the all-black tail (no brown tips) and in both sexes having broadly white-tipped upper tail coverts. Until recently, regarded as a full species. (2) *C. c. osgoodi* Bishop: Yukon and n. B.C. (Atlin, Telegraph Creek, Fort Nelson) and w. Mackenzie (Norman Wells; Canol Road between Carcajou and Mackenzie rivers; intergradation eastward not well understood). (3) *C. c. canadensis* (Linnaeus): c.-e. B.C. (Peace River), c. Alta., c. Sask., Man., n. Ont., n. and c. Que., and Labrador. (4) *C. c. canace* (Linnaeus): s. Ont. (n. to Temagami and Georgian Bay), s. Que. (n. to Lake St. John), N.B., and N.S.

Remarks. The Spruce Grouse is deserving of its other name 'Fool Hen.' Unlike the Ruffed Grouse, it has never learned to fear man greatly. Ridiculously tame, it can often be killed with a stick or stone. Consequently it disappears rapidly with the advance of settlement and is now gone from most southern parts of its former range where man has thickly settled. It feeds to a large extent on the needles and buds of coniferous trees, especially in winter. Berries of various kinds are much relished when they are available.

1

2

3

4

Crosby

5a

5b

1

2 a

3 a

3 b

4 a

4 b

5

Crosby

Crosby

PLATE 18

1 Prairie Falcon, adult

2 Peregrine Falcon,
   (a) first-year immature
   (b) adult

3 Gyrfalcon,
   (a) immature, dark
       phase
   (b) adult, white phase

4 Pigeon Hawk,
   (a) first-year immature
   (b) adult male

5 Sparrow Hawk, male

RUFFED GROUSE

La Gelinotte huppée. *Bonasa umbellus* (Linnaeus)
Plate 21. L. 16 to 19 in.

Head slightly crested. Tail, many-barred and with broad subterminal band. Separable from other grouse by black or reddish brown ruff (soft, broad, longish feathers on sides of neck) and broad subterminal dark tail bar. Two colour phases occur regardless of age, sex, or season. Grey phase is commoner in interior western Canada, and both phases are more or less common in eastern Canada, but in extreme southwestern British Columbia reddish brown is predominant. Female smaller than male, with shorter ruffs and tail, and the tail band is usually incomplete across the two central tail feathers.

Measurements (*B. u. togata*). *Adult male:* wing, 174.5–187 (179.6); tail, 144–184 (157.2); exposed culmen, 14–16.5 (15.4); tarsus, 42–45 (43.3). *Adult female:* wing, 170.5–184.5 (176.6) mm.

Field Marks. A chicken-like woodland grouse with fan-like many-barred tail. Diagnostic *dark* subterminal tail band is noticeable, especially in flight. Ruffs diagnostic at close range. Springs suddenly from ground with noisy whirring rapid flight. Drumming of male, beginning with slow dull thuds which quickly increase in tempo until they die away in a muffled roll, suggests the starting of a car in the distance.

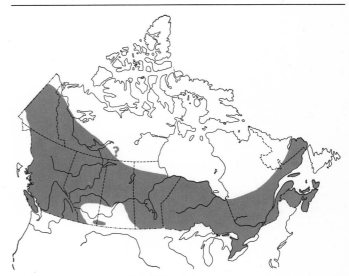

Breeding Distribution of Ruffed Grouse

Habitat. Mainly second growth deciduous and mixed woodland, wood edges and openings, alder- and willow-bordered ravines and stream edges, old orchards. Much less partial to extensive stands of mature forest, but uses coniferous woods for shelter.

Nesting. Nest, a hollow in the ground lined with leaves and a few feathers, is usually in second-growth woodland, often at the base of a tree, rock, log, or brushpile. *Eggs*, usually 9 to 12; buffy, sometimes sparsely spotted with browns. Incubation, about 24 days (Bump, *et al.*) by the female.

Range. Permanent resident from central Alaska and much

of forested Canada (except Newfoundland) south to northern California, central Idaho, central Utah, western South Dakota, Minnesota, central Arkansas, northern Georgia, and northeastern Virginia.

Range in Canada. Permanent resident (numbers subject to periodic fluctuations) in southern and central Yukon (north to about Old Crow, Lapierre House), southwestern Mackenzie (forts Resolution and Simpson, Wrigley; perhaps Fort Rae and Roche-qui-Trempe-à-l'Eau); British Columbia (except Queen Charlotte Islands, the islands in Queen Charlotte Sound, and apparently most of the northern mainland coast, although observed near head of Rivers Inlet); Alberta (except most of southeastern corner); Saskatchewan (north at least to Lake Athabasca and Reindeer Lake, but absent from most of southern plains; introduced into Cypress Hills), southern and central Manitoba (north at least to Thicket Portage; probably York Factory), Ontario; southern and south-central Quebec (north to Lake Albanel and the north shore of Gulf of St. Lawrence; introduced on Anticosti Island); southern Labrador (north to Goose Bay, Hamilton Inlet), New Brunswick, Nova Scotia (including Cape Breton Island), and Prince Edward Island. Not found on Newfoundland or Magdalen Islands.

Subspecies. (1) *Bonasa umbellus yukonensis* Grinnell: Yukon, sw. Mackenzie, n. Alta. (2) *B. u. umbelloïdes* (Douglas): interior B.C. (except certain southern parts; see *sabini, phaia*), sw. and c. Alta., Sask. (except southern part), and Man. (except sw. part). Birds from much of interior B.C. average somewhat darker than *umbelloïdes* and have been named *affinis* Aldrich and Friedmann; but for the present at least I follow the A.O.U. Check-List (1957) and Dickinson (1953) in placing them with *umbelloïdes*. (3) *B. u. brunnescens* Conover: Vancouver I. and adjoining mainland from Vancouver north at least to Kingcome River. (4) *B. u. sabini* (Douglas): extends into Canada to Chilliwack region of Fraser Valley (Munro and Cowan, 1947). (5) *B. u. phaia* Aldrich and Friedmann: se. B.C.; distribution poorly understood. (6) *B. u. incana* Aldrich and Friedmann: s. Sask., sw. Man. (7) *B. u. obscura* Todd: n. Ont., c. Que. e. at least to Lake Mistassini. Additional material needed farther e. and from s. Labrador. (8) *B. u. togata* (Linnaeus): c. Ont. (between *obscura* and *monticola*), s. Que. including Gaspé Pen., N.B., N.S., and P.E.I. (9) *B. u. monticola* Todd: extreme s. Ont. s. to Seaforth, Glen Morris, and Hamilton.

Remarks. The Ruffed Grouse is known to most people simply as 'partridge.' It is a great favourite with the sportsman because it makes a challenging target when flying and is a delicious table bird. It bursts into the air with a startling clatter of wings, flies fast, takes advantage of any cover between it and the hunter, and before the startled novice can raise his gun, it is out of range. Its numbers are subject to drastic fluctuations periodically, the cause of which is poorly understood. Its drumming (*see* Field Marks) is one of the pleasantly mysterious sounds of the spring woodlands. This is produced by quick forward and upward strokes of the male's wings as he stands erect on his drumming log.

WILLOW PTARMIGAN
Le Lagopède des saules. *Lagopus lagopus* (Linnaeus)
Plate 22. L. 14 to 17 in.

Recognizable as a ptarmigan by feathered toes and large amounts of white (wings white even in summer). Black tail feathers separate it from the White-tailed Ptarmigan. Most similar to Rock Ptarmigan but much red on neck and breast separates summer males. Females of Willow Ptarmigan separable by larger size and heavier, broader bill. In winter it never shows the black stripe through the eye, possessed by male Rock Ptarmigan, but as this is lacking in many female Rock Ptarmigan, its absence is not diagnostic. Then larger size and heavier bill must be relied upon. *Adult male* (summer): Head, neck, and upper breast, chestnut; feathers about base of bill and chin, more or less white; eye-ring white; back, scapulars, rump, and upper tail coverts, mixed blacks, browns, and a little white; wings, white with dusky shafts to the primaries (except in *L. l. leucopterus*); tail blackish, tipped narrowly with white; belly and legs, white; comb red. *Adult male* (early autumn): Similar to male in summer but reddish brown of head, neck, and breast paler; upper parts, paler and more decidedly barred. *Adult male* (winter): All white except most of tail feathers, which are black tipped with white; shafts of wing primaries dusky (except in *L. l. leucopterus*). *Adult female* (summer): Upper parts intricately patterned with blacks, buffs, and white; under parts more decidedly barred with black; wings mostly white (except some wing coverts like the back) and dusky shafts of primaries (except *leucopterus*); tail blackish, tipped white; comb, paler red than in male. *Adult female* (early autumn): Similar to adult male in similar dress, the head, neck, and breast with more or less reddish brown but usually enough of the heavily barred plumage of the summer female's under parts is retained to distinguish her. *Adult female* (winter): Like adult male in winter, but the concealed bases of the crown feathers are often more greyish.

Measurements (*L. l. leucopterus*). *Adult male:* wing, 210.5–226 (217.9); tail, 129–140 (133.2); exposed culmen, 12.5–17.5 (14.1); tarsus, 34.5–38 (36.4). *Adult female:* wing, 196.5–205 (200.4) mm.

Field Marks. Ptarmigan are smallish arctic or alpine grouse, readily separable from other grouse by large amounts of white in the plumage (brown with white wings and abdomen in summer; mainly white in winter). Canada has three species, but the White-tailed is restricted to the western mountains. Willow and Rock Ptarmigan both have semi-concealed black tails, visible in flight, thus differing in all plumages from the White-tailed Ptarmigan. Summer adult male Willow Ptarmigan differ from the other two in the reddish brown of head, neck, and breast. Summer females are difficult to distinguish from other ptarmigan in the field, as are birds of both sexes in white winter dress. Willow Ptarmigan in white winter plumage never have the black eye stripe shown by male Rock Ptarmigan, but as this is lacking in many females of the latter its absence is not diagnostic.

Habitat. In the Arctic, low tundra preferring moister

better-vegetated country than the Rock Ptarmigan. In the western mountains frequents willow-grown meadows just above timberline, shrubby mountainsides, willow-bordered stream bottoms mostly near or just above timberline. In winter many descend to intermontane lowlands and from the arctic tundra to well south of treeline, inhabiting muskegs, lake and river margins, and forest openings.

Nesting. Nest on the ground, a depression lined with grasses or leaves. *Eggs*, usually 7 to 10; yellowish, thickly and handsomely spotted and blotched with blackish brown. Incubation by female, probably about 22 days (Conover *in* Bent).

Range. Circumpolar. Breeds in Alaska, northern Canada, northern Europe, and northern Asia. Mainly permanent resident but somewhat migratory.

Breeding Distribution of Willow Ptarmigan

Range in Canada. Breeds in the arctic islands north to Banks, southern Melville, Prince of Wales, and Baffin (north probably to southern Admiralty Inlet – Gifford Fiord but evidently absent from most of east coast) islands; Yukon; northern Mackenzie (Kittigazuit, Anderson River, Great Bear Lake, Artillery Lake); Keewatin (south to Nueltin Lake) and Southampton Island; British Columbia (interior mountains south to Kleena Kleene region; also Porcher Island); southwestern Alberta (northern Jasper Park); northeastern Manitoba (Churchill, Herchmer); northern Ontario (very locally: Cape Henrietta Maria region); some James Bay islands; north and central Quebec (locally south in the interior to Lake Bienville and Irony Mountain, perhaps to Eastmain Hills; farther south along James Bay coast and small islands to Moar Bay; and on the outer north shore of Gulf of St. Lawrence: The Bluff Harbour; Kegashka; St. Augustin); Labrador, and Newfoundland.

Winters throughout much of breeding range north to Banks and southern Baffin islands but migrates irregularly south to south-central Alberta (Camrose, Sullivan Lake), south-central Saskatchewan (Qu'Appelle Valley rarely), southern Manitoba (Gypsumville, Ashern, southern Lake Manitoba), central Ontario (rarely south to Whitby), and southern Quebec (rarely south to Montreal).

Subspecies. (1) *Lagopus lagopus leucopterus* Taverner: arctic islands including southern Baffin and Southampton islands; also east coastal Mack. (Dolphin and Union Strait east) and north coast of Keewatin (Adelaide Pen.). (2) *L. l. albus* (Gmelin): Yukon, west coastal and interior Mackenzie (north to mouth of Anderson River, Cape Dalhousie, Great Bear Lake), Keewatin (but replaced by *leucopterus* in extreme north), ne. Man., w. coast of Hudson B. (north at least to Chesterfield Inlet), B.C. (except nw., intergradation areas with *alexandrae* imperfectly understood), and sw. Alta. (3) *L. l. alexandrae* Grinnell: nw. B.C. (Porcher Island; also according to A.O.U. Check-List, Atlin and Dease Lake). (4) *L. l. ungavus* Riley: Que. and Lab. (5) *L. l. alleni* Stejneger: Nfld.

Remarks. Ptarmigan are arctic grouse. They are found also at higher elevations in the western mountains. They have separate summer, autumn, and winter plumages. In winter they are mainly white, in summer largely brown and grey. Thus they are well camouflaged at all seasons—excellent examples of 'protective coloration.'

ROCK PTARMIGAN

Le Lagopède des rochers. *Lagopus mutus* (Montin)
Plate 22. L. 12.75 to 15.50 in.

Black tail instead of white separates it from White-tailed Ptarmigan. Similar to Willow Ptarmigan. Males in summer lack any suggestion of dull red on head and neck feathers; in late summer plumage, upper parts of both sexes are more finely marked than in Willow. In white winter plumage, the black loral bar through eye (usually absent in females) instantly identifies Rock Ptarmigan. The slighter bill and smaller size of Rock Ptarmigan will help identify similar individuals of these two species.

Measurements (*L. m. rupestris*). *Adult male:* wing, 178–195.5 (187); tail, 101–117.5 (107.7); exposed culmen, 11.5–14.5 (12.8); tarsus, 31–33.5 (32.2). *Adult female:* wing, 173.5–188 (179) mm.

Field Marks. In white winter plumage, black bar at eye, when present (often absent), separates it from the other two ptarmigan. Black tail (often concealed) eliminates White-tailed Ptarmigan (*see* Willow Ptarmigan).

Habitat. In breeding season generally prefers higher, drier, barer country than Willow Ptarmigan; arctic and alpine highlands. In winter and during migration both species sometimes utilize similar habitats.

Nesting. Nest, a depression in ground or moss, lined with available vegetation and feathers, often sheltered by a rock, hummock, or low vegetation. *Eggs*, usually 6 to 9; very similar to those of Willow Ptarmigan but smaller, creamy to buffy, heavily spotted and blotched with blackish brown. Incubation, 21 days (A. Pedersen), is by female.

Range. Circumpolar. Arctic Ocean islands and coasts south in Eurasia to Iceland and locally in the mountains to Scotland, France, Spain, Austria, central Asia, and northern Japan; and in North America south to southern Alaska, northern Canada, and southern Greenland.

Range in Canada. The most boreal ptarmigan. Breeds

111

from Prince Patrick, Ellef Ringnes, and northern Ellesmere islands south through the Arctic Archipelago, through Yukon (including Herschel Island), north and middle interior British Columbia (Atlin, Ingenika River. Probably to southern part: occurs in June near Bella Coola, Yule Lake, Seymour Mountain near Vancouver); northern and middle Mackenzie (south to Cap Mountain and Artillery Lake; probably south to southwestern mountains); southern Keewatin (south to Alder Lake), Boothia and Melville peninsulas; Southampton Island; northern Quebec (south to Knob Lake region); northern Labrador (Cape Chidley, Ramah); and Newfoundland. Reports of breeding on Anticosti Island probably erroneous.

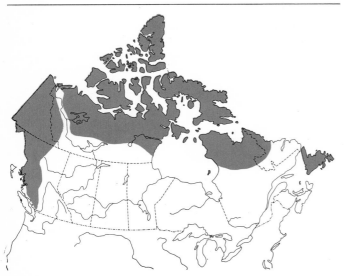

Breeding Distribution of Rock Ptarmigan

Winters mainly within breeding range (north at least to Melville and Devon islands but probably most withdraw from northernmost parts) and south to southern Mackenzie (Great Slave Lake); northern Saskatchewan (Athabasca Lake); northern Manitoba (Lynn Lake, York Factory); northwestern Ontario (Fort Severn, Winisk); central Quebec (James Bay and high barren country 150 to 200 miles inland from it; outer north shore Gulf of St. Lawrence); Labrador; and Newfoundland.

Casual in summer on Bonaventure Island, Quebec (July 9, 1922). Accidental in Nova Scotia (Elmsdale, April 20, 1922).

Subspecies. (1) *Lagopus mutus nelsoni* Stejneger: northern Yukon. (2) *L. m. welchi* Brewster: Nfld. (3) *L. m. rupestris* (Gmelin): currently all Canadian populations except those of the two previously mentioned races are included in *rupestris*. Birds from northern Ellesmere I. tend toward *L. m. captus* Peters. It is asserted by some that populations extending across northern Baffin Island and along the arctic coast of the mainland to Coronation Gulf should be referred to *L. m. saturatus* Salomonsen.

Remarks. Ptarmigan are notable for their remarkable seasonal plumage changes. The adults acquire no less than three different plumages annually, and in spring, summer, and autumn seem to be continuously molting.

WHITE-TAILED PTARMIGAN
Le Lagopède à queue blanche
Lagopus leucurus (Richardson)
Plate 22. L. 12.3 to 13.5 in.

Smallest ptarmigan. A small grouse with white wings in summer; all-white plumage in winter identifies it as a ptarmigan. All-white tail separates adults in all seasons from other ptarmigan.

Measurements (*L. l. leucurus*). *Adult male:* wing, 168–181.7 (173.9); tail, 95–109 (101.6); exposed culmen, 11.6–14.9 (13.6); tarsus, 28.5–34.5 (30.9). *Adult female:* wing, 162.5–178.6 (169.8) mm.

Field Marks. Not an arctic grouse, it is to be expected only in mountains of the West. All-white tail and small size separate adults in all plumages from other ptarmigan. Other ptarmigans have a black tail.

Habitat. High altitudes of the western mountains from treeline to the highest most barren tops, preferring alpine rocky meadows and slide-rock slopes. Some descend to timber in winter.

Nesting. Nest, a depression in the ground sparsely lined with available grasses or grass-like vegetation, leaves, and feathers. *Eggs*, usually 6 to 8, buff, dotted, spotted, or small-blotched, leaving decidedly more ground colour exposed than in other ptarmigan.

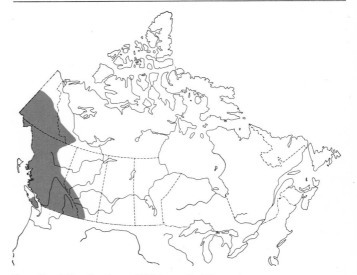

Breeding Distribution of White-tailed Ptarmigan

Range. South-central Alaska and Yukon, south through the Cascade Mountains to Washington; and in the Rockies through British Columbia and southwestern Alberta through Montana, Wyoming, and Colorado, to northern New Mexico.

Range in Canada. Resident in higher mountains of Yukon (north at least to Lapierre House), southwestern Mackenzie (Nahanni Mountains), British Columbia (higher mountains of most of the interior and Vancouver Island), and southwestern Alberta (Jasper, Banff, and Waterton Lakes parks).

Subspecies. (1) *Lagopus leucurus leucurus* (Richardson): B.C. (except Vancouver Island) and sw. Alta. Yukon birds, included in this race by current authors, require further study. (2) *L. l. saxatilis* Cowan: Vancouver I., B.C.

GREATER PRAIRIE CHICKEN
La Poule des prairies. *Tympanuchus cupido* (Linnaeus)
Plate 21. L. 16.50 to 18.75 in.

A medium-sized grouse with heavily barred body, short rounded tail, tarsi feathered to toes (bare behind), and in adults a group of stiff, narrow elongated feathers (poorly developed in female) over an inflatable sac on sides of neck. It is widely confused with Sharp-tailed Grouse, but the barred (instead of V-marked) under parts; the rounded, mostly dark (instead of pointed, mostly whitish) tail; and the elongated neck feathers (when present) readily mark the Prairie Chicken. Compared with the Ruffed Grouse, it has a shorter tail without a dark subterminal band, tarsi are feathered to toes, and the elongated neck feathers are very different from the soft, square-tipped ruffs of the Ruffed Grouse.

Measurements (*T. c. pinnatus*). *Adult male:* wing, 215.5–234 (222.7); tail, 76.5–106 (95.7); exposed culmen, 15.8–19.9 (17.7); tarsus, 46.5–51 (49.8). *Adult female:* wing, 202.5–219 (213) mm.

Field Marks. The dark rounded tail (best seen in flight), *barred under parts*, and elongated neck feathers instantly separate it from the Sharp-tailed Grouse. The barred *upper parts* and shorter tail without a dark subterminal bar distinguish it from the Ruffed Grouse. Very different habitat preferences make confusion with female Spruce Grouse unlikely, but Spruce Grouse never have profuse whitish bars on secondaries and wing coverts.

Habitat. Natural grassland, broadly open to fairly brushy. Cultivated lands, especially grainfields, but near open to semi-brushy wild land. More extensive man-made clearings.

Nesting. Nest on the ground, a depression lined with grasses and similar available material, usually in tall grass clumps or low bushes. *Eggs,* average clutch 11 to 12; olive, lightly dotted or spotted with pale brown. Incubation (about 23 or 24 days) is by female.

Range. Prairies of Alberta, Saskatchewan, and Manitoba, and southern Ontario south to northern Texas; also in southwestern Louisiana and coastal Texas. Formerly also on the Atlantic seaboard from eastern Massachusetts (possibly southern Maine) south to Maryland and Washington, D.C., and in Kentucky. Range now much less extensive than formerly.

Status in Canada. Range known to have expanded and recently contracted drastically; now greatly restricted. Southern Alberta: early history obscure but reportedly present in late 1890's. In early part of present century ranged north to Lac la Biche. Now very rare or extirpated. Last sight record 1940 (near Medicine Hat). Southern Saskatchewan: early history obscure. During first quarter of present century fairly common locally. Has been recorded north to Emma Lake and Nipawin regions. Now very rare. Recent sight records from Old Wives Lake (August 25, 1959); Stoughton (October 1960); and Sidewood (1959). Manitoba: apparently colonized southern Manitoba about

1880, became fairly common in southern parts during first quarter of present century. Specimen records north to Peonan Point, sight records to Grand Rapids. Now very rare. Specimen killed near Langruth, autumn, about 1961. Southern Ontario: formerly Essex County (1824–1836), and Kent County (until 1897). Reappeared in Ontario about 1925 on St. Joseph's Island, spreading to Manitoulin Island about 1938, where still (1961) present but with much hybridizing with Sharp-tailed Grouse.

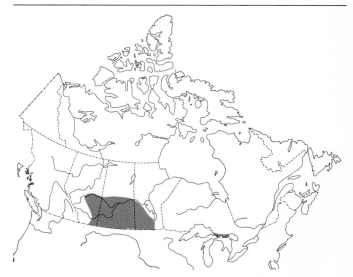
Breeding Distribution of Greater Prairie Chicken

Although partially migratory, it has been reported in winter north to Emma Lake and Nipawin, Saskatchewan; Winnipeg, Manitoba; and Manitoulin Island, Ontario.

Subspecies. *Tympanuchus cupido pinnatus* (Brewster).

SHARP-TAILED GROUSE
La Gelinotte à queue fine
Pedioecetes phasianellus (Linnaeus)
Plate 21. L. 16.4 to 18.5 in.

A medium-sized grouse with short pointed tail and V-marked under parts. It is widely miscalled 'Prairie Chicken,' but its V-marked under parts and pointed whitish (except central feathers) tail instantly distinguish it from that species. Sage Grouse also has pointed tail but is much larger, tail is grey, and there is a large black patch on its abdomen. Other grouse have broader rounded tails.

Measurements (*P. p. phasianellus*). *Adult male:* wing, 199–212.5 (205.6); tail, 119–127.9 (124.4); exposed culmen, 14.2–19.6 (16.2); tarsus, 41.5–50 (44.9). *Adult female:* wing, 195–206 (198.9) mm.

Field Marks. A medium-sized grouse with short pointed tail. Separable from Prairie Chicken by V-marks (instead of conspicuous bars) on under parts and in flight by white outer sides of tail (Prairie Chicken has dark rounded tail). Pointed white-sided tail separates it from most other grouse. Sage Grouse has a pointed grey tail, is much larger, and has a black belly patch. Ring-necked Pheasant has a long coloured (not white) tail.

113

Habitat. On the prairies: grassland, shrubby sandhills, coulees, creeks, brushy patches; in parklands: grassland and grain-bearing land near brush or open woodland; in coniferous areas, openings made by burns or man; muskegs and bogs.

Nesting. Nest on the ground, lined with grasses, is usually situated in a clump of grass or under or near a bush or tree in areas varying from open grassland to open woodland. *Eggs*, usually 10 to 13; brown or buff with or without fine dark brown spots. Incubation probably lasts about 24 days and is by the female.

Range. Breeds from north-central Alaska and Yukon east to central-western Quebec and south through the western North American interior to eastern Oregon, northern Utah, Colorado, Minnesota, and northern Michigan. Formerly farther south. Northern populations irregularly migratory.

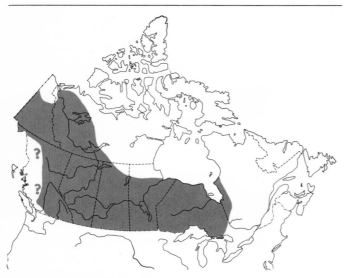

Breeding Distribution of Sharp-tailed Grouse

Range in Canada. Populations fluctuate numerically periodically. Breeding range peripheries subject to change and far from static: central and southern Yukon (north at least to Dawson, where sometimes common, and Mayo Landing), western Mackenzie (Fort Smith; Hay River; forts Providence and Rae; Canol; St. Charles Rapids; Fort Good Hope; valley of Lockhart and Anderson rivers, Conjuror Bay; occurrences reported north to Fort McPherson); northern and southern interior British Columbia (distribution local and poorly understood: Tagish Lake, Prophet River, and in southern interior west to Kleena Kleene region, north at least to Vanderhoof region, east to Baynes Lake and probably Elko); Alberta; Saskatchewan; Manitoba (Ilford, Bird, and probably Herchmer southward); western and northern Ontario (south to Lake of the Woods, Thunder Bay, Manitoulin Island, Geraldton, Hearst, Cochrane, Lake Abitibi); and central-western Quebec (Rupert House, probably north to Fort George, breeding distribution poorly known).

Winters within much of breeding range but is partly migratory or nomadic in northernmost segment. Occasional irruptive movements occur involving large numbers as in autumn 1932 in eastern Ontario and western Quebec, when the species was recorded south to Gravenhurst, Ontario; and Pontiac and Papineau counties, Quebec (*see* Snyder 1935, *Univ. Toronto Studies*, Biol. Ser. 40). Old records east to Saguenay River and Quebec City.

Subspecies. (1) *Pedioecetes phasianellus phasianellus* (Linnaeus): c.-w. Que., n. and c. Ont., n. Man. (2) *P. p. kennicotti* Suckley: w. Mack. south to Great Slave L. (3) *P. p. caurus* Friedmann: Yukon, n. and nw. B.C., n. Alta. (to Peace River – Lesser Slave Lake region) and nw. Sask. (Lake Athabasca). Area of intergradation with *phasianellus* unknown. (4) *P. p. columbianus* (Ord): interior c. and s. B.C. (5) *P. p. jamesi* Lincoln: c. and s. Alta., except mountains, s. Sask., and extreme sw. Man. (Whitewater Lake). (6) *P. p. campestris* Ridgway: s. Manitoba (except sw. corner) north to northern Lake Winnipeg and The Pas, and contiguous parts of w. Ont. (Lake of the Woods, Thunder Bay). No Manitoulin I. material available; therefore race unknown but probably *campestris*.

Remarks. The Sharp-tailed Grouse is the common grouse of the prairies. It is commonly miscalled 'prairie chicken,' but the real Prairie Chicken is another species altogether, which has all but disappeared from the Canadian prairies.

In spring the Sharp-tails gather on ancestral dancing grounds, and in the dawn the males perform a peculiar courtship dance, characterized by rapid stamping of the feet, lowered head, ruffled plumage, and a low booming sound, produced through the mouth by air from inflated purplish sacs on the sides of the neck.

SAGE GROUSE (Sage Hen)
La Gelinotte des armoises
Centrocercus urophasianus (Bonaparte)
Plate 21. L. male 26 to 29; female 21.75 to 23 in.

Unmistakable. A very large grouse. Upper parts finely marked with browns, buff, dull white, and black. Abdomen with large black patch (somewhat smaller in female). Tail of peculiarly shaped feathers, each one narrow, tapering gradually to a sharp point.

Measurements (*C. u. urophasianus*). *Adult male:* wing, 282–317.5 (299.4); tail, 241–285 (263.4); exposed culmen, 31.6–37 (35.1); tarsus, 52.4–58 (56.4). *Adult female:* wing, 247.5–279 (261.2) mm.

Field Marks. A very large greyish brown grouse of the sagebrush plains with a large black patch on the abdomen, and a rather long tail composed of narrow pointed feathers (*see* Ring-necked Pheasant).

Habitat. Plains and intermontane valleys where sagebrush (*Artemisia*) flourishes.

Nesting. Nest, a shallow depression in the ground, usually sparsely lined with grass and usually sheltered by a sage brush or clump of grass. *Eggs*, usually 7 to 9; an olive-buff, evenly spotted with brown. Incubation by female.

Range. Locally distributed permanent resident, now reduced numerically, from central Washington, southern Idaho, Montana, southeastern Alberta, southwestern Saskatchewan, and western North Dakota south to eastern California, Nevada, southern Utah, and western Colorado.

Breeding Distribution of Sage Grouse

Formerly extreme southern interior British Columbia and northern New Mexico.

Range in Canada. Permanent resident in southeastern Alberta (commonest in Manyberries – Wildhorse region with recent peripheral sight records at Magrath, Milk River, and Champion) and southwestern Saskatchewan (plains between International Boundary and Cypress Hills east to Wood Mountain). Formerly southern British Columbia (locally: Osoyoos Lake) but now extirpated there.

Subspecies. *Centrocercus urophasianus urophasianus* (Bonaparte) is the only race known to occur in Canada today. Formerly *C. u. phaios* Aldrich occurred in s. B.C. but is now extirpated.

Family **Phasianidae** – Quails, Pheasants, Peacocks

Number of Species in North America 9; in Canada 6

Fowl-like birds with legs, toes, and nostrils bare. In some species the legs are equipped with spurs. Some species have more or less extensive areas of bare skin on the head. Tail varies from short to very long. The family, which is widely distributed, contains some of the most gorgeous fowl.

BOBWHITE
Le Colin de Virginie. *Colinus virginianus* (Linnaeus)
Plate 23. L. 9.5 to 10.60 in.

Male: White stripe above eye; throat patch white framed by black. In female the white of these areas is replaced by buff, and the black by reddish brown. Upper parts predominantly reddish brown and flanks striped (not barred) in both sexes. Completely unfeathered tarsi and diminutive size separate it from Canadian grouse. Ruddy upper parts distinguish it from other quail. Striped (instead of barred) flanks eliminate confusion with the larger Chukar and the Gray Partridge.

Measurements (*C. v. virginianus*). *Adult male:* wing, 109.8–116.2 (112.7); tail, 61.5–65.8 (63.4); exposed culmen, 13–14.9 (13.8); tarsus, 31.5–33.5 (32.6). *Adult female:* wing, 109.6–115 (112.5) mm.

Field Marks. Distinctive face markings and ruddy upper parts distinguish it from other quails; diminutive size from our grouse, partridges, and pheasants. Its whistled *bobwhite* is unmistakable.

Habitat. Cultivated areas growing grain and corn, or weedy abandoned farms near brushy patches or edges for shelter.

Nesting. Nest, a hollow in the ground, lined with grass and usually well concealed by an arch woven from the surrounding vegetation. *Eggs*, 14 to 16, more or less; plain dull white. Incubation lasts about 23 to 24 days (various authorities) and is by both parents.

Range. Eastern Wyoming, southern Minnesota, central Michigan, extreme southern Ontario, New York, and Massachusetts south through eastern New Mexico and western Texas to Guatemala, southeastern United States and Cuba. Introduced in Washington.

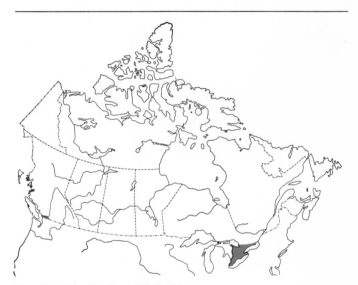

Breeding Distribution of Bobwhite

Range in Canada. Permanent resident in extreme southern Ontario: north to southern Huron, Middlesex, Oxford, Brant, and Lincoln counties (Snyder, 1957). Range has fluctuated violently within historic times. With settlement and clearing of southern Ontario, it spread rapidly to a maximum in the 1840's (Clarke, 1954, *Fed. Ontario Nat. Bull.* 63: 6–15) north to Kingston, Muskoka, and south Georgian Bay but now much decreased. Introduced into other parts of Canada mostly without permanent success but reported still breeding in southwestern British Columbia at Huntingdon (Munro and Cowan, 1947).

Subspecies. *Colinus virginianus virginianus* (Linnaeus) is the native subspecies. Origin of B.C. stock unknown.

Remarks. As a destroyer of harmful insects, as a game bird, or just as a pleasant aspect of the countryside, the Bobwhite rates highly. Unfortunately it is not more widely distributed in Canada.

115

CALIFORNIA QUAIL

Le Colin de Californie. *Lophortyx californicus* (Shaw)
Plate 23. L. 9.5 to 10.5 in.

A small, chicken-like, brown and blue-grey bird with a black forward-curved plume standing up from the crown. To be looked for in Canada only in southern British Columbia. Male has jet-black throat with white border, white streaks on flanks, scaly abdomen with small chestnut patch. Female similar but lacks the black-and-white head pattern, has smaller crown plume, and shows little, if any, chestnut on abdomen. Bobwhite has no crown plume and is very differently coloured. Mountain Quail has chestnut throat patch, conspicuously barred flanks, and the crown plume is longer, *straight*, not forward-curved.

Measurements. *Adult male:* wing, 105.6–114.5 (110.5); tail, 76–95.5 (85.6); exposed culmen, 11.8–13.8 (12.4); tarsus, 30–33.7 (31.9). *Adult female:* wing, 105.6–114 (110.1) mm.

Field Marks. As above.

Habitat. Tall shrubbery or low trees interspersed with less extensive open areas (grassy or weedy ground for foraging); hence frequent about man's dwellings, gardens, and parks; mainly in low country.

Nesting. Nest, a hollow in the ground lined with grass or leaves, usually more or less hidden by shrubbery. *Eggs,* usually 10 to 18, are creamy white to buffy, more or less irregularly marked with brown.

Range. Oregon and western Nevada south to southern Baja California. Introduced into southern British Columbia, Washington, and Utah.

Breeding Distribution of California Quail

Range in Canada. Introduced and well established locally for many years in southern British Columbia: southern Vancouver Island (Victoria, Comox); Vancouver; Okanagan Valley (Osoyoos to Vernon); Keremeos; Cache Creek to Twenty Mile House.

Subspecies. Parent stocks appear to include more than one race, now mixed. It seems best not to try to refer present stock to any one race.

MOUNTAIN QUAIL

Le Colin des montagnes. *Oreortyx pictus* (Douglas)
L. 10.6 to 11.5 in.

Unmistakable. A small chicken-like bird distinguished from other quail by a long *straight* crown plume, chestnut throat, bold white bars on chestnut flanks. Sexes similar.

Measurements (*O. p. palmeri*). *Adult male:* wing, 129–136 (131.2); tail, 71–82 (76.5); culmen from base, 15.7–17.9 (16.9); tarsus, 35–37 (36.3). *Adult female:* wing, 125–134 (130.2) mm (Ridgway and Friedmann).

Habitat. Mountains and hills but little definite information is available on preferences of this introduced species in its restricted range in Canada.

Nesting. A depression in the ground scantily lined with grass or leaves. *Eggs,* 6 to 15 in United States, are pale cream to buff, unmarked.

Range. Washington and southwestern Idaho south to northern Baja California. Introduced to southwestern British Columbia and Washington.

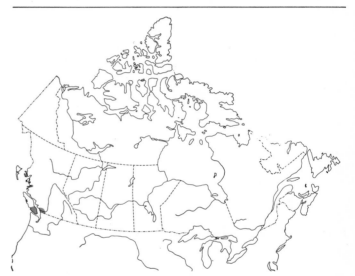

Breeding Distribution of Mountain Quail

Range in Canada. Scarce local resident in extreme southwestern British Columbia where probably introduced many years ago, possibly native, but history obscure. Vancouver Island: small numbers present for over a century, mainly in hills between Victoria and Sooke Harbour; reported north to Duncan. In November 1958 six were observed on Mount Finlayson, and the species was heard calling in spring, 1959 (G. A. Poynter, MS.). Southwestern mainland: Three shot on Vedder Mountain, September 26, 1921.

Subspecies. *Oreortyx pictus palmeri* Oberholser.

RING-NECKED PHEASANT

Le Faisan à collier. *Phasianus colchicus* Linnaeus
Plate 21. L. male 32.5 to 36; female 18.0 to 22.5 in.

The gorgeous male with long (16 to 18 in.) tapering pointed tail, bill resembling that of a domestic rooster, and spurred tarsus is quite unlike any other wild bird in Canada. The white ring about neck is variable in extent and sometimes lacking. Female very differently coloured: a dark-spotted, pale-brownish hen-like bird with very long (11 to 12 in.), slender, tapering, pointed tail. Females might be confused with the locally distributed Sage Grouse but lack the black abdominal patch of that species and have unfeathered legs (tarsi).

Measurements. *Adult male:* wing, 228.5–244.5 (236.6); tail, 428.5–514.5 (460.9); exposed culmen, 28.5–32 (30.7); tarsus, 66.5–75 (71). *Adult female:* wing, 198–224 (207.1) mm.

Habitat. Mainly farmland with fields of grain, corn, alfalfa, soybeans, grass, and weeds near cover, such as hedges, ditch shrubbery, ground-hugging shrub patches, marsh edges, ungrazed woodland borders, groves with underbrush. Irrigated areas on the prairies.

Nesting. Nest, a depression in the ground lined with grass or leaves, is usually in fields, wood edges, or under bushes. *Eggs*, 8 to 15, are plain olive brown. Incubation 22¼ to 25 days, by female (various authors).

Range. It is native from the Ukraine east through central Asia to Manchuria and southern China; also in Japan and Formosa. Introduced and widely established in Europe (including British Isles), New Zealand, and North America. In North America from southern Canada south locally to California, Utah, New Mexico, northwestern Texas, northwestern Oklahoma, southern Illinois, Pennsylvania, New Jersey, and Maryland.

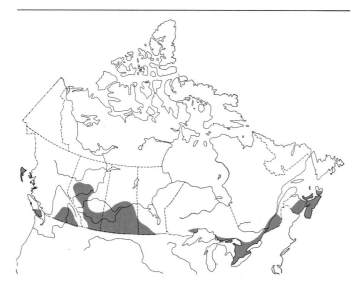

Breeding Distribution of Ring-necked Pheasant

Status in Canada. Introduced. Permanent resident, locally distributed across southern Canada: British Columbia (southern parts: notably successful in Osoyoos-Keremeos area; dry country north of Ashcroft; parts of southern Vancouver Island; established also on Queen Charlotte Islands); southern Alberta (particularly successful on irrigated southern parts but ranging north to near Athabasca; introduced also in Grande Prairie district); southern Saskatchewan (north to about the Battleford and Carlton areas; introduced at Nipawin where in 1959 it was existing precariously); southwestern Manitoba; southern Ontario (mainly south of southern Bruce Peninsula, Lake Simcoe, and Kingston; especially successful on Pelee Island; locally in small numbers north to Ottawa and St. Joseph's Island; also Thunder Bay district); southwestern Quebec (Eastern Townships, Montreal; reported also from Hudson, Hull, and even Charlesbourg); New Brunswick, Prince Edward Island, and Nova Scotia (but rare on Cape Breton Island where status is uncertain).

Subspecies. Populations, introduced from several subspecies, now mingled and composite, are best referred to species only; hence *Phasianus colchicus* Linnaeus.

CHUKAR
La Perdrix bartavelle. *Alectoris graeca* (Meisner)
Plate 23. L. 13 to 15.5 in.

A medium-sized chicken-like bird. Sexes similar. Upper parts greyish brown with pinkish wash. Black band from forehead through eye, down side of neck, and broadening across upper breast. Rest of breast bluish grey. Throat patch and abdomen, buff. Flanks, boldly barred with black and chestnut. Outer tail, reddish brown terminally. Bill, feet, and eyelids, red to pink.

Measurements. *Adult male* (2 specimens): wing, 166.5–167.9; tail, 97.5–101.2; exposed culmen, 21–21.9; tarsus, 47.5–49.1. *Adult female* (1 specimen): wing, 153.5 mm.

Field Marks. Black border around throat patch, bold black bars on flanks, red bill and legs. In flight shows reddish outer tail like Gray Partridge, but Gray Partridge has no black on head, breast, or flanks and no red on legs and bill.

Habitat. Rugged steep terrain in areas of light precipitation, relatively snow-free in winter.

Breeding Distribution of Chukar

Range. Native to mountainous central and southern Europe and Asia. Introduced into drier mountainous western United States and north to extreme southern British Columbia and southern Alberta.

Range in Canada. Recently introduced to interior southern British Columbia (1950–1955) where good populations are currently present in the Similkameen valley: U.S. border to Keremeos; Okanagan Valley: U.S. border to Penticton; Thompson Valley: Shuswap Lake to Lytton; and Fraser Valley: extent unknown but Lytton to probably mouth of Chilcotin River (Patrick W. Martin, in litt. May 5, 1961); also Alberta: Milk River Valley, but introductions not too promising. Has been introduced into Saskatchewan but success unknown.

GRAY PARTRIDGE

(European Partridge; Hungarian Partridge)
La Perdrix européenne. *Perdix perdix* (Linnaeus)
Plate 23. L. ca. 12 to 13 in.

The *unmarked reddish brown* outer tail feathers distinguish it from other chicken-like game birds found in Canada except the Chukar (*see* Field Marks). The very finely vermiculated breast separates it from all others including the Chukar. The chestnut horseshoe-shaped patch on the abdomen when present is diagnostic, but it is smaller or absent in females. Crown in males has narrow pale streaks; in females the crown streaks are broadened into spots.

Measurements. *Adult male:* wing, 151–161.6 (154.2); tail, 77–86.8 (80.8); exposed culmen, 14.8–16.4 (15.6); tarsus, 40–43.1 (41.3). *Adult female:* wing, 144–158 (151.3) mm.

Field Marks. A smallish shortish-tailed partridge (but obviously larger than any quail) with plain, pale brown eyebrow line, cheeks, and throat, greyish breast, chestnut-brown bars on the flanks, and (in male) a chestnut abdominal patch. Reddish brown outer tail feathers, unmarked, separate it from all but Chukar (red phase Ruffed Grouse show a conspicuous dark subterminal tail band), but the present species differs from the Chukar in lacking a broad black head and neck stripe, in having no suggestion of red on bill or legs, and in possessing brown (not mainly black) flank bars. Voice in Spring a raspy *túr-ip*.

Habitat. Open grassland and agricultural land.

Nesting. Nest, a hollow scraped in the ground and lined with grasses, usually in shelter of grass or low shrubs. *Eggs,*

usually 9 to 20, are plain olive brown. Incubation, 23 to 25 days (Witherby, *et al.*), is by female.

Range. Native of western Eurasia from the British Isles, southern Norway, southern Sweden, and middle Russia south to northern Portugal, northern Spain, Italy, Rumania, and southern Russia, east about to western Mongolia. Widely introduced and established in parts of North America from southern Canada to northern and middle United States.

Range in Canada. Introduced. Permanent resident, more or less well established in suitable southern parts of the country. Numbers subject to fluctuations and range limits uncertain because of repeated introduction attempts on marginal or submarginal habitat. Resident in southern British Columbia (locally), including a small southern Vancouver Island population; southern and central Alberta; southern Saskatchewan (north about to Prince Albert, Carlton, Nipawin); southern Manitoba; southern and central Ontario (mostly east: locally north to North Bay, Timmins, Cochrane; also Thunder Bay district); extreme southwestern Quebec (north probably to St. Justin); southern New Brunswick; Prince Edward Island; and Nova Scotia (locally).

Subspecies. Origin of imported stocks is poorly known, and probably several of the many subspecies recognized in its native range are intermixed.

Remarks. This little foreigner was imported into North America as a game bird and, as such, has proved to be a great success in many parts of its new home. It flushes warily with a clatter of wings and a rapid cackle. It flies and glides speedily but never very high above the ground. The reddish spread tail shows prominently in flight.

The Gray Partridge is a hardy species, able to withstand the cold and ordinary snow of winter in most southern parts of Canada. At times very heavy snows can cause high mortality, but even at that the species manages to hold its own in marginal territory through its surprisingly high reproductive potential.

In mid-winter, when snow lies deep over the land, coveys of Gray Partridge often appear about farmyards and even on the grounds about suburban dwellings.

Breeding Distribution of Gray Partridge

Family **Meleagrididae**–Turkeys

Number of Species in North America 1; in Canada 1

A small family of two species, confined to the New World. The domestic turkey, familiar to everyone, is derived from the wild bird and illustrates the main characters of the family.

TURKEY

Le Dindon sauvage. *Meleagris gallopavo* Linnaeus
L. 36 to 48 in.

Like domestic turkey, but tail of Canadian wild birds tipped with brown instead of whitish or pale buff.

Measurements (*M. g. silvestris*). *Adult male:* wing, 480–

550 (512.9); tail, 370–440 (397.2); culmen (from cere), 31–38 (34.8); tarsus, 146–181.5 (162.6). *Adult female:* wing, 382–438 (414.3) mm (Ridgway and Friedmann).

Habitat. Extensive mature deciduous forest.

Nesting. On the ground. *Eggs,* pale buff spotted with purplish grey. Incubation 28 days (A. C. Bent).

Range. Native to eastern and southwestern United States and Mexico; formerly southern Ontario. Now extirpated or reduced in much of former range.

Range in Canada. Extirpated. Formerly a permanent resident (in fluctuating but sometimes fair numbers) in extreme southern Ontario, north to Lambton, Middlesex, Oxford, Brant, and Wentworth counties; also Simcoe County; range extended also eastward through parts of Halton, Peel, and York counties to Durham County. Apparently it was temporarily greatly reduced in unusually severe winters, as in 1842, but was able to recover while suitable habitat remained. Destruction of its timber habitat was undoubtedly the primary factor in its extirpation, and its decline kept pace with the depletion of the forests during the 19th century. Its final extirpation in Canada was completed probably about 1902 (Clarke, 1948, *Sylva* 4 (6): 5–12; 24). Modest reintroduction attempts have been made in its former range.

Success could at best be only extremely local today because of paucity of suitable habitat.

Subspecies. *Meleagris gallopavo silvestris* Vieillot.

Remarks. Many people are surprised to learn that wild turkeys once inhabited even a small part of Canada. Here these large birds were on the northern periphery of their range, and their existence seems to have been somewhat precarious at best because of heavy mortality suffered in severest winters. As long as their hardwood forest habitat remained and hunting pressure was light, the surviving population was able to recover from such winter kills. Once ever-widening settlement decimated the forests, and as more and more gunners roamed the land, the wild turkey in Ontario had no chance.

The wild turkey very closely resembles the domesticated variety. The latter originated from a Mexican subspecies, however; it can be distinguished from the wild bird by its whitish or pale buffy tips to the upper tail coverts and tip of the tail. The wild turkey of Canada had the upper tail coverts and tail-tip rusty or chestnut.

In the Prairie Provinces, the Sandhill Crane is commonly miscalled 'Wild Turkey,' but the crane is an entirely different kind of bird.

Order Gruiformes–Cranes, Rails, and Allies

Family Gruidae–Cranes

Number of Species in North America 3; in Canada 3

Large, long-necked, long-legged birds with rather long straight bills. Superficially they resemble herons, but they differ from them in having no partition between the nostrils; shorter hind toe, which is elevated above the level of the other toes; middle toe-nail with no comb-like inner edge; adults (in Canadian species) with the forehead bare; plumage denser and firmer; tertials, very long and curving down over the primaries.

In flight, cranes carry the neck straight and extended; herons fold the neck in an S-shape.

WHOOPING CRANE
La Grue blanche d'Amérique
Grus americana (Linnaeus)
Plate 23. L. 50 to 56 in.

Adults: Mainly white; wing tips, alula, and a very small patch on back of head, black; crown, lores, and cheeks below and behind eye, bare (except for sprinkling of blackish hair-like feathers) and dull red. *Immatures (first autumn):* Variable. Rusty brown, buffy, and white in various proportions, brown predominating on head and neck, white on under parts and back; no bare red face patch.

Measurements. *Adult male:* wing, 550–630 (601.7); tail, 205–245 (223.8); exposed culmen, 129–147 (138.5); tarsus, 265–301 (276.5). *Adult female:* wing, 583–610 (one 535), (597.9) mm (Ridgway).

Field Marks. A very large long-legged, long-necked, heron-like bird, white in colour with black wing tips (more or less hidden when wing is folded) and red face. In flight it carries neck outstretched, a characteristic that separates it from herons, and the upstroke of the wing is quicker than the downstroke. The Snow Goose and White Pelican also are large white birds with black wing tips, but both have short legs; in addition, the pelican flies with neck folded back against the shoulders.

Habitat. For nesting, marshy or swampy slough country, formerly mainly in the aspen belt of the Prairie Provinces. In migration, it visits grainfields near sloughs or ponds.

Nesting. Nest, a flat-topped mound of marsh vegetation with a slight depression in the centre, usually in shallow water. *Eggs*, usually 2; buff marked with various browns. Incubation 34 to 35 days (R. P. Allen) by both sexes.

Range. Now precariously near extinction. Currently known to breed only in southern Mackenzie and to winter in Aransas National Wildlife Refuge, coastal Texas. Formerly bred in southern Mackenzie, the Prairie Provinces, North Dakota, Minnesota, Iowa, Illinois, and Louisiana (White Lake). Formerly wintered from coastal Texas, Louisiana, Alabama, Georgia, and Florida south to central Mexico.

Range in Canada. Perilously close to extinction. The few wild individuals left are known to breed only in Wood Buffalo Park, Mackenzie. Migrates through Saskatchewan and eastern Alberta.

Known former breeding range included southern Mackenzie (Fort Resolution, Salt River); Alberta (near Killam, Whitford Lake, Wainwright; probably elsewhere but records either lacking or uncertain); Saskatchewan (Battleford, Baliol, Bradwell, Muddy Lake, north of Davidson, Yorkton, Moose Mountain); Manitoba (Oak Lake, Shoal Lake, Winnipeg region). In migration east rarely to southern Ontario (Yarker, September 27, 1871).

Whooping Crane Population (Autumn 1955–1964)

Year	Wild Population			Number in Captivity	Total Population
1955	28			3	31
1956	24 including 3 young			3	27
1957	26	”	3 ”	5	31
1958	32	”	9 ”	6	38
1959	33	”	2 ”	6	39
1960	36	”	6 ”	6	42
1961	38	”	5 ”	7	45
1962	32	”	no ”	8	40
1963	33	”	7 ”	7	40
1964	42	”	10 ”	8	50

(Data compiled by Canadian Wildlife Service)

Reported former occurrences, without evidence of breeding, and mostly unsatisfactorily documented, north to northern Mackenzie (Fort Anderson, Mackenzie Delta), Keewatin (Baker Lake, Eskimo Point), and northern Manitoba (Churchill).

Remarks. The Whooping Crane, the tallest of Canadian birds, has for some years tottered on the brink of extinction.

Formerly it ranged over a large part of western North America. Since the white man's coming to the Prairies, with his extensive agriculture and his gun, the Whooping Crane's numbers have dwindled. Now only a pitiful remnant is all that stands between it and extinction. Needless to say, it is highly illegal to molest this fine species at any time. A large bird with a low reproductive potential, deprived of the greater part of its former breeding range, and with the added handicap of having to make a long, dangerous migration flight twice a year between Texas and Mackenzie, its chances of long survival seem poor.

SANDHILL CRANE (Little Brown Crane)
La Grue canadienne. *Grus canadensis* (Linnaeus)
Plate 23. L. 34 to 48 in.

A large heron-like bird of general slaty coloration, usually more or less stained with rusty (adventitious in adults), black wing tips, and in adults a bare (except for sparse black hair-like feathers) reddish patch on forehead and upper face. Young more brownish and without bare forehead patch. Most likely to be confused with Great Blue Heron (which is widely miscalled 'crane'), but the Sandhill Crane is readily distinguished by (1) its more even grey coloration lacking any decided stripes or other pattern, (2) broad perforate nostrils (one can readily look through them to other side of bill), (3) the much shorter hind toe which is elevated above the level of the others, and (4) the middle toenail is not pectinate (*see* Fig. 15).

Measurements (*G. c. canadensis*). *Adult male:* wing, 427.5–474 (460.9); tail, 146–183.5 (170.3); exposed culmen, 88–102 (95.6); tarsus, 160–206 (187.9). *Adult female:* wing, 423–456 (440.3) mm.

Field Marks. Heron-like appearance, large size, even slaty coloration, and at closer range, reddish forehead. The Great Blue Heron is widely miscalled 'crane,' but true cranes including the present species are easily distinguished from all herons, even at great distances, by the crane habit of flying with outstretched neck and noticeably quicker wing upstrokes. The voice of the Sandhill also is distinctive — a vibrant, far-carrying *gar-oo-ooo*.

Habitat. In breeding season, marshes, bogs, broad flat arctic valleys, marshy tundra, and neighbouring vicinities. In migration it visits fields, marshes, and shallow-water edges of lakes.

Nesting. Nest, a mass of aquatic vegetation in shallow water or a depression in the ground, often lined with grass or willow sticks, on hummocks, sometimes on a muskrat house. *Eggs*, usually 2; buff to olive buff, spotted and blotched with browns. Incubation, by both parents, requires about 29 to 30 days (L. H. Walkinshaw), or perhaps a little more.

Range. Breeds from northeastern Siberia, northern Alaska, and middle arctic Canada (Banks and Devon islands), south locally to northeastern California, Nevada, Wyoming, Colorado, South Dakota, and Michigan; also from southern Mississippi, Alabama, and Georgia south through Florida to Cuba and the Isle of Pines. Winters from southern United States south to central Mexico and Cuba.

Range in Canada. Transient and summer resident. Breeds or formerly bred (extirpated from much of southern parts of former range) from Banks Island (Mercy Bay, Kellett River, Sachs Harbour) and southeastern Devon Island (Dundas Harbour) southward through the Arctic Archipelago and southeast to Cumberland Peninsula of Baffin Island; northern Yukon (north coast, breeding unknown in interior); Mackenzie; Keewatin (south to McConnell River and mouth of Thlewiaza River); Southampton Island; southern and coastal British Columbia (Lulu Island; northern Vancouver Island; Queen Charlotte Islands; parklands of the Cariboo; Kleena Kleene region; Quesnel region; formerly Okanagan Valley, Sumas Prairie, Pitt Meadows); Alberta (now mainly from Athabasca Valley north. Formerly south to Innisfail, Rocky Mountain House, Spotted Lake, Sedgwick); Saskatchewan (central and northern parts; formerly south to Touchwood Hills, Saltcoats, Balgonie, Grayson, Kutawagan Lake); Manitoba (formerly Shoal Lake, Sperling, Eden; Lake St. Martin in 1933, but present status unknown there; nesting not definitely known in northern Manitoba, but there are breeding season occurrences near Churchill and Ilford); and Ontario (junction Asheweig and Winisk rivers and junction of Attawapiskat and Muketei rivers; noted in summer between Kapuskasing and Moosonee, and near Big Sandy Lake; formerly bred in southern Ontario: Lake St. Clair).

Migration primarily west of Hudson Bay. As a transient (in addition to breeding range) it is found through Yukon, interior British Columbia, and southern parts of the Prairie Provinces (locally large flocks). Spectacular concentrations at north end of Last Mountain Lake, Quill Lakes and Kindersley – South Saskatchewan River region, Saskatchewan, in southward migration. Rare transient in southern Ontario (e.g., Guelph, Toronto, Rondeau, Beaumaris; also Thunder Bay region). Casual in Prince Edward Island (Alexandra, September 22, 1905; Earnscliffe, October 25, 1905) and in Newfoundland.

Subspecies. (1) *Grus canadensis tabida* (Peters), the more southern of the two races inhabiting Canada (B.C., the Prairie Prov. except n. Man.; formerly s. Ont.) is now extirpated from much of its former range in settled country. (2) *Grus canadensis canadensis* (Linnaeus), a smaller race, occupies the vast northern remainder of the breeding range mostly in unsettled country and therefore less often molested by man. It makes up the bulk of the large flocks that migrate across the settled West today and has been taken in migration east to Beaumaris, Ont., and casually in P.E.I.

COMMON CRANE
Grus grus subsp.

Has appeared in Alberta on three occasions: one near Cavendish, December 11–20, 1957; Stirling Lake, south of Lethbridge, March 20, 1958; and near Athabasca, September 19, 1958 (Wishart and Sharp, 1959, *The Auk* 76: 358). Identifiable photographs were taken. It is not known whether these concerned the same individual or the same as that seen in Alaska on April 24, 1958 (Kessel and Kelly 1958, *The Auk* 75: 465). Both Sharp and Wishart (in litt.)

found the Alberta bird wary, and there is nothing to suggest that it was an escaped captive.

Family **Rallidae** – Rails, Gallinules, Coots

Number of Species in North America 13; in Canada 10

Rails are predominantly marsh birds. They are expert skulkers and move among the marsh vegetation with mouse-like dexterity. When approached, they usually prefer to run instead of fly. When they do fly, flight is weak and slow, and the bird quickly drops back into the cover of the marsh. They are often noisy, especially at night, and are far more often heard than seen. Their laterally compressed bodies, enabling them to pass through small spaces in dense marsh vegetation, have given rise to the expression 'thin as a rail.'

The legs are strong, the front toes long and slender; wings are short, rounded, and rather weak; tail short; bill variable from short to long in the different species. Food is largely seeds, insects, and snails.

KING RAIL

Le Râle élégant. *Rallus elegans* Audubon
Plate 23. L. 15.5 to 19 in.

A large, long-billed rail. Similar in colour and outline to the Virginia Rail but cheeks not grey. The King Rail's much larger size separates it from all other rails of *regular* occurrence in Canada (but *see* Clapper Rail).

Measurements. *Adult male:* wing, 159–177 (163.4); tail, 56–72.5 (65.9); exposed culmen, 58–65.5 (62.5); tarsus 52–64 (58.4). *Adult female:* wing, 147–162 (154.3) mm (Ridgway and Friedmann).

Habitat. Freshwater marshes, but more inclined than most rails to wander onto adjacent fields.

Nesting. Nest, a well-made structure of marsh vegetation supported a few inches above water in clumps of marsh vegetation or bushes; sometimes a grass-lined scrape in moist ground in or near a marsh. *Eggs,* usually 5 to 11; pale buff with small spots of several shades of brown. Incubation 21 to 24 days, by both sexes.

Range. Breeds from eastern Nebraska, central Minnesota, southern Michigan, southern Ontario, central New York, and (rarely) Massachusetts, south to southern Texas and Florida; also Cuba and Isle of Pines. Winters mainly in southern United States and Cuba; occasionally much farther north.

Range in Canada. Breeds in extreme southern Ontario (St. Clair flats, Point Abino, Niagara River near Welland, Port Rowan, Long Point, Hamilton, Toronto, Terra Cotta). Non-breeding birds recorded in Ontario to Crane Lake on Bruce Peninsula; Port Perry; Nottawasaga River, Simcoe Co.; Kingston; Ottawa. Casual or accidental in Manitoba (Long Lake, October 26, 1921), Quebec (Sabrevois, October 1899), and Newfoundland (near St. John's, October 20, 1935). Casual in winter in southern Ontario (Point Pelee, Toronto, La Salle, Kingston).

Subspecies. *Rallus elegans elegans* Audubon.

CLAPPER RAIL

Le Râle gris. *Rallus longirostris* Boddaert
L. 14 to 16 in.

A large long-billed rail, likely to be confused only with the King Rail. The Clapper Rail's markings are similar but less conspicuous; colours usually considerably paler and more greyish; dimensions in average slightly smaller. These characters separate most specimens, but some individuals are perplexingly like King Rails and should be identified by specialists. Most races frequent salt marshes where King Rails are seldom found.

Measurements (*R. l. crepitans*). *Adult male:* wing, 142.5–159.5 (151.1); tail, 55–69 (64.6); exposed culmen, 55–69.5 (63.3); tarsus, 48–56 (51.7). *Adult female:* wing, 135.5–160 (146.8) mm (Ridgway and Friedmann).

Range. Coasts from California south to Ecuador and northwestern Peru; and from Connecticut southward coastally through southern United States, Mexico, Central America to Sao Paulo, Brazil; also the West Indies and in freshwater marshes in Distrito Federal, Mexico, and the lower Colorado Valley.

Status in Canada. Casual in New Brunswick (Grand Manan, January 17, 1952; Pt. Lepreau, September 21, 1952; Kent Island, April 1, 1953; near Alma, October 4, 1954); Nova Scotia (Lawrencetown, May 10, 1892, and October 1893. Sight records: Sable River, September 2, 1957; Brier Island, September 23, 1957); and Prince Edward Island (Mount Stewart, December 21, 1957).

Subspecies. *Rallus longirostris crepitans* Gmelin. Possibly one or more other races are represented by the specimens, but they have not been examined by the writer.

VIRGINIA RAIL

Le Râle de Virginie. *Rallus limicola* Vieillot
Plate 23. L. 8.9 to 10.2 in.

A small cinnamon-breasted rail with long slender reddish bill and grey cheeks. Our other long-billed rails, the King and the Clapper, are obviously much larger with more than twice its body bulk. Our other small rails have stubby bills. Adult-size young in late summer are mostly black.

Measurements. *Adult male:* wing, 101–107.9 (105.4); tail, 40–48.6 (44.5); exposed culmen, 35.3–41.8 (39.9); tarsus, 33.1–38.2 (36.4). *Adult female:* wing, 94.2–102.2 (98.1) mm.

Field Marks. As above.

Habitat. Fresh-water, bulrush, cattail, or sedge marshes.

Nesting. Nest, in a marsh, a loosely woven basket of marsh vegetation with grass lining, attached to stalks of a clump of vegetation a little above the mud or water. *Eggs,* 7 to 12; very pale buff to whitish, sparingly spotted with reddish brown. They are paler and less heavily spotted than those of the Sora. Incubation 19 to 20 days (L. H. Walkinshaw) by both sexes.

Range. Breeds from southern Canada south locally to southern South America (Straits of Magellan). Winters mainly from southern United States southward; irregularly farther north.

Range in Canada. Breeds in southern British Columbia

(Vancouver Island, Tatton Lake, 150 Mile House); Alberta (definitely breeding at Vermilion, Brooks, and Czar; observations at Glenevis, Many Island Lake, Millet, Lac Ste. Anne, Spruce Grove; probably at Fort Chipewyan—specimen in breeding condition June 30, 1945); central and southern Saskatchewan (Regina, Yorkton district, Dafoe, Simpson, Kutawagan Lake, Kazan Lake, Prince Albert, Mountain Cabin on Carrot River); southern Manitoba (Hillside Beach, Winnipeg, Dog Lake, Indian Bay, Riding Mountain; recorded in summer and probably breeds north

Breeding Distribution of Virginia Rail

to Halcrow Lake near The Pas and to Moose and Cedar lakes); central and southern Ontario (north at least to Wabigoon, Maskinonge Bay, Bigwood, Ottawa; recorded in summer, probably breeds, north to Kapuskasing, Timmins, Cochrane); southern Quebec (Hatley; Montreal, Senneville, Quebec City, St. Fulgence on Saguenay River, Gaspé, Magdalen Islands); New Brunswick (Grand Manan; Midgic); and southwestern Newfoundland (Doyles). Breeding records lacking for Nova Scotia and Prince Edward Island.

Scarce visitor to Prince Edward Island (Tignish, Belle River; Mount Stewart: three taken in muskrat traps November 17 to 30, 1957). Winters in small numbers in southern (mainly southwestern) British Columbia, and casually southern Ontario and Nova Scotia.

Subspecies. *Rallus limicola limicola* Vieillot.

SORA

Le Râle de Caroline. *Porzana carolina* (Linnaeus)
Plate 23. L. 8.0 to 9.5 in.

A chunky small rail with short yellowish bill. *Throat and front of face, black. Breast grey.* Upper parts olive brown, inconspicuously streaked with black and narrowly (feather edges) with white. Young are similar but have no black on throat or face, and no grey on breast: throat white, breast light brown. Young Soras resemble Yellow Rail but are larger; white streaks on back are longitudinal (not trans-

verse), and there is no white on the tips of the secondaries. Downies are black with orange bristles on throat.

Measurements. *Adult male:* wing, 100.4–108.9 (104.8); tail, 40.5–50.6 (45.7); exposed culmen, 21–24.1 (22.2); tarsus, 31.2–36.5 (33.8). *Adult female:* wing, 97.6–108.4 (101.9) mm.

Field Marks. Short yellow bill eliminates all rails of regular occurrence in Canada except Yellow Rail, but grey breast, black throat, and face of adult Sora distinguish it. Vocally a far-carrying whinny on a descending scale is characteristic (*see* Yellow Rail).

Habitat. In breeding season freshwater or brackish marshes. In migration sometimes also salt marshes.

Nesting. Nest, a shallow basket woven of dead marsh vegetation attached to stalks of marsh plants; sometimes a heap of marsh vegetation; sometimes on ground in grass near marsh or pond. *Eggs,* usually 8 to 13; buffy spotted with browns. Eggs are darker and more heavily spotted than those of Virginia Rail. Incubation 16 to 20 days (L. H. Walkinshaw) by both sexes.

Range. Breeds from Canada south to northern Baja California, Nevada, southern New Mexico, northern Missouri, Ohio, West Virginia, and Pennsylvania. Winters mainly from southern United States south to the West Indies, Colombia, and Peru; occasionally farther north in the United States.

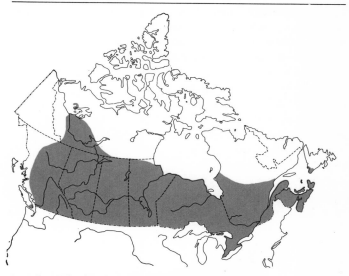

Breeding Distribution of Sora

Range in Canada. Breeds in central and southern British Columbia (north at least to Nulki Lake and Peace River, west to southern Vancouver Island; recorded in summer northwest to Hazelton), southern Mackenzie (Mills Lake; Great Slave Lake; and Fort Simpson. Probably farther north: sight records of three, Brackett Lake, July 10; of four, 20 miles east of Fort Franklin, July 15; and of one east of Norman Wells—S. D. MacDonald and W. J. Smith), Alberta, Saskatchewan, Manitoba (north to Churchill), Ontario, central-western and southern Quebec (Rupert House, Great Whale River, Lake St. John, Godbout, Montreal, Hatley, Gaspé, Magdalen Islands), New Brunswick, Nova Scotia, Prince Edward Island, and Newfoundland (Codroy: nest and eggs—L. M. Tuck).

Casual in southern Labrador (Sandwich Bay, Battle Harbour), southeastern Quebec (Harrington Harbour); and Queen Charlotte Islands (Masset), British Columbia. Occasional in winter in southwestern British Columbia (Lulu Island, Pitt Meadows).

YELLOW RAIL

Le Râle jaune. *Coturnicops noveboracensis* (Gmelin)
Plate 23. L. 6.5 to 7.7 in.

A small short-billed buffy rail, similar in outline to the Sora. Breast buffy, throat light. Back marked with fine *white crossbars*. Separable from Sora by white tips of the secondaries and by fine white crossbarring on back (Sora has white longitudinal stripes). Downies are black but differ from downy Soras in lacking orange bristles on throat.

Measurements. *Adult male:* wing, 73–93 (86.7); tail, 27.5–38 (33.3); exposed culmen, 11.5–15.5 (13.9); tarsus, 21–27.5 (23.7). *Adult female:* wing, 75.5–89 (84.2) mm (Ridgway and Friedmann).

Field Marks. Short bill distinguishes it from other rails of regular occurrence in Canada except the Sora. Adult Soras have a grey breast and a black throat and face. Immatures of the two species are difficult to distinguish in the field except in flight during which the Yellow Rail shows a white wing patch (white tips to secondaries) or at close range when the fine white *crossbarring* on the upper parts of the Yellow can be seen. A common call is a clicking *tick-tick*, *tick-tick-tick* (in twos and threes) easy to recognize once learned.

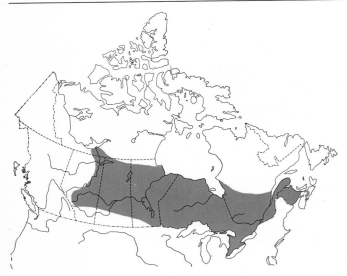

Breeding Distribution of Yellow Rail

Habitat. Grassy (or grass-like) marshes. In migration also grainfields and hayfields.

Nesting. Nest, in a grassy marsh, is a well-concealed cup of finer grasses or sedges in a tussock or on a mat of dead grass. *Eggs*, usually 8 to 10; a rich buff speckled mostly about larger end with reddish brown.

124

PLATE 19

1 Red-tailed Hawk,
  (a) adult
  (b) immature

2 Red-shouldered Hawk,
  (a) adult
  (b) immature

3 Broad-winged Hawk

4 Swainson's Hawk,
  (a) adult, dark phase
  (b) adult, pale phase
  (c) immature, pale
    phase

5 Rough-legged Hawk,
  (a) immature, pale
    phase
  (b) immature, dark
    phase

6 Ferruginous Hawk,
  adult, pale phase

1a

2a

1b

3

2b

4a

5a

4b

5b

Crosby

4c

6

PLATE 20

1 Sparrow Hawk, adult
  male

2 Gyrfalcon, intermediate
  colour phase

3 Pigeon Hawk

4 Peregrine Falcon, adult

5 Prairie Falcon, adult

6 Goshawk, immature

7 Cooper's Hawk,
  immature

8 Sharp-shinned Hawk,
  immature

9 Osprey

10 Marsh Hawk, adult
   male

11 Turkey Vulture

12 Bald Eagle, immature

13 Golden Eagle, immature

Range. Locally from Canada (*see* Range in Canada) south to North Dakota, Minnesota, Wisconsin, Michigan, Ohio, and Massachusetts; also eastern California and, apparently, in Valley of Toluca, Mexico. Winters from Oregon to California and in the Gulf States.

Range in Canada. Breeds very locally in southern Mackenzie (Fort Resolution, Little Buffalo River, Salt River), Alberta (Red Deer, Dried Meat Lake, Athabasca district), Saskatchewan (Jackfish Lake, Medstead, Scentgrass Lake, Maidstone, Lloydminster, Battleford, Last Mountain Lake), Manitoba (Churchill, York Factory, Reader Lake, Overflowing River, Brandon, Whitemouth, Rennie), Ontario (widely but very locally north to marshes bordering coasts of James and Hudson bays, including Ship Sands Island, south to Lake St. Clair and Holland Marsh, and perhaps Ottawa; apparently absent from large areas), southern Quebec (near Gaspé, Ste. Anne de la Pocatière; possibly north on James Bay to Fort George), and New Brunswick (near Milltown, Midgic). Probably breeds in Nova Scotia (Noel), but evidence not quite satisfactory.

Rarely reported migrant in Nova Scotia (Wolfville region, Meadowville, Little River). Casual in Labrador (Hamilton Inlet).

Subspecies. *Coturnicops noveboracensis noveboracensis* (Gmelin).

[**Black Rail.** Le Râle noir. *Laterallus jamaicensis* (Gmelin). Hypothetical. Recorded from southern Ontario, southern Quebec, and Nova Scotia. Most supposed records are based on mistaken identifications of the black young of other rails or on old specimens, the origin of which is uncertain. Plausible sight records are from Rondeau, Ontario (Baillie 1951, *Audubon Field Notes* 5: 253), and Hatley, Quebec (Mousley, 1921, *The Auk* 38: 56–57).]

CORN CRAKE
Le Râle des genêts. *Crex crex* (Linnaeus)
L. ca. 10.5 in.

A short-billed buffy rail with blackish streaking on upper parts, chestnut wing coverts, and chestnut bars on flanks. Its much larger size and the extensive chestnut on its wings distinguish it from our native short-billed rails.

Status in Canada. Accidental. A straggler from Europe. Specimens are from Baffin Island (Cape Dorset, September 24, 1928); Newfoundland (two evidently from St. Shotts: one in 1859; one September 28, 1928); and Nova Scotia (near Pictou, October, about 1874).

PURPLE GALLINULE
La Gallinule pourprée. *Porphyrula martinica* (Linnaeus)
L. 12 to 14 in.

Adults somewhat similar to Common Gallinule (next species), but head, neck, and breast deep purple (looks black at distance), back and wing coverts glossy olive green, under tail coverts *all* white. Frontal shield bluish. Autumn immatures have no purple on them; the head, neck, and breast being brownish, becoming whitish on throat and abdomen, but the upper body showing at least some olive green. Adults are unmistakable. Immatures differ from immature Common Gallinules in having more greenish colour of upper body, more oval-shaped (less elongated) nostrils, no black (all white) in under tail coverts, middle toe not longer than tarsus. Lack of scallops on toes separates them from Coots.

Range. Breeds from the Gulf States and South Carolina south through Mexico, Central America, and the West Indies to Uruguay, northern Argentina, Brazil, and Peru.

Status in Canada. Casual visitor to southeastern Canada: southern Ontario (near Toronto, April 8, 1892; Guelph, St. Clair flats), southern Quebec (Quebec City, mid-September 1909; October 1930); New Brunswick (near St. John, April 1881; Gagetown, September 1880: Quaco, September 1881; Grand Manan); Nova Scotia (Halifax: January 30, 1870; April 1889; January 1896; Chezzetcook: January 1896; Scateri Island: ca. July 1, 1915; Canard: about May 1, 1927), and Newfoundland (Lamaline; Torbay, May 24, 1933; Borgeo, May 10, 1945; St. John's, May 1948; Iona, May 1948; Broad Cove, May 1933; Millertown, April 17, 1953; Badger, November 8, 1950; Rencontre West, November 8, 1951; Port Rexton, October 1959).

COMMON GALLINULE (Florida Gallinule)

La Gallinule commune. *Gallinula chloropus* (Linnaeus)
Plate 23. L. 12 to 14.8 in.

Adults: Head and neck black, becoming slate on breast and flanks. Flanks streaked with white. Back, brown to brownish olive. Outer under-tail coverts white, inner ones black.

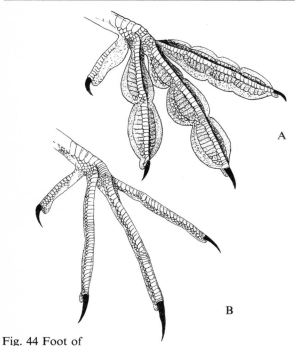

Fig. 44 Foot of
    (A) American Coot   (B) Common Gallinule

whitish flecked with black, under parts more mixed with white, no red on bill. *Downies* are blackish with white beard and reddish bill. Gallinules (*see also* Purple Gallinule) are separable from coots in any plumage by their unlobed toes (Fig. 44).

Measurements (*G. c. cachinnans*). *Adult male:* wing, 171.9–185 (177.9); tail, 68–77 (72.1); culmen (from base of frontal shield), 29.2–34.6 (31.9); tarsus, 55–58 (56.9). *Adult female:* wing, 162–172.5 (165.7) mm.

Field Marks. A blackish grey freshwater marsh bird with chicken-like red bill and white line along flanks. The red bill distinguishes it from coots; the white flank line separates it from both coots and Purple Gallinule. Its small head and the habit of bobbing the head in time with each foot stroke when swimming distinguish gallinules and coots from small ducks (except the very differently marked Wood Duck, which bobs its head, too, while swimming).

Habitat. Freshwater marshes of various sizes, usually where there is at least a small area of open water; waterside vegetation on edges of lakes, ponds, or slow rivers.

Nesting. More or less colonial. Nest, often a basket-like platform of marsh vegetation attached to living marsh plants above or at water-level. Usually other nestlike platforms are built nearby. *Eggs,* usually 9 to 12; buffy, irregularly dotted and spotted with browns. Incubation, about 21 days, by both sexes (A. C. Bent).

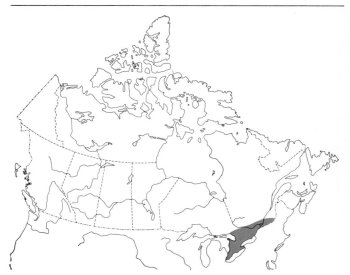

Breeding Distribution of Common Gallinule

Range. Except for colder parts of the world, nearly cosmopolitan but not in Australia. In Western Hemisphere breeds in California (locally) and central Arizona; and from Nebraska, Iowa, Lower Michigan, southern Ontario, southwestern Quebec, and Massachusetts south through Mexico, Central America, and the West Indies to northern Chile and Argentina. Winters mainly from the Gulf States and California and Arizona southward.

Range in Canada. Summer resident and transient. Breeds from southern Ontario (Point Pelee north at least to southern Georgian Bay and Ottawa) and southwestern Quebec (Sorel, Montreal, La Prairie, Magog).

Middle of abdomen whitish. Frontal shield and bill red, bill tipped yellowish. Toes long (middle toe longer than tarsus), without webs or scallop-shaped lobes. Nostrils narrow, elongated. *Immatures:* Similar but paler and duller, throat

Casual in southern Manitoba (Sandy Bay Indian Reserve: July 12, 1931), central Ontario (north shore Lake Superior; Lake Nipissing), eastern Quebec (Gaspé, Anticosti Island), New Brunswick (Grand Manan, Dick's Lake, South Bay), Nova Scotia (Halifax, Canard River, Yarmouth, Sable Island), and Newfoundland (St. John's, St. Shotts, Colinet).

Subspecies. *Gallinula chloropus cachinnans* Bangs.

EUROPEAN COOT

La Foulque noire. *Fulica atra* Linnaeus
L. 15 in.

Similar to American Coot and most easily distinguished from it by colour of all under tail coverts which are slaty or blackish, like rest of under parts, instead of mostly white.

Range. Breeds across Eurasia, including Iceland; in northern Africa, Australia, Tasmania, and New Guinea. Accidental in North America.

Status in Canada. Accidental in Labrador (Separation Point in Sandwich Bay, mid-December 1927; Tangnaivik Island in Anaktalak Bay, December 1927), and Newfoundland (Exploits Harbour, December 1927).

Subspecies. *Fulica atra atra* Linnaeus.

AMERICAN COOT

La Foulque américaine. *Fulica americana* Gmelin
Plate 23. L. 13 to 16 in.

Distinguished from gallinules by broad scallop-like lobes on toes (Fig. 44). *Adults:* Body, even dark slate becoming black on head and neck. Wing edged narrowly with white and secondaries with white tips (usually hidden by folded wing). Outer under-tail coverts white, inner ones blackish. Bill whitish with spot of chestnut near tip; frontal shield mostly chestnut. *Immature (early autumn):* Similar to adults but paler; under parts more mixed with white. *Downies* blackish with bristle-like orange down on throat, cheeks, neck, back, and wings. Under plumage more or less grey-tipped. Bill reddish.

Measurements. *Adult male:* wing, 189–199.8 (195.9); tail, 51.6–57.2 (54.7); culmen (from base of frontal shield), 31.9–39.2 (34.5); tarsus, 56–64.2 (58.1). *Adult female:* wing, 168–193 (182.5) mm.

Field Marks. American Coot and Common Gallinule are dark grey (often look black) marsh birds, the size of small ducks but with chicken-like bills, much smaller heads than ducks, and a habit of bobbing the head with each swimming stroke. Coot's white bill and lack of white line along the flanks separate it from Common Gallinule. In flight the Coot shows a white line on hind edge (secondaries) of wing. The name 'Coot' is often erroneously applied to scoters.

Habitat. Mainly freshwater marshes, ponds, sloughs, lakes, and slow rivers. Although often frequenting the same marsh as gallinules, coots tend to use broader expanses of open water.

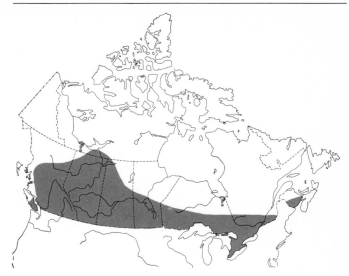
Breeding Distribution of American Coot

Nesting. Usually more or less colonial. Nest on a mass of marsh vegetation, either floating and anchored to living marsh plants or resting on the marsh. *Eggs,* usually 8 to 12 but often more or less; buffy to greyish, thickly and evenly fine-spotted with dark brown. Incubation, 23 to 24 days (G. W. Gullion), is by both sexes.

Range. Breeds from Canada southward through the United States, West Indies, Mexico, and Central America; in the northern Andes of South America; and on most of the Hawaiian Islands. Winters from Maryland and southern British Columbia southward.

Range in Canada. Breeds in southern and central British Columbia (north to Vanderhoof and Peace River district; west to southern Vancouver Island); Alberta; central southern Mackenzie (Little Buffalo River); Saskatchewan (northern Lake Athabasca, Crean Lake, Cumberland House); southwestern Manitoba (north to Moose and Cedar lakes); western and southern Ontario (western Lake Erie north to Whitefish Lake, Lillabelle Lake, and Ottawa, summer records on southern James Bay); southwestern Quebec (uncommon, local: near Kilmar Mines; Montreal region); and southern New Brunswick (scarce, local: Williamston Lake, Harvey Station; possibly Midgic).

Winters in southern British Columbia (Okanagan Valley, Arrow Lake, and on the coast including Vancouver Island) and occasionally in southern Ontario.

Casual in southern Yukon (Pelly River, Little Atlin Lake), northern Manitoba (Churchill), northern Ontario (Fort Severn), central and eastern Quebec (Pierce Lake, Mingan, Whale Head, Johan Beetz Bay, Mecatina Island, Old Fort, Anticosti Island), Labrador (Table Bay), Newfoundland (about seventeen specimen records through 1956, mostly autumn), Prince Edward Island, and Nova Scotia (mostly autumn). Accidental in Franklin District (Bellot Strait).

Subspecies. *Fulica americana americana* Gmelin.

PLATE 21

1 Ruffed Grouse,
  (a) grey phase (flying)
  (b) red phase

2 Sharp-tailed Grouse

3 Greater Prairie Chicken

4 Ring-necked Pheasant,
  (a) female
  (b) male

7 Sage Grouse,
  (a) female (flying)
  (b) adult male in
      autumn

PLATE 22

1 Sooty Grouse
   (race *fuliginosus*),
      (a) adult male
      (b) adult female

2 Spruce Grouse
   (race *canadensis*),
      (a) adult female
      (b) adult male

3 Spruce Grouse
   (race *franklinii*),
   adult male

4 Willow Ptarmigan,
      (a) head in winter
      (b) adult male, early
          summer
      (c) adult female, early
          summer
      (d) winter

5 Rock Ptarmigan,
      (a) male in winter
      (b) adult female,
          summer
      (c) adult male, summer
      (d) male in winter

6 White-tailed Ptarmigan,
      (a) head in winter
      (b) adult male, early
          summer
      (c) adult female
      (d) winter

Order **Charadriiformes**–Shorebirds, Gulls, Auks, and Allies

Family **Haematopodidae**–Oystercatchers

Number of Species in North America 3; in Canada 2

Large shorebirds, coloured either in contrasting black and white or all blackish, with long, stout, laterally compressed bright red bills. Their hind legs and feet are heavy, and they have no hind toe.

AMERICAN OYSTERCATCHER

L'Huîtrier américain. *Haematopus palliatus* Temminck
L. 17 to 21 in.

Bill laterally compressed (height greater than width) and about twice as long as head. *Adults:* Head, neck, and upper chest, black. Back and most of wings, greyish brown. Broad band across wings, white. Upper tail coverts mostly white. Tail, dark brownish grey to blackish. Under parts (posterior to breast) white. Bill mainly red. Legs, pale flesh. (*See also* Black Oystercatcher.) The European Oystercatcher (*H. ostralegus*) is very similar to the American species, but the back (hidden when the wings are folded but visible in flight) is white, and the upper surface of the wings is black instead of brown.

Field Marks. A crow-sized black-and-white shorebird with a large reddish bill and conspicuous white wing patches. In flight shows dark back and white rump (both back and rump white in European Oystercatcher).

Range. Breeds from New Jersey south on the Atlantic, Gulf, and Caribbean coasts to middle Argentina; some of the West Indies; and from Baja California on the Pacific coast to Chile; also the Galápagos Islands.

Status in Canada. Casual visitor. Ontario: One, presumably the same bird, in 1960 was first observed at Toronto, May 22; it was photographed by D. R. Gunn at Presqu'ile Point on May 29, and collected at Rosehill on July 21 for the Royal Ontario Museum. New Brunswick: Grand Manan. Nova Scotia (hypothetical): An oystercatcher was carefully identified on May 19, 1957, at Grand Desert by Charles Allen, T. H. Morland, and John Comer, three competent observers (R. W. Tufts, in litt.). It was not collected, and the possibility of the occurrence of the similar European Oystercatcher was not completely ruled out.

Audubon's assertion that in 1833 he found it breeding in the Bay of Fundy and northward to the north shore of the Gulf of St. Lawrence cannot now be corroborated.

Subspecies. *Haematopus palliatus palliatus* Temminck.

BLACK OYSTERCATCHER

L'Huîtrier noir. *Haematopus bachmani* Audubon
Plate 29. L. 17.0 to 17.7 in.

Bill as in American Oystercatcher. A crow-sized all-black shorebird with a red laterally compressed bill twice the length of the head. Unmistakable. *Young* similar, but more brownish; bill dusky, orange at base.

Field Marks. A crow-sized all-black shorebird with robust red bill and pinkish feet. *Voice:* a repeated loud *queep*.

Habitat. Rocky, outer saltwater shores and islands.

Nesting. Eggs are laid in a depression on a bare rock, often lined with bits of stone and shell chips; or in a hollow in beach gravel or other ground. *Eggs*, usually 2 to 3, are buffy and are uniformly spotted and scrawled with blackish browns and some bluish grey. Incubation period 26 to 30 days, usually 27 days (J. Dan Webster). Incubation by both parents.

Breeding Distribution of Black Oystercatcher

Range. Breeds on the Pacific coasts of North America from Attu Island, Aleutians, Alaska, eastward and southward to central-western Baja California.

Range in Canada. Permanent resident on the outer coast

and rocky coastal islands of British Columbia from southern and western Vancouver Island north to the Alaska boundary.

Family **Charadriidae**—Plovers, Surfbirds, and Turnstones

Number of Species in North America 16; in Canada 14

Plovers are plump-bodied shorebirds with short necks, rather large eyes, and short thickish bills (not longer than head). The bill is rather soft basally with a hard tip somewhat suggesting the bill of a pigeon (Fig. 47). Hind toe usually absent or obsolete (present in Black-bellied Plover).

Turnstones are similar to plovers but have pointed, more woodpecker-like bills. Both turnstones and surfbirds have hind toes.

LAPWING

Le Vanneau huppé. *Vanellus vanellus* (Linnaeus)
Fig. 45. L. 12 to 13 in.

A rather large plover with long slender crest (shorter in young). Looks black and white at a distance, but at closer range upper parts show glossy green. Broad black band across breast (extends to throat in summer). Sides of head mainly whitish. Belly white. Under tail coverts chestnut. Tail white with broad black subterminal bar. The Lapwing is not likely to be confused with any other bird of probable occurrence in Canada.

Fig. 45 Head of Lapwing, adult male

Range. Breeds in Eurasia: British Isles, the Faroes, northern Sweden, Russia (north to lat. 62°) and Siberia (north to lat. 57°), south to Spain, north Italy, northern China. Winters from southern parts of breeding range south to northern Africa, India, Indochina, Formosa, and Japan.

Status in Canada. Accidental. A great storm-borne flight in December 1927 accounts for most of the records: Baffin Island (Pangnirtung Fiord, October 1926). Labrador (The 1927 flight carried large numbers to the coast from Battle Harbour, Sandwich Bay, and Hamilton Inlet north to

Hopedale). Quebec (Harrington Harbour, St. Augustin). Newfoundland (large numbers at numerous localities between December 17, 1927, and January 15, 1928. One specimen had been banded in England. Specimens also from Quidi Vidi, November 23, 1905; St. Anthony, November 19, 1944; Glenwood, January 7, 1955; and Fogo Island, January 30, 1960). New Brunswick (In 1927 specimens were taken at Three Islands, Outer Wood Island, Hay Island, Saint John). Nova Scotia (Ketch Harbour, March 17, 1897; Upper Prospect, December 12, 1905; and from the 1927 flight, specimens were taken in Richmond, Antigonish, and Colchester counties).

In January 1966 (as this goes to press) another sizeable flight occurred bringing Lapwings to Newfoundland, Nova Scotia, New Brunswick, Prince Edward Island, and southern Quebec (Manicouagan).

RINGED PLOVER

Le Grand Gravelot. *Charadrius hiaticula* Linnaeus
Average total length 7.5 in.

Extremely like Semipalmated Plover but has no web between the basal parts of inner and middle toes (a small web between outer and middle toes is possessed by both species; Fig. 46); it has a broader black breast band; and the white areas of head are slightly more extensive.

Field Marks. Not safely separable in the field from Semipalmated Plover except by direct comparison under excellent conditions.

Nesting. Nest a hollow in sand, gravel, or turf, often lined with small stones or bits of shell. *Eggs,* usually 4; pale buff spotted with blackish brown and small amounts of grey. Incubation by both sexes.

Breeding Distribution of Ringed Plover

Range. Breeds in northeastern arctic Canada, Greenland, Iceland, and across northern Eurasia east to Chukotski Peninsula. Winters from the British Isles, Mediterranean Sea, Asia Minor, and China south to southern Africa and India.

131

Range in Canada. Summer resident. Breeds from northern Ellesmere Island (Alert, Nansen Sound) south through Bylot Island and eastern Baffin Island (Clyde and Pond inlets, probably Admiralty Inlet. Possibly Cumberland Sound). Winters in the Old World.

Subspecies. *Charadrius hiaticula hiaticula* Linnaeus.

SEMIPALMATED PLOVER

Le Pluvier à collier. *Charadrius semipalmatus* Bonaparte
Plate 24. L. 6.5 to 7.7 in.

Bill short. No hind toe. Front toes partly webbed, including small web at base of inner and middle toes (Fig. 46). *Adults (spring and summer):* Narrow black patch from base of bill to cheeks. Black bar above white forehead. Upper parts brown. Black breast band on otherwise white under parts. Legs and base of bill, rich yellow. Tip of bill black. *Autumn adults and young:* Similar but black areas replaced by dark brown. Young have black bills.

Fig. 46 Foot of
(A) Ringed Plover
(B) Semipalmated Plover

Measurements. *Adult male:* wing, 114.9–123.9 (118.8); tail, 52.5–59.2 (56); exposed culmen, 11.9–14.4 (13); tarsus, 22–25.3 (23.9). *Adult female:* wing, 118–126 (121.3) mm.

Field Marks. A small short-billed brown-backed plover with well-defined single breast band. Similar to Piping Plover but upper parts much darker brown (like wet sand rather than dry sand) and with black (dark brown in young) area extending from base of bill to cheeks. The much larger Killdeer has a double breast band. Semipalmated Plover often calls *pe-wit*, the second syllable higher pitched (*see* Ringed Plover).

Habitat. Both fresh and salt mud flats, beaches, flat open margins of ponds, lakes, and rivers. In nesting season inhabits also sparsely vegetated low gravel ridges, gravelly plains, beaches, and sand dunes.

Nesting. Nest a depression in sand, gravel, moss, or dead seaweed, sparsely, if at all, lined with bits of shell or plant material. *Eggs,* 3 to 4; buffy, variously spotted with blackish browns. Incubation, about 23 days, by both sexes.

Range. Breeds in Alaska (north to Colville Delta) and Canada (*see* Range in Canada). Winters from southern California, the Gulf of Mexico coast, and South Carolina south (including the West Indies) to southern Argentina and Chile.

Range in Canada. Summer resident and transient. Breeds

from Banks Island (Sachs Harbour, Kellett River), Victoria Island (Cambridge Bay, perhaps Holman Post), Boothia Peninsula (Sagvak Inlet, Krusenstern Lake), northern Melville Peninsula (Fury and Hecla Strait), and central and southern Baffin Island (north at least to Clyde Inlet) south through Yukon (Old Crow, Carcross, Rose-Lapie Pass) to northwestern British Columbia (Mile 85 Haines Road; Atlin; Graham Island; also south-central interior: Le Blanc Lake — *see* Hesse, *Murrelet* 42: 3), through Mackenzie (Mackenzie Delta, Anderson River, and the Arctic Coast, Great Slave Lake), throughout Keewatin, northern Saskatchewan (Lake Athabasca), northern Manitoba (Churchill, Herchmer, Bird), northern Ontario (Big Piskwanish, Cape Henrietta Maria), Quebec (mainly coastal apparently, but probably locally also in the interior: north to Hudson Strait and Ungava Bay; south to southern James Bay, the north shore of the Gulf of St. Lawrence: St. Mary's and Fog islands; Magdalen Islands); Labrador (entire coast), Newfoundland, Nova Scotia (very locally: near Englishtown; mouth of Chebogue River; Sable Island), and formerly southern New Brunswick (Grand Manan).

Breeding Distribution of Semipalmated Plover

Transient, more or less common, through most of southern Canada (but scarce in south-interior of British Columbia and mountainous southwestern Alberta). In the Maritime Provinces much more numerous in autumn.

PIPING PLOVER

Le Pluvier siffleur. *Charadrius melodus* Ord
Plate 24. L. 6.0 to 7.7 in.

Small web between outer and middle toes. Similar in size, proportions, and markings to Semipalmated Plover, but brown of upper parts much paler, more greyish; black on head confined to a bar above white forehead and lacking on cheeks; breast band often broken or (in autumn adults and immatures) very poorly defined or lacking.

Measurements (*C. m. melodus*). *Adult male:* wing, 114.8–127 (121.3); tail, 48.2–56.8 (53.1); exposed culmen, 10.3–13

(12.1); tarsus, 22–22.9 (22.4). *Adult female:* wing, 110–122 (118.1) mm.

Field Marks. A very pale edition of the Semipalmated Plover from which it is readily separable by much paler upper parts (colour of dry, instead of wet sand); and lack of any black or dark brown on the cheeks. Breast bar often broken; poorly defined or almost absent in autumn adults and young. Its whistled, ventriloquial *queep,* or *queeplo,* is very different from calls of the Semipalmated Plover.

Habitat. Sandy beaches on both salt and fresh water.

Nesting. Nest, a shallow depression in sand above the high-water mark of ocean or lake beaches, is either unlined or scantily lined with pebbles and bits of shell. *Eggs,* usually 4; light buff to whitish, sparsely but usually quite evenly dotted with blackish brown; ground colour paler, spots smaller and sparser than in Semipalmated Plover. Incubation, 27 to 31 days, by both sexes (L. Wilcox).

Range. Breeds from southern Canada (Alberta to Newfoundland) south to South Dakota, Nebraska, southern shores of lakes Michigan and Erie, and on the Atlantic coast to Virginia. Winters on the Atlantic Coast from South Carolina to Florida and westward along the Gulf of Mexico to Texas.

Range in Canada. Local summer resident and transient. Breeds in southeastern central Alberta (Bittern, Miquelon, Buffalo, Gull, Baxter, and Beaverhill lakes), southern Saskatchewan (Bigstick, Quill, Johnston, and Last Mountain lakes; Indian Head), southern Manitoba (Dawson Bay on Lake Winnipegosis; lakes Manitoba and Winnipeg; Shoal Lake), southern Ontario (Point Pelee, Long Point, Hamilton, Toronto, Consecon, Rockport, Ipperwash Beach, Wasaga Beach), southeastern Quebec (New Carlisle; Magdalen Islands; probably Natashquan), southwestern Newfoundland (Grand and Little Codroy river mouths; probably Stephenville Crossing); New Brunswick (Tabusintac, Neguak Beach; probably Miscou Island), Prince Edward Island (Stanhope, Howe Bay), and southern Nova Scotia (Cape Sable and various other 'white' sand beaches on the South Shore; Sable Island).

Breeding Distribution of Piping Plover

Subspecies. (1) *Charadrius melodus melodus* Ord, characterized by having the black pectoral band more frequently broken, breeds from se. Que. and Nfld. south through the Maritimes. (2) *C. m. circumcinctus* (Ridgway), with usually an unbroken pectoral band, breeds from the Great Lakes westward.

SNOWY PLOVER

Le Pluvier neigeux. *Charadrius alexandrinus* Linnaeus
L. 5.75 to 6.75 in.

A diminutive plover (wing chord not over 107 mm) with relatively longish slender bill (culmen 13 to 15.5 mm). Upper parts pale brown as in Piping Plover. Very narrow black bar above white forehead. No breast band, just a single dark patch on either side of chest. Rest of under parts white. Bill black. Legs grey. Distinguished from Piping Plover by smaller size, relatively (and actually) longer bill, and grey legs (Piping and Semipalmated plovers have yellow legs).

Status in Canada. Casual. One was taken on July 6, 1897, at Toronto. Another specimen, taken at Toronto in May 1880, was identified, not entirely without misgivings, by Seton (1885, *The Auk* 2: 335–336) and was subsequently destroyed. At Buck Lake, 18 miles south of Regina, Saskatchewan, a male was collected on May 31, 1964.

Subspecies. The Toronto records have been referred to *Charadrius alexandrinus tenuirostris* (Lawrence); the Regina specimen to *C. a. nivosus* (Cassin). The species breeds in many widely separated parts of the world including western and southern United States.

WILSON'S PLOVER

Le Pluvier de Wilson. *Charadrius wilsonia* Ord
L. 7.0 to 8.1 in.

Another brown-backed plover with single breast band, thus resembling Semipalmated and Piping Plover but readily distinguishable by its longer, thicker, all-black bill. Brown of upper parts darker than Piping Plover. Slightly larger than both.

Status in Canada. Casual in Nova Scotia: on Brier Island one was collected on April 28, 1880; Halifax: a summer adult listed without date by Sharpe (1896, *Catalogue of Birds in the British Museum* 24: 216).

Subspecies. *Charadrius wilsonia wilsonia* Ord which breeds on the Atlantic coast of the U.S. from Virginia to Florida, along the entire coast of the Gulf of Mexico, and in the West Indies.

KILLDEER

Le Pluvier kildir. *Charadrius vociferus* Linnaeus
Plate 24. L. 9.0 to 11.25 in.

The double black band across the breast and cinnamon-coloured rump and upper-tail coverts readily identify it.

Measurements. *Adult male:* wing, 148.8–165 (158); tail, 86–99.6 (94); exposed culmen, 18.8–21.2 (20.3); tarsus, 35.1–38 (36.4). *Adult female:* wing, 153–167.8 (161.4) mm.

Field Marks. The double black band across breast and the cinnamon-buffy rump and upper tail coverts are unmistakable (other 'ringed' plovers have only one breast band and are smaller and shorter-tailed). Its ringing *kill-dee*, rapidly and frequently repeated, is a common summer voice of upland fields in most of southern Canada west of the Maritimes.

Habitat. Open uplands. Pastured, mowed, or plowed fields, bare gravel, golf courses, roadside ditches, and similar disturbed areas where grass is short, sparse, or absent. After nesting, it frequents margins of ponds and lakes, muddy and moist places. Rarely salt marshes.

Nesting. Nest, a shallow depression in the ground, sparsely lined with a few pebbles and bits of weeds. *Eggs*, usually 4; light buff, boldly blotched and spotted with blackish. Incubation, usually 24 to 26 days (W. P. Nickell), by both sexes.

Range. Breeds from southern Canada south to central Mexico, the Gulf coast of the United States, south-central Florida, and the West Indies; also in Peru. Winters from southern British Columbia, Colorado, the Ohio Valley, and Long Island south to northern South America.

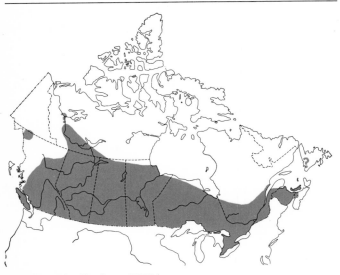

Breeding Distribution of Killdeer

Range in Canada. Common summer resident in much of southern Canada, scarcer east of southwestern Quebec. Breeds in British Columbia (Bulkley Lake and Peace River valley southward locally through the interior; also Vancouver Island and Vancouver; probably north to Atlin); Mackenzie (Fort Simpson, Slave River; perhaps Fort Norman; possibly Aklavik: short-winged juvenal, but capable of flight, taken by W. J. Smith, August 18, 1958; two adults were present also); Alberta, Saskatchewan, and Manitoba (north at least to Churchill); Ontario (probably throughout but scarcer northward and definite data wanting from northwest); southwestern Quebec (Montreal, Quebec, Lake St. John, Pointe des Monts; Trois Pistoles); New Brunswick (uncommon: near Bathurst, Riley Brook, St. Andrews, Jemseg), Nova Scotia (rarely: Debert), and Prince Edward Island (rarely: Dundas).

Recorded in summer in Yukon (Fortymile, Pine Creek, Burwash Landing, Old Crow), southern Keewatin (Windy and McConnell rivers). Casual on the north shore of the Gulf of St. Lawrence (lower Moisie River; near Mingan; Johan Beetz Bay; Whale Head), Anticosti Island, Gaspé Peninsula (Fox River), Newfoundland (various records 1930–1957, mostly late autumn; two for spring). Accidental in Labrador (Nain).

Winters in small numbers in southern British Columbia (Vancouver, Okanagan Landing) and occasionally southern Ontario (Toronto).

Subspecies. *Charadrius vociferus vociferus* Linnaeus.

Remarks. The handsome, noisy Killdeer derived its name from one of its numerous calls. It is common in most of southern Canada except in the extreme east. Although a shorebird, it favours open interior uplands more often than the seashore. It is among the earliest of birds to appear in the spring, soon after the first patches of bare ground begin to show in the fields.

MOUNTAIN PLOVER
Le Pluvier montagnard. *Eupoda montana* (Townsend)
L. 8.25 to 9.25 in.

Bill rather slender. Legs rather long for a plover. *Adults (breeding plumage):* Upper parts plain greyish brown, some feathers margined with buffy. Front of crown and line from bill to eye, black. Forehead and superciliary stripes, white. Under parts plain dull white with buffy-greyish wash across breast. Bill black. Legs pale brownish yellow. *Adults and young in autumn:* Similar to breeding adults but black head markings absent. The Mountain Plover approaches the Killdeer in size but lacks black breast bands. Its plain back distinguishes it from autumn Golden and Black-bellied plovers. A bird of the dry short-grass plains of the United States, it is to be expected in Canada only in southern parts of the Prairie Provinces.

Status in Canada. Rare summer visitor to southeastern Alberta (near Wild Horse: four on June 22, 1941) and southwestern Saskatchewan (near Bracken: one on June 5, 1939). Soper (1941, *Can. Field-Nat.* 55: 137), the authority for both records, suspected that the Alberta birds were nesting.

EURASIAN GOLDEN PLOVER
Le Pluvier doré eurasien. *Pluvialis apricaria* (Linnaeus)
L. 11 in.

Very similar to the slightly smaller American Golden Plover but axillars white in all plumages.

Range. Breeds in Iceland, the Faroe Islands, and eastward across northern Europe through northern Scandinavia, northern Russia, and western Siberia (to Yenisei River), south to the British Isles, the Netherlands (formerly), Denmark, northern Germany, Poland, and the Baltics. In migration occurs regularly in southern Greenland.

Status in Canada. Accidental in Newfoundland: specimen received on April 20, 1961, by L. M. Tuck from Cappahayden, Avalon Peninsula. Others, presumably this species, reported to Tuck about the same time, suggest that a flight arrived in Newfoundland a few days earlier.

Subspecies. The Newfoundland specimen is referable to *Pluvialis apricaria altifrons* (Brehm).

AMERICAN GOLDEN PLOVER
Le Pluvier doré d'Amérique. *Pluvialis dominica* (Müller)
Plates 24, 31. L. 9.75 to 11.0 in.

Lacks hind toe. Axillars grey. *Adults (spring and summer)*: Upper parts, including crown and upper tail coverts, blackish or dusky, speckled with yellow and often a few white spots. Forehead, line over eye and down side of neck, white. Lower cheeks, throat, middle of breast, abdomen, sides and under tail coverts, black. Bill black. Legs dark bluish grey. *Adults and young in autumn:* Upper parts duller, no black on face or under parts. Vague whitish line over eye but not down side of neck. Breast pale greyish brown, faintly barred with dusky.

Measurements (*P. d. dominica*). *Adult male:* wing, 175.1–188.4 (180.3); tail, 66–72.7 (68.9); exposed culmen, 22–24.5 (23.3); tarsus, 42.2–44.8 (43.5). *Adult female:* wing, 172–183 (179.6) mm.

Field Marks. Similar to Black-bellied Plover but in breeding plumage distinguishable from it by dark crown and consequent white line over eye and down side of neck; black of abdomen extends to under tail coverts. Both adults and young are separable from Black-bellied in any plumage by their grey (instead of black) axillars and dark (instead of whitish) rump and tail.

Habitat. Tends to prefer drier habitats than the Black-bellied Plover. In migration, short-grass and stubble fields, pastures, plowed land; and to some extent beaches and shores of both fresh and salt water. In the Arctic, relatively dry uplands, ridges, slopes, and tundra knolls, both coastal and inland.

Nesting. Nest a shallow depression in lichens or soil, lined with pieces of lichen. *Eggs*, usually 4; buffy, boldly spotted and blotched with blackish. Incubation, 26 days (D. F. Parmelee), by both sexes.

Range. Breeds in northern Siberia, Alaska, and northern Canada. Winters on South American plains from southern Bolivia and southern Brazil south to central Argentina; also from India, southern China, and the Hawaiian Islands south to Australia, and New Zealand. Main migration in North America in spring is up the Mississippi Valley over the Prairie Provinces and west of Hudson Bay. In autumn, southward both east and west of Hudson Bay, with a considerable proportion apparently flying over the Atlantic Ocean from southeastern Canada and northeastern United States to South America.

Range in Canada. Summer resident and transient. Breeds from Banks Island (De Salis Bay), Victoria Island (Cambridge Bay, Prince Albert Peninsula), Prince of Wales Island (Fisher Lake), Boothia Peninsula, and Bylot Island south through Yukon (Herschel Island, Keno Hill; probably mountains near Burwash Creek, Edith Creek, Tepee Lake; and near Klutlan Glacier) to northwestern British Columbia (Kliweguh Creek), central Mackenzie (Great Bear Lake;

Artillery and Prairie lakes), Keewatin (Adelaide Peninsula, Whale Point; perhaps lower Back River; distribution poorly known), northeastern Manitoba (Churchill), Southampton Island, Prince Charles Island, and south-central Baffin Island (Amadjuak Lake, Cape Dorchester). Probably north to Melville and Devon islands, but confirmation is needed.

Spring and autumn migrant in British Columbia, Alberta, Saskatchewan, Manitoba; mainly-autumn migrant in Ontario; and autumn migrant in Quebec, Labrador, Newfoundland, New Brunswick, Prince Edward Island, and Nova Scotia. Although Nova Scotia is frequently mentioned in the literature as the place where allegedly large numbers rest and fatten in preparation for the long transocean flight to South America, the writer is aware of no such concentrations there in the present century. Its status is given by Tufts (1962) as an uncommon fall migrant. The possibility of change in the eastern migration route has been suggested by some. This may be correct, for the concept of large numbers converging on Nova Scotia does not hold today.

Breeding Distribution of American Golden Plover

Subspecies. (1) *Pluvialis dominica dominica* (Müller) is the only subspecies known to breed in Canada. It migrates through most of the southern parts. (2) *P. d. fulva* (Gmelin), breeding from Siberia east to w. coastal Alaska (Cape Lisburne to Kuskokwim River), a smaller bird with brighter, more profusely yellow colouring especially in fall, is a scarce autumn transient on the coast of B.C. and has been taken once in Alta. (Tofield; September 9, 1925).

BLACK-BELLIED PLOVER
Le Pluvier à ventre noir. *Squatarola squatarola* (Linnaeus)
Plates 24, 31. L. 10.5 to 13.5 in.

A small hind toe usually present. Axillars black. Similar in all plumages to American Golden Plover, but in spring and summer the crown is mostly whitish, upper parts lack yellow speckles, and the black of under parts does not extend so far backward, thus leaving the rear abdomen and under tail coverts white. Autumn Black-bellies have much less yellow speckling on upper parts than do autumn Goldens. The presence of a small hind toe and the distinctions under 'Field Marks' separate it from the slightly smaller Golden Plover.

Measurements. *Adult male:* wing, 180.2–191 (187.8); tail, 71.2–79.7 (74.8); exposed culmen, 27.2–31.8 (29.9); tarsus, 45–50.2 (47.2). *Adult female:* wing, 182–199 (187.7) mm.

Field Marks. Likely to be confused only with the American Golden Plover but is easily recognizable in all plumages by its whitish tail and upper tail coverts and by its black axillars (arm-pits), which are visible in flight at some distance. In spring and summer its whitish crown and the white rear part of the abdomen are additional distinctions. Its flight call is a trisyllabic whistled *tee-yu-eee*, the middle syllable lowest.

Habitat. Although it often frequents short-grass fields, especially moist ones, it is more likely to be found on mud flats, muddy shores and pools, beaches, and sand bars, in the vicinity of either fresh or salt water. In the Arctic, dry gravel ridges are popular for nesting purposes, but wetter tundra areas also are used.

Nesting. Nest, a shallow depression in the ground lined with bits of lichen or moss. *Eggs*, usually 4; vary from light buff or greyish to pinkish, greenish, or brownish, spotted or blotched with blackish brown especially on larger end. Incubation 27 days (W. H. Drury).

Breeding Distribution of Black-bellied Plover

Range. Breeds in Alaska and the middle and low Arctic of Canada; also in northern Russia (Kanin Peninsula eastward) and across northern Siberia. Winters from southwestern British Columbia southward along the Pacific coast to Chile; and on the Atlantic and other eastern coasts from New Jersey south to southern Brazil; also the West Indies. Winters also from the British Isles, the Mediterranean, southern China, and Hawaii south to South Africa, Australia, and New Zealand.

Range in Canada. Breeds from Banks, Prince of Wales, Devon, and Bylot islands south to northern Mackenzie

PLATE 23

1 Gray Partridge,
  adult male

2 Bobwhite, adult male

3 California Quail,
  (a) adult female
  (b) adult male

4 Chukar, adult male

5 Whooping Crane, adult

6 Sandhill Crane, adult

7 American Coot, adult
  in summer

8 Common Gallinule,
  (a) immature
  (b) adult in summer

9 Yellow Rail, summer
  adult

10 Sora,
  (a) summer adult
  (b) autumn immature

11 King Rail, summer adult

12 Virginia Rail, summer
  adult

(Cape Bathurst, Cockburn Point, Perry River), southern Victoria Island (Cambridge Bay), northern Keewatin (Adelaide Peninsula), Melville Peninsula, Southampton Island, and southwestern Baffin Island (Bowman Bay).

Recorded in summer north to Melville Island (Winter Harbour) and northern Ellesmere Island (Cape Belknap).

Scarce transient in Yukon (Dawson: in spring). Spring and autumn transient in southern Mackenzie (apparently local and uncommon: forts Simpson, Resolution, and Rae; Great Bear Lake), and southern Keewatin (mainly the coast; also locally in the interior: Aberdeen and Beverly lakes). Spring and autumn transient in British Columbia (common on coast; scarcer in interior where most records are for autumn; one spring record for Rolla, Peace River), Alberta, Saskatchewan, Manitoba, Ontario, southern and central-western Quebec (coast of Hudson and James bays and the north shore of the Gulf of St. Lawrence; in the interior records lacking north of Lake St. John), the Maritime Provinces (common in autumn; scarcer in spring), and Newfoundland (fairly common in autumn; rare in spring). Rare transient in Labrador (autumn records: Cartwright, Okak).

Spring migration from coastal northeastern United States appears to be mainly to James and Hudson bays. Perhaps many fly there non-stop. Smaller numbers pass northward farther east through the Maritimes. In autumn more birds spread farther east, and the species is common in Anticosti Island, eastern Gaspé, the Maritimes, and even Newfoundland. Evidence of any significant migration in northern Quebec and Labrador is lacking.

Winters regularly in small numbers in southwestern British Columbia (southern Vancouver Island; mouth of Fraser River).

SURFBIRD

L'Échassier du ressac. *Aphriza virgata* (Gmelin)
Plate 29. L. 9.5 to 10 in.

Bill plover-like, rather slender, with slightly enlarged horny tip. Legs short. *Adults (spring and summer)*: Head and neck streaked dark grey and white. Upper body and wing coverts dark grey, the back feathers with whitish margins; scapulars with admixture of chestnut. Base of tail and upper tail coverts white; rest of tail brownish black. Wing stripe white. Under parts white, the fore-neck streaked with dusky, breast heavily spotted and V-marked with greyish brown, the flanks V-marked with same. Legs and base of lower mandible yellowish. *Adults (autumn and winter)*: Similar to above but upper parts (except upper tail coverts) plain dark greyish brown. Breast plain dark greyish brown, the lower breast often inconspicuously spotted with dusky. *Immatures:* Similar to autumn adults, but scapulars and wing coverts narrowly margined with white, and breast much mixed with whitish.

Measurements. *Adult male:* wing, 160.5–173.4 (165.6); tail, 60.3–67.2 (63.9); exposed culmen, 21.5–25 (23.6); tarsus, 31–32 (31.1). *Adult female:* wing, 171–183.2 (176.9) mm.

Field Marks. A chunky, short-legged shorebird of the rocky West Coast, most likely to be confused with turnstones, Rock Sandpiper, or the autumn Knot. Its upper parts and breast are darker than those of the Knot, and its white rump patch contrasts sharply with its dark hind tail and lower back (the Knot often shows lightish rump, but this is never conspicuous). The Surfbird has a tail pattern similar to that of turnstones, but flight exposes its dark lower back (turnstones show white in lower back and more white in wings). Its white rump patch separates it from the Rock Sandpiper.

Habitat. Rocky wave-swept ocean shores in migration and winter in British Columbia. Probably will be found nesting in the western mountains above timberline.

Nesting. In Alaska, on barren rocky mountains above timberline. Nest a shallow depression in rocky ground. *Eggs*, 4; buff, boldly marked usually with bay and browns, thus in colour somewhat like eggs of certain falcons, although the pyriform shape is, of course, similar to the eggs of many other shorebirds. The nest and eggs were unknown until 1926 (Dixon, *Condor* 29: 2–16).

Range. At present only two breeding localities are known, both in Alaska (Mount McKinley Park and the Fortymile River system). Winters along the Pacific Coast from southeastern Alaska south to the Straits of Magellan.

Range in Canada. Fairly common spring and autumn transient along the outer coasts and islands of British Columbia (sometimes recorded there also in July); winter resident on both coasts of Vancouver Island and probably elsewhere on the British Columbia coast. Recorded rarely in Yukon: specimen taken at Carcross, May 27, 1924; eight observed at Whitehorse, August 14, 1945 (Schmid, *The Auk* 64: 308).

As the Surfbird has been found breeding just west of the Yukon border, its breeding should be looked for in the mountains of Yukon Territory and northern British Columbia.

RUDDY TURNSTONE

Le Tourne-pierre roux. *Arenaria interpres* (Linnaeus)
Plate 24. L. 8.0 to 9.9 in.

Bill tapering to a point, hard, blackish, very woodpecker-like. Legs short, orange. Woodpecker-like bill identifies it as a turnstone. The peculiar black, white, and russet colour pattern of spring and summer adults is unmistakable. Autumn adults and immatures are much duller, the blacks being replaced by greyish browns; the russet patches are lacking or reduced to buffy feather edges, and the sides of head and neck are heavily streaked with dusky. But the breast patches, although more brownish and somewhat obscured by whitish feather tips, retain their characteristic shape, thus separating this species from the Black Turnstone. Bill shape and white lower back separate it from the Surfbird (which has only a white rump).

Measurements (*A. i. morinella*). *Adult male:* wing, 135.9–151.7 (146); tail, 56.9–64.6 (60.5); exposed culmen, 21.1–24 (22.6); tarsus, 24.8–27 (26.5). *Adult female:* wing, 140–156.3 (146.9) mm.

Field Marks. A stocky shorebird with shortish neck; short orange legs; pointed, often slightly upturned blackish bill; and in spring and summer a striking black, white, and russet colour pattern. Autumn adults and immatures, although more brownish and without the russet patches, still show enough of the peculiar breast pattern to identify them. Both species of turnstone and the Surfbird have a broad dark band near the end of the tail, but in flight turnstones show a white lower back. The orange legs and peculiar breast patches separate this species from the Black Turnstone. The white lower back, dark rump band, white upper tail coverts, and dark hind half of the tail form a striking pattern that in flight separates the turnstones from the rest of our shorebirds.

Habitat. In migration, rocky shores, pebbly and sandy beaches, muddy places strewn with sea debris, kelp piles along saltwater tide lines; shores and beaches of freshwater lakes of the interior; sometimes crowberry flats. For nesting, in the Arctic, habitat varies from tundra, well-vegetated with willow and dryas, to rather bare and open places, and from the plateau tops of gravelly ridges to low, flat sandy islands and hummocky moist tundra.

Nesting. Nest, a shallow depression in the ground, usually (not always) lined with leaves of available vegetation. *Eggs*, usually 4; greyish green variously streaked and spotted with browns. Incubation 21 to 22 days (Parmelee and MacDonald), by both sexes but, until the approach of hatching, mainly by the female. Young leave the nest within a day after hatching.

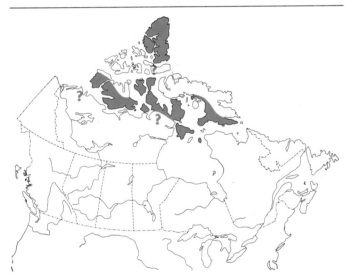

Breeding Distribution of Ruddy Turnstone

Range. Circumpolar. Breeds (usually not far from coasts) in northern Alaska (south to the delta of Yukon River; St. Lawrence and St. Matthew islands), northern Canada, northern and central Greenland, Iceland, north coasts of Europe (locally south to islands in the Baltic), northern Siberia, and Wrangell Island. Winters from southern United States south to Chile and southern Brazil; and from southern Europe (north on the Atlantic Coast to the British Isles), coastal southern Asia, and the Hawaiian Islands south to southern Africa, the East Indies, Australia, and New Zealand.

Range in Canada. Breeds on Banks, Victoria, Prince of Wales, and King William islands, and perhaps Somerset Island; Boothia Peninsula, Igloolik Island, southwestern Baffin Island (Bowman Bay, Taverner Bay), and Southampton Island (probably also Mansel Island); also Ellesmere (Alert, Slidre Fiord) and Axel Heiberg islands. Probably also in northwestern coastal Mackenzie (Franklin and Liverpool bays, Cape Bathurst), but evidence is not completely satisfactory.

Recorded northwest to Prince Patrick Island (Wilkie Point) and Melville Island, but evidence of breeding is lacking. Possibly there is a hiatus between the extreme northeastern population and that of the remainder of the breeding range in Canada.

Spring and autumn transient in much of southern Canada but absent or rare in the mountains of Yukon, interior British Columbia, and southwestern Alberta. Much commoner in autumn from southern Quebec eastward than in spring. Generally commoner coastally than in the interior, but concentrations occur on the Great Lakes. Spring and autumn transient in British Columbia (coast and islands only, uncommon), Alberta (east of the mountains, scarce), Saskatchewan (scarce to locally fairly common), Manitoba (scarce to locally fairly common in interior; common on Hudson Bay coast), Ontario (common on James and Hudson bays and on the Great Lakes; elsewhere generally scarce), Quebec (commoner on southeast coasts in autumn than in spring; scarce in southern interior; known to migrate on coasts of Hudson, James, and Ungava bays but extent and numbers poorly known; no records available from northern interior north of Lake St. John), Labrador (uncommon autumn migrant), Newfoundland (fairly common autumn migrant), Maritime Provinces (uncommon spring, common autumn migrant). Non-breeding birds occasionally are found in summer in widely scattered localities in the country.

Subspecies. (1) *Arenaria interpres morinella* (Linnaeus) occupies most of the breeding range in Canada except the northeast part (*see* next subspecies). It is the common migrant race of all of southern Canada, but on the B.C. coast it is scarce and the following race also occurs there. (2) *Arenaria interpres interpres* (Linnaeus) has more extensive black and less extensive paler russet in the upper parts. Breeds on Ellesmere and Axel Heiberg is. (perhaps also Devon Island) and winters in the Old World. More blackish migrants on the B.C. coast are referred to this race, although in some specimens (three males, Clayoquot, May 15, 1907) the russet in the upper parts is darker than in Ellesmere I. and Greenland *interpres*. They doubtless originate in Alaska. Some authors consider Alaskan and Siberian birds separable from the nominate race, as *A. i. cinclus* (Pallas), but the writer has not seen adequate material to be sure of the validity of *cinclus*.

BLACK TURNSTONE

Le Tourne-pierre noir. *Arenaria melanocephala* (Vigors)
Plate 29. L. 8.9 to 10 in.

Bill pointed, woodpecker-like, blackish as in Ruddy Turnstone. Legs short, dusky. *Adults in breeding plumage:* Head,

neck, breast, and upper parts, mainly sooty black. Lower back (partly concealed by folded wings) white, separated from white base of tail by blackish rump band as in Ruddy Turnstone. Hind half of tail black, narrowly margined white. In high plumage, forehead, sides of neck, and sides of breast, spotted with white. Line over eye and spot in front of eye, white. Wing stripe, belly, sides, and under tail coverts, white. *Adults and young in autumn:* Similar to above but without any white on head or neck.

Measurements. *Adult male:* wing, 144–150.8 (147.1); tail, 59–64.4 (61.8); exposed culmen, 21–24.9 (23); tarsus, 25–27.6 (26.3). *Adult female:* wing, 141.5–157 (150.9) mm.

Field Marks. A chunky, short-legged, black-and-white shorebird of the west coast. In flight it shows the same white lower back and base of tail separated by dark band as in Ruddy Turnstone, but differs from the Ruddy in darker all black-and-white coloration, dusky instead of orange legs, and uniform (not patchy) dark breast. Surfbird also has base of tail and upper tail coverts white, but the lower back is dark and the spread wing shows much less white.

Habitat. Exposed, rocky, or kelp-covered ocean shores and wave-washed reefs.

Range. Breeds on the coast of western and southern Alaska (Cape Prince of Wales south to Chichagof Island). Winters along the Pacific Coast of North America from southeastern Alaska south to Baja California and Sonora.

Range in Canada. Very common transient and winter resident on the coast of British Columbia. Casual in migration in the interior of British Columbia (Vanderhoof region) and Yukon (Teslin, Watson Lake).

Family **Scolopacidae** – Woodcock, Snipe, Sandpipers

Number of Species in North America 45; in Canada 36

This, the sandpiper family of the shorebirds, is a large and very widely distributed one. Members of the family show great differences in size and colour. The bill is slenderer than

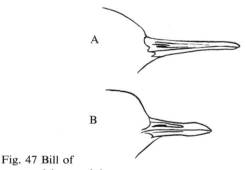

Fig. 47 Bill of
(A) a sandpiper
(B) a plover

that of plovers, is soft and rather flexible throughout its length, and does not have the well-marked horny tip of plovers' (Fig. 47). Bill is usually straight but sometimes downcurved (curlews) or somewhat upturned (godwits). Legs are slender, long or medium, and usually a hind toe is present (absent in Sanderling). Most are gregarious and are found in companies or flocks on shores and wet ground and in marshes with either fresh or salt water.

AMERICAN WOODCOCK

La Bécasse américaine. *Philohela minor* (Gmelin)
Plates 25, 31. L. 10 to 12 in. (including 2½- to 3-in. bill)

Bill long and straight; eyes large and set high in the head; wings short, rounded, outer three primaries very much narrower than rest (Fig. 48). General cinnamon coloration: 'autumn leaf' patterns above, plain below.

Fig. 48 Emarginate outer primaries of American Woodcock

Measurements. *Adult male:* wing, 122–128 (125); tail, 53–61 (57.8); exposed culmen, 63.9–67.7 (65.8); tarsus, 30–34.8 (31.5). *Adult female:* wing, 129.6–139.6 (136) mm.

Field Marks. A plump, cinnamon-coloured shorebird of thickets, with very long bill, large eyes set high in the head, short neck and tail. Usually it is not seen until it flies up at close range, its short wings producing a *twittering whistle*. The Common Snipe, also a long-billed shorebird, is very differently coloured, and the wings do not whistle in flight. The wings of the Mourning Dove produce a distinct whistling sound in flight, but its body proportions are very different (short bill, long tail).

Habitat. In spring the singing grounds of the males are in clearings and openings of various sizes in or near areas of low immature open mixedwood or hardwood or alder-willow thickets. These young open woodlands serve as nesting places and, along with alder thickets, as the male's daytime territory. In autumn, alder runs and moist alder thickets are popular, but dry open second growth is also frequented. Woodcock feed largely on earthworms and are likely to be found in the vicinity of soft moist soils suitable for the production of earthworms. Sometimes in dusk or darkness the birds feed in open fields or roadside ditches at considerable distances from woodland.

Nesting. On the ground in young open mixedwood or deciduous woodland, alder thickets, or sometimes in brushy or weedy fields. Nest, a depression in the ground sparsely lined with leaves. *Eggs*, usually 4; less pear-shaped (more ovate) than those of most shorebirds; buffy, rather sparingly

140

PLATE 25

1a

1b

2a

2b

3a

3b

4

5a

5b

6

7

Crosby

PLATE 26

1 Solitary Sandpiper,
    (a) autumn immature
    (b) summer adult

2 Spotted Sandpiper,
    (a) autumn immature
    (b) summer adult

3 Stilt Sandpiper,
    (a) summer adult
    (b) autumn immature

4 Willet,
    (a) autumn immature
      (flying)
    (b) summer adult

5 Greater Yellowlegs

6 Lesser Yellowlegs

spotted with brown and some grey. Incubation, 19 to 21 days (O.S. Pettingill, Jr.), by the female.

Range. Breeds from southeastern Canada south to Louisiana, Mississippi, southern central Alabama, and central Florida; west to southeastern Manitoba and extreme eastern Texas. Winters chiefly in southeastern Arkansas, Louisiana, and southwestern Mississippi, and in smaller numbers somewhat farther north and west.

Breeding Distribution of American Woodcock

Range in Canada. Breeds from southeastern Manitoba (Red River valley; species noted west to Delta), southern and south-central Ontario (north at least to Fort William–Port Arthur region and Michipicoten Island, northern Lake Superior; North Bay; Lake Timagami; Westmeath; Ottawa); southern Quebec (Hull, Montreal, Magog, Quebec, Rivière-du-Loup, eastern Gaspé Peninsula: Forillon and Bonaventure Island; recorded in breeding season in La Vérendrye Park and at Lake St. John), Newfoundland (Indian Head, Doyles; probably sparsely in other southwestern and southern parts; singles, including one 'ground calling,' reliably reported north to St. Anthony, July, 1955 and 1956), New Brunswick, Prince Edward Island, and Nova Scotia (including Cape Breton Island).

Casual on north shore of the Gulf of St. Lawrence (Johan Beetz Bay, Havre St. Pierre).

Occasional winter occurrences in Canada may be wounded or otherwise unhealthy individuals.

Remarks. Although a shorebird, the Woodcock is found mostly in moist brushy tangles and alder thickets. It sleeps during the day, and when disturbed it springs from the ground with whistling wings, whirs up over the alder tops, then soon drops back into cover.

It is one of the earliest birds to return in spring, while snow patches still remain in the woods. When dusk settles over the alder patches on a spring evening, the male's well-spaced nasal *peent* is a common sound. It is similar to a call of the Nighthawk and is often mistaken for that bird long before the Nighthawk has returned from the south. This note is given by the Woodcock while on the ground. Every few minutes, however, it whirs up from the ground, wings whistling loudly, mounts high in the semi-darkness where it does a peculiar sky dance on wings, then plummets back to earth and resumes its ground calling.

The long slender bill has a flexible tip and is ideal for probing the ground for earthworms, which make up a large part of the Woodcock's food.

EUROPEAN WOODCOCK

La Bécasse européenne. *Scolopax rusticola* Linnaeus
L. 13 to 14 in.

Decidedly larger than American Woodcock with greyer, distinctly barred under parts. The three outermost primaries are not narrow as in American Woodcock. An Old World species which breeds across Eurasia from the British Isles to northern Japan.

Status in Canada. Accidental in Quebec (one shot at Chambly, November 11, 1882) and in Newfoundland (one taken near St. John's, January 9, 1862).

COMMON SNIPE (Wilson's Snipe)

La Bécassine ordinaire. *Capella gallinago* (Linnaeus)
Plates 25, 31. L. 10.3 to 11.7 in. (including 2½- to 2¾-inch bill)

Bill long, straight. Upper parts mixed browns, buff, ochre, and blackish with buff stripes down back. Crown with light buff or whitish median stripe. Tail stubby, with subterminal area of brick-red crossed by narrow black bar near end and tipped buff or whitish. Breast buffy brown, variously marked with dusky. Belly white. Sides and flanks barred with blackish brown. Woodcock and dowitchers also have long straight bills, but American Woodcock is coloured very differently, and the outermost three primaries are extremely narrow. Dowitchers have the lower back (partly hidden by folded wings) mainly white, no brick-red in the tail, and no median crown stripe.

Measurements. *Adult male:* wing, 122.3–128.4 (125.2); tail, 53.2–58 (55.3); exposed culmen, 61–70.3 (65.2); tarsus, 31–35.6 (32.4). *Adult female:* wing, 121.9–132.5 (127) mm.

Field Marks. A long-billed shorebird that flies up, usually from low marshy places, with a peculiar zig-zag flight, uttering a characteristic raspy *scaipe* and showing at close range a little brick-red in the tail. In spring it is frequently detected by the hollow tremolo 'winnowing' sound, produced by the tail and wings in the air overhead. The dowitcher is a long-billed shorebird of similar proportions, but in flight it shows a conspicuously white lower back and has no red in the tail and no light median crown stripe.

Habitat. In breeding season, various types of large and small freshwater marshes, bogs, marshy edges, moist meadows and similar places that provide soft mud and low cover. In migration, also plowed and puddly fields, wet stubbles, ditches, and creeks; also upper salt marshes. Water edges trampled into black mud by the hoofs of animals are often very inviting. Sometimes more open wet alder runs and occasionally even wet woodland. The few that winter in eastern Canada usually resort to springs.

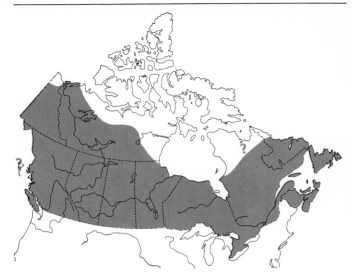

Breeding Distribution of Common Snipe

Nesting. On the ground, in a slight depression lined with grass in or near a marsh, bog, slough, or lake, or sometimes in the grass of prairie or fields near by. *Eggs*, usually 4; greenish buff to brownish, heavily marked with dark browns. Incubation about 20 days, by both sexes (H. Mousley).

Range. Holarctic. In North America breeds from northwestern Alaska and the northern mainland of Canada south to California, Arizona, Nebraska, central Iowa, northern Illinois, northwestern Pennsylvania, and northern New Jersey. Winters mainly from southern British Columbia, Utah, central Nebraska, Indiana, and North Carolina south to the West Indies, Colombia, Venezuela, and southern Brazil. Breeds also in Iceland, the Faroes, and widely across much of Eurasia, and winters south as far as central Africa, Ceylon, Java, and the Philippines.

Range in Canada. Breeds from northern Yukon (Old Crow, Lapierre House), northwestern and central Mackenzie (Aklavik, Thelon River marshes), southern Keewatin (McConnell and Windy rivers), northern Quebec (Great Whale River, Knob Lake, and perhaps Fort Chimo) and central Labrador (Webb's Bay) south through British Columbia (breeding records lacking from Queen Charlotte Islands), Alberta, Saskatchewan, Manitoba, Ontario, Quebec (including Magdalen Islands), Newfoundland, New Brunswick, Prince Edward Island, and Nova Scotia.

Winters regularly in southern British Columbia (small numbers on coast and southern interior); casually and irregularly elsewhere (southern Ontario, New Brunswick, Nova Scotia, and Newfoundland).

Subspecies. (1) *Capella gallinago delicata* (Ord) is the breeding subspecies of N. America and the only subspecies likely to occur at any time. (2) The Eurasian subspecies *Capella gallinago gallinago* (Linnaeus) is of accidental occurrence in Labrador (Jack Lane's Bay, December 24, 1927).

Remarks. A common spring sound, high in the air, over low-lying areas is a hollow tremolo *who-who-who-who-who*. This is a courtship performance of the Common Snipe. The sound is produced in flight by the rush of air past the spread tail feathers, and the tremolo effect by the rapidly beating wings. Another common spring sound, produced vocally, usually while the bird is perched on the ground or on a fence post, is a harsh *kak-kak* repeated various times. At any season a harsh *scaipe* is given while the bird is in flight, especially when flushing.

[Great Snipe. *Capella media* (Latham). Hypothetical. The type specimen of *Scolopax leucurus* Swainson, later identified as this species, was alleged to have come from 'Hudson's Bay' (Swainson and Richardson, 1831, *Fauna Boreali-Americana* 2:501).]

EUROPEAN JACKSNIPE
La Bécassine sourde. *Lymnocryptes minimus* (Brünnich)
L. 7.4 to 8.7 in.

Smaller than Common Snipe with much shorter bill (bill little more than 1½ in.). Lacks median crown stripe. Flanks not barred. Tail has no brick-red colour; *middle tail feathers longest.*

Status in Canada. Accidental visitor from the Old World. Labrador (Makkovik Bay, specimen taken December 24, 1927).

LONG-BILLED CURLEW
Le Courlis à long bec. *Numenius americanus* Bechstein
Plate 28. L. 20 to 26 in. (of which bill, in adults, is 5 to 7½ in.).

Bill extremely long, slender, downcurved. Larger size and sickle bill distinguish curlews from other shorebirds (*see* ibises). This, our largest shorebird, can always readily be distinguished from the Whimbrel, a slightly smaller curlew, and from the Eskimo Curlew by its plain, unbarred, cinnamon-coloured axillars.

Measurements (*N. a. parvus*). *Adult male:* wing, 249–271 (258.6); tail, 92–105.5 (99.2); exposed culmen, 112–134 (123.4); tarsus, 73.6–81.5 (76). *Adult female:* wing, 265.5–284.5 (274.6) mm.

Field Marks. Large size for a shorebird, sickle bill, and brownish coloration mark it as a curlew (*see also* ibises). Most likely to be confused with the Whimbrel, a somewhat smaller curlew. Greater length of bill is not always a safe criterion as some immature Long-bills have bills as short as some adult Whimbrels or shorter. Its lack of a dark stripe through the eye and more pinkish buff coloration, especially on the lining of the spread wing, distinguish it from the Whimbrel. Also it lacks any well-defined median crown stripe, but this is usually hard to ascertain in the field.

Habitat. Grasslands of the southern prairies and grassy intermontane valleys of southern interior British Columbia.

Nesting. Nest, a depression in the ground, lined (often sparsely but sometimes well) with grass and weeds. *Eggs,* usually 4; olive buff, more or less evenly spotted with browns and olive. Incubation is evidently by both sexes.

Range. Breeds from southern western Canada south to Utah, New Mexico, Texas (formerly east to Wisconsin and Illinois). Winters from California, western Nevada, Texas, and Louisiana south to Guatemala; also in South Carolina, Georgia, and Florida.

Range in Canada. Summer resident in southern part of western Canada, much scarcer than formerly. Breeds in southern interior British Columbia (Osoyoos, Kamloops, Riske Creek, Baldy Mountain, Dog Creek), southern Alberta (Sullivan Lake, Rosebud, Fort Macleod, Brooks, Medicine Hat), southern Saskatchewan (Cypress Lake, Rusk Lake, Elbow, Quill Lakes, Saskatoon, Moose Mountain), and southern Manitoba (now very scarce but bred formerly at Aweme and on the prairies of the Red and Souris rivers).

Casual in southern Mackenzie (Fort Simpson), on James Bay, and in New Brunswick. Records elsewhere in eastern Canada are unsatisfactory, but there is a convincing sight record for southern Ontario (Ajax).

Breeding Distribution of Long-billed Curlew

Subspecies. (1) *Numenius americanus parvus* Bishop is the only breeding subspecies known in Canada. (2) *Numenius americanus americanus* Bechstein, a longer-billed race breeding farther south in the U.S. is a casual visitor to N.B. (one specimen).

WHIMBREL (Hudsonian Curlew)
Le Courlis corlieu. *Numenius phaeopus* (Linnaeus)
Plate 28. L. 15 to 18.8 in. (of which bill, in adults, is 2¾ to 4 in.).

Bill downcurved, slender but usually shorter than in Long-billed Curlew. Separable from that species also by Whimbrel's barred axillars, dark stripe through eye, light median crown stripe, more greyish (less pinkish cinnamon) plumage, and smaller size. Both the Whimbrel and Long-billed Curlew have a characteristic saw-tooth colour pattern on the inner webs of the primaries, which is lacking in the smaller Eskimo Curlew.

Measurements (*N. p. hudsonicus*). *Adult male:* wing, 223–241.5 (232.8); tail, 83.7–95.2 (91.3); exposed culmen, 74.4–88.2 (81.9); tarsus, 54.7–58.5 (56.4). *Adult female:* wing, 221.5–250.5 (240.7) mm.

Field Marks. Long, slender, downcurved bill, large size

for a shorebird, and brownish coloration mark it as a curlew. Presence of head stripes and lack of conspicuous pinkish-cinnamon wing linings distinguish it from the larger Long-billed Curlew (*see also* Eskimo Curlew).

Habitat. Variable. For nesting, hummocky, grass-sedge, heath, and mossy tundras varying from wet tussocky lowland types to dry uplands of hills, sedge-hummocked alpine tundra, and moderately dry tundra ridges with scattered three-foot-high dwarf birch. In migration tidal mud flats, beaches, lakeshores, sparsely vegetated parts of marshes, short-grass fields and stubbles, and heaths, especially those with crowberry (*Empetrum*).

Nesting. Nest, a depression in the ground or on a tussock of vegetation in either wet or dry tundra; nest lined with lichens, sedge leaves or other vegetation. *Eggs*, 4, olive-buff to greenish, spotted and blotched with various browns and lavender. Incubation period 22 to 23½ days (J. R. Jehl and D. J. T. Hussell).

Range. Breeds in Alaska, Canada, Iceland, the Faroes, and northern Eurasia east to Ob River, and from Yana River eastward across northeastern Siberia. Winters from coastal southern United States south to the Galápagos Islands, southern Chile, and Brazil; and elsewhere south to southern Africa, Australia, Tasmania, and islands in the south Pacific Ocean.

Breeding Distribution of Whimbrel

Range in Canada. Breeding range apparently two disjunct areas. Breeds in Yukon (Old Crow Mountains, probably Burwash Creek summit), and northwestern Mackenzie (Richards Island, Caribou Hills, Anderson River); also in southern Keewatin (Upper Kazan Lake region, Boundary Lake), northeastern Manitoba (Churchill), and northern Ontario (Cape Henrietta Maria, Lake River). Recorded in the breeding season on Southampton Island and Banks Island.

Spring and autumn (including late summer) transient, mainly coastwise and on lower Great Lakes. In spring up the Pacific Coast and the lower Great Lakes and west side of Hudson Bay with small numbers in the interior between.

In late summer and autumn, southern Southampton Island, both coasts of Hudson Bay, spreading east to Newfoundland, the north shore of the Gulf of St. Lawrence, and the Maritimes. A spring and autumn transient in British Columbia (common on coast; very rare in interior); scarce spring transient in Alberta, Saskatchewan, and interior southern Manitoba. In interior Ontario it is locally fairly common in spring in extreme southern parts near lakes Erie and Ontario, much scarcer there in autumn; scarce elsewhere; in extreme eastern parts (Ottawa) more frequently reported in autumn. Quebec (mainly autumn transient on Hudson and James bays; common on north shore of the Gulf of St. Lawrence, Anticosti and Magdalen islands, and the St. Lawrence River east of Quebec; scarcer in interior west of Quebec; scarce along Ungava Bay; not recorded from the northern interior). Labrador (uncommon autumn transient on coast). Newfoundland (common autumn transient). Locally common to very common autumn transient in the Maritimes, notably Cape Breton Island.

Accidental on northern Baffin Island (Arctic Bay).

Subspecies. (1) *Numenius phaeopus hudsonicus* Latham is the only subspecies known to nest in Canada and is the common transient. (2) *Numenius phaeopus phaeopus* (Linnaeus), of Europe and nw. Siberia, is of accidental occurrence in southern Lab. (Red Bay, May 14, 1932). It has a whitish lower back and rump. (3) *Numenius phaeopus islandicus* Brehm, of Iceland and the Faroes, is of accidental occurrence in N.S. (Sable Island, May 23, 1906) and Nfld. (Pistolet Bay, June 27, 1943). Similar to the nominate race but averages larger.

ESKIMO CURLEW

Le Courlis esquimau. *Numenius borealis* (Forster)
L. 12 to 14.5 in. (of which bill is 2 to 2.5 in.)

Similar to Whimbrel but considerably smaller with (usually) shorter, not so decidedly downcurved, bill; and with primaries plain brown, completely lacking the bars or sawtooth markings that characterize those of the Whimbrel. Crown somewhat mottled with buff, but light crown stripe less well defined than in the Whimbrel. The short bill is not always a reliable species criterion, as immature Whimbrels often have the bill almost or quite as short. The unmarked primaries are the best criterion (Fig. 49).

Fig. 49 Outermost primary of
(A) Whimbrel (B) Eskimo Curlew

Measurements. *Adult male:* wing, 200.5–214 (206.3); tail, 77–83.5 (80.1); exposed culmen, 48–53 (51.3); tarsus, 39.5–44 (42.1). *Adult female:* wing, 189.5–215 (203.8) mm (Ridgway).

Field Marks. The almost extinct Eskimo Curlew cannot safely be separated from the Whimbrel in the field except under extremely favourable circumstances. A small-bodied curlew with short, slender, less decidedly decurved bill. Crown with no well-defined median stripe; dark line in front of eye poorly developed. Breast tends to have more definitely arrow-shaped markings than in the Whimbrel, and the under parts, especially in spring, are more buffy.

Nesting. Nest, a depression in the ground lined with a few dead leaves or a little dry hay. *Eggs*, usually 4; brownish green to olive blotched with brown. Little is known of its nesting habits.

Range. Extent of former breeding range now uncertain but known to have included northwestern Mackenzie and perhaps northern Alaska. Wintered from southern Brazil south to southern Argentina and Chile.

Range in Canada. Now almost extinct. Formerly a locally very common transient and summer resident. Known to have bred in northwestern Mackenzie (Fort Anderson, Lac Rendez-vous, Franklin Bay, Point Lake). Breeding range probably larger but extent unknown.

Spring migration in North America was mainly through the interior, over the drainage of the Mississippi and Missouri rivers and west of the Great Lakes and Hudson Bay. Therefore it undoubtedly occurred as a spring transient in the Prairie Provinces (Swainson and Richardson), but more definite data apparently were not recorded. Known as a spring migrant in southern Mackenzie (forts Resolution and Simpson). In autumn, formerly an abundant transient on the coast of Labrador (numbers falling off sharply just prior to 1888–1890), the north shore of the Gulf of St. Lawrence, Newfoundland, Magdalen Islands, Nova Scotia, Prince Edward Island, and New Brunswick. Rare in southern Ontario (near Kingston, October 10, 1873; Toronto, 1864; and Hamilton), and in interior southwestern Quebec (Lake St. Peter). Casual in southern Baffin Island.

The last recorded specimen taken in Canada was at Battle Harbour, Labrador, on August 29, 1932.

Remarks. Excessive shooting seems to have been the most plausible main reason for the decline of this little curlew. Migrating in flocks, often large ones, numbers could often be killed by a single shotgun blast. Sometimes the confused and decimated flocks returned to the decoys only to receive another barrage from the ambushed hunters. One needs to look no further for a reason for this curlew's decline.

Recent sight records in the United States and Canada, as well as an unfortunate shooting of one in the West Indies recently, show that the species is not yet extinct and provide a basis for hope that the Eskimo Curlew may yet be saved. Needless to say, the hunting or molesting of it is strictly forbidden.

UPLAND PLOVER
La Maubèche des champs
Bartramia longicauda (Bechstein)
Plate 30. L. 11 to 12.8 in.

Bill (1 to 1.3 in.), straight but upper mandible slightly downcurved at tip. Inner web of outermost wing primary

(often others also) with sawtooth-shaped markings, which distinguish it from our other shorebirds except the Whimbrel and the Long-billed Curlew (both larger birds with much longer, decidedly downcurved bills). Although called 'plover,' this bird is really a sandpiper.

Measurements. *Adult male:* wing, 157.8–169.8 (163.4); tail, 76.4–88 (82.6); exposed culmen, 27.7–30.5 (28.9); tarsus, 47–51.3 (48.9). *Adult female:* wing, 161–177.9 (168.2) mm.

Field Marks. A rather large buffy upland sandpiper without any very conspicuous markings, but with slender neck, rather small head, straight shortish bill (slightly shorter than head), and rather long tail for a sandpiper. On alighting, it often extends wings straight up for a moment, exposing black-and-white barring of entire wing lining. In flight, blackish lower back is exposed. These points, combined with its habit, unlike most sandpipers, of frequenting upland habitats, make recognition easy.

Habitat. Open grassy uplands: hayfields, pastures, and prairies; also (in Yukon) sandy, sparsely vegetated flats and bogs up to timberline.

Nesting. Nest, a depression in the ground lined with grass and usually hidden in grass or other low vegetation. *Eggs*, usually 4, rather large for the size of the bird; pale buff, small-spotted with browns and a little bluish grey. Incubation 21 days, by both sexes (I. O. Buss and A. S. Hawkins).

Range. Breeds from southern Alaska and Canada (*see* Range in Canada) south to northeastern Oregon, southeastern Wyoming, northwestern Oklahoma, northern Texas, southern Illinois, central Virginia, and Maryland. Winters in southern South America.

Breeding Distribution of Upland Plover

Range in Canada. Breeds locally in southern Yukon (Duke River meadows, Wolverine Creek, Hutshi Lake, Burwash Landing), southern Mackenzie (probably Fort Smith and Fort Simpson; recorded in summer near Norman Wells), British Columbia (interior locally: Peace River District, perhaps elsewhere in interior), Alberta, south-central and southern Saskatchewan (Prince Albert, Nipawin, Maple

Creek, Grenfell), southern Manitoba (Garland, Aweme, probably Lake St. Martin), southern Ontario (north to about Ottawa, Manitoulin Island, and Fort William), and extreme southwestern Quebec (Aylmer, Montreal, Hatley).

Migrates through the interior. Rare transient in coastal British Columbia (Comox, Victoria, Vancouver). Casual in eastern Quebec (Godbout), New Brunswick (Kent Island), and Nova Scotia (Grand Pré, Canard, Sable Island); also southeastern Keewatin (50 miles below Cape Eskimo).

Remarks. Although named 'Upland Plover,' this interesting bird is not a plover at all. It is a true sandpiper, aberrant only in its preference for uplands to shores and mud flats. It would be much more accurately called 'Upland Sandpiper.'

SPOTTED SANDPIPER

La Maubèche branle-queue. *Actitis macularia* (Linnaeus)
Plates 26, 31. L. 7 to 8 in.

Adults in breeding plumage are unmistakable with roundish black spots on the white underparts and a slight metallic lustre to the greyish brown upper parts. Autumn birds have unspotted white under parts, shading to grey on upper breast, and narrow dusky bars on wing coverts. Separable from Solitary Sandpiper by all-white axillars.

Measurements. *Adult male:* wing, 94–102.5 (99.7); tail, 47–53 (49.1); exposed culmen, 21.6–25 (23.1); tarsus, 23.3–25.1 (24.3). *Adult female:* wing, 99.3–108.3 (105.7) mm.

Field Marks. The common breeding sandpiper all across southern Canada. On the ground a pale-legged sandpiper with a pale area at base of lower mandible and a habit of teetering almost constantly, the tail figuring prominently in this. In flight the stiffly-held, down-bowed wings and quick shallow wing-strokes with frequent short glides are characteristic. Black roundish spots on the under parts of spring and summer adults are unmistakable. Young and adults in autumn have plain white under parts with grey shading on upper breast. Although less well marked, they have the same characteristic motions, pale legs, and pale area at base of lower mandible and usually show a whitish area just in front of the folded wing. Most likely to be confused with the Solitary Sandpiper, but the peculiar flight, white stripe in spread wing, much less white in tail, and yellowish or flesh-coloured legs mark the Spotted. Common call: a sharp *peet-weet;* a series of *weet.*

Habitat. Sandy, rocky, or muddy shores of interior lakes, ponds, rivers, and streams as well as on coastal salt water, usually in open to fairly open places. Often forages on floating logs.

Nesting. Nest, a hollow in the ground with a sparse lining of grass, moss, bits of weeds, or similar vegetation, usually not too far from water. *Eggs,* usually 4; buffy with spots and blotches of dark brown and often a few spots of bluish grey. Incubation 20 to 22 days (J. K. and J. T. Miller). Incubation is largely by male (Mousley).

Range. Breeds from northwestern Alaska eastward across Canada and south to southern California (mountains), central Texas, northern Alabama, western North Carolina (mountains), and eastern Maryland. Winters from south-

western British Columbia, southern Texas, the Gulf States, and coastal South Carolina south to northern Chile and southern Brazil.

Range in Canada. Common and widely distributed summer resident and transient. Breeds from northern Yukon (Old Crow), northwestern and central Mackenzie (Mackenzie Delta, Lockhart and Anderson rivers, marshy parts of Thelon River), southwestern Keewatin (Windy River mouth), northern Quebec (Richmond Gulf, Fort Chimo, Indian House Lake), and northern Labrador (Okak) south

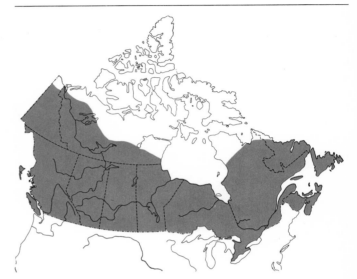

Breeding Distribution of Spotted Sandpiper

through British Columbia (including southern Vancouver Island), Alberta, Saskatchewan, Manitoba, Ontario, Quebec, New Brunswick, Prince Edward Island, Nova Scotia, and Newfoundland.

Occasionally winters in southwestern British Columbia (Vancouver Island, Chilliwack).

[**Green Sandpiper.** *Tringa ochrophus* Linnaeus. Hypothetical. Swainson and Richardson (1831, *Fauna Boreali-Americana*) recorded a specimen of this Old World species from Hudson Bay, and Brewer (1878, *Bull. Nuttall Orn. Club* 3: 49) discussed another specimen allegedly from Halifax, Nova Scotia. Neither record is completely satisfactory.]

SOLITARY SANDPIPER

Le Chevalier solitaire. *Tringa solitaria* Wilson
Plates 26, 31. L. 7.5 to 9 in.

Upper parts including rump very dark blackish brown with slight green sheen, speckled in summer adults with white, in immatures with buffy white. Legs, dark olive green. Heavy black-and-white barring of axillars distinguishes it from similar small sandpipers. Yellowlegs have finer and sparser barring on the axillars but are decidedly larger and have bright yellow legs and whitish upper tail coverts.

Measurements (*T.s. solitaria*). *Adult male:* wing, 124.5–130 (127.2); tail, 53.2–58.5 (55.2); exposed culmen, 28–31 (29.3); tarsus, 29.8–33.5 (31.2). *Adult female:* wing, 126–135 (130.2) mm.

Field Marks. A rather slender, straight-billed, dark-backed sandpiper with dark green legs and a habit of nodding. Both species of yellowlegs also have a habit of nodding, but the Solitary Sandpiper's dark legs, dark rump, and smaller size distinguish it. From the Spotted Sandpiper, it is distinguished by its darker upper parts and legs, streaked breast, and different nodding motions involving mainly the front of the body instead of mainly the rear. In flight, it differs further from the Spotted Sandpiper in showing no white wing stripe and much more white in outer tail. Its full wing-stroke differs from the markedly shallow stroke of the Spotty. Common call, *peet weet*, like that of the Spotted Sandpiper but shriller.

Habitat. More inclined to frequent quiet woodland pools and tarns than most sandpipers, but also inhabits more open places; shallow muddy edges of fresh and brackish water, margins of lakes, rivers, sloughs, open muddy parts of marshes, cattle wallows. In breeding season, muskegs and shallow water edges in or near woodland.

Nesting. Eggs are laid in old nests of tree-nesting birds, such as American Robin, Rusty Blackbird, Gray Jay, and Cedar Waxwing, at various heights in both coniferous and deciduous trees. The four *eggs* are greenish or buffy, spotted and blotched with browns and a little bluish grey. Relatively little is known concerning its nesting habits.

Range. Breeds in central-eastern and southern Alaska and in more northern wooded parts of Canada. Winters from Baja California, the Gulf of Mexico, Florida, and southeastern Georgia south to Argentina.

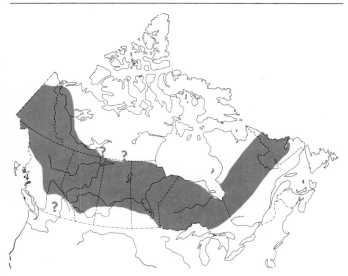

Breeding Distribution of Solitary Sandpiper

Range in Canada. Summer resident and transient. Breeds north to near tree-limit from Yukon (Old Crow, Kathleen River, Lapie River), Mackenzie (Mackenzie Delta, Wood Buffalo Park; probably Fort Norman, Brackett Lake, and possibly Thelon River), south to central British Columbia (Peace River District, Heart Lake), south-central Alberta (Jasper Park, Bowden), central Saskatchewan (Emma Lake, Hudson Bay Junction, Torch River), Manitoba (Churchill, Ilford, Herchmer south perhaps to Lake St. Martin),

northern and central Ontario (Raft River, Moosonee, High Falls on Frederick House River), Quebec (probably Knob Lake and 90 miles south, Indian House Lake; Paul Bay), and Labrador (near Nain and Hopedale).

Spring and autumn transient through British Columbia (scarcer on coast), Alberta, Saskatchewan, Manitoba, Ontario, central and southern Quebec, New Brunswick, Prince Edward Island, Nova Scotia, and rarely Newfoundland. In the Maritimes commoner in southward migration than in spring.

Subspecies. (1) *Tringa solitaria solitaria* Wilson is the breeding form throughout the eastern part of the range and in w. Canada north to se. Yukon (Lapie River) and n.-c. Man. (Ilford). (2) *T. s. cinnamomea* (Brewster), with more ashy upper parts, slightly larger size, and (usually) with white mottling near the base of the under side of the outer primary, and in autumn immatures with deeper buff spots on the back, breeds in the northern part of the range in the West (east to northeastern Manitoba) and south to nw. B.C., Great Slave Lake, and Churchill, Man.

WANDERING TATTLER
Le Chevalier errant. *Heteroscelus incanus* (Gmelin)
Plate 29. L. 10.5 to 11.3 in.

Bill straight. Upper parts plain slaty grey, unrelieved from crown to tip of tail and without wing stripes. Adults in breeding plumage have the under parts heavily barred with dark grey and white. Winter adults and immatures lack bars on the under parts, these replaced by a grey suffusion over breast and sides. In all plumages a well-defined white eyebrow line is present. Legs yellow-green to dull orange-yellow.

Measurements. *Adult male:* wing, 161.2–179.9 (170.1); tail, 72.3–80 (74.9); exposed culmen, 34–40.3 (37.7); tarsus, 32.5–36.5 (33.9). *Adult female:* wing, 167.4–181.6 (173.8) mm.

Field Marks. A medium-sized shorebird of the far West with plain dark grey upper parts, longish straight bill, well-defined white eyebrow line, and in migration showing a preference for outer coasts. The heavily barred under parts of breeding plumage are unlike those of other shorebirds, except the Stilt Sandpiper, which is a smaller, brownish-backed bird with a white rump. Winter-plumaged adults and immatures have plain grey breast and sides, but the *uniform* dark grey of the upper parts distinguishes them from the Surfbird, Black Turnstone, Knot, and both yellowlegs, all of which show some white or whitish near the tail. In flight it shows no white wing stripe. It has the habit of teetering.

Habitat. In migration, usually outer rocky sea-coasts and islands. In breeding season, mountain streams and meadows.

Nesting. The few nests known have been on gravel bars of high mountain streams. Nest, a depression in gravel, compactly lined with twigs and rootlets. *Eggs,* 4; greenish, spotted and blotched with browns. Incubation is said to be by both parents.

Range. Breeds in the mountains of interior Alaska, Yukon, and northwestern British Columbia; also evidently in northeastern Siberia. Winters on the Pacific Coast from southern California to Ecuador, on the Hawaiian Islands, and on many islands of the south Pacific south to Fiji, Tonga, and Society islands.

Range in Canada. Breeds (extent of breeding range poorly known) in high mountains of Yukon (probably Rose River at Canol Road; perhaps upper Macmillan River) and northwestern British Columbia (Haines Road near Mile 84; probably Atlin and Dease Lake).

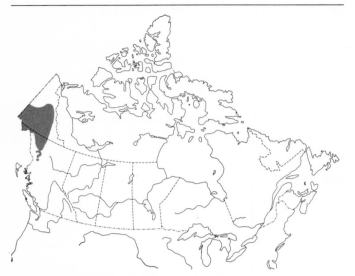

Breeding Distribution of Wandering Tattler

Migrant, fairly common, along outer coast and islands of British Columbia. Casual in central-eastern British Columbia (Tupper Creek, May 30, 1938). There are two sight records for southern Ontario, but no specimen was taken.

WILLET

Le Chevalier semi-palmé
Catoptrophorus semipalmatus (Gmelin)
Plate 26. L. 14 to 17 in.

A large grey-and-white shorebird with bill straight and slightly longer than head, white upper tail coverts, and very broad white band across the wing, contrasting with the blackish flight feathers. The wing markings are diagnostic in any plumage. American Oystercatcher and Avocet are other large shorebirds with much white in the wings, but the bills and markings of both are very different.

Measurements (*C. s. inornatus*). *Adult male:* wing, 196.3–208.1 (203.9); tail, 74.9–81.8 (78.3); exposed culmen, 56.3–66 (61.1); tarsus, 64–71.4 (66.7). *Adult female:* wing, 202.2–213.1 (207.3) mm.

Field Marks. A large greyish straight-billed shorebird somewhat suggesting a robust Greater Yellowlegs but with grey-blue legs. In flight it flashes a very conspicuous black-and-white wing pattern, visible at considerable distances, a pattern unlike that of any other greyish straight-billed shorebird. Noisy on breeding grounds. Common call: when on ground in nesting season, a loud, long-continued series of *yips*; in flight *pil-willet, pil-willet,* or *pil-will-willet*.

Habitat. In the West, moist and wet meadows, grassy edges of prairie sloughs and lakes. In the East, salt marshes and beaches on the coast.

Nesting. Nest, a depression in the ground, lined with grass and weeds. *Eggs,* usually 4; olive-buff, spotted and blotched with browns.

Range. Breeds from eastern Oregon, Idaho, and southern parts of the Prairie Provinces of Canada south to northeastern California, northern Colorado, and South Dakota; and on the Atlantic Coast in Nova Scotia, and locally from New Jersey to Florida, Texas, and Tamaulipas; also in the West Indies. Winters from southern United States south to Peru and Brazil.

Range in Canada. Locally common summer resident. Breeds in two disjunct areas: (1) southeastern and central-eastern Alberta (Miquelon Lake, Brooks, Dominion Range Station on Milk River), southern Saskatchewan (Carlton), Maple Creek, Yorkton), and southwestern Manitoba; and (2) Nova Scotia (coastal localities in Annapolis, Digby, Yarmouth, Shelburne, Queens, Lunenburg, Halifax counties, and recently Avonport, Kings Co.; also southern Cape Breton Island: Madame Island).

Breeding Distribution of Willet

Scarce summer visitant to New Brunswick (Grand Manan) and Prince Edward Island (in addition to old records, there are numerous recent observations at Wood Island). Casual in southwestern British Columbia (Comox, Victoria), northern Manitoba (Churchill), southern Ontario (Toronto; sight records for Kenora, Niagara River, Ottawa), and Newfoundland (Argentia, St. Andrews, Grand Banks), and southwestern Quebec (Godbout; also detailed sight record near Montreal).

Subspecies. (1) *Catoptrophorus semipalmatus semipalmatus* (Gmelin) breeds in N.S. (2) *C. s. inornatus* (Brewster), a larger, decidedly paler race, is the bird of the interior, breeding in the Prairie Provinces.

Remarks. This large wader, with its noisy ways and showy wing pattern, is an impressive bird on its nesting grounds. In Nova Scotia it has substantially expanded its breeding range during recent years.

GREATER YELLOWLEGS
Le Grand Chevalier à pattes jaunes
Totanus melanoleucus (Gmelin)
Plates 26, 31. L. 12.5 to 15 in.

A large shorebird with almost straight or very slightly uptilted bill (2.0 to 2.3 in.); marked with grey, black, and white (in autumn, adults and immatures have the black replaced by grey), rump more whitish than rest of upper parts, and long bright yellow legs. Distinguished from Lesser Yellowlegs by much larger size.

Measurements. *Adult male:* wing, 182–197.5 (189.4); tail, 69–84.2 (77.2); exposed culmen, 53.3–59.5 (56.1); tarsus, 59.4–67 (63.4). *Adult female:* wing, 183–198.4 (188.6) mm.

Field Marks. A large, slim, grey-and-white shorebird with long *bright yellow legs*. In flight it shows whitish rump and no wing stripe. A large edition of the Lesser Yellowlegs, and when, as often happens, the two are together they are readily distinguishable by size. Otherwise size is tricky. The bill of the Greater tends to turn up slightly. In migration its ringing whistled calls are in series of *three* or *four* on a descending scale, very different from the *one* or *two* softer whistles of the Lesser. On the ground, when disturbed, a loud long-continued monotonous series of *keks*. Both yellowlegs on the ground have frequent nodding motions (actually they begin with a backward jerk of the head).

Habitat. In migration, pools, sloughs, shallow margins of lakes and sluggish streams, flooded land; and on the coast, salt marshes, tidal pools, mud flats, and bays, but is not partial to outer wave-swept shores. In breeding season, wooded muskeg country, its bogs, ponds and lakes, low sparsely wooded ridges, and burntlands; also open woodlands, not necessarily very close to water.

Nesting. Nest, a depression or scrape in the ground or moss, lined with grasses, moss, or leaves, in boggy places or sparsely wooded ridges. *Eggs*, usually 4; buffy, spotted and blotched with browns. Nesting activities poorly known. Male takes active part in caring for the young.

Range. Breeds in southern Alaska and in wooded muskeg country across Canada (*see* Range in Canada). Winters from central California (rarely southern British Columbia), southern Arizona, the Gulf of Mexico coast, and South Carolina south to southern South America, including the West Indies.

Range in Canada. Breeding range rather poorly known. Breeds in south-central British Columbia (Fort St. James, Nukko Lake, Kleena Kleene, Mile 93 Caribou Road; possibly Peace River parklands), northern and central Alberta (Lake Athabasca, Fawcett, Athabasca, Entrance, Nordegg, Rocky Mountain House, Sundre, Jasper National Park), northwestern and central Saskatchewan (Lake Athabasca, probably Kazan Lake), north-central and central Manitoba (probably Ilford, Bird, Moose and Cedar lakes, perhaps Kalavala), northern Ontario (probably muskegs inland from James and Hudson bays), central Quebec (Lake Mistassini, Knob Lake region, south to the Gulf of St. Lawrence and Anticosti Island), central and southern Labrador (Hopedale, Cartwright), Newfoundland (Gaff Topsail), and northeastern Nova Scotia (Cape Breton Island).

Migrates through the southern interior and along the Pacific and Atlantic coasts. Stragglers north to southern Mackenzie (Great Slave Lake, Fort Simpson), southern Keewatin (probably: sight records 50 miles below Cape Eskimo; Windy River), and northern Quebec (Ungava Bay, Povungnituk). Casual on Southampton Island. Accidental in Baffin Island (Cumberland Sound). Irregularly a few winter in southwestern British Columbia (southern Vancouver Island).

LESSER YELLOWLEGS
Le Petit Chevalier à pattes jaunes
Totanus flavipes (Gmelin)
Plate 26. L. 9.3 to 11.1 in.

Bill straight, 1.3 to 1.5 in. Almost exactly like Greater Yellowlegs in all plumages, but decidedly smaller and lacks any suggestion of an uptilted bill. Lacks faint whitish marbling usually present on under side of the flight feathers of Greater Yellowlegs.

Measurements. *Adult male:* wing, 146.2–158.3 (152.1); tail, 58–66 (60.9); exposed culmen, 33.6–37 (35.4); tarsus, 46.8–53.6 (50.4). *Adult female:* wing, 150.1–158.5 (156.2) mm.

Field Marks. Long, bright-yellow legs, grey-and-white coloration, whitish rump and tail identify it as a yellowlegs. Its smaller size is obvious, when compared directly with Greater Yellowlegs, but is less helpful otherwise. Bill straight, not slightly uptilted. On take-off, utters one or two call-notes which are much softer, flatter and usually very different from the loud, ringing three or four of the Greater. Lesser Yellowlegs might be confused with autumn Stilt Sandpiper, a smaller bird with more greenish legs and a whitish line extending completely over and behind the eye.

Habitat. In migration very similar to that of Greater Yellowlegs, often in company with that species. For nesting, open woodland and burntland in country interspersed with muskegs, ponds, and lakes, the wet areas used for feeding and raising of young.

Breeding Distribution of Greater Yellowlegs

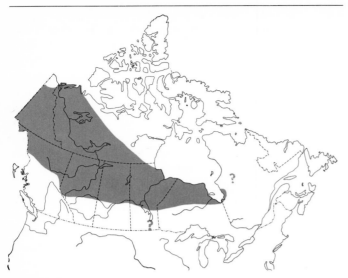
Breeding Distribution of Lesser Yellowlegs

Nesting. Nest, a depression in the ground lined with grasses and leaves, near a log, stump, small tree, or in the open. *Eggs*, usually 4; buffy, spotted and blotched with browns. Incubation by both parents. As in Greater Yellowlegs, the male apparently assumes a large part of caring for the young.

Range. Breeds in Alaska and much of western Canada east to James Bay. Winters from South Carolina, the Gulf States, and Mexico south to Chile and Argentina; also in the West Indies.

Range in Canada. Breeds from northern Yukon (Old Crow), northwestern and east-central Mackenzie (Mackenzie Delta, Fort Anderson, Artillery Lake), southern Keewatin (Nueltin Lake), northern Manitoba (Churchill), northern Ontario (probably inland from James and Hudson bays), and central-western Quebec (Moar Bay), south to central British Columbia (Peace River District), south-central Alberta (Buffalo Lake), central Saskatchewan (Amyot Lake, Whitefox River), central Manitoba (The Pas; unconfirmed reports south to Kalavala), and northern Ontario (Favourable Lake).

In southward migration common in most of extreme southern Canada from interior British Columbia to Nova Scotia, but spring migration is mainly through the interior, at which time the bird is much scarcer in British Columbia, Quebec, and the Maritimes. Rare to casual in Labrador and Newfoundland. Scarce on British Columbia coast.

[Redshank. *Totanus totanus* (Linnaeus). Hypothetical. A careful observation in Halifax County, Nova Scotia, on January 2, 1960, by L. B. Macpherson and Fred Dobson (Tufts, 1962) was of one of this species or possibly the Spotted Redshank, *Totanus erythropus*.]

KNOT

Le Bécasseau à poitrine rousse. *Calidris canutus* (Linnaeus) Plates 25, 31. L. 10 to 11 in.

Bill straight, 1.2 to 1.5 in., slightly longer than head. Legs short. In breeding plumage, unmarked robin-red throat and breast combined with a short straight bill distinguish it from all others. Dowitchers have long bills, and the accidental Curlew Sandpiper has a definitely downcurved bill. Autumn Knots have white under parts with fine dusky streaking on the breast; light grey upper parts, the feathers of the back with faint white narrow margins and a fine black submarginal line, giving a semicircular pattern to the feather tips. Upper tail coverts white, barred with dusky. Legs yellowish olive.

Measurements. (*C. c. rufa*). *Adult male:* wing, 155.9–173.9 (162.5); tail, 58–66.5 (62.2); exposed culmen, 33.5–37.8 (35.4); tarsus, 31–32.8 (32). *Adult female:* wing, 166–172.1 (168.7) mm.

Field Marks. In spring, a sturdy sandpiper with brick-red breast and *short* straight bill (dowitchers and others with reddish breast have *long* bills; the accidental Curlew Sandpiper has definitely downcurved bill). In autumn, a chunky large sandpiper with light grey upper parts; white under parts, finely streaked with dusky on breast; short legs; and short straight bill. In flight it shows a narrow white wing stripe and a rump obviously lighter than the rest of the upper parts. On the west coast, autumn Knots might be confused with the Surfbird or Wandering Tattler. The Knot has a poorly defined lighter rump compared with the rest of the upper parts. The Surfbird has a sharply defined white rump, and in the Wandering Tattler the rump is dark grey, exactly like the rest of the upper parts.

Breeding Distribution of Knot

Habitat. In migration it favours beaches and mud flats, also rocks covered with seaweed. In breeding season (Ellesmere and Prince Patrick islands) favours well-vegetated moist tundra for nesting, feeding, and rearing of young; nests also on higher, stony ridges.

Nesting. Nest, a shallow depression in the ground, lined with willow twigs, dry leaves, grass, and bits of moss. May be located on hummocks in moist ground or in glacial gravel on higher, drier arctic hills. *Eggs*, usually 4; buffy, spotted and scrawled with brown. Incubation almost certainly by both parents, and both care for the young.

Range. Breeds locally in the Arctics of both the New and Old Worlds; in the New World in northern Alaska (Point Barrow), locally in the Canadian Arctic, and in northern Greenland. In the New World, winters from southern California and Massachusetts (rarely) south along the coasts to southern South America.

Range in Canada. Breeds locally in the Arctic from Prince Patrick Island (Mould Bay), Ellef Ringnes Island (Isachsen), Axel Heiberg Island, and northern Ellesmere Island (Alert) south to southern Victoria Island (Cambridge Bay) and Southampton Island; probably Adelaide Peninsula and Mansel Island.

Spring migration is mainly west of Quebec and James and Hudson bays. In autumn it spreads farther east to the Maritimes and rarely to the coast of Labrador and Newfoundland. An uncommon spring and autumn transient on the coast of British Columbia (but not recorded from the interior), eastern Alberta, Saskatchewan, interior Manitoba, interior Ontario. Common transient on west coasts of James and Hudson bays. Autumn transient, rare in spring, from southern Quebec east to the Maritimes.

Subspecies. (1) *Calidris canutus canutus* (Linnaeus) breeds in the Old World and also occupies the northern part of the breeding range in N. America on Prince Patrick, Ellef Ringnes, Ellesmere, southern Melville (Winter Harbour) is., and probably n. Prince of Wales I. At least the Ellesmere I. birds winter in the Old World, but the winter range of other segments of the Canadian population of this race is not certainly known. Some migrate along the coast of B.C., but the writer has seen no evidence of its migration in se. Canada. (2) *C. c. rufa* (Wilson), a well-marked race characterized by paler coloration above and below and with the rufous of under parts decidedly less extensive posteriorly, occupies the southern part of the breeding range from southern Victoria I. east at least to Southampton I., but its areas of intergradation with the nominate race are not known. It is the migrant through most of s. Canada east of the Pacific Coast. However, little material has been examined from the Prairie Provinces.

PURPLE SANDPIPER
Le Bécasseau maritime. *Erolia maritima* (Brünnich)
Plate 25. L. 8.1 to 9.5 in.

Bill slightly longer than head, nearly straight or slightly downcurved, yellowish or orange basally. Legs short, dull greenish yellow to yellowish brown. In winter plumage, back is almost blackish *with purplish gloss*; head, neck, and breast dark grey, feathers of breast with white edges broader toward white belly; throat whitish; flanks with heavy grey streaks. In breeding plumage, blackish brown back is variegated with buff and white, breast heavily spotted and streaked.

Measurements. *Adult male:* wing, 117.9–130 (124.9); tail, 55.9–63 (60.2); exposed culmen, 27.2–32 (29.2); tarsus, 22–23.8 (23.1). *Adult female:* wing, 122.6–132.6 (126.9) mm.

Field Marks. A chunky, often tame, short-legged sandpiper, typical of rocky Atlantic shores, the most likely *winter* sandpiper on the east coast. In winter plumage, very dark grey coloration, short dull-yellowish legs, and yellowish or orange basal part of bill. In flight shows, as do many others, a white wing stripe and a dark rump.

Habitat. In migration and winter, rocky coastal shores; less often sand beaches and muddy pools. Even when it is found in the interior it is likely to be on the stones of breakwaters or similar stony situations. In breeding season, it nests on moss and lichen tundra, often at considerable elevations and sometimes far inland but often also on low tundra near shore and on coarse gravel-sand beaches along rivers. Many continue to use the shore for feeding.

Nesting. Nest, a depression in the ground or moss, well lined with leaves of dwarf birch or other available vegetation. The four *eggs* are said to be greenish or buffy, spotted and blotched with various browns. Apparently incubation is largely by the male, but more information is needed on this and most other phases of the breeding cycle.

Range. Breeds locally from eastern arctic Canada, Greenland, Iceland, and northern Eurasia from northern Scandinavia to Taimyr Peninsula and on Spitsbergen, Franz Josef Land, Novaya Zemlya, and the New Siberian Islands; formerly the Faroes. Winters in southwestern Greenland and Iceland, and on the Atlantic Coast from Newfoundland to Maryland; also in the British Isles and on shores of the North and Baltic seas.

Breeding Distribution of Purple Sandpiper

Range in Canada. Breeds (more definite data are needed to show western and northern limits) from Devon Island (probably) and northern Bylot Island, south to Southampton Island, Belcher Islands, and southern Baffin Island (Cape Dorset, Amadjuak Lake, probably Cumberland Sound); probably west at least to Cornwallis and Somerset islands, where recorded without evidence of breeding. Observed in summer west to Banks Island (Mercy Bay) and Prince Patrick Island (Mould Bay). On Prince of Wales Island, a fairly common spring and autumn migrant.

Winters on the Atlantic Coast in Newfoundland, New Brunswick, Prince Edward Island, and Nova Scotia. Casual in southern Ontario (Crystal Beach, Toronto, Ottawa).

Accidental in southern Manitoba (southwestern Lake Winnipeg). Rare in extreme southwestern Quebec (Montreal, Lake St. Peter) becoming commoner below Quebec on the St. Lawrence. Migration mainly east of Hudson Bay and presumably mainly coastal. Common transient in autumn, at least along the Labrador coast from Button Islands south.

ROCK SANDPIPER (Aleutian Sandpiper)
Le Bécasseau aléoutien. *Erolia ptilocnemis* (Coues)
L. ca. 9 in.

Like Purple Sandpiper, but in breeding plumage the upper parts have much more rusty colouring, and the breast has a poorly defined dusky patch or extensive dusky blotches.

Measurements (*E. p. couesi*). *Adult male:* wing, 109–118.5 (114.3); tail, 50.8–55 (52.4); exposed culmen, 25.2–27.9 (26.8); tarsus, 22.3–24.2 (23.2). *Adult female:* wing, 116–125 (120.9) mm.

Field Marks. In winter plumage like Purple Sandpiper (q.v.). A bird of the west coast likely to be found on rocky outer shores with Black Turnstones, Surfbirds, and Wandering Tattlers. It lacks the white rump of the Surfbird and the intricate white patterns shown in flight by the Black Turnstone. The Rock Sandpiper's white wing stripe, evident in flight, distinguishes it from the Wandering Tattler. In breeding plumage the rusty upper parts and dusky *breast* patch are a little suggestive of the Dunlin, but the Dunlin has dark (instead of yellowish) legs, an all-dark bill, and much more extensive black *abdominal* patch.

Habitat. In migration and winter, rocky ocean shores are the usual habitat.

Range. Breeds in northeastern Siberia, the Commander, Kurile, and Sakhalin islands, many islands in Bering Sea, and from central-western Alaska south to western Alaska Peninsula, the Shumagin and Aleutian islands. Winters within much of breeding range and south on the North American Pacific coast to Oregon and locally southern California and northwestern Baja California.

Range in Canada. Common winter resident and transient on the coast of British Columbia. One record inland (Atlin, October 29, 1932).

Subspecies. *Erolia ptilocnemis tschuktschorum* (Portenko).

SHARP-TAILED SANDPIPER
Le Bécasseau à queue fine. *Erolia acuminata* (Horsfield)
Plate 29. L. 8.5 in.

Similar to Pectoral Sandpiper, but tail feathers, especially outer ones, more sharply pointed at tips; *basal* part of outermost primary shaft brownish instead of white as in Pectoral (*see* Field Marks).

Field Marks. Closely resembles Pectoral Sandpiper, but breast markings never sharply cut off against white of under parts. Winter adults have the breast more lightly streaked and spotted (Pectoral's breast much more heavily and regularly streaked, not spotted). Immatures distinguishable from Pectoral by strong suffusion of cinnamon on breast; much finer and much more restricted dusky streaking on breast.

Habitat. Similar to Pectoral Sandpiper.

Range. Breeds in northern Siberia. Winters south to Australia and New Zealand, migrating mainly through eastern Siberia and along the Pacific coast of Asia; also along the Pacific coast of North America from about Kotzebue Sound, Alaska, south to Washington, rarely to California.

Range in Canada. Scarce autumn transient on the coast of British Columbia (Masset, Queen Charlotte Islands; Comox and Victoria, Vancouver Island, River Inlet). Two specimens from Masset, December 27, 1897, suggest occasional wintering.

PECTORAL SANDPIPER
Le Bécasseau à poitrine cendrée
Erolia melanotos (Vieillot)
Plate 30. L. 8.0 to 9.6 in. (male larger than female)

A medium-sized sandpiper with straight bill (.95 to 1.3 in.). Tail with two middle feathers pointed and extending well beyond the others. Broad buffy band across the breast and fore-neck, heavily and evenly streaked with dusky, and sharply cut off from white belly. Throat white. Rump blackish brown. Bill greenish yellow at base becoming black at tip. Legs yellowish green or greenish yellow.

Measurements. *Adult male:* wing, 136–142.8 (138.7); tail, 60.4–63.9 (62.2); exposed culmen, 28.7–30 (29.3); tarsus, 27.8–30 (28.9). *Adult female:* wing, 123.9–129 (126.3) mm.

Field Marks. A medium-sized sandpiper with a broad, buffy, heavily streaked breast band, *sharply cut off from white of belly.* Baird's and White-rumped sandpipers have a similar streaked band on the breast, but it is less sharply defined. Pectoral's legs are greenish-yellowish (black in the somewhat smaller Baird's), and it lacks the white rump shown in flight by the White-rumped Sandpiper. Least and Semipalmated sandpipers are much smaller birds. The neck of the Pectoral is longer than that of any of the others mentioned. Hunters often flush it in places frequented by Common Snipe, but as the Pectoral flies away it shows a broad black mark down lower back and rump, which the snipe lacks. On the arctic breeding grounds, males inflate the throat immensely in courtship, this giving them a different appearance from any of our other shorebirds. At the same time they emit grunting notes. On migration when flushed or flying, the common note is a grating *kriek*.

Habitat. In migration, grassy marshes, moist grassy edges of pools and ponds, flooded fields; sometimes short-grass drier fields. In the breeding season, sedge, grass, or shrub tundra and tundra meadows, especially moist or wet ones and with tussocks and hummocks; also mounds and ridges in such places; rolling tundra.

Nesting. Nest on the ground, often well hidden in the grass and sedge of a tussock or bunch of similar vegetation. It is substantially made of grasses and leaves. *Eggs,* usually 4; greenish to buffy, heavily blotched and spotted with browns. Incubation and care of the young are by the female. Incubation said to require 21 to 23 days (A. C. Bent).

Range. Breeds mainly along the coasts from eastern Siberia, northern and western Alaska, and locally in the low Arctic and Subarctic of Canada east to Southampton

Breeding Distribution of Pectoral Sandpiper

Measurements. *Adult male:* wing, 117–126 (120.4); tail, 47.5–53.6 (51.4); exposed culmen, 20–23.6 (21.7); tarsus, 21–24.5 (22.9). *Adult female:* wing, 117.5–124 (120.6) mm.

Field Marks. A small sandpiper with bill about as long as head, dark legs, and with a white patch completely across the rump (often hidden by wings when at rest, but readily noticeable in flight). Stilt Sandpiper also has a white rump, and its autumn plumage is somewhat like that of the White-rump, but the Stilt Sandpiper is a slender bird with obviously longer legs and longish bill. Other white-rumped sandpipers are obviously larger or are otherwise very distinctive. Common calls: in migration a distinctive high-pitched *jeet.*

Habitat. In migration, muddy shores, mud flats, and sand or gravel beaches on both salt and fresh water. Also, in the breeding season, wet and moist grassy tundra.

Nesting. Nest, usually on a tussock or mound in wet or moist tundra, is a shallow depression in soil or moss, lined with grasses and dead leaves. *Eggs,* usually 4; greenish to olive-buff, blotched and spotted with browns. Incubation apparently is mainly, if not entirely, by the female.

Range. Nearctic. Breeds in northern Alaska (rarely) and in the Canadian Arctic. Winters in southern South America.

Island. Winters in southern South America and in small numbers south to Australia and New Zealand.

Range in Canada. Breeds on the coast of Mackenzie (Richards Island, Bernard Harbour, Perry River), Banks Island, Victoria Island (Cambridge Bay), Prince of Wales Island, Keewatin (Adelaide Peninsula, probably McConnell River), Southampton Island, and south locally along the coast of Hudson and James bays to Cape Henrietta Maria. Probably breeds also on the coast of Yukon (definite data lacking). Reports of breeding in interior Mackenzie and interior Keewatin require confirmation.

Migration in spring is mainly through the interior west of Hudson Bay; in autumn, spreading eastward to the Atlantic and westward to the Pacific coast. A spring and autumn migrant in British Columbia (but rare in spring on the coast), Alberta, Saskatchewan, Manitoba, and Ontario (but much scarcer in spring in eastern localities). Mainly an autumn transient in Quebec (down coast of Hudson and James bays, the north shore of the Gulf of St. Lawrence where it is uncommon to rare, the southern interior and coast), Labrador (coast; uncommon), Newfoundland (uncommon), and commonly in New Brunswick, Prince Edward Island, and Nova Scotia. Casual north to Prince Patrick and Bylot islands, N.W.T. Casual in winter in southwestern British Columbia (Chilliwack).

WHITE-RUMPED SANDPIPER
Le Bécasseau à croupion blanc
Erolia fuscicollis (Vieillot)
Plates 27, 31. L. 6.8 to 8 in.

A small sandpiper with straight bill about as long as head (.85 to 1.0 in.). The only *small, moderately short-legged* sandpiper with a completely white rump patch. Might be confused with Stilt Sandpiper, which also has a white rump and is somewhat similar in autumn dress, but the Stilt Sandpiper's longer bill is abruptly broadened near the tip, and its legs are much longer than those of the White-rump, extending the feet well beyond the tip of the folded wing.

Breeding Distribution of White-rumped Sandpiper

Range in Canada. Breeds across the Arctic from Banks Island (Big River), Melville Island (Winter Harbour), Prince of Wales Island, and northwestern Bylot Island south to northern Mackenzie (Franklin Bay; Cockburn Point; 50 miles east of Fort Anderson), northern Keewatin (Adelaide Peninsula, Pelly Bay; probably Chesterfield Inlet; perhaps inland on Back River), Southampton Island, and southern Baffin Island (Jordan River, Cape Dorset).

Spring migration is mainly through the interior east of the Rockies and west of western Quebec and Hudson Bay, much more rarely farther east; in fall, mainly down the Atlantic Coast and the eastern interior. Transient, mainly in spring, in Alberta (rare), Saskatchewan, and interior Manitoba (common on the Hudson Bay coast, in both spring and fall); an uncommon transient in spring and fall in eastern interior Ontario (but common on coast of James

153

and Hudson bays); mainly autumn transient, rare in spring, in Quebec (all the coasts and at least the southern interior: Montreal, Saguenay – Lake St. John region, Labrador (abundant in autumn along coast), Newfoundland, New Brunswick, Prince Edward Island, and Nova Scotia. In British Columbia two spring records (Atlin, Peace River District). Casual on Prince Patrick Island (Mould Bay).

BAIRD'S SANDPIPER
Le Bécasseau de Baird. *Erolia bairdii* (Coues)
Plate 27. L. 7.0 to 7.6 in.

Bill rather short, straight, slender, .8 to 1.0 inch long. A small sandpiper with rather buffy upper parts (in immatures, feathers of back with narrow white margins, giving back a scaly appearance), buffy band across the breast, lightly streaked with dusky. Rump sooty brown, the feathers narrowly edged with buffy brown. Bill blackish. Legs blackish with slight suggestion of olive. From the Pectoral Sandpiper it is distinguished by its smaller size, less well-defined and more lightly streaked breast band, blackish legs, and by the middle tail feathers which are more obtuse, with tips extending little beyond the others; from the Least, by its blackish legs and larger size; from the Semipalmated and Western, by its completely unwebbed toes, larger size, and more decidedly buffy breast band; and from the White-rumped, by its dark rump and more buffy breast.

Measurements. *Adult male:* wing, 117.6–125.3 (121.5); tail, 50–57 (52.1); exposed culmen, 20.5–24.5 (22.4); tarsus, 21.3–24.2 (22.9). *Adult female:* wing, 120–128 (122.7) mm.

Field Marks. One of several similar small sandpipers collectively known as 'peeps.' Larger than the Least, Semipalmated, and Western sandpipers; about the same size as the White-rump; and smaller than the Pectoral. In addition to size differences, which usually are not too reliable in the field unless birds can be compared side by side, its blackish legs distinguish it from the Pectoral and the Least. These tend to have streaked upper parts, but Baird's, especially autumn immatures, has a faintly scaly pattern on the back.

Its more buffy breast band, less greyish upper parts, and, in flight, lack of a white rump patch distinguish it from the White-rump. Spring and summer Sanderlings show much rusty about head, neck, and upper breast, but at other times they are very different. The Sanderling shows a broad white wing stripe in flight; Baird's an obscure one. The Buff-breasted Sandpiper is entirely different with the entire under parts uniformly buffy and with yellow legs.

Habitat. In migration it tends to prefer drier parts of muddy areas (often with patches of grass or other low vegetation) near both fresh and salt water; also beaches; flooded and sometimes dry fields. Less inclined to feed in water than many other sandpipers. In the Arctic it nests usually in drier situations than many sandpipers; ridges, flats, and rocky slopes, both inland and coastal; occasionally in moister places.

Nesting. Nest, a shallow depression on the ground, lined with grass and perhaps a few willow leaves. *Eggs,* usually 4, sometimes 3; buffy, rather thickly spotted with browns. Incubation is by both sexes and lasts 21 days (W. H. Drury).

154

Range. Breeds in northeastern Siberia, northwestern Alaska, arctic Canada, and northwestern Greenland. Winters mainly in western and southern South America.

Range in Canada. Breeds from Prince Patrick Island (Mould Bay), Melville Island (Winter Harbour), Ellef Ringnes Island (probably), and northern Ellesmere Island (Fosheim Peninsula, Lake Hazen) south to northern Yukon (Herschel Island), northern Mackenzie (barrens east of Anderson River; Dolphin and Union Strait), northern Keewatin (Adelaide Peninsula, Mount Meadowbank on lower Back River), southern Melville Peninsula (Gore Bay), and south-central Baffin Island (Nettilling Lake).

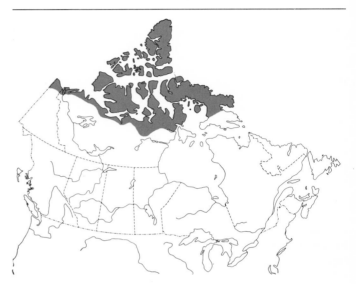

Breeding Distribution of Baird's Sandpiper

Spring migration is mainly through the interior west of Hudson Bay. In autumn, largely over the spring route but also regularly in small numbers west to the Pacific Coast and much farther east, rarely to Newfoundland. Migrates spring and fall through interior British Columbia (also in fall west to the coast), commonly through Alberta, Saskatchewan, and Manitoba. Uncommon autumn migrant, rare in spring, in eastern interior Ontario and the Ontario coasts of James and Hudson bays. Scarce fall migrant in Quebec (Montreal, Quebec, Arvida, Cape Weggs, Great Whale River, Cabbage Willows Bay). Rare fall migrant in New Brunswick (Campobello Island, St. Andrews) and Nova Scotia (Grand Pré). Very rare in Newfoundland (Argentia).

LEAST SANDPIPER
Le Bécasseau minuscule. *Erolia minutilla* (Vieillot)
Plates 27, 31. L. 5 to 6.8 in.

The tiniest of our sandpipers. Bill straight, rather slender, about .65 to .85 in. long. In the hand, its small size separates it from all other sandpipers except Semipalmated and Western. Its completely unwebbed (instead of partly webbed) toes distinguish it from them (*see also* Field Marks).

Measurements. *Adult male:* wing, 84.4–90.9 (86.7); tail, 37–40.4 (39.5); exposed culmen, 17–20 (18.2); tarsus, 18.2–20 (19.1). *Adult female:* wing, 82.3–91.2 (89) mm.

Field Marks. Our tiniest sandpiper, but only slightly smaller than Semipalmated and Western. The Least is more ruddy above, has usually a buffier breast, slenderer bill, and greenish-yellowish legs (those of other two are blackish). The Least is coloured very much like Baird's but is smaller, with yellowish-green legs (black in Baird's). In flight its common call *queeeeeet* differs from that of the Semipalmated, which lacks the long *e*.

Habitat. In migration, muddy margins of fresh or salt water with or without low vegetation, mud flats, wet fields; sometimes beaches and dry fields. In breeding season, sedge, grass, and mossy bogs; hummocky marshes; sometimes also higher drier situations with low vegetation.

Nesting. On the ground. A shallow depression lined sparsely with dry leaves or grass. *Eggs*, usually 4; pale buff, spotted and blotched, sometimes very heavily, with various browns. The male takes a large part in incubation of the eggs. Incubation period 19½ to 21½ days (Jehl and Hussell).

Range. Breeds in southern Alaska and across subarctic Canada. Winters from southern United States south to central Peru and Brazil; also in the West Indies.

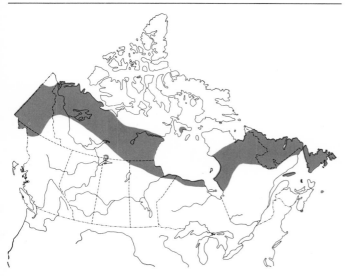

Breeding Distribution of Least Sandpiper

Range in Canada. Breeds in Yukon (Old Crow, Lake Marsh); northwestern British Columbia (Chilkat Pass); northern Mackenzie (Franklin Bay, Coppermine, Aklavik; and probably Fort Norman and Thelon Sanctuary), southern Keewatin (Nueltin Lake; probably Tha-anne River), Southampton Island (rarely: Coral Harbour), northern Manitoba (Churchill, Herchmer), northern Ontario (coast of Hudson and James bays: Cape Henrietta Maria), Quebec (Port Harrison, Bush Lake; Lake Bienville; Knob Lake; Blanc Sablon; Anticosti and Magdalen Islands; recorded in breeding season at numerous other northern localities north to Lake Aigneau and Fort Chimo), Labrador (Indian Harbour, Goose Bay, Nain, possibly north to Ramah; and in the interior: upper Hamilton River), Newfoundland, and locally in Nova Scotia (Sable Island and Cape Sable Island). Alleged breeding on southern Victoria Island, N.W.T., requires confirmation.

A common to locally abundant spring and autumn transient through most southern localities from coast to coast. Casual in southern Baffin Island.

CURLEW SANDPIPER
Le Bécasseau cocorli. *Erolia ferruginea* (Pontoppidan)
L. 7 to 9 in.

In breeding plumage unmistakable: rich chestnut breast, white rump with a few dark bars, and a rather long *down-curved* bill. Knots and Dowitchers also have reddish breasts, but their bills are straight. In winter plumage the red of breast is lacking (although some immatures have a faint rusty suffusion). The decidedly downcurved bill separates it from other small and medium-sized sandpipers except the Dunlin. The two are then similar in colour, but the Curlew Sandpiper has a white patch completely across the rump.

Range. Breeds in northern Siberia. Winters from southern Eurasia and the Philippines south to southern Africa, Australia, Tasmania, and New Zealand.

Status in Canada. Casual visitor to British Columbia (Masset, Queen Charlotte Islands, July 31, 1936), Ontario (Toronto about 1886; Whitby, October 21, 1961; sight record at Dundas, October 10, 1954), New Brunswick (Red Head, August 3 and 31, 1895; St. Andrews; Grand Manan), and perhaps Nova Scotia (Halifax, September 1868, but specimen was not examined by an authority).

DUNLIN (Red-backed Sandpiper)
Le Bécasseau à dos roux. *Erolia alpina* (Linnaeus)
Plate 25. L. 7.5 to 9.3 in.

Bill blackish, rather long (1.2 to 1.7 in.), and slightly down-curved. Legs greenish black. Spring and summer adults, with a large black patch on the abdomen contrasting with the white of the rest of the under parts, and much cinnamon on the back, are likely to be confused with only the Rock Sandpiper of the West Coast, which has vague black blotches on the lower breast, not on the abdomen. In winter dress, the grey of the back is uniform (but before the molt is complete a few black feathers with buffy borders may still be present), not streaked as in most sandpipers of similar or smaller size, and there is a greyish suffusion, faintly streaked, across the breast. Winter White-rumps and Sanderlings also have clear grey backs, but the former has a completely white rump and the latter has no hind toe. The longer, slightly decurved bill of the Dunlin is different from both. The Curlew Sandpiper of the Old World is very similar to the Dunlin in winter, but the former has a completely white rump. Juvenal Dunlins (seen mostly on or near the breeding grounds) are very buffy above, and the sides of the abdomen and lower breast have large spots and streaks of dusky brown.

Measurements (*E. a. pacifica*). *Adult male:* wing, 111.7–119.6 (114.9); tail, 41.5–53.7 (47.8); exposed culmen, 34–37.5 (35.9); tarsus, 26.1–27.8 (26.7). *Adult female:* wing, 112.5–121.2 (117.3) mm.

Field Marks. A medium-sized sandpiper with longish bill, noticeably downcurved near the tip. In spring and summer the reddish back and large black patch on the belly make it readily recognizable (Rock Sandpiper of the West Coast has some blackish blotches on the under parts, but they are on the lower breast not the belly, and its legs are yellowish not black). In fall and winter: unpatterned grey back, grey suffusion across the breast, and longish downcurved bill. Western Sandpiper often has a slightly downcurved bill, but it is an obviously smaller bird with less uniformly grey back. White-rumps in winter plumage have uniformly grey backs but a white rump patch. Sanderlings have snowy white under parts in fall and winter, thus lacking the grey suffusion of the Dunlin across the breast. The Curlew Sandpiper (of casual occurrence in Canada) in fall and winter looks like a Dunlin but with a white patch across the rump.

Habitat. In migration, muddy margins of both salt and fresh water, mud flats, flooded grassland, sandy beaches and bars. On breeding grounds, usually moist to wet grassy or hummocky tundra; also coastal salt marshes.

Nesting. Nest on the ground, usually a grass-lined depression on a hummock or mound in moist grassy tundra or coastal salt marsh. *Eggs*, usually 4; greenish to buffy, with some gloss, spotted and blotched with browns. Incubation by both sexes.

Breeding Distribution of Dunlin

Range. Holarctic, breeding southward from the Arctic Ocean to southwestern Alaska, the northern mainland of Canada east to Southampton Island and down the west coast of Hudson Bay; the British Isles, the Baltics, northern parts of Russia and Siberia; also Greenland, Iceland, Spitsbergen, and Novaya Zemlya. Winters from southern Alaska to Baja California and from Massachusetts to Florida and the Gulf Coast of the United States; and from the British Isles, Mediterranean and Red seas, south to northern Africa; also India, southern China, Japan, and Formosa.

Range in Canada. Breeds in northern Mackenzie (Baillie Island), southern Somerset Island (Fort Ross), Southampton Island, Keewatin (Baker Lake, Chesterfield Inlet, McConnell River), northeastern Manitoba (Churchill), and north-

PLATE 27

1 Semipalmated Sandpiper,
  (a) summer adult
  (b) autumn immature

2 Least Sandpiper,
  (a) summer adult
  (b) autumn

3 White-rumped Sandpiper,
  (a) summer adult
  (b) autumn adult

4 Western Sandpiper,
  (a) summer adult
  (b) autumn immature

5 Baird's Sandpiper,
  autumn

6 Sanderling,
  (a) autumn immature
  (b) summer adult

PLATE 28

1 Hudsonian Godwit,
   (a) summer adult
   (b) autumn plumage

2 American Avocet,
   summer adult

3 Whimbrel

4 Marbled Godwit,
   summer adult

5 Long-billed Curlew,
   summer adult

western Ontario (Cape Henrietta Maria). Noted in summer in southwestern Baffin Island (West Foxe Islands, Bowman Bay) and southern Melville Island.

Spring and autumn transient in British Columbia (abundant on coast, much scarcer in interior), Alberta (scarce), Saskatchewan (uncommon), Manitoba (locally common), Ontario (locally common), Quebec (mainly autumn: Montreal, Quebec, Arvida, mouth of Kegashka River, Gaspé, Great Whale River), and in New Brunswick, Prince Edward Island, and Nova Scotia (locally scarce to common in fall, rare in spring). Scarce transient in interior Yukon (Coal Creek, Dawson), and apparently very scarce in interior western Mackenzie. Casual in Newfoundland (Stephenville Crossing, October 2, 1946). Hypothetical in Labrador (sight record: Port Manvers).

Winters regularly and commonly on the coast of British Columbia.

Subspecies. *Erolia alpina pacifica* (Coues).

SHORT-BILLED DOWITCHER
Le Bécasseau roux. *Limnodromus griseus* (Gmelin)
Plates 25, 31. L. 10.5 to 12 in.

Bill straight, twice as long as head. Dowitchers (there are two very similar species) have such long, straight bills that, in the hand, they are likely to be confused with only the Common Snipe and the Woodcock (*see also* Stilt Sandpiper). The whole lower back of dowitchers (concealed by the folded wings) is white, and the rump is white with a few black bars and spots. Woodcock and Common Snipe have no white on those parts. (For distinctions between the two species of dowitchers *see* Long-billed Dowitcher.)

Measurements (*L. g. griseus*). *Adult male:* wing, 132.8–145.3 (139.2); tail, 51.5–57.3 (53.4); exposed culmen, 51.9–57.5 (54.8); tarsus, 32.9–35.9 (34.1). *Adult female:* wing, 131–146.1 (139.8) mm.

Field Marks. Dowitchers are medium-sized sandpipers with long straight bills. The lower back (concealed by folded wings but conspicuous in flight) and rump are white. Common Snipe and the Woodcock also have long straight bills but no white on rump or lower back. Dowitchers in autumn resemble also the Stilt Sandpiper, a smaller bird that in flight shows a white rump but no white on the back and lacks the white wing stripe of the dowitchers. There are two species of dowitchers (*see* Long-billed Dowitcher).

Habitat. In migration, soft muddy margins of fresh, brackish, and salt water; mud flats; beaches. In nesting season, muskegs and similar boggy and marshy places with low vegetation.

Nesting. The nest is lined with grasses and moss and is usually a depression on or near a hummock in wet sedge or grassy meadows or muskegs. The *eggs*, usually 4, are greenish to olive-buff, spotted with browns. Incubation period 21 days (Jehl and Hussell).

Range. Breeds in southern Alaska and widely but locally in Canada. Winters from southern United States south through Central America and the West Indies to Brazil and Peru.

Range in Canada. Breeding range poorly known. Breeds

Breeding Distribution of Short-billed Dowitcher

locally in northwestern and probably central-eastern British Columbia (Chilkat Pass, probably Peace River District), southern Mackenzie (probably), Alberta (various localities: Edmonton north to Lesser Slave Lake), northern Saskatchewan (probably Kazan Lake), northern Manitoba (Churchill), and northern Quebec (Knob Lake region; probably Fort Chimo).

Regular spring and autumn transient in British Columbia, southern Alberta, southern Saskatchewan, Manitoba, and on the west coast of Hudson and James bays, southern Ontario (but apparently very scarce in interior western localities and rather scarce in extreme east: Ottawa), Quebec (locally: Montreal, Quebec, Lake St. John, north shore of the Gulf of St. Lawrence, Percé), Labrador (rare: Turnavik West, Henley Harbour), Newfoundland (autumn transient, uncommon), and the Maritimes (uncommon in spring, more common in autumn).

Subspecies. Three, all well-marked. (1) *Limnodromus griseus griseus* (Gmelin): cinnamon of under parts pale and much restricted posteriorly with belly mainly white; spotting dense but mainly on breast; upper parts dark; white bars on tail narrow, thus closely approaching those of the Long-billed Dowitcher; bill shorter than in other races. Breeds in Que. (2) *L. g. hendersoni* Rowan: Cinnamon of under parts darker and more extensive than in (1); spotting sparser but more extensive, often extending to belly; upper parts paler; white bars on tail broader; bill slightly longer. Breeds from e. B.C. to Man., north to s. Mack. (3) *L. g. caurinus* Pitelka: averages larger than (1) and (2) and intermediate between them in spotting and extent of cinnamon on under parts. Known breeding range, southern Alaska. Occurs in B.C. as a transient.

LONG-BILLED DOWITCHER

Le Bécasseau à long-bec. *Limnodromus scolopaceus* (Say)
Plate 25. L. 11 to 12.5 in.

Like Short-billed Dowitcher, but bill averages decidedly longer; in breeding plumage the cinnamon of the under parts consistently extends over belly and usually over undertail coverts; ventral spotting is dense and is restricted to upper breast and throat; markings of sides of breast are well-formed bars rather than spots; light bars on tail are buffier and narrower than in western races of the Short-billed Dowitcher.

Measurements. *Adult male:* wing, 139–146.2 (141.2); tail, 52.1–57.9 (55); exposed culmen, 57–64 (61.5); tarsus, 36–41 (38.2). *Adult female:* wing, 139–148 (144.3) mm.

Field Marks. So similar to the Short-billed Dowitcher that many individuals cannot be safely distinguished in the field. Bill lengths overlap, and only extremes can serve as useful indicators. In breeding plumage however, birds with well-formed bars on the sides of the *breast* instead of spots (caution: both species have bars on sides and flanks) and with obviously longer bills can safely be called Long-bills. Individuals with extensive white on the belly, no bars on sides of breast, and short to moderate bills are Short-bills. Also the Long-bill's upper parts are darker than those of the Short-bills breeding in the Prairie Provinces (subspecies *hendersoni*), but the eastern nominate race of the Short-bill has the upper parts as dark as those of the Long-bill. Eastern Short-bills are best distinguished in breeding plumage from the Long-billed by their much more extensively white bellies. The common call of the Short-billed Dowitcher is a double or triple *tu*; that of the Long-bill is said to be a thin *keek*. Needless to say, field identification of the two species should be attempted with caution.

Habitat. In migration, it favours freshwater situations more than the Short-billed Dowitcher.

Nesting. Apparently similar to the Short-billed Dowitcher but has not been closely studied.

Breeding Distribution of Long-billed Dowitcher

Range. Breeds in northeastern Siberia, northwestern coastal Alaska, and probably northwestern Mackenzie. Winters from southern United States (California to Florida) and south through Mexico (mainly western) to Guatemala.

Range in Canada. Probably breeds in extreme northwestern Mackenzie (Anderson River, Franklin Bay) and

158

perhaps northern Yukon. Spring and fall transient mainly in the western provinces: British Columbia (coast and interior), Alberta, Saskatchewan, and Manitoba. Less commonly in southern Ontario (Toronto, Hamilton). Casual in Nova Scotia (Sable Island).

STILT SANDPIPER
Le Bécasseau à échasses
Micropalama himantopus (Bonaparte)
Plate 26. L. 7.5 to 9.3 in.

Bill rather long, nearly straight but slightly depressed at tip, the tip expanded and flattened. Legs relatively long, dull greenish yellow or yellowish olive (*see* Field Marks).

Breeding Distribution of Stilt Sandpiper

Measurements. *Adult male:* wing, 120–127 (123.9); tail, 48–55 (51.7); exposed culmen, 38.6–41.9 (39.6); tarsus, 36–45 (40.4). *Adult female:* wing, 126.1–133.9 (131.4) mm.

Field Marks. A slender sandpiper with longish legs, longish bill very slightly depressed at tip, and white patch across the rump, characters that distinguish it from most small and medium sandpipers. In breeding dress, the heavily and closely barred under parts distinguish it from all but the Wandering Tattler, a larger bird with no white rump patch at any time. In autumn plumages the under parts are not barred, but the longer legs and bill separate it from most other sandpipers. Possibly it might be confused with the Lesser Yellowlegs, but smaller size, a light line over the eye, and dull yellowish-green legs (yellowlegs have bright yellow legs) should distinguish it. It does not have the frequent bobbing motions of the yellowlegs. Its appearance and the habit of plunging its long bill vertically into the mud or shallow water suggest a dowitcher. If unsure, flush the bird. The Stilt Sandpiper has only the rump white, but the dowitcher in flight shows a white lower back and a white wing stripe. Stilt Sandpiper's long legs and bill readily distinguish it from the obviously smaller White-rumped Sandpiper.

Habitat. In migration it prefers shallow quiet water and edges of pools, ponds, sloughs, and lakes; sometimes beaches. In nesting season, wet tundra and the vicinity of ponds, lakes, and marshes; occasionally drier ridges.

Nesting. Nest, a depression sparsely lined with a few leaves or grasses in tundra moss or ground. *Eggs*, apparently usually 4; pale buff with large irregularly shaped spots. Very little is known of the breeding cycle. Incubation period at least 21 days (Jehl and Hussell).

Range. Breeds in extreme northeastern Alaska and the low Arctic of western Canada east to western Hudson Bay. Winters in South America.

Range in Canada. Breeds in southern Victoria Island (Cash Point, Cambridge Bay), northern Mackenzie (mouth of Anderson River, Cockburn Point, probably Perry River), southeastern Keewatin (McConnell River, Boundary Lake), northeastern Manitoba (Churchill), and north coastal Ontario (Cape Henrietta Maria). Possibly breeds in northern Yukon (has occurred in summer on Herschel Island) and in the interior of Mackenzie south perhaps to treeline.

Migrates spring and autumn, mainly through the western provinces: Alberta, Saskatchewan, Manitoba, and in smaller numbers, British Columbia (mainly interior, rare on coast); scarce mainly-autumn transient in southern Ontario; rare autumn visitant to southern Quebec (Laprairie, Amos, Quebec, Arvida, Magdalen Islands), New Brunswick (North Head, Kent Island, Saint John), and Nova Scotia (Sable Island, Lawrencetown Beach). Evidence of occurrence in Newfoundland is unsatisfactory.

SEMIPALMATED SANDPIPER
Le Bécasseau semi-palmé. *Ereunetes pusillus* (Linnaeus)
Plate 27. L. 5.5 to 6.8 in.

Bill rather short (.6 to .9 in.), straight, black Front toes with small basal webs. Legs black. Its very small size distinguishes it from all but the Least and Western sandpipers. Small webs between the front toes separate it from the Least. (For distinctions from Western Sandpiper, *see* next species.)

Measurements. *Adult male:* wing, 90.9–97.8 (94.7); tail, 39.1–45.5 (42.4); exposed culmen, 17.9–20.3 (19.2); tarsus, 19.9–21.9 (21.1). *Adult female:* wing, 90.7–100.1 (97.1) mm.

Field Marks. The Semipalmated, Least, and Western sandpipers are our tiniest shorebirds (sparrow-sized). They are similar in appearance. The present species differs from the Least by black (not greenish or yellowish) legs, slightly thicker bill, and greyer, paler upper parts. Its bill is usually noticeably shorter than that of the Western and has no tendency to be slightly downcurved as in many Westerns. In breeding plumage it has greyer upper parts, lacking the bright cinnamon shown on head and back of the Western. Its breast is less heavily streaked, and there are no V-marks on the breast or flanks. In autumn plumages the two are very similar, and the shorter, straighter bill of the Semipalmated is the best means of distinguishing them. There is some overlapping, however, and only typical individuals of the two can be safely identified in the field.

Habitat. In migration, sand beaches, mud flats, open edges of pools, ponds, lakes, rivers, and shores, both fresh

159

and salt. In nesting season, moist or wet sedge-grass or heath tundra, sandy places along arctic rivers, and pond-dotted sand dunes.

Nesting. Nest, a depression in a hummock or knoll in wet tundra or in sand near ponds or rivers. It is lined with grass and willow leaves. *Eggs*, usually 4; vary from dull white to olive-buff, speckled and spotted with reddish browns, often coalescing into blotches on larger end. They are similar to those of the Least and Western sandpipers. Incubation is by both sexes; lasts 18 to 19 days (D. F. Parmelee).

Range. Breeds in northern Alaska (arctic coast south to Yukon Delta) and across the low Arctic of Canada. Winters from South Carolina and the Gulf Coast of the United States, the West Indies, and eastern Mexico south to northern Chile and southern Brazil.

Breeding Distribution of Semipalmated Sandpiper

Range in Canada. Breeds widely in the Arctic and Sub-arctic: Banks Island (Sachs Harbour, De Salis Bay), Victoria Island (Read Island; Cambridge Bay), King William Island, and central and southern Baffin Island (Frustration Bay, Taverner Bay, Nettilling Lake, Frobisher Bay, West Foxe Islands); coastal Yukon, northern and central-eastern Mackenzie (islands north of and coast east of Mackenzie Delta, Baillie Island, shores of Dolphin and Union Strait, Bathurst Inlet, Perry River; also in the interior: Thelon River), northwest coastal and southern Keewatin (Adelaide Peninsula, Beverly Lake, Chesterfield Inlet, Windy River, McConnell River), Southampton Island, the Hudson Bay coast of Manitoba (Churchill) and of northern Ontario (Cape Henrietta Maria), northwestern Quebec (Port Harrison, Payne Lake, Ungava Bay, and south along the coast to Comb Islands), and Labrador (Ramah and probably south to Seal Island). Recorded in summer on southern Somerset Island (Fort Ross), N.W.T.

Common to abundant in migration in most parts of southern Canada except the coast of British Columbia where rare (Sumas and Calvert Island). Much scarcer in spring than autumn in British Columbia and from eastern

PLATE 29

1 Black Turnstone,
   (a) summer adult
   (b) winter
   (c) flight pattern

2 Surfbird,
   (a) flight pattern
   (b) winter
   (c) summer adult

3 Sharp-tailed Sandpiper, autumn immature

4 Wandering Tattler,
   (a) summer adult
   (b) autumn and winter

5 Black Oystercatcher, summer adult

Crosby

1b

1a

2b

2a

3a

3b

4

6

5

Crosby

Ontario eastward. In Newfoundland, a common autumn transient but has not been recorded there in spring. In autumn it is common to abundant in the Maritimes.

WESTERN SANDPIPER
Le Bécasseau du Nord-Ouest. *Ereunetes mauri* Cabanis
Plate 27. L. 5.8 to 7.1 in.

Bill and legs blackish, the former often slightly downcurved. Front toes with small basal webs. Small size separates it from all but the Least and Semipalmated sandpipers. Presence of small webs at the base of the front toes distinguishes it from the Least in any plumage. It is less easily distinguished from the Semipalmated Sandpiper except in breeding plumage, at which time the Western has much more rusty in the upper parts and heavier streaking on the breast, *this often forming V-marks, which frequently extend to the sides.* In autumn plumages the two are often very difficult to distinguish, but the longer bill of the Western (.85 to 1.2 in.) will separate typical individuals. Frequently there is overlap, however, but in most individuals the longer, usually slightly downcurved bill of the Western is fairly obvious.

Measurements. *Adult male:* wing, 91.7–95.9 (94); tail, 39.8–45.6 (41.3); exposed culmen, 21.9–23.6 (22.7); tarsus, 21–23 (22.2). *Adult female:* wing, 94.9–98.9 (96.9) mm.

Field Marks. One of our three tiniest sandpipers. Its blackish (not yellowish-green) legs and usually longer bill, when discernible, are sure distinctions from the Least Sandpiper. Compared with the Semipalmated Sandpiper, it shows much more rusty on crown and other upper parts in breeding plumage; also the breast streaks tend to be arrow-shaped. In autumn, however, the two are often very similar. In typical Westerns the bill is noticeably longer and is slightly downcurved, but many autumn individuals of the two cannot safely be identified in life.

Habitat. In migration similar to that of Semipalmated Sandpiper.

Range. Breeds on the coast of western and northern Alaska east to Camden Bay. Winters mainly from the coast of California, the Gulf Coast of United States, and North Carolina south to Venezuela, and in Peru; also the West Indies.

Status in Canada. Spring and autumn transient, common only on the coast of British Columbia (scarce mainly-autumn transient in the interior. Spring records for the Cariboo: May 18, 1950, and May 24, 1951). Rare transient in southern Ontario (specimen records: Port Franks, Long Point, Toronto, Fort Erie). Sight records for southern Mackenzie and southern Quebec (Kamouraska) require confirmation.

BUFF-BREASTED SANDPIPER
Le Bécasseau roussâtre. *Tryngites subruficollis* (Vieillot)
Plate 30. L. 7.5 to 8.9 in.

Bill shorter than head. A very buffy sandpiper, the buff coloration extending over all the under parts, darkest on breast becoming buffy white on abdomen and under tail coverts. In autumn the feathers of the back are narrowly margined with white. The extensive buff on the under parts combined with considerable dark marbling and spotting on inner webs of the flight feathers readily identifies it in the hand. Bill blackish, paler near base. Legs, greenish yellow.

Measurements. *Adult male:* wing, 128.2–138.7 (133.4); tail, 56.8–61.4 (59); exposed culmen, 19.9–21.3 (20.5); tarsus, 31.8–34 (33.1). *Adult female:* wing, 120.4–127 (123.9) mm.

Field Marks. The extensive buffy coloration on the under parts, the dove-like head (short bill, high forehead), the unmarked buffy sides of head, and the yellowish legs make it one of the easy sandpipers to identify. The silvery white wing linings are conspicuous in flight or when, as frequently happens in courtship, the wings are raised high. Because of the buffy coloration and, in autumn, 'scaly' back, it might be confused with Baird's Sandpiper, but Baird's has black legs, the buff of the breast is cut off rather sharply from the white of the abdomen, and the sides of the head are entirely different. Buff-breasts often assume an erect posture like the Upland Plover.

Habitat. In migration short-grass prairies, fields, grain stubbles, and drier grassy places near water. On nesting grounds either drier grassy and mossy tundra or wet, marshy tundra.

Nesting. Nest, a slight depression in dry ground sparsely lined with grass and leaves. *Eggs,* usually 4; buff to dull white, marked especially at larger end with dark browns and with small spots or blotches over the entire egg. Its nesting routine is very poorly known.

Range. Breeds locally in northern Alaska (Point Barrow) and in the western Arctic of Canada. Winters in central Argentina.

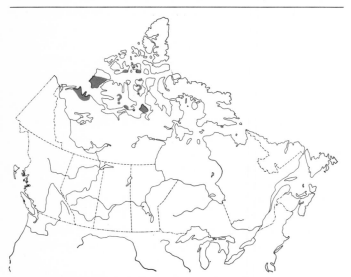
Breeding Distribution of Buff-breasted Sandpiper

Range in Canada. Breeding range very poorly known. Breeds in northwestern Mackenzie (barrens between Horton River and Franklin Bay; probably Harrowby Bay), Banks Island, Victoria Island (Cambridge Bay, Jenny Lind Island), King William Island; probably Melville Island (Winter Harbour), Bathurst Island (probably near Cape Cockburn),

162

and perhaps northern Yukon (Herschel Island), and Victoria Island (Cambridge Bay).

Migration is mainly through the western interior (Alberta, Saskatchewan, and Manitoba) and southern Mackenzie (Fort Simpson, Great Slave Lake), and in small numbers through southern Keewatin (McConnell River). Scarce in southern Yukon (Mayo Landing, Teslin) and British Columbia (recorded on the coast and in the interior). Rare in southern Ontario (casually east to Ottawa) and southern Quebec (Montreal, Lake St. Peter, Godbout); casual in Labrador (Henley Harbour, probably Port Burwell), Newfoundland (Argentia), Magdalen Islands, and Nova Scotia (Halifax).

MARBLED GODWIT
La Barge marbrée. *Limosa fedoa* (Linnaeus)
Plate 28. L. 16.8 to 20 in. (including bill, 3 to 5.5 in.)

Godwits are very large shorebirds with very long slender bills (slightly upturned or straight) and long legs. (American Avocet and Black-necked Stilt are also large with upturned bills but are coloured entirely differently. Curlews have downcurved bills.) The Marbled Godwit, our largest godwit, is a buffy brown bird with much pinkish cinnamon in the plumage, especially the wings. It is distinguished from the Hudsonian Godwit and the Black-tailed Godwit (of accidental occurrence in Canada) in any plumage by its lack of white upper tail coverts, lack of white wing stripe, and its larger size (*see also* Bar-tailed Godwit).

Measurements. *Adult male:* wing, 216.5–230.5 (223.5); tail, 77.2–84.4 (80.9); exposed culmen, 88.2–101.5 (95.9); tarsus, 64–73.6 (69.4). *Adult female:* wing, 221–242.5 (233.6) mm.

Field Marks. A very large buffy-brown shorebird with a very long, slightly upturned or straight bill. Shows much pinkish cinnamon on the under side of the wing in flight. In size and colour it resembles the Long-billed Curlew and, like it, inhabits the southern prairies in summer, but curlews have decidedly downcurved bills. Avocets and Black-necked

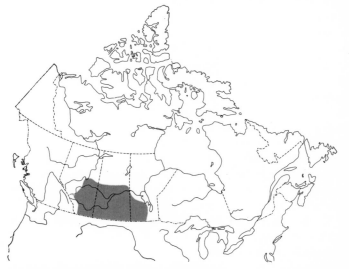
Breeding Distribution of Marbled Godwit

Stilts are other large shorebirds that, like the godwits, have upcurved bills, but they are so differently coloured that they could not be confused with godwits. The Marbled Godwit is *the* breeding godwit of the Prairie Provinces, where it is a noisy and conspicuous bird. Its calls include a monotonous *caráck* (sounds like *correct*) repeated loudly at varying speeds; *ack-ack* in couplets or triplets; and *karática, rática, rática, rática*.

Habitat. In breeding season, grasslands of the Prairies and the edges of prairie sloughs and lakes. In migration, also beaches and tide flats.

Nesting. Nest, a depression in either dry or moist grassland, sometimes at a considerable distance from water. It is sparsely lined with grass. *Eggs*, usually 4; buffy, rather sparingly blotched (mainly at the larger end) and spotted with browns.

Range. Breeds from southern parts of the Prairie Provinces of Canada south to central Montana, North Dakota, northeastern South Dakota, and west-central Minnesota. Winters from southern United States south to Guatemala and British Honduras, more rarely to South America.

Range in Canada. Breeds in the grasslands of central and southern Alberta (Beaverhill Lake, Brooks), southern Saskatchewan (10 miles east of Nipawin, Crane Lake, Regina), southern Manitoba (Oak Lake, Lake St. Martin). Occurs in the breeding season north to The Pas region of Manitoba and on James Bay. Rare transient in British Columbia (Clayoquot, Fort Simpson, Victoria, Columbia Lake); very rare in southern Ontario (Toronto, Ottawa), southern Quebec (Montreal, Lake St. Peter, Rivière Ouelle, Métis), New Brunswick (Mace's Bay, autumn, 1879), and Nova Scotia (near Halifax; reliable sight records at Sable River and Lawrencetown Beach).

BAR-TAILED GODWIT

La Barge de Laponie. *Limosa lapponica* (Linnaeus)
L. 15 to 17.5 in.

A large shorebird with slender slightly upturned bill. In breeding plumage, the under parts are plain cinnamon, this extending up on the sides of the neck and head. Upper tail coverts white, barred and spotted with dusky. Tail brownish, barred with white or buff. Adults in autumn and winter have dull whitish under parts, and immatures have the breast greyish buff. Distinguished from Hudsonian Godwit by heavy bars and spots on the white of the upper tail coverts, barred axillars (instead of solid sooty brown or blackish), lack of a white wing stripe, and narrowly barred tail (no solid black masses). The narrowly barred tail, lack of a white wing stripe, and barred axillars (instead of plain white ones) distinguish it from the Black-tailed Godwit. The heavily black-and-white barred axillars and lack of pinkish cinnamon on the under side of the wing separate it from the larger Marbled Godwit.

Range. Breeds in northern Eurasia and western and northern Alaska. Winters from southern Eurasia south to Australia and New Zealand.

Status in Canada. Accidental in British Columbia (Colebrook, October 30, 1931).

Subspecies. The one Canadian specimen is referable to the Alaskan subspecies *Limosa lapponica baueri* Naumann.

HUDSONIAN GODWIT

La Barge hudsonienne. *Limosa haemastica* (Linnaeus)
Plate 28. L. 14.5 to 16.7 in.

A large shorebird with slightly upturned slender bill. This and the Marbled Godwit are the only godwits of regular occurrence in Canada. Its mainly black tail strongly contrasting with immaculate white upper tail coverts, solid blackish or dark brown axillars, and white wing stripe readily separate it in any plumage from the larger Marbled Godwit. (For distinctions from the Bar-tailed and Black-tailed godwits, both of which are of accidental occurrence in Canada, see those species.)

Measurements. *Adult male:* wing, 195.5–208.5 (203.4); tail, 70–83.8 (74.9); exposed culmen, 68.2–81.2 (75.2); tarsus, 53.5–59.5 (56.6). *Adult female:* wing, 207–219 (212.8) mm.

Field Marks. Large size, long slender slightly upturned bill, and general coloration make it a godwit (Avocet and Black-necked Stilt also are large waders with upturned bills, but their coloration and markings are entirely different). The black tail and sharply contrasting white rump patch, white wing stripe, blackish axillars, and lack of bright cinnamon on the wing linings distinguish it at any season from the Marbled Godwit, the only other godwit of regular occurrence in Canada. Its blackish tail separates it from the Willet and Greater Yellowlegs, with which it might be confused in autumn. Its bluish grey legs are very different from those of either species of yellowlegs.

Habitat. In autumn migration, largest concentrations on tidal mud flats, gently sloping beaches, and sand bars; smaller numbers (and in spring migration nearly the whole species), shores and shallow water of lakes, ponds, and rain pools. For nesting, wet grassy or sedge tundra seems to be preferred.

Nesting. Few detailed descriptions. What appears to be a typical nest is on a hummock or low mound in wet sedge or grass tundra with widely scattered small trees; nest proper, a shallow scrape usually in or under the edge of a prostrate dwarf birch, and unlined except for a few dead leaves, perhaps windblown (J. A. Hagar). *Eggs* 4; olive buff, variously marked with darker spots and blotches of olive brown; general effect dark, markings obscure. Incubation period about 22 days (Hazel Ellis); 23½ (J. R. Jehl and D. J. T. Hussell).

Range. Breeds locally in western subarctic Canada; also southern Alaska (Cook Inlet). Winters in southern South America.

Range in Canada. Breeding range not fully known, but apparently in two disjunct areas: (1) northwestern Mackenzie (inner deltas of Mackenzie and Anderson rivers; Fort Anderson region; reportedly Burnside River on Bathurst Inlet) and (2) northeastern Manitoba (Churchill), northwestern Ontario (Sutton River), and probably Akimiski Island in James Bay. Suggested nesting on Southampton Island appears unlikely.

Spring migration crosses western Ontario, the Prairie

163

Provinces, and southern Mackenzie and is therefore somewhat dispersed. Southward movement in the autumn is remarkably concentrated, passing down the west coast of Hudson and James bays in a lane only a few miles wide. Main body of adults reaches James Bay in late July and early August, settling in large groups on tidal flats; at the same time a few hundred over-flying adults appear in the Magdalen Islands and in Prince Edward Island, Nova Scotia, and New Brunswick (J. A. Hagar). Exodus of adults from James Bay is in the last ten days of August, in flocks of 150 to 350. Since there are no observations of large flocks anywhere on the Atlantic coast or in the West Indies, a non-stop flight of at least 3,000 miles to some stopping place in northern South America seems likely (J. A. Hagar). Young of year begin to gather on the west coast of James Bay in early September and depart in much the same way as adults from mid-September to early October.

Breeding Distribution of Hudsonian Godwit

Except on main routes outlined above, the species is infrequent to casual, usually in very small numbers. Rare spring transient in British Columbia (Atlin, Peace River District, 150-Mile House) and in southern Ontario (near Toronto, Point Pelee). In autumn, recorded in small numbers on the east coast of James Bay (casually north to Great Whale River on east Hudson Bay), in southern Ontario, the north shore of the Gulf of St. Lawrence (Bonne Espérance); Gaspé, Quebec; and casually in Newfoundland. Sight records for southern Labrador (Flatwaters Cove). A regular autumn transient in small numbers in the Maritimes. Casual on Igloolik Island, southern Melville Peninsula (Repulse Bay), and southern Baffin Island (Cumberland Sound).

BLACK-TAILED GODWIT
La Barge à queue noire. *Limosa limosa* (Linnaeus)
L. 15 to 17.5 in.

Bill long, slender, slightly upturned or straight. Adults in breeding plumage have most of head, neck, breast, and sides pinkish cinnamon; the belly and under tail coverts white, broadly barred with dusky. Its mainly-black tail, white upper tail coverts, and white wing stripe distinguish it from the Marbled and Bar-tailed godwits, but not from the Hudsonian. In any plumage it can be distinguished from the Hudsonian Godwit by its white axillars and extensively white wing lining (these are blackish in the Hudsonian).

Range. Breeds in Iceland and widely in Eurasia.

Status in Canada. Accidental in Newfoundland (Placentia Bay, May 20, 1954).

Subspecies. The one Canadian specimen is of the Iceland subspecies, *Limosa limosa islandica* Brehm.

RUFF
Le Chevalier combattant. *Philomachus pugnax* (Linnaeus)
L. 8.5 to 11.5 in. (male larger than female)

Bill about as long as head, slightly tapering when viewed from the side. Adult male in breeding plumage is exceedingly variable in colour but is unmistakable by its extraordinary ruff (an erectile shield of feathers on the neck) and by two broad ear-tufts. The shield may be black (with purplish gloss), brown, white, and various combinations. These adornments are lacking in fall and winter plumage when adult male resembles the dull-coloured female. Fall and winter birds are nondescript; the feathers of the upper parts have dark centres and sandy margins; breast is buffy, sometimes spotted with dusky; chin and belly white. Legs variable in colour. In any plumage a broad dark stripe extends down the rump and centre of tail. This stripe is bordered on either side by white, the white broadening to form an oval white patch on either side of the tail. These oval white patches are quite unlike anything shown by the Upland Plover, Greater and Lesser yellowlegs, or any similar species.

Status in Canada. An accidental visitor from Eurasia. It has occurred in Ontario (specimen records: Fort Severn, Toronto, Crystal Beach. Sight records: Hamilton; Rockhouse Point near Dunnville); Quebec (Seven Islands, May 27, 1933); New Brunswick (Grand Manan), Nova Scotia (Cornwallis River, Cole Harbour), and Saskatchewan (near Regina, May 8, 1965).

SANDERLING
Le Sanderling. *Crocethia alba* (Pallas)
Plates 27, 31. L. 7.1 to 8.7 in.

Bill about as long as head, rather heavy, black. Toes three (hind toe lacking or very rarely rudimentary). Lack of a hind toe distinguishes it from other sandpipers.

Measurements. *Adult male:* wing, 114.5–121.6 (118.3); tail, 47.3–53 (50.6); exposed culmen, 22.5–26.6 (24.4); tarsus, 23.5–25.8 (24.7). *Adult female:* wing, 122.3–128.9 (124.4) mm.

Field Marks. A chunky sandpiper with short heavy black bill and (in flight) a conspicuous white wing stripe. In autumn more extensively white than other sandpipers. The short stout black bill and black legs contrast sharply with the nearly immaculate snowy whiteness of the under parts. Young birds show a faint buffy suffusion on sides of breast.

In breeding plumage the feathers of the upper parts are edged with rusty; breast and sides of head and neck rusty, spotted and barred with dusky and white.

Habitat. In migration it favours sand beaches on either salt or fresh water, but sometimes one finds it on mud flats and other muddy places. In the nesting season, stony, sparsely vegetated, usually drier tundra and rock desert.

Nesting. Nest, a slight hollow on dry stony ground, usually in or at the edge of a patch of vegetation, and lined with grasses. *Eggs* usually 4; olive with brown spots, especially on the larger end, and sometimes a few blackish ones. Incubation period said to be 23 to 24 days (Manniche). Female incubates, but there is a difference of opinion whether the male assists.

Range. Holarctic. Breeds on arctic tundra around the world. In North America: the Arctic of Canada and Greenland. Winters in many parts of the world: in North America from southern British Columbia, Massachusetts, and the Gulf Coast of the United States south to southern Chile and southern Argentina; also the West Indies. In the Old World winters south to South Africa, Australia, and New Zealand.

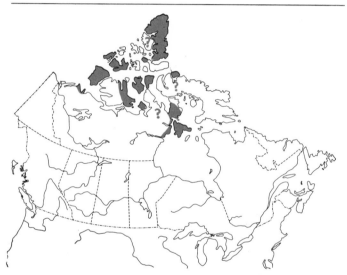

Breeding Distribution of Sanderling

Range in Canada. Breeds in the Arctic from Prince Patrick Island (Mould Bay) and northern Ellesmere Island (Lake Hazen, Fosheim Peninsula, probably Alert) south through Banks Island (Collinson Point, Sachs Harbour) to northwestern Mackenzie (rarely: near Franklin Bay), Victoria Island (De Haven Point), Prince of Wales Island, King William Island, Melville Peninsula, and Southampton Island, Cape Fullerton, and Bylot Island. Breeding not reported from Baffin Island except Bylot Island.

In migration it disperses widely and is a common transient in most of the country south of the breeding range and in all the provinces. Very scarce in Yukon and interior British Columbia (recorded only in autumn) but common on the British Columbia coast, Alberta, Saskatchewan, Manitoba; but from Ontario eastward it is mainly an autumn transient, particularly in Quebec, Labrador, Newfoundland,

and the Maritimes. Non-breeding birds occur in summer south of the breeding range.

Winters in small numbers in southwestern British Columbia (Fraser River mouth, Vancouver Island), and Nova Scotia.

Family **Recurvirostridae** – Avocets and Stilts

Number of Species in North America 2; in Canada 2

Large shorebirds with extremely long legs; long, very slender bills, slightly upcurved in avocets, nearly straight in the Black-necked Stilt; heads smallish, necks rather long.

AMERICAN AVOCET

L'Avocette américaine. *Recurvirostra americana* Gmelin
Plate 28. L. 16 to 20 in. (male larger than female)

Bill extremely slender, long, and slightly flattened; usually upturned, often decidedly so (but sometimes the extreme tip is downcurved in a slight hook). Legs long, pale bluish, front toes webbed. The peculiar awl-like bill, large size, and striking coloration make it unmistakable. Winter adults and immatures are similar to adults in breeding plumage, but the pinkish buff coloration of head, neck, and breast is largely replaced by white and some grey.

Measurements. *Adult male:* wing, 222–228.5 (224.6); tail, 76.5–89 (86.1); exposed culmen, 91.5–92 (91.8); tarsus, 95.5–102.5 (99.1). *Adult female:* wing, 214.5–236.5 (224.1) mm.

Field Marks. This very large, strikingly coloured shorebird with very slender upturned bill and very long legs is unmistakable. Young lack most of the vinaceous coloration on head, neck, and breast but are otherwise so similar to breeding adults that they are easily recognized. Common call when alarmed is a strident *kleep*, many times repeated.

Habitat. Shores and flats of sparsely vegetated lakes and sloughs, especially alkaline ones.

Nesting. Often in loose colonies. Nest, a depression in the ground usually on dried-out mud shores or islands of shallow lakes or sloughs. Nest lined with grasses, weeds, and similar available material, sometimes only sparsely but often forming a considerable structure. *Eggs* 3 to 5, usually 4; vary in colour from dark olive to light brown, rather profusely spotted and blotched with dark browns and a few spots of lavender. Nests are not infrequently found with up to eight eggs, but these are probably the product of more than one female.

Range. Breeds from eastern Washington, southern Idaho, and southern parts of the Prairie Provinces of Canada south to southern California, southern Nevada, central Colorado, and southern Texas; perhaps also locally in central Mexico (San Luis Potosi). Winters from California and southern Texas south through Mexico to Guatemala.

Range in Canada. Breeds on the prairies of central and southern Alberta (Beaverhill Lake, Bittern Lake, High River, Milk River; formerly north to Lesser Slave Lake), southern Saskatchewan (Edam, Saskatoon, Big Quill Lake,

Maple Creek, Yorkton; perhaps north to Wakaw: Frank Roy, in litt.), and southwestern Manitoba (Oak Lake, West Shoal Lake, Delta, Dog Lake). Formerly bred north to southern Mackenzie (Fort Rae about 1861). That the species formerly ranged more widely is indicated by specimens taken in the nineteenth century at Fort Rae and Fort Resolution, Mackenzie; Fort Chipewyan and Lesser Slave Lake, Alberta.

Breeding Distribution of American Avocet

Casual in British Columbia (mouth of Fraser River, Arrow Lake, Okanagan Landing), southern Ontario (Toronto), and New Brunswick (Quaco; Charlotte County; perhaps St. John).

BLACK-NECKED STILT
L'Échasse américaine. *Himantopus mexicanus* (Müller)
Fig. 50. L. 13.5 to 15.5 in.

Bill twice as long as head (2.0 to 2.7 in.), slightly upturned, very slender, sharp-pointed. Legs extremely long, slim, stilt-like, red in colour. *Adults* (female duller and more brownish than male): hind part of crown, back of head (to below eye), hind-neck, upper back, and wings, black. Forehead, spot above eye, front of face and lower cheeks, sides and front of neck, rump, and under parts, white. Tail greyish. Immatures similar to female but still duller, the feathers of the dark upper parts margined with brownish or whitish.

Field Marks. A large shorebird contrastingly attired in black and white, with slender upturned bill (twice as long as head) and excessively long stilt-like red or pink legs. Wings solid black with no white stripe.

Range. Breeds locally from southern Oregon, northern Utah, southern Colorado, and the Gulf Coast of Texas south through the West Indies, Mexico, and Central America to northern Brazil, the Guianas, and northern Colombia.

Range in Canada. Accidental in Newfoundland (Trepassey, June 23, 1947). Casual in New Brunswick (Grand

Fig. 50 Black-necked Stilt

Manan, Mace's Bay). There is a sight record for Ontario at Timmins, September 1, 1955, following a hurricane. A set of eggs in the National Museum of Canada was, according to the label, taken at Qu'Appelle, Saskatchewan, on June 13, 1894, by Edward Arnold. This is so far from the known breeding range that the possibility of an error in the data seems probable.

Family **Phalaropodidae** – Phalaropes

Number of Species in North America 3; in Canada 3

Phalaropes are small swimming 'sandpipers.' Their toes are equipped with lobes (which sandpiper's toes lack), and there are small webs at their bases. The tarsi are laterally flattened. Plumage is dense and waterproof. They are the only small shorebirds that habitually swim. Often they feed by swimming in small circles, picking up bits of food as they go. The males are smaller and much duller in colour than the females. Females take the initative in courtship, and the males incubate the eggs and care for the young.

RED PHALAROPE
Le Phalarope roux. *Phalaropus fulicarius* (Linnaeus)
Plates 30, 31. L. 7.7 to 9 in. (female larger and more brightly coloured than the male)

A sandpiper-like shorebird with scalloped membranes along the sides of the front toes is a phalarope (Fig. 51). Front toes half-webbed at bases. In breeding plumage the entire under parts (except blackish throat) are chestnut red, quite unlike any other phalarope. Adults and young in autumn are mainly white below and similar to the other species. In any plumage the broader, flattened bill of the Red Phalarope is diagnostic compared with the slender bill of the other two species.

Measurements. *Adult male:* wing, 121–132 (125.1); tail, 58.5–67.1 (63); exposed culmen, 21–23 (22.3); tarsus, 21.8–23 (22.3). *Adult female:* wing, 128–136.3 (131.9) mm.

Field Marks. A sandpiper-like bird with a persistent habit of swimming is a phalarope. In spring and summer the all-red under parts and yellow (with dark tip) bill readily distinguish this species. In autumn and winter it closely resembles the other two species. At close range its flatter, thicker bill, often with a small light area at the base of the lower mandible, distinguishes it from the other two. In flight its white wing stripe separates it from the Wilson's Phalarope.

Fig. 51 Foot of Red Phalarope

Habitat. In migration mainly the open sea, where it swims buoyantly; comes closer inshore occasionally, especially during storms, occasionally coming to land; more rarely freshwater bodies of the interior. In the breeding season, grass, sedge, and moss tussocky tundra interspersed with shallow freshwater ponds and shallow lakes, generally not very far from the coast.

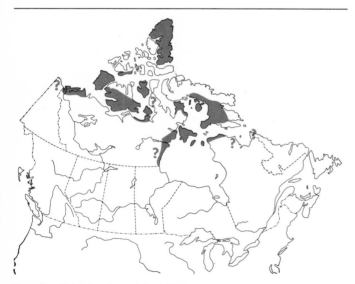

Breeding Distribution of Red Phalarope

Nesting. Nest, often a depression in the ground, usually (not always) lined with grass or similar vegetation. Usually it is situated on a dry spot or tussock near a tundra pond; sometimes a cup-shaped structure attached to vegetation over water. *Eggs*, usually 4; dark to light greenish buff, heavily and irregularly marked, most heavily at larger end, with dark browns. Incubation mainly by the male, but Brandt (*Alaska Bird Trails*, p. 396) twice observed a female on eggs in Alaska, and Sutton (1932) suspected that the

female may incubate to a limited extent. Incubation period 18 to 19 days (D. F. Parmelee).

Range. Circumpolar. Breeds on tundra mostly near the coast across North America and Eurasia. Winters at sea, mainly in the Southern Hemisphere off both coasts of South America and western Africa; small numbers farther north.

Range in Canada. Breeds from Banks Island (Kellett River; probably Mercy Bay), Melville Island (probably Winter Harbour), and Ellesmere Island (Fosheim Peninsula) south to northern Mackenzie (Franklin Bay, Perry River), Keewatin (Adelaide Peninsula, Chesterfield Inlet, McConnell River), Southampton Island, Mansel Island (probably), northern Quebec (Digges Island), and probably northern Labrador. The species has been recorded on Prince Patrick Island and Ellef Ringnes Island but without evidence of breeding.

Migrates mainly at sea and along both the Pacific and Atlantic coasts. Rare in the interior, most records for autumn; in interior British Columbia (Swan Lake, Okanagan; Sirdar Lake), Alberta (Beaverhill Lake, Didsbury, Banff National Park, Stirling), Saskatchewan (Sandfly Lake on Churchill River), Ontario (Rondeau; Toronto; Middlesex County; White Lake; Ottawa), and Quebec (Valleyfield, Brosseau, Disraeli, Beauport).

WILSON'S PHALAROPE

Le Phalarope de Wilson. *Steganopus tricolor* Vieillot
Plates 30, 31. L. 8.4 to 10 in.

Female larger and more brightly coloured than male. Bill very slender and awl-like, not obviously flattened, thus different from that of Red Phalarope. Front toes with very narrow lateral membranes and very small basal webs. Differs from other phalaropes in larger size, lack of a white wing stripe, and absence of distinct scallops on the lateral membranes of the front toes.

Measurements. *Adult male:* wing, 116.5–128 (121.1); tail, 45.8–53.7 (51.3); exposed culmen, 28.4–33 (30.8); tarsus, 29.9–33.5 (31.7). *Adult female:* wing, 128.9–137.3 (132.5) mm.

Field Marks. Phalaropes are swimming sandpipers. However, the Wilson's Phalarope wades and walks on shore more often than the other two species. When on land its needle-like bill and slender neck distinguish it from sandpipers. Lack of a white stripe in the spread wing separates it from the two other phalaropes in any plumage. In breeding plumage the female, with a black stripe from the eye down the side of the neck merging posteriorly into chestnut, is easily recognized. The male is smaller and duller and, like the Northern Phalarope, has a cinnamon suffusion on sides of neck. It lacks the buffy streaks present on the back of the Northern and usually shows a small whitish area on the back of the neck which the Northern lacks. Common call: harsh grunts seemingly out of keeping with the daintiness and relatively small size of the bird.

Habitat. In the breeding season, sloughs, shallow lakes, and freshwater marshes.

Nesting. Nest, a depression in the ground, sparsely to well lined with dry grasses, and usually near shallow water. *Eggs*, usually 4; pale buff, well spotted and blotched with blackish brown. Incubation, by the male, lasts about 20.2 days (D. F. Parmelee).

Range. Breeds from southern interior of western Canada south in the interior to south-central California, northern Utah, central Kansas, and northern Indiana; locally southern Ontario. Winters mainly in Argentina and rarely Chile.

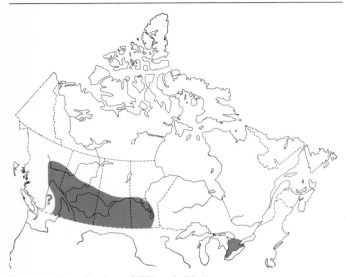

Breeding Distribution of Wilson's Phalarope

Range in Canada. Breeds in interior central and southern British Columbia (Nulki Lake, 149 Mile Lake, Dale Lake, Cranbrook; Peace River District), Alberta (north at least to Bear Lake in Grande Prairie region), central and southern Saskatchewan (north at least to Nipawin and Prince Albert and probably to Niska Lake), central-western and southern Manitoba (north to Reader and Halcrow lakes near The Pas); also very locally in southern Ontario (Luther Marsh near Orangeville; Holland Marsh near Bradford; Dunnville, Haldimand Co.; West Lorne, Elgin Co.). Recorded in summer without evidence of breeding to Lake Athabasca, Alberta, and Ile à la Crosse, Saskatchewan.

Rare transient in southeastern Ontario (Kingston, Ottawa), southern Quebec (Montreal, Anticosti Island, Magdalen Islands), New Brunswick (Point Lepreau, probably Grand Manan). There is a convincing sight record of ten seen off the coast of Nova Scotia, June 19, 1934 (Gross 1937, *The Auk* 54: 27). Casual in migration off the coast of British Columbia.

Remarks. This phalarope is a common summer inhabitant of the prairie sloughs and pools. On the water it rides as lightly as thistledown, often spinning in small circles and seizing by quick thrusts of its slender bill bits of food stirred up in the shallow water. It is more inclined, however, to feed on land than are the other phalaropes. Land and aquatic insects (especially the larvae of mosquitoes), brine shrimps, and amphipods provide a large part of its diet.

As in all phalaropes, the male is a 'hen-pecked husband.' He is smaller and plainer than the female. He builds the nest, incubates the eggs, and cares for the young. The female takes the initiative in courtship. The writer once saw a little male being ardently pursued by five females at one time!

168

PLATE 31

1 Least Sandpiper

2 White-rumped Sandpiper

3 Sanderling

4 Red Phalarope, autumn

5 Spotted Sandpiper, autumn

6 Wilson's Phalarope, summer female

7 Northern Phalarope, autumn

8 Solitary Sandpiper

9 American Golden Plover, autumn

10 Black-bellied Plover, autumn

11 Knot, autumn

12 American Woodcock

13 Common Snipe

14 Dowitcher, autumn

15 Greater Yellowlegs

Crosby

1a
1b
1c
1d
2a
2b
2c
2d
3a
3b
3c
4a
4b
4c
4d
5a
5b
5c
5d
6a
6b
6c
7a
7b
7c

Crosby

PLATE 32

1 Glaucous Gull,
    (a) wing tip of adult
    (b) juvenal
    (c) adult
    (d) details of head
       (adult)

2 Iceland Gull,
    (a) wing tip of adult
       (nominate race)
    (b) wing tip of adult
       (*kumlieni* race)
    (c) juvenal
    (d) adult (nominate
       race)

3 Thayer's Gull,
    (a) wing tip of adult
    (b) head of adult
    (c) leg and foot of
       adult

4 Ivory Gull,
    (a) wing of first-year
       immature
    (b) wing of adult
    (c) head of adult
    (d) leg and foot of
       adult

5 Herring Gull,
    (a) wing of adult
    (b) juvenal
    (c) adult
    (d) head details (adult)

6 Mew Gull,
    (a) wing of adult
    (b) head of adult
    (c) foot of adult

7 California Gull,
    (a) wing of adult
    (b) head of adult
    (c) foot of adult

NORTHERN PHALAROPE

Le Phalarope hyperboré. *Lobipes lobatus* (Linnaeus)
Plates 30, 31. L. 6.5 to 8 in.

Female larger and in breeding plumage more brightly coloured than the male. A shorebird with lobed membranes along the sides of the front toes is a phalarope. White wing stripe separates it in all plumages from Wilson's Phalarope. Its very slender pointed bill distinguishes it from the Red Phalarope.

Measurements. *Adult male:* wing, 101–106.5 (104.6); tail, 45–51 (48.4); exposed culmen, 20.2–23.5 (21.8); tarsus, 19.8–21.6 (20.7). *Adult female:* wing, 106.7–114.9 (111.6) mm.

Field Marks. A small shorebird that swims for sustained periods, often with spinning motions, is a phalarope. In breeding plumage, lack of extensive red on the under parts easily distinguishes it from the Red Phalarope. In winter and immature plumages, these two species are very similar, but at close range the much slenderer needle-like bill of the Northern can often be discerned. Both Northern and Red phalaropes have a white wing stripe, visible in flight or when the wing is raised, which separates them from the Wilson's Phalarope at all times.

Habitat. In the breeding season low arctic and subarctic freshwater pools and their low-vegetation margins. In migration, mostly the open ocean and sea-coast, but interior lakes and ponds are also frequented to a smaller extent.

Nesting. Nest, a depression lined with grass or leaves in a tussock or mound in a marshy place with scattered ponds. *Eggs,* usually 4; olive buff, well spotted or blotched with brown. Incubation about 20 days (H. B. Conover), by the male; 22½ days (Jehl and Hussell).

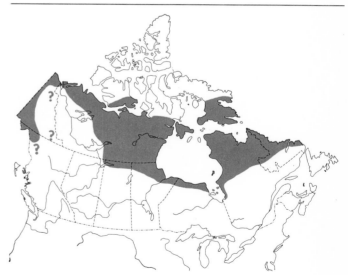

Breeding Distribution of Northern Phalarope

Range. Breeds across the low Arctic or Subarctic of both the New and Old Worlds. Winters at sea in both Hemispheres, mainly south of the equator.

Range in Canada. Breeds in the low Arctic and Subarctic from southern Victoria Island (Simpson Bay, Cambridge Bay), central Keewatin (Beverly Lake, Chesterfield Inlet),

Southampton Island, and southern Baffin Island south to northwestern British Columbia (Atlin, Chilkat Pass), southern Yukon, Mackenzie (barrens east of Mackenzie Delta, Franklin Bay, Coronation Gulf, Bathurst Inlet, probably Perry River and indefinitely southward), northern Saskatchewan (Lake Athabasca), southern Keewatin (McConnell River), northeastern Manitoba (Churchill), northern Ontario (Cape Henrietta Maria, Little Cape), James Bay (Grey Goose Island), northern Quebec (islands in Ungava Bay; Gregory Lake; Knob Lake region and south on the James Bay coast to Rupert Bay); and Labrador coast (south to Battle Harbour). Non-breeding birds are found in summer south of the breeding range.

Migrates commonly along both the Atlantic and Pacific coasts and at sea, with good numbers also passing through interior British Columbia, Alberta, and Saskatchewan. Scarce in interior Manitoba, infrequent to rare in the southern interior of Ontario and Quebec (mainly in autumn), but likely to turn up eventually almost anywhere. Occurs in all the coastal provinces, mostly as an offshore migrant.

Family **Stercorariidae** – Jaegers and Skuas

Number of Species in North America 4; in Canada 4

Gull-like, graceful, swift, and predatory sea birds which rob other birds of food. They spend most of the year on the ocean but nest on the arctic tundra. Bill is strongly hooked. Wings long and pointed. Front toes fully webbed, claws hooked and sharp. In flight they show more or less white at the base of the primaries on the under side of the wing. Adult jaegers have the central tail feathers elongated.

Their size and strongly hooked bills (gulls have only slightly hooked bills) combined with webbed feet distinguish them from most other birds of regular occurrence in Canada except cormorants, shearwaters, and petrels. The presence of open nostrils and of two instead of three webs on each foot distinguishes them from cormorants. The nostrils are not enclosed in tubes as in shearwaters, petrels, and albatrosses.

These dashing pirates commonly pursue gulls and terns, forcing them to disgorge their food. With a graceful swoop the jaegers snap up the disgorged fish or other item before it hits the water. They capture fish, small mammals, large insects, and sometimes adult birds for food, and they eat also eggs and young of other birds as well as carrion.

POMARINE JAEGER

Le Labbe pomarin. *Stercorarius pomarinus* (Temminck)
Plate 35. L. 20 to 23 in.

The most robust of the jaegers (although the extremely long tail of the smaller Long-tailed Jaeger gives it an almost equal total length) with decidedly heavier and longer bill and usually longer wing. Adults are distinguishable from adults of the other jaegers by the tips of the elongated central tail feathers, which are blunt and are usually twisted so that they are nearly or quite vertical (projection beyond other tail feathers 2 to 4 in., Fig. 52). There are two colour phases.

Adults (*light phase*): Top of head black. Wings and tail, sooty greyish brown. Primaries whitish at bases with whitish shafts. Throat, neck, and breast white, the sides of the neck suffused with golden yellow, and usually there is a more or less complete band of dusky mixed with white across the breast and more or less dusky markings on sides (dusky markings on breast and sides variable in extent, sometimes almost absent). Posterior abdomen and tail coverts, greyish brown. Adults in *dark phase* are uniform greyish brown above and below, but with whitish areas on wings as in light phase. *First-year Immatures* (*light phase*): Upper parts dark brown with buff spots on scapulars and rump; head and neck, dark brown; under parts barred buffy and dark brown. Central tail feathers project little beyond others. Young separable from those of other jaegers by larger size.

Fig. 52 Tail of adult Pomarine Jaeger

Measurements. *Adult male:* wing, 340–359.5 (346.4); tail, 174.5–238.5 (212.7); exposed culmen, 34.9–40.9 (36.9); tarsus, 49.4–55 (53.1). *Adult female:* wing, 355.5–367 (359.9) mm.

Field Marks. Adults separable from other jaegers in both colour phases by the tips of the central tail feathers, which are blunt and twisted to a vertical plane. Projecting central tail feathers much shorter (2 to 4 in.) than in adult Long-tailed. Young of all jaegers are almost impossible to distinguish in the field, but direct comparison may distinguish Pomarine by larger size and heavier bill (*see also* Skua).

Habitat. In the breeding season, low tundra interspersed with lakes, pools, or sluggish streams, often on coastal plains but also at variable distances (usually not great) inland. In migration the ocean, mainly well off shore; rarely large interior lakes.

Nesting. Nest, a slight depression, lined with grass or sometimes unlined, on a mound or other rise of ground in usually low tundra. *Eggs*, usually 2; brownish olive, spotted with browns. Incubation by both sexes.

Range. Breeds in northern Alaska, arctic Canada, Greenland, Spitsbergen, Novaya Zemlya, northern Russia, and northern Siberia. Winters at sea mainly from the latitude of North Carolina to the West Indies and off Africa, and from the latitude of southern California south to Peru, and off eastern Australia.

Range in Canada. Breeds in the Arctic from Banks Island, Melville Island (Winter Harbour), Prince of Wales, Somerset, and Devon islands south to northwestern Mackenzie (Baillie Island), southern Victoria Island (abundantly Anderson Bay to Wellington Bay and elsewhere), Southampton Island (Itiuachuk), southern Baffin Island (Lake Amadjuak), and northwestern Quebec (Port Harrison). Recorded in summer on Cornwallis Island.

Non-breeding birds are found in summer off northern British Columbia (Goose Island Banks), in Hudson Bay, the coast of Labrador, Newfoundland, and the north shore of the Gulf of St. Lawrence.

Breeding Distribution of Pomarine Jaeger

Migrates mainly at sea and off both the Pacific and Atlantic coasts and has occurred in all the coastal provinces. Very rare in the interior of British Columbia (Chilcotin), southern Yukon (Teslin Lake), Saskatchewan (Yellow Grass), Manitoba (mouth of Red River), Ontario (Niagara River, Hamilton, Detroit River), and interior Quebec (St. Lambert).

PARASITIC JAEGER

Le Labbe parasite. *Stercorarius parasiticus* (Linnaeus)
Plate 35. L. 18 to 21 in.

Smaller than Pomarine Jaeger. Central tail feathers of adults pointed and never twisted, thus differing from adult Pomarine Jaeger (Fig. 53). Central tail feathers much shorter than in adult Long-tailed Jaeger (projecting only 2½ to 3½ inches beyond others). There are two colour phases, light and dark, both similar to Pomarine. The light phase of the Parasitic is slightly paler above; breast band and markings on sides when present are decidedly paler and more uniform (little or no white mottling or bars); yellow suffusion on sides of head and neck less extensive and intensive; and the feathers at the base of the upper mandible are whitish. Young of the year somewhat smaller than Pomarine and have more decided streaking on the head (*see also* Long-tailed Jaeger).

Measurements. *Adult male:* wing, 317–334.5 (325); tail, 195–232.5 (209.7); exposed culmen, 28.6–32.8 (30.4); tarsus, 44–48.7 (45.8). *Adult female:* wing, 305–335.5 (325.6) mm.

Field Marks. The pointed, untwisted central tail feathers distinguish it from the Pomarine. The shorter central tail feathers (extending no more than 3½ inches beyond the others) separate it from the adult Long-tailed Jaeger which has long streaming tail feathers (except of course when molting). Especially in the light phase the Parasitic usually shows a pale area at the base of the upper mandible, often a useful character at close range. First-year birds are almost impossible to distinguish in the field from young of other jaegers.

Habitat. In nesting season, low grassy or mossy tundra interspersed with ponds or lakes; also low stony country. In migration open ocean and coasts; rarely large lakes of the southern interior.

Nesting. Often tends to be colonial in nesting. Nest, a depression in moss or grass, sometimes sparsely lined with available vegetation. *Eggs,* usually 2; greenish or brownish, spotted and blotched with dark brown; sometimes only lightly spotted or nearly immaculate. Incubation period given by various authors as 23, 24, 25 to 26, and up to 28 days. Incubation by both sexes.

Range. Holarctic. Breeds in the Arctic and Subarctic of Alaska, Canada, Greenland, Iceland, northern Scotland, northern Norway, Sweden, Finland, northern Russia, and northern Siberia south near the coast to Kamchatka and the Sea of Okhotsk. Winters at sea; in the Atlantic offshore from Maine and the British Isles south to Argentina and southern Africa; in the Pacific from Baja California south to southern Chile, Australia, and New Zealand.

Fig. 53 Tail of adult Parasitic Jaeger

Range in Canada. Breeds in the Arctic and Subarctic from Banks Island, southern Melville Island, Cornwallis and southern Ellesmere islands south to central Mackenzie, southern Keewatin (Angikuni Lake, McConnell River), Southampton Island, northwestern Manitoba (Churchill), northern Ontario (Cape Henrietta Maria), northern Quebec (Kogaluk River) and northern Labrador (Metik Islands). Non-breeding birds found in summer south of the breeding range.

Migration mainly at sea and along the Pacific and Atlantic coasts, usually well off shore. Scarce in the interior:

171

Breeding Distribution of Parasitic Jaeger

Yukon (Old Crow), Alberta (Beaverhill Lake; sight records elsewhere), Saskatchewan (Old Wives Lake, Imperial Beach), southern Manitoba (Scanterbury, Pelican Island), southern Ontario (numerous records for the Great Lakes; also recorded from Ottawa; sight records elsewhere).

LONG-TAILED JAEGER

Le Labbe à longue queue. *Stercorarius longicaudus* Vieillot
Plate 35. L. 20 to 23 in. (including long tail).

The smallest of the jaegers, although the extremely long tail gives it a total length equal to or exceeding that of the Parasitic. In adults the long slender central tail feathers, projecting 5 to 9 inches beyond the others, distinguish it from other jaegers (Fig. 54). Bill sheath (or false cere) is about equal to chord of remainder of upper mandible (in

Fig. 54 Tail of Long-tailed Jaeger

PLATE 33

1 Ring-billed Gull,
   (a) head of adult
   (b) adult
   (c) first autumn
   (d) wing of first-year immature
   (e) wing of adult

2 Black-legged Kittiwake
   (a) adult
   (b) immature

3 Heermann's Gull,
   (a) head of first-year immature
   (b) adult
   (c) wing of adult

4 Glaucous-winged Gull,
   (a) head of adult
   (b) adult
   (c) juvenal
   (d) wing of adult

5 Herring Gull, juvenal

6 Western Gull,
   (a) head of adult
   (b) adult
   (c) juvenal
   (d) wing of adult

7 Great Black-backed Gull,
   (a) head of adult
   (b) adult
   (c) juvenal
   (d) wing of adult

1a

1b

1c

1d

1e

2a

2b

3a

3b

3c

4a

4b

4c

4d

5

6a

6b

6c

6d

7a

Crosby

7b

7c

7d

PLATE 34

1 Bonaparte's Gull,
   (a) summer adult
   (b) winter adult
   (c) first-year immature
   (d) summer adult
   (e) head of juvenal

2 Black-headed Gull,
   (a) wing tip of adult
      (upper side)
   (b) wing tip of adult
      (under side)
   (c) head of adult in
      summer
   (d) head of adult in
      winter
   (e) head of first-winter
      immature

3 Little Gull,
   (a) summer adult
      (dorsal view)
   (b) winter adult
      (ventral view)
   (c) first-winter
      immature

4 Sabine's Gull,
   (a) adult
   (b) juvenal

5 Ross's Gull,
   (a) adult in summer
   (b) first-winter
      immature

6 Laughing Gull,
   (a) wing tip of adult
      (upper surface)
   (b) wing tip (upper
      surface) of first-year
      immature
   (c) adult in summer
   (d) juvenal

7 Franklin's Gull,
   (a) wing tip (upper
      surface) of adult
   (b) wing tip (upper
      surface) of first-year
      immature
   (c) adult in summer
   (d) head of juvenal

Parasitic, bill sheath longer than chord of remainder of upper mandible), and the bill of the Long-tailed, viewed dorsally, is actually and relatively slenderer. Similar in coloration to Parasitic Jaeger, but a dark phase in adult Long-tailed is excessively rare, if indeed it exists at all. Adult, like light phase Parasitic but consistently lacks a breast band (some Parasitics and Pomarines also lack breast band); cap decidedly more blackish (less greyish); there is no whitish area at the base of the upper mandible; and the legs, but not feet, are bluish grey (blackish in other jaegers). Smaller size distinguishes it in any plumage from the Pomarine Jaeger.

Measurements. *Adult male:* wing, 294–315.5 (301); tail, 268–334.5 (289.9); exposed culmen, 26.4–28.5 (27.4); tarsus, 38.5–45.4 (42.2). *Adult female:* wing, 294–324 (307.5) mm.

Field Marks. Adults with fully developed, long, streaming central tail feathers are readily recognizable. Adults in molt with only partly developed tail resemble Parasitic Jaeger but have blacker (less brownish) cap, and bluish grey instead of black legs. They have no band across the breast. First-year immatures are very difficult to separate from those of other jaegers but show less white in the spread wing.

Habitat. In nesting season vegetated upland rolling tundra, often wet but by no means always on ponds and streams; stony plateaus; flat coastal tundra, tending to prefer better-drained areas than the Parasitic Jaeger. In migration, mainly the open ocean, rarely large freshwater lakes of the southern interior.

Nesting. Nest, a depression in the ground either unlined or sparsely lined with available vegetation. *Eggs,* 1 to 2; similar to those of the Parasitic Jaeger but averaging slightly smaller. Incubation 23 days, by both sexes (Manniche).

Range. Circumpolar. Breeds in the Arctic of Alaska, Canada, and Greenland; and in the Old World from Jan Mayen, Spitsbergen, and Novaya Zemlya south to northern Scandinavia, northern Russia, and northern Siberia including Kamchatka and the northeast coast of the Sea of Okhotsk. Winters at sea in the Atlantic and Pacific oceans, most commonly in more southern parts.

Breeding Distribution of Long-tailed Jaeger

Range in Canada. Breeds in the Arctic from Prince Patrick, Ellef Ringnes, and northern Ellesmere Islands south to northern Yukon (north coast; probably Old Crow), northern Mackenzie (Baillie Island, Anderson River, Perry River), southern Keewatin (Aberdeen Lake; McConnell River), Southampton Island, northern Quebec (25 miles north of Port Harrison; Povungnituk; perhaps George River).

Migrates mainly at sea, uncommon to rare at inshore coastal localities on the Pacific and Atlantic coasts. Very rare in the interior: British Columbia (Buffalo and Okanagan lakes), southern Manitoba (Lake Winnipeg), southern Ontario (Ottawa, Kempenfeldt Bay, Point Pelee).

SKUA

Le Grand Labbe. *Catharacta skua* Brünnich
Plate 35. L. 20 to 22 in.

A large dark-brown sea bird with robust 2-inch bill, strongly hooked at the tip, a large white patch at the base of the primaries, and white primary shafts. Larger and much more robust than jaegers. Unlike adult jaegers, it never has elongated central tail feathers. In adults the feathers of the head, neck, and back have yellowish or whitish tips. Immatures are more uniform brown and have less conspicuous white patches in the wing.

Measurements. (*C. s. skua*) *Adult male*: wing, 367–389.5 (378.3); tail, 140.9–163 (149.8); exposed culmen, 44.8–48.3 (46); tarsus, 63.5–69.8 (66.9). *Adult female*: wing, 377–395.9 (387.8) mm.

Field Marks. A large dark sea bird with a conspicuous white patch at the base of the flight feathers and a robust hooked bill. Central tail feathers never elongated, thus differing from adult jaegers. A much larger and more robust bird than immature jaegers, and with a much larger white patch in its broader, more rounded wings.

Habitat. In Canada, the open ocean, usually well offshore, seldom coming within sight of land.

Range. Breeds in Iceland, the Faroes, Shetlands, and Orkneys; wandering widely over the North Atlantic. Breeds also on the coasts of the Antarctic Continent, southern South America (southern Chile, Tierra del Fuego, Falkland Islands) and on islands in the southern seas; wandering widely over the ocean northward in the Pacific to British Columbia and Japan.

Status in Canada. A non-breeding visitant to offshore coastal waters: British Columbia (Vancouver Island, Goose Island Banks); Labrador (sight records only); Newfoundland (off Fogo, Funk Island, Cape Broyle, Argentia. Up to 20 per day on the Grand Banks, mid-September 1961 — S.W. Gorham. One banded in Iceland on July 11, 1952, was shot off Horse Island, Newfoundland, late October 1952 — L. M. Tuck); and Nova Scotia (Lockeport, Yarmouth). Alleged occurrences in the Canadian Arctic require confirmation.

Subspecies. (1) *Catharacta skua skua* Brünnich is the only race known to occur on our Atlantic Coast and its offshore waters. (2) *C. s. lönnbergi* Mathews has been taken off the B.C. coast (Goose Island Banks).

Family **Laridae** – Gulls and Terns

Number of Species in North America 41; in Canada 33

Long-winged swimming birds with front toes more or less fully webbed, the hind toe small (absent rarely) and somewhat elevated. Adults are typically coloured in greys and white, often with black on the wing tips, head, or elsewhere. Immatures are attired mostly in browns, greys, and white.

Gulls have a suggestion of a hook at the end of the upper mandible (but not a strong hook, and the bill is not divided distinctly into a horny tip and a long cere, as is the case in the jaegers); the tail is usually square or rounded (but forked in Sabine's Gull). Terns are usually smaller than gulls, have sharp-pointed bills, shorter legs, and usually deeply forked tails.

Terns dive from the air for food. Gulls usually pick their food up from the water or land surface. In flight, gulls tend to hold the bill straight out in line with the body, but terns tend to point it downward toward the water.

GLAUCOUS GULL

Le Goéland bourgmestre. *Larus hyperboreus* Gunnerus
Plate 32. L. 26 to 30 in.

A very large heavy-billed gull with white wing tips in adults and nearly white in immatures. Adults with pale grey mantle, rest of plumage including wing tips immaculate white (but in winter, head and neck are vaguely marked with brownish grey). First-year immatures are extensively marked with pale greys and buffs, the wing tips slightly paler (nearly white). Second-year birds are extremely pale, sometimes almost white. The white (or in immatures very pale) wing tips distinguish it from all but the Iceland Gull and the otherwise very different Ivory Gull. Larger size and very much heavier, longer bill separate it from the very similar Iceland Gull.

Measurements. *Adult male:* wing, 447–477.2 (459.2); tail, 188.5–201 (196.3); exposed culmen, 53–64.6 (60.4); tarsus, 67.3–76.6 (72.7). *Adult female:* wing, 411.5–437 (425.1) mm.

Field Marks. A very large gull without any dark colour on the wing tips, thus separable from other gulls except the Iceland and Ivory. The latter is so much smaller and otherwise different that confusion is unlikely. Adults likely to be confused only with Iceland Gull, but Glaucous is a larger bird than the Iceland with decidedly longer, heavier bill and yellowish eye-ring (reddish in Iceland). First-year immatures have all the basal part of the bill pale, contrasting with the dark tip; whereas yearling Icelands have an almost uniformly dark bill. Second-year Glaucous are extremely pale or whitish all over.

Habitat. In winter and migration, sea-coasts, bays, and harbours, and less often offshore waters; also, in small numbers, inland lakes and rivers. For nesting purposes, arctic cliffs near the coast, coastal islands, islands in freshwater lakes near the coast, edges of coastal lagoons.

Nesting. Usually colonial on cliffs (often shares cliffs with other species), solitary on islands, usually on or near coast, rarely considerably inland: Garry Lake, Keewatin (A. H.

Macpherson). Nest, an accumulation of grass, seaweed, moss, and debris, often added to from year to year. *Eggs* 2 to 3 (usually 3); buffy brown to olive brown, spotted and blotched with dark browns and often with some grey or lavender grey. Incubation 27 to 28 days (Swenander), apparently by both sexes.

Range. Breeds on arctic coasts and islands from northern Alaska eastward across northern Canada, Greenland, Iceland, and across northern Europe to eastern Siberia. Winters from the southern part of the breeding range south to southern California and New York; also, in small numbers, on the Great Lakes; and in the Old World south to the British Isles and coasts of western Europe, China, and Japan; casually farther south.

Breeding Distribution of Glaucous Gull

Range in Canada. Breeds on arctic coasts and islands from Prince Patrick, Ellef Ringnes, and northern Ellesmere islands south to northern Yukon (coast and Herschel Island), northern Mackenzie (arctic coast), northern Keewatin (Adelaide Peninsula, and in the interior near Garry Lake), Southampton Island, Coats Island, and Belcher Islands in Hudson Bay, northern Quebec (Digges Sound, Payne Bay, Richmond Gulf), and northern Labrador (south to about Hopedale). Not known to breed on the west coast of Baffin Island.

Winters from southern parts of the breeding range southward, mostly on the Atlantic and Pacific coasts and islands of southern Canada; also Hudson Bay and in small numbers on the Great Lakes and St. Lawrence River. In most of the southern interior, it is scarce and irregular even in migration. It is, however, regular in small numbers on the upper St. Lawrence River and its drainage system (including the Ottawa) and on the Great Lakes.

Subspecies. *Larus hyperboreus hyperboreus* Gunnerus is the subspecies of most of the breeding range in Canada. Populations breeding in n. Yukon and w. Mack. (east to about Harrowby B.) are closer to *L. h. barrovianus* Ridgway, characterized by somewhat smaller size, particularly of bill, and slightly darker mantle.

ICELAND GULL (Kumlien's Gull)
Le Goéland arctique. *Larus glaucoides* Meyer
Plate 32. L. 23 to 25 in.

Two subspecies: *L. g. glaucoides*, a somewhat smaller edition of the Glaucous Gull, including white wing tips, but with decidedly smaller, slenderer bill and reddish eye-ring. *L. g. kumlieni*, similar to *L. g. glaucoides*, but adults have pale grey markings of variable but usually slight extent on the primaries. Yearlings of the two subspecies perhaps not distinguishable from each other (*see also* Thayer's Gull).

Measurements. *Adult male:* wing, 395.5–423 (408.4); tail, 167–177.5 (173.5); exposed culmen, 43–46.9 (44.9); tarsus, 58.2–62.9 (60.9). *Adult female:* wing, 372–423 (394.1) mm.

Field Marks. Herring Gull size but with pale wing tips. A somewhat smaller edition of the Glaucous Gull with noticeably slenderer and smaller bill. Adults have a reddish eye-ring, the Glaucous a yellowish one. Adults of the *kumlieni* race (Kumlien's Gull) have pale grey markings, usually not extensive, in the wing tips, thus differing from the Glaucous, but these markings are always paler and much less extensive than in the Herring and Thayer's gulls. First-year Iceland Gull closely resembles the Glaucous Gull of similar age but has an all-dark bill (basal part pale in yearling Glaucous).

Habitat. In migration, shores of saltwater and, less often, freshwater lakes and rivers; sometimes feeds at dumps. In nesting season, arctic coastal or near-coastal cliffs, or rocky islands.

Nesting. Nests in colonies, sometimes with other species. Nest of grass, moss, and seaweed is usually on cliff ledges, sometimes on islands. *Eggs*, usually 2 to 3, sometimes only 1; similar to those of the Glaucous Gull but somewhat smaller.

Breeding Distribution of Iceland Gull

Range. Breeds in low-arctic eastern Canada and southern Greenland. Winters mainly on the Atlantic Coast from southern Labrador south to Virginia; and from Iceland, the Faroes, Norway, and Sweden south to the British Isles,

175

northern France, and the Baltic Sea. Small numbers winter also on the Great Lakes.

Range in Canada. Breeds on coastal southern Baffin Island from southern Foxe Peninsula eastward, and northward on the east coast to Home Bay; also in extreme northwestern Quebec (Erik Cove, Digges Island).

Winters mainly on the Atlantic Coast in southern Labrador, Newfoundland, coasts of southern Quebec, and the Maritime Provinces; also in small numbers on the Great Lakes and the upper St. Lawrence River (Quebec, Montreal). Transient in small numbers on the upper St. Lawrence River and its drainage. Reported from northern Hudson Bay, but to what extent it uses that bay in migration is not known.

Subspecies (For descriptions, *see* paragraph one). (1) *Larus glaucoides kumlieni* Brewster, formerly known as 'Kumlien's Gull,' is the breeding bird of the Canadian part of the breeding range and is the commoner of the two subspecies found in migration and winter. (2) *Larus glaucoides glaucoides* Meyer, which breeds in Greenland, is only a transient and winter resident in Canada, being found over much the same winter grounds as *kumlieni* but much less commonly.

GLAUCOUS-WINGED GULL

Le Goéland à ailes glauques. *Larus glaucescens* Naumann
Plate 33. L. 24 to 28 in.

A large, rather heavy-billed gull. Wing tips grey, similar in coloration to the mantle, not blackish as in other large gulls of the Pacific Coast. Adults of the geographically widely separated *kumlieni* race of the Iceland Gull have similar pale grey on the wing tips, but the Glaucous-winged is a larger bird with much heavier bill, somewhat darker mantle, and the grey coloration of wing tips is much more extensive. First-year Glaucous-winged, compared with yearling Herring, Western, and California gulls, are paler generally with grey wing tips instead of blackish brown. First-year Glaucous-winged Gulls are often very similar to first-year Thayer's, but the former has a heavier bill.

Measurements. *Adult male:* wing, 393–443.5 (422.9); tail, 132.5–195 (173); exposed culmen, 50–61 (55.1); tarsus, 65–73 (69.6). *Adult female:* wing, 363.5–414 (396.3) mm.

Field Marks. A large pink-legged gull of the Pacific Coast. Adults with grey wing tips, not blackish as in other large West Coast gulls. Yearlings have greyish brown wing tips, not noticeably darker than the back. In very much worn immatures the wing tips sometimes bleach white.

Habitat. Primarily the vicinity of salt and brackish water along the Pacific Coast: bays, islands, estuaries, the ocean (usually not far off shore), beaches, mud flats, wharves, dumps, fish canneries. Often follows boats. Follows rivers for various distances but is not normally found very far inland.

Nesting. Nests colonially. Nest, a heap of seaweed, kelp, rockweed, and grasses, is often on flat low islands, rock ledges of higher islands or headlands. *Eggs*, 2 or 3; similar to those of other large gulls, have buffy to olive buff ground colour, spotted and blotched with darker browns and some lavender grey. Incubation period 26 to 28 days (R. H. Drent).

176

Range. Breeds from western and southern Alaska south to northwestern Washington; also on the Commander Islands, St. Lawrence Island, the Pribilof and Aleutian islands. Winters from southeastern Alaska south coastally to southern Baja California and casually to Sonora.

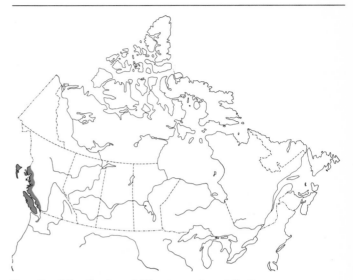

Breeding Distribution of Glaucous-winged Gull

Range in Canada. Breeds and winters along the entire coast of British Columbia. Accidental far in the interior: St. Paul and Bear Lake, Alberta.

GREAT BLACK-BACKED GULL

Le Goéland à manteau noir. *Larus marinus* Linnaeus
Plate 33. L. 28 to 31 in.

A very large gull of the eastern part of the continent, the adult with a distinctive black mantle, thus unlike any other gull likely to be found in eastern Canada. In winter, white of head lightly streaked with dusky. Immatures are separable from other eastern gulls except the Glaucous by large size and large heavy bill. From Glaucous Gull, by much darker general coloration and blackish brown wing tips. First-year birds show more white in the tail, particularly the outer feathers, than Herring Gull of similar age, and the upper and under parts are paler. Full adult plumage is not assumed until at least the fourth year, but the first few black feathers begin to appear in the mantle the second year.

Measurements. *Adult male:* wing, 446–486.5 (471.6); tail, 191–199 (195.4); exposed culmen, 62.5–66 (64.3); tarsus, 76–82.5 (79.9). *Adult female:* wing, 445.5–461.5 (455.5) mm.

Field Marks. A very large gull of the east, mainly the coast. Much larger, with heavier bill, than the Herring Gull. Black mantle and great size characterize adults. First-year birds are separable from Herring Gull of similar age by whiter under parts, usually whiter head, paler back, larger size, and heavier bill. *Voice:* Notes varied and many similar to those of other gulls, but a deep hoarse *érr-ul* is distinctive.

Habitat. Nesting is on coastal islands and cliffs; sometimes on islands of freshwater lakes usually (not always) near the coast. In other seasons almost any shoreline situation,

Breeding Distribution of Great Black-backed Gull

---

including coastal islands; also freshwater lakes and rivers mostly near the coast, but a few winter far inland on large lakes with open water.

Nesting. Nests singly or in colonies on coastal islands and cliffs; also less commonly on islands of freshwater lakes near the coast; rarely far inland. Nest, a depression lined with grass and seaweed, a mound of vegetable material, or sometimes an unlined depression. *Eggs*, usually 3, sometimes 2; usually buff to olive brown, blotched and spotted with browns and purplish greys. Incubation by both sexes, 26 to 28 days (various authors).

Range. Breeds along the east coast of North America from Labrador south to New York. Also southern Greenland, Iceland, the Faroes, Spitsbergen, Bear Island, and northern Norway, south mainly on the coast through the British Isles, northern France, and Denmark. Winters south to North Carolina, and in the Old World south to the Mediterranean, Black, and Caspian seas.

Range in Canada. Breeds on or near the coast from northern Labrador (Eclipse Harbour) southward in south coastal Quebec (entire north shore of the Gulf of St. Lawrence, lower St. Lawrence River west at least to Ile aux Lièvres, Anticosti, and Magdalen Islands), Newfoundland and the Maritime Provinces. Also rarely and very locally inland in southern Ontario (Little Haystack Rock, Lake Huron; Presqu'ile Park). Non-breeding wanderers occur north at least to southern Baffin Island (Bowman Bay) and west to Hudson Bay (Chesterfield Inlet, Great Whale River). Sight records of black-backed gulls reported from the high Arctic may refer to this species.

Winters mainly on the east coast from the Strait of Belle Isle southward: Newfoundland, coastal southern Quebec, New Brunswick, Prince Edward Island, and Nova Scotia; also small numbers on St. Lawrence River (Quebec, Montreal), and on lakes Ontario, Erie, and Huron.

[**Slaty-backed Gull.** Le Goéland à manteau ardoisé. *Larus schistisagus* Stejneger. L. 24 to 27.5 in. *Adults:* Similar to both Western and Great Black-backed in appearance but intermediate between them in size.

Resembles Western Gull but somewhat larger (wing of male 430–472; of female 405–452 mm), iris yellowish (instead of dark), eye-ring reddish (instead of yellow), and wing pattern with longer tongues of grey and a white spot on usually two primaries. Similar also to Great Black-backed Gull but considerably smaller; mantle paler (slaty rather than black); and white areas on outer primaries more extensive.

Range. Breeds from extreme western Siberia (Gulf of Anadyr), Kamchatka, and Commander Islands south through the Kuriles to Hokkaido, Japan.

Status in Canada. Hypothetical. One male (Museum of Comparative Zoology) was, according to the label, collected from the nest on Harrowby Bay, Mackenzie, on June 9, 1901, by Captain H. H. Bodfish (Bent, 1921) while he was in charge of a whaling expedition that had wintered on Baillie Island nearby. There is no other evidence that this east Asian gull ever bred on this continent. Bodfish in his narrative *Chasing the Bowhead* does not mention taking any such gull in Canada, and his itinerary shows that he visited the Siberian coast on his way north in June of the previous year. A distinct possibility exists that the specimen was actually taken in Siberia on the voyage north and was perhaps later erroneously labelled from memory.]

WESTERN GULL

Le Goéland de l'Ouest. *Larus occidentalis* Audubon
Plate 33. L. 24 to 27 in.

Adults: The dark mantle distinguishes it from other common Pacific Coast gulls except the otherwise very different Heermann's Gull (*see* Field Marks). Its wing tips (white spot on only the outermost primary; inner webs of outermost primaries usually without grey tongues) and in life yellow eye-ring and dark iris distinguish it from the dark Siberian race of the Herring Gull (*L. a. vegae*), and these characters plus smaller size from the Slaty-backed Gull, which is of accidental occurrence in North America. *First-year:* The much darker primaries distinguish it from the Glaucous-winged; relatively deeper bill and more evenly dark tail (less light spotting or marbling) from the Herring Gull; heavier bill and darker general coloration from the California Gull in first-year dress.

Measurements. *Adult male:* wing, 400–420 (412.3); tail, 166–177 (170); exposed culmen, 52–58 (55.6); tarsus, 65–74 (69.2). *Adult female:* wing, 384–408 (397.6) mm (J. Dwight).

Field Marks. *Adults:* A large dark-backed gull with white head, tail, and under parts, yellow bill with red spot, and pinkish legs. The dark back and upper surface of the wings distinguish it from all other common Pacific Coast gulls except the Heermann's, from which it differs in its yellow bill, pink legs, white under parts, white tail, and much larger size. First-year Westerns are less easily distinguished, but they can be recognized from other large gulls of similar age by characters given in the first paragraph.

Habitat. Sea-coasts of the Pacific.

Range. Breeds on the Pacific Coast from northern Washington (Destruction Island) south to Baja California and the coast of Sonora. Winters in much of its breeding range and north to southern coastal British Columbia.

Range in Canada. Regular winter visitor in small numbers to the coast of southern British Columbia (mainly Vancouver Island; also Seymour Inlet).

Subspecies. *Larus occidentalis occidentalis* Audubon is the only race so far ascertained to occur in Canada. Additional races breed in west coastal United States.

HERRING GULL

Le Goéland argenté. *Larus argentatus* Pontoppidan
Plates 32, 33. L. 23 to 26 in.

A large, broadly distributed gull, widely known as 'sea-gull.' *Adults* (*L. a. smithsonianus*): Mantle pearl grey. Wing tips black, each feather tipped white; outermost primary with large white spot usually separated from white tip by a narrow, sometimes broken, black bar; ninth primary with or without a small white spot; a tongue of grey extends out from base of primaries usually not reaching white spot on either ninth or tenth primaries. Head, neck, tail, and under parts white (in winter head and neck more or less streaked dusky). Bill yellow with red spot on lower mandible; iris yellow, occasionally lightly freckled with brown; eye-ring yellowish; legs pinkish flesh. *First-year* birds are mottled brown in general colour with plain dark brown wing tips, dark bill, and brown irides. *Second-winter* birds, paler brown more mixed with white, and with some grey beginning to show in the mantle; unevenly banded tail; basal part of the bill and extreme tip, flesh; remainder dark. *Third-winter* birds show extensive grey in the mantle, pale bill with enough dark coloration often remaining to form a dark band somewhat similar to that of adults of the smaller Ring-billed Gull.

The combination of pearl grey mantle, blackish wing tips, and flesh-coloured legs separates adults from those of other larger Canadian gulls except Thayer's Gull, which has a different wing tip pattern and a reddish eye-ring.

Measurements (*L. a. smithsonianus*). *Adult male:* wing, 414–462 (432.7); tail, 167–192.5 (176.4); exposed culmen, 57–61.5 (59.4); tarsus, 66–70.9 (68.4). *Adult female:* wing, 400.5–430 (403.2) mm.

Field Marks. A largish gull. Adults with pearl grey mantle, white-spotted black wing tips, and pinkish flesh legs. The pearl grey mantle distinguishes it from adults of the Great Black-backed and Western; blackish wing tips from Glaucous, Iceland, and Glaucous-winged; flesh-coloured legs from adult Ring-billed (which has a black band on the bill and no red spot), adult California (which often has a black spot on the bill in addition to the red one), Mew Gull (which is much smaller with no red spot on bill), and the smaller Black-legged Kittiwake. Very similar to Thayer's Gull and probably not distinguishable in the field, unless the sometimes darker wing tips or yellowish eye-ring (instead of reddish) of the Herring can be discerned.

First-year bird is mottled brown, with dark bill and eye. The dark wing tips distinguish it from the Glaucous, the Iceland, and the Glaucous-winged. Darker body colour, particularly below, from first-year Great Black-backed. First-year Herring Gull has a darker body than first-year Ring-billed, and the all-dark tail is very different from the banded tail of immatures of that species, but leg colour is not reliable as young Ring-bills sometimes have pinkish legs also. Very similar to first-year Western Gull, but under excellent conditions the Herring's slenderer bill may help to distinguish it. Not usually safely separable from first-autumn California Gull in the field, although yearling California Gull shows a flesh-coloured base of the bill and

a dark tip, while first-year Herring has a mainly dark bill. In succeeding plumages Herring Gull often shows a dark terminal band on the tail, suggestive of immature Ring-billed, but in the latter the band is usually (not always) narrower, more uniform in width, and more sharply defined. In doubtful cases the smaller size of the Ring-bill is apparent if the two are together.

Habitat. Various types of shores and islands on the coast as well as inland freshwater lakes and rivers. Often feeds at dumps, canneries, open fields; frequently follows ships but seldom to great distances from land.

Nesting. Mostly in colonies of various sizes, sometimes in single pairs, not infrequently with other species like cormorants, terns, and other gulls. Nest is usually on the ground, a depression lined (sometimes very sparsely) with grass, moss, seaweed, or sometimes vegetation and rubbish. Most often on coastal islands, or on islands and boulders in inland lakes and rivers, situations varying from low islets to the flat tops and ledges of high ones; also on cliff ledges and occasionally in trees. *Eggs*, usually 2 or 3; vary from bluish grey to brownish with irregular spots and blotches of dark brown and some lilac. Incubation, variously recorded, 25 to 28 days, the greater part by the female.

Range. In North America from central and north-central Canada and western Greenland south to western interior Canada, northern Minnesota, central Wisconsin, central Michigan, northern New York (south along the coast to Long Island), and casually to north coastal Virginia; also in Iceland, Europe, and northern Siberia. Winters from southern parts of the breeding range south to the West Indies, Panama, northern and central Africa, Indo-China, and the northern Philippines.

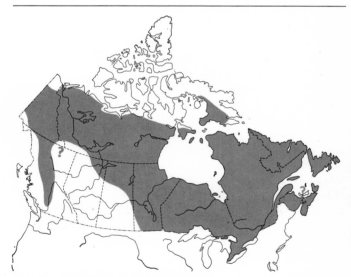

Breeding Distribution of Herring Gull

Range in Canada. Breeds from interior Yukon, northern Mackenzie (wooded parts of Mackenzie Delta; inland 15 to 25 miles from the coast at Perry River), southern and central Keewatin, northern Melville Peninsula (probably), Southampton Island (Bay of God's Mercy, Prairie Point), and central-western and southern Baffin Island (Straits Bay,

Taverner Bay, Dorset, Frobisher Bay) south (except on the Pacific Coast) to south-central interior British Columbia (108 Mile Lake, Bridge Lake), northeastern Alberta (Lake Athabasca), northern Saskatchewan (Lake Athabasca, Peter Pond Lake), southern Manitoba (Lake Winnipeg, Shoal Lake), southern Ontario (lakes Erie and Ontario), southern Quebec (commonly in northern and eastern parts south to Magdalen Islands; locally in extreme southwest: Lac des Isles, Lac Simon, Razades, Basques, and Pèlerin islands), Labrador, Newfoundland, New Brunswick, Nova Scotia, and Prince Edward Island.

Common to abundant in migration in most parts of southern Canada including the Pacific Coast but is not frequently reported from southern parts of Alberta or Saskatchewan. Winters on the coast of British Columbia, the southern Great Lakes, St. Lawrence River, and along the Atlantic Coast from Newfoundland through the Maritimes.

Subspecies. (1) *Larus argentatus smithsonianus* Coues occupies the range outlined above. (2) *L. a. vegae* Palmén, characterized by somewhat larger size and much darker mantle, is a casual visitant from Siberia to coastal B.C. (one specimen record: Henderson L., Vancouver I., November 27, 1922). *Larus thayeri* Brooks, treated as a subspecies of *L. argentatus* by many authors (A.O.U. *Check-list of North American Birds*, Fifth Edition), is here regarded as a separate species.

Remarks. Although the name 'sea gull' has no official status, it has wide popular usage with reference to large gulls in general. Probably the Herring Gull is the species most often called 'sea gull'; this, despite the fact that it is widely distributed in the interior as well as on the coast and rarely travels very far out on the ocean.

The Herring Gull is largely a scavenger, often gathering in noisy numbers about fishing boats and fish-processing plants for the offal thrown on the water. It scavenges also at garbage dumps and sewer outlets; and along the shores it cleans up dead or stranded aquatic animals in great numbers. Its menu includes fishes and marine and freshwater invertebrates of many kinds; occasionally eggs and young of other birds. Sometimes it flocks to the fields where it devours larger insects, especially grasshoppers; occasionally mice. Often it takes wild berries like blueberries or crowberries.

It is a lively and graceful addition to our waterways, and our shores would indeed be duller places without it and its numerous interesting congeners.

THAYER'S GULL

Le Goéland de Thayer. *Larus thayeri* Brooks
Plate 32. L. ca. 22.5 to 25.0 in.

Very similar to Herring Gull but differs as follows: *Adults:* Wing tips with black areas less extensive and often decidedly paler or greyish; the white tongue in outermost primary often joining a long white tip and on the next primary reaching to, or nearly to, the white spot; mantle slightly darker grey; irides, lightly to heavily speckled with brown or grey; eye-ring red or purplish; size averages smaller. *First-year* birds variable, often very similar to those of Herring Gull but usually distinguishable by paler wing

tips which often are as pale as those of first-year Glaucous-winged Gull.

Measurements. *Adult male:* wing, 397–425.5 (411.4); tail, 160.5–186 (172.3); exposed culmen, 47.1–52.7 (50.6); tarsus, 62.5–66.2 (64.5). *Adult female:* wing, 361.5–408.5 (390.1)mm.

Field Marks. Very similar to Herring Gull. Some adults have obviously paler wing tips, but in many individuals these are as black as in the Herring Gull; in adults with heavily speckled irides the eye appears dark. Most immatures not safely distinguishable from young Herring or Glaucous-winged.

Habitat. In the breeding season, arctic shores and islands, breeding on ledges of coastal or near-coastal cliffs. In winter, the Pacific Coast. Primarily a saltwater gull, but migrants or non-breeders visit freshwater lakes and rivers in Yukon and northern Mackenzie.

Nesting. Nest of grass and other available vegetation is placed on a cliff ledge usually at salt water but sometimes at fresh water near the coast. *Eggs*, usually 2 or 3; similar in coloration to those of Herring Gull.

Range. Breeds in arctic Canada and in a small area in northwest Greenland (Middle Thule District). Winters on the Pacific Coast of North America from southern British Columbia south to California; casually to central Baja California.

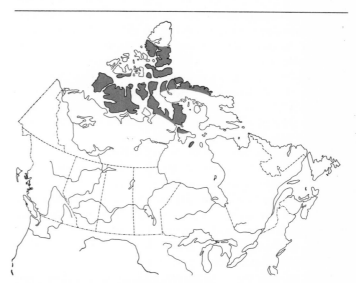

Breeding Distribution of Thayer's Gull

Range in Canada. Breeds in the Arctic from Banks Island (Cape M'Clure, Cape Lambton), southern Melville Island (probably), northern Victoria Island (Minto Inlet), Prince of Wales Island, Cornwallis Island, Axel Heiberg Island (Mökka Fiord), and central Ellesmere Island (Buchanan Bay) south to southern Victoria Island (Cambridge Bay), Boothia Peninsula (Sagvak Inlet), Pelly Bay, northern Southampton Island, Coats Island (Neal Smith, in litt.), northern and central-eastern Baffin Island (south at least to Home Bay—Neal Smith, pers. comm.).

Casual in summer in northwestern Saskatchewan (Lake Athabasca).

Winters in coastal British Columbia.

Remarks. *Larus thayeri* has been treated as a subspecies of *L. argentatus* (A.O.U. *Check-list of North American Birds*, Fifth Edition) and by other authors as a subspecies of *L. glaucoides*. It is now known to breed sympatrically with *L. argentatus* (A. H. Macpherson, 1961, Arctic Inst. North America, Tech. Pap. 7: 1–40; Neal Smith, in litt.) and, in the Home Bay region of central-eastern Baffin Island, with *L. g. kumlieni* (Neal Smith, pers. comm.). For these reasons it is here treated as a separate species.

CALIFORNIA GULL
Le Goéland de Californie. *Larus californicus* Lawrence
Plate 32. L. 20.5 to 23.0 in.

Adults similar to Herring Gull (*L. a. smithsonianus*) but differ as follows: Legs greenish to yellowish; lower mandible with usually a black spot or bar in addition to a red spot; iris usually brown, sometimes grey; eye-ring reddish; gape orange to reddish; mantle averages darker grey; size averages smaller, sex for sex. Outermost primary more often with long all-white tip, but this often crossed by a subterminal black bar similar to that of Herring Gull. Similar also to Thayer's Gull, but adult Thayer's has different wing tip pattern (grey tongue on two outermost primaries usually reaches the white mirrors), flesh-coloured legs, and lacks any black spot on the bill. *First-year* California Gull closely resembles Herring Gull of similar age, but by late summer the basal half of the bill becomes flesh coloured, contrasting with dark tip instead of remaining mostly dark as in first-year Herring. Resembles first year Ring-billed Gull, but the body plumage is darker and more uniform, the under parts less whitish and more uniform (less spotted). Like the Herring Gull, adult plumage is not attained until the fourth year (For details *see* Behle and Selander, *The Auk* 70: 239–260).

Measurements. *Adult male:* wing, 369–419.5 (391.7); tail, 142.8–171 (153.6); exposed culmen, 44.9–55 (49.5); tarsus, 55–64.5 (60.5). *Adult female:* wing, 361.5–386.5 (375) mm.

Field Marks. Adults similar to Herring Gull but distinguishable by greenish or yellowish legs, and often by the presence of a blackish area (not always present) in addition to the red one on the lower mandible. Ring-billed and Mew Gulls both are similar to California Gull and, like it, have greenish legs, but the Ring-billed has a well-defined black band around the bill and no red spot, and the Mew Gull, a smaller species, has a plain greenish-yellow bill. First-year California Gull is a somewhat darker bird with less spotted under parts than first-year Ring-billed, and the tail is dark (the Ring-bill has a white tail with a sharply-defined dark subterminal bar). In later plumages the California shows a dark bar across the end of the tail, but it is usually broader and less well defined than in the Ring-billed. Many immatures of the two species are difficult to separate in the field.

Habitat. In nesting season the vicinity of inland freshwater and alkaline lakes, rivers, and marshes, but the birds also spread out over wide areas to fields, especially newly-plowed ones. In migration frequents also various coastal situations.

Nesting. Nests in colonies, often with Ring-billed Gulls and other birds, on islands of lakes, marshes, and rivers. Nest, a depression in the ground or on bare rock, lined with grass, weeds, and rubbish, often sparsely; but nest sometimes a substantial structure up to a foot high. *Eggs,* usually 3; similar to those of other large gulls but often more boldly marked. Variable from bluish white to buffy brown, spotted and often boldly marked with browns and some purplish grey. Average incubation time for first egg, 26.7 days; the second, 25; the third, 23.6 in Utah (Behle and Goates).

Range. Breeds from interior Mackenzie south through the Canadian Prairie Provinces to Washington (Benton County), southeastern Oregon, northeastern California, northwestern Utah, northwestern Wyoming, central Montana, and east-central North Dakota. Winters from southern Washington south along the Pacific coast to Guatemala.

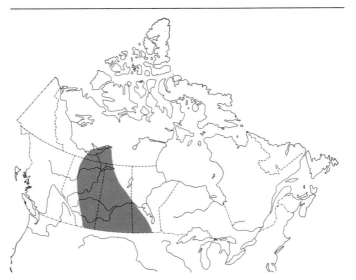

Breeding Distribution of California Gull

Range in Canada. Breeds in southern Mackenzie (Great Slave Lake), Alberta (east of the mountains: Lake Athabasca, Lac la Biche, Lake Winnifred, Camrose, Lake Newell near Brooks); Saskatchewan (Lake Athabasca, Redberry Lake, Last Mountain Lake, Bigstick Lake) and southern Manitoba (Dog Lake).

In migration, spring and autumn, small numbers occur on the south coast and in the interior of British Columbia and in the mountains of southwestern Alberta (Jasper, Banff).

RING-BILLED GULL
Le Goéland à bec cerclé. *Larus delawarensis* Ord
Plate 33. L. 18 to 20 in.

Adult is a grey-mantled gull with black wing tips (two outermost primaries with a white subterminal spot), and with remainder of plumage white; decidedly smaller than the Herring and somewhat smaller than the California Gull. Adults with black band across yellow bill, yellow iris, reddish eye-ring and gape, greenish-yellow legs. The black band on the bill with no red on lower mandible distinguishes adults from adults of other gulls. In the California Gull when black is present on the bill, a red spot also is present on lower mandible. Some immatures of other gulls (e.g., third-year Herring) often show a more or less well-marked black band on the bill but show signs of immaturity by presence of dusky feathers in tail, mantle, or under parts; such Herring Gulls often have a faint red spot on lower mandible, which the Ring-billed never has.

First-year Ring-billed, like most gulls of similar age, has much brown in the body plumage and dark brown wing tips, but compared with Herring, Thayer's, Western, California, and Mew gulls it has a decidedly greater amount of white in the body plumage, especially the under parts which appear white mottled with brown, instead of rather uniform dark brown or grey. Tail with usually a narrow, dark, sharply defined subterminal band of uniform width. (In some individuals, however, this band is poorly defined, and therefore for identification purposes this character cannot always be relied upon.) Iris, brown; basal part of bill flesh, tip dark; legs pinkish or greyish. The first feathers of the grey mantle appear in the first winter, and it assumes adult plumage early in its third year. In the hand, smaller size easily distinguishes otherwise doubtful specimens from Herring, Thayer's, and Western gulls, and usually from the California Gull. The Ring-billed is only slightly larger than the Mew Gull, which is rather similar in first year. The Ring-billed has much whiter brown-mottled under parts (first-year Mew Gull more uniform dark grey), and its upper parts have more whitish feather edges, and dark parts are paler, more brownish (less greyish).

Measurements. *Adult male:* wing, 362–383.3 (369.9); tail, 139–152 (146.8); exposed culmen, 37.8–44 (40.9); tarsus, 53–62 (58.1). *Adult female:* wing, 339.5–377 (353.5) mm.

Field Marks. Smaller than Herring Gull, but size is useful only when the two are together. Black band on yellow bill (no red spot) and greenish-yellow legs distinguish adults from adults of other gulls. Third-year Herring Gull sometimes shows a black band-like area on bill, but the Herring is larger with pinkish legs. California Gull adult frequently shows a black area on bill but also a red spot on the lower mandible which Ring-billed lacks. First-year Ring-billed Gull is more whitish, particularly in under parts, than other gulls of similar age with which it is likely to be confused. Tail with dark narrow band, usually of even width and very sharply defined (second-year Herring and California Gulls show a dark tail band, but it is poorly defined and usually not of even width. However the occasional Ring-billed also has the tail band poorly defined, and this difference is by no means infallible). Paler, more spotted body coloration, especially under parts, separates it from first-year Mew Gull.

Habitat. Shores, islands, and water surfaces of freshwater lakes, ponds, and rivers, and saltwater shores on the coast; commonly frequents also garbage dumps and fields (especially newly plowed ones); follows boats.

Nesting. In colonies often with other species, usually on islands (sometimes beaches, etc.) in fresh or alkaline waters in the interior and on islands in salt water off the coast. Nest on the ground, of grass, weeds, and rubbish. *Eggs*, usually 3; buffy, variously spotted and blotched with browns and some underlying purplish grey. Incubation period in incubator, 26 to 27 days (James Moffitt).

Range. Breeds from southern Canada south to northeastern California, central Idaho, central Colorado, northeastern South Dakota, northern Michigan, southern Ontario, and northern New York. Winters from Oregon, the lower Great Lakes (where water remains open), and Maine south into Mexico.

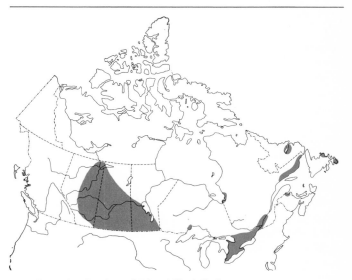

Breeding Distribution of Ring-billed Gull

Range in Canada. Breeds in Alberta (east of the mountains: Lake Athabasca, Lac la Biche, Buffalo Lake, Lake Newell), Saskatchewan (Kazan Lake, Redberry Lake, Maple Creek, Last Mountain Lake), south-central and southern Manitoba (north at least to Moose Lake), southern Ontario (Black Bay on Lake Superior, North Channel, Georgian Bay, Lake Erie, Lake Ontario), southern Quebec (locally: north shore of the Gulf of St. Lawrence: Betchouane, Gull Island, Green Island, Parson Island, Romaine, Fog Island, St. Augustin; mouth of Eastmain River; also near St. Lambert. Reports of breeding on Hudson Bay require confirmation), southern Labrador (Lake Melville), Newfoundland (Browsey Island, South Penguin Island); recently northeastern New Brunswick (Bathurst Harbour).

Non-breeding birds are reported in summer in interior British Columbia, southern Mackenzie (Great Slave Lake), southern Keewatin (Nueltin Lake), Hudson Bay, Prince Edward Island, and probably elsewhere in the Maritimes.

In migration, found also in southern British Columbia (but scarce on coast), Gaspé Peninsula, New Brunswick, Prince Edward Island, and Nova Scotia. Winters in extreme southern Ontario (lower Great Lakes, where water remains open); rarely southern Nova Scotia (Yarmouth).

Remarks. These gulls eat insects, grubs, worms, and occasionally mice or the eggs of other birds. They often congregate where grasshoppers abound and gorge themselves on the insects. They are useful scavengers.

MEW GULL (Short-billed Gull)
Le Goéland cendré. *Larus canus* Linnaeus
Plate 32. L. 16 to 18 in.

Adults: Grey mantle; black wing tips, the primaries tipped with white and the outermost two with a large white subapical spot; rest of plumage white (in winter, head and neck streaked with dusky); bill plain greenish yellow; irides variable, brown to grey, often flecked with yellow; eye-ring red; legs yellowish green. Small size separates it from all similar gulls except Kittiwake (which lacks white subapical spots on primaries and has no well-developed hind toe). *First-year* Mew Gull is similar in plumage coloration to first-year Herring or California gulls but has a dark terminal tail band, rather poorly defined against the grey basal two-thirds of tail. Compared with first-year Ring-billed, it has darker more uniform body plumage, and the basal part of the tail is darker grey. Adult plumage is acquired with assumption of third-winter dress.

Measurements. *Adult male:* wing, 324–360.5 (346.7); tail, 129–149 (139.9); exposed culmen, 32–36.3 (34.1); tarsus, 49–53.2 (50.8). *Adult female:* wing, 321–350.5 (335.5) mm.

Field Marks. A small gull of the Northwest and Pacific coasts with general Herring Gull type of plumage coloration. Adults with relatively small, plain, greenish-yellow bill without any red or black markings, thus different from Ring-billed and California gulls; also shows more white in wing tip and is smaller than those gulls. Obviously smaller than Herring and Thayer's gulls. The Kittiwake, also a small gull, has no white spots in the black wing tip.

Habitat. In nesting season, marshes, lakes, and rivers. In migration and winter, marine outer coasts, harbours, bays, mud flats, beaches, garbage dumps, often with the larger gulls.

Nesting. Both in colonies and as solitary pairs. Nest usually on the ground about lakes or on islands in marshy places; sandpits; occasionally in trees. *Eggs*, usually 3, less often 2; buffy variously marked with browns. Incubation 22 to 23 days, probably sometimes longer (*in* Witherby) by both sexes.

Range. Breeds in central and southern Alaska, northwestern continental and west coastal Canada; also across Europe and Asia from near the Arctic Circle south to the British Isles, Netherlands, the Black and Caspian seas, northern Mongolia, Kamchatka, and the Kuriles. Winters from southeastern Alaska to southern California; in Europe south to the Mediterranean Sea, and in eastern Asia on the coasts of China and Japan to Formosa.

Range in Canada. Breeds in southern Yukon (commonly; north probably at least to Dawson), Mackenzie (Mackenzie Delta, Fort Anderson, mouth of Horton River, Great Slave Lake, Fort Smith; perhaps east to Thelon River marshes), northwestern Saskatchewan (Lake Athabasca); also northwestern and coastal British Columbia (Atlin Lake and locally southward on the coast to Kennedy Lake, Vancouver Island).

In migration, regularly through interior British Columbia, northern Alberta, and northern Yukon (Old Crow). Rare in southern Alberta (Brooks, Camrose, Jasper). Recorded in

Breeding Distribution of Mew Gull

summer north to the arctic coast of Mackenzie (Baillie Island), east to Thelon River marshes, and northeastern Saskatchewan (Reindeer Lake).

Winters commonly on British Columbia coast.

Subspecies. (1) *Larus canus brachyrhynchus* Richardson is the breeding form. (2) *L. c. canus* Linnaeus is a casual visitor (Specimen at Locks Cove, Nfld., April 19, 1956, had been banded as a chick on the White Sea).

BLACK-HEADED GULL
La Mouette rieuse d'Europe. *Larus ridibundus* Linnaeus
Plate 34. L. 14 to 15 in.

Adults (breeding plumage): Head dark brown, a narrow white border behind eye; mantle grey; wing pattern similar to that of Bonaparte's Gull but inner edge of inner webs of primaries blackish; rest of plumage white; bill and legs crimson. *Adults (winter):* Similar to summer adults but head largely white with small dark patch in front of eye and a larger patch on ear coverts with varying amounts of greyish brown on hind crown and nape. *First-winter* birds similar to winter adults but with some brownish feathers in the grey mantle, a black band across the end of the tail, duller wing tips with white areas more restricted, bill flesh with dark tip, legs yellowish flesh. It is somewhat larger than Bonaparte's Gull.

Measurements. *Adult male:* wing, 284–315 (300); tail, 113–124 (117.5); exposed culmen, 31–37 (33.6); tarsus, 43–47 (44.7). *Adult female:* wing, 280–297 (288.2) mm (J. Dwight).

Field Marks. A rare visitor from the Old World. Closely resembles Bonaparte's Gull (often accompanies it), with similar wing pattern but is larger with relatively longer, differently coloured bill. *Adults:* Similar to Bonaparte's Gull but bill reddish, under side of wing tip much more extensively blackish, with mainly the outermost primary showing white (Plate 34), head in breeding plumage dark brown instead of black. First-winter birds are similar to Bonaparte Gull but bill slightly longer, flesh basally with blackish tip.

Range. Breeds in Iceland, the Faroes, and across Eurasia to Kamchatka.

Status in Canada. Rare non-breeding visitant to Labrador (Stag Bay: specimen banded in Holland), Newfoundland (Badger, Green Island, Chapel Arm, Placentia, Fermeuse), and Nova Scotia (Halifax, Cole Harbour – Chezzetcook area, Port Hawkesbury) and Quebec (Havre St. Pierre). In recent years, at least, a regular winter visitor in small numbers to Newfoundland, Nova Scotia, and New Brunswick. Rare visitor to southern Ontario (Oshawa, July 23, 1963. Sight records have been reported from Hamilton, Niagara River, Toronto, Whitby).

Subspecies. *Larus ridibundus ridibundus* Linnaeus.

LAUGHING GULL

La Mouette rieuse d'Amérique. *Larus atricilla* Linnaeus
Plate 34. L. 15 to 17 in.

Adult a smallish, white-bodied, grey-mantled gull of the Atlantic Coast; in breeding plumage with black head; primaries black with *no white spots*, only narrowly tipped with white, the *outermost and usually the next* without white tip. Mantle darker than that of other small east coast gulls. *First-autumn:* Upper parts greyish brown, feather edges pale; wing tips brownish black, all but outermost primaries tipped white; secondaries white tipped; rump and upper tail coverts white; tail with dark subterminal bar; throat and breast greyish brown blending into white on abdomen; bill blackish; legs brownish.

Measurements. *Adult male:* wing, 308–330 (321); tail, 113–133 (122.6); exposed culmen, 37–44 (40.2); tarsus, 50–54 (51.6). *Adult female:* wing, 295–326 (312.3) mm (J. Dwight).

Field Marks. Adult a small gull of the Atlantic Coast with dark grey mantle, a white line along hind edge of spread wing, primaries appearing all black (adults of other gulls show light areas in primaries; Kittiwake shows no white spots in primaries, but only the tips are black), reddish bill, and in breeding season a black head. Because of its black head it is most likely to be confused with Bonaparte Gull but is a somewhat larger bird with darker mantle, dark reddish bill. *First-autumn:* Slightly smaller than Ring-billed Gull, but darker; breast darker, uniform grey, not spotted.

Habitat. Coastal: harbours, river mouths, coastal islands, mud flats, occasionally wanders inland on rivers or lakes.

Nesting. Usually in colonies. Nest on the ground of grass and weeds. *Eggs,* usually 3; buffy to olive with spots and blotches of brown and some underlying grey or purplish. Incubation reportedly about 20 days (A. C. Bent).

Range. Breeds from southern Nova Scotia south locally along the Atlantic Coast to Florida, the Bahamas, and Greater and Lesser Antilles; around the Gulf of Mexico in Florida, Louisiana, Texas, and Mexico; off northern Venezuela; and Salton Sea, southern California south to the coasts of Sonora and Sinaloa. Winters on the coasts from North Carolina and the Gulf of Mexico south to northern South America and on the Pacific Coast from southern Mexico to Ecuador.

Range in Canada. Breeds very locally in Nova Scotia

(islands off Halifax County) and southern New Brunswick (Machias Seal Island). Casual in Prince Edward Island (Wood Island) and Newfoundland (Burnt Islands, Grey River, Isle-aux-Morts, Boswarlos, all in 1958); southern Quebec (Montreal), and southern Ontario (various records on lakes Ontario and Erie); accidental in northern Ontario (Winisk).

FRANKLIN'S GULL

La Mouette de Franklin. *Larus pipixcan* Wagler
Plate 34. L. 13.5 to 15.5 in.

Adults with basal part of central tail feathers grey, thus differing from other white-tailed gulls. In breeding season adults have a black head, thus resembling Bonaparte's and Laughing gulls (*see* Field Marks). Larger than Bonaparte's, slightly smaller than Laughing. First-year birds similar to those of Laughing Gull but smaller, usually paler on breast, and with subterminal dark tail band not extending to outer tail feathers.

Measurements. *Adult male:* wing, 262.5–290 (279.7); tail, 95.4–109.3 (104.9); exposed culmen, 28–31 (29.5); tarsus, 39.5–45 (42.8). *Adult female:* wing, 261–285 (273.1) mm.

Breeding Distribution of Franklin's Gull

Field Marks. A smallish gull of the prairies. Adults in breeding plumage with black head thus resembling Bonaparte's, from which Franklin's differs in larger size, stouter *red* bill, and very different wing tip pattern in flight (Plate 34). First-year birds of both species have dark tail band, but Franklin's has much grey on crown and face (Bonaparte's shows well-defined dark ear spot) and dark white-tipped primaries (Bonaparte's shows long tongues of white reaching to near primary tips). It closely resembles Laughing Gull, but the two are widely separated geographically except as wanderers to the Great Lakes. The large amount of white in the spread wing tip of Franklin's distinguishes adults from those of Laughing Gull. First-year birds of the two are more difficult to separate in the field, but Franklin's usually has a paler breast and forehead.

183

Habitat. In the breeding season, prairie lakes and marshes; foraging regularly on grassy fields and ploughed land, often in large numbers.

Nesting. In colonies. Nest, a floating anchored mass of marsh vegetation in lake or marsh. *Eggs*, usually 3; buffy or greenish brown, variously spotted and blotched with browns.

Range. Breeds from the Prairie Provinces of Canada south to eastern Oregon, northwestern Utah, south-central Montana, northeastern South Dakota, and northwestern Iowa. Winters in the Pacific from Guatemala south to the Gulf of Panama, the Galápagos Islands, and Chile; also coastal Louisiana and Texas.

Range in Canada. Breeds commonly in Alberta (east of the mountains: Many Island Lake, Beaverhill Lake, Lake Athabasca), central and southern Saskatchewan (north to Kazan and Torch lakes), and southwestern Manitoba (Overflowing River and Lake Winnipeg southward).

Recorded in summer in central-eastern British Columbia (Peace River District) and northeastern Manitoba (Hayes River). Migration from breeding grounds mainly southward. Uncommon transient in British Columbia (Okanagan Lake, Alta Lake, Sirdar Lake, Comox) and southern Ontario (Toronto. Sight records east to Ottawa). Accidental in New Brunswick (Grand Manan, December 6, 1925).

Remarks. The swirling flocks and high-pitched cries of this pretty gull are a pleasant summer aspect of the prairies. In spring they descend on the freshly ploughed fields where they seek out myriads of cutworms and wire-worms. Later in the season they feast on grasshoppers.

BONAPARTE'S GULL

La Mouette de Bonaparte. *Larus philadelphia* (Ord)
Plate 34. L. 12.0 to 14.5 in.

A small gull. *Adults* with grey mantle; mainly white wing tips with broad black ends and a narrow black border on outer side of outermost primary; head black in breeding plumage, mainly white with dusky ear spot in autumn and winter; rest of plumage white; bill black; legs red. *First-year* birds similar to winter adults but have dark subterminal tail band, more black in primaries, grey mantle mixed with brown; legs flesh. Adult plumage is assumed in second autumn. Wing tip pattern (largely white, narrowly bordered by black) distinguishes it from other North American gulls. The mostly white *under side* of the wing tips distinguishes adults from Black-headed Gull.

Measurements. *Adult male:* wing, 251–273 (258.7); tail, 95.9–105.6 (101.9); exposed culmen, 27.9–30.6 (29.2); tarsus, 34.5–38.2 (36). *Adult female:* wing, 245.5–261.2 (251.5) mm.

Field Marks. A small gull. Adults in breeding plumage with black head thus resembling Franklin's, Laughing, and Black-headed gulls, but bill black instead of reddish. The largely white wing tip *with narrow black borders* flashes conspicuously in flight at considerable distances and distinguishes it at any season and age from terns and other gulls except the rare Black-headed. The under side of the wing tip in Bonaparte's is mostly white (in Black-headed, dark with the outer primary showing white). Winter adult and immature Bonaparte's have mainly white head with a conspicuous dark ear patch.

Habitat. For nesting, the vicinity of muskegs, ponds, and lakes in coniferous woodland. Post-breeders and non-breeders frequent lakes, rivers, marshes, coastal bays and harbours, sand bars, and mud flats.

Nesting. Nest is placed in a coniferous tree usually in the vicinity of a muskeg lake or pond and is composed of twigs, grass, moss, and lichen. *Eggs*, usually 3; buffy grey to buffy green, spotted and blotched with browns. Incubation period 23 days, 20 hours (D. F. Parmelee); 24 days (J. R. Jehl and D. J. T. Hussell).

Range. Breeds in western and central Alaska and in the coniferous belt of western and central Canada. Winters from southern British Columbia, lakes Erie and Ontario, and Massachusetts south to northern Mexico, Bermuda, Cuba, and Haiti.

Range in Canada. Breeds from southern Yukon (Canyon–Aishihik lakes, Lapie and Pelly rivers) northwestern interior Mackenzie (Anderson River, Keith Arm), northern Saskatchewan (Black Lake), and northeastern Manitoba (Churchill) south to south-central interior British Columbia (Kleena Kleene, Bridge Lake), central Alberta (between Camrose and Edmonton), central Saskatchewan (10 miles southwest of Glaslyn; Nipawin), south-central Manitoba (Riding Mountain), and central Ontario (Lake Miminiska, Rat Rapids, probably Schumacher), and James Bay (near the Ontario-Quebec boundary).

More or less common migrant south of breeding range and on the Pacific Coast; also in southern Ontario, southern Quebec (St. Lawrence River, inner north shore of the Gulf of St. Lawrence, Lake St. John, Gaspé Peninsula, Magdalen Islands), New Brunswick, Prince Edward Island, and Nova Scotia. Scarce visitant to Newfoundland (Bonavista, Stephenville Crossing, Chance Cove, Fermeuse). Records for Labrador require confirmation. Non-breeders are commonly found in summer outside the breeding range. Rare or casual in winter in southwestern British Columbia (Georgia Strait), and southern Ontario (Hamilton, Toronto).

Breeding Distribution of Bonaparte's Gull

LITTLE GULL

La Mouette pygmée. *Larus minutus* Pallas
Plate 34. L. about 11 in.

Our smallest gull.

Measurements. *Adult male:* wing, 210–230 (220.5); tail, 85–95 (91.9); exposed culmen, 21–25 (23.2); tarsus, 25–28 (26.5). *Adult female:* wing, 212–227 (220.5) mm (J. Dwight).

Field Marks. Diminutive size. Smaller than Bonaparte's Gull, which it resembles and often associates with. Adults in summer with black head, reddish brown bill; in winter, mainly white head with dark ear patch and often a slaty patch on hind crown. Adults at all seasons are identifiable in flight by dark under surface of wings and plain grey white-tipped upper side of primaries (occasionally one, perhaps not mature, has outermost web of outermost primary black, with black smudges on other primaries and with paler grey wing linings). First-year birds have under side of wing white, a black ear spot, and a black terminal band, thus very similar to Bonaparte's of similar age, but Little Gull shows in flight a blackish bar diagonally across the upper surface of wing which *continues around the bend of wing to join the base of the black primaries;* also the Little Gull shows more extensive black in wing tips. Young Sabine's Gull and Kittiwake also have a dark bar diagonally across upper wing, but Sabine's Gull has a forked tail and the young Kittiwake shows a black bar across back of neck.

Status in Canada. Until recently it was considered a scarce, non-breeding visitant from the Old World. In 1962, however, a few were found nesting at Oshawa, Ontario (J. L. Baillie, Jr., pers. comm.), the first known breeding record for the Western Hemisphere. Previously it was known in Canada as follows—Southern Ontario: specimen, Toronto, October 4, 1950; numerous sight records mainly along lakes Ontario and Erie. J. L. Baillie (*Audubon Field Notes* 5: 13) considers it a rare but regular associate of Bonaparte's Gull at Niagara, Hamilton, and Toronto. Atlantic Coast: Probably more or less regular in small numbers as is indicated by several sight records in Newfoundland (L. M. Tuck), a sight record of an adult in Prince Edward Island (B. Stupart, *Ontario Field Biologist* 11: 21), old sight records for southern New Brunswick (Squires, 1952), and a sight record of an adult for Nova Scotia (Pictou, October 10, 1960—E. Holdway). The species is listed as of casual occurrence in Saskatchewan (A. O. U. Check-list, Fifth Edition), presumably on the basis of a specimen taken by Franklin's first expedition, but this is questioned by Houston (*Blue Jay* 16: 45) on the grounds that it might have been collected elsewhere. A male was collected in the Lake Athabasca region, Saskatchewan, June 28, 1962 (R. W. Nero, in litt.).

HEERMANN'S GULL

La Mouette de Heermann. *Larus heermanni* Cassin
Plate 33. L. 18 to 21 in.

Measurements. *Adult male:* wing, 337–368 (347.3); tail, 138–154 (142.3); exposed culmen, 37–48 (43.7); tarsus, 52–58 (54.8). *Adult female:* wing, 329–344 (337.7) mm (J. Dwight).

Field Marks. An easily recognized medium-sized gull of the west coast. *Adult:* Dark grey coloration above and below with white head (much obscured by dusky in autumn) white trailing edge to spread wing, black tail with white tip, red bill, and black legs. *First year:* Even more uniformly dark with black wing tips, tail, and head; bill buffy or pinkish with dark tip; legs blackish.

Habitat. Saltwater coasts and islands.

Range. Breeds on islands on the west coast of Mexico (March–June). After breeding, it migrates northward along the Pacific Coast as far as southwestern British Columbia. Winters on the Pacific Coast from Oregon to Guatemala.

Status in Canada. Fairly common non-breeding summer and early autumn visitor to south coastal British Columbia (Vancouver Island north to Alert Bay from late June to late October or early November).

IVORY GULL

La Mouette blanche. *Pagophila eburnea* (Phipps)
Plate 32. L. 15.5 to 19.3 in.

Measurements. *Adult male:* wing, 328–346 (338); tail, 141–160 (148.3); exposed culmen, 33–38 (35.9); tarsus, 37–42 (39.6). *Adult female:* wing, 320–340 (329.2) mm (J. Dwight).

Field Marks. *Adults:* The only gull having the *entire* plumage pure white with black legs. *First-year* birds also are easily recognized: a white gull with black legs, a narrow dark subterminal tail band, the flight feathers and many wing coverts tipped with blackish brown, and frequently a 'dirty face' caused by dark smudges on face and throat. Under good conditions when the gull is perched, one may see that the feathering of tibia extends down to near the top of the tarsus, and the legs therefore appear short. Less inclined to alight on water than other gulls.

Habitat. In summer, mainly high-arctic coastal situations with both permanent ice and open water; also islands, including floating ice islands; uses both flat land and cliff ledges for nesting; often ranges inland for considerable

Breeding Distribution of Ivory Gull

distances. At other seasons, mainly edges of pack-ice and drift-ice.

Nesting. In colonies either on flat ground or on cliff edges. Nest varies from a depression lined sparsely with only a few feathers to a bulky structure of moss, lichen, saxifrages, and grass. *Eggs*, 1 to 3; buffy olive, spotted or blotched with dark brown and some ashy grey. Incubation (in Spitsbergen) 24¼ to 25¼ days, by both sexes (Bateson and Plowright).

Range. Breeds in the high Arctic of Canada, northern Greenland, Spitsbergen, Franz Josef Land, Novaya Zemlya, and Severnaya Zemlya. Winters over northern drift-ice and edges of pack-ice casually south in North America to the New England coast.

Range in Canada. Breeds in the high Arctic. Range imperfectly known. Breeding localities include: northern Prince Patrick Island (Cape Krabbé), and the Polynia Islands; reefs west to Meighen Island; a floating ice island at 79° 13.2′ N, 97° 29.1′ W on June 20, 1960; and perhaps in the interior of Brodeur Peninsula and possibly Port Bowen. Reports of breeding heretofore at other localities are unsatisfactory.

Winters over arctic drift-ice south to the arctic coasts, Labrador, pack-ice off northeastern Newfoundland, and occasionally in numbers on the north shore of the Gulf of St. Lawrence (Harrington Harbour, Whale Head, Mutton Bay, Anticosti Island), more rarely in Nova Scotia and New Brunswick. Very rare in British Columbia (Penticton, Dease Lake), interior Manitoba (Egg Lake, Woodland), Ontario (Fort Albany, Oba, Toronto), and southwestern Quebec (St. Jean Port Joli, St. Raymond, Vandry).

BLACK-LEGGED KITTIWAKE (Atlantic Kittiwake)
La Mouette tridactyle. *Rissa tridactyla* (Linnaeus)
Plate 33. L. 16 to 18 in.

The rudimentary condition of the hind toe (a tiny fleshy lump with no toe nail) separates it from all our other gulls except the Red-legged Kittiwake, which is of accidental occurrence in Canada. Tail slightly forked.

Measurements. *Adult male:* wing, 295–322 (305.1); tail, 124–136 (128.5); exposed culmen, 33–39 (35.7); tarsus, 32–36 (33.6). *Adult female:* wing, 285–314 (297.9) mm (Dwight).

Field Marks. *Adults:* A smallish grey-mantled saltwater gull with the extreme wing tips sharply black (as though dipped in ink) and without white spots, bill plain yellow without red spot, legs dark brown to blackish. *First-year:* Clear white below (thus unlike most gulls at that age), grey mantle with dark bar diagonally across wing coverts, dark band across back of neck, dark ear spot, dark tail tip, and blackish bill and legs. The black band across back of neck distinguishes it from other gulls except Red-legged Kittiwake (which, however, lacks both dark band across wing coverts and dark tail band).

Habitat. Marine. In breeding season rocky coasts where cliff ledges provide nest sites. In other seasons mostly offshore and pelagic waters. Rare or accidental inland.

Nesting. In colonies, often large. Nest, a neat well-cupped structure of seaweed, grass, moss, and so on, is placed on ledges or similar projections of cliffs beside or near the sea. *Eggs*, usually 2, sometimes 1 or 3; varying from buffy to greenish or bluish, spotted and blotched with browns and grey. Incubation by both sexes, said to be 21 to 24 days (Hantzsch).

Range. Circumpolar. Breeds on islands and shores of the Arctic Ocean south to the Aleutian Islands and southern Alaska, southern Newfoundland, France, the Kurile Islands, and Sakhalin. Winters south to Baja California, southern New Jersey, northwestern Africa, and Japan.

Breeding Distribution of Black-legged Kittiwake

Range in Canada. Breeds on coasts and islands off eastern Canada: Prince Leopold, Bylot, and eastern Somerset islands (perhaps southeastern Devon Island), eastern Hudson Strait (Resolution and Button islands), southeastern Quebec (north shore of the Gulf of St. Lawrence west to Carrousel Island; Anticosti Island, Bonaventure Island, Percé Rock, Bird Rocks), and Newfoundland (commonly on cliffs on all coasts). Common in summer off Labrador but breeding not known.

Wanders widely over salt water outside breeding season to Hudson Bay, west to Victoria Island (Prince Albert Land), and north rarely to within 150 miles of the Pole (Fletcher's Ice Island, between 85° 15′ N and 86° 10′ W). Transient and winter resident on the coast of British Columbia and from the Gulf of St. Lawrence southward off New Brunswick, Nova Scotia, and more rarely Prince Edward Island. Numerous individuals banded in Greenland, the British Isles, Russia, Iceland, and Denmark have been recovered in Newfoundland and elsewhere on the Atlantic Coast. Casual or accidental inland in southern Ontario (Kingston, Toronto, Lake Nipissing).

Subspecies. (1) *Rissa tridactyla tridactyla* (Linnaeus) is the only subspecies that breeds in Canada and the only one known from Canadian localities except the Pacific Coast. (2) *R. t. pollicaris* Ridgway (longer bill and slightly larger size, slightly better developed hind toe, and slightly more extensive black on primaries) is the subspecies known to visit B.C. in migration and winter.

RED-LEGGED KITTIWAKE

La Mouette à pattes rouges. *Rissa brevirostris* (Bruch)
L. 14.0 to 15.8 in.

Adult similar to Black-legged Kittiwake but with red legs and grey (instead of white) wing linings. First-year bird similar to first-year Black-legged Kittiwake but lacks dark diagonal bar across wing coverts and has no black tip to the tail; smaller size.

Status in Canada. Accidental. Specimen found dead near Fortymile, Yukon, October 15, 1899.

ROSS'S GULL

La Mouette rosée. *Rhodostethia rosea* (MacGillivray)
Plate 34. L. 12.5 to 14.0 in.

Tail distinctly wedge-shaped. Adults (breeding plumage): Mantle grey, secondaries white-tipped; primaries grey, but outer web of outermost is black; wing linings bluish grey; fine black collar around neck; rest of plumage white with distinct rosy tinge strongest on breast; bill black, legs red. *Adults (winter plumage):* Similar to breeding plumage but lacks black neck-ring; white parts less rosy, more washed with grey. First-year birds have considerable blackish in wing coverts and wing tips, a black ear spot, black tip to tail (except outermost feathers), and as in adults the wing lining is bluish grey.

Measurements. *Adult male:* wing, 248–265 (255.1); tail, 121–138 (125.3); exposed culmen, 18–20 (19.3); tarsus, 30–33 (32.1). *Adult female:* wing, 252–260 (256) mm (J. Dwight).

Field Marks. A small gull of the Arctic, rare in Canada, with distinctly wedge-shaped tail in all plumages. Adults with rosy tinge to white of body, grey wing tips, blue-grey wing lining, and in breeding plumage a fine black collar around neck. First-year birds with boldly marked wing-pattern resemble several other small gulls but have wedge-shaped tails and blue-grey wing linings.

Habitat. In Canada, arctic drift-ice, as far as is known.

Range. Poorly known. Breeds in northern Siberia; also one breeding record at Disko Bay, Greenland. Winter range unknown but probably on open waters of the Arctic.

Status in Canada. Rare visitor to the Arctic: Boothia Peninsula (Felix Harbour), Melville Peninsula (Igloolik), Cornwallis Island, and Keewatin (McConnell River). Sight record of four, eastern Baffin Island (Broughton Island) by Neal G. Smith.

SABINE'S GULL

La Mouette de Sabine. *Xema sabini* (Sabine)
Plate 34. L. 13 to 14 in.

Distinctly forked tail distinguishes it in all plumages from other Canadian gulls.

Measurements (*X. s. sabini*). *Adult male:* wing, 259.2–278 (268.2); tail, 112.2–129 (120.4); exposed culmen, 22.4–25.4 (24.1); tarsus, 31.9–36 (33.8). *Adult female:* wing, 257–278.7 (262.8) mm.

Field Marks. No other Canadian gull has a *distinctly* forked tail (Kittiwake shows just a suggestion of forked tail). Adult in breeding plumage with dark grey hood narrowly bordered by black, black bill with yellow tip, black legs, and boldly patterned spread wing (unlike any tern) is unmistakable. Juvenal shows similar spread-wing pattern but has brown back and wing coverts, greyish brown wash on crown and face, black-tipped tail. In the Arctic it is likely to be confused only with young of the rare Ross's Gull, but the forked tail, lack of sharply marked dark ear spot, and white (instead of bluish grey) wing linings distinguish the Sabine Gull.

Habitat. In nesting season, low wet tundra and tundra lakes usually not very far inland, low coasts, and islands. Outside breeding season, mostly coastal waters, rarely on southern interior fresh water.

Nesting. Usually in small colonies, occasionally single pairs; sometimes in association with Arctic Terns. Nest a shallow depression in a tundra hummock, pond or lake edge or island, either unlined or lined with grasses and willow twigs. *Eggs,* 2 or 3; brown to olive-brown, rather faintly spotted and blotched with somewhat darker browns. Incubation, by both sexes, lasts about 21 days, 6 hours (D. F. Parmelee); also variously given by others as 23 to 26 days.

Range. Breeds on arctic coasts and islands in Alaska (south to Bristol Bay), arctic Canada, Greenland, Spitsbergen, and Siberia (south to Anadyr). Winter range poorly known but includes coastal Peru.

Breeding Distribution of Sabine's Gull

Range in Canada. Breeds on arctic coasts and islands from Banks Island (probably west coast), southern Victoria Island (Austin Bay, Cambridge Bay), Prince of Wales Island (Little Browne Bay), and Bylot Island (Canada Point) south to northwestern Mackenzie (Richards Island, Cape Bathurst, Franklin Bay), King William Island, southern Southampton Island, and southwestern Baffin Island (northern Foxe Peninsula to Taverner Bay). According to Snyder (1957) breeds also in central-eastern Ellesmere Island.

Migration is mainly along the Pacific Coast: British

187

Columbia (regular fall transient on coast, less common in spring; rare in interior). Rare migrant in the Canadian interior but recorded in Alberta, Saskatchewan, Manitoba, Ontario, and Quebec. Rare autumn visitor to Labrador (Okak, Jack Lane's Bay); casual in New Brunswick (Indian Island; Grand Manan).

Subspecies. *Xema sabini sabini* (Sabine) is the only subspecies known to breed in Canada. On the Pacific coast of B.C., *X. s. woznesenskii* Portenko (averages slightly darker) is a migrant to and from its breeding grounds in w. Alaska.

GULL-BILLED TERN
La Sterne à gros bec. *Gelochelidon nilotica* (Gmelin)
L. 13 to 15 in.

Characteristic tern-like coloration, about the size of the Common Tern but with much heavier somewhat gull-like bill (black in adult), large black feet and legs. Tarsus measures over one inch. Hind toe well developed, about half as long as inner one. Tail only moderately forked.

Status in Canada. Accidental. New Brunswick: specimen, Grand Manan, August 1879. It is normally found on warm temperate waters of both the New and Old Worlds.

Subspecies. *Gelochelidon nilotica aranea* (Wilson).

FORSTER'S TERN
La Sterne de Forster. *Sterna forsteri* Nuttall
Plate 35. L. (including long tail) 14 to 15 in.

Dark inner web (instead of outer web) of outermost tail feathers distinguishes it in all plumages from other similar terns.

Measurements. *Adult male:* wing, 250–265.5 (257.3); tail, 146–180.5 (169.1); exposed culmen, 36.5–41.8 (39.4); tarsus, 21.2–25.2 (24). *Adult female:* wing, 253–260 (256.5) mm.

Field Marks. Similar to Common Tern but adults in breeding plumage with tail greyish (instead of white); upper side of primaries paler, especially near their bases, than wing coverts; breast and belly white instead of slightly greyish; and bill more yellowish orange. Adults in winter plumage and in first autumn are easily recognized by a well-defined but more limited dark bar extending from the eye across the ear *but not around back of head.* Voice also is somewhat different (more nasal) from other similar terns.

Habitat. Marshes (in Canada only inland), frequently those bordering lakes.

Nesting. On floating mats of aquatic vegetation, muskrat houses, or islets. *Eggs,* 2 to 4 (usually 3); buff to olive buff, marked with small spots and less often blotches of dark brown, and some purplish grey. Incubation 23 days, probably by both sexes (A. C. Bent).

Range. Breeds from the Prairie Provinces of Canada south through eastern parts of Washington and Oregon to south-central California, central Idaho, northern Utah, southeastern Wyoming, eastern Colorado, eastern South Dakota, central Iowa, and southeastern Wisconsin; also from southeastern Maryland and eastern Virginia to southern Louisiana, and southeastern Texas. Winters from central California to Guatemala and from Virginia to

PLATE 35

1 Skua

2 Pomarine Jaeger, adult (light phase)

3 Long-tailed Jaeger, adult

4 Parasitic Jaeger,
   (a) adult (light phase)
   (b) juvenal
   (c) adult (dark phase)

5 Common Tern,
   (a) summer adult
   (b) head of first-autumn immature

6 Forster's Tern,
   (a) summer adult
   (b) head of first-autumn immature

7 Arctic Tern, summer adult

8 Caspian Tern, summer adult

9 Black Tern,
   (a) summer adult
   (b) juvenal

10 Roseate Tern, summer adult

Crosby

Crosby

PLATE 36

1 Common Murre,
  (a) winter plumage
  (b) summer adult
  (c) summer adult
      ('ringed murre'
      phase)

2 Thick-billed Murre,
  (a) winter plumage
  (b) summer adult

3 Razorbill,
  (a) first-winter
      immature
  (b) summer adult

4 Tufted Puffin,
  breeding plumage

5 Horned Puffin,
  breeding plumage

6 Common Puffin,
  breeding plumage

7 Rhinoceros Auklet,
  (a) breeding plumage
  (b) immature

8 Cassin's Auklet

9 Pigeon Guillemot,
  (a) breeding plumage
  (b) winter plumage

10 Black Guillemot,
   breeding plumage

11 Ancient Murrelet,
   (a) winter plumage
   (b) breeding plumage

12 Marbled Murrelet,
   (a) winter plumage
   (b) breeding plumage

13 Dovekie,
   (a) winter plumage
   (b) breeding plumage

northern Florida and along the Gulf of Mexico from western Florida to Mexico.

Range in Canada. Breeds in south-central and southeastern Alberta (Buffalo and Dried Meat lakes, Wabamun Lake; probably Many Island Lake), southern Saskatchewan (Waterhen Lake, near Kinistino; Rush Lake, probably Regina), southern Manitoba (lakes Winnipeg, Winnipegosis, and Manitoba, Shoal Lake; perhaps north to Moose and Cedar lakes); and formerly southern Ontario (Lake St. Clair).

Breeding Distribution of Forster's Tern

Scarce transient in southern Ontario (Toronto, Fort Erie). Casual in British Columbia (Okanagan Lake, August 3, 1938). Accidental in Nova Scotia (near Dartmouth, September 4, 1924).

COMMON TERN

La Sterne commune. *Sterna hirundo* Linnaeus
Plate 35. L. 13 to 16 in.

Adults (*breeding*): Crown and nape black; back and upper side of wings pearl grey; tips and outer webs of primaries dusky to silvery grey; tail forked, white with grey outer webs; under parts very pale greyish becoming white on chin, cheeks, under tail coverts, and wing linings; bill red, usually with black tip; legs reddish; *Adults* (*winter*): Similar but forehead white, a broad black patch extends from in front of eye back around back of head; bill dusky red. *Immature:* Head pattern similar to adult but feathers of mantle extensively tipped with blackish and buff; lesser wing coverts blackish; bill dusky, orange near base; legs pinkish or yellowish.

Measurements. *Adult male:* wing, 252.5–274 (262.6); tail, 133.4–149 (140.9); exposed culmen, 32.5–40.8 (37.1); tarsus, 19.6–22.5 (20.8). *Adult female:* wing, 245.8–268.2 (258.9) mm. Tarsus longer than in Arctic Tern (*see* Forster's and Roseate terns).

Field Marks. Very similar in all plumages to Arctic Tern and often very difficult to distinguish. Bill of summer adults more orange-red and usually tipped with dusky (Arctic has blood-red bill usually with no dusky tip); under parts less greyish, face whiter. Immatures extremely difficult to distinguish. When at rest the longer legs of both adult and immature Common Tern compared with those of Arctic Tern are often noticeable (*see also* Forster's and Roseate terns). *Voice:* A harsh *ke-ar-r-r;* also *kit, kit.*

Habitat. For nesting, open edges of sandy and gravelly beaches, flat areas on islands frequently near edges of sparse low vegetation, thus usually different from nesting habitat of Forster's Tern, although Common Tern occasionally nests in a similar marshy situation, even on muskrat houses. Forages over inshore coastal waters and interior lakes and larger rivers.

Nesting. Usually colonial, sometimes single pairs; often with other terns. Nest a shallow depression in sand, gravel, turf, or rock, variously lined with grass, twigs, pebbles, or bits of shell. *Eggs,* usually 3, often 2 or 4; variable, pale buff to brown or olive, spotted and blotched with darker browns and some purplish grey. Incubation (by both sexes) 21 to 30, average 25.7, days (O. L. Austin, Jr.).

Range. Breeds widely in the Northern Hemisphere of both the New and Old Worlds. In North America, from Alberta east to Newfoundland and south to northeastern Montana, South Dakota, southern Michigan, northern Ohio, northern New York, and on the Atlantic Coast to North Carolina; also southeastern Texas and Florida. Does not breed on the Pacific Coast of North America. Winters from southern Baja California and South Carolina south to the Straits of Magellan and in the Old World south to southern Africa.

Breeding Distribution of Common Tern

Range in Canada. Locally common summer resident and transient. Breeds in southern Mackenzie (Great Slave Lake), Alberta (east of the Rocky Mountains: Lake Athabasca, Miquelon Lake, Many Island Lake), Saskatchewan (Lake Athabasca, Flotten Lake, Crane Lake, Regina), north-central to southern Manitoba (Bird, Cedar Lake, Shoal Lake; probably northwest to Kasmere Lake), central and

southern Ontario (lat. 53°–54° N on Manitoba boundary and Lake Abitibi south to Lake Erie, Lake Ontario, and St. Lawrence River), James Bay (Charlton Island), southern Quebec (Lake Mistassini, north shore of Gulf of St. Lawrence, Montreal, Magdalen Islands), southern Labrador (Lake Melville, Cartwright), Newfoundland, New Brunswick, Prince Edward Island, and Nova Scotia.

Transient in British Columbia (Georgia Strait and the southern interior).

Subspecies. *Sterna hirundo hirundo* Linnaeus is the only subspecies known in N. America.

ARCTIC TERN
La Sterne arctique. *Sterna paradisaea* Pontoppidan
Plate 35. L. 14 to 17 in.

Very similar to Common Tern but legs (tarsi) shorter; bill of breeding adults of a deeper red and without (usually) a dusky tip; under parts more distinctly grey, this extending farther up on lower face. Adults in winter plumage have forehead and front of crown whitish, under parts white, blackish bill and feet. Autumn immatures have shorter tarsi than Common Tern, but the plumage is very similar.

Measurements. *Adult male:* wing, 251.7–272.5 (264.2); tail, 147.3–197 (170.1); exposed culmen, 29.8–33.9 (31.5); tarsus, 15–16.7 (15.8). *Adult female:* wing, 251.5–273 (261) mm.

Field Marks. Very difficult to distinguish from Common Tern except under favourable conditions. Bill of Arctic is of darker blood red, usually lacks dusky tip; lower face slightly more greyish. Autumn adults and immatures of the two usually are not separable. When on land or perched, however, the shorter legs of the Arctic are noticeable to those familiar with the two species. Roseate Tern in breeding plumage has a mostly black bill, white under parts (instead of distinctly grey), and longer tail and legs.

Habitat. For nesting, the vicinity of either salt or fresh water, on sandspits, dunes, deltas, sand and gravel beaches, rocky shores and islands, marshy tundra. Forages over either salt or fresh water. Outside nesting season it is marine.

Nesting. In colonies, sometimes single pairs; sometimes with other species. Nest, a depression in ground, moss, or rock, frequently unlined but sometimes lined with various amounts of grass. *Eggs,* usually 2 or 3; very similar to those of the Common Tern. Incubation 21 to 22 days (R. Dircksen), by both sexes; 20 to 21 (D. F. Parmelee).

Range. Circumpolar, breeding in the Arctic and Subarctic of both the New and Old Worlds; in North America: Alaska, northern Canada, and Greenland, south on the Atlantic Coast to Massachusetts. Eastern North American populations in migration cross the north Atlantic and pass along the west coast of Europe and Africa. Winters in the oceans of the Southern Hemisphere.

Range in Canada. Breeds from northern Yukon (Herschel Island and arctic coast), northern Mackenzie (Mackenzie Delta, Baillie Island), Banks Island (Sachs Harbour), Bathurst Island, and northern Ellesmere Island (Ravine Bay), south through Yukon to northern British Columbia (Atlin, Chilkat Pass; probably Dease Lake), southern Mackenzie

(Great Slave Lake), northwestern Saskatchewan (Lake Athabasca), southern Keewatin (Nueltin Lake), northern Manitoba (Churchill), northern Ontario (Cape Henrietta Maria), James Bay (Gasket Shoal), central and southeastern Quebec (James Bay coast, Boundary Lake, near Knob Lake; north shore of the Gulf of St. Lawrence, Magdalen Islands), Labrador (coast; also interior: Attikamagen Lake), Newfoundland, and the coast of New Brunswick and Nova Scotia (Cape Breton Island, Sable Island, Mud Island). Occurs in summer and perhaps breeds in northeastern Alberta (Athabasca Lake) and probably in Prince Edward Island.

Breeding Distribution of Arctic Tern

Post-breeding movements are to the Atlantic and Pacific oceans. Transient in southern British Columbia (coast and interior) and very rarely in central Alberta (Lac la Nonne). Accidental in southern Ontario (Toronto).

Remarks. The Arctic Tern makes one of the longest and most remarkable of all migratory journeys. Those that nest in eastern Canada start their autumn migration by launching out across the vast Atlantic Ocean. Once on the other side, they travel southward along the west coasts of Europe and Africa and thus reach their winter range in waters off South Africa and southward to the Antarctic Circle.

Probably this tern sees more daylight during its lifetime than any other animal. It summers in the North while up to 24 hours of daylight daily prevail and 'winters' in the South where the periods of daylight greatly exceed the hours of darkness.

Bird banding has dispelled most of the secrets surrounding the long migrations of the Arctic Tern. One banded on July 22, 1927, in Labrador, was recovered near La Rochelle, France, on October 1 of the same year. Another banded in Labrador on July 23, 1928, was retaken in Natal, South Africa, on November 14, 1928. Additional similar recoveries of banded birds have revealed the major details of these great journeys. Banding also has provided information on the longevity of this tern. One banded as a flightless young

in Norway died, in the same tern colony in which it was raised, 27 years later, the longest life-span yet known for any species of tern.

ROSEATE TERN

La Sterne rosée. *Sterna dougallii* Montagu
Plate 35. L. 14 to 17 in.

Similar to Common Tern but both webs of outer tail feathers white; bill of breeding adults usually black (sometimes with various extent of red at base); wing shorter; tail longer.

Measurements. *Adult male:* wing, 222–231.5 (230); tail, 166–214.5 (187.6); exposed culmen, 36–40.5 (38.1); tarsus, 18–20 (19). *Adult female:* wing, 218.5–233 (230) mm (Ridgway).

Field Marks. Most breeding Roseate Terns have a black bill which distinguishes them from the Common, Arctic, and Forster's terns. Some, however, may show considerable red on the basal half of the bill, in which case the Roseate's longer, more deeply forked tail, and white, faintly rosy under parts (instead of greyish) will help separate it from breeding Common and Arctic terns.

Habitat. Coastal salt water, nesting on islands and shores.

Nesting. In colonies often with other species on coastal islands and shores. Nest, on the ground either unlined or sparsely lined. *Eggs*, 2 or 3; similar to those of Common Tern but average a little paler and slightly longer. Incubation variously recorded 21 to 26 days, by both sexes; 21 days (L. Jones).

Range. Breeds locally on coasts and islands on both sides of the Atlantic from Nova Scotia to Virginia and south to the West Indies and the north coast of Venezuela, and from the British Isles to southern Africa; also in the Indian Ocean; China and the Philippines to Australia and islands in the South Pacific. In North America winters from the West Indies to Brazil.

Range in Canada. Breeds locally in small numbers in southern Nova Scotia (Thrumcap Island, Guysborough County; Indian Island; Sable Island; Mud Islands; Little Bald Island, but apparently no longer nests on some of these islands).

Subspecies. *Sterna dougallii dougallii* Montagu.

SOOTY TERN

La Sterne fuligineuse. *Sterna fuscata* Linnaeus
L. 15 to 17 in.

Contrasting black upper parts and white under parts are entirely unlike any tern of regular occurrence in Canada (*see* Black Tern, Black Skimmer, and Bridled Tern). Tail well forked. Forehead (and narrow extension back to top of eye) and under parts, white; crown, hind-neck, broad line eye to bill, and rest of upper parts, black (except outermost tail feathers *mostly* grey to whitish); bill and legs black. Young are brown above and slightly paler below; feathers of back, tipped white.

Status in Canada. Accidental visitor from the tropics and subtropics where widely distributed in the world. Nova Scotia: specimen found dead near Wolfville, August 28,

1924, after a hurricane. Not examined by the writer but probably referable to the subspecies *S. f. fuscata* Linnaeus.

BRIDLED TERN
La Sterne à collier. *Sterna anaethetus* Scopoli
L. 14 to 15.5 in.

Adults resemble Sooty Tern but back more greyish brown, crown black and separated from the dark back by *whitish hind-neck;* white of forehead less extensive but white extension backward over eye reaching well past eye. Young resemble adults, but head mainly grey or dusky mottled brown, feathers of upper parts with pale edges. The under parts are greyish white (brown in young Sooty Tern).

Status in Canada. Accidental in Newfoundland: An immature now in the Museum of Comparative Zoology at Harvard College was taken at Custlett on January 21, 1891 (L. M. Tuck, R. A. Paynter, in litt.). On September 6 and 7, 1955, Tuck studied at close range at Fermeuse, Newfoundland, another immature which he identified as this species. The Newfoundland specimen of this tropical and subtropical species has been referred to the subspecies *S. a. recognita* (Mathews).

LEAST TERN
La Petite Sterne. *Sterna albifrons* Pallas
L. 8.5 to 9.7 in.

A tiny tern similar in general coloration to the much larger Common Tern, but in breeding plumage bill and legs are orange-yellow, and the black cap has a large white forehead patch, leaving only a narrow black bar between eye and base of bill. In any plumage diminutive size distinguishes it from other terns.

Measurements. *Adult male:* wing, 163–178 (168.1); tail, 70–93 (81.2); exposed culmen, 26–31 (28.8); tarsus, 14–15.5 (14.5). *Adult female:* wing, 160–167 (162.9) mm (Ridgway).

Status in Canada. Accidental in Nova Scotia (Barrington, Polly Bog) and New Brunswick (hypothetical: a sight record for Kent Island of several after a hurricane in September 1944). These are probably referable to the subspecies *S. a. antillarum* (Lesson), which breeds on the Atlantic Coast from Massachusetts southward.

ROYAL TERN
La Sterne royale. *Thalasseus maximus* (Boddaert)
L. 18 to 21 in.

A large tern similar to Caspian Tern but smaller, with slenderer more orange (less deep red) bill, much more deeply forked tail (outer feathers reach to wing tips; Caspian has shorter, broader, outer tail feathers which fall well short of wing tips), under side of primary tips much paler, black nuchal feathers of cap longer and pointed. Royal Tern has complete black cap for only a short period in spring, after which forehead and forecrown become white, only the hind part remaining black. Immatures are distinguishable from young Caspians by the more deeply forked tail.

192

PLATE 37

Crosby '63

1

2

3a

3b

4

5

Crosby

Measurements. *Adult male:* wing, 360–382 (371); tail, 147.5–192 (171.9); exposed culmen, 59–68 (64.1); tarsus, 29.5–34.5 (31.8). *Adult female:* wing, 357–393 (374) mm (Ridgway).

Status in Canada. Accidental in Nova Scotia (Brier Island: specimens, October 1, 1958; September 13, 1960).

Subspecies. *T. m. maximus* (Boddaert). The species breeds from Maryland southward on the Atlantic Coast as well as in other parts of the world.

SANDWICH TERN
La Sterne caugek. *Thalasseus sandvicensis* (Latham)
L. 14 to 16 in.

Another black-capped, grey-mantled tern with white under parts. Somewhat resembles the Common Tern, but the bill is black with yellowish tip and is much longer; legs black and longer; black nuchal feathers longer and pointed. No other tern has a black, yellow-tipped bill.

Status in Canada. Accidental in southern Ontario (Lucknow, spring 1882).

Subspecies. *T. s. acuflavidus* (Cabot). Nearest point of breeding is Atlantic coastal U.S. (Carolinas).

CASPIAN TERN
La Sterne caspienne. *Hydroprogne caspia* (Pallas)
Plate 35. L. 19 to 23 in.

A very large tern with heavy coral red bill, black cap (only slightly crested, black nuchal feathers with blunt tips), black feet, and only slightly forked tail, the outermost feathers not greatly elongated. By late summer the forehead and crown become heavily streaked with white (winter plumage). Immatures similar to winter adults but upper parts mottled with dusky; bill, dull orange.

Measurements. *Adult male:* wing, 400–422 (411.1); tail, 130–150 (137.9); exposed culmen, 65–75 (69.4); tarsus, 40.5–46 (43.2). *Adult female:* wing, 404–423 (416) mm (Ridgway).

Field Marks. Large size (as big as the medium-sized gulls) and slower wing-beats in flight distinguish it from all other terns of regular occurrence in Canada. The pointed tapering red bill and dark cap eliminate confusion with any gull. Its hoarse voice is distinctive, a low *ca-arrrr ka-ka-ka-kaow*, higher pitched in early autumn young.

Habitat. Lakes and larger rivers in the interior; also coasts. Often rests on sand bars and beaches. For nesting usually sandy or rocky islands in interior lakes; in Quebec coastal islands.

Nesting. Usually in colonies often near other terns or gulls; sometimes single pairs. Nest, on the ground, may be a mere depression or be fairly well lined with vegetation. *Eggs*, usually 2 or 3; buffy, usually sparingly spotted with browns. Incubation 20 to 22 days (Grobbels *in* Witherby), by both sexes.

Range. Breeds locally in North America, Europe, Asia, Africa, Australia, and New Zealand. In North America, locally from Canada to southern United States and central Baja California. In the Western Hemisphere, it winters from

193

central California south through Baja California; the Gulf of Mexico, the Caribbean, and the West Indies.

Range in Canada. Breeds very locally in southern Mackenzie (Great Slave Lake), northeastern Alberta (Lake Athabasca), central Saskatchewan (Doré Lake), south-central and southern Manitoba (lakes Winnipeg and Winnipegosis), southern Ontario (Georgian Bay, North Channel of Lake Huron, Lake Ontario, Thousand Islands group in upper St. Lawrence River), southeastern Quebec (Fog Island), and probably Newfoundland (locally). Recorded in summer in western Ontario (Lake of the Woods).

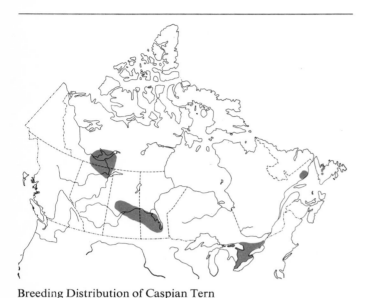

Breeding Distribution of Caspian Tern

Scarce transient in central and southern Alberta, Saskatchewan, southwestern Quebec (Ile aux Noix), New Brunswick (Buctouche, Nantucket Island), Prince Edward Island (Tracadie Bay, Conway Inlet), and Nova Scotia (Cole Harbour, Cape Sable Island). Sight records only for British Columbia. Wanders occasionally to northern Manitoba (Churchill) and northern Ontario (James Bay). A specimen taken at Boxey, Newfoundland, September 30, 1958, had been banded on July 10, 1958, at Rogers City, Michigan.

BLACK TERN

La Sterne noire. *Chlidonias niger* (Linnaeus)
Plate 35. L. 9 to 10.5 in.

A small dark tern with slightly forked tail. Colour and small size are diagnostic.

Measurements. *Adult male:* wing, 195.5–214.5 (207.5); tail, 73–83.9 (79.9); exposed culmen, 26.7–29.5 (27.9); tarsus, 15.3–17 (16.5). *Adult female:* wing, 193.3–215 (205.7) mm.

Field Marks. Adults in breeding plumage, with all-black head, neck, and under body (except white under tail coverts) and with dark slate mantle, rump, and tail, are easily identified. Adults in winter plumage and young are mainly white below but have the characteristic slaty mantle and tail, and head markings shown in Plate 35. They are darker above than other terns of regular occurrence in Canada and have the tail uniformly dark grey.

Habitat. In Canada, mainly interior watery marshes, lakes, ponds, sloughs, and rivers in either treeless or wooded country.

Nesting. Nest, a hollow on rafts or mats of marsh vegetation floating in shallow water of lakes or marshes, sometimes on muskrat houses or on solid ground. *Eggs*, usually 2 or 3; buffy or olive, marked (usually heavily) with browns or blackish brown. Incubation 21 to 22 days (R. E. Goodwin), by both sexes.

Range. Breeds widely in the Northern Hemisphere of both the New and Old Worlds. In North America from much of interior-southern Canada south to south-central California, northern Nevada, Colorado, Nebraska, Kentucky, Pennsylvania, western New York, and Maine. Winters coastally from Panama to Peru and to Surinam.

Range in Canada. Summer resident, commonest in the Prairie Provinces. Breeds in central-southern Mackenzie (Buffalo Lake, probably Slave River Delta), interior-central and southern British Columbia (Nukko Creek; Swan Lake, Peace River; Kleena Kleene, Cranbrook), Alberta (except extreme northwest corner and perhaps the mountainous southwest), Saskatchewan (north at least to Kazan Lake), Manitoba (north regularly to The Pas and Pikwitonei Lake; also locally near Churchill), Ontario (north to Favourable Lake; 9 miles south of Fort Albany; perhaps Lake Abitibi), southwestern Quebec (Ile aux Noix, lakes St. Peter and St. Louis, Lac Trois Saumons, perhaps Lake Abitibi), and southern New Brunswick (very locally: Big Timber Lake).

Rare transient (mainly in fall) in Prince Edward Island (Tignish), Magdalen Islands, and Nova Scotia (Sable Island, Cape Sable Island, Barrington Passage, Devil's Island, Crescent Beach).

Subspecies. *Chlidonias niger surinamensis* (Gmelin).

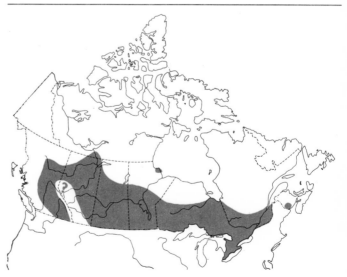

Breeding Distribution of Black Tern

Remarks. This graceful inhabitant of inland lakes and marshes, while in Canada, feeds on grasshoppers, dragonflies, beetles, flies, moths, and other insects, most of which it catches on the wing.

Family **Rynchopidae** – Skimmers

Number of Species in North America 1; in Canada 1

Large, long-winged tern-like birds of tropical and subtropical coasts, with webbed front toes and a strange, thin, knife-like, laterally compressed bill, the lower mandible much longer than the upper, comprise this family (Fig. 55).

Fig. 55 Black Skimmer

BLACK SKIMMER
Le Bec-en-ciseaux. *Rynchops nigra* Linnaeus
L. 16 to 20 in.

Unmistakable. A long-winged bird of Atlantic coasts with peculiar thin knife-like bill, the lower mandible of which extends far beyond the upper one. Forehead, sides of head below eye, and under parts, white. Rest of head, hind-neck, back, and upper side of wings, black. Tips of secondaries and inner primaries white, giving a conspicuous white hind edge to wing. Tail, white mixed with brown, forked. Basal half of bill red, terminal half black.

Range. Breeds along the Atlantic and Gulf of Mexico coasts from Massachusetts to Yucatan; northern and eastern South America; and on the Pacific Coast from northern Mexico to southern South America.

Status in Canada. Casual in Nova Scotia (Cole Harbour, Cape Sable, August 1924, numbers, following a hurricane) and New Brunswick (Grand Manan: August 1879, large flock; also three taken there in October 1924. Kent Island: 50 counted September 15, 1944). Accidental in Newfoundland (between September 30 and October 10, 1958, numbers appeared near Burgeo, St. Alban's, Boxey, Brigus Junction, Milltown, Placentia, Heart's Content, Happy Adventure, Gaultois, and other localities), and southwestern Quebec (Lake St. Peter: specimen October 26, 1938). Occurrences in Canada usually a result of hurricanes.

Subspecies. *Rynchops nigra nigra* Linnaeus.

Family **Alcidae** – Auks, Murres, and Puffins

Number of Species in North America 21; in Canada 14

Birds of this family frequent salt water and come ashore only to breed. They are expert swimmers and divers. All species are short-necked and stout-bodied, and most are coloured mainly black and white. The short narrow wings beat very rapidly in flight. Legs are short and are set far back near the end of the body, thus accounting for an upright posture on land; hind toe absent or vestigial, front toes fully webbed. The bill is short but highly variable in shape. Small fishes and marine invertebrates are the staple foods.

GREAT AUK
Le Grand Pingouin. *Pinguinus impennis* (Linnaeus)
Fig. 56. L. 28 to 30 in.

A big auk with large, laterally compressed, much-grooved bill, rudimentary wings too small for flight. Upper parts black, becoming dark brown on sides of head and neck and on throat. Large white patch in front of eye. Secondaries tipped white. Under parts (except head and neck) white. Bill black with whitish grooves.

Fig. 56 Great Auk

Measurements. *Adult male:* wing, about 146; tail, about 76; exposed culmen, 80–89; tarsus, 42.16 mm (Ridgway).

Habitat. Coastal waters of the north Atlantic, nesting on rocky coasts and islands.

Nesting. In large colonies on rocky islands and coasts. The single *egg* was laid on bare rock. It was pale buff with brown, black, or grey scrawls and blotches, and about 5 inches long.

Range. Extinct. Last definite record on June 3, 1844, on Eldey Rock off Iceland. Bred along coasts on both sides of the north Atlantic: Eastern Canada, Iceland, the outer Hebrides (St. Kilda); probably the Orkneys; possibly Greenland, the Faroes, and Lundy. Wintered on salt water from southern Greenland south to Florida and southern Spain.

Range in Canada. Extinct. Formerly bred in Newfoundland (Funk Island; possibly elsewhere), possibly the Magdalen Islands (Bird Rocks), Quebec. Its former occurrence in southern New Brunswick (shores of the Bay of Fundy, Nantucket Island) and Nova Scotia (Port Joli, St. Margaret's Bay, Mahone Bay) is indicated by bones found in Indian shell heaps, but evidence of breeding is lacking. The supposed reference in the diaries of Champlain to breeding on Mud Islands, Nova Scotia, seems to be based on erroneous translation from the French and doubtless refers to the Gannet. It probably wintered more or less commonly in waters off the East Coast and in numbers on the Grand Banks of Newfoundland.

RAZORBILL (Razor-billed Auk)

Le Gode. *Alca torda* Linnaeus
Plate 36. L. 16 to 18.5 in.

Bill laterally compressed (deep and thin), grooved with white line (absent in young) across it; tail pointed, central tail feathers somewhat elongated. Winter plumage similar to breeding plumage, but throat and sides of neck are white, and the white line from eye to base of bill is obscure or lacking, although the one crossing the bill remains. Young in first autumn are similar to winter adults, but bill is smaller, shallower, without grooves or a white line; thus it somewhat resembles winter murres, but in the hand the more laterally compressed bill and pointed tail distinguish the Razorbill.

Measurements (*A. t. torda*). *Adult male:* wing, 186.2–204 (196.4); tail, 73.9–89 (81.7); exposed culmen, 32–37.4 (34.8); tarsus, 31.8–35.5 (33.5). *Adult female:* wing, 196–201 (197.9) mm.

Breeding Distribution of Razorbill

Field Marks. A black-and-white sea diver the size of a small duck but with deep, laterally compressed bill entirely different from that of any duck. Most likely to be confused with the murres, but the Razorbill's much deeper bill (with strongly arched culmen) with white line across it, is very different from the slender, pointed, unmarked bill of murres. In breeding plumage the Razorbill has a narrow white line from eye to base of bill. Autumn immatures, with small unmarked black bill, are more difficult to distinguish from winter Thick-billed Murres, but usually the deeper, more rounded bill profile is evident. Winter Common Murres are readily separable also by their well-defined dark spur extending backward from the eye. Young Common Puffins have enough of the characteristic puffin face-pattern to identify them; also they are smaller, chunkier, and lack white tips to the secondaries.

Habitat. Marine. In winter, mostly offshore waters of the ocean. In nesting season, sea cliffs on coasts or islands, boulder-strewn shores near salt water.

Nesting. In colonies, sometimes with murres, on sea cliffs or among boulders and rocks. No nest is constructed, the egg being laid in natural crevices, holes, or under rocks or overhangs. *Egg*, usually one only; strongly tapered and elongated, buffy to greenish white, spotted and blotched with browns or blacks. Incubation, by both sexes, 33 to 36 days (Keighley and Lockley).

Range. Breeds along coasts from western Greenland, Iceland, Norway, and northern Russia, south to Maine, northern France, and southern Finland. In winter ranges south to South Carolina (rarely) and the Canary Islands.

Range in Canada. Atlantic coasts and islands. Breeds in extreme southeastern Baffin Island (Harper Islands south of Loks Land—V. G. Wynne-Edwards, in litt.), Labrador coast, southeastern Quebec (north shore of the Gulf of St. Lawrence, Les Pèlerins on lower St. Lawrence River, Anticosti Island, Bonaventure Island, Magdalen Islands), Newfoundland, northeastern Nova Scotia (Ciboux and Hertford islands), and southern New Brunswick (Yellow Murr Ledge, south of Grand Manan; formerly Machias Seal Island).

Winters mostly in offshore waters from southern Labrador and Newfoundland southward. Accidental in southern Ontario (Toronto, Hamilton, Upper Rideau Lakes) and southwestern Quebec (Lake St. Louis).

Subspecies. *Alca torda torda* Linnaeus.

COMMON MURRE (Atlantic or California Murre)

La Marmette commune. *Uria aalge* (Pontoppidan)
Plate 36. L. 16.5 to 18 in.

Bill long (for an alcid), rather slender, pointed, all black. Breeding plumage is illustrated, but in Atlantic populations a variation is found in some individuals which have a white eye-ring and a white line extending backwards from it. This was once thought to be a distinct species and was named 'Ringed Murre,' *Uria ringvia*. Bill characters, size, and markings distinguish the Common Murre from most other members of the family. In breeding plumage, however, it is very similar to the Thick-billed Murre, from which it differs in its more slender, longer bill and in lacking a bare pale line (bluish white in life) along the cutting edge of the upper mandible near the gape. The 'Ringed Murre' variation has no counterpart in the Thick-billed Murre. Winter adults and immatures of the two species of murres are easily distinguished (*see* Field Marks).

Measurements (*U. a. aalge*). *Adult male:* wing, 192–200 (196.5); tail, 39.3–50.6 (45.4); exposed culmen, 40.8–43.5 (42.3); tarsus, 37.2–38.7 (38.1). *Adult female:* wing, 194.5–204 (199.9) mm.

Field Marks. The relatively long, slender, pointed bill as well as the size and the markings distinguish it from most species of the family. In breeding plumage, it is very similar to the Thick-billed Murre, from which it differs by having the white of the breast meet the black of the fore-neck in a less distinct peak (in the Thick-billed Murre, the white on breast forms a distinct peak at the junction with the black of the fore-neck; Fig. 57), the longer slenderer bill, and the lack of a pale line along cutting edge of upper mandible near gape. Adults and immatures in winter plumage have a spur of dark colour extending backwards from the eye region, quite different from the Thick-billed.

Habitat. Strictly marine. In winter, offshore coastal waters (between 5 miles from shore and the edge of the continental shelf). In breeding season, the vicinity of sea cliffs or rocky islands.

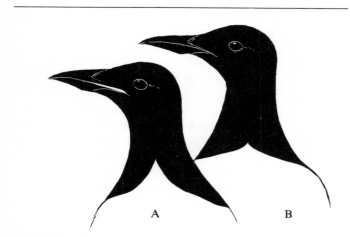

Fig. 57 Field marks of
(A) Thick-billed Murre
(B) Common Murre

Nesting. In colonies, sometimes immense, often with other species. Egg is laid on bare rock of cliff ledge or rocky island. *Egg*, one only; pear-shaped, pale greenish to bluish, variously spotted, blotched, and scrawled with browns or black. Incubation, by both sexes, period variable 28 to 35 days (various authors), but probably rarely less than 30 days.

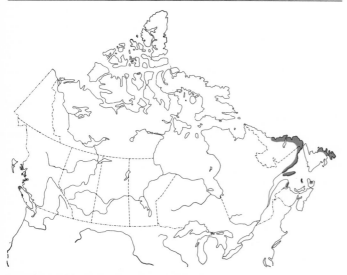

Breeding Distribution of Common Murre

Range. Breeds along coasts and islands of the North Pacific and North Atlantic from Bering Strait south to northern Japan (perhaps eastern Korea) and to central California; and from western Greenland, Iceland, Bear Island, and Novaya Zemlya south to Nova Scotia and to northern France and Portugal.

Range in Canada. Breeds on Atlantic and Pacific coasts: British Columbia (Triangle Island, outermost of the Scott Islands), Labrador (locally north to Nunarsuk Island), southeastern Quebec (north shore of the Gulf of St. Lawrence: Fog Island to Bradore Bay; Anticosti Island, Bonaventure Island, Bird Rocks), Newfoundland (Funk, Baccalieu, Green islands; Cape St. Mary's), and Nova Scotia (formerly at least: Bird Islands).

Winters on offshore waters from northern Newfoundland southward; also along the coast of British Columbia.

Subspecies. (1) *Uria aalge aalge* (Pontoppidan) is the subspecies of the Atlantic coast. (2) *Uria aalge inornata* Salomonsen is the only subspecies known to occur in B.C.

THICK-BILLED MURRE (Brünnich's Murre)

La Marmette de Brünnich. *Uria lomvia* (Linnaeus)
Plate 36. L. 17 to 19 in.

Similar to Common Murre but bill heavier and plumage markings somewhat different (*see* preceding species and Field Marks below).

Measurements (*U. l. lomvia*). *Adult male:* wing, 194.9–215 (207.6); tail, 44.5–53 (48.9); exposed culmen, 30.3–37.2 (33.7); tarsus, 34.7–37.8 (35.6). *Adult female:* wing, 195–212.5 (204.8) mm.

Field Marks. Very similar to Common Murre, differing from it as follows (breeding plumage): presence of a pale line along the cutting edge of the upper mandible near the gape and by a more acute-angled peak of white from the breast into the dark fore-neck. Adult in winter plumage and immature: black of crown extends down uniformly over the ear region (in Common Murre the ear region is whitish with a dark spur extending back across it from the eye). Although the bill is at all seasons thicker and shorter, this is often very difficult to discern and is not always a reliable criterion in immature birds.

Habitat. Marine. In breeding season, sea cliffs and nearby cold turbulent water. In winter, offshore waters. Has slightly less tolerance for warmish waters than the Common Murre.

Nesting. In colonies, often immense, frequently with other birds. No nest, the egg being laid on bare rock of cliff ledge or on flat top. *Egg*, one only; usually pear-shaped, extremely variable in colour but most often bluish green irregularly spotted, scrawled, and blotched with browns, sometimes clouded with lilac. Incubation period variable, 30 to 35 days (L. M. Tuck), by both sexes.

Range. Breeds on islands and coasts in the Arctic of North America and Eurasia and south to the Commander, Aleutian, and Kodiak islands, the Gulf of St. Lawrence, southern Greenland, Iceland, and Jan Mayen; also in Spitsbergen, Bear Island, Franz Josef Land, Novaya Zemlya, Murmansk coast of northern Russia, Severnaya Zemlya, New Siberian Islands, and Wrangel Island. Winters on salt water within much of the breeding range and somewhat south of it, in North America south to southeastern Alaska and Delaware.

Range in Canada. Breeds in northwest Mackenzie

(locally: Cape Parry); and in the eastern Arctic (Coburg, Prince Leopold, and Bylot islands, eastern Baffin Island, Coats Island, Digges Sound, and Akpatok Island; probably northwest Somerset Island); the Labrador coast, Newfoundland, Magdalen Islands (Bird Rocks); and St. Mary Islands on outer north shore of Gulf of St. Lawrence.

Winters in offshore waters within the breeding range (where open water permits) and southward, commonly on the Grand Banks, and in smaller numbers off Nova Scotia, New Brunswick, and Prince Edward Island. Accidental, usually in late autumn, sometimes in numbers, in southern Ontario and southwestern Quebec (upper St. Lawrence, Great Lakes, Ottawa River); recorded once in interior southern Keewatin (Edehon Lake). Rare migrant in northern Yukon (Herschel Island). Casual on coastal British Columbia (near Vancouver).

Breeding Distribution of Thick-billed Murre

Subspecies. (1) *Uria lomvia lomvia* (Linnaeus) is the subspecies inhabiting the e. Arctic and the Atlantic Coast. Birds taken in the southern interior of Ont. and sw. Que. are of that race. (2) *U. l. arra* (Pallas) is the only race known to visit the coast of B.C. and the coast of Yukon. Perhaps the population breeding on Cape Parry, Mackenzie, is referable to it (no specimens available).

DOVEKIE

Le Mergule nain. *Plautus alle* (Linnaeus)
Plate 36. L. 7.5 to 9 in.

A diminutive sea diver of eastern waters with stubby bill; short thick neck; black-and-white coloration. Small size readily distinguishes it from other eastern Canadian sea divers. In winter plumage it somewhat resembles some west coast species but does not normally come into contact with them (*see* Ancient Murrelet, and Cassin's and Least auklets).

Measurements (*P. a. alle*). *Adult male:* wing, 111–116.5 (114.3); tail, 31.3–37.5 (34.3); exposed culmen, 12.9–16 (14.3); tarsus, 19.5–21.3 (20.5). *Adult female:* wing, 108–114 (112) mm.

Field Marks. Small size, stubby (half an inch) bill, and markings distinguish it from our other eastern sea divers.

Habitat. Marine. In winter offshore salt water, edges of pack-ice, openings in drift-ice. Occasionally numbers are storm-blown inland or to inshore waters. For nesting (not known in Canada) talus slopes of rocky cliffs near the sea.

Nesting. (Unknown in Canada but should be looked for in the eastern Arctic near Greenland.) In colonies, often immense. The single egg is laid on a rock crevice or among rock rubble of talus slopes of arctic cliffs near the sea. *Egg,* usually one, is pale bluish, usually unmarked.

Range. Breeds from northern Greenland, Jan Mayen, Spitsbergen, Novaya Zemlya, and Franz Josef Land south to southern Greenland, Iceland, and Bear Island. Winters from within the breeding range in suitable open water south to New Jersey and to the Azores, Canary Islands, France, and the Baltic Sea; irregularly farther south.

Range in Canada. Not known to breed, although perhaps might do so. Occurs commonly as a migrant, winter resident, or summer non-breeder along the Canadian coasts of Baffin Bay and Davis Strait; Jones Sound, Lancaster Sound, Hudson Strait, and northern Hudson Bay; rarely west to Melville Island and northeastern Mackenzie (Perry River), and north to northern Ellesmere Island (Parr Inlet). Winters in northern Hudson Bay and Hudson Strait (probably also farther north) and southward off the coast of Labrador, southeastern Quebec, Newfoundland, and the Maritimes. Accidental inland, sometimes in large numbers, due to storms, very rarely west to the Great Lakes and Manitoba (Warren's Landing).

Subspecies. *Plautus alle alle* (Linnaeus).

BLACK GUILLEMOT

Le Guillemot noir. *Cepphus grylle* (Linnaeus)
Plate 36. L. 12 to 14 in.

Bill rather long, straight, pointed, black in colour. *Breeding plumage:* All black except large white wing patch and white under wing coverts and red legs. *Winter adults:* Wings and tail as in breeding plumage; head, neck, and under parts mainly white, more or less mixed with black; crown and back, black variously mixed with white. *Young:* Resemble winter adults but are less extensively whitish; white wing patch mottled with blackish. Its large white wing patches differ from any other alcid of eastern Canada but are very much like those of the Pigeon Guillemot of the west coast (*see* Pigeon Guillemot).

Measurements (*C. g. ultimus*). *Adult male:* wing, 155.2–164.1 (160.7); tail, 46–51 (49.3); exposed culmen, 24–30 (27.6); tarsus, 30–33 (31.5). *Adult female:* wing, 154.0–170.2 (158.8) mm.

Field Marks. A teal-sized sea-diver with slender pointed bill and large white wing patch. Not likely to be confused with any other species of the Atlantic Coast or eastern Arctic. The White-winged Scoter is larger with an entirely different bill. The Pigeon Guillemot of coastal British Columbia is very similar, but the Black Guillemot is not known to have occurred in British Columbia. *Voice:* Vague, weak, shrill whistles. Usually a silent bird.

Habitat. Marine (also rarely brackish water). In nesting season, the rocky coasts where cliffs, talus slopes, fractured rocks, and rock rubble provide nesting places. In winter, offshore waters; edges and leads of pack-ice; also to some extent, where open water permits, inshore waters. Forages in waters of various depths.

Nesting. Nests in colonies, frequently small, or in single pairs, in crevices and crannies of talus slopes and rock rubble, in cliff faces, even in soft red clay bluffs (the birds perhaps excavating holes themselves), often at no great height above high tides, but also up to considerable height on cliffs. *Eggs*, usually 2, sometimes 1; white to greenish or buffy, spotted and blotched, often handsomely, with various browns and purplish grey. Incubation 27 to 33 days, usually 28 (H. E. Winn), by both sexes.

Breeding Distribution of Black Guillemot

Range. Almost circumpolar. Breeds in the Arctic of both the New and Old Worlds (but apparently not in western arctic Canada) south to northern Alaska (probably), James Bay, Maine, southern Greenland, Iceland, Scotland, southern Scandinavia, and northern Siberia. Slightly farther south in winter.

Range in Canada. Breeds on suitable coasts and islands near the sea from Ellesmere Island south through Somerset (Port Leopold), Devon, and Bylot islands, eastern and southern Baffin Island, Melville Peninsula, Southampton Island, Hudson and James bays, Hudson Strait, Ungava Bay, Labrador, southern Quebec (north shore of Gulf of St. Lawrence, St. Lawrence River west at least to Saguenay River and Pèlerin Islands, Anticosti and Magdalen islands, Gaspé Peninsula), Newfoundland, New Brunswick, Prince Edward Island, and Nova Scotia. Summer sight records of single birds: Banks Island and Adelaide Peninsula, N.W.T.

Winters off the breeding places, as open water permits, north at least to Iglulik, Baffin Bay, and Davis Strait, and southward along the entire Atlantic Coast of Canada; also near Southampton Island, and in Hudson Bay and Hudson Strait. Accidental in southern Ontario (Toronto; sight record for Kingston).

Subspecies. *Cepphus grylle atlantis* Salomonsen breeds from southern Labrador (where it intergrades with the following subspecies), the Gulf of St. Lawrence, and Nfld. southward. *C. g. ultimus* Salomonsen occupies the remainder of the known breeding range in Canada from the high Arctic south to James B. and northern Labrador. Possibly sight records in the western Arctic refer to yet another race *C. g. mandtii*, which is like *ultimus* but with longer bill.

PIGEON GUILLEMOT
Le Guillemot du Pacifique. *Cepphus columba* Pallas
Plate 36. L. 12.5 to 14.5 in.

A west coast species very similar to the Black Guillemot of the Canadian Arctic and the Atlantic Coast, differing by (1) brownish grey under wing coverts (but sometimes mixed with considerable white), (2) a black bar cutting part way across the white patch on upper side of wing, and (3) somewhat larger size.

Measurements (*C. c. columba*). *Adult male:* wing, 167–180.9 (174.1); tail, 46.5–53.2 (49.1); exposed culmen, 31–34.9 (31.7); tarsus, 33.2–36.7 (35.1). *Adult female:* wing, 166.8–175 (171.7) mm.

Field Marks. Pacific Coast. Adults are readily distinguishable from all but the Black Guillemot, which is not known to visit the Pacific Coast. The black bar part way across white wing patch of adults (unreliable in immatures) and the brownish under wing coverts, when they can be seen, would distinguish the Pigeon Guillemot. In immatures the white wing patch is often heavily obscured.

Habitat and Nesting. Similar to Black Guillemot. Birds sometimes excavate own burrows. Incubation said to be 30 days (Drent and Guiguet). *Eggs*, usually 2; slightly larger and more heavily marked than in Black Guillemot.

Breeding Distribution of Pigeon Guillemot

Range. North Pacific. Breeds from the Chukotski Peninsula, islands in Bering Sea (except the Pribilofs), and the Aleutian Islands south to the Kurile Islands and California (Santa Barbara Islands).

Range in Canada. Breeds commonly on the coast of British Columbia wherever suitable conditions are found. Winters off the breeding grounds.

Subspecies. *Cepphus columba columba* Pallas is the breeding and common permanent resident of coastal B.C. Dickinson (1953) has assigned a specimen from Lund, B.C., to *C. c. kaiurka* Portenko, which breeds in the w. Aleutians.

MARBLED MURRELET

L'Alque marbrée. *Brachyramphus marmoratus* (Gmelin)
Plate 36. L. 9.5 to 10.5 in.

Bill slender, pointed. *Breeding plumage:* Upper parts dusky, the back feathers with rusty brown tips; under parts mottled brown and white. *Winter plumage:* Blackish above, feathers of back tipped with bluish, narrow white band (often incomplete) on back of neck, scapulars mixed with white, under parts white. *Autumn immatures* similar to winter adults, but white under parts are finely barred with dusky.

Measurements (*B. m. marmoratus*). *Adult male:* wing, 122–130 (128.1); tail, 30–34 (32.9); exposed culmen, 16.5–20 (17.6); tarsus, 16.9–17.9 (17.3). *Adult female:* wing, 121.5–128.6 (125.8) mm.

Field Marks. In breeding plumage, small size and colour. In winter plumage, its white stripe above the folded wing distinguishes it from the similar Ancient Murrelet.

Habitat. Mainly coastal salt water but, according to Munro and Cowan (1947), sometimes larger lakes on the coast of British Columbia are used. Nesting habitat not known but is inland, perhaps at times as much as 25 miles from the sea.

Nesting. Not certainly known. For an account of the evidence available in British Columbia, *see* Drent and Guiguet (1961, Occas. Papers, British Columbia Prov. Mus., No. 12). Nests inland within 25 miles of the sea, probably usually much nearer.

Range. Apparently breeds on or near the Pacific Coast from southeastern Alaska to northwestern California.

Range in Canada. Permanent resident along the coast of British Columbia. Although the nest is not certainly known, the bird obviously breeds commonly along virtually all the coast of that province as attested by, (1) eggs taken from oviduct of adult females (Harrison Lake; off Mitlenatch Island; Swanson Bay), (2) the finding of flightless young (Vancouver, Masset, and elsewhere), (3) the finding of an adult with a broken partly-incubated egg in debris of a felled tree (Masset), and (4) numerous observations of adults carrying food inland.

Subspecies. *Brachyramphus marmoratus marmoratus* (Gmelin).

ANCIENT MURRELET

L'Alque à cou blanc. *Synthliboramphus antiquus* (Gmelin)
Plate 36. L. 9.5 to 10.5 in.

Measurements. *Adult male:* wing, 130.2–140.2 (134); tail, 32.7–38.8 (35.3); exposed culmen, 13–14.9 (14.2); tarsus, 25.7–28.9 (27.2). *Adult female:* wing, 132.9–141.2 (135.7) mm.

Field Marks. A small alcid of the west coast. *Breeding*

PLATE 39

1 Spotted Owl

2 Great Gray Owl

3 Barred Owl

4 Short-eared Owl

Crosly

Crosby

plumage: black bib contrasts with white breast, sides of neck, and pale bill; white stripe over eye extends backward onto nape. *Winter plumage:* similar to Marbled Murrelet but lacks white line along scapulars.

Habitat. Marine. Nests on coastal islands.

Nesting. In colonies. Nest of dried grasses in burrows (or crevices) beneath stones, roots, or fallen logs on grassy or wooded slopes of coastal islands. *Eggs,* usually 2; often elongate and surprisingly large for size of bird, variable from bluish milky white through creams and buffs, marked with different shades of brown and bluish greys. Incubation (period unknown), by both sexes. Young leave nesting burrows when very small (variously estimated at one to four nights after hatching) and scramble down to join adults on the sea at night.

Range. North Pacific. Breeds from the Aleutian, Sanak, and Kodiak islands to the Queen Charlottes, British Columbia, and casually to Carroll Island, Washington; also from the Commander Islands and Kamchatka to Amurland, Sakhalin, the Kuriles, Korea, and Dagelet Island. Ranges farther south in winter, in North America to northern Baja California.

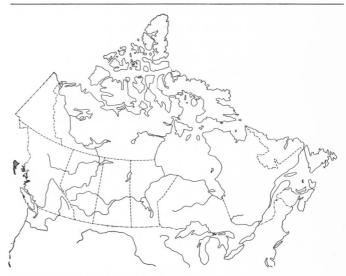

Breeding Distribution of Ancient Murrelet

Range in Canada. Breeds in north coastal British Columbia (north and west coasts of Graham Island; Langara Island). Winter resident and transient along the entire coast of British Columbia. Accidental in the interior of British Columbia (Swan Lake in Okanagan Valley, October 26, 1939), Yukon (Pelly Lake, November 1951), Manitoba (Winnipeg, October 8, 1953), Ontario (Toronto, November 18, 1901; Lake Erie, November 15, 1908); and Quebec (Montreal, April 13, 1913).

CASSIN'S AUKLET

L'Alque de Cassin. *Ptychoramphus aleuticus* (Pallas)
Plate 36. L. 8 to 9 in.

A small sea diver, without much plumage-change seasonally and lacking breeding plumage adornments. Adults blackish

201

slate above with dull brownish-grey throat and fore-neck, sides mixed with grey; breast and abdomen white; small white spot above and below eye; bill blackish, the basal third of lower mandible yellowish or flesh; iris white (as in other auklets, but not murrelets). Immatures similar to adults but with more white on throat.

Measurements. *Adult male:* wing, 109.5–129 (120.7); tail, 28–34.5 (31.4); exposed culmen, 18.5–20 (19.3); tarsus, 23.5–25 (24.6). *Adult female:* wing, 120–122 (121) mm. (Ridgway).

Field Marks. Pacific Coast. Smaller than Marbled and Ancient murrelets. On water (when white abdomen is hidden) looks all dark with, at close range, a tiny white spot over eye and a pale area at base of lower mandible. There is little seasonal change (young have more white on the throat), and in winter plumage it is the only *small* sea diver with dark fore-neck; however, Ancient Murrelet often retains black bib until late fall. Rhinoceros Auklet is obviously larger.

Habitat. Marine. Nests on coastal islands.

Nesting. In colonies. Nest, an accumulation of plant rubbish in burrows similar to those of Ancient Murrelet. *Egg,* one only; dull white, sometimes tinged with bluish or greenish, is unmarked. Incubation by both parents. The young, like other burrow-inhabiting alcids except the Ancient Murrelet, remain in the burrows until fledged. The incubation period appears to be unknown.

Range. Breeds on the Pacific Coast of North America from Sanak Islands (formerly), Shumagin and Kodiak islands, Alaska, south to Baja California (San Geronimo and San Martin islands) and Guadaloupe Islands. Winters from Vancouver Island to northern Baja California.

Breeding Distribution of Cassin's Auklet

Range in Canada. Breeds on coastal islands of British Columbia: northwestern Queen Charlotte Islands, Queen Charlotte Strait (Tree Islets, Pine Island), the Scott Islands, and Solander Island (off Cape Cook). Winters, apparently in very small numbers, off Vancouver Island (Barclay Sound).

Subspecies. *Ptychoramphus aleuticus aleuticus* (Pallas).

202

[**Parakeet Auklet.** L'Alque perroquet. *Cyclorrhynchus psittaculus* (Pallas). Hypothetical. Included in Taverner's *Birds of Canada* on grounds of probability only. There is a specimen in the L. B. Bishop collection labelled 'Franklin Bay, Arctic America' and taken either in 1903 or 1905 by H. H. Bodfish. Bishop (in litt. January 28, 1929) expressed serious doubts concerning the correctness of these data because the original labels of the specimens in the lot, including this specimen, were not attached, and in at least one case two labels were known to have become transposed.]

LEAST AUKLET

L'Alque minuscule. *Aethia pusilla* (Pallas)
L. ca. 6 to 6.5 in.

The tiniest alcid. Breeding plumage blackish above with white patch in scapulars, narrow white tips to secondaries; forehead and face in front of and below eye, streaked with narrow white feathers, these extending backward across ear; chin blackish, rest of under parts white, irregularly spotted or mottled with dusky; bill stubby, with a little knob near base of culmen. Winter plumage similar but under parts (except blackish chin) unmarked white and knob on bill lacking.

Measurements. *Adult male:* wing, 90–97.5 (92.9); tail, 25.5–29 (27.1); exposed culmen, 8–9 (8.6); tarsus, 17–19.5 (18.3). *Adult female:* wing, 88.5–96 (93.6) mm (Ridgway).

Habitat. Marine.

Range. Breeds from the coast of Chukotski Peninsula, Diomede Islands, and Cape Lisburne, Alaska, south on islands in Bering Sea to the Aleutian and Shumagin islands.

Status in Canada. Accidental in northwestern Mackenzie (Kittigazuit: specimen found on bare ice of small lake, January 1927).

RHINOCEROS AUKLET

L'Alque à bec cornu. *Cerorhinca monocerata* (Pallas)
Plate 36. L. 14 to 15.5 in.

Measurements. *Adult male:* wing, 175–183 (177.8); tail, 42.5–60.5 (55); exposed culmen, 32.5–36 (34); tarsus, 27–30 (28.2). *Adult female:* wing, 169–181 (175.6) mm (Ridgway).

Field Marks. A largish west coast alcid (between murrelets and murres in size), blackish brown above; with greyish brown cheeks, throat, fore-neck, sides, and flanks; whitish belly; side of head with two lines of white plume-like feathers (shorter in winter) extending backward, one from above the eye, the other from the corner of the mouth. In breeding season only, the yellowish bill is equipped with a vertical knob at the base of the culmen; hence the name 'Rhinoceros Auklet.' Immatures similar to winter adults, but head plumes are lacking; bill is much smaller and more dusky. Adults are easily identified, but immatures resemble immature Tufted Puffins but have smaller bill and whiter belly. Immatures are similar also in colour to Cassin's Auklet but are obviously larger.

Habitat. Marine. Nests on coastal islands.

Nesting. In colonies. Nests in a chamber at the end of a long burrow in the ground of wooded islands. The egg is laid on a small heap of miscellaneous grasses, twigs, and leaves. *Egg,* one only, is dull white, sometimes immaculate, but usually spotted with lavender, grey, or light brown; sometimes rather heavily spotted with darker browns. Incubation period is 31 days or more (Richardson). Young remain in the burrow until fledged.

Range. Breeds from southeastern Alaska (Saint Lazaria and Forrester islands) south to northwestern Washington (Destruction Island), formerly to California (Farallon Islands); also from the Kurile Islands south to northern Honshu and Korea. Winters from southern part of breeding range to Baja California and to Korea and Japan.

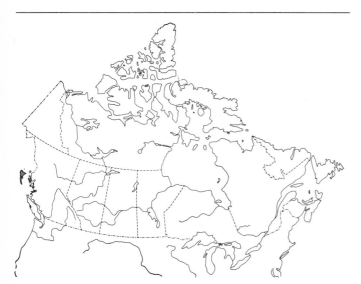

Breeding Distribution of Rhinoceros Auklet

Range in Canada. Breeds on coastal islands of British Columbia: Queen Charlotte Islands (Langara, Halgesen, Lihou, and Kunghit islands), Chatham Sound (Lucy Island), Queen Charlotte Strait (Pine Island). Winters in small numbers off southern Vancouver Island and in Georgia Strait.

COMMON PUFFIN (Atlantic Puffin)

Le Macareux arctique. *Fratercula arctica* (Linnaeus)
Plate 36. L. 11.5 to 13.5 in.

The grotesque, triangular, laterally compressed, and highly-coloured bill makes this bird unmistakable as a puffin, the only puffin of normal occurrence on the east coast. Winter adults and immatures have the bill much reduced in size and a darker face, but the characteristic face and other puffin markings are evident enough.

Measurements (*F. a. arctica*). *Adult male:* wing, 157–166.5 (160.8); tail, 47–52.2 (50.6); exposed culmen, 47.5–53.2 (50.5); tarsus, 26.9–29 (28.3). *Adult female:* wing, 157–161.8 (155.5) mm.

Field Marks. East coast. Adults in breeding plumage unmistakable as a puffin, the only puffin of our east coast. Winter adults and immatures have much smaller and duller bills, and the sides of the head are darker than in breeding birds. However, usually the characteristic puffin colour pattern (black band around fore-neck, paler throat and sides of head), as well as the big head and thick short neck will be evident. Shows no white anywhere on upper side of wing

(other *east* coast alcids have either a white line along the ends of the secondaries or a white wing patch).

Habitat. Marine. For nesting, coastal islands or sea cliffs.

Nesting. In colonies. Nest, either in a chamber at the end of a burrow in the ground or in a crevice or cranny in the rock of a cliff. *Egg*, usually one, is most often plain dull white but sometimes is somewhat spotted with browns and lilac. Incubation 40 to 43 days (R. M. Lockley), the greater part by the female. Young remain in the burrows until fledged.

Range. Breeds from Greenland, Jan Meyen, Spitsbergen, and Novaya Zemlya south to Maine, Iceland, the British Isles, northern France, Norway, and northwestern Russia. Winters south to Massachusetts and the western Mediterranean Sea.

Range in Canada. Breeds along the coast of Labrador (north at least to Nain), southeastern Quebec (north shore of the Gulf of St. Lawrence west to Perroquet Islands; Anticosti, Bonaventure, and Magdalen Islands), northern and eastern Newfoundland (St. John Bay, Walham Islands, Funk Island, Witless Bay, Baccalieu Island), Nova Scotia (very locally: Hertford and Ciboux islands; formerly Seal Island), and southwestern New Brunswick (Machias Seal Island). Reports of nesting on Resolution Island, N.W.T., require investigation.

Winters from Newfoundland southward in Atlantic waters. Accidental in Ontario (Ottawa, late October 1881) and southwestern Quebec (Lake St. Peter).

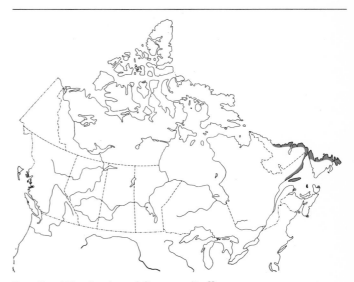

Breeding Distribution of Common Puffin

Subspecies. (1) *Fratercula arctica arctica* (Linnaeus) is the only subspecies known to breed in Canada and is the common winter resident. (2) *F. a. grabae*, a slightly smaller subspecies, is known as a winter visitor from Europe to Nfld. (two specimens banded at St. Kilda, British Isles, were taken, one at Herring Neck, the other on Bonavista B., in December 1939).

Remarks. There is a comical solemnity about the puffin with its serious facial expression and oversized, brightly-coloured bill. Its parrotlike appearance has given it the names 'sea parrot' and 'perroquet'. Much of the bulk and bright colour of the bill are shed after the breeding season; consequently this is much less impressive during autumn and winter.

Puffins are usually unwary, often even curious. At their nesting places they walk with a dignified gait, standing up on the toes unlike other alcids that shuffle more awkwardly with the tarsi pressed flat on the ground for support. On the water they are excellent swimmers and divers. Under water they use their wings for propulsion. Unless a wind is blowing, they have difficulty in becoming air-borne, often splashing over the water surface for considerable distances. Once in the air, however, their little rapidly-beating wings propel them swiftly with frequent side-to-side swaying, usual in the alcids.

Fishes, caught by underwater pursuit, are the main food of puffins. They are carried to the young in the parent's bill. The slippery fish are held crosswise in the beak, and it is surprising how many can be carried at one time.

Like other birds that nest in burrows in the ground, puffins are vulnerable to such mammal predators as cats, rats, dogs, and foxes. Consequently they choose islands for nesting purposes. Colonies quickly disappear, even from islands, once mammal predators have gained access to them. Numbers of the Common Puffin have declined in recent years, especially near settled areas.

[**Horned Puffin.** Le Macareux cornu. *Fratercula corniculata* (Naumann). Plate 36. L. ca. 14.5 in. A North Pacific species most similar to the Common Puffin of the Atlantic but with the black band around the fore-neck extending forward to the chin, a somewhat differently shaped and coloured bill, and greater dimensions, expecially those of tail. On the Pacific Coast it is more likely to be confused with the Tufted Puffin but has mainly white under parts and more extensive white on sides of head and lacks head plumes; it has a less deeply grooved bill, and the bird's dimensions are slightly smaller (except tail, which averages slightly longer). The pure white abdomen and lower breast distinguish it from the Tufted Puffin.

Measurements. *Adult male:* wing, 170–187.5 (181.4); tail, 60–68 (64.1); exposed culmen, 46–55 (50.6); tarsus, 27–30 (27.9). *Adult female:* wing, 168–185 (177.9) mm (Ridgway).

Status in Canada. Hypothetical. There are very convincing sight records for the coast of northern Queen Charlotte Islands, but no specimen has yet been taken in Canada. As the species breeds on the Alaska side of Dixon Entrance on Forrester Island and as there are specimens from Washington and Oregon, it is doubtless only a matter of time before the species will be established on the list of Canadian birds.]

TUFTED PUFFIN
Le Macareux huppé. *Lunda cirrhata* (Pallas)
Plate 36. L. 14.5 to 15.5 in.

Bill is unmistakable as that of a puffin. The dark grey under parts distinguish it from the Horned and Common puffins.

Measurements. *Adult male:* wing, 189.5–208 (197.5); tail, 60.0–64.2 (62.6); exposed culmen, 58.1–62.8 (59.8); tarsus, 34.8–36 (35.4). *Adult female:* wing, 183.5–197.8 (191.2) mm.

Field Marks. Pacific Coast. Puffin bill, dark grey-brown under body and straw-coloured head tufts are unmistakable. In winter the bill is much smaller, the face is mostly dusky, and the head tufts are missing. The under parts (although

PLATE 41

1 White-throated Swift

2 Black Swift

3 Vaux's Swift

4 Chimney Swift

5 Poor-will

6 Common Nighthawk

7 Whip-poor-will

PLATE 42

1 Black-chinned
   Hummingbird,
   adult male

2 Ruby-throated
   Hummingbird,
   (a) adult male
   (b) female

3 Rufous Hummingbird,
   (a) adult female
   (b) adult male

4 Calliope Hummingbird
   (a) adult male
   (b) female

5 Red-bellied Woodpecker,
   male

6 Yellow-bellied Sapsucker,
   (a) adult male
      (nominate race)
   (b) adult female
      (nominate race)
   (c) adult male
      (*ruber* race)

7 Williamson's Sapsucker,
   (a) adult male
   (b) adult female

in young birds light greyish) are always darker than the white under parts of the Horned Puffin.

Habitat. Marine. Breeds on coastal islands.

Nesting. In colonies. Nests either in burrows in the soil of higher grassy slopes of coastal islands or in natural crevices and cavities in rock; occasionally on the ground surface. Nest, whether in burrows or in rock crevices, is usually an accumulation of grass and leaves. *Egg*, one only, is dull white, and many are marked with greys or light brown. Incubation is by both parents.

Range. Breeds from the Kolyuchin Islands and East Cape, Siberia, and the Diomede Islands south to Kamchatka, Commander and Kurile islands, Sea of Okhotsk, Sakhalin, and Hokkaido; from Cape Lisburne, Alaska south to southern California; and islands in Bering Sea south to the Aleutians.

Breeding Distribution of Tufted Puffin

Range in Canada. Breeds along the coast of British Columbia: Queen Charlotte Islands, Moore Islands, Queen Charlotte Strait (Pine and Storm islands), Scott Islands, Vancouver Island (Solander, Clark, Cleland, and Mandarte islands). Winter record for Victoria, B.C., but apparently most of the population winters at sea.

Order **Columbiformes**–Sand-Grouse, Pigeons, and Doves

Family **Columbidae**–Pigeons and Doves

Number of Species in North America 16; in Canada 5

Pigeons and doves resemble in a general way the familiar domesticated pigeon or Rock Dove and are not difficult to recognize. The head is small in proportion to body size; the bill is soft and fleshy basally, with a horny tip; legs short; toes four, the hind toe on the same level as the others. Tail is variable, short to long. The family is poorly represented in Canada, but it is a large one with greatest diversity in tropical parts of the world. About 290 species are recognized. The names 'dove' and 'pigeon' are not based on trenchantly-different taxonomic characters and consequently do not represent two distinct groups. The Rock Dove, for example, in captivity is called 'domestic pigeon.'

BAND-TAILED PIGEON

Le Pigeon du Pacifique. *Columba fasciata* Say
Plate 37. L. 14.2 to 15.5 in.

A large pigeon, in Canada found west of the Coast Range. Adult female similar to but duller than adult male. Immatures lack the narrow white band across back of neck; head, neck, and breast are brownish grey; and the feathers of the chest and smaller wing coverts have narrow pale margins (*see* Field Marks).

Measurements (*C. f. fasciata*). *Adult male:* wing, 209–228.5 (218.5); tail, 133.8–155.9 (146.2); exposed culmen, 17.5–21 (19.8); tarsus, 26.5–30 (28.2). *Adult female:* wing, 209.9–219.5 (215.8) mm.

Field Marks. A large pigeon of western British Columbia, always distinguishable from the smaller Mourning Dove and the extinct Passenger Pigeon by its squarish or slightly rounded (not pointed) tail. Most likely to be confused with Rock Dove (domestic pigeon) which also has squarish tail, but Band-tailed Pigeon differs in, (1) broad pale band across end of tail with narrow dark band anterior to it, (2) yellowish feet and base of bill, (3) lack of black band across wing coverts, (4) uniformly coloured lower back and upper tail coverts (therefore no white patch shows in flight), (5) adults having narrow white band across back of neck (but absent in young), and (6) frequently alighting in trees (Rock Dove infrequently does so). *Voice:* two or three notes, the first pigeon-like; the others lower, and somewhat suggesting the voice of a Great Horned Owl.

Habitat. More open woodland (both coniferous and deciduous) and edges. In spring and autumn it visits grain-fields, but it may be found in various situations where foods like elderberry, cherries, cascara, arbutus, and acorns are available. It especially likes tall trees, including dead ones, for perching.

Nesting. Nest, a loose, often frail, platform of twigs on a horizontal branch of a coniferous or deciduous tree, at various heights between 8 and 40 feet or more. *Egg*, usually one, rarely two; white, slightly glossy. Incubation period probably 18 to 20 days (C. E. Bendire), by both sexes.

Range. Breeds from southern British Columbia, Utah, and north-central Colorado south to Baja California (Cape region), the Mexican tableland, and the mountains of Guatemala, Honduras, El Salvador, and northern Nicaragua. Winters from southwestern United States (occasionally north to British Columbia) southward.

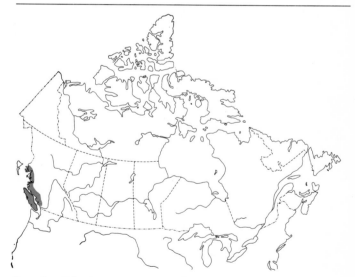

Breeding Distribution of Band-tailed Pigeon

Range in Canada. Breeds in southwestern British Columbia (De Horsey Island, Saltspring Island, Victoria, Coquitlam). Species has been recorded inland as far as Spuzzum and Lytton, and north to Terrace, B.C. Winter records for Victoria.

Subspecies. *Columba fasciata monilis* Vigors.

206

ROCK DOVE (Domestic Pigeon)
Le Pigeon biset. *Columba livia* Gmelin
Plate 37. L. 11 to 13.5 in.

In addition to the normal wild plumage (Plate 37), selective breeding has produced many variations in colour and form. In Canada it is not likely to be confused with any living species except the Band-tailed Pigeon of western British Columbia, but the Rock Dove's two dark wing bars, reddish legs, dark bill, and, in flight, white rump patch readily distinguish it. Occasionally the Rock Dove is mistaken by the novice for the extinct Passenger Pigeon, but regardless of colour variations the squarish tail of the Rock Dove is entirely different from the long, pointed tail of the Passenger Pigeon.

Habitat. In Canada, mainly in cities, towns, and farms; nesting in or on buildings and foraging in cultivated fields, barnyards, garbage dumps, railway yards, and streets. Usually avoids extensive forest but occasionally perches in trees.

Nesting. Nest, a shallow, slightly hollowed accumulation of twigs and straws placed (in Canada) usually inside or outside a building or cliff. *Eggs*, usually two; white and glossy. Incubation 17 to 19 days (Witherby, *et al.*), by both sexes. Young at first are fed 'pigeon milk' (a substance produced within the crop of the parents), later on regurgitated grain. Two or three broods are raised annually, as nesting may be attempted even in winter.

Range. Native to the Old World from islands in the eastern Atlantic eastward across southern Europe to parts of China and across northern Africa. Now widely established by feral domestic stock in North, Central, and South America, the Hawaiian Islands, parts of the West Indies, Australia, New Zealand, and in other scattered parts of the world.

Range in Canada. Introduced by establishment of feral domestic stock. Permanent resident in cities and farmland in Southern Canada from coast to coast.

Subspecies. North American populations are derived from several Old World subspecies, and consequently this mongrel stock can be referred to species only.

WHITE-WINGED DOVE
La Tourterelle à ailes blanches
Zenaida asiatica (Linnaeus)
L. 11 to 12.3 in.

Similar to Mourning Dove in size and general coloration but has greater wing coverts largely white (forming a conspicuous white bar); secondaries narrowly tipped white; tail roundly and broadly white-tipped except central feathers. In the field, looks like a Mourning Dove with white wing patch, and tail as described.

Status in Canada. Accidental in British Columbia (Renfrew, Vancouver Island, July 1918) and northern Ontario (Fort Albany, June 17, 1942). Both specimens, not examined by the writer, have been referred to *Z. a. mearnsi* (Ridgway). The species breeds from southern United States, south through Mexico and Central America; in northwestern South America, and in the West Indies.

MOURNING DOVE (Domestic Pigeon)
La Tourterelle triste. *Zenaidura macroura* (Linnaeus)
Plate 37. L. 11 to 13.2 in.

Tail long, pointed when closed, the central feathers longest. Female similar to male but duller with shorter tail. Late summer and early autumn immatures are duller than adult females and lack the black spot under the ear; the feathers of fore-neck, scapulars, and wing coverts have paler margins. The pointed tail distinguishes it from all other living Canadian doves and pigeons (the extinct Passenger Pigeon also had a long pointed tail but was much larger and never possessed a black spot below the ear.

Measurements (*Z. m. marginelle*). *Adult male:* wing, 141–153.5 (146); tail, 119.9–149.1 (135.4); exposed culmen, 13–15.3 (14.1); tarsus, 18.9–21.4 (20.1). *Adult female:* wing, 139.2–147 (143.3) mm.

Field Marks. A small slender brown bird with obviously pigeon-like head and motions, a long pointed tail; at close range the adults show a small black spot under the ear. Rises with a twittering whistle of the wings and in flight exposes much white in outer tail feathers. *Voice:* A mournful slow *Oh-woe-woe-woe*.

Habitat. Open woods, groves, and woodlots of both deciduous and coniferous trees. Forages in a variety of situations, such as weedy wasteland, cultivated fields and stubbles, grassland, roadsides, beaches, and gravel pits.

Breeding Distribution of Mourning Dove

Nesting. Usually single pairs; sometimes colonies. Nest, a fragile platform of twigs in coniferous (preferred) or deciduous trees, most often 15 to 25 feet up; also, especially on the prairies, on the ground. Sometimes the nest is placed on an old nest of another species. *Eggs*, usually 2; pure white. Incubation 15 days (O. L. Austin), by both parents. Young in nest are fed first on 'pigeon milk,' then on regurgitated seeds. Usually two broods annually.

Range. Breeds from southern Canada (and possibly southeastern Alaska) south to Panama and the West Indies. Northernmost populations move farther south to winter.

Range in Canada. Breeds in southern British Columbia (commonly in southern interior north to Williams Lake; very locally and in small numbers on the coast: Victoria, New Westminster), central and southern Alberta (Jasper, Dried Meat Lake, Milk River), south-central and southern Saskatchewan (Carlton, Prince Albert, Nipawin, Cypress Hills, Regina, Yorkton), southern Manitoba (Garland, Shoal Lake, Aweme, Hillside Beach), southern Ontario (north to Fort William, Sault Ste. Marie, Lake Doré, Ottawa; range has expanded northward in recent times), southwestern Quebec (Montreal, Lanoraie, St. Nicolas), southern New Brunswick (rarely: Glenwood), and very locally in Nova Scotia (Gaspereau).

Wanders widely outside breeding range, especially in autumn: northern British Columbia and Yukon (Dawson, Teslin, Carcross), southern Mackenzie (sight records: Fort Reliance, Hay River), northern Manitoba (Brochet, Churchill), northern Ontario (Moose Factory, Attawapiskat), southern James Bay (Ship Sands Island), central and eastern Quebec (Cabbage Willows, Pointe des Monts, Seven Islands, Johan Beetz Bay, Anticosti and Magdalen Islands, Gaspé Peninsula), Labrador (Nain, Red Bay, Spotted Islands, Battle Harbour), Newfoundland (very numerous autumn records), Prince Edward Island, and Nova Scotia (mainly an autumn visitant).

Winters in southern Ontario (north rarely and precariously to Ottawa), and in small numbers in southern British Columbia (Okanagan Landing, Victoria), Nova Scotia, and rarely Prince Edward Island and Newfoundland (St. John's). In the Maritimes, few survive the entire winter.

Subspecies. (1) *Zenaidura macroura marginella* (Woodhouse) is the breeding bird of w. Canada eastward through Man. (2) *Z. m. carolinensis* (Linnaeus), with slightly darker, less greyish coloration and slightly smaller size, breeds from s. Ont. eastward. Breeding specimens from w. Ont. (Fort William) have not been examined, and their affinities are uncertain.

PASSENGER PIGEON

La Tourte. *Ectopistes migratorius* (Linnaeus)
Plate 37. L. 15 to 18 in.

A large extinct pigeon with long, pointed, much-graduated tail feathers. Adult male as illustrated. Adult female much duller, browner above; fore-neck, breast, and abdomen, greyish brown; tail shorter. Juvenal similar to adult female but feathers of head, neck, upper breast, and scapulars tipped with whitish. The long, pointed tail distinguished it from Rock Dove and Band-tailed Pigeon. It differed from the Mourning Dove in its much larger size, different coloration, especially of adult male, and lack of a black spot under the ear in adults of both sexes.

Measurements. *Adult male:* wing, 196.5–214.5 (204.9); tail, 173–211 (193.5); exposed culmen, 15–18 (16.7); tarsus, 26–29 (27.4). *Adult female:* wing, 175–210 (198.1) mm (Ridgway).

Field Marks. Unnecessary as the species is extinct.

Nesting. Usually in colonies, sometimes incredibly immense; occasionally in single pairs. Nest, a frail platform loosely made of sticks and twigs on a branch of a deciduous (preferred) or coniferous tree at heights from 8 to 50 feet. A single white *egg* (sometimes two), was laid. Incubation about 14 days, by both sexes (A. C. Bent). Two or more broods annually, sometimes only one.

Range. Extinct. The last individual died in captivity in Cincinnati, Ohio, September 1, 1914. Last known specimen taken in the wild at Sargento, Ohio, March 24, 1900. Formerly bred from central Montana, North Dakota, southern Manitoba and southeastern Canada south to eastern Kansas, Oklahoma, Mississippi, and Georgia. Wintered in southeastern United States.

Status in Canada. Extinct. Details of former breeding range poorly known. Bred in central-eastern Saskatchewan: Cumberland House (Drummond, 1830, *Botanical Miscellany* 1: 180–181). Manitoba: Probably nested widely, abundantly in southern parts, and wandered north to Churchill and York Factory; known breeding colony at Waterhen River between lakes Manitoba and Winnipegosis; last known Manitoba specimen taken at Winnipegosis, April 13, 1898. Ontario: Bred in great numbers in southern parts; also west to northern Lake of the Woods and north to Moose Factory. Margaret H. Mitchell (1935, *Contrib. Royal Ont. Mus. Zool.* 7: 1–181) has presented an excellent history of the species in Ontario and includes breeding records for 45 of the 55 Ontario counties and districts. Last known Ontario specimen taken was at Sherkston, near Niagara, mid-September, 1891; last reliable sight record was at Penetanguishene, May 18, 1902. Quebec: Formerly southwestern parts, north rarely to perhaps Fort George and east probably to Gaspé Peninsula; species recorded east to Pointe des Monts and Anticosti Island. New Brunswick: Was abundant in summer with breeding records for Scotch Lake, Grand Falls, and possibly Grand Manan; last known specimen killed at Scotch Lake, 1899. Nova Scotia: Former breeder and transient; last definite record about 1857. Prince Edward Island: Apparently it was common and probably bred.

West of Saskatchewan there is no definite evidence of breeding, although it may have done so. It is known to have occurred in British Columbia (specimen: Chilliwack, June 29, 1859) and Mackenzie (formerly wandered down the Mackenzie Valley to forts Simpson, Norman, and Good Hope). Accidental on Baffin Bay, July 31, 1829.

Remarks. Probably no other medium-sized North American bird existed in such vast numbers as did the Passenger Pigeon. In migration great flocks darkened the sky; in roosting places, limbs of trees crashed under the sheer weight of its numbers; largest nesting colonies occupied hundreds of square miles. Its habit of concentrating in immense flocks facilitated its mass slaughter. Trainloads were shipped from favoured areas. It laid only one or two eggs to a clutch, and its reproductive potential was therefore inadequate to cope with the vast drain on its numbers. It was gunned, trapped, and clubbed off the face of the earth. Today the Passenger Pigeon, whose myriads not so long ago were one of the wonders of this continent, is gone forever. We, and all who follow us, will never see a living one.

Order **Cuculiformes**–Cuckoos and Plantain-eaters

Family **Cuculidae**–Cuckoos, Roadrunners, Anis

Number of Species in North America 7; in Canada 2

The cuckoo family containing 125 or more species is represented in the tropical and temperate parts of all the continents of the world. The North American species build fragile nests, but many of the Old World species are parasitic, laying their eggs in the nests of other birds.

Although the species of the world vary greatly in appearance, the two Canadian species are very similar. Long slender birds, plain brown above, plain white below, with long graduated tails, slightly downcurved bills, and zygodactylous (two toes in front, two behind) feet. Economically, cuckoos are extremely valuable because they devour vast numbers of insects and have a particularly voracious appetite for caterpillars.

YELLOW-BILLED CUCKOO

Le Coulicou à bec jaune. *Coccyzus americanus* (Linnaeus)
Plate 37. L. 11 to 12.6 in.

Sexes alike (*see* Field Marks). Young resemble adults but are duller; the black of the lateral tail feathers is much greyer, and the white tips are less of a contrast.

Measurements (*C. a. americanus*). *Adult male:* wing, 137–142 (139); tail, 140.2–143.9 (141.1); exposed culmen, 23.9–26.1 (24.9); tarsus, 26.3–26.9 (26.6). *Adult female:* wing, 140–156.5 (148.1) mm.

Field Marks. Plain brown upper parts, unmarked greyish-white under parts, downcurved bill, long graduated tail, and slender outline mark it as a cuckoo. The yellow lower mandible, broad white tips to the otherwise black outer tail feathers (best observed from below as they are concealed from above by brown central tail feathers), and a cinnamon-rufous area in the primaries (conspicuous in flight) separate it from the Black-billed Cuckoo. *Voice:* A long series of hollow wooden clucks, characteristically becoming slower near the end.

Habitat. Open woodland; willow and alder tangles; thickets.

Nesting. The nest, a frail flat loose structure of twigs sparsely lined with soft plant material, is placed usually 4 to 9 feet above ground in shrubbery or a low tree. The three or four light greenish-blue *eggs* are said to be incubated by both sexes but mainly by the female. Rarely it lays eggs in other birds' nests, including that of the Black-billed Cuckoo.

Range. Breeds from southern Canada (locally) south to northern Mexico and parts of the West Indies. Winters in South America.

Range in Canada. Breeds in southwestern British Columbia (Victoria, Pitt Meadows); southern Manitoba (rarely: Selkirk); southern Ontario (commonly in Lake Erie region but rarely north to Ottawa and Rosseau); rarely in extreme southwestern Quebec (Montreal Island, Ulverton), and southern New Brunswick (Saint John).

Breeding Distribution of Yellow-billed Cuckoo

Accidental, due mainly to autumn storms, in Nova Scotia (many records September–December), Prince Edward Island (Brackley Point, Mount Stewart), Newfoundland (St. John's region: specimens October 12, 1954, and November 15, 1955), north shore of the Gulf of St. Lawrence (Moisie River, P.Q., October 6, 1953), and Labrador (Hamilton River). Notable was October 1954, when large numbers appeared in Nova Scotia and New Brunswick, and small numbers in Newfoundland.

Subspecies. (1) *Coccyzus americanus americanus* (Linnaeus) breeds from Ont. eastward; probably the small Man. breeding population also is referable to it, but no specimens were examined by me. (2) *C. a. occidentalis* Ridgway, averaging somewhat larger in size, is the subspecies breeding in B.C.

BLACK-BILLED CUCKOO

Le Coulicou à bec noir. *Coccyzus erythropthalmus* (Wilson)
Plate 37. L. 11 to 12.6 in.

Sexes similar (for distinctions from Yellow-billed Cuckoo, *see* Field Marks). Young resemble adults, but white tips of tail feathers are less distinct and eye-ring is not red.

Measurements. *Adult male:* wing, 132.9–140.9 (136.5); tail, 147.4–159.8 (152.6); exposed culmen, 20.2–23.9 (21.9); tarsus, 21.1–24.1 (22.9). *Adult female:* wing, 130.4–148.9 (141.1) mm.

Field Marks. Longer than Robin. Long graduated tail, slender outline; brown upper parts, plain white under parts, and downcurved bill mark it as a cuckoo. All black bill (no yellow on lower mandible), red eye-ring, narrower much less

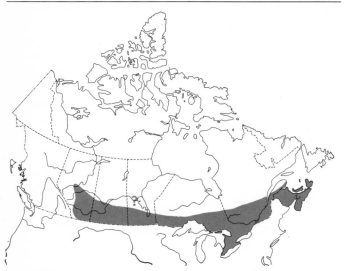

Breeding Distribution of Black-billed Cuckoo

sharply defined white tips to the tail feathers, and in flight lack of a conspicuous cinnamon-rufous area in the wing separate it from Yellow-billed Cuckoo. *Voice:* Hollow wooden clucks, tending to phrases of three or four clucks, with a slight pause between phrases.

Habitat. More open woodland; tangles of willow, alder, vines, and similar cover.

Nesting. Nest is of twigs. It usually is fragile but often is more substantially made than that of the preceding species and is usually better lined with soft vegetable material. It is placed most often 2 to 7 feet above the ground (occasionally more or less) on a branch in a low bush or tree, either deciduous or coniferous. *Eggs*, 2 to 4, usually 3; blue-green averaging slightly smaller and darker than those of the Yellow-billed. Incubation, by both sexes, requires 10 or 11 days (Ruth Spencer). Occasionally lays in nests of other birds including that of the Yellow-billed Cuckoo.

Range. Breeds from southern Canada (Alberta east), south to eastern Wyoming, Nebraska, Kansas, Tennessee, and South Carolina (Mount Pleasant). Winters in north-western South America.

Range in Canada. Breeds in central-eastern and south-eastern Alberta (Athabasca, Duhamel, Camrose, Sullivan Lake, Castor), southern Saskatchewan (Cypress Hills, Somme, Yorkton, Regina), southern Manitoba (Riding Mountain National Park, Hartney, Hillside Beach, Indian Bay, Shoal Lake, probably Cedar Lake), southern and central Ontario (commonly in the south; in small numbers north at least to Savanne, Port Arthur, and Matheson; probably Sioux Lookout), southwestern Quebec (Meach Lake, Montreal, Chambly, Hatley, Quebec, Rivière du Loup), New Brunswick, Prince Edward Island, and Nova Scotia.

Recorded in summer north to north-central Ontario (Moosonee) and in Quebec to Lake Waswanipi and eastern Gaspé Peninsula (Sandy Beach, Percé). Accidental in Newfoundland (St. John's, October 12, 1955). There are sight records for British Columbia.

Order **Strigiformes**–Owls

This order has a worldwide distribution. Owls have large heads, more or less flattened in front, with broad facial discs. Eyes are large and are directed forward. Bills are strongly hooked; the toes are armed with sharp, curved talons. The outer toe is reversible. The legs are feathered in most species. Plumage is extremely soft and fluffy facilitating silent flight.

Most owls hunt at night, but some, like the Snowy, Short-eared, and Hawk owls, hunt in daylight or at dusk. Even the nocturnal owls have excellent vision in daylight except when brought suddenly from darkness into strong light. Rodents, particularly mice and rats, are the staple food of most of these interesting birds of prey. Their great value in keeping rodent numbers in check would be difficult to overestimate.

Family **Tytonidae**–Barn Owls

Number of Species in North America 1; in Canada 1

Face, long and triangular, or heart-shaped; eyes rather small for an owl. Legs are long and are covered with short scanty feathers, the toes with a sparse covering of bristles, the middle toenail pectinate on inner edge. Structurally these owls differ greatly from other owls, but their general habits are similar.

BARN OWL

L'Effraie. *Tyto alba* (Scopoli)
Plate 38. L. 14.5 to 17.5 in.

Head rather large without ear tufts, facial disc distinctly heart-shaped, eyes black and not large, lower legs and toes scantily feathered. Adults of both sexes and immatures, similar in coloration. Upper parts mainly buffy, back to top of head frosted over with greyish and spotted with blackish and greyish; under parts variable from tawny to white, without any bars or stripes, but finely spotted or speckled with black.

Measurements. *Adult male:* wing, 314–345 (328.6); tail, 126–152.5 (138.1); culmen from cere, 21–24 (22.1). *Adult female:* wing, 320–360 (336.9) mm (Ridgway).

Field Marks. A medium-sized, slender-bodied, pale, generally buffy owl with long heart-shaped face, black eyes, no ear tufts, and no stripes or bars on the finely spotted under parts. The Short-eared Owl, another buffy owl of about the same size, is easily distinguished from it by striped under parts, well-feathered legs and toes, yellow eyes, and very differently shaped facial disc. *Voice:* hisses and rasping cries and a variety of weird notes.

Habitat. Forages over fields and similar open places particularly where small rodents abound. Roosts and nests in buildings, hollow trees, and cavities in cliffs and banks.

Nesting. In dark sheltered places, such as hollows in trees or cliffs, barn lofts, towers of abandoned or less disturbed buildings. No nest is made, but as the site is used year after year, piles of rodent fur and bones accumulate. *Eggs,* usually 5 to 8; white. Incubation period 30 to 34 days (Niethammer). Young fed by both parents.

Breeding Distribution of Barn Owl

Range. Nearly cosmopolitan. In the New World from extreme southern Canada (locally) south to southern South America and the West Indies.

Range in Canada. Breeds in extreme southwestern British Columbia (Crescent Beach, Ladner, probably southern Vancouver Island), extreme southern Ontario (Kingsville,

211

Chatham, Strathroy, Blenheim, Queenston), and rarely southwestern Quebec (Berthierville). Winters in breeding range.

Wanders casually north to southern Saskatchewan (Aylesbury), southern Manitoba (La Rivière, Whitewater Lake, Ste. Anne des Chênes), southern Ontario (Sault Ste. Marie, Ottawa). Accidental in New Brunswick (Cape Tormentine), Nova Scotia (Tusket, December 16, 1910), and Newfoundland (St. Anthony, November 29, 1957).

Subspecies. Although many subspecies of the Barn Owl are found in various parts of the world, *Tyto alba pratincola* (Bonaparte) is the only one known from North America.

Family **Strigidae** – Typical Owls

Number of Species in North America 17; in Canada 14

A large family including all the owls except the Barn Owls and represented in most parts of the world. Face more rounded, less triangular, than in the Tytonidae; eyes usually larger, ear tufts often present. It differs also in numerous structural details.

SCREECH OWL

Le Petit Duc. *Otus asio* (Linnaeus)
Plate 38. L. 7 to 10 in.

A small eared owl with yellow eyes. With the exception of the rare and local Flammulated Owl, it is our only *eared* owl with folded wing under 7 inches long. Eastern and mid-west populations have two well-marked (grey and red) colour phases regardless of sex and age.

Measurements (*O. a. naevius*). *Adult male:* wing, 156.5–174.9 (164.3); tail, 77.1–86.9 (81.2); culmen from cere, 14–15.9 (15.2). *Adult female:* wing, 155.2–177.9 (166.5) mm.

Field Marks. A small nocturnal owl with prominent ear tufts and yellow eyes, eastern birds in two distinct (a grey and a red) colour phases. The rare Flammulated Owl of southern British Columbia is very similar but has dark eyes. Long-eared and Great Horned owls also have ear tufts, but the Screech Owl is obviously smaller and in flight has entirely different, rapid wing beats. *Voice:* In the East, a long, tremulous, low whistle descending rapidly toward the end. In western birds there is less tendency for the call to descend in pitch.

Habitat. Open woodlands, groves, orchards, and shade trees about houses in backwoods or city.

Nesting. Nests in holes in trees (natural cavities and especially old woodpecker holes); also in bird houses. Heights vary from a few to 80 feet above ground. *Eggs*, usually 4 or 5; white. Incubation about 26 days (A. R. Sherman), mostly, if not entirely, by female.

Range. Resident from southeastern Alaska, much of southern Canada, and Maine south to south-central Mexico and Florida.

Range in Canada. Permanent resident in western and southern interior British Columbia (coast of mainland, Vancouver and Goose islands; southern interior, north

rarely to Vanderhoof region), southern Saskatchewan (Yorkton; breeding range not well known, but the bird has been reported occurring west to Cypress Hills region and north to Saskatoon), southern Manitoba (Red and Assiniboine river valleys, Riding Mountain, Oak and Whitewater lakes, Aweme), southern Ontario (commonly in south and northward at least to Port Sydney and Ottawa; presence of species reported north to Lake Nipissing and Lake of the Woods), and extreme southwestern Quebec (Chelsea, Montreal).

Possibly breeds also in central Alberta (two specimens: Flatbush, Kinuso; one sight record: Belvedere). Casual or accidental in Nova Scotia (Indian Lake, September 1892). Records for New Brunswick are not completely satisfactory.

Breeding Distribution of Screech Owl

Subspecies. (1) *Otus asio naevius* (Gmelin), with well-marked grey and red colour phases, is the breeding bird of Ont. and Que. (2) *O. a. swenki* Oberholser, a much paler race also with two well-marked colour phases, breeds in s. Man. (Winnipeg). (3) *O. a. macfarlanei* (Brewster), which averages larger and darker than *naevius* and has no red colour phase, is the subspecies of interior B.C. (4) *O. a. kennicottii* (Elliot), much darker and more brownish than *macfarlanei*, is the bird of coastal B.C. The writer has examined no material from sw. Sask. for the possible occurrence there of *O. a. maxwelliae* (Ridgway).

FLAMMULATED OWL (Flammulated Screech Owl)

Le Duc nain. *Otus flammeolus* (Kaup)
L. 6.3 to 7.5 in.

Suggests the Screech Owl but is smaller and has dark instead of yellow eyes and shorter ear tufts and quite naked toes.

Measurements. *Adult male:* wing, 128–138 (132.9); tail, 58–63.5 (59.7); culmen from cere, 8.5–10 (9.5). *Adult female:* wing, 128.5–144 (135.2) mm (Ridgway).

Field Marks. Looks like a small Screech Owl with dark brown eyes (instead of yellow).

Habitat. Pine and other coniferous woodland.

Nesting. In a woodpecker hole or similar tree cavity. *Eggs*, usually 3 or 4; white.

Range. Breeds from southern British Columbia south through the mountains west of the Great Plains to the highlands of Mexico and Guatemala.

Range in Canada. Very rare and local breeder in southern British Columbia (the only known nest was located about 20 miles west of Penticton). There are two other British Columbia specimen records (Penticton, 1902; and near Kamloops, August 11, 1935).

Subspecies. *Otus flammeolus flammeolus* (Kaup). Some authors regard the Flammulated Owl as a subspecies of the Old World *Otus scops*.

GREAT HORNED OWL

Le Grand Duc. *Bubo virginianus* (Gmelin)
Plate 38. L. male, 18 to 23; female, 22 to 25 in.

A large owl, the only Canadian owl over 16 inches in total length with prominent ear tufts. Sexes similarly coloured, but populations are geographically variable in colour (*see* Subspecies).

Measurements (*B. v. virginianus*). *Adult male:* wing, 337–380.5 (356.9); tail, 193–223.5 (209.9); culmen from cere, 27–31.4 (29.8). *Adult female:* wing, 357.5–395.5 (380.8) mm.

Field Marks. Large size and prominent ear tufts. *Voice:* a series of deep *hoo* notes, often five, which are less varied and deeper than the Barred Owl's; also a scream.

Breeding Distribution of Great Horned Owl

Habitat. Both deciduous and coniferous woods varying from extensive heavy forests to isolated groves, woods of city parks, and, on the prairies, wooded coulees and river valleys.

Nesting. Nest, usually in an old nest of a hawk, crow, or squirrel in trees; sometimes in a cavity in a tree or on a cliff ledge. *Eggs*, usually 2 or 3; white. Incubation 30 days (A. K. Gilkey, *et al.*).

Range. North and South America from the northern limit of trees south (except the West Indies) to the Straits of Magellan. There is limited migration and wandering.

Range in Canada. Resident throughout most wooded parts north to the limit of trees in Yukon, Mackenzie, British Columbia (except Queen Charlotte Islands), Alberta, Saskatchewan, Manitoba, Ontario, Quebec (north at least to Chimo, but apparently not recorded from Magdalen Islands), Labrador (north to Okak), Newfoundland, New Brunswick, Prince Edward Island, and Nova Scotia.

Recorded without evidence of breeding in Keewatin (mainly in winter: Windy River; mouth of Thlewiaza River. Casual at Chesterfield Inlet: Specimen, June 10, 1935). Winters within breeding range including northern parts, and sometimes probably also north of breeding range; for example, in Keewatin and perhaps elsewhere where winter ptarmigan abound. Individuals wander over long distances, perhaps in all directions but mainly southward.

Subspecies. (1) *Bubo virginianus virginianus* (Gmelin), medium dark coloration with distinctive amount of redness in the plumage: s. Ont., s. Que., N.B., P.E.I., and N.S. (tends toward *heterocnemis* in n. Cape Breton I.). (2) *B. v. heterocnemis* (Oberholser), very dark: Nfld., Lab., c. and n. Que. (3) *B. v. subarcticus* Hoy (*wapacuthu* of the A.O.U. Check-list, Fifth Edition), extremely pale, extensively white: Mack. (status in extreme nw. part uncertain), c.-e. B.C. (Peace River parklands), Alta. (except mountains), Sask., Man., w. and n. Ont. (however, w. and n. Ont. populations have recently been considered separable and named *scalariventris* Snyder, 1961, *Roy. Ont. Mus., Cont.* 54: 5. As I have examined little pertinent breeding material, I cannot express an opinion as to the validity of *scalariventris*. Also, birds of southern parts of the Prairie Prov. are referred to *occidentalis* in A.O.U. Check-list, Fifth Edition, but our large series from the southern parts of the Canadian prairies are not separable from *subarcticus* from farther north). (4) *B. v. lagophonus* (Oberholser), much darker than *subarcticus*, usually less tawny than *virginianus:* Yukon, interior B.C. (except Peace River parklands), and sw. Alta. (mountains); possibly extreme w. Mack. (but only one non-breeding specimen available). Outside breeding season individuals wander considerably, often widely.

Remarks. The Great Horned Owl is savage and powerful. It preys on a wide variety of birds and small mammals, notably rabbits, rats, mice, grouse, ducks, crows, poultry, and skunks. Occasionally it even attacks a porcupine. It is our only owl that is considered really destructive. Small animals are eaten entire. The indigestible bones, fur, and feathers are regurgitated as pellets, as is usual in owls.

It hunts mostly at night or at dusk. The daylight hours are spent dozing in the branches of a tree. Crows detest it. When a sharp-eyed Crow spots an owl, the Crow lets out a peculiarly intonated *caw* which soon tells every other Crow within hearing that an owl is in the vicinity. Crows quickly gather in numbers about the dozing owl, and, perching as near as they consider expedient, all *caw* at the top of their voices. When the owl seemingly can stand it no longer, it flies but is closely followed by the noisy black mob, and several such attempts to get away may be necessary before the owl is finally able to shake off its tormentors.

SNOWY OWL

Le Harfang des neiges. *Nyctea scandiaca* (Linnaeus)
Plate 38. L. 22 to 27 in. (female larger than male)

A large owl, as large as the Great Horned but lacks ear tufts; general coloration white, more or less barred and spotted with dark brown; eyes yellow; legs and toes very heavily feathered. Adult male is mainly white (occasionally immaculate). Adult female is more heavily marked than adult male, and immatures are more profusely (often heavily) marked than adult females.

Measurements. *Adult male:* wing, 375.5–407.5 (396.4); tail, 210–219.5 (214.1); culmen from cere, 24.7–29 (27). *Adult female:* wing, 415–438.5 (414.9) mm.

Field Marks. A large, bulky, very white owl (often heavily barred and spotted with dark brown) with round head lacking ear tufts. Unlikely to be confused with anything but whitish races of the Great Horned Owl, but lack of ear tufts distinguishes it. It is active in daylight and frequents open places.

Habitat. For nesting, low or high arctic tundra, preferably hummocky or rolling. In migration and winter in the south, open places such as fields, prairies, marshes, coasts, shores of lakes and large rivers. Perches on the ground, fence posts, straw stacks, trees, radio towers, and buildings.

Nesting. On the ground, a slight depression often thinly lined with moss or grass in a high spot on rolling tundra. *Eggs,* 5 to 7, occasionally more or less; white. Incubation 32 to 33 days (Witherby, *et al.*), by the female.

Range. Circumpolar; arctic tundras of the world. Winters within breeding range and south to central Europe, central Asia, and northern United States; occasionally south to southern United States.

Breeding Distribution of Snowy Owl

Range in Canada. Breeds from Prince Patrick Island (probably) and northern Ellesmere Island (Cape Sheridan) south through the Arctic Archipelago to northern Yukon (Herschel Island), northern Mackenzie (Baillie Island, Perry River, and probably inland for an undetermined distance),

Keewatin, northern Manitoba (Churchill), Southampton Island, northern Quebec (Povungnituk, Kogaluk River, Fort Chimo), and northern Labrador (south to Okak, possibly to Nain).

Winters within parts of the breeding range, but probably south of the zone of 24-hour winter darkness, and south in irregular numbers to southernmost parts of all the provinces. Largest flights to southern localities occur about every four years, these being correlated with periodic low points in numerical fluctuations of small mammals in the Arctic, especially lemmings, which are a staple arctic food.

Remarks. The hardy Snowy Owl is a winter visitor to the settled southern parts of Canada. Its luxurious feather coat is ideal for a life in the cold. Its feet are densely feathered to the tips of the toes, and the bill is almost hidden in the warm feathers of the face. Only the searching yellow eyes are fully exposed. It spurns the protection of heavy forest and frequents instead more open expanses where winter's bitterest blasts blow unimpeded. Unlike many other owls, this one is active during the daylight hours.

In the Arctic, this owl depends for food on lemmings and other rodents and, to some extent, on birds and fishes. Lemmings, its staple diet in the Arctic, tend to fluctuate violently in numbers periodically, building up to great abundance every four years or so, then suddenly dying off. In the resulting periods of lemming scarcity the owls must wander southward to find adequate food. Thus in southern Canada relatively large numbers of Snowy Owls appear, usually during one winter in four. Sometimes flights will occur in two successive winters, the second involving smaller numbers.

HAWK OWL

La Chouette épervière. *Surnia ulula* (Linnaeus)
Plate 40. L. 14.5 to 17 in.

A medium-sized slender owl without ear tufts; tail longish, decidedly graduated, its feathers tapering toward tip. Sexes alike in colour. Upper parts, dark brown spotted with white. Chest and abdomen, sharply and regularly barred with brown; greyish white facial disc with black outer border, the border extending down to sides of breast. Eyes and exposed part of bill, yellow. The sharply barred chest, sides, and abdomen, and the long tail are distinctive.

Measurements. *Adult male:* wing, 210–231 (222.4); tail, 167–187 (177.9); culmen from cere, 18.6–19.8 (19). *Adult female:* wing, 223–235.5 (228.6) mm.

Field Marks. A medium-sized, slender, long-tailed owl (often flicks tail) with sharply barred under parts and without ear tufts. Black outer margin of facial disc extends down to sides of chest. Active in daylight. Often perches on tree tops. Long slender tail gives it a hawk-like appearance. Flight, swift and hawk-like with rapid wing beats, occasionally hovers. *Voice:* A series of *kip, kip,* or *kleep, kleep;* a rising *skree-e-e-e-e-yip,* the *yip* emphatic.

Habitat. Open coniferous or mixed woodland, muskeg, or burntland with standing stubs.

Nesting. Nests in hollow top of a dead tree stub, in an old woodpecker hole, or in an old hawk or crow nest. *Eggs,* usually 3 to 7; white.

214

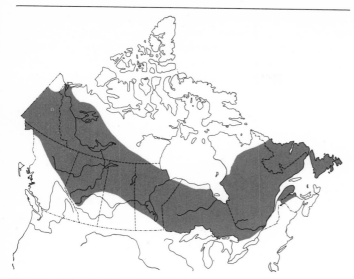

Breeding Distribution of Hawk Owl

Range. Holarctic. Breeds in the northern coniferous belts, north to tree limit, across Eurasia and North America. Winters in the breeding range and somewhat farther south, in North America south to southern Canada and northern United States.

Range in Canada. Breeds (north to treeline) from northern Yukon (Lapierre House, Old Crow), northwestern and central Mackenzie (Mackenzie Delta, Anderson River, Great Slave Lake), northern Saskatchewan (Lake Athabasca), northern Manitoba, northern Ontario, northern Quebec (Fort Chimo, Indian House Lake), central Labrador (Okak, Udjutok Bay), and Newfoundland south locally to northern British Columbia (Atlin, Peace River region), south-central Alberta (near Banff, probably Red Deer), central-eastern Saskatchewan (Hudson Bay Junction), southern Manitoba (Riverton, Kalevala), south-central Ontario (Thunder Bay, Lake Abitibi, Ottawa; perhaps Cameron), southern Quebec (Lochaber, Gaspé Bay), and New Brunswick (rarely: Tabusintac).

Winters from northernmost parts of breeding range (Mackenzie Delta, Indian House Lake) south irregularly and in variable numbers to southern parts of all provinces.

Subspecies. *Surnia ulula caparoch* (Müller).

PYGMY OWL

La Chouette naine. *Glaucidium gnoma* Wagler
Plate 40. L. 6.3 to 7.3 in.

A tiny western owl, smaller even than the Saw-whet Owl, with small head and no ear tufts. Sexes alike. Upper parts greyish to reddish brown, finely spotted with buffy white especially top of head, scapulars, and wings; around back of neck a narrow half-collar of mixed black and white. Lower breast and abdomen, white striped with dark brown. Tail dark brown with 6 or 7 white cross-bars. Eyes yellow. Distinguished from other Canadian owls by very small size and black-and-white half-collar on back of neck. Young similar to adults but top of head dark grey with only a few spots on forehead.

Measurements (*G. g. swarthi*). *Adult male:* wing, 87.3–93.3 (89.6); tail, 57.5–65 (62.2); culmen from cere, 10.6–11.9 (11.2). *Adult female:* wing, 90.9–96 (92.8) mm.

Field Marks. A bluebird-sized western owl with small head, no ear tufts, and rather longish tail often held quite high. Might be confused with the Saw-whet Owl, which is slightly larger. The Pygmy's sharper, darker stripes on the under parts, the black-and-white half-collar on hind-neck, the small head, and the often slightly elevated tail distinguish it. The Pygmy is active during the day, especially early morning and evening. *Voice:* A series of hollow, low, whistled, spaced *ook* notes, which are easily imitated.

Habitat. Open or broken coniferous and mixed woodland, edges and openings of coniferous forest.

Nesting. In abandoned woodpecker holes in trees, either deciduous or coniferous. *Eggs,* 2 to 7, usually 3 or 4; white, almost spherical. Incubation by female.

Range. Southeastern Alaska and northwestern and central British Columbia south through the Rockies and California to Guatemala.

Range in Canada. Found in British Columbia (permanent resident in southern and central parts including Vancouver Island. Recorded, but without evidence of breeding, northwest to Atlin and Driftwood River. Absent from Queen Charlotte Islands and probably from the northeastern corner) and Alberta (probably breeds in mountains of southwest near Banff and Jasper, but definite evidence is lacking. Wanders in winter farther east: to Nordegg, Peers, Fort Assiniboine, Phoenix, Sedgewick, McLeod Valley, Calgary, and Alexo).

Subspecies. There is considerable disagreement on the subspecies and their nomenclature. The A.O.U. Check-list (Fifth Edition) recognizes three races in B.C.: (1) *G. g. swarthi* Grinnell (Vancouver Island), (2) *G. g. grinnelli* Ridgway (western mainland), and (3) *G. g. californicum* Sclater (interior of B.C. and w. Alta.). However, *see* Munro and Cowan (1947) and Jewett, Taylor, Shaw, and Aldrich (1953). A study of critical material from both Canada and United States is needed.

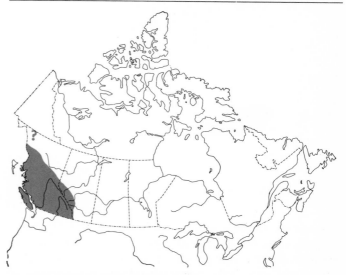

Breeding Distribution of Pygmy Owl

BURROWING OWL

La Chouette de terrier. *Speotyto cunicularia* (Molina)
Plate 40. L. 9 to 10 in.

A smallish round-headed owl with no ear tufts, poorly developed facial disc, long slim legs (tarsi unfeathered except sparsely in front), and short tail. Adults, above greyish brown, thickly spotted with whites and buffs; eyebrows and throat white, the lower throat crossed by a dark brown half-collar; breast and abdomen whitish, barred with brown; eyes yellow. Young for a short time lack brown bars on under parts. Size, sandy coloration, and long, slim, almost-bare legs and toes make the species unmistakable.

Measurements (*S. c. cunicularia*). *Adult male:* wing, 166–176 (171.5); tail, 77–84.5 (81.6); culmen from cere, 13.9–15 (14.4). *Adult female:* wing, 169–178.5 (172.5) mm.

Field Marks. A smallish sandy-coloured owl with short tail and long, slim, almost-bare legs. Active both day and night, mostly at dusk. Usually seen on the ground, or on a low fence post, in open country. Has bobbing motion when disturbed. Short-eared Owl also is found in similar open places but is much larger, is differently shaped, and has striped instead of barred under parts.

Habitat. Drier open short-grass treeless country.

Nesting. Nests at the end of a 5- to 10-foot ground burrow, dug and abandoned by a mammal. *Eggs,* 6 to 10; white, often nest-stained.

Range. Plains and treeless areas from southern parts of western Canada through western United States (west from Minnesota, Iowa, Oklahoma, and rarely Louisiana) to Honduras, central and southern Florida, the West Indies, Central America, and much of South America. In winter, it retreats from its northernmost breeding grounds.

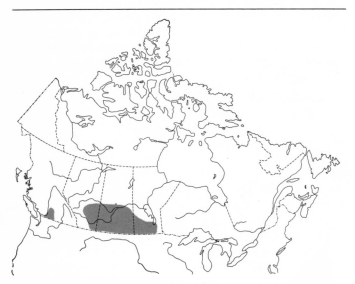

Breeding Distribution of Burrowing Owl

Range in Canada. Breeds in southern interior British Columbia (Kamloops; Similkameen and Okanagan valleys), southern Alberta (southern plains north to about Red Deer Lake), southern Saskatchewan (southern plains north to Livelong, St. Louis, and Nipawin), southwestern and cen-

tral-southern Manitoba (Whitewater Lake, Virden, Emerson, Winnipeg vicinity).

A few winter in extreme southwestern British Columbia (Comox; Trail and Snake islands; rarely Victoria). Casual in Ontario (Ajax). Accidental in southern Quebec (Arvida).

Subspecies. *Speotyto cunicularia hypugaea* (Bonaparte).

BARRED OWL

La Chouette rayée. *Strix varia* Barton
Plate 39. L. 18 to 23 in.

A largish brown-and-white round-headed owl without ear tufts. Sexes alike. Upper parts greyish brown, barred on head, neck, tail and flight feathers, and spotted elsewhere, with buffy white. Under parts whitish, the chest closely barred, the abdomen striped with brown; eyes blackish; bill yellowish. The combination of barred breast and striped abdomen distinguishes it.

Measurements (*S. v. varia*). *Adult male:* wing, 310.5–330 (320.1); tail, 209–230.5 (218.6); culmen from cere, 21.5–25 (23.6). *Adult female:* wing, 320.5–334 (328.5) mm.

Breeding Distribution of Barred Owl

Field Marks. A largish brown-and-white, nocturnal, round-headed owl with no ear tufts. It has black eyes, a barred breast, and a striped abdomen. Resembles Great Gray Owl and also the Spotted Owl of western British Columbia. The Barred Owl's barred breast, black eyes, and smaller size exclude the Great Gray. Striped abdomen and paler coloration separate it from the Spotted Owl. *Voice:* Hooting is less deep and more varied than that of the Great Horned Owl, closing with an extra syllable. Sounds like, "*Who cooks for yo—all?*"

Habitat. Denser darker forests, woodlands, even isolated woodlots of maturer trees (apparently prefers coniferous or mixed woods to deciduous), especially near lakes, streams, swamps, or marshes.

Nesting. Usually in hollows in trees (either deciduous or coniferous) but also in deserted tree nests of hawks or crows. *Eggs,* 2 or 3; plain white.

216

Range. Southern wooded Canada (from eastern British Columbia east to Nova Scotia) southward through the United States (east of the Rocky Mountains), and the mountains of Mexico to western Guatemala and Honduras.

Range in Canada. Permanent resident in woodlands of eastern British Columbia (scarce: Liard Crossing; Hart Lake, 47 miles north of Prince George; near Likely; Birch Creek; Salmon River, northwest of Vernon), central and western Alberta (Smoky River, north of Jasper; and northward in wooded country at least to Lesser Slave Lake region and probably Fort McMurray), central Saskatchewan (Klogei Lake, Cumberland House), south-central and south-eastern Manitoba (woodland north to Reader Lake near The Pas), central and southern Ontario (north at least to Ingolf, Port Arthur, Amyot, Timmins, and Moose Factory), southern Quebec (north to Lake Waswanipi; Lake Paterson, Mistassibi watershed; Godbout; Anticosti Island), New Brunswick, Prince Edward Island, and Nova Scotia. Winters throughout breeding range.

Subspecies. *Strix varia varia* Barton.

SPOTTED OWL

La Chouette tachetée. *Strix occidentalis* (Xantus)
Plate 39. L. 16.5 to 19 in.

A largish round-headed hornless owl with black eyes. Most closely resembles the Barred Owl but averages slightly smaller; browns are much darker and richer; top of head and hind-neck are spotted (instead of barred) with whitish; and abdomen is barred instead of striped. Sexes alike.

Measurements. *Adult male:* wing, 310–326 (320.5); tail, 210–220 (215.8); culmen from cere, 21–22 (21.3). *Adult female:* wing, ca. 328 mm (Ridgway).

Field Marks. A largish dark brown hornless owl with black eyes, found in forests of southwestern British Columbia. Our only other owls with black eyes are the Barred Owl and the obviously different Barn Owl. The Spotted is easily distinguished from the Barred by the former's lack of stripes on the abdomen and by its darker, richer coloration.

Breeding Distribution of Spotted Owl

Habitat. Dense forests, mainly coniferous, wooded ravines.

Nesting. Little known in Canada. In a tree cavity or crevice in a cliff. *Eggs*, 2 or 3; plain white.

Range. Permanent resident from southwestern British Columbia southward in coastal forests to southern California; and in the southern Rocky Mountains, from central Colorado south through eastern Arizona, New Mexico, and western Texas to central Mexico.

Range in Canada. Scarce permanent resident in extreme southwestern mainland British Columbia (north to Alta Lake, east to Hope and Manning Park). Not known to occur on Vancouver Island.

Subspecies. *Strix occidentalis caurina* (Merriam).

GREAT GRAY OWL

La Chouette cendrée. *Strix nebulosa* Forster
Plate 39. L. 25 to 33 in.

A very large (our largest), grey, round-headed, hornless owl with very large facial disc, yellow eyes, and long tail. Sexes alike. Most closely resembles Barred Owl but is much larger, more greyish (less brownish) in coloration, lacks distinct bars on back of neck and breast, has yellow eyes.

Measurements. *Adult male:* wing, 396–437.5 (416.3); tail, 295.5–305 (299.1); culmen from cere, 22.5–25.3 (24.3). *Adult female:* wing, 417–461.5 (433.4) mm.

Field Marks. An extremely large grey hornless owl with very large facial disc, yellow eyes, long tail, and indistinctly striped under parts. Below the bill is a black area which divides a narrow but surprisingly conspicuous white throat patch. Distinguished from Barred Owl by bright yellow eyes, unbarred breast, conspicuous white throat markings, and much more definite concentric rings on facial disc. It usually is quite tame. Frequently forages in daylight.

Habitat. Boreal forests, either coniferous or deciduous; wooded muskegs. While wintering in settled parts of the country, various woodland types, frequently deciduous. Often hunts meadow mice in open fields using fence posts, low trees, shrubbery, and wood edges as lookouts.

Nesting. In an abandoned nest of hawk or crow, 12 to 50 feet up in either a broadleafed or coniferous tree. *Eggs*, 2 to 5, most often 3; dull white, rather small for the size of the bird and less rounded, more oval, than is usual in owls.

Range. Northern coniferous belt across North America and Eurasia. In North America breeds from near treeline in central Alaska and Canada south in the western mountains to California (Madera County), northern Idaho, western Montana, Wyoming, northern Minnesota, and south-central Ontario. Winters within breeding range and irregularly south of it.

Range in Canada. Definite breeding data relatively few. Breeds sparsely in wooded country from northern Yukon (Old Crow, Lapierre House), northwestern and central Mackenzie (Lockhart River, Great Slave Lake), northern Saskatchewan (probably Lake Athabasca), northern Manitoba (The Pas), and northern Ontario (probably Severn River, Moose Factory) south through southern Yukon and interior British Columbia (probably south at least to Hulcar, 14 miles north of Vernon), northern and central Alberta (Fort

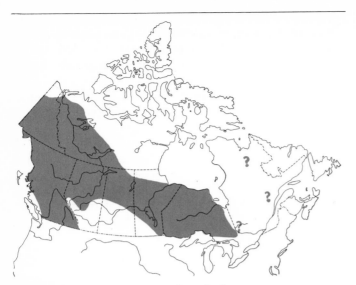

Breeding Distribution of Great Gray Owl

Habitat. Denser parts of woods (not necessarily extensive) and copses, probably preferring coniferous or mixed wood when available but in the Prairie Provinces regularly uses deciduous types also. Hunts over open country as well as in woodland. Often roosts gregariously.

Nesting. Nests in woodland, 10 to 30 feet up in a tree, usually using a nest of a hawk, crow, or magpie; occasionally on the ground. *Eggs*, 3 to 7; white. Incubation period about 28 days (E. L. Summer).

Range. Holarctic. Breeds in woodland across Eurasia and south to northwest Africa, and across North America. In North America from southern Canada south to northwest Baja California, southern Arizona, Oklahoma, Arkansas, and Virginia.

Range in Canada. Breeds in woodlands in southern Mackenzie (Fort Simpson, Fort Providence), southern British Columbia (Nulki Lake, Vancouver Island, Lulu Island, Vaseaux Lake), Alberta, Saskatchewan, central and southern Manitoba (Shoal Lake, Aweme; probably north to The Pas and Herb Lake), central and southern Ontario (north to southern James Bay), southern Quebec (north to St. Félicien: probably to Gaspé Bay; recorded in summer north to Great Whale River and Richmond Gulf), New Brunswick (Saint John, St. Stephen; probably St. Leonard), Nova Scotia (Kings County), and probably Prince Edward Island (summer occurrence records). In winter withdraws from northern colder parts of the range but winters in warmer parts (British Columbia, southern Ontario, and the Maritimes); one record for Labrador (Red Bay, December 8, 1930).

Chipewyan, Whitemud Lake, Belvedere, Edson, Rocky Mountain House, Jasper), Manitoba (Lake Winnipeg), and central Ontario (Nipissing District). Probably Quebec but breeding evidence lacking (reported in summer at Fort Mackenzie, Little Cape Jones River, and north of Lake St. John).

Winters throughout breeding range (north to Mackenzie Delta) and in irregular small numbers south of it in wooded parts of southern Canada and southeastward casually to New Brunswick and Nova Scotia (Pictou County).

Subspecies. *Strix nebulosa nebulosa* Forster.

LONG-EARED OWL

Le Hibou à aigrettes longues. *Asio otus* (Linnaeus)
Plate 38. L. 13 to 16 in.

Ear tufts long, conspicuous. Sexes similar (female larger and slightly darker). Upper parts dark brown, mixed with tawny and speckled and mottled with greyish white. Face tawny. Abdomen and sides white, boldly striped and narrowly cross-barred with brown. Eyes yellow. Canada has three owls with conspicuous long ear tufts, one very large (Great Horned), one small (Screech Owl), and one medium-sized (Long-eared) (*see also* Field Marks).

Measurements (*A. o. wilsonianus*). *Adult male:* wing, 269.5–295 (285.7); tail, 141.5–153.5 (148.1); culmen from cere, 15–17.7 (17.1). *Adult female:* wing, 274.8–300 (283.6) mm.

Field Marks. A not large (crow-sized) owl with long ear tufts, which are usually visible when it is at rest. Great Horned and Screech owls also have conspicuous ear tufts. Long-eared Owl's much smaller size, slenderer build, position of ear tufts nearer centre of head, and stripes on abdomen distinguish it from the Great Horned Owl; and its larger size and tawny face separate it from the grey-phased Screech Owl. In flight when the ear tufts are flattened, its greyer (less buffy) general coloration distinguishes it from the Short-eared Owl. It is nocturnal, whereas the Short-eared Owl is active during the day as well as at night.

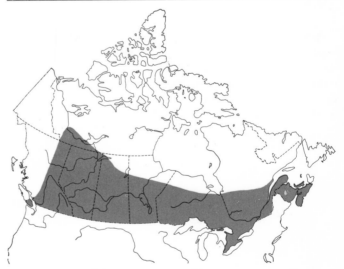

Breeding Distribution of Long-eared Owl

Subspecies. (1) *Asio otus wilsonianus* (Lesson) breeds across e. Canada intergrading with the following subspecies in sw. Man. (2) *Asio otus tuftsi* Godfrey, a paler western subspecies, breeding from extreme sw. Man. (Whitewater Lake), and Sask. westward (no material examined from Mack. or n. Alta.).

Remarks. Dozing away the daylight hours deep in tangles of prairie coulees or in coniferous or alder thickets in the

East, this owl is not often seen. Mice and other small rodents are its staple food. Although usually silent, its calls include soft hoots, mews, and shrieks.

SHORT-EARED OWL
Le Hibou des marais. *Asio flammeus* (Pontoppidan)
Plate 39. L. 13 to 17 in.

Ear tufts very short, scarcely discernible. A medium-sized buffy to buffy white owl, the upper parts broadly but softly streaked, the abdomen narrowly and more sharply streaked with brown. Flight feathers and tail barred with brown. Eyes yellow, framed by a small poorly-defined blackish area on facial disc.

Measurements. *Adult male:* wing, 283.5–307.5 (302.9); tail, 135.5–149.5 (146); culmen from cere, 16–18.2 (16.8). *Adult female:* wing, 291–315 (302) mm.

Field Marks. A crow-sized brown-streaked buffy owl (ear tufts usually not perceptible), active in daylight, especially at dusk, and inhabiting open places (not a woodland owl). Like the Long-eared Owl, it shows in flight a black patch near the wrist on the under side of the wing, but the more buffy general colour and complete lack of any cross-barring on the abdomen of the Short-ear should distinguish it. The Rough-legged Hawk shows a similar black wrist mark in flight, but the owl has a very different big-headed silhouette and lighter, more buoyant flight. Marsh Hawks, inhabiting similar open areas, have a conspicuous white rump patch which the owl lacks.

Habitat. Open grassland, grassy or bushy meadows, fresh and salt marshes, bogs, low-arctic tundra.

Nesting. On ground in open places, a depression often sparsely lined with grasses and similar material, sometimes sheltered by a clump of grass or weeds. *Eggs,* 4 to 9, usually 5 to 7; white. Incubation period 24 to 28 days (J. Vincent, *in* Witherby).

Range. Europe, Asia, North and South America, Hawaiian Islands. Withdraws in winter from northernmost parts of range.

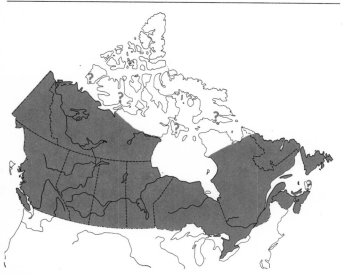

Breeding Distribution of Short-eared Owl

Range in Canada. Breeds from northern Mackenzie (Franklin Bay, Coronation Gulf), southern Keewatin (north probably to Baker Lake), southern coasts of Hudson Bay, James Bay, northern Quebec (Chimo), and northern Labrador (Ramah), south through southern Yukon to southern British Columbia, Alberta, Saskatchewan, Manitoba, Ontario, Quebec, the Maritimes, and Newfoundland. Perhaps breeds north to northern Yukon, southern Banks Island, and southern Victoria Island, where the species has been reliably reported in summer. Perhaps also on southern Baffin Island (old breeding reports at Greater Kingwah and Kingnait Fiord require confirmation).

Winters in southern British Columbia, southern Ontario, occasionally in the Maritimes and Newfoundland; rarely and precariously elsewhere.

Subspecies. *Asio flammeus flammeus* (Pontoppidan).

Remarks. With easy buoyant wingbeats, the Short-eared Owl quarters marsh and meadow. Now and then it pauses to pounce on any unwary mouse. It is most often observed in the evening, but it is more or less active also at other times of the day or night. Like most of our owls, it is a valuable and efficient destroyer of rodent pests.

BOREAL OWL (Richardson's Owl)
La Nyctale boréale. *Aegolius funereus* (Linnaeus)
Plate 40. L. 8.5 to 11.5 in.

A small owl lacking ear tufts. Adults (sexes similarly coloured): Upper parts chocolate brown spotted with white, thickly so on forehead; under parts white, blotchily streaked with brown; greyish white facial disc has a narrow dark brown or blackish outer border. Eyes yellow. Bill yellowish.

Measurements. *Adult male:* wing, 159.5–173.5 (165.9); tail, 88–102.5 (96.5); culmen from cere, 13.2–16 (14.4). *Adult female:* wing, 164.8–179.9 (173.6) mm.

Field Marks. A smallish nocturnal (diurnal in northernmost part of range) dark brown-and-white owl without ear tufts. Separable from the Saw-whet Owl by larger size, yellowish bill, and round white spots on forehead (instead of narrow streaks). Round hornless head distinguishes it from the Screech Owl, which is of similar size.

Habitat. Coniferous and mixedwood forests. When it wanders into settled country in winter, it may roost in a variety of situations including isolated deciduous trees as well as coniferous woodland, sometimes buildings, and even on a haystack.

Nesting. Nests in cavities in trees (abandoned nests of larger woodpeckers or in natural cavities). The tree may be either broadleaf or conifer. *Eggs,* 3 to 7, usually 4 to 6; white. Incubation probably largely, if not entirely, by female. Incubation period 27 days (A. Norberg).

Range. Breeds in boreal woodlands across Eurasia and North America. In North America from Alaska eastward across the coniferous forest belt of Canada. In winter, south irregularly to northern United States.

Range in Canada. Breeds (details of full breeding range not well known) in woodland from central Yukon (Fortymile; possibly north to Old Crow), Mackenzie (Fort Simpson; probably north to Lake Hardisty and possibly even to

PLATE 43

Mackenzie Delta where early autumn occurrence has been reported), northern Saskatchewan (Lake Athabasca), northern Manitoba (probably York Factory), central Quebec (probably Paul Bay; possibly Lac Aulneau), and Labrador (Hopedale), south to northern British Columbia (Flood Glacier; probably Laurier Pass), central Alberta (Belvedere, Jasper, perhaps Banff), central-eastern Saskatchewan (Nipawin), southern Manitoba (near Winnipeg, Shelley), central Ontario (probably Kapuskasing), southern New Brunswick (Grand Manan), and Magdalen Islands, Quebec. Possibly breeds also in Newfoundland, but evidence is inconclusive.

Breeding Distribution of Boreal Owl

Winters within breeding range and southward: north at least to northern British Columbia (Atlin), southern Mackenzie (Fort Simpson), central Manitoba (Herb Lake), and south-central Quebec (Lake Mistassini), and southern Labrador, south in irregular (occasionally substantial) numbers to southern parts of all the provinces including the Maritimes and Newfoundland.

Subspecies. *Aegolius funereus richardsoni* (Bonaparte).

SAW-WHET OWL

La Petite Nyctale. *Aegolius acadicus* (Gmelin)
Plate 40. L. 7 to 8.5 in.

Our smallest *eastern* owl, only the Pygmy Owl of the West being smaller. No ear tufts. Adults most similar to Boreal Owl but smaller; browns (especially of under parts) more reddish; crown with narrow white *streaks* instead of spots; outer sides of facial disc tinged buffy and marked with dusky lines radiating outward; bill black. Juvenal plumage (worn only a short time after leaving nest) is solid brown above (but wings white-spotted as in adults), a brown band across breast, plain cinnamon-buff abdomen and sides; facial disc blackish brown, except whitish space between and over eyes.

Adults easily distinguished from Pygmy Owl by their larger size, softer more luxuriant plumage, well-feathered

1 Downy Woodpecker,
   (a) adult male
   (b) adult female

2 Hairy Woodpecker,
   adult male

3 Red-headed Woodpecker,
   (a) first-autumn
       immature
   (b) adult

4 Black-backed Three-toed
   Woodpecker,
   (a) adult male
   (b) adult female

5 Northern Three-toed
   Woodpecker,
   adult male

6 Lewis's Woodpecker

7 Pileated Woodpecker,
   adult male

8 Red-shafted Flicker,
   adult male

9 Yellow-shafted Flicker,
   (a) adult female
   (b) adult male

1b

4a

4b

3b

1a

2

3a

5

6

7

8

9a

9b

Crosby. /65

toes (sparsely feathered in young), larger head, lack of spots on sides.

Measurements (*A. a. acadicus*). *Adult male:* wing, 127–139.2 (133.2); tail, 66.9–74 (70.3); culmen from cere, 11.6–12.9 (12.4). *Adult female:* wing, 131.5–144.9 (140.3) mm.

Field Marks. A very small hornless nocturnal owl. Black bill, forehead streaked instead of spotted, and smaller size distinguish it from the Boreal Owl. Separable from Pygmy Owl of the West by broader more diffuse reddish brown abdominal streaks (dark, sharply defined in Pygmy), larger size and heavier build, larger head. Unlike the Pygmy Owl, the Saw-whet is not active in the daytime (but both hunt at dusk). *Voice:* Various calls, but the commonest is a long-continued series of monotonous, short, evenly spaced, low whistles.

Habitat. Coniferous and deciduous woodlands, especially moister ones; also dense alder thickets and cedar and tamarack bogs.

Nesting. Nests in old woodpecker holes or other cavities in trees. *Eggs*, 4 to 7, usually 5 or 6; white. Incubation period variously reported from 21 to 28 days. At least 26 days (L. M. Terrill).

Range. Breeds from southeastern Alaska and across southern Canada south to southern California, Arizona, Mexico (Oaxaca, Puebla, Veracruz), Oklahoma, Missouri, Ohio, West Virginia, and Maryland.

Range in Canada. Permanent resident where woodland habitat is available all across extreme southern Canada from Vancouver Island, B.C., to Cape Breton Island, N.S., and north to central British Columbia (northern Queen Charlotte Islands, Topley, Nulki Lake; possibly northwest to Atlin where twice taken in winter), central Alberta (Big Mouth Creek on Athabasca River), central Saskatchewan (Prince Albert, Nipawin), southern Manitoba (Cedar Lake), central Ontario (Lake Nipigon; probably Moose Factory), southern Quebec (La Vérendrye Park, Gaspé Peninsula, Magdalen Islands, possibly to Fort George and Anticosti Island), northern New Brunswick, Prince Edward Island, and northern Nova Scotia (Sydney, Cape North).

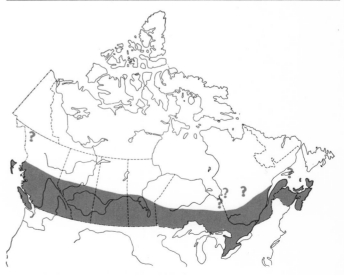

Breeding Distribution of Saw-whet Owl

Winters within breeding range, but many individuals move to more southern points, occasionally in incursion numbers. Casual in Newfoundland (Colinet, April 1940).

Subspecies. (1) *Aegolius acadicus acadicus* (Gmelin) is the breeding bird of all Canada except Queen Charlotte Is., B.C. (2) *Aegolius acadicus brooksi* (Fleming), a more heavily-pigmented subspecies, is confined to Queen Charlotte Is., B.C.

Remarks. One misty evening in early September on northern Cape Breton Island, I was setting out a line of mouse traps in an alder thicket. There came a soft flutter of wings, and quite suddenly a Saw-whet Owl was sitting on an alder branch not more than ten feet from my face. It seemed overcome with curiosity. Its contortions were comical as its head twisted sideways and up and down until sometimes its chin almost rested on its feet as its wide round eyes strove to get a better look at me. After a few minutes of this, it fluttered off into the fast-gathering dusk, its flight suggesting that of a Woodcock.

Tameness is a characteristic of this tiny owl. Perched motionless and silent in shadowy woodlands during the day, it is readily overlooked. It is active at night, and in the dusk and during spring it is often quite vocal. It derives its name from one of its calls which sounds like the filing of a saw. Its ringing, metallic, one-syllabled call-notes may be delivered monotonously for a considerable time, with only short pauses between, during the darker hours and in the evening and morning dusk, mostly in spring.

The Saw-whet Owl's food consists mainly of mice, but it takes also bats, shrews, young squirrels, insects, and the occasional small bird. In the severest parts of the winter, especially if the snow is very deep, Saw-whets seem to have difficulty securing adequate food, and at such times they may suffer considerable mortality.

Order **Caprimulgiformes** – Goatsuckers, Oilbirds, and Allies

Family **Caprimulgidae** – Goatsuckers

Number of Species in North America 6; in Canada 4

Plumage soft and coloured in mixture of wood browns, buffs, white, and black. Head rather flattened; bill tiny; mouth enormous, opening back under the ears; feet small and weak, the middle toenail with comb-like serrations on its edge. The name 'goatsucker' was long ago derived from an erroneous belief that these birds with their large mouths sucked milk from goats in pastures. Doubtless the birds flew about over the pastures only to feed on the insects attracted or stirred up by the animals. Birds of this family are extremely beneficial as their food is mostly insects taken on the wing. They have nearly noiseless flight, large eyes, and nocturnal vision. Their soft plumage closely resembles that of the owls, their nearest relatives. They build no nest, the eggs being laid on the ground.

CHUCK-WILL'S-WIDOW

L'Engoulevent de Caroline
Caprimulgus carolinensis Gmelin
L. 11 to 13 in.

The largest goatsucker known to occur in Canada. Similar to Whip-poor-will but decidedly larger and readily distinguishable from it in the hand by differences in the long bristles on sides of mouth. These bristles have fine branches near their base, while those of the Whip-poor-will are bare, unbranched. Adult male Chuck-will's-widow also differs from the male Whip-poor-will by brown instead of black throat; less conspicuous white in the tail, the white there confined to the *inner webs* of three outer tail feathers (in the male Whip-poor-will, white occupies both webs of the three outer tail feathers). Females and immatures are similar to those of Whip-poor-will but much larger size, and branched mouth bristles are always diagnostic.

Measurements. *Adult male:* wing, 206.5–225 (213.9); tail, 138.5–151 (144.1); exposed culmen, 9–14.5 (12.5); tarsus, 17.5–19 (18.4). *Adult female:* wing, 201.5–215 (209) mm (Ridgway).

Status in Canada. Casual in southern Ontario (Point Pelee, May 21, 1906); New Brunswick (Saint John, May 20, 1916); and Nova Scotia (Pictou, about 1890; Canso, June 1, 1905). Its breeding range is in southeastern United States north to southern Maryland, New Jersey, southern Ohio, southern Illinois, and eastern Kansas.

WHIP-POOR-WILL

L'Engoulevent bois-pourri. *Caprimulgus vociferus* Wilson Plate 41. L. 9 to 10.2 in.

Bill small, mouth enormous. Wings long, tail rounded. Sides of mouth with long black bristles. Colours somewhat variable. *Adult male* coloured in browns, greys, and mottled with black, the top of head streaked with black; throat blackish with narrow white band across lower part; large white area on both webs of the three outermost tail feathers extending to tips. *Adult female* similar but throat band narrower and more buffy; white areas lacking in tail, the three outermost feathers broadly tipped with buff.

Measurements. *Adult male:* wing, 154–167.5 (161.9); tail, 112.5–134.5 (128.2); exposed culmen, 8–11.5 (10.1); tarsus, 15.5–18.5 (17.3). *Adult female:* wing, 148.6–158.5 (152.7) mm.

Field Marks. Perches on the ground or lengthwise on a horizontal branch. A longish Robin-sized bird with tiny down-bent bill. Most similar to the Nighthawk when perched, but the Whip-poor-will's wing tips do not reach the tip of the *rounded* tail (in Nighthawk they reach to or beyond the slightly forked tail tip), its sides and abdomen are never obviously regularly barred. In flight it shows no

Breeding Distribution of Whip-poor-will

white wing patch and never flies at any great height as the Nighthawk does. *Voice:* Far-carrying *whip-poor-will*, the last syllable accented and loudest, repeated tirelessly at dusk and during the night in spring and early summer.

Habitat. Ungrazed woodlands of various developments, especially those with openings; woodland edges; woodlots. Perhaps prefers mixedwood or deciduous types, but open coniferous woods sometimes harbour good numbers too.

Nesting. Eggs are laid on bare ground or leaf litter, usually on the outer fringes of ungrazed woodland. *Eggs,* 2; white, small-blotched and spotted irregularly with grey and some browns. Incubation 19 to 21 days (G. S. Raynor), mainly by the female.

Range. Breeds in woodlands from southern Canada (Saskatchewan to Nova Scotia) south (east of the Great Plains) to northeastern Oklahoma, northeastern Texas, northern Louisiana, northwestern South Carolina, and eastern Virginia; also from central Arizona, New Mexico, and southwestern Texas to Honduras. Winters from southeastern United States and northern Mexico south to El Salvador and Honduras.

Range in Canada. Breeds in central Saskatchewan (rarely: Nipawin; probably Prince Albert and Yorkton), southern Manitoba (Gypsumville, Shoal Lake, Sprague), central-southern and southern Ontario (Off Lake, Port Arthur, Sault Ste. Marie, Uno Park), southern Quebec (Ville Marie, southern La Vérendrye Park, Wakefield, Montreal, Brompton Lake, Coleraine, Quebec), New Brunswick (Scotch Lake, Saint John), and rarely Nova Scotia (Waverley Game Sanctuary, La Have Lake). Casual on Gaspé Peninsula and at St. Félicien, Quebec. Accidental on outer north shore of the Gulf of St. Lawrence (14 miles west of Harrington Harbour, June 11, 1936).

Subspecies. *Caprimulgus vociferus vociferus* Wilson.

POOR-WILL

L'Engoulevent de Nuttall
Phalaenoptilus nuttallii (Audubon)
Plate 41. L. 7 to 8.5 in.

Small bill, immense mouth, and general coloration mark it as a goatsucker. Upper parts finely mottled with greys and browns and sharply marked with black. Tail short, rounded, the outermost three feathers tipped with white (more narrowly in female); cheeks, throat, and upper breast blackish, the throat crossed by a white band. Its small size and short tail distinguish it from our other goatsuckers. From the Nighthawk it is distinguished further by its rounded (instead of slightly forked) tail, bristles on sides of mouth, and lack of any white patch on the wings. The white of tail is *at* the tip; in Nighthawk (male only) the white is a bar *near* the tip.

Measurements. *Adult male:* wing, 141–151 (144.4); tail, 84.6–90.2 (87.9); exposed culmen, 7.6–10.6 (9.3); tarsus, 16.8–18.2 (17.4). *Adult female:* wing, 137.5–141 (139.5) mm.

Field Marks. In Canada the only goatsucker normally found in the range of the Poor-will is the Nighthawk. Poor-will shows no white patch in the spread wing, is smaller with shorter wing and shorter rounded tail (which when

PLATE 45

1 Least Flycatcher

2 Traill's Flycatcher

3 Yellow-bellied Flycatcher

4 Acadian Flycatcher

5 Hammond's Flycatcher

6 Western Flycatcher

7 Dusky Flycatcher

Crosby

spread may show small white tips to the outer feathers). Male Nighthawk shows a white band on tail but not a white tip. Poor-will's voice is an emphatic and far-carrying *poor-will* (accent on second syllable), at close range *poor-will-uck*, usually heard at dusk or at night.

Habitat. Semi-arid sagebrush benchlands or grassy openings in dry open woodland of the Canadian southwest.

Nesting. Eggs laid on bare ground or on a rock, often partly shaded by a bush. The two eggs are pinkish white.

Range. Breeds from southern interior British Columbia, southern Alberta, northwestern South Dakota, and southwestern Iowa south (on the Pacific Coast from central California to southern Baja California) and through eastern Kansas and central Texas to central Mexico. Winters from southwestern United States southward.

Breeding Distribution of Poor-will

Range in Canada. Breeds in southern interior British Columbia (commonly in semi-arid parts: Okanagan Valley; Kamloops; Ashcroft, Fraser Valley; 18 miles south of Lillooet; Hope) and southern Alberta (locally: Cypress Hills); probably also in southwestern Saskatchewan (Calf Creek).

Subspecies. *Phalaenoptilus nuttallii nuttallii* (Audubon).

COMMON NIGHTHAWK
L'Engoulevent commun. *Chordeiles minor* (Forster)
Plate 41. L. 8.3 to 10 in.

Wings long. Tail slightly forked. No bristles on sides of mouth. Very small bill and enormous mouth mark it as a goatsucker. White wing patch, pronounced barring of abdomen and sides, slightly forked tail, lack of buffy bars on primaries, and lack of bristles on sides of mouth distinguish it from other goatsuckers that occur in Canada. *Adult male:* Upper parts blackish, marbled and spotted irregularly with greys, white, and buffs; a conspicuous white patch across the middle of four or five wing primaries; a white bar across tail near its tip; a white band across throat extending backward to below ear coverts; abdomen and sides whitish, regularly barred with blackish.

225

Adult female: Similar but broad white patch across tail wanting (although several narrow bars are present); white patches in primaries smaller; throat band often more buffy white. *Juvenals* resemble adult female, but white throat band absent or faintly indicated; primaries with narrow white margins at tips.

Measurements (*C. m. minor*). *Adult male:* wing, 189–208.5 (198.3); tail, 103.5–120 (101.7); exposed culmen, 6.2–7.5 (6.8); tarsus, 13.3–15.9 (14.9). *Adult female:* wing, 184.2–208 (194.4) mm.

Field Marks. Most often seen on summer evenings (but sometimes at other times of day), high in the air over city or country. The long, slender, pointed wings show a characteristic conspicuous white patch, and the tail is slightly forked (male shows a white tail bar near the tip). Flight graceful, wing beats often erratic. Occasionally it nose-dives, the wings producing a hollow booming sound at the bottom of the dive. Spends day perched lengthwise on a tree branch, on a fence post, on the ground, or on a flat roof of a building. When at rest it resembles the Whip-poor-will, from which it is distinguishable by a white wing patch (often not visible in folded wings), longer wing (reaching to or beyond tip of tail), slightly different position of white throat band (nearer base of bill), slightly forked tail, and decidedly barred sides and abdomen, but no bars on primaries. *Voice:* Mostly in flight, a single harsh nasal *peent*.

Habitat. Forages in the air over city or wilderness. Roosts in trees in open woodlands, fence posts in open areas, or on the ground in woodland openings and clearings, natural open areas, burntlands, flat tops of buildings.

Nesting. No nest is made, the eggs being laid on the ground on sand, gravel, or rock in open places such as woodland openings, clearings, burntlands, prairies and plains, and flat (preferably gravelled) roofs of buildings. *Eggs*, 2; variable in colour, creamy white to pale olive grey or olive buff, speckled with greys, browns, and black.

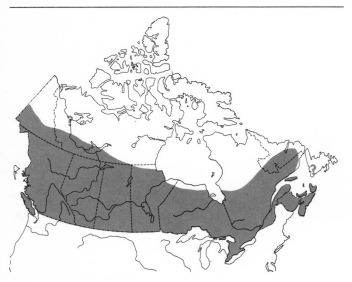

Breeding Distribution of Common Nighthawk

Incubation 19 days (H. Mousley, A. O. Gross), by female, but some authors doubtfully report assistance by male.

Range. Southern Canada south to southern California, central Nevada, Arizona, northeastern Sonora, Chihuahua, Tamaulipas, Durango, Bahama Islands, Jamaica, and Puerto Rico. Winters in South America.

Range in Canada. Breeds all across southern Canada from Vancouver Island, British Columbia east to Cape Breton Island, Nova Scotia; and north through British Columbia (but apparently not recorded for Queen Charlotte Islands) to southern Yukon (Mile 40 Canol Road, Kathleen River), north through Alberta to southern Mackenzie (Fort Simpson, perhaps somewhat farther north in Mackenzie Valley), and to northern Saskatchewan (Lake Athabasca, Black Lake area), northern Manitoba (Lynn Lake, Bird; probably Churchill and Lac du Brochet), northern Ontario (north to Favourable Lake and western James Bay coast), south-central Quebec (north to Fort George, to Lake Mistassini; the inner north shore of the Gulf of St. Lawrence, east probably to about Natashquan; Anticosti Island; eastern Gaspé Peninsula), New Brunswick, Prince Edward Island, and Nova Scotia. Scarce summer resident in interior southern Labrador (Goose Bay, Grand Falls, Sawbill). Rare summer visitor to Newfoundland (Bonavista Bay, Bay of Islands, Port aux Basques; no evidence of breeding).

Casual in northern Yukon (Lapierre House), coastal Labrador (Makkovik). Accidental on Melville Island, N.W.T.

Subspecies. (1) *Chordeiles minor minor* (Forster) is the breeding bird of all e. Canada and the greater part of w. Canada except the dry belt of extreme se. B.C. (Trail, Cranbrook, Elko, Flathead), which is occupied by (2) *C. m. hesperis* Grinnell, a somewhat paler race; and se. Alta. (Milk River, Cypress Hills), s. Sask. (Cypress Hills, Davidson), and extreme sw. Man. (Whitewater Lake), which is occupied by (3) *C. m. sennetti* Coues, the palest and most greyish race in Canada. Specimens from extreme sw. Alta. (south of Banff), not examined by me but said (Salt and Wilk, 1958) to be intermediate between *hesperis* and *sennetti*.

Remarks. Most people easily recognize the common Nighthawk with a white spot on each of its long wings as it courses back and forth high in the air on summer evenings. Its nasal *peent*, and the deep booming sound produced by its wings as it pulls out of a steep dive are common sounds over city and country.

It feeds almost entirely on insects, which it captures on the wing. Its mouth is so large that it opens back under the ear and is ideal for this kind of insect catching. As many as 500 mosquitoes have been found in the stomach of a single Nighthawk. Another, accidentally killed, had 2,175 flying ants in its stomach. Many kinds of beetles are eaten voraciously. When the bird flies close to the ground, it often takes grasshoppers. Although called 'Nighthawk' it is not related to the hawks at all, its small soft beak and weak feet being entirely different. Needless to say, it is illegal to molest this valuable and interesting bird at any time.

Order **Apodiformes**–Swifts, Hummingbirds

It surprises many to learn that swifts and hummingbirds are classed in the same order. Although their bills, mouths, and some aspects of their appearance are very different, many important anatomical features are similar. Obvious external similarities common to both swifts and hummingbirds include long, narrow wings (due to very long primaries and very short secondaries) and very small feet.

Family **Apodidae**–Swifts

Number of Species in North America 6; in Canada 4

Small, long-winged, mostly dull-coloured birds with very small bill and very large mouth; small but strong feet, the hind toe reversible; primaries very long, stiff, somewhat bowed, reaching when closed well beyond tip of tail; plumage (in all Canadian species) rather hard and stiff. On the wing they somewhat resemble swallows, but their wing action is very different. The wings of swifts buzz and twinkle and often seem, erroneously, to beat alternately. There are frequent short glides on stiff bowed wings. All are insect eaters and feed entirely on the wing.

BLACK SWIFT

Le Martinet noir. *Cypseloides niger* (Gmelin)
Plate 41. L. 6.5 to 7.3 in.

Our largest swift, but only slightly larger than the differently-coloured White-throated Swift. Large size and lack of spines on the tips of the tail feathers distinguish it from the Chimney and the Vaux's swifts. *Adult male:* Very dark sooty, almost black, above and below, slightly paler on head and neck; forehead and crown feathers with narrow pale margins; small black area in front of eyes; tail slightly forked and lacking spines on feather tips. *Adult female:* Similar, but feathers of abdomen and under tail coverts more likely to be tipped with white; tail even less forked (almost truncate).

Measurements (*C. n. borealis*). *Adult male:* wing, 160.3–170 (164); tail, 56–64.9 (61.5); exposed culmen, 6–7 (6.5); tarsus, 12.5–13.9 (13). *Adult female:* wing, 155.5–171 (164.7) mm.

Field Marks. Large size for a swift, all-black appearance, and slightly forked tail. Vaux's Swift (also Chimney Swift, which is unknown in Black Swift's range in Canada) is obviously smaller, with greyish under parts, and short rounded tail. The White-throated Swift, another large swift with forked tail, has extensive white on throat, breast, and mid-abdomen. The Purple Martin might be confused with it but for its typical swallow outline and flight, very different from that of swifts.

Habitat. Forages in the air in mountain country at various heights. In fair weather high in the air, often at great heights; in dull, threatening, or rainy weather near the ground or low over water. For nesting, walls of mountain canyons.

Nesting. Relatively few nests have been discovered. Nest is of mosses, bits of ferns and grasses, in a crevice in the wall of a mountain canyon or cliff, or sea cliff. Nests found have usually been in moist places, often near waterfalls. *Egg,* one only, is dull white.

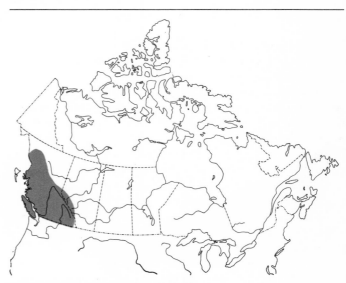

Breeding Distribution of Black Swift

Range. Breeds in mountains or sea cliffs from southeastern Alaska, northern British Columbia, and southwestern Alberta south to Costa Rica; also in the West Indies and in British Guiana. Winters probably in tropical America.

Range in Canada. Summer resident, breeding in British Columbia (throughout southern parts including Vancouver Island and northwestward at least to Telegraph Creek; near Kleena Kleene, Clinton, and at Chilliwack); also in southwestern Alberta (Banff and Jasper parks).

Subspecies. *Cypseloides niger borealis* (Kennerly).

CHIMNEY SWIFT

Le Martinet ramoneur. *Chaetura pelagica* (Linnaeus)
Plate 41. L. 4.8 to 5.7 in.

Our only eastern (Saskatchewan eastward) swift. Its very long wings (longer than the bird itself and extending far beyond the tail) and short tail with the feather shafts projecting as spines beyond the webs (Fig. 58) distinguish it from other eastern birds. Upper parts dark sooty brown (slight gloss), palest on rump, blackish on wings; abdomen dark like the back, paling to brownish grey on throat. Smaller size and spiny tail distinguish it from the Black and the White-throated swifts. It is very similar, however, to Vaux's Swift, but its somewhat smaller size and darker under parts identify it in the hand.

Fig. 58 Tail of Chimney Swift

Measurements. *Adult male:* wing, 124–131.6 (127.8); tail, 40.5–44 (42.3); exposed culmen, 4.7–5.9 (5.2); tarsus, 11.9–13.9 (12.2). *Adult female:* wing, 124.5–131.5 (128.4) mm.

Field Marks. Any swift in eastern Canada and west to Saskatchewan is almost certainly this one. Usually seen in flight, often high in the air. A small sooty bird, likely to be mistaken for a swallow but readily distinguished from swallows by its cigar-shaped body (seems to lack a tail, unless the short rounded tail is spread), long, narrow, pointed wings, its silhouette bowed slightly backward, quick jerky flight (sometimes giving the illusion of alternating wing beats), often interspersed with short glides. The voice, once learned, also distinguishes it from the swallow. Not safely separable in the field from Vaux's Swift, a slightly smaller swift of the western mountains with somewhat paler under parts, but the ranges of the two in Canada are widely separated. *Voice:* A far-carrying, sharp, staccato *chit-chit-chit*, at times running together into a prolonged chittering.

Habitat. Forages in the air, often at considerable heights in fair weather but tending to fly lower during threatening or rainy weather, then often preferring the air over open water or open land. Nested and roosted originally in hollow

Breeding Distribution of Chimney Swift

trees, but most have now adapted to man's chimneys. Highly gregarious.

Nesting. Nested formerly inside hollow trees or in crevices of rock cliffs. Now most have adapted to the interior of man's chimneys and, less often, the interior of old buildings. In remote areas a few still nest in hollow trees. Nest is of twigs glued together and to the chimney wall by the bird's saliva to form a shallow bracket-like structure. *Eggs,* usually 4 or 5; white. Incubation averages 19 days, but variable, by both parents (R. B. Fischer).

Range. Breeds from southern Canada (Saskatchewan east to Nova Scotia) south to southeastern Texas, the Gulf States, and central Florida. Winters in the upper Amazon river drainage of South America.

Range in Canada. Breeding summer resident in central-eastern Saskatchewan (Nipawin), southern Manitoba (Dauphin, St. Laurent, Selkirk, Winnipeg, Indian Bay), southern and south-central Ontario (north to about Kenora, Wabigoon, Savanne, Port Arthur, Missanabie, Cochrane), southern Quebec (north to Amos, Senneterre, Lake St. John, Percé), New Brunswick, Prince Edward Island, and Nova Scotia (including Cape Breton Island). Possibly breeds also in southwestern Newfoundland (numerous summer records of occurrence, especially at Codroy where observed in several summers, but breeding evidence lacking). Casual on the north shore of the Gulf of St. Lawrence (Matamek, Harrington Harbour).

Remarks. Swifts are well named, for they are indeed fast flyers. On calm summer evenings they may fly so high as to be mere specks in the sky, and their voices, like the clicking of knitting needles, drift faintly down to earth. In cloudy weather they fly low. They always seem in a hurry, and as they zigzag across the sky their wings seem almost to twinkle. This bird does not intentionally alight on the ground. It feeds on flying insects, taken on the wing. When thirsty it can skim close to the water, touching the surface lightly with its bill. Nesting twigs are snapped off as the bird hovers at a tree branch. It sleeps clinging to the vertical wall of a chimney or hollow tree.

VAUX'S SWIFT

Le Martinet de l'Ouest. *Chaetura vauxi* (Townsend)
Plate 41. L. 4.0 to 4.5 in.

Our smallest swift. Similar to Chimney Swift (including spiny tail) but decidedly smaller (wing ca. 4½ in. or under) and paler, especially the under parts, the throat being greyish white.

Measurements. *Adult male:* wing, 107.9–112.8 (111.6); tail, 34.9–37.7 (36.1); exposed culmen, 4.1–5 (4.6); tarsus, 11–11.3 (11.1). *Adult female:* wing, 105–116.5 (111.5) mm.

Field Marks. A small swift of the western mountains with greyish under parts and no obvious tail (unless spread, when it looks short and rounded). Black and White-throated swifts are obviously larger with different under parts, and definite, slightly forked tails. Probably not safely separable in the field from the Chimney Swift, but the ranges of the two in Canada are well separated.

Breeding Distribution of Vaux's Swift

Habitat. Forages in the air at various heights and over many different types of country. When flying low, appears to favour the vicinity of water, woodland openings, burnt-lands, flats, river valleys. For nesting, hollows in trees, sometimes in chimneys.

Nesting. Nest, a narrow bracket of twigs, weed stems, or conifer needles, cemented together and to the inside of a hollow tree or, less often, chimney interior. Has adapted less readily to using man's chimneys than has the Chimney Swift. *Eggs,* usually 4 to 6; dull white. Incubation period 18½ to 20 days (Baldwin and Zaczkowski).

Range. Southeastern Alaska and northern British Columbia south to central California (mainly west of the Cascades and Sierra Nevada); also Mexico to Panama and in northern Venezuela. Winters mainly from southern Mexico southward.

Range in Canada. Breeding summer resident in British Columbia (across southern parts, Vancouver Island east to Elko and northwestward through Horsefly to Telegraph Creek; perhaps to Mile 45 Haines Road; apparently not recorded on Queen Charlotte Islands). Probably occurs sparingly in southwestern Alberta (sight record only: Berg Lake, August 31, 1943).

Subspecies. *Chaetura vauxi vauxi* (Townsend)

WHITE-THROATED SWIFT

Le Martinet à gorge blanche
Aëronautes saxatalis (Woodhouse)
Plate 41. L. 6 to 7 in.

A large western swift, only slightly smaller than the Black Swift. Wings long; tail ample, decidedly forked, lacking spine-like projections. Upper parts brownish black or sooty brown; line over eye, tips of secondaries, patch on either side of rump, the throat, breast, and median part of abdomen, white; sides blackish. The only Canadian swift with extensive patches of white.

Measurements (*A. s. saxatalis*). *Adult male:* wing, 137–145.5 (141.9); tail, 50.5–61 (58.9); exposed culmen, 5.5–6.2 (5.9); tarsus, 10.7–11.4 (11.1). *Adult female:* wing, 136.2–145.1 (141.5) mm.

Field Marks. White throat, breast, and middle of abdomen contrast with dark sides, and there is a conspicuous white patch on either side of rump. No other Canadian swift has extensive white patches. Beginners might confuse it with the Violet-green Swallow because of the white patches on the sides of the rump, but the swallow's outline and flight action are very different.

Habitat. Forages widely over various types of mountain country, roosting and nesting on mountain cliffs and canyon walls.

Nesting. Nest, usually in a crevice in a wall of a cliff (often inaccessible), is a shallow cupped bracket of feathers and often grass and other plant material, glued together and to the rock by the bird's saliva. *Eggs,* usually 4 or 5; white.

Range. Breeds from central-southern British Columbia south in the mountains to Guatemala and El Salvador. Winters from central California and southwestern New Mexico southward.

Breeding Distribution of White-throated Swift

229

Range in Canada. Breeds in central-southern British Columbia (on cliffs in and near Okanagan Valley: Osoyoos Lake, Summerland, White Lake, Vaseaux Lake, Okanagan Falls, Rutland, Vernon).

Subspecies. *Aëronautes saxatalis saxatalis* (Woodhouse) is the subspecies inhabiting c.-s. B.C. If the species is eventually found in Alta., specimens should be examined for the possibility of a larger race, *sclateri*.

Family **Trochilidae**—Hummingbirds

Number of Species in North America 18; in Canada 4

This very large family, which contains the smallest of birds, is confined to the New World. Most of the more than 300 species are found in the tropics, but the family is represented from Alaska to Patagonia. Hummingbirds are easily recognized by their diminutive size, brilliant iridescent colours, especially in the males, and by the darting, hovering (even backward) flight, which is accompanied by a characteristic humming sound. The wings are long, slender, and pointed; the feet small and weak; the bill is slender and in Canadian species straight (but the shape is extremely variable elsewhere). The long extensile tongue is ideal for reaching nectar and tiny insects deep inside flowers.

RUBY-THROATED HUMMINGBIRD

Le Colibri à gorge rubis. *Archilochus colubris* (Linnaeus) Plate 42. L. 3 to 3.7 in.

Adult male: Tail forked, its feathers tapering toward tips; upper parts glossy green; throat bright metallic red (changeable in different positions to dull blackish); breast and middle of abdomen, greyish white; sides, greyish brown mixed with glossy green. *Adult female:* Similar to adult male but throat greyish white; tail not forked, feather tips more rounded, the outer three tail feathers tipped with white. *Young:* Similar to adult female, but young males have throat streaked with dusky, sometimes showing traces of red.

Measurements. *Adult male:* wing, 39.9–43.2 (40.9); tail, 26.4–30.4 (28); exposed culmen, 14.2–16.7 (15.2). *Adult female:* wing, 44.3–48 (45.7) mm.

Field Marks. The only hummingbird to be expected from eastern Alberta eastward. Small size and buzzing insect-like flight distinguish it as a hummingbird.

Habitat. Gardens, orchards; woodland clearings and edges; almost anywhere where flowers provide tiny insects and nectar and not too far from trees or tall shrubbery for perching, shelter, and nesting. Feeds at flowers of many kinds, both wild and cultivated; often takes insects fly-catcher-fashion; occasionally feeds at sapsucker borings.

Nesting. Nest, a neat little cup saddled on a limb of a tree. It is composed of bud scales and plant down, the outside covered with bits of lichen and held together by spider silk. *Eggs,* 2; white. Incubation 16 days (A. F. Skutch), by female alone.

Range. Breeds from southern Canada (Alberta eastward

to Nova Scotia) south to the Gulf States and west in the United States to eastern North Dakota, central Nebraska, central Oklahoma, and east-central Texas. Winters from northern Mexico and southern Texas south to Costa Rica; also in southern Alabama and southern Florida.

Breeding Distribution of Ruby-throated Hummingbird

Range in Canada. Breeds in central and southeastern Alberta (Lesser Slave Lake, Belvedere, Elk Island National Park, Brooks), central Saskatchewan (Flotten Lake, Prince Albert, Nipawin, Buchanan), southern Manitoba (The Pas: 20 miles north; Swan River, Lake St. Martin, Red River, Hillside Beach, Indian Bay; probably Overflowing River), southern and south-central Ontario (north to about Lake of the Woods, Wabigoon, Lake Nipissing, Kapuskasing, perhaps Lake Abitibi), southern Quebec (north to La Vérendrye Park, Lake St. John, and eastern Gaspé Peninsula), New Brunswick, Prince Edward Island, and Nova Scotia (including Cape Breton Island).

Casual in northern Ontario (Moose Factory, Attawapiskat), north shore of the Gulf of St Lawrence (Seven Islands, Johan Beetz Bay), and Newfoundland (Avalon Peninsula, St. Anthony). Accidental in central Labrador (Davis Inlet, July 17, 1882).

Remarks. Hummingbirds feed on minute insects and nectar which they obtain from flowers. Their tiny wings move so rapidly in flight that they produce a characteristic humming sound, hence the name. They are capable of rapid direct flight, of remaining perfectly stationary in the air as they feed at flowers, and of even flying backwards for short distances.

The males take no part in nesting duties and leave the drudgery of incubating the eggs and raising the young entirely to the females. They quarrel frequently among themselves, and when so engaged their squeaky, high-pitched voices are incessantly audible.

The Ruby-throated has the widest distribution in Canada of all hummingbirds and is the only species found in the eastern part of the country. Beginners sometimes confuse it with large hawk moths which also feed at flowers.

BLACK-CHINNED HUMMINGBIRD

Le Colibri à gorge noire. *Archilochus alexandri* (Bourcier and Mulsant)
Plate 42. L. 3 to 3.8 in.

Adult male: Above, metallic green; chin and upper throat black, lower throat iridescent purplish violet (but changeable: black in some positions); breast whitish, median abdomen greyish, sides and flanks darker overlaid with green. *Adult female:* Above, metallic green, forehead and crown duller and more greyish brown; tail rounded, outer three tail feathers tipped with white; under parts dull white (more purely so on abdomen). From Rufous Hummingbird, the Black-chinned is easily distinguished by its lack of any rufous coloration in body plumage or at base of tail; from the Calliope by larger size, solid dark throat in male, and complete lack of rufous in the female.

Measurements. *Adult male:* wing, 43.8–45.3 (44.4); tail, 23.5–28.7 (26.7); exposed culmen, 16.5–18.3 (17.4).

Field Marks. *Adult male:* Throat patch looks black, but in certain positions the shiny violet lower throat can be seen. Female differs from Rufous and Calliope by lack of buffy on sides. *Caution:* Throats of some other hummingbirds may look black in certain lights.

Nesting. Nest, of vegetable downs held together with cobwebs, is saddled on a tree branch. *Eggs;* 2; white.

Range. From southern British Columbia and northwestern Montana south to northern Baja California, northwestern Mexico, and northwestern Texas. Winters from southeastern California south to southwestern Mexico.

Range in Canada. Scarce summer visitant, probably breeding, in southern interior British Columbia (Chilliwack east to Creston, north to Grindrod).

[**Anna's Hummingbird.** Le Colibri d'Anna. *Calypte anna* (Lesson). L. 3.6 to 4.1 in. Somewhat larger than other Canadian hummingbirds. *Adult male* has both crown and throat patch (the latter elongated laterally onto sides of neck) iridescent purplish red; rest of upper parts rich glossy green; sides and flanks mainly greenish but duller than on back. The reddish crown (changeable: both it and throat patch may look blackish in certain lights) readily distinguishes the adult male from other Canadian hummingbirds.

Range. Breeds in California west of the higher mountains and south to northwestern Baja California.

Status in Canada. Hypothetical. Various sight records by competent observers at Victoria, British Columbia, August 1958 to April 1961 (C. J. Guiguet, *in litt.*; also *Murrelet* 40: 13).]

RUFOUS HUMMINGBIRD

Le Colibri roux. *Selasphorus rufus* (Gmelin)
Plate 42. L. 3.3 to 3.8 in.

Adult male: Upper parts cinnamon-rufous, glossy green on crown and often more or less on back; throat patch metallic scarlet (changeable to greenish or dark brown); sides, flanks, tail coverts, and much of tail feathers, cinnamon-rufous paling to whitish on breast. *Adult female:* Upper parts bronze-green; tail with much cinnamon-rufous basally, largely blackish terminally, but three outermost feathers tipped white; throat, breast, and median abdomen, whitish; many of the throat feathers tipped with scarlet to greenish

(sometimes forming a patch); sides, flanks, and under tail coverts, pale cinnamon rufous.

The adult male's rufous coloration and flaming extensive throat patch distinguish it from all others of regular occurrence in Canada (but individuals showing green speckling on the back might be mistaken for the smaller, decidedly green-backed Allen's Hummingbird with narrower outer tail feathers, which is found farther south in the United States). Adult females and young resemble Calliope Hummingbirds of similar sex and age, but in the hand they are obviously larger and have much more cinnamon-rufous in the base of the tail than Calliopes. Ruby-throated and Black-chinned in all plumages lack cinnamon rufous colouring everywhere (an occasional young bird may have just a suggestion of buffy on the flanks but never in the tail or elsewhere).

Measurements. *Adult male:* wing, 40.2–42.8 (41.3); tail, 27.2–30 (28.8); exposed culmen, 15.5–16.9 (16.1). *Adult female:* wing, 43.3–45.3 (44.2) mm.

Field Marks. As given above. Females and young difficult to distinguish from Calliope of similar sex or age.

Habitat. Forages over a great variety of habitats, mainly where flowers are available, from sea-coast, coastal islands, and valley bottoms to meadows above timberline.

Nesting. In a variety of trees, bushes, and vines. Probably favours a low sloping branch of a conifer. Nest, a firm cup of plant downs and mosses, with lichens on the outside, held together by cobwebs. *Eggs* 2; white.

Range. From southeastern Alaska, southwestern Yukon, east-central British Columbia, and southwestern Alberta south through Washington and Oregon to northwestern California and southern Idaho. Winters in Mexico.

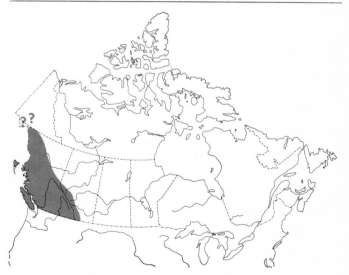

Breeding Distribution of Rufous Hummingbird

Range in Canada. Breeds in British Columbia (commonly across the southern part, including Vancouver Island, northward through Queen Charlotte Islands and Vanderhoof, and northwestward at least to Dokdaon Creek. Found in summer, possibly breeds, northwest to Chilkat Pass and Atlin. Probably absent from northeastern corner), and southwestern Alberta (Waterton, Banff, and Jasper parks). Scarce summer visitant in southwestern Yukon (Carcross, Marsh Lake, Whitehorse). Wanders eastward occasionally to east-central Alberta (Red Deer, probably Camrose) and rarely to southwestern Saskatchewan (Eastend).

CALLIOPE HUMMINGBIRD

Le Colibri de Calliope. *Stellula calliope* (Gould)
Plate 42. L. 2.8 to 3.3 in.

Our smallest hummingbird. *Adult male:* Above, iridescent green; throat with long narrow purple feathers (elongated on sides of throat and extending down side of neck) forming distinct streaks on whitish background. *Adult female:* Above, iridescent bronzy green; throat whitish, usually more or less faintly streaked with dusky; breast and middle of abdomen, white merging into cinnamon on sides and flanks; tail with three outermost feathers tipped white, cinnamon coloration restricted to very narrow margins near the base of some of the feathers. The adult male's decidedly purple, heavily streaked throat with elongated feathers down sides of neck is unmistakable. Females and young are more difficult but are distinguishable from Ruby-throated and Black-chinned in similar plumages by decidedly cinnamon flanks. Closely resembles female and young Rufous, but in the hand the Calliope is seen to have much less cinnamon in the base of the tail (very narrow margins, not extending to middle pair of feathers).

Measurements. *Adult male:* wing, 37.6–43.5 (39.1); tail, 18.7–23 (20.9); exposed culmen, 13–14.9 (13.8). *Adult female:* wing, 41.3–45 (43.1) mm.

Field Marks. Adult male with heavy purple streaks on throat (these feathers elongated laterally thus extending down sides of neck) is very distinct. Females and young show considerable cinnamon on the flanks which distinguishes them from Ruby-throated and Black-chinned hummingbirds; but they are so similar to female Rufous that they cannot ordinarily be safely distinguished in the field.

PLATE 47

1 Blue Jay

2 Steller's Jay

3 Black-billed Magpie

4 Gray Jay

5 Clark's Nutcracker

6 Northwestern Crow

7 Common Crow

8 Common Raven

Breeding Distribution of Calliope Hummingbird

1

2

3

4

5

6

7

8

Crosby '63.

Crosby

Habitat. In mountains: openings in woodland, glades, burntlands, flowery meadows; for nesting open woodland either coniferous, deciduous, or mixedwood.

Nesting. Typically saddled on a sloping branch (various heights) of a coniferous or deciduous tree, often beneath another protecting overhanging branch. Nest, a firm neat cup of plant downs, lichens, and mosses, bound together with cobwebs. *Eggs*, 2; white.

Range. Breeds in mountainous country from south-central British Columbia and southwestern Alberta south to northern Baja California and east to western Colorado. Winters in Mexico.

Range in Canada. Breeds in interior British Columbia (Princeton, Okanagan Valley, Elko, north to Vanderhoof region; possibly northwest to Topley: specimen taken) and in mountainous southwestern Alberta (Waterton Lakes and Banff national parks; probably also Jasper Park: three June specimens). Casual in southwestern Saskatchewan (Shaunavon).

Remarks. This is the tiniest bird in Canada. Its average weight is about one-tenth of an ounce. Yet it does not hesitate to dive-bomb birds much larger than itself. A mother bird, with half-grown young in the nest, has been known to chase a squirrel from the nest tree. Even large hawks are occasionally 'attacked.'

As in other hummingbirds, its food is nectar, tiny insects, and little spiders, most of which it finds in flowers. Most brightly coloured flowers attract it, but red ones appear to be preferred. Often it takes insects on the wing, flycatcher-fashion.

Order **Coraciiformes** – Kingfishers, Motmots, Rollers, and Allies

Family **Alcedinidae** – Kingfishers

Number of Species in North America 3; in Canada 1

Stocky birds with rather large heads which are crested in many species; heavy, straight, pointed bills; very short legs; middle and outer toes joined together *for over half their length* (Fig. 59). The North American species are all fish eaters and are usually seen in the vicinity of water. The family is widely distributed in warmer parts of the world, especially in the Australian region.

Fig. 59 Foot of Belted Kingfisher

BELTED KINGFISHER

Le Martin-pêcheur. *Megaceryle alcyon* (Linnaeus)
Plate 37. L. 11 to 14.8 in.

Head large, crested. Bill straight, tapering to a point. Legs short; feet small, three of the four toes directed forward, the two outermost joined for basal half of their length. *Adult male:* Upper parts greyish blue with wide white collar around neck; white spot in front of eye; under parts white; except sides, flanks, and a broad band across breast, blue. *Adult female:* Similar to adult male, but sides, flanks, and a second breast band (below the blue one), cinnamon-rufous. *Young:* Resemble adults but bill shorter and breast bands much-mixed with reddish brown. Some young males show vestiges of a red second breast band.

Measurements (*M. a. alcyon*). *Adult male:* wing, 151.3–159.5 (156.7); tail, 82–90 (86.7); exposed culmen, 48–52.9 (50.4); tarsus, 10.6–12 (11.2). *Adult female:* wing, 147–163.5 (155.4) mm.

Field Marks. Larger than a robin, with large crested head, blue back, very short legs, rather long pointed bill. Male with one blue band across white breast; female with an additional reddish band below the blue one. Usually seen near water, often perches motionless for long periods, dives with resounding splash, sometimes hovers over water on rapidly beating wings. *Voice:* A loud, harsh rattle. Blue Jay also is a crested blue-backed bird but is easily distinguished by its *black* necklace (which extends right up sides of neck), longer legs, and much longer tail.

Habitat. The vicinity of fish-inhabited water (preferably clear) either fresh or salt: lakes, ponds, rivers, streams, salt water near shore or islands and not too far from elevated perching places such as trees, posts, telephone wires. For nesting, steep earth banks (when obtainable), not necessarily in the immediate vicinity of water. Breeding populations in rocky areas limited by availability of nesting sites. Sometimes utilizes man-made cutbanks of roads and railways, gravel pits, sawdust piles (often unsuccessfully); rarely even wheel tracks through earth mounds; occasionally an earth-filled root of an upturned tree.

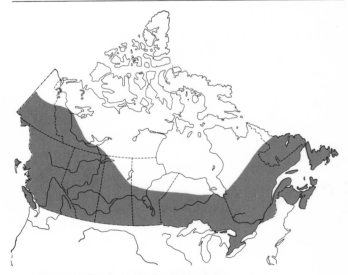

Breeding Distribution of Belted Kingfisher

Nesting. Nests in a circular chamber at the end of a burrow excavated by both sexes in the face of a steep earth bank. Burrow, usually 3 to 7 feet long, rarely considerably longer, is horizontal or slightly up-slanting. Usually (not

234

always) near the top of the bank. Eggs are laid on bare chamber floor in which a lining of fish bones gradually accumulates. *Eggs*, 5 to 8, usually 6 or 7; white, somewhat glossy. Incubation 23 to 24 days (H. Mousley), mainly by female, but apparently the male at least sometimes assists.

Range. Breeds from central Alaska and across much of forested Canada south to southern United States (including southern California, southern Texas, and southern Florida). Winters from southeastern Alaska, southern British Columbia, Wyoming, Nebraska, Illinois, extreme southern Ontario, Vermont, New Hampshire, and Maine south through much of Central America and the West Indies to Panama, Curaçao, and Trinidad.

Range in Canada. Breeds through the southern parts of all provinces and northward through British Columbia (including Queen Charlotte and Vancouver islands) to southern Yukon (Teslin Lake, Nisutlin River), through Alberta to western and central-southern Mackenzie (certainly northwest to Norman Wells; possibly to Fort McPherson and Anderson River where it has been noted in summer), northwestern and central-eastern Saskatchewan (Lake Athabasca, Nipawin region), central Manitoba (north to about Thicket Portage and Oxford Lake), Ontario (north at least to Casummit-Birch lakes and Moose Factory), central Quebec (north at least to Lake Mistassini, the north shore of the Gulf of St. Lawrence, and the Knob Lake region), and from New Brunswick, Prince Edward Island, and Nova Scotia north to northern and eastern Newfoundland and Labrador (Hopedale).

Winters in coastal and southern interior British Columbia (regularly on the coast; occasionally and locally in the interior) and extreme southern Ontario. Occasional individuals sometimes present in winter in Nova Scotia, Prince Edward Island, and southern Newfoundland, but apparently most attempts at over-wintering there are unsuccessful.

Subspecies. (1) *Megaceryle alcyon alcyon* (Linnaeus) breeds throughout e. Canada and extends westward to Yukon Territory (Teslin Lake), ne. B.C. (Peace River, Liard River), and Alta. e. of the foothills. (2) *M. a. caurina* (Grinnell), of somewhat larger size, occupies extreme sw. Alta. (Waterton Lakes, MacLeod), s. and coastal B.C., and perhaps extreme sw. Yukon. Because of the lack of suitable study material, areas of intergradation with the nominate race are not well understood.

Remarks. The tousle-headed silhouette of the kingfisher is a familiar sight to all who frequent Canadian waters. On one of its numerous favourite perches it patiently watches for fishes in the water below. It may dive either from a perch or from the air. Sometimes it hovers in the air for a moment and then hits the water with a resounding splash. If successful in catching a fish, it carries it out of the water in its bill. Although the kingfisher feeds mainly on small fishes, it sometimes eats beetles, grasshoppers, crickets, and even frogs. Most of the fishes taken are of little economic value. Some are actually harmful destroyers of young trout. At fish hatcheries kingfishers can be destructive, but screens placed over pools will protect the young fish.

Ordinarily, kingfishers are wary and difficult to approach closely. Often they would go unseen were it not for their harsh rattle which draws attention to them as they disappear around a bend in the river. Swift, graceful, and picturesque, the Belted Kingfisher adds colour to the scene.

PLATE 49

1 Bewick's Wren

2 Rock Wren

3 Carolina Wren

4 Winter Wren

5 House Wren

6 Brown Creeper

7 American Dipper

8 Long-billed Marsh Wren

9 Short-billed Marsh
   Wren

PLATE 50

1 Northern Mockingbird

2 Catbird

3 Brown Thrasher

4 Sage Thrasher

5 Water Pipit,
    (a) summer
    (b) autumn

6 Sprague's Pipit

7 Skylark

8 Horned Lark

Order **Piciformes**–Woodpeckers, Jacamars, Toucans, and Barbets

Family **Picidae**–Woodpeckers and Wrynecks

Number of Species in North America 23; in Canada 13

Woodpeckers are highly specialized for climbing the trunks and branches of trees and for digging out wood-boring insects. The bill is hard, straight, and chisel-like, ideal for digging holes in either dead or living wood; the tongue is slender, fitted with a horny spear at its tip (Fig. 60), and is capable of being extended far beyond the bill tip to impale and withdraw insect larvae from deep cavities. The skull is extremely thick and heavy, enabling it to withstand the shock of using the head as a hammer. The legs are short; the three or four toes, usually four, with two in front and two behind, are fitted with sharp claws for climbing. The tail is very stiff and is well fitted for bracing against tree trunks.

Most species feed mainly on insects, and as their diet includes a high proportion of wood-boring species the importance of these avian tree surgeons is great.

Fig. 60 (A) extensile tongue of Pileated Woodpecker
(B) detail of tongue tip (magnification 4X)

YELLOW-SHAFTED FLICKER

Le Pic doré. *Colaptes auratus* (Linnaeus)
Plate 43. L. 12 to 13 in.

Adult male: Crown and back of neck grey, a scarlet crescent across nape; back, wing coverts, and most of secondaries, olive brown barred with black; rump white; sides of head, throat, and upper breast, vinaceous brown; 'moustache' patches and large crescent across breast, black; rest of under body brownish white to yellowish white, heavily spotted with black; shafts of flight feathers, under side of wing, and much of under side of tail, yellow. *Adult female:* Similar to adult male but lacks black 'moustache' patches.

Young in juvenal plumage (worn for only a short time while in and after leaving nest): Similar to adult male, but both sexes have black 'moustache' patches (sometimes poorly indicated); often there is some reddish on the forehead, and the throat is more greyish.

Measurements (*C. a. luteus*). *Adult male:* wing, 150.9–164 (157.4); tail, 98.7–111.5 (105.9); exposed culmen, 31.3–39 (34.3); tarsus, 25.9–30.8 (28.7). *Adult female:* wing, 152.1–166.9 (156.9) mm.

Field Marks. A brown woodpecker, larger than a robin, with a large white rump patch conspicuous in flight. Often feeds on the ground. Easily recognizable in the East but in the western part of its range must be distinguished from the Red-shafted Flicker. The Yellow-shafted has the wing linings and under side of tail yellow (instead of red), and the male has black (instead of red) 'moustache' patches which are lacking in the adult female. These two flickers both have loud varied calls, which further distinguish them from other woodpeckers but not from each other. A loud, far-carrying series of rapid *yucks;* a more deliberate *flicker-flicker-flicker,* are common examples.

Habitat. This wide-ranging and adaptable species inhabits a variety of habitat but prefers moderately open situations including open woodland of all kinds: farmland, burntland, pastures and similar open places with, or not too far from, trees. Forages on the ground (especially where ants are present) as well as in trees. Uses trees also for cover, roosting, drumming, and nesting. On treeless plains or prairies telephone poles or fence posts may serve to some extent instead of trees; or it may nest in a building, rarely even in a haystack, earth bank, or other strange place.

Nesting. A cavity, excavated by both sexes, most often in a tree, frequently a dead one, at heights from 2 to 60 feet; often in a telephone pole or fence post, sometimes in a building and more rarely in a variety of other situations. Bird boxes are sometimes used. *Eggs,* usually 6 to 9; glossy white. Incubation 11 to 12 days (Althea Sherman), by both sexes.

Range. Breeds from about tree limit in Alaska and across Canada south (east of the Rocky Mountains) to southern Texas, the Gulf coast of United States, Florida Keys, Cuba, and Grand Cayman.

Range in Canada. Breeds from about tree limit in northern

238

Yukon (Old Crow), northwestern and central Mackenzie (Mackenzie Delta, Anderson River, Fort Enterprise, and Fort Reliance), northern Manitoba (Kasmere River, Churchill), northern Ontario, north-central Quebec (probably Great Whale River; Knob Lake region), south-central Labrador (Kaipokok Bay, Goose Bay), and Newfoundland south to central British Columbia (where it hybridizes with Red-shafted Flicker), southern Alberta (east of the Rockies), through Saskatchewan, Manitoba, Ontario, Quebec, New Brunswick, Prince Edward Island, and Nova Scotia. Extensive areas of introgression and hybrid populations where the breeding range is in contact with that of *C. cafer* in British Columbia, southern Alberta, and southwestern Saskatchewan (Cypress Hills) make exact delimitation of range in those areas difficult.

Winters in southern Ontario (Plover Mills, Hamilton, Toronto) and in very small numbers in southwestern Quebec (Montreal rarely), southern Newfoundland, southern New Brunswick, and Nova Scotia. Casual in northern Quebec (Cape Wolstenholme, July 1925; Ungava Bay, October 1882).

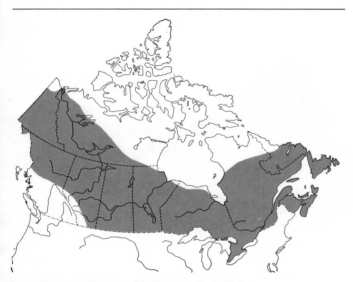

Breeding Distribution of Yellow-shafted Flicker

Subspecies. (1) *Colaptes auratus luteus* Bangs is the breeding bird of e. Canada. (2) *C. a. borealis* Ridgway, of slightly larger average size, is generally understood to include the northern part of the breeding population from Alaska east to Labrador. Birds from Ont. eastward, however, are best referred to *luteus*. There is a slight increase in size northwestward, and if *borealis* is recognized it should be restricted to western populations, east perhaps to Man., but boundaries are rather arbitrary.

Remarks. Flickers are woodpeckers that feed on the ground more often than our other woodpeckers do. The tongue can be extended far beyond the bill tip and is provided with a sticky substance that assists in catching insects. Flickers often feed voraciously at ant hills, and one individual is known to have consumed 5,000 ants at a single meal. They devour also a large variety of other insects they find on or under the bark of trees.

RED-SHAFTED FLICKER

Le Pic rosé. *Colaptes cafer* (Gmelin)
Plate 43. L. 12.5 to 13.5 in.

Similar to the Yellow-shafted Flicker, but yellow is replaced by red on the shafts of the flight feathers, under side of wings, and under side of tail; top of head is brown; throat grey; and the male has red (instead of black) 'moustache' patches (lacking in female or only faintly indicated by brown). In juvenal plumage only the male shows 'moustache' patches (which are red). (*Note:* In areas where the ranges of these two flickers come together, extensive interbreeding produces various combinations of characters in the individual.)

Measurements (*C. c. collaris*). *Adult male:* wing, 161.5–173 (168.9); tail, 109–125 (117); exposed culmen, 35–38 (36.6); tarsus, 29–30.8 (29.8). *Adult female:* wing, 158.5–174 (166.5) mm.

Field Marks. A rather large brown woodpecker whose broad white rump patch, very conspicuous in flight, distinguishes it as a Flicker. Red (instead of yellow) wing linings and under side of tail; lack of a red bar on nape; and in males, the red (instead of black) 'moustache' patches separate it from Yellow-shafted Flicker. (*Caution:* In areas where the two flickers interbreed freely, various combinations of these characters occur.) *Voice* is similar to that of Yellow-shafted Flicker.

Habitat. Very similar to that of Yellow-shafted Flicker, from near timberline in the mountains down to sea-level.

Nesting. Similar to that of Yellow-shafted Flicker.

Range. Breeds from southeastern Alaska, western and southern British Columbia, southern Alberta, southwestern Saskatchewan, and central North Dakota southward along the western edge of the Great Plains (where it interbreeds with *C. auratus*) to northern Baja California and in the highlands south to southern Mexico. Winters from southeastern Alaska and southern British Columbia southward.

Range in Canada. Breeds in coastal and southern interior British Columbia (entire coast including Vancouver Island

Breeding Distribution of Red-shafted Flicker

239

and Queen Charlotte Islands, and the southern interior north at least to Lac la Hache Valley, probably to Cottonwood and Indianpoint Lake. Interbreeds with *C. auratus* along northern and eastern parts of the range), southern Alberta (in the mountains north to Jasper Park; interbreeds commonly with *C. auratus* in Rosebud Valley and Cypress Hills), and southwestern Saskatchewan (Cypress Hills, where practically entire population is mixed with *C. auratus*).

Winters in British Columbia (regularly on the coast; small numbers in the southern interior: Okanagan Valley). Casual in migration northeast to southern Keewatin (Red River) and east to Manitoba (Churchill, Winnipeg), but whether these are pure *cafer* is unknown. Obvious hybrids occur in migration east to eastern Ontario (Ottawa).

Subspecies. (1) *Colaptes cafer cafer* (Gmelin) is the breeding bird of coastal B.C., west of the Cascades. (2) *C. c. collaris* Vigors, paler and more greyish, slightly larger, breeds in s. B.C. (east of the Cascades), s. Alta., and sw. Sask. The evidence is strong that this species is conspecific with *C. auratus*, but for the present at least the writer follows the A.O.U. Check-list (Fifth Edition) in treating the Red-shafted and Yellow-shafted Flickers as separate species.

Remarks. Although, like other woodpeckers, Flickers secure much of their insect food from the trunk and branches of trees, they are much more terrestrial. Ants make up a substantial part of their diet. In addition to insects, they eat limited amounts of acorns, grains, and small fruits. Their overall economic effect is very beneficial.

PILEATED WOODPECKER

Le Grand Pic. *Dryocopus pileatus* (Linnaeus)
Plate 43. L. 16 to 19.5 in.

By far our largest woodpecker. Patterned in broad masses of black and white and with a conspicuous bright red pointed crest (not just a red bar across nape). Males have the whole forehead and a patch behind the base of the bill red also.

Measurements (*D. p. abieticola*). *Adult male:* wing, 230.4–246.8 (236); tail, 148.5–163 (157); exposed culmen, 50–58.8 (55.2); tarsus, 33.5–37.8 (35.3). *Adult female:* wing, 220.2–238 (228.5).

Field Marks. Unmistakable. A crow-sized woodpecker with conspicuous bright red crest; rest of plumage mainly black with white stripe on side of head and down sides of neck; white areas in and under the wings show prominently in flight. *Voice:* Commonly a *cuk-cuk-cuk*, a little like that of a flicker, but more deliberate, lower-pitched, more powerful.

Habitat. Mature woodlands of various kinds, especially those containing some standing dead trees. Although it probably prefers, especially in the breeding season, more extensive wilder forests, these are not essential. Where unmolested, it also inhabits woodlots, parks, and other less extensive stands of mature trees. Sometimes, especially in winter, it forages close to dwellings in city suburbs if maturer trees are present.

Nesting. Nests in a cavity excavated by the birds, 15 to 70 feet up in a dead or, less often, living tree, either deciduous or coniferous. *Eggs*, 3 to 4; white. Incubation 18 days (J. S. Y. Hoyt), by both sexes.

Range. Resident in forested parts of Canada and the United States south to central California, central Texas, the United States Gulf coast, and southern Florida.

Range in Canada. Breeds in forested regions from southern Mackenzie (Fort Simpson, Upper Buffalo River) south through northeastern, central, and southern British Columbia (Vancouver Island, Elko, Thutade Lake, Fort Nelson River), Alberta (except southeastern corner), northwestern and central Saskatchewan (Lake Athabasca, Nipawin); central and southern Manitoba (north to about Thicket Portage and Herb Lake), central and southern Ontario (north to southern James Bay), southern Quebec (north at least to Lake Waswanipi, Lake St. John, Gaspé Peninsula; possibly Anticosti Island), New Brunswick, Nova Scotia (including Cape Breton Island), and formerly Prince Edward Island (apparently extirpated).

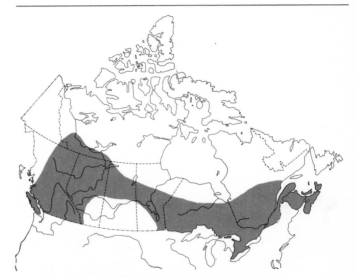

Breeding Distribution of Pileated Woodpecker

Winters mostly in the breeding range, but perhaps withdrawing from northernmost parts. Occasionally wanders to southeastern Alberta (Brooks) and somewhat south of breeding range in Saskatchewan (Yorkton).

Subspecies. (1) *Dryocopus pileatus picinus* (Bangs): B.C. (area of intergradation with the following race not well understood). (2) *D. p. abieticola* (Bangs), average larger size and paler coloration, occupies the remainder of the range in Canada from Mack. and w. Alta. eastward.

RED-BELLIED WOODPECKER

Le Pic à ventre roux. *Centurus carolinus* (Linnaeus)
Plate 42. L. 8.8 to 10 in.

Adult male with whole back, scapulars, and wings (except primaries), black barred with white; whole top of head, nape, and back of neck, bright red; under parts (including throat), brownish grey with more or less red in middle of abdomen. *Female* is similar to male but top of head grey, red coloration being confined to nape, back of neck, and forehead; red of mid-abdomen more restricted.

Measurements. *Adult male:* wing, 123.5–139 (131); tail,

72.5–85 (77.7); exposed culmen, 28–33 (29.8); tarsus, 20–23 (21.9). *Adult female:* 122–133 (128.3) mm (Ridgway).

Field Marks. Extensive black-and-white zebra-like barring of back and wings, combined with red on the head, distinguishes it from other Canadian woodpeckers. Males have the whole top of head, nape, and back of neck red; females have a grey crown, but the nape and back of neck are like those of the male. The red suffusion on the belly is hard to see in both sexes.

Habitat. Varies from mature timber to dooryard trees. Too rare in Canada for generalization but is known to nest in mature deciduous woodland in southern Ontario.

Nesting. The usually 4 or 5 white *eggs* are laid in a cavity in a tree, often a dead one, excavated by the birds at heights up to 40 feet.

Range. Breeds from southeastern Minnesota, extreme southern Ontario, western New York, and Delaware south to southern Texas and southern Florida.

Range in Canada. Rare and local permanent resident in extreme southern Ontario, breeding in Middlesex County; but formerly north to Wellington County and east to Halton County. Occasionally occurs at other points in southern Ontario (north to Minden and east to Kingston and Ottawa).

Accidental in southern Saskatchewan (Regina, May 26, 1959: specimen) and Nova Scotia (Middleton, January 1962: photographs). There are sight records for southern Manitoba (Winnipeg, Sanford, Brandon) and southwestern Quebec (Montreal).

Subspecies. *Centurus carolinus zebra* (Boddaert).

RED-HEADED WOODPECKER
Le Pic à tête rouge
Melanerpes erythrocephalus (Linnaeus)
Plate 43. L. 8.7 to 9.7 in.

Adults (sexes alike) characterized by solid, unspotted masses of red, white, and black. Whole head, neck, and upper breast, crimson red; back, scapulars, and wing coverts, black; rump, secondaries, upper tail coverts, and under body (lower breast to under tail coverts), white. *Young* differ from adults in having head and neck mostly greyish brown to blackish, the throat streaked; feathers of back and scapulars tipped with grey; and the white secondaries are crossed by one or two black bars, the tertials often by three or more. The basic patterns of the young (particularly the large white wing patch formed by the white secondaries) are so similar to those of adults that there is no mistaking them.

Measurements (*M. e. erythrocephalus*). *Adult male:* wing, 131.8–142 (136.4); tail, 71.6–79.9 (73.9); exposed culmen, 21.2–28.7 (25.9); tarsus, 19.2–23.5 (21.6). *Adult female:* wing, 131–138 (134.9) mm.

Field Marks. The completely red head and neck, contrasting masses (unspotted) of black and white on the body, especially the large white patch on the wing, can be mistaken for nothing else that occurs within the Red-headed Woodpecker's range. Young have blackish-brown head and dusky-streaked throat (little or no red), and there are some black bars on the mainly white wing patch, but their basic

patterns are so suggestive of those of adults (especially the large white wing patch) that there should be no difficulty in distinguishing them. *Voice:* Varied. Commonly a harsh *churr-churr* suggesting the call of a tree frog (*Hyla versicolor*). (*Note:* A western form of the Yellow-bellied Sapsucker (*Sphyrapicus varius ruber*) has the whole head and neck red but is otherwise very different. Its range and that of the Red-headed Woodpecker are widely separated.)

Habitat. Open woods, burntlands, groves, and scattered large trees in open places.

Nesting. Nests in a cavity excavated in dead wood of a tree, telephone pole, or fence post. *Eggs,* 4 to 7; white. Incubation said to be about 14 days (A. C. Bent), by both sexes.

Range. Breeds from southern Canada (Saskatchewan to New Brunswick) south to northern New Mexico, central Texas, the United States Gulf coast, and Florida. Somewhat migratory in northernmost part of range.

Breeding Distribution of Red-headed Woodpecker

Range in Canada. Breeds in southern Saskatchewan (rarely and locally: Cypress Hills), southern Manitoba (Dauphin, Winnipeg Beach, Sprague), southern Ontario (northward in diminishing numbers to about Malachi, Port Arthur, Sault Ste. Marie, North Bay, Ottawa), southwestern Quebec (Hudson Heights, Lachine, Hatley) and formerly, at least, in southern New Brunswick (Saint John). Possibly breeds in southwestern Alberta (Cypress Hills). Range somewhat less extensive than formerly.

Irregularly wanders west to southern Alberta (Waterton Lake, Foremost, Calgary, Elk Island Park), and east rarely to Nova Scotia (Ketch Harbour, Windsor). Winters in southern Ontario and rarely southern Manitoba (St. Vital).

Subspecies. *Melanerpes erythrocephalus caurinus* Brodkorb, occupies the western part of the breeding range east to w. Ont. *M. e. erythrocephalus* (Linnaeus), slightly smaller in size, breeds from s. Ont. eastward.

Remarks. There is a common tendency in Canada to misapply the name 'Red-headed Woodpecker' to any of the various woodpeckers that show a red mark on the head. Anyone who has seen the real Red-headed Wood-pecker, however, is unlikely to mistake it.

This species takes insects on the wing, flycatcher-fashion, more frequently than do most other woodpeckers. It eats also fruits and nuts in some quantities and is not above taking eggs and young of other birds on occasion. Except in extreme southern Ontario, it is nowhere a common bird in Canada.

LEWIS'S WOODPECKER
Le Pic de Lewis. *Asyndesmus lewis* (Gray)
Plate 43. L. 10.5 to 11.5 in.

Adults (sexes similar): Upper parts glossy greenish black except narrow grey collar; face, dull dark red; breast grey (black feather bases sometimes show through) shading into rose on abdomen, sides, and flanks. Feathers of under body rather hairlike. *Young* are similar to adults but lack red face and grey collar; rose on under body duller.

Measurements. *Adult male:* wing, 159.3–174.9 (169.9); tail, 83.5–101 (91.9); exposed culmen, 28.2–30.9 (29.6); tarsus, 23.7–26.2 (25.2). *Adult female:* wing, 153.8–171 (163) mm.

Field Marks. Adults with solid black upper parts, narrow grey collar around back of neck, grey breast, rose-tinted abdomen. Flight not undulating like that of other wood-peckers, often glides; wings solid black and rather broad. Frequently catches insects in the air, flycatcher-fashion. *Voice:* Rather silent but in breeding season a harsh *krar*.

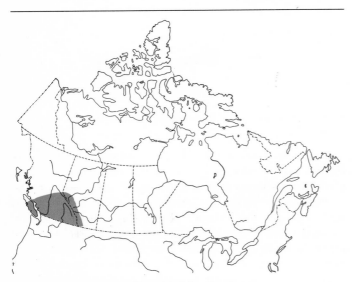

Breeding Distribution of Lewis's Woodpecker

Habitat. Open areas with scattered trees, such as burnt-lands with standing dead wood, logged-over places, wooded roadsides, open woodland.

Nesting. Nest in an excavated tree cavity, typically a dead tree. *Eggs*, usually 6 or 7; dull white. Incubation is by both sexes.

Range. Breeds from southern British Columbia, south-western Alberta, Montana, and southwestern South Dakota, south to California, Arizona, and New Mexico.

Range in Canada. Breeds in southern British Columbia (including Vancouver Island; north at least to Williams Lake) and southwestern Alberta (Jasper National Park, probably Waterton Lake). Winters in southern British Columbia (southern coast, Okanagan Valley, and rarely southern Vancouver Island).

Wanders irregularly north to central British Columbia (rarely as far as Masset and Takla Lake) and east to central and southeastern Alberta (Lesser Slave Lake, Belvedere, Camrose, Sullivan Lake, Brooks). Casual in Saskatchewan (Herschel, Tisdale, Saltcoats, Eastend, Tuxford, Qu'Appelle Valley), southern Manitoba (Winnipeg), and probably western Ontario (Emo: sight record only).

YELLOW-BELLIED SAPSUCKER
Le Pic maculé. *Sphyrapicus varius* (Linnaeus)
Plate 42. L. 8 to 9 in.

There are three subspecies in Canada different enough to cause confusion. A broad longitudinal white stripe down the closed wing distinguishes them as sapsuckers (*see also* Williamson's Sapsucker).

Sphyrapicus varius varius (Linnaeus), of eastern Canada west to Alberta (east of the mountains), northeastern British Columbia (Peace River Valley) and southern Yukon. *Adult male:* Crown red, bordered by black; from nasal tufts back-ward across face to side of neck, a white band; back, black copiously marked with white; throat, red with black border expanding into a posteriorly rounded black patch on breast; rest of under body, yellowish white with black V-marks down sides and flanks; upper surface of wing, black with conspicuous longitudinal white patch along wing coverts, a row of white spots along outer edge of primaries and secondaries. *Adult female:* Similar to adult male but throat white instead of red; red of crown often reduced and quite often completely replaced by black. *Young in juvenal plumage:* Little or no red on head; no black patch on breast; breast and sides brownish or olivaceous, the former cross-barred with dusky. Wings similar to adult.

Measurements (*S. v. varius*). *Adult male:* wing, 119–127 (122.5); tail, 59–78.1 (69.7); exposed culmen, 21.2–25 (22.9); tarsus, 18.9–21.5 (20.3). *Adult female:* wing, 119.2–125.3 (121.8) mm.

Sphyrapicus varius nuchalis Baird, of the Cariboo Park-lands of southeastern British Columbia and mountains of southwestern Alberta. Adults similar to *S. v. varius* but with some red on nape (posterior to black border of crown) and with the white on back much reduced; red throat patch of male usually more extensive; throat of female at least partly red with only chin and upper throat white.

Sphyrapicus varius ruber (Gmelin), of coastal British Columbia west of the Cascade mountains, and between latitudes 54° and 57° extending inland from the coast to Peace River Parklands. *Adults* (sexes similar): Whole head, neck, and breast, red; the paler markings of head of *nuchalis* much obscured; but usually the nasal tufts and a bar back-ward a short distance are whitish.

Field Marks. White longitudinal patch on side of folded wing marks it as a sapsucker. East of the Rockies it is distinguished readily from other woodpeckers: male has red crown and throat; female red crown (usually but occasionally all black) and white throat; both with black patch on breast and yellowish (yellow often hard to see) white abdomen. Populations in southeastern British Columbia and mountainous southwestern Alberta (*nuchalis*) are similar to eastern birds, but female shows partly red throat. In coastal and central-interior British Columbia (*ruber*) both sexes have the whole head, neck, and breast red and lack the black breast patch, but the white longitudinal wing patch and the remainder of the body plumage are similar to other populations. Young in juvenal plumage (all races) look brown, have no black breast patch, show only a little or even no red on head, but, like adults, have the long white sapsucker wing patch (*see* Williamson's Sapsucker, of southern interior B.C.).

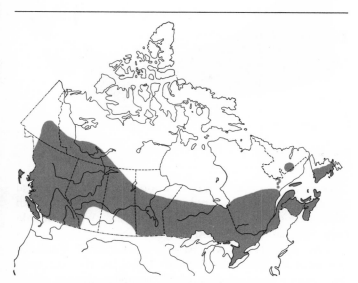

Breeding Distribution of Yellow-bellied Sapsucker

Habitat. In breeding season prefers deciduous or deciduous-coniferous woodlands, particularly where poplars and birches are important components.

Nesting. Nest in a cavity excavated by the birds in a tree (usually dead or partly so) at various heights. *Eggs,* 3 to 7; white. Incubation by both sexes.

Range. Breeds in woodlands of southeastern Alaska and southern Canada south to southern California, northern New Mexico, southeastern South Dakota, central Illinois, northern Ohio, and northern New York, and central New England south in the Alleghanies to Tennessee, North Carolina, and northern Georgia. Winters from southeastern Alaska and coastal British Columbia and north-central United States south to northern Baja California, western Panama, the Gulf coast, and Florida; in small numbers also in the West Indies.

Range in Canada. Breeds in wooded parts from southern Yukon (Mayo), southwestern Mackenzie (Fort Simpson, Great Slave Lake), northwestern and central-eastern Saskatchewan (Milliken Lake, Cumberland House); central Manitoba (Thicket Portage), north-central Ontario (Moose Factory), southern Quebec (Lake Mistassini, Gaspé Penin-

sula, Anticosti Island), interior Labrador (Hamilton River), and central Newfoundland (east at least to Swift Current) south through British Columbia (including Queen Charlotte and Vancouver islands), Alberta (south at least to Red Deer; breeding status uncertain in the Rocky Mountains but recorded in summer in Jasper and Banff national parks), south-central Saskatchewan (Wingard, Good Spirit Lake), southern Manitoba, southern Ontario, southern Quebec, and throughout New Brunswick, Prince Edward Island, and Nova Scotia.

Winters in coastal British Columbia.

Subspecies. Three (*see* above).

WILLIAMSON'S SAPSUCKER
Le Pic de Williamson. *Sphyrapicus thyroideus* (Cassin)
Plate 42. L. 9 to 9.7 in.

Adult male: Upper parts black. Rump patch, spots on flight feathers, and conspicuous longitudinal wing patch (along wing coverts), white; sides of head with two white stripes; throat and breast, black with narrow red median throat patch. Belly yellow. *Adult female:* Very different. Back, scapulars, and wing coverts, barred black and whitish; head brown with black streaks; rump patch white; throat brown (occasionally a trace of red); breast and sides barred black and whitish, middle of breast usually with black patch; belly yellowish. *Young male:* Resembles adult male but is duller, median throat patch white. *Young female:* Resembles adult female but is duller, belly whitish, no black breast patch.

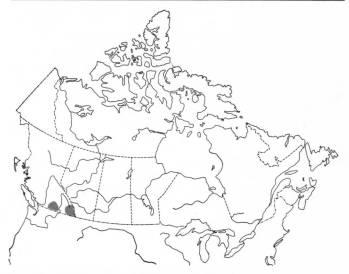

Breeding Distribution of Williamson's Sapsucker

Measurements (*S. t. nataliae*). *Adult male:* wing, 131.6–139 (135.7); tail, 76.9–90 (83.5); exposed culmen, 23.2–27 (24.9); tarsus, 20.3–23.5 (21.9). *Adult female:* wing, ca. 135 mm.

Field Marks. Adult male, a black-backed woodpecker with white rump and conspicuous long white patch on wing coverts; head black with two white stripes on each side and a narrow red throat patch (white in juvenal). Female is entirely different and lacks a white patch in the wing. The extensive regular barring of upper parts combined with white rump distinguishes her from other Canadian woodpeckers.

Habitat. Open coniferous woodland (especially western larch, Douglas fir, and yellow pine), sometimes burntlands, in the mountains of interior southern British Columbia.

Nesting. Nest, a cavity excavated by the birds in a tree, often dead or partly dead. *Eggs*, usually 5 or 6; white. Incubation by both parents.

Range. Breeds in the mountains from southern interior British Columbia and western Montana south to southern California, central Arizona, and northern New Mexico.

Range in Canada. Breeding summer resident in extreme southern interior British Columbia in two areas, (1) Okanagan region (mountains on International Border from Similkameen east to Midway and north to Schoonover Mountain), and (2) East Kootenay (Cranbrook, Newgate).

Subspecies. (1) *Sphyrapicus thyroideus thyroideus* (Cassin) breeds in the Okanagan region of B.C. east to Midway. (2) *S. t. nataliae* (Malherbe) breeds in the East Kootenay of B.C. The latter has a shorter, more slender bill.

HAIRY WOODPECKER

Le Pic chevelu. *Dendrocopos villosus* (Linnaeus)
Plate 43. L. 8.5 to 10.5 in.

A black-and-white (but on West Coast whites are tinged with sandy brown) four-toed woodpecker, with broad white stripe down middle of back and bill nearly as long as head. Varies geographically (*see* Subspecies). Adult male with bright red bar (often divided into two spots) on nape but lacking in female. Young not long out of the nest often show reddish or yellowish spots on crown, but young male does not have red on nape. A large edition of the common Downy Woodpecker but decidedly larger with much longer bill.

Measurements (*D. v. septentrionalis*). *Adult male:* wing, 127–137.5 (131); tail, 71.5–92.1 (81.9); exposed culmen, 29–38.6 (33.6); tarsus, 22–26.3 (24.3). *Adult female:* wing, 119–138.1 (127.8) mm.

Field Marks. A black-and-white woodpecker with a broad white stripe down middle of back, the adult male with a small bar of red on the nape. Closely resembles the Downy Woodpecker but is larger. However, size is hard to judge unless the two are together. The best distinction is the Hairy's relatively much longer bill (nearly as long as head), that of the Downy being more stubby and obviously shorter than the head. Another distinction valid in most parts of the continent (except the Pacific Coast region and Newfoundland) is the immaculate (no black spots or bars) white outer tail feathers of the Hairy. The Northern Three-toed Woodpecker has heavily barred sides and flanks.

Habitat. In nesting season more mature woodlands and forests but in heavy forests prefers more open parts, edges or openings; also burns and logged-over areas. Inhabits deciduous, coniferous, or mixedwood forests but over most of its range prefers at least an admixture of deciduous trees. Tends to be less tolerant than the Downy Woodpecker of young, smaller tree growth. In winter inhabits a wide variety of trees, often visiting ornamental trees and tall shrubbery even in urban areas.

Nesting. In a cavity excavated by the birds in a living or dead tree. *Eggs*, 3 to 5; white. Incubation reportedly 14 days (F. L. Burns), by both sexes.

Range. Breeds in wooded areas from central Alaska and across Canada south to Panama and the Bahamas. Winters mainly within breeding range, although there is some migratory movement, especially in more northern populations.

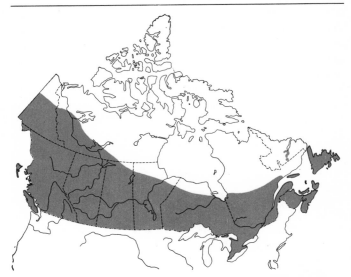

Breeding Distribution of Hairy Woodpecker

Range in Canada. Breeds in wooded areas from central Yukon (Fortymile), southwestern and central southern Mackenzie (forts Providence and Simpson, Wood Buffalo Park; probably northwest to Fort Norman), northern Saskatchewan (Lake Athabasca), north-central Manitoba (probably Bird, perhaps Reindeer Lake), northern Ontario (Favourable Lake, Fort Albany), southern Quebec (Eastmain, Lake St. John, Moisie River, Anticosti Island), and Newfoundland southward through British Columbia (including Queen Charlotte and Vancouver islands), Alberta, Saskatchewan, Manitoba, Ontario, southern Quebec, New Brunswick, Prince Edward Island, and Nova Scotia (including Cape Breton Island). Summer sight records for interior Labrador (Hamilton River). Winters north to southern Mackenzie and northern Newfoundland, but there is a certain amount of migration from such northern points.

Subspecies. (1) *Dendrocopos villosus septentrionalis* (Nuttall): Yukon, n. and c. B.C. (including Peace River Parklands, Chezacut), s. Mack., Alta. (east of the Rocky Mts.), Sask., Man., w. and c. Ont. (Kapuskasing), Que. (Temiskaming, Lake St. John, Anticosti I.). A large race with copiously white-marked black upper parts, all-white under body, including sides and flanks. (2) *D. v. villosus* (Linnaeus): s. Ont., s. Que. (including Gaspé Pen.), N.B., P.E.I., and N.S. Similar to (1) but averaging smaller. (3) *D. v. terraenovae* (Batchelder): Nfld. Similar to (2) but whites in upper parts reduced; sometimes white outer tail feathers with black spots and occasionally lightly dark-barred flanks. (4) *D. v. monticola* (Anthony): interior s. and s.-c. B.C., sw. Alta. (southern mts. intergrading northward with (1) in Jasper Park); similar to (1) but white spotting of wing coverts reduced. (5) *D. v. sitkensis* (Swarth): n. coast region of B.C. (but not Queen Charlotte Is.) south to Calvert I. and Rivers Inlet; like (4) in reduction of white spotting on wings but white of under parts more tinged with brownish. (6) *D. v. harrisi* (Audubon): s. coast and Vancouver I. of B.C. Differs from (5) in still darker, more smoky under parts. (7) *D. v. picoideus* (Osgood): Queen Charlotte Is., B.C. The most heavily pigmented of all the races. White spotting on wings sparse and small, white stripe down back, brownish and often spotted or barred with black, white outer tail feathers often spotted or broadly barred with black; flanks often barred, and sides streaked with black; under parts more heavily smoky brown than in (6). (8) *D. v. orius* (Oberholser) has been taken in sw. B.C. and possibly breeds in the Cascades near the International Boundary.

DOWNY WOODPECKER

Le Pic mineur. *Dendrocopos pubescens* (Linnaeus)
Plate 43. L. 6.3 to 7.2 in.

A small black-and-white woodpecker with broad white stripe down middle of back, rather short bill (shorter than head), and in the adult male a small bright red bar on back of head. Young only shortly out of the nest often have red, yellow, or white spots on the crown. South coastal British Columbia populations have the white under parts tinged with smoky brown (*see* Subspecies). Colour and markings like Hairy Woodpecker, but very much smaller size and much shorter bill (shorter than head) easily distinguish it in the hand. Our smallest woodpecker.

Measurements (*D. p. medianus*). *Adult male:* wing, 92.1–98.7 (94.7); tail, 50.6–61 (57.7); exposed culmen, 14.4–18.1 (16.2); tarsus, 15.9–17.1 (16.8). *Adult female:* wing, 92–98.7 (95.2) mm.

Field Marks. A small black-and-white woodpecker, the male with a small red bar on the back of the head. A broad white stripe down the middle of the black back distinguishes it from other woodpeckers except the Hairy, which it very closely resembles. Much smaller size of the Downy is often hard to judge, and the best field mark is the short bill of the Downy (much shorter than head). In most parts of Canada the presence of black spots on the white outer tail feathers distinguishes the Downy from the Hairy (however, on the west coast of British Columbia and in Newfoundland this is useless as many Hairy Woodpeckers have similar markings). The Northern Three-toed Woodpecker has the sides and flanks heavily barred.

Habitat. Open deciduous or mixed deciduous and coniferous woodland and tall shrubbery, and in various situations from wilderness areas to city parks and shade trees, farm groves, woodlots, and orchards. Forages in trees, shrubbery, and sometimes, especially in winter, on non-woody plants in fields. Prefers deciduous trees and tall shrubbery.

Nesting. In an excavated cavity in a dead tree or dead part of a living one, at heights varying from a few to 60 feet above the ground. *Eggs,* usually 4 or 5; white. Incubation reported as 12 days (F. L. Burns), by both sexes.

Range. Breeds in woodlands from southeastern Alaska and across southern Canada (*see* below) south to southern California, central Arizona, south-central Texas, and along the Gulf coast from Louisiana to Florida.

Range in Canada. Breeds from southern Yukon (probably Dezadeash Lake), southwestern Mackenzie (Carcajou River west of Fort Norman; Fort Simpson; probably Wood Buffalo Park), northern Alberta, northwestern and central-eastern Saskatchewan (Lake Athabasca), north-central Manitoba (Thicket Portage), western and northern Ontario (north probably to central-western James Bay), southern Quebec (Lake Mistassini, Matamek, Anticosti Island, Little Mecatina River, St. Augustin), and Newfoundland, south through the International Boundary through British Columbia (including Vancouver Island but not Queen Charlotte Islands), Alberta, Saskatchewan, Manitoba, Ontario, southern Quebec, and through New Brunswick, Prince Edward Island, and Nova Scotia. Winters within most of the breeding range north at least to southern Mackenzie, northwestern Saskatchewan, and Lake Mistassini, Quebec. There is some migratory movement of individuals.

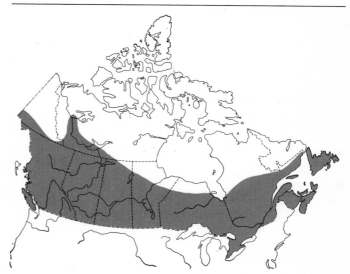

Breeding Distribution of Downy Woodpecker

Subspecies. (1) *Dendrocopos pubescens nelsoni* (Oberholser): s. Mack., n. and ne. B.C., Alta. (except extreme sw. but south to Banff), Sask., Man. (intergrading in south with *medianus*), and probably nw. Ont. (intergrades with *medianus* in Rainy River district). In whiteness of under parts and white spotting on wings it is similar to *medianus* but averages slightly larger with perhaps less black barring on white of tail (very variable), whites a little purer. A poorly characterized race. As size variation is a cline, delimitation of range, apart from that of *medianus*, is arbitrary. (2) *D. p. medianus* (Swainson): s. and e. Ont., Que., Nfld., and the Maritimes. Averages slightly smaller than *nelsoni*. (3) *D. p. leucurus* (Hartlaub): c. and s. B.C. (except sw. coast and s. Vancouver Island) and extreme sw. Alta. (Waterton Lakes Park). Similar in size to *nelsoni*, but wing coverts with white spots reduced and white of under parts not so pure. (4) *D. p. gairdnerii* (Audubon): s. coastal B.C. and Vancouver Island. Like *leucurus* in reduced white spotting of wing coverts but under parts decidedly tinged with smoky brown; size

245

averages smaller. (5) *D. p. glacialis* (Grinnell): wanderer to Queen Charlotte Is., August 24, 1920 (Munro and Cowan, 1947); possibly occurs regularly on northern coast of B.C., but no specimens are available for determination of racial affinities. Additional material is needed also from southwestern Yukon.

Remarks. This is our smallest woodpecker and in many parts of the country our commonest. It is a confiding bird and is more likely to come closer to our dwellings than would most of its relatives. In winter it is easily attracted by a supply of suet to the backyard feeding shelf.

In appearance it is almost a counterpart of the larger Hairy Woodpecker. The males of both species have a little red bar on the nape and, for that reason, are often mistaken for the very different Red-headed Woodpecker.

Insects constitute over 75 per cent of the food of this woodpecker. Almost all insects eaten are economically harmful and include some wood-boring species. An interesting study of the effects of the Downy and Hairy woodpeckers on the coddling moth have recently been made in Nova Scotia by C. R. MacLellan (1958, *The Canadian Entomologist* 90(1): 21). In the years 1950 to 1956 he found that these woodpeckers reduced the overwintering population of the coddling moth on his study area by 52 per cent!

WHITE-HEADED WOODPECKER

Le Pic à tête blanche. *Dendrocopos albolarvatus* (Cassin) L. 9 to 9.5 in.

Adults are all black, except white head, fore-neck, patch on primaries of the wing, and, in the male only, a red bar across the nape. Young are similar to adults, but black is duller.

Field Marks. Unmistakable, as described above.

Range. Eastern Washington and northern Idaho south to southern California and western Nevada.

Status in Canada. Casual in extreme southern British Columbia (Okanagan Landing, Okanagan Centre, Similkameen Valley).

Subspecies. *Dendrocopos albolarvatus albolarvatus* (Cassin).

BLACK-BACKED THREE-TOED WOODPECKER

(Arctic Three-toed Woodpecker)
Le Pic à dos noir. *Picoïdes arcticus* (Swainson)
Plate 43. L. 9 to 10 in.

Three instead of four toes distinguish it from other woodpeckers except the Northern Three-toed. *Adult male:* Above, bluish black (including whole back) except yellow crown patch, white spots on flight feathers, and mainly white outer tail feathers; sides of head with narrow white line (sometimes absent) running back from eye and a broad white stripe below eye; under parts mostly white, the sides and flanks heavily barred black and white. *Adult female:* Like adult male but crown black without yellow patch. *Young:* Resemble adult male, there being a smaller yellow crown patch in the young male and frequently young females too have yellow feathers in the crown.

Measurements. *Adult male:* wing, 126.1–132 (128.6); tail, 73.8–84.6 (79.4); exposed culmen, 31–34 (32.2); tarsus, 22.5–24.9 (23.8). *Adult female:* wing, 121–132 (126.3) mm.

Field Marks. Solid black back, yellow crown patch in male (lacking in female), white under parts, the sides and flanks extensively barred with black. All-black back distinguishes it from Northern Three-toed. Williamson's Sapsucker male, of southern British Columbia, has white patch on sides of wings, white rump, and mostly black breast and should be easily distinguishable.

Habitat. Coniferous woodlands and burned areas with standing dead trees.

Nesting. In an excavated cavity in a dead or living tree, usually (not always) coniferous. Generally at no great height (2 to 20 feet) but exceptionally (mainly in the West) up to 80 feet. Incubation said to be 14 days (A. C. Bent), by both sexes.

Range. Breeds from central Alaska and across Canada (*see* Range in Canada) south to central California, western Nevada, northwestern Wyoming, southwestern South Dakota, northern Minnesota, Upper Peninsula of Michigan, northern New York (Adirondacks), Vermont (Green Mts.), New Hampshire (White Mts.), and Maine.

Range in Canada. Breeds in coniferous woodland from southern Yukon (Sixmile River; north probably to Fort Reliance), central-western and southern Mackenzie (Norman Wells, Fort Simpson, Great Slave Lake), northern Saskatchewan (Lake Athabasca), northern Manitoba (Bird, York Factory), northern Ontario (Favourable Lake, southern James Bay), south-central Quebec (southern James Bay, Lake Mistassini, north shore of the Gulf of St. Lawrence, Anticosti Island), central Labrador (Hamilton Inlet, Sandgirt Lake), and Newfoundland south through British Columbia (east of the Cascades), central and southwestern Alberta (Battle River region), central Saskatchewan, southern Manitoba (High Lake), western and southern Ontario (south to Georgian Bay, Algonquin Park), southern Quebec (Inlet, Lac Trois Saumons, Gaspé Peninsula), New Brunswick, Prince Edward Island, and Nova Scotia.

Winters mainly in the breeding range, but individuals

Breeding Distribution of Black-backed Three-toed Woodpecker

246

wander south irregularly in small numbers. In certain years, irregularly spaced, relatively large numbers move southward.

NORTHERN THREE-TOED WOODPECKER
(American Three-toed Woodpecker)
Le Pic à dos rayé. *Picoïdes tridactylus* (Linnaeus)
Plate 43. L. 8 to 9.6 in.

Three instead of four toes distinguish it from the other woodpeckers except the Black-backed Three-toed Woodpecker. The present species differs from the Black-backed in having white bars on the back (in western populations the white bars are sometimes coalesced into a longitudinal white stripe down the back) and is somewhat smaller in size. As in the Black-backed, the male has a yellow crown patch, which is lacking in the adult female. In female Northerns there is usually (not always) white spotting on the black crown.

Measurements (*P. t. bacatus*). *Adult male:* wing, 111.2–119 (114.1); tail, 64.9–77.3 (71.5); exposed culmen, 25.5–29 (27); tarsus, 20.1–22.3 (21.3). *Adult female:* wing 109.8–115 (112.1) mm.

Field Marks. Large yellow crown patch identifies male three-toed woodpeckers, and white areas in the middle of the back (usually white bars) denote the present species. Females of this species, lacking a yellow crown patch and with white down the middle of the back (usually at least some barring can be detected) might be confused by beginners with female Hairy Woodpecker. In eastern populations especially, the Northern Three-toed has obvious white barring on the back instead of a solid white longitudinal stripe, but in some western individuals the whites are more extensive and occasionally are fused into a solid white stripe. The sides and flanks of the three-toed woodpeckers are heavily barred; those of the Hairy Woodpecker *over most of its range* are plain white. (*Caution:* On the west coast and in Newfoundland, Hairy Woodpeckers often have lightly barred *flanks*, but the barring does not include the sides. The Queen Charlotte Island Hairy, however, often has black streaks on the sides *and* barred flanks.)

Habitat. Coniferous woodlands and burntlands (or similar stands of dead trees); muskegs.

Nesting. Similar to Black-backed Three-toed Woodpecker.

Range. Breeds north to tree limit in North America, Europe, and Asia. In North America: northern Alaska and across Canada (*see* Range in Canada) south to southern Oregon, Arizona, New Mexico, Minnesota, central Ontario, northern New York (Adirondack Mts.), northern Vermont (Green Mts.), northern New Hampshire (White Mts.), and Maine.

Range in Canada. Breeds from near tree limit in northern Yukon (Old Crow), northwestern and central Mackenzie (Mackenzie Delta, Fort Anderson, Great Slave Lake), northern Saskatchewan (Lake Athabasca, Reindeer Lake), northern Manitoba (Churchill; perhaps Sandhill Lake), northern Ontario (probably Severn River), northern Quebec (Richmond Gulf; Chimo), northern Labrador (Saglek Bay), and Newfoundland south to southern British Columbia (including Vancouver Island rarely), southwestern and central-eastern Alberta (Battle River Region), central Saskatchewan (Nipawin), southern Manitoba (Riding Mountain, Whitemouth), central Ontario (Savanne; Fort William–Port Arthur area; Abitibi Lake), Quebec (south at least to Lake Mistassini, Pointe des Monts, Anticosti Island; probably Gaspé Peninsula; southern limits poorly known), and New Brunswick. Casual in southwestern Keewatin (Windy River). Winters within the breeding range, but individuals move south of the breeding range irregularly into southern Ontario and southwestern Quebec. Sight records only for Nova Scotia.

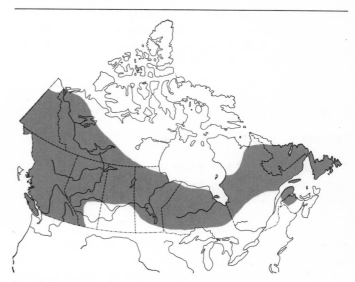

Breeding Distribution of Northern Three-toed Woodpecker

Subspecies. (1) *Picoïdes tridactylus bacatus* Bangs: Man. eastward. White bars on back narrower but usually quite distinct, rarely very few and indistinct. (2) *P. t. fasciatus* Baird: Yukon, Mack., B.C., Alta., w. Sask. Similar to *bacatus* but with more white on back, white bars larger and often partly, occasionally completely, coalesced forming a more or less unbroken longitudinal patch; white spots on forehead larger.

Order **Passeriformes**–Perching Birds

The passerine or perching birds make up by far the largest avian order, containing, as it does, almost half of the more than 8,000 species of the world's living birds. All species have four toes, three in front, one behind, the hind toe well developed and on the same level as the others. The feet are ideal for grasping limbs in perching. Most have well-developed songs. All are land birds, and the open sea has no useful place in their existence; indeed, it is just another migration hazard for many species.

Family **Tyrannidae**–Tyrant Flycatchers

Number of Species in North America 32; in Canada 22

This large family of 360 species, more or less, is confined to the Western Hemisphere with its centre of abundance in the tropics. The bill is typically flattened, broad at the base, slightly hooked at the tip, and has stiff bristles at its base. Legs and feet are weak but ideal for perching. Song is less well developed than in other families of this order. Fly-catchers usually perch with alert upright posture, occasionally to frequently jetting the tail. Passing insects are taken by a short quick flight and a snap of the bill, after which the bird resumes perching to watch for other insects.

EASTERN KINGBIRD

Le Tyran tritri. *Tyrannus tyrannus* (Linnaeus)
Plate 44. L. 7.8 to 8.7 in.

Adults: Upper parts blackish slate, the top and sides of head black with a concealed orange to scarlet patch in centre of crown; tail, black with white tip; under parts white, the breast shaded with grey. *Young (in juvenal plumage):* Like adults but without orange-red crown patch, upper parts duller, the head little if any darker than the back.

Measurements. *Adult male:* wing, 115–126.5 (119.2); tail, 82–92.5 (86.3); exposed culmen, 18.3–20.6 (19.0); tarsus, 17.5–19.5 (18.6). *Adult female:* wing, 109.5–118.5 (113.9) mm.

Field Marks. A large flycatcher; blackish above, white below, the black tail tipped with white. Usually seen perched on a fence or tree in open places. Posture erect, alert. Flies with rapid, quivering wing strokes. *Voice:* Commonly a single strident *dzeet* and a more prolonged shrill twittering in which *kitter* sounds are frequent.

Habitat. More open places: fields, pastures, and prairies (with trees, shrubbery, or fence posts for perching and nesting), parklands, scattered trees, orchards, wood edges, farmland, standing drowned trees on rivers, lakes, and bogs.

Nesting. At various heights, usually 8 to 20 feet, on a branch of a tree or bush, occasionally on a fence post or tree stump. Nest, a rather bulky structure of twigs and grasses lined with animal hair, rootlets, dry grasses, and plant fibre. *Eggs,* usually 3 or 4; white—spotted, dotted, and blotched with browns and often some greys. Incubation 12 to 13 days (F. L. Burns), 13 days (O. W. Knight), by the female.

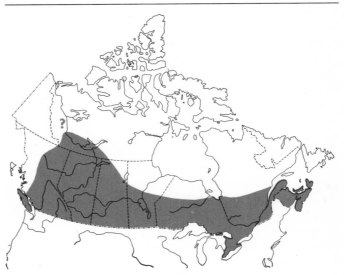

Breeding Distribution of Eastern Kingbird

Range. Breeds from southern Canada south to northeastern California, northern Nevada, northern Utah, northeastern New Mexico, central Texas, the Gulf coast of United States, and southern Florida. Winters in South America.

Range in Canada. Summer resident, breeding from northcentral British Columbia (Nulki Lake, Bouchie Lake, Peace River parklands; recorded in summer, possibly breeds,

248

north to near Trutch and Muskwa), southern Mackenzie (Nyarling and Little Buffalo rivers, probably Fort Simpson; recorded in summer north to Norman Wells), northwestern and central-eastern Saskatchewan (Lake Athabasca, Cumberland House), central Manitoba (Thicket Portage), central Ontario (Favourable Lake, Kapuskasing, Moose Factory), southern Quebec (Lake St. John, Rivière du Loup, Rimouski; probably Percé), south through southern parts of British Columbia (including Vancouver Island), Alberta, Saskatchewan, Manitoba, Ontario, Quebec, and through New Brunswick, Prince Edward Island, and Nova Scotia (including Cape Breton Island).

Casual in southern Yukon (Champagne), central Quebec (Moar Bay; north shore of the Gulf of St. Lawrence: Mingan, Natashquan, Wolf Bay; Anticosti Island), and Newfoundland (St. Andrews, Tompkins, Cappahayden). Accidental in northern Hudson Bay (Coats Island, August 1955) and Labrador (Killinek, Hopedale).

Remarks. Eastern Kingbirds are pugnacious and will not tolerate the presence of any large bird near their nesting territory. A crow, hawk, heron, or other large bird passing nearby is immediately and ignominiously driven off by the fury and agility of the kingbird's attack.

Kingbirds are flycatchers and therefore are insect eaters. The Eastern Kingbird perches with erect posture on a post or tree in an open place and alertly watches for passing insects. With a short dash and an audible snap of the bill, it picks off its prey in mid-air and nonchalantly returns to its perch to await another insect.

GRAY KINGBIRD

Le Tyran gris. *Tyrannus dominicensis* (Gmelin)
L. 8 to 9.2 in.

Similar to Eastern Kingbird but upper parts paler (ashy grey); ear coverts dusky; tail lacks white tip; bill decidedly larger and longer; size somewhat larger.

Measurements. *Adult male:* wing, 111–122 (116.2); tail, 82–100 (90.3); exposed culmen, 24.5–28 (26.1); tarsus, 17.5–19.5 (18.5). *Adult female:* wing, 107.5–120 (113.2) mm (Ridgway).

Range. Breeds in coastal southeastern United States (South Carolina, Georgia, Florida) and the West Indies south to northern Venezuela.

Status in Canada. Accidental. A specimen was taken at Cape Beale, Vancouver Island, British Columbia, on September 29, 1889.

Subspecies. *Tyrannus dominicensis dominicensis* (Gmelin).

TROPICAL KINGBIRD (Couch's Kingbird)

Le Tyran mélancolique. *Tyrannus melancholicus* Vieillot
L. 8 to 9.5 in.

Similar to Western Kingbird but tail uniform dusky brown (instead of black with white outer margin) and slightly forked; has dark area through eye and across ear, and larger bill. Its reddish orange crown patch (adults), slightly forked tail, and attenuated outer primary tips distinguish it from the Crested Flycatcher.

Range. Southeastern Arizona, northern Mexico, and southern Texas south to Bolivia and Argentina.

Status in Canada. Accidental. A specimen taken at French's Beach, Renfrew District, southern Vancouver Island, British Columbia, in February 1923, is of the subspecies *Tyrannus melancholicus occidentalis* Hartert and Goodson.

WESTERN KINGBIRD (Arkansas Kingbird)

Le Tyran de l'Ouest. *Tyrannus verticalis* Say
Plate 44. L. 8 to 9.3 in.

Adults: Head, neck, and breast, pale grey (whitish on chin); top of head with concealed orange-red patch; through eye to ear, a suggestion of a faint dusky patch; belly yellow; tail black except contrasting white outer web of outermost feather on each side; tips of outer primaries of the wing narrowed to a point (less so in female). *Young in juvenal plumage:* Similar to adults but crown patch lacking, colours duller and paler, tips of outer primaries more rounded, only outermost tending to be pointed.

Measurements. *Adult male:* wing, 125.5–133.5 (129.4); tail, 88.5–96.5 (93); exposed culmen, 20.5–22.5 (21.7); tarsus, 18.5–19.5 (19.1). *Adult female:* wing, 118.5–127.0 (123.5) mm.

Field Marks. A large flycatcher, primarily western in distribution, with yellow belly, pale grey head and breast (sometimes whitish on throat), black tail with narrow white outer edges (white edges sometimes hard to see because of wear). Of birds occurring regularly in Canada, the Great Crested Flycatcher is most likely to be confused with it, but the Western Kingbird's *black tail* and lack of definite white wing bars (if such bars are present in the kingbird, it is only a suggestion of them) distinguish it. *Voice:* Various shrill twitters and squeaks; or a series of harsh notes; often a single *kip*. Voice usually lower pitched than that of Eastern Kingbird.

Habitat. Open situations such as prairies but in the vicinity of at least one or two trees, shelter belts, telephone

Breeding Distribution of Western Kingbird

249

poles, or houses for perching and nesting; and in the mountains open areas among scattered trees.

Nesting. In trees and shrubs and on telephone poles and buildings. It is a rather bulky structure of grasses, hair, wool, and various fibrous materials. *Eggs*, 3 to 5, usually 4; very similar to Eastern Kingbird. Incubation period is given variously by authors as 12 to 14 days.

Range. Breeds from southern western Canada (interior southern British Columbia east to southern Manitoba; rarely extreme southern Ontario) south to northern Baja California, northwestern Mexico, and west-central Texas, and east to northwestern Ohio and (rarely) north-central Missouri. Winters mainly from Mexico south to Nicaragua; in small numbers in coastal southeastern United States (South Carolina to Florida).

Range in Canada. Summer resident, breeding in southern interior British Columbia (Okanagan Valley, Williams Lake, southern Wells Grey Park, Cranbrook), southern Alberta (north at least to Scollard and Bodo, west at least to Pearce, Rosebud, Munson), southern Saskatchewan (Cypress Hills region, Davidson, Simpson, Melville), southern Manitoba (Oak Lake, Winnipeg, Whitemouth), and once in extreme southern Ontario (Port Alma in 1943).

Rare visitant to Vancouver Island (Ucluelet, etc.). Casual in southern Ontario (mainly in migration), southeastern Quebec (Moisie River, September 22, 1958; sight record Magdalen Islands), New Brunswick (Machias Seal Island; Sackville vicinity; etc.), Nova Scotia (West La Have, November 17, 1940, to January 26, 1941, and various other records) and Newfoundland (Cappahayden, November 5, 1957; Exploits Bay, August 7, 1890).

CASSIN'S KINGBIRD

Le Tyran de Cassin. *Tyrannus vociferans* Swainson
L. 8.75 to 9 in.

Another large flycatcher with a yellow belly, but its black tail distinguishes it from all other Canadian flycatchers but the Western Kingbird. Closely resembles Western Kingbird and, like it, has a black tail, but the outer margins of the tail in Cassin's are not conspicuously white (at most only a suggestion of white or pale brown) and the grey of head and breast is darker.

Range. Central California and southern Montana south to Guerrero, Mexico. Farther south in winter.

Status in Canada. Accidental. Specimen collected June 5, 1953, at Achray, Grand Lake, northeastern Algonquin Park, Ontario.

Subspecies. *Tyrannus vociferans vociferans* Swainson.

SCISSOR-TAILED FLYCATCHER

Le Moucherolle à longue queue
Muscivora forficata (Gmelin)
L. 12 to 15 in. (including long tail)

Tail extremely long, forked 8 to 10 inches in males. *Adult male:* Upper parts light grey, the crown with a concealed patch of orange-red; wings blackish, their coverts and secondaries edged in white; middle tail feathers blackish,

the outer three on each side white (often with pinkish tinge) with black ends; throat whitish, shading to pale grey on breast; sides, flanks, and undertail coverts, salmon; wing linings pale pinkish; axillars and patch on under wing coverts, red. *Adult female:* Similar to adult male but duller, crown patch small or wanting, tail shorter. *Young:* Similar to adult female but crown patch always absent, greys more brownish; pinkish of under wings paler, the sides more buffy than pink.

Range. Breeds from eastern New Mexico, southeastern Colorado, western Oklahoma, central Kansas, western Arkansas, and western Louisiana south to southern Texas.

Status in Canada. Casual or accidental: Manitoba (York Factory, 1880; also October 2, 1924; Portage la Prairie, October 31, 1884; Delta, October 20, 1951). Quebec (Noranda, October 30, 1938; Pointe des Monts, August 14, 1894; Seven Islands, May 10, 1955). New Brunswick (Clarendon Station, May 21, 1906; Alma, June 20, 1907; Grand Manan, October 26, 1924). There are two sight records for Alberta (Salt and Wilk, 1958), and about seven for Ontario, but to date no specimen has been secured in either province.

GREAT CRESTED FLYCATCHER

Le Moucherolle huppé. *Myiarchus crinitus* (Linnaeus)
Plate 44. L. 8 to 9.2 in.

About the size of the Eastern Kingbird. Upper parts olive brown, the feathers of crown with darker centres (but crown never has a concealed red patch); inner webs of tail feathers (except central pair) cinnamon rufous; throat and breast grey; belly, sides, flanks, and under tail coverts, yellow; wings greyish brown, the secondaries and wing coverts edged with white (forming two wing bars), the edges of the primaries tinged with chestnut.

Measurements. (*M. c. boreus*). *Adult male:* wing, 102.5–111 (106.5); tail, 91–98.5 (93.9); exposed culmen, 18.8–21.5 (20.1); tarsus, 21–22.5 (21.6). *Adult female:* wing, 97–103.5 (99.7) mm.

Field Marks. A large (about kingbird size) flycatcher, typically of woodlands, with yellow belly, grey throat and upper breast, *much rufous in tail* (especially under side) and a little in the wings, and two white wing bars. The only other flycatcher of regular occurrence in Canada that closely resembles it is the Western Kingbird (both occur regularly in Manitoba and eastern Saskatchewan). The Crested Flycatcher's rufous tail, white wing bars, different habitat, and voice will prevent confusion between the two. *Voice:* Varied. A loud harsh whistled *kweep* is characteristic and common, often followed by several *wick-wick-wick*'s.

Habitat. More mature woodlands, preferring deciduous or mixedwood types; maturer woodlots, groves of taller trees, orchards near woodland. Usually frequents the upper branches.

Nesting. In a cavity in a dead or living tree, most frequently a deciduous one. The cavity may be a natural one or a woodpecker hole. Bird boxes are used also. Nest, often bulky, an accumulation of leaves (including pine needles), hair, feathers, moss, twine, miscellaneous litter, and often

Breeding Distribution of Great Crested Flycatcher

one or more cast snake skins. (However, snake skins are by no means always used, even in areas where snakes are common.) *Eggs*, most often 4 to 6; creamy white to buffy, heavily and handsomely blotched, lined, and streaked with browns and sometimes a little grey or lavender. Incubation, variously given by authors, 13 to 15 days, by both sexes.

Range. Southern Canada (eastern Saskatchewan east to Nova Scotia) south to western Oklahoma, central Texas, the Gulf coast of United States, and Florida. Winters from Florida and eastern and southern Mexico south to Colombia.

Range in Canada. Summer resident, breeding in southeastern Saskatchewan (High Hill, Indian Head; pairs noted north to near Cumberland House), southern Manitoba (Aweme, Lake St. Martin, Hillside Beach, Whitemouth), southern western and southern Ontario (north at least to MacLennan, Lake Nipissing, Petawawa; also Rainy River) southwestern Quebec (Montreal, Hatley, Blue Sea Lake, Quebec, Ste. Anne de la Pocatière) southwestern New Brunswick (Woodstock), and recently Nova Scotia (rarely and very locally: Port Wallis).

Subspecies. *Myiarchus crinitus boreus* Bangs.

Remarks. There has been considerable speculation as to why the Crested Flycatcher so frequently places a piece of cast-off snake skin in its nest. A popular belief is that the snake skin acts as a scarecrow to repel would-be nest intruders. However, the snake skin is often buried deep under other nesting materials, or it may be replaced by something similar such as cellophane or onion skins. Perhaps the truth of the matter is that snake skin is used simply because it makes good nesting material and because its shininess attracts the flycatcher's attention.

Beetles, bees and wasps, flies, bugs, grasshoppers and crickets, butterflies and moths including their caterpillars, dragonflies, and spiders constitute the bulk of its food. A few berries are eaten also.

Erect and alert, it perches on a high branch. Every so often it dashes out and snaps up a passing insect. Like most of its relatives, it is aggressive toward other birds that venture too close to its nest.

ASH-THROATED FLYCATCHER

Le moucherolle à gorge cendrée
Myiarchus cinerascens (Lawrence)
L. 8 to 8.5 in.

Similar to Crested Flycatcher, but upper parts browner (less greenish), under parts very much paler, the throat and belly sometimes nearly white; bill smaller.

Range. Breeds from southwestern Oregon (probably rarely eastern Washington), southern Idaho, southwestern Wyoming, Colorado, and northern and central Texas south to Guerrero, and southern Baja California.

Status in Canada. Casual in British Columbia: Vancouver, October 7 and 11, 1953; also sight record: August 24, 1958.

Subspecies. *Myiarchus cinerascens cinerascens* (Lawrence).

EASTERN PHOEBE

Le Moucherolle phébi. *Sayornis phoebe* (Latham)
Plate 44. L. 6.3 to 7.2 in.

Adults (sexes similar): Top and sides of head and back of neck, blackish brown (darker than back); back and scapulars greyish olive; wings and tail mostly dark brown; edges of wing coverts slightly paler but not forming conspicuous wing bars; under parts white with yellowish tinge (in autumn decidedly yellowish); sides of breast pale greyish olive; bill black above and *below*. *Young:* Similar to autumn adults, but upper parts more brownish, two buffy wing bars present.

Measurements. *Adult male:* wing, 80.7–90.3 (85.3); tail, 70–76 (73.1); exposed culmen, 13.8–15.4 (14.7); tarsus, 17–19 (18). *Adult female:* wing, 80.1–87.8 (83.7) mm.

This is one of the larger of the small dull-coloured flycatchers. Most similar to the pewees, but its dark *under* side of bill, lack of *distinct* white wing bars, larger stouter legs, and less-pointed wings distinguish it.

Field Marks. A bluebird-sized dull-coloured flycatcher, the top of the head more blackish than the back. Its lack of *conspicuous* white wing bars (young have buffy wing bars), its habit when perched of frequently wagging the tail, its black *lower* mandible, and its voice distinguish it from pewees and other similar small flycatchers. *Voice: Fee-be* with accent on first syllable (very different from the drawn-out call of the Eastern Wood Pewee); also a sharp *chip*.

Habitat. In nesting season, often the vicinity of streams and lakes where rocky walls or bridges provide nesting places, and trees or shrubbery furnish foraging places, also frequently the vicinity of buildings often remote from water.

Nesting. Nest, rather bulky, of mud (not always used), moss, grasses, rootlets, lined with fine grasses, hair, and plant fibres, is placed on ledges of rock, under bridges, culverts, and overhangs of buildings. *Eggs*, usually 5; white (occasionally a few spots of brown). Incubation apparently variable: 14, 16, 17 days (W. P. Smith); 13 days (Knight); 15 to 20 days (L. deK. Lawrence); by the female.

Range. Breeds from Canada (*see* Range in Canada) south to southwestern South Dakota and eastern New Mexico, central and northeastern Texas, central Alabama, western South Carolina, and North Carolina. Winters mainly from

251

Breeding Distribution of Eastern Phoebe

PLATE 51

1 Wheatear, adult male in summer

2 Townsend's Solitaire, adult

3 Hermit Thrush

4 Veery

5 Gray-cheeked Thrush

6 Wood Thrush

7 Swainson's Thrush

Virginia south through the states on the Atlantic Coast and west through states on the Gulf coast and south to southern Mexico.

Range in Canada. Summer resident, breeding from central-western and southern Mackenzie (Norman Wells, Fort Simpson, Fort Rae, Fort Resolution), northern Saskatchewan (Lake Athabasca, Reindeer River), northern Manitoba (Bird; recorded in summer north to Churchill), and central Ontario (Favourable Lake, Lake Nipigon, Lake Abitibi), south to central-eastern British Columbia (Peace River parklands), southern Alberta (Jasper Park, Brooks), south-central and southeastern Saskatchewan (Cochin; St. Louis; Yorkton region), southern Manitoba (except extreme southwestern corner), and through southern Ontario; also southwestern Quebec (Blue Sea Lake, Montreal, Hatley, Quebec, Rivière du Loup; probably north to Amos), and western New Brunswick (St. Leonard, Woodstock, Fredericton).

Casual in Nova Scotia (Wolfville, Gaspereau, Sable River, Bon Portage Island) and southeastern Quebec (Moisie River, May 9, 1953). Probably of casual occurrence also (sight records only but by competent observers) in southwestern Yukon (Pine Creek) and central-western Quebec (Great Whale River).

BLACK PHOEBE

Le Moucherolle noir. *Sayornis nigricans* (Swanson)
L. 6.3 to 7 in.

Dull black except white abdomen; edges of secondaries and outer web of outer tail feathers whitish; under tail coverts white, frequently streaked with dusky. The only Canadian flycatcher with a black breast.

Range. California, southwestern Utah, southern New Mexico, and central Texas south in the highlands to Argentina.

Status in Canada. Accidental in British Columbia (Vancouver, November 11, 1936). The specimen represents the subspecies *Sayornis nigricans semiatra* (Vigors).

252

1

2

3

4

5

6

7

Crosby

SAY'S PHOEBE

Le Moucherolle à ventre roux
Sayornis saya (Bonaparte)
Plate 44. L. 7 to 8 in.

Adults (sexes similar): Upper parts brownish grey (darkest on top and sides of head); tail black; breast greyish, becoming very pale on throat and with buffy wash; abdomen and under tail coverts cinnamon; wings dark brownish grey, the inner secondaries and ends of greater wing coverts edged with dull whitish. *Young:* Similar to adults but middle and greater wing coverts tipped with cinnamon (forming two cinnamon wing bars).

Measurements (*S. s. saya*). *Adult male:* wing, 104.0–108.5 (106.1); tail, 80.0–85.0 (83.0); exposed culmen, 14.3–16.8 (15.4); tarsus, 20.0–21.5 (20.6). *Adult female:* wing, 95.0–104.0 (100.3) mm.

Field Marks. A bluebird-sized flycatcher of the West. Its cinnamon belly and black tail identify it. *Voice:* A plaintive *pee-urr*.

Habitat. Open, usually dry, places where bushes, fences, buildings, or even low rocks and earth hummocks provide look-out perches. For nesting, rocky walls, buildings, bridges, and similar locations that provide a place for the nest with, preferably, at least some overhang above.

Nesting. Nest a flattish structure of grasses, plant fibres, wool, and hair, placed on a sheltered ledge, in natural situations or man-made structures, or similar situations. *Eggs,* usually 4 or 5; white, sometimes with a few brownish spots. Incubation two weeks (I. G. Wheelock), by the female.

Breeding Distribution of Say's Phoebe

Range. Breeds from central Alaska, Yukon, western Mackenzie, and the Prairie Provinces of Canada south to northern Mexico. Winters from California and southern Texas south to Mexico.

Range in Canada. Breeds from northern Yukon (Old Crow), western Mackenzie (Mackenzie Delta, McTavish Arm, Fort Norman; occurs at least in migration at Fort

253

Simpson and other southern Mackenzie localities, but evidence of breeding at these southern localities is not known to the writer), central Alberta (Athabasca district, perhaps Dixonville), and central Saskatchewan (Kazan Lake, probably Carlton House) south through southern British Columbia (east of Cascade and Coast ranges), southern Alberta, southern Saskatchewan, and southwestern Manitoba (Aweme). (*Note:* Definite evidence of breeding is needed for a very large area comprising southern Mackenzie, northern Alberta, and northeastern British Columbia.)

Scarce transient on coastal British Columbia (Victoria, Chilliwack). Accidental in Ontario (London: 20 miles northwest) and Quebec (Godbout).

Subspecies. Two races are recognized in Canada in the A.O.U. Check-list (1957): (1) *Sayornis saya yukonensis* Bishop, with darker, clearer grey upper parts than in the following race, breeding in Yukon, nw. B.C. (Telegraph Creek), and nw. Mack. (2) *Sayornis saya saya* (Bonaparte) inhabiting the rest of the Canadian breeding range. Taxonomists differ greatly in delimiting the range of *yukonensis* (for example, *see* Aldrich in Jewett, *et al.*, 1953; Dickinson, 1953; Rand, 1948). The geographically limited material available to the writer at present is equally confusing.

YELLOW-BELLIED FLYCATCHER
Le Moucherolle à ventre jaune
Empidonax flaviventris (Baird and Baird)
Plate 45. L. 5.1 to 5.8 in.

Adults (sexes alike): Upper parts greenish olive; tail deep greyish brown; wings blackish, the middle and greater coverts tipped with pale yellowish or whitish (forming two wing bars), and the secondaries margined with same; eyering pale yellow; under parts including throat, pale yellow, the chest decidedly tinged with olive; wing linings pale yellowish, decidedly yellow on bend of wing. *Young:* Similar to adults but wing bars slightly buffy, yellow of under parts paler, the upper parts duller.

Measurements. *Adult male:* wing, 62.5–70.9 (67.2); tail, 51.0–56.0 (53.5); exposed culmen, 9.9–11.3 (10.5); tarsus, 16.0–17.5 (16.8). *Adult female:* wing, 61.2–68.2 (63.7) mm.

The uniformly yellow under parts *including throat and chin* distinguish it from all our other similar flycatchers except the Western. Differs from the Western in more greenish (less brownish or greyish) upper parts, chest less buffy or brownish; bend of wing *yellow* instead of buffy; the outermost (tenth) primary is usually longer than the fifth, instead of shorter.

Field Marks. A small greenish flycatcher, with two whitish wing bars and *yellowish under parts including throat.* The yellow under parts separate it from other eastern flycatchers of similar size (sometimes in the fall others show a yellowish tinge below, but in only the present species does the yellow extend onto the throat). *Voice:* Chelék (more liquid than the *chebéc* of Least Flycatcher); a plaintive *pe-wheep*, second syllable rising, with slight suggestion of the *pee-wit* of Semipalmated Plover. The Western Flycatcher (of western and southern British Columbia and southwestern Alberta) is very similar, but its range is different.

Habitat. Shady, moss-floored thickets and woodland; alder-willow shrubbery often mixed with conifers; bogs; wooded streams. Forages mainly in shady lower stratum of woodlands but on breeding grounds sometimes uses perches 30 to 40 feet high in the sunny top of either a coniferous or deciduous tree for singing (*chelék* song).

Nesting. Nest of rootlets, grass, and moss is usually placed on the ground (often sunk in moss) or sometimes in the roots of a fallen tree. *Eggs*, 3 to 5; white, sparingly spotted with browns. Incubation 12 to 14 days (E. H. Forbush), largely, if not entirely, by the female.

Range. Breeds from southern Canada (east of the Rockies) south locally to northern parts of North Dakota, Wisconsin, northeastern Pennsylvania (Pocono Mts.), and New York (Adirondack and Catskill mts.). Winters from eastern Mexico south to eastern Panama.

Breeding Distribution of Yellow-bellied Flycatcher

Range in Canada. Summer resident, breeding in central western and southern Mackenzie (Fort Norman, Soulier Lake), northern British Columbia (probably Trutch and McDonald Creek; recorded also from Atlin but status there uncertain), northern and central Alberta (south at least to Glenevis), northern and central Saskatchewan (south at least to Glenevis), northern and central Saskatchewan (south at least to Nipawin), Manitoba (north probably to Churchill), Ontario (south at least to Algonquin Park and Ottawa; also locally on Amherst Island in northeastern Lake Ontario), central and southern Quebec (Knob Lake region south to Hatley and the Magdalen Islands), southern Labrador (Goose Bay, Chateau Bay), Newfoundland, New Brunswick, Prince Edward Island, and Nova Scotia.

ACADIAN FLYCATCHER
Le Moucherolle vert. *Empidonax virescens* (Vieillot)
Plate 45. L. 5.6 to 6.3 in.

Similar to Traill's Flycatcher but upper parts olive green (less brownish or greyish); upper mandible (in skins) usually more brownish (less blackish). Wing tip longer: from end of secondaries to tip of longest primary averages in males 19.3 mm; in females 17.3 (compared with 14.2 and 12.8 for Traill's). (*See* Snyder 1953, *Contrib. Roy. Ont. Mus. Zool.* 35: 1–26.)

Measurements. *Adult male:* wing, 71–80.5 (74.3); tail, 55–61.5 (59.3); exposed culmen, 11.5–13 (12.6); tarsus, 14.5–16 (15.5). *Adult female:* wing, 67.5–75.5 (70.2) mm (Ridgway).

Field Marks. In appearance practically indistinguishable from Traill's Flycatcher and often from Least Flycatcher. Voice and habitat are the best characters. *Voice: Ka-zeep,* second syllable higher; also commonly *peep.* In breeding plumage, the under parts are only faintly tinged with yellowish, and the throat is white, thus distinguishing it from the Yellow-bellied Flycatcher. In fall plumage, however, some individuals are very yellowish below, this extending onto the throat, and the two are then not safely distinguishable. In Canada, however, the Acadian has a very restricted range.

Habitat. Shady maturer woodland, especially beech. Frequents lower levels well below the treetops. Does not ordinarily leave woodlands in the nesting season.

Nesting. Nest, a rather untidy shallow structure, *suspended* hammock-wise from the fork of a branch, usually 8 to 15 feet above ground, frequently near a stream. *Eggs,* usually 3; white sparingly dotted, mostly near larger end, with browns. Incubation period 13 to 15 days (Walkinshaw).

Range. Breeds mainly from southeastern North Dakota, northern Iowa, southern Michigan, extreme southern Ontario, southern New York, and southwestern Connecticut south to central Texas, the Gulf coast, and central Florida. Winters from Costa Rica to northern South America.

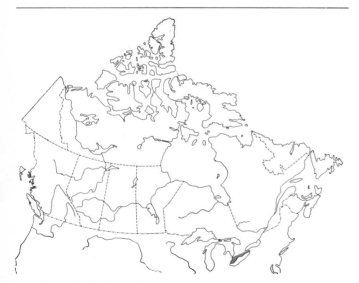

Breeding Distribution of Acadian Flycatcher

Range in Canada. Breeds in extreme southern Ontario (Rondeau and elsewhere along Lake Erie). Recorded without evidence of breeding at Toronto. Accidental in British Columbia (Leonie Lake, June 9, 1934) according to Todd (*Condor* 59: 211); also at Point Natashquan, Quebec.

TRAILL'S FLYCATCHER (Alder Flycatcher)

Le Moucherolle des aulnes. *Empidonax traillii* (Audubon)
Plate 45. L. 5.2 to 6 in.

Tail not forked. Variable geographically (*see* Subspecies). *Adults* (*E. traillii traillii*): Sexes similar. Upper parts greenish olive (darker and less pure green than in Acadian Flycatcher); eye-ring and wing edging whitish; wing bars buffy whitish; throat white; breast and sides greyish olive; belly, flanks, and under tail coverts whitish, usually more or less (sometimes decidedly) suffused with yellow. Tenth (outermost) primary usually longer or equal to fifth in eastern populations (but in *E. t. brewsteri* of southern British Columbia this is reversed). *Young:* Similar to adults but wing bars decidedly buff, upper parts browner.

Measurements. (*E. t. traillii*). *Adult male:* wing, 68.7–75.6 (72.3); tail, 54.0–64.5 (59.6); exposed culmen, 10.5–12.3 (11.6); tarsus, 15.5–18.0 (16.7). *Adult female:* wing, 63.2–70.9 (67.4) mm.

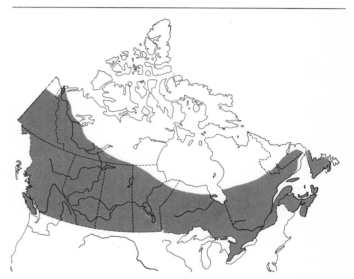

Breeding Distribution of Traill's Flycatcher

Field Marks. One of the larger members of the small *Empidonax* flycatchers, but size is of little help. It is best identified by voice and habitat. A widely distributed species inhabiting alders, willows, and similar thickets in moist, but sometimes drier, situations. *Voice:* In most of Canada the 'song' is a raspy *fee-be-o* (the second syllable often slurred so that it often sounds like *fee-beer*), which easily distinguishes the species, but on Pelee Island in extreme southern Ontario and in parts of southern British Columbia the song is *fits-bew.* Common alarm note a low *wit;* also *wée-oo.*

Habitat. Typically, alder and willow thickets, or bushy shrubbery of similar form, usually along streams, lakes and ponds, bogs and swamps; damp cut-over or burned-over places growing up in alders and similar thickets; also tall shrubbery or young aspens on uplands; bushy upland fields (parts of Nova Scotia), occasionally low spruces in bogs; and rarely even in orchards (on British Columbia coast).

Nesting. Nest is of grasses, weed stalks, and vegetable

fibres, often a bit untidy externally owing to hanging grasses, with neat cup-lining of fine grasses. It is placed in an upright crotch of a bush (various kinds) usually 2 to 6 feet above ground. *Eggs*, 3 or 4; white, usually (not always) more or less finely spotted with browns, mostly near larger end. Incubation usually 12 days but up to 14 days (R. C. Stein), by the female.

Range. Breeds from central Alaska and across southern Canada south to northern Baja California, western Texas, Missouri, and Virginia. Winters from southern Mexico to Argentina.

Range in Canada. Breeds in northern Yukon (Old Crow), northwestern and central-southern Mackenzie (Fort McPherson, Fort Norman, Fort Resolution), northern Alberta, northern Saskatchewan (Lake Athabasca), northern Manitoba (Ilford), northern Ontario, southern Quebec (Lake Mistassini, Matamek, Havre St. Pierre; possibly Piagochiwi River near northern James Bay), southern Labrador (Goose Bay) and southern Newfoundland (Bay of Islands, Doyles) south through southern British Columbia, southern Alberta (locally), southern Saskatchewan (locally), southern Manitoba, southern Ontario, southern Quebec, New Brunswick, Prince Edward Island, and Nova Scotia.

Subspecies. Although much has been written recently on the perplexing taxonomy of this bird, there is wide disagreement among authors as to the number of valid subspecies, their geographic extent, and even whether or not two separate similar species may be involved. The A.O.U. Check-list (1957) recognizes only two subspecies: (1) *Empidonax traillii brewsteri* Oberholser, which breeds across s. B.C. from Vancouver Island to extreme se. B.C. (Flathead River) and north to near Hagensborg and at least to Kamloops; (2) *E. t. traillii* (Audubon), with more greenish (less brownish) upper parts, paler wing bars, and slightly shorter bill, occupies the rest of the range in Canada and south in the western mountains to s.-c. B.C. Recently Stein (1963, *Proc. Am. Phil. Soc.* 107: 21–50) has proposed the recognition of two separate species, *E. traillii* (Audubon) and *E. brewsteri* Oberholser.

LEAST FLYCATCHER
Le Moucherolle tchébec
Empidonax minimus (Baird and Baird)
Plate 45. L. 5 to 5.5 in.

The smallest Canadian flycatcher. *Adults:* Very similar to Traill's Flycatcher but averaging slightly paler and usually a bit more greyish, under parts more whitish (less yellowish), wing bars and edging more whitish, tail very slightly forked; bill rather broad. *Young:* Similar to adults but wing bars dull buff, upper parts slightly more brownish.

Measurements. *Adult male:* wing, 60.6–68.5 (64.3); tail, 51.8–59.3 (55.9); exposed culmen, 9.4–10.5 (9.9); tarsus, 15.5–16.5 (16.1). *Adult female:* wing, 56.5–64.5 (60.6) mm.

Field Marks. Although it averages whiter underneath and is slightly smaller than other small flycatchers in Canada, these points are seldom very helpful in the field. Its emphatic, often-repeated *chebéc* identifies it instantly in spring and early summer.

PLATE 53

1 Golden-crowned Kinglet,
  (a) adult female
  (b) adult male

2 Ruby-crowned Kinglet,
  (a) adult male
  (b) adult female

3 Blue-gray Gnatcatcher

4 Loggerhead Shrike

5 Northern Shrike

6 Bohemian Waxwing

7 Cedar Waxwing,
  (a) juvenal
  (b) adult

Crosby

Habitat. More open deciduous or mixed woodland, forest edges, and openings, deciduous second growth, woodlots, copses, orchards, suburban shade trees, city parks, alder thickets.

Nesting. Nest, a neat thin-walled cup usually set deep in an upright crotch of a branch, either deciduous or coniferous, or on a horizontal branch supported by upright twigs; sometimes in alder or other tall shrubbery. Nest usually 5 to 25 feet above ground. *Eggs*, 3 to 6 (usually 4); creamy white. Incubation 12 days (O. W. Knight) and evidently mainly, if not entirely, by the female.

Range. Breeds from southern Canada (but absent from much of British Columbia) south to Montana, northeastern Wyoming, southwestern Missouri, northern Ohio, and western North Carolina. Winters from north-central Mexico to Panama.

Breeding Distribution of Least Flycatcher

Range in Canada. Summer resident, breeding from southwestern and southern Yukon (Haines Junction, Watson Lake), central-western and central-southern Mackenzie (Fort Norman, Fort Simpson, southern Great Slave Lake; perhaps Norman Wells and Fort Rae), northern Alberta, northern Saskatchewan (Lake Athabasca, Stony Rapids), north-central Manitoba (Thicket Portage, Oxford Lake), northern Ontario (Favourable Lake, southern James Bay), southwestern and central-southern Quebec (Mistassini Post, Matamek, Percé, perhaps Anticosti Island) and northern Nova Scotia south through northern and central-eastern British Columbia (Dease Lake, Lower Post, Fort Nelson, Trutch, Peace River parklands, Indianpoint Lake; Murtle Lake; near 100-Mile House; near Clinton), southern Alberta (including the southwestern mountains south to Waterton Lakes Park), southern Saskatchewan, southern Manitoba, southern Ontario, southern Quebec, and throughout New Brunswick, Prince Edward Island, and Nova Scotia.

Remarks. This, our smallest flycatcher, is one of several closely related species that look so much alike that many people despair of identifying them. Fortunately most of them have distinctive voices in spring and early summer. The

257

Least Flycatcher's emphatic *chebéc* is easily recognizable. Like other small flycatchers it is an avid eater of insects, and as it inhabits our orchards and gardens much more often than the others, its usefulness is enhanced.

HAMMOND'S FLYCATCHER
Le Moucherolle de Hammond
Empidonax hammondii (Xantus)
Plate 45. L. 5 to 5.7 in.

Bill rather narrow. Tail definitely emarginate. *Adults* (sexes alike): Upper parts greyish olive (most greyish on head); outer web of outer tail feathers more or less greyish; eyering dull white; breast and sides, pale olive grey, throat paler grey; abdomen and under tail coverts yellowish to whitish. *Young:* Similar to adults but wing bars buffy, upper parts more brownish.

Measurements. *Adult male:* wing, 64.5–73.0 (69.9); tail, 53.5–63.0 (58.2); exposed culmen, 9.3–10.3 (9.8); tarsus, 16.0–17.5 (16.8). *Adult female:* wing, 66.0–70.4 (67.5) mm.

Similar to Dusky Flycatcher but tenth (outermost) primary usually longer than fifth; difference between length of wing and tail greater: 10.0–14.8 mm (av. 11.9) in Hammond's; 5.0–8.6 mm (av. 7.2) in Dusky; throat grey (less whitish), outer web of outer tail feather, greyish (less whitish). From Least Flycatcher it is distinguished by longer wing and tail (tail more decidedly emarginate), relatively narrow bill, and decidedly darker under parts; from Traill's Flycatcher by emarginate tail, narrower bill, and darker under parts; and usually the lower mandible is darker than that of either Least or Traill's.

Field Marks. A small flycatcher of the western mountains. Extremely difficult and often impossible to distinguish from Dusky Flycatcher in the field. Hammond's has slightly more uniformly dingy under parts, and the tail is a little shorter, but these points are of little help without considerable field experience with the two. The voices too are very similar. Song, usually in three parts *seweép, tsurp, seep* (the last rising), is very similar to that of the Dusky Flycatcher. The song of Hammond's tends to be more emphatic than that of the Dusky and the second part more burred. Habitat differences are often helpful.

Habitat. Typically mature coniferous or mixed forests of the western mountains up to near timberline with much of its activity in the higher forest strata.

Nesting. Nest, a cup-like structure of plant fibres, lined with grasses and hairs. It is usually placed in the fork of a horizontal branch, most often of a conifer, and usually 25 to 60 feet up; a few nests have been reported at much lower levels, however. *Eggs,* usually 3 or 4; white and generally immaculate, but some have small brown spots. Incubation period 15 days (D. E. Davis).

Range. Breeds from southern Alaska, northern British Columbia, southwestern Alberta, central-southern Montana, and northwestern Wyoming south to northwestern and central-eastern California, Utah, western Colorado, and central-northern New Mexico. Winters in southeastern Arizona, the western mountains and central plateau of Mexico, and south in the highlands to Nicaragua.

258

Breeding Distribution of Hammond's Flycatcher

Range in Canada. Breeds in much of British Columbia (throughout the south and northward through Fort St. James and northwestward to Atlin; not known in Peace River parklands and the northeastern corner) and southwestern Alberta (mountains: Jasper, Banff, and Waterton Lakes parks). Perhaps also in southern Yukon (Dawson) but evidence unsatisfactory.

DUSKY FLYCATCHER (Wright's Flycatcher)
Le Moucherolle sombre. *Empidonax oberholseri* Phillips
Plate 45. L. 5.2 to 6 in.

Similar to Hammond's Flycatcher, but tenth (outermost) primary usually shorter than fifth; difference between length of wing and length of tail less, averaging 7.2 mm (extremes 5.0–8.6 mm); colour of anterior under parts, paler and less uniform (throat whitish, instead of grey, contrasting more with grey of breast); outer web of outer tail feathers more whitish; bill averages longer, and lower mandible is more variable in colour, blackish to flesh (usually blackish in Hammond's).

Measurements. *Adult male:* wing, 68.4–72.8 (70.1); tail, 59.5–65.5 (62.8); exposed culmen, 10.1–12.0 (11.1); tarsus, 17.5–19.5 (18.4). *Adult female:* wing, 60.0–73.0 (65.7) mm.

Field Marks. (*See* Hammond's Flycatcher, which is extremely similar.) Song sounds to the writer like *seweép, hreek, seep* (sometimes with a fourth part) and is very similar to that of Hammond's (but very different from that of Traill's or Least flycatchers). Habitat is often useful in helping to distinguish it from Hammond's.

Habitat. Usually stands of tall shrubbery (such as willows) among which are trees, either deciduous or coniferous; open deciduous or mixed woodland in drier situations. It is not a bird of extensive mature damp coniferous forests, such as are preferred by Hammond's. Usually forages and nests at lower levels than Hammond's but sometimes perches in the tops of fair-sized trees (40 feet or so).

Nesting. Nest, a neat cup of vegetable fibres and grasses, is most often placed in an upright crotch of a willow, alder, aspen, or similar tree (less often in a conifer) at heights between 3 and 7 feet (rarely up to 20 feet). *Eggs*, 3 or 4; dull white. Incubation period 12 to 15 days (Howsley *in* Bent); 14 days (N. K. Johnson).

Range. Breeds from southwestern Yukon, northwestern and central-eastern British Columbia, southwestern Alberta, southwestern Saskatchewan, and Wyoming south to southern California, central Arizona, and central-northern New Mexico. Winters from southeastern Arizona and northern Mexico south to southern Mexico.

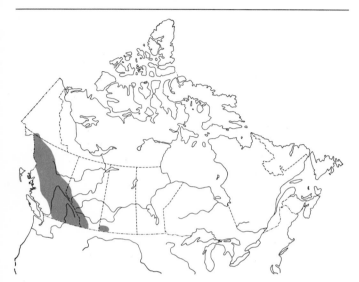

Breeding Distribution of Dusky Flycatcher

Range in Canada. Summer resident, breeding in southwestern Yukon (Carcross), British Columbia (the southern half, apparently east of the Coast and Cascade ranges, and northwestward through the Vanderhoof region to Telegraph Creek and Atlin; unknown in the northeastern corner and Peace River parklands), southwestern and probably (locally) southeastern Alberta (Jasper, Banff, and Waterton Lakes parks; also Cypress Hills), and extreme southwestern Saskatchewan (Cypress Hills). Uncommon migrant on the coast of British Columbia and rarely noted there in summer but without evidence of breeding.

WESTERN FLYCATCHER
Le Moucherolle du Pacifique. *Empidonax difficilis* Baird
Plate 45. L. 5.5 to 6 in.

Resembles Yellow-bellied Flycatcher in extensive yellow of under parts (including throat) but differs as follows: Outermost (tenth) primary shorter than fifth, olive of upper parts more brownish or greyish (less greenish), bend of wing buffy instead of yellow, breast and sides more brownish olive; tail averages slightly longer. The extensively yellow under parts (including throat) distinguish it from similar species other than the Yellow-bellied.

Measurements (*E. d. difficilis*). *Adult male:* wing, 63.1–71.8 (66.9); tail, 56–63 (58.5); exposed culmen, 10.5–11.7 (11.1); tarsus, 16–18 (17.3). *Adult female:* wing, 60.4–63.5 (61.8) mm.

Field Marks. A western species. The extensively yellow

under parts *including throat* separate it from other small flycatchers in its range. Other small western mountain flycatchers show some yellow on the under parts but not on the throat. Probably indistinguishable in the field, however, from the more eastern Yellow-bellied Flycatcher, but fortunately the breeding ranges of the two are not known to overlap. *Voice:* Variable. Song is often *pseet, ptsick, seet* (the last highest).

Habitat. Shady, more open areas below the tree crowns of woodland, mixed or coniferous, especially about depressions and similar moist parts, ravines, and streams. However, dense thickets of tall shrubbery, such as those preferred by the Traill's Flycatcher, are not usually frequented by the present species.

Nesting. Nest, a cup made of plant fibre, mosses, rootlets, and sometimes feathers or hair, is placed in a variety of situations such as rock ledges on streams, in the roots of an upturned tree, in a small tree, on a stump or building. *Eggs*, 3 or 4; white lightly to moderately spotted and blotched with reddish browns. Incubation period about 15 days (Laidlaw Williams).

Range. Breeds from southern Alaska, southern British Columbia, southwestern Alberta, and western Montana, northern Wyoming, and southwestern South Dakota south in the highlands to Baja California, Honduras, and western Texas. Winters from northern Mexico southward.

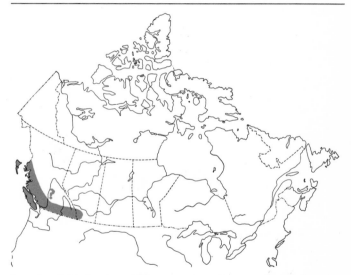

Breeding Distribution of Western Flycatcher

Range in Canada. Summer resident, breeding in British Columbia (commonly on the coast and coastal islands including Queen Charlotte and Vancouver islands; more rarely in southern interior: Coldstream in Okanagan Valley), and southwestern Alberta (Gorge Creek in Turner Valley; Little Red Deer River, 43 miles northwest of Crossfield). Possibly breeds also in Cariboo District of British Columbia, as single specimens have been reported from Riske Creek, Alkali Lake, and Bowron Lake but without evidence of breeding.

Subspecies. *Empidonax difficilis difficilis* Baird is the breeding bird of B.C.

259

EASTERN WOOD PEWEE

Le Pioui de l'Est. *Contopus virens* (Linnaeus)
Plate 44. L. 6 to 6.5 in.

Larger than any of our *Empidonax* flycatchers, wing much longer, coloration darker, greyer (much less greenish), lacks eye-ring. Pale lower mandible, wing bars, and somewhat smaller size distinguish it from Eastern Phoebe. *Adults* (sexes alike): Upper parts dark greyish olive; crown feathers rather long with dark centres; wing and tail dusky; wing bars pale greyish, edging on secondaries and tertials whitish; breast and sides greyish olive; throat whitish, abdomen pale yellowish white; bill brownish black above, pale yellowish or whitish below with dusky tip. *Young:* Buffy wing bars and often the pale area of the lower mandible is more restricted, sometimes mainly dusky.

Measurements. *Adult male:* wing, 80.8–86.8 (84.1); tail, 63–68 (65.5); exposed culmen, 12.3–13.1 (12.9); tarsus, 12.5–14 (13.7). *Adult female:* wing, 78.3–86.2 (82.1) mm.

Very similar to Western Wood Pewee but upper parts more olivaceous (less greyish), under parts less extensively olive-greyish, this colour paler, lower mandible usually paler.

Breeding Distribution of Eastern Wood Pewee

Field Marks. Between the Eastern Phoebe and the *Empidonax* flycatchers in size. It is much darker and less greenish than the *Empidonax* flycatchers and lacks an eye-ring, and its longer wing extends halfway down the tail. Its obvious wing bars and lack of the tail-wagging habit distinguish it from the Phoebe; also at close range its pale lower mandible, smaller size, smaller bill, and less definite breast patches distinguish it from the Olive-sided Flycatcher. Its plaintive lazy whistled *pee-a-wee*, the second syllable lowest, the third rising, distinguishes it from all others. Also *pee-wee* dropping in pitch.

Habitat. Prefers maturer open deciduous woodland and openings; forests, woodlots, tall shade trees in towns, old orchards, mixed woods. Sometimes more open coniferous woodland.

Nesting. Nest, of grasses, plant fibres, and similar material, is covered on the outside with lichens. It is saddled on a horizontal branch (most often deciduous) at heights from 8 to 60 feet. *Eggs*, 2 to 4, usually 3; creamy white with a ring of brown dots, spots, and blotches around the large end. Incubation 12 to 13 days, by the female (*in* Bent).

Range. Breeds from southern eastern Canada (southern Manitoba east to Cape Breton Island) south to central and southwestern Texas, the Gulf coast of United States, and central Florida. Winters from Costa Rica, Colombia, and Venezuela south to Peru.

Range in Canada. Summer resident, breeding in central-southern and southwestern Manitoba (Delta, Shoal Lake, Whitemouth; probably Lake St. Martin), western and southern Ontario (north to about Malachi, Sioux Lookout, Port Arthur, Agawa, Timagami, New Liskeard), southern Quebec (north to about Ville Marie, Blue Sea Lake, Quebec, Rivière du Loup), New Brunswick (St. Leonard, Fredericton; probably Campbellton and Bathurst), Prince Edward Island, and Nova Scotia (including Cape Breton Island). Recorded rarely in summer in eastern Gaspé Peninsula (Grande Grève, Percé).

Accidental at sea (200 miles off Hopedale, Labrador, August 31, 1929).

WESTERN WOOD PEWEE

Le Pioui de l'Ouest. *Contopus sordidulus* Sclater
Plate 44. L. 6 to 6.6 in.

Very similar to Eastern Wood Pewee but upper parts a little more greyish; olive greyish of under parts darker and more extensive; lower mandible usually darker.

Measurements (*C. s. veliei*). *Adult male:* wing, 83.7–87.1 (85.5); tail, 62–68 (65.7); exposed culmen, 12.1–13.2 (12.7); tarsus, 12.5–14.5 (13.7). *Adult female:* wing, 79.1–86.1 (82.1) mm.

Field Marks. *Voice* is the only field distinction from Eastern Wood Pewee. Fortunately its harsher nasal *pe-ear* is very different from the calls of the Eastern Pewee. Its larger size, much darker coloration, and lack of an eye-ring readily separate it from the *Empidonax* flycatchers.

Habitat. More open woodland (mixed, deciduous, or coniferous) openings and edges; trees and tall shrubbery along coulées and rivers; orchards.

Nesting. Nest, usually saddled on a horizontal limb (deciduous or coniferous). It tends to be a bit larger and deeper than that of the Eastern Wood Pewee, and lichens are apparently not so often used in its exterior. *Eggs*, 2 to 4, usually 3; similar to those of the Eastern Wood Pewee.

Range. Breeds from central-eastern Alaska and Western Canada (east to central-southern Manitoba) south to western Panama. Winters from Panama to Venezuela and Bolivia.

Range in Canada. Summer resident, breeding from southern Yukon (north at least to Little Salmon River and Lapie River), southern Mackenzie (Hill Island Lake), northern Alberta, northwestern and central-eastern Saskatchewan (Lake Athabasca, Kazan Lake, Cumberland House), and south-central Manitoba (northwestern Lake Winnipegosis,

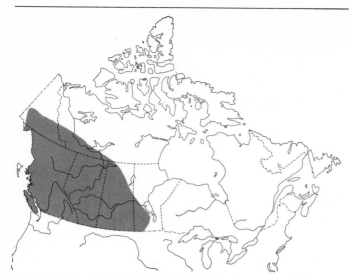
Breeding Distribution of Western Wood Pewee

Lake St. Martin) south through southern British Columbia (including Vancouver Island; not recorded from Queen Charlotte Islands), southern Alberta (locally: Milk River, Waterton Lakes), southern Saskatchewan (locally: Regina region, probably Cypress Hills), and southwestern Manitoba (east to Delta where outnumbered by *virens*).

(*Note:* Eight late-July pewees recently collected, with song types recorded on the labels by W. John Smith at Delta, Manitoba, comprise seven *virens* (plumage and song), one *sordidulus* (plumage and song). They show no obvious evidence of intergradation and support the concept that these two pewees are separate species.)

Subspecies. Two races in Canada are recognized in the A.O.U. Check-list (1957): (1) *Contopus sordidulus veliei* Coues, breeding in all the Canadian part of the range except w. B.C.; (2) *C. s. saturatus* Bishop, characterized by average slightly darker coloration, inhabiting w. B.C.; areas of intergradation with *veliei* vaguely understood. Several authors, perhaps with good reason, regard *saturatus* as a synonym of *veliei*. Certainly, the extent of individual variation in breeding populations is great.

OLIVE-SIDED FLYCATCHER
Le Moucherolle à côtés olive
Nuttallornis borealis (Swainson)
Plate 44. L. 7.1 to 7.8 in.

Adults (sexes similar): Upper parts dull greyish olive, darkest on crown; sides of rump with a patch of white feathers (often concealed by folded wings); wings and tail dusky, the wing coverts with paler tips, the secondaries and tertials narrowly edged whitish; sides of breast, sides, and flanks, dark greyish olive; throat, centre of breast, and belly, whitish or pale yellowish (contrasting with sides of breast). Bill blackish above, pale brownish below becoming dusky toward tip.

Measurements. *Adult male:* wing, 103.2–112.4 (106.9); tail 67.5–75 (70.9); exposed culmen, 16.8–17.9 (17.4); tarsus, 13.5–15.5 (14.6). *Adult female:* wing, 98.6–105.1 (101.9) mm.

Field Marks. A stout, short-necked flycatcher with very erect posture, larger than the pewees, smaller than kingbirds. The dark sides of the breast extend well down on the sides of the abdomen and contrast with the white belly. Often the fluffy white tufts on either side of the rump partly show from under the folded wings (they are quite noticeable as the bird flies away). Usually perches well up, near or at the top of a tree (often in dead one). *Voice* is unmistakable: an emphatic whistled *Come right here* or *Quick-three beers;* also commonly when even mildly excited, *pip-pip-pip* in threes, slightly descending.

Habitat. Perches high in trees, often dead ones or those with high dead branches or living trees with slender tops. Burntlands with standing dead trees, bogs, lakeshores with water-killed trees, lumbered areas and other clearings in woodland; sometimes tall trees about farmland, occasionally orchards (Nova Scotia).

Nesting. Nest is placed well out on a branch of a conifer (less often a deciduous tree, rarely even an apple tree) ordinarily at considerable height but may rarely be as low as seven feet. It is made of twigs, rootlets, lichens, and mosses and lined with fine grasses and rootlets. *Eggs*, 3 or 4; are handsome: creamy to light buff with a broad wreath around the larger end of brighter browns and more or less purplish grey in spots and blotches. Incubation 16 to 17 days (L. H. Walkinshaw).

Range. Breeds in wooded regions from central Alaska east to Newfoundland and south to northern Baja California, central Arizona, northern New Mexico, central Minnesota, northern Michigan, and Massachusetts; and in the mountains south to North Carolina and Tennessee. Winters in South America.

Breeding Distribution of Olive-sided Flycatcher

Range in Canada. Summer resident, breeding from central western and southern Yukon (probably north to Yukon River; species recorded north to Old Crow), central-western and southern Mackenzie (north to southern Great Slave Lake and Snowdrift; and in the upper Mackenzie Valley north probably to Fort Norman), northern Saskatchewan (Lake Athabasca), north-central Manitoba (Thicket Portage, Bird), northern Ontario (Favourable Lake, southern James Bay), south-central Quebec (Lake Mistassini, Lac Méchant), southern Labrador (Goose Bay) and Newfoundland south through British Columbia (including Vancouver Island but not Queen Charlotte Islands) through northern, central, and southwestern Alberta (south in the mountains and foothills to Waterton Lakes and to the edge of wooded country in central-eastern parts: Pigeon and Battle lakes; absent from the southeastern plains), south-central Saskatchewan (south to about Nipawin; absent from the plains), southern Manitoba (Duck Mountains, Whitemouth); southern Ontario (south to about Mount Forest, Holland Swamp, Lindsay, Sharbot Lake), southern Quebec (south to Gatineau Park, Hatley, Gaspé Peninsula, Anticosti and Magdalen islands), and through New Brunswick, Prince Edward Island, and Nova Scotia.

Remarks. Although the Olive-sided Flycatcher is usually a forest recluse, this is not always so. When the writer was a boy in Wolfville, Nova Scotia, this fine flycatcher summered regularly on the edge of that town and sometimes nested in apple orchards.

VERMILION FLYCATCHER

Le Moucherolle vermillon
Pyrocephalus rubinus (Boddaert)
L. 5.5. to 6.5 in.

Adult male: Crown and under parts bright red (under parts somewhat paler and sometimes tinged with orange); sides of head and upper parts greyish brown; wings and tail mainly dusky or blackish; bill brownish black. *Adult female:* Upper parts brownish grey; under parts whitish, the breast, sides, and flanks distinctly but narrowly streaked with dusky, belly pale salmon to buffy.

Range. Southwestern United States south to Guatemala and Honduras; also South America.

Status in Canada. Accidental in southern Ontario (Toronto, October 29, 1949).

Subspecies. *Pyrocephalus rubinus mexicanus* Sclater.

Family **Alaudidae**–Larks

Number of Species in North America 2; in Canada 2

Larks are ground birds that run instead of hopping. The hind toenail is very long and sharp. The tarsus is scutellate (scaled) and is rounded behind (not sharply ridged as in most passerines). Wings are rather long and pointed and have nine primaries. Bill rather slender, rather short, and pointed. Many larks have an impressive flight song. They eat large numbers of weed seeds and also a considerable number of insects. The family is primarily an Old World one. North America has only one native species, the Horned Lark. The famous Skylark of Europe has been introduced into southern Vancouver Island, British Columbia, and is established there. The so-called Meadowlark is not a lark at all but belongs to the family Icteridae.

SKYLARK

L'Alouette des champs. *Alauda arvensis* Linnaeus
Plate 50. L. 7 to 7.5 in.

Bill slender, feathers of hind-crown longish, hind toenail much elongated. *Adults:* Upper parts buffy brown to greyish brown, heavily streaked with blackish brown; line over eye buffy white; ear coverts brown streaked with dusky; outer two-thirds of outermost tail feathers mostly white, the next with white outer web; throat whitish with short brown streaks; breast buffy brown, heavily streaked with blackish brown, sides and flanks more lightly streaked; belly and tail coverts plain white.

Measurements. *Adult male:* wing, 109.5–116 (113.3); tail, 68.5–73 (70.4); exposed culmen, 11–13.5 (12.2); tarsus, 24–26 (24.8). *Adult female:* wing, 98–111 (104.2) mm (Ridgway).

The much elongated hind toenail distinguishes it from most birds of similar colour, except longspurs, pipits, and the Horned Lark. The slender bill separates it from longspurs; its much larger size from our pipits; its different head and breast markings from the Horned Lark.

Field Marks. Somewhat larger than a sparrow. A streaky brown bird with short crest and white outer tail feathers. It is usually seen either on the ground or in flight. Spends up to three or four minutes in continuous song on the wing at considerable heights, often with sustained hovering. Slender bill separates it from sparrows; stouter body and less slender bill from our pipits; and different head and breast markings from the Horned Lark (which has similar habits).

Habitat. Open sparsely vegetated ground: airfields, pastures, cultivated land, golf courses. Avoids narrow valleys and small fields bordered by trees.

Nesting. Nest of grasses in a depression on the ground. *Eggs*, usually 3 or 4; greyish white, thickly spotted with browns. Incubation 11 days, by the female (*in* Witherby).

Range. Eurasia and northern Africa. Has been introduced and established in some other parts of the world.

Range in Canada. Introduced to southern Vancouver Island, B.C., but dates given by authors vary by a few years. Two introductions seem to have been made, the first in 1902 or 1903, from which there appear to have been some survivors. In 1908 or 1913, a second introduction was made. Now well established on Saanich Peninsula, southern Vancouver Island, B.C. In March 1962, the total population was estimated by D. Stirling and R. Y. Edwards at about one thousand.

Subspecies. *Alauda arvensis arvensis* Linnaeus.

HORNED LARK

L'Alouette cornue. *Eremophila alpestris* (Linnaeus)
Plate 50. L. 6.8 to 8 in.

Bill slender, pointed, shorter than head; hind toenail much elongated, nearly straight. The elongated hind toenail, large black patch on upper breast, and narrow black face patch curving from the bill backward under the eye are a combination that identifies Horned Larks. Tail mostly black except central feathers, which are brown like back, and outer web of outermost feathers, which is white. In addition, the male has a black band across the front of the crown, which extends backward narrowly to join a pair of slender black 'horns' (erectile feathers). Juvenal plumage (worn only a short time) lacks these black areas and has white spots on the upper parts.

Measurements (*E. a. alpestris*). *Adult male:* wing, 108–118 (111.5); tail, 66.5–75 (71.8); exposed culmen, 11–13 (12.2); tarsus, 22–25 (24). *Adult female:* wing, 101–109 (103.8) mm (H. C. Oberholser).

Field Marks. A brown-backed, slender-billed ground bird, larger than a sparrow, usually seen in companies or flocks. The black breast-shield and black face-patch curving downward from bill to below the eye are easily recognized. The tiny black 'horns' are often difficult to see. Runs or walks instead of hopping. Flight somewhat undulating; overhead, the black of tail contrasts with white under parts. *Voice:* At all seasons sibilant high-pitched notes, one to three to a series, given especially when flushing or in flight. In the breeding season the tinkling wiry song is given either in flight or from the ground.

Habitat. Open terrain with a minimum of ground cover. In the East, ploughed or sparsely vegetated fields, airports, upper beaches, and barren shores; on the prairies, short-grass plains, sparse sagebrush flats; in the mountains, grasslands, meadows, and sparsely vegetated places above and below timberline; in the Arctic, gravel ridges, hills, plateaus, rock desert, raised beaches—mostly drier situations. In winter, various types of open terrain, especially where weeds protrude above the snow or where weed seeds or grain are available, such as weedy fields, grain stubbles, and weedy shores.

Nesting. In a hollow of the ground in drier open places. Nest, usually composed of grasses and similar available vegetation, lined with plant down, hair, or feathers. *Eggs,* 3 to 5; greyish, thickly speckled with pale brown; speckling sometimes confluent and occasionally forming a wreath of solid brown around larger end. Incubation 11 days (G. B. Pickwell) in Illinois and New York, perhaps varies somewhat in other parts of the vast range of the species.

Range. Alaska and arctic Canada south to southern Mexico, with an isolated population in Colombia, South America; also northern Eurasia south to northern Africa. In North America it winters from southern Canada southward.

Range in Canada. Breeding range governed by availability of suitable habitat, therefore absent or extremely local in a broad belt of unsettled forested non-mountainous country stretching from Alberta to Quebec. Breeds from the arctic islands (Prince Patrick, Devon, and northern Baffin) southward through Yukon, Mackenzie (but apparently absent from Mackenzie Valley above the delta), Keewatin (including Southampton Island); through British Columbia (locally; status on Vancouver and Queen Charlotte islands uncertain but probably breeds near Victoria); central and southern Alberta (absent or very local in northern half but perhaps breeds about Lake Athabasca; breeds commonly from about Tofield and Clyde southward in mountains and plains); northwestern and southern Saskatchewan (Lake Athabasca, and from south-central parts

southward); Manitoba (Churchill and Hudson Bay coast, and in the southern part from about Swan River and Lake St. Martin southward); Ontario (coasts of James and Hudson bays; also the southern parts from about Sudbury and Ottawa southward; locally on north shore of Lake Superior: Rossport and Peninsula; also locally in extreme west: Emo); northern, central, and southern Quebec (south to Hatley, Gaspé Peninsula, and Magdalen Islands; local in forested interior where barren higher parts of mountains provide habitat), Labrador, Newfoundland, New Brunswick, Prince Edward Island (recently—apparently since early 1900's), and Nova Scotia (recently).

Winters in southern parts of most provinces: British Columbia, Alberta, Saskatchewan, Manitoba, Ontario (rarely north to Ottawa), Quebec (rarely north to Anticosti Island), Newfoundland (rarely: Argentia), New Brunswick, Nova Scotia, and probably Prince Edward Island.

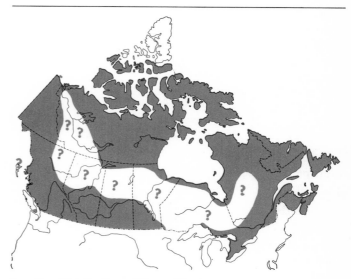

Breeding Distribution of Horned Lark

Subspecies. (1) *Eremophila alpestris arcticola* (Oberholser): Yukon, Mackenzie Delta, and high mountains of B.C. and sw. Alta. (2) *E. a. hoyti* (Bishop): arctic islands south to ne. Alta., nw. Sask., ne. Man., extreme nw. Ont. (Fort Severn). (3) *E. a. alpestris* (Linnaeus): n. Que. and n. Lab. south to s. James Bay, se. Que. (Gaspé Pen., Magdalen Is., and Nfld.). (4) *E. a. leucolaema* Coues: s. Alta. (east of the mts.), sw. Sask. (5) *E. a. enthymia* (Oberholser): c.-e. Alta. (Tofield, Clyde), c. Sask., s. Man., extreme w. Ont. (Emo)—affinities of (4) and (5) require study. (6) *E. a. praticola* (Henshaw): s. Ont., sw. Que. (Gatineau Point, Lake St. John basin), N.B., P.E.I., N.S. (7) *E. a. strigata* (Henshaw): sw. B.C. west of Cascade Mts. (8) *E. a. merrilli* (Dwight): intermontane valleys of s. B.C.

Remarks. On open prairie, arctic tundra, the sea coast, or on man's cultivated fields, there the Horned Lark thrives, for it has no use for trees. Its foraging is done on the ground. Weed seeds make up the bulk of its food, although many insects are eaten also. Many Horned Larks remain in the southern parts of Canada during the winter months. In some parts of the country just north of the usual winter range, such as Ottawa, Ontario, the Horned Larks are the earliest spring arrivals, as a rule before mid-February. While the snow is still deep, many congregate along the bare shoulders of roads and highways in companies and flocks. They also seek food in other open places where weed stalks protrude above the snow. When a flock alights, its members disperse, running hither and thither in their energetic search for weed seeds. When they have worked over one weed patch, away they fly to another, leaving behind an intricate lacework of tiny tracks in the snowy field.

Family **Hirundinidae** – Swallows

Number of Species in North America 12; in Canada 7

The swallow is found in both hemispheres of the world. It has long pointed wings, a more or less forked tail, slender body, short neck, flattish head, a small flat bill which broadens at the gape to form a wide mouth, and small weak feet. Its food is insects, which are taken on the wing. Swallows are not outstanding singers, but their pleasant twitterings, graceful flight, and gentle ways have earned them a high place in the affection of man. Barn and Cliff swallows use our buildings for nesting. Tree Swallows and Purple Martins take advantage of the nesting boxes we provide for them.

VIOLET-GREEN SWALLOW
L'Hirondelle à face blanche
Tachycineta thalassina (Swainson)
Plate 46. L. 5 to 5.5 in.

Tail not deeply forked. *Adult male:* Crown and back, green with bronze tint, especially on crown; rump and upper tail coverts violet or purplish (white of under parts extends up onto sides of rump); under parts white, extending up over cheeks to the eye. *Adult female:* Similar to male but much duller, crown and nape often mostly brownish, this colour extending down much of cheeks. *Young:* Upper parts greyish brown, darkest on back where faintly glossed purplish; under parts white but breast often tinged with brown.

Measurements. *Adult male:* wing, 111–118.5 (114.6); tail, 44.0–47.0 (45.7); exposed culmen, 4.7–5.4 (5.0); tarsus, 10.5–11.5 (11.2). *Adult female:* wing, 106.0–111.0 (109.2) mm.

Adults with green and violet coloration are unmistakable. Young resemble young Tree Swallows, but throat is less pure white, and the brown on sides of face is not sharply cut off from the white.

Field Marks. The green and violet upper parts are distinctive at close range. In flight a small white patch on each side of the rump distinguishes it from other swallows (*see* White-throated Swift), although this is sometimes suggested in the Tree Swallow (in which the pair of spots are much more widely spaced). In the adult male the cheeks are white up to and around the back of the eye. Young have greyish brown upper parts and resemble young Tree Swallows, but brown on top of head is less sharply cut off from the white below on the face.

PLATE 55

1 Parula Warbler,
(a) adult male
(b) adult female
(c) autumn immature

2 Yellow Warbler,
(a) adult male
(b) adult female

3 'Brewster's Warbler,'
hybrid Golden-winged
x Blue-winged Warbler

4 Blue-winged Warbler,
adult male in breeding
plumage

5 Golden-winged Warbler,
(a) adult female
(b) adult male

6 Worm-eating Warbler

7 Prothonotary Warbler,
adult male

8 Black-and-white
Warbler,
(a) adult male in
breeding plumage
(b) autumn immature

1a

1b

2a

2b

3a

3b

4a

4b

5a

5b

5c

6

Crosby

PLATE 56

1 Tennessee Warbler,
   (a) male in breeding
      plumage
   (b) autumn immature

2 Orange-crowned Warbler,
   (a) adult male in
      breeding plumage
   (b) autumn immature

3 Nashville Warbler,
   (a) adult in breeding
      plumage
   (b) autumn immature

4 Magnolia Warbler,
   (a) adult male in
      breeding plumage
   (b) autumn immature

5 Cape May Warbler,
   (a) adult male in
      breeding plumage
   (b) adult female in
      breeding plumage
   (c) autumn immature
      female

6 Kirtland's Warbler,
   adult male in
   breeding plumage

Habitat. Forages over various terrain, open country, water, and above forest tops. Forages at various heights depending on weather factors affecting height of flying insects.

Nesting. In cavities and crevices of cliffs (often at great heights), in woodpecker holes, cavities in buildings, in bird boxes, even rarely in piled lumber. Nesting material consists of grasses and small twigs with a lining of feathers. *Eggs*, 4 to 6; white. Incubation period about 15 days (J. M. Edson).

Range. Breeds from Alaska, Yukon, southwestern Alberta, central Montana, and southwestern South Dakota south to northern Baja California and Sonora and through Colorado, New Mexico, and western Texas to southern Mexico. Winters mainly in Mexico and northern Central America.

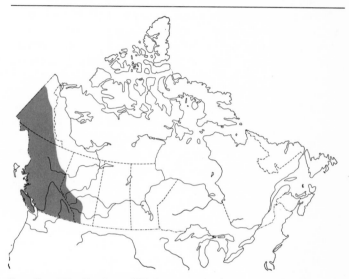

Breeding Distribution of Violet-green Swallow

Range in Canada. Summer resident, breeding in Yukon (north to Old Crow), throughout British Columbia, and southwestern Alberta (mountains from Jasper south to Waterton Lakes; also near Red Deer).

Accidental in Manitoba (Sandilands, April 1945).

Subspecies. *Tachycineta thalassina lepida* Mearns.

TREE SWALLOW

L'Hirondelle bicolore. *Iridoprocne bicolor* (Vieillot)
Plate 46. L. 5 to 6.2 in.

Tail slightly forked. *Adult male:* Upper parts glossy steel blue, with greenish reflections, this extending down on sides of head well below the eye; under parts white. *Adult female:* Similar to adult male but upper parts usually duller, often mainly dusky greyish brown with only the feather tips bluish. *Young:* Upper parts dull brownish grey, this extending down on sides of head to well below the eye and more sharply cut off from the white of the under parts than in young Violet-green Swallow.

Measurements. *Adult male:* wing, 114–125 (118.3); tail, 52–60 (55.8); exposed culmen, 6–7.8 (6.7); tarsus, 11.5–13 (12.5). *Adult female:* wing, 109–124 (113.5) mm.

Field Marks. All-white under parts and steel blue upper

parts separate it from all other swallows in the East. In the West another species has all-white under parts (*see* Violet-green Swallow). Young have brownish grey upper parts (as do some adult females) and often show a greyish wash on the breast, but this is never so dark nor so well defined as the breast band of the Bank Swallow. Unlike the Rough-winged Swallow, the young Tree Swallow has a pure white throat.

Habitat. Forages in the air, preferably over water or moist ground: lakes, ponds, sloughs, dams, larger streams, fresh and brackish marshes, wet meadows, and bogs. In nesting season availability of suitable nesting places governs numbers. Flooded places such as beaver dams or those made by man, flooded shores, and similar places with numerous standing dead trees near water attract concentrations.

Nesting. In a cavity in a tree, either natural or made by a woodpecker, sometimes in buildings; uses bird boxes where available. Nest, a collection of grass and similar material lined with feathers. *Eggs*, usually 4 to 6; white. Incubation period 13 to 16 days (Austin and Low), by both sexes.

Range. Breeds from north-central Alaska and across Canada (north to near tree limit) south to southern California, western Colorado, northeastern Kansas, northeastern Louisiana, and Virginia. Winters from southern United States (in the East occasionally north to Massachusetts) south to Honduras, Nicaragua, and Cuba.

Range in Canada. Breeds from northern Yukon (Old Crow), central-western and southern Mackenzie (Fort Norman, Great Slave Lake; probably Aklavik), northern Alberta, northern Saskatchewan (Lake Athabasca), northern Manitoba (Churchill), northern Ontario, northern Quebec (Knob Lake region, perhaps Chimo), central Labrador (Goose Bay, Ashuanipi Lake; recorded north to Davis Inlet without evidence of breeding), and Newfoundland, south throughout southern Canada from western British Columbia (Queen Charlotte and Vancouver islands) east to eastern Nova Scotia (Cape Breton Island), and Newfoundland, but locally absent in parts of southeastern Alberta and southern Saskatchewan where nest sites are few.

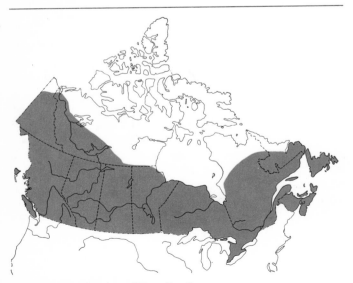

Breeding Distribution of Tree Swallow

266

Casual in Keewatin (Chesterfield, Southampton Island, Windy River) and on Boothia Peninsula (Levesque Harbour), and Banks Island (Sachs Harbour), N.W.T.

BANK SWALLOW
L'Hirondelle des sables. *Riparia riparia* (Linnaeus)
Plate 46. L. 4.8 to 5.5 in.

Tail somewhat forked. Upper parts greyish brown (some feathers with paler edges), darkest on head and extending down over ear coverts; under parts white with well-defined greyish-brown band across breast.

Measurements. *Adult male:* wing, 97.4–106.7 (101.4); tail, 45–50.5 (47.7); exposed culmen, 5.9–6.9 (6.3); tarsus, 10.5–11.0 (10.9). *Adult female:* wing, 95.1–105.9 (101.3) mm.

Field Marks. A brown-backed smallish swallow with a *clearly-defined dark breast band* on otherwise white under parts. Rough-winged Swallow also has brown upper parts, but the whole throat and breast are greyish with no clearly-defined breast band. *Voice:* A harsh twitter.

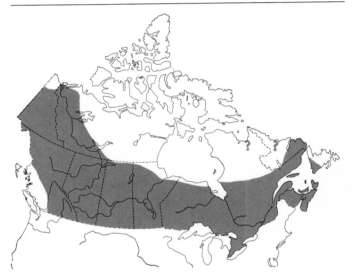

Breeding Distribution of Bank Swallow

Habitat. Forages over water and open land. Breeding populations are rather locally distributed, being confined to the general vicinity of suitable nesting places (*see* Nesting) and usually at no great distance from water.

Nesting. In colonies. A long tunnel is excavated by the birds in steep banks (tunnels tend to be concentrated near the top) of sand, sandstone, clay, gravel, and in similar softer earths in gravel pits, railway and road cuts, river banks, and shores. Nest, of grass and feathers, is placed in a chamber at the end of the tunnel. *Eggs*, 4 to 6; white. Incubation 14 to 16 days (Dayton Stoner), by both sexes.

Range. Breeds in North America (north-central Alaska east to northern Quebec and Newfoundland and south to southern United States) and across Eurasia. North American populations winter in South America.

Range in Canada. Summer resident; breeding where suitable nesting sites are available, from northern Yukon (Old Crow), northwestern and central-southern Mackenzie (beyond tree limit on Mackenzie Delta, Kittigazuit, Fort Anderson, Slave River), northern Alberta, northern Saskatchewan (Lake Athabasca), northern Manitoba (Herchmer), northern Ontario (Severn River), central Quebec (Roggan River, Moisie River, Mingan River, Havre St. Pierre, possibly lower Whale River), southern Labrador (Goose Bay, perhaps near Hopedale) and southwestern Newfoundland (Highlands, Swift Current) south through southwestern Yukon (Burwash Landing; Canyon), through southern interior British Columbia, southern Alberta, southern Saskatchewan (locally), southern Manitoba, southern Ontario, southern Quebec (including Gaspé Peninsula and Magdalen Islands), New Brunswick, Prince Edward Island, and Nova Scotia.

Its status as an accidental visitant to Melville Island, N.W.T. (June 12, 1820) is based on a sight record and is unsatisfactory.

Subspecies. *Riparia riparia riparia* (Linnaeus).

ROUGH-WINGED SWALLOW
L'Hirondelle à ailes hérissées
Stelgidopteryx ruficollis (Vieillot)
Plate 46. L. 5 to 5.7 in.

Adults have outer web of outer primary furnished with fine recurved hooklets (Fig. 61), difficult to see but readily felt by passing the finger along the edge of the wing toward the tip. *Adults* (sexes similar): Resemble Bank Swallow but whole throat, breast, and sides brownish grey, paling gradually to white on abdomen; brown of upper parts slightly paler than in Bank Swallow. *Young:* Similar to adults but wing coverts and tertials tipped with pale cinnamon, the throat and upper breast more or less tinged with same; hooklets on outer web of outer primary lacking or nearly so.

Fig. 61 Wing of Rough-winged Swallow showing hooklets (much magnified) on outer edge of outer primary

Measurements. *Adult male:* wing, 103.2–114.3 (110.8); tail, 47.0–51.5 (50.5); exposed culmen, 6.0–6.8 (6.4); tarsus, 11.0–11.5 (11.1). *Adult female:* wing, 99.0–108.0 (103.5) mm.

Field Marks. A brown-backed swallow resembling the Bank Swallow but whole throat and breast are plain greyish (instead of white with sharply defined dark breast band). Young Tree Swallows often show a vague greyish suffusion on the breast but have a white throat and dull grey upper parts.

Habitat. In the breeding season the vicinity of suitable nesting places (*see* Nesting), foraging over both water and dry land (even the driest parts of semi-arid plains).

Nesting. Often singly, not so highly colonial as is the Bank Swallow. In burrows in banks of sand, clay, or gravel, excavated by the swallows themselves, or in deserted kingfisher burrows, natural cavities, holes in cement walls, bridges, culverts, and similar situations. Nest of grasses, rootlets, leaves, and similar material depending on locality. *Eggs,* usually 6 or 7; white. Incubation period, 16 days (W. A. Lunk), mainly, if not entirely, by the female.

Range. Breeds from southern Canada (locally) south to Peru, Paraguay, and Argentina; not in the West Indies. Winters from southern United States southward, but only small numbers in the West Indies.

Breeding Distribution of Rough-winged Swallow

Range in Canada. Summer resident, breeding in southern and central British Columbia (Hazelton, Vanderhoof, Kleena Kleene, Victoria, Creston), southern Alberta (north to Jasper and Camrose), southern Saskatchewan (Maple Creek, Regina), southern Manitoba (Indian Bay), western and southern Ontario (Rainy River District; and from the extreme southern part north to about Manitoulin Island and Ottawa), and southwestern Quebec (Lac Simon, Batiscan, Lachine, Lennoxville).

Subspecies. *Stelgidopteryx ruficollis serripennis* (Audubon).

BARN SWALLOW
L'Hirondelle des granges. *Hirundo rustica* Linnaeus
Plate 46. L. 5.8 to 7.7 in.

Tail deeply forked, the outer feathers decidedly elongated. *Adult male:* Forehead chestnut; rest of upper parts dark

267

PLATE 57

steel blue; each tail feather (except central pair) with a patch of white on inner web; throat and middle breast chestnut, bordered on sides of neck and sides of breast by an extension downward of the blue of upper parts; rest of under parts cinnamon-rufous to cinnamon (sometimes quite pale). *Adult female:* Usually duller above and paler below than adult male; tail shorter. *Young:* Much duller above and paler below than adults; tail shorter.

Measurements. *Adult male:* wing, 116.0–122.0 (119.1); tail, 82.0–108.0 (89.5); exposed culmen, 7.2–7.8 (7.5); tarsus, 10.5–11.5 (11.3). *Adult female:* wing, 116.0–122.0 (118.3) mm.

Field Marks. Our only swallow with a *deeply* forked tail or with white in the tail feathers. The combination of blue upper parts and chestnut throat also separates it from all but the Cliff Swallow. The Barn Swallow has a uniformly blue back and rump (no brownish rump patch). The cinnamon abdomen, visible in flight at considerable distances, and long tail will distinguish it from other swallows. Young Barn Swallows have less deeply forked tail than adults, but nevertheless it is usually more deeply forked than in other swallows. *Voice:* Song a pleasant bubbly chatter, occasionally punctuated with a little, slightly rising, grating trill; also, especially in the air, *kvick, kvick.*

Habitat. In the breeding season the vicinity of a suitable nesting site (*see* Nesting) and within cruising radius of water for drinking, foraging, and providing mud for nest building. Forages over water, marshes, and open land; often low but also at great heights in fair weather.

Breeding Distribution of Barn Swallow

Nesting. Either in single pairs or small colonies. In protected places such as inside buildings of various kinds, under bridges, in caves, and under rocky overhangs of cliffs. Nest is of mud, bonded with grasses and lined with fine grasses, hair, and feathers, often on a beam in a building, on a ledge, or plastered against a wall. *Eggs,* usually 4 to 6; white, variously dotted or spotted with bright reddish browns and duller browns. Incubation 14 to 15 days (W. P. Smith), mainly by the female with some irregular assistance from the male.

1 Townsend's Warbler,
  (a) adult female in
      breeding plumage
  (b) autumn immature
  (c) adult male in
      breeding plumage

2 Myrtle Warbler,
  (a) autumn
  (b) male in breeding
      plumage
  (c) female in breeding

3 Audubon's Warbler,
  male in breeding
  plumage

4 Black-throated
  Green Warbler,
  (a) male in breeding
      plumage
  (b) female in breeding
      plumage
  (c) autumn immature

5 Black-throated
  Blue Warbler,
  (a) female
  (b) male in breeding
      plumage

6 Black-throated
  Gray Warbler, male in
  breeding plumage

7 Cerulean Warbler,
  (a) female in breeding
      plumage
  (b) male in breeding
      plumage

1a

1b

1c

2a

2b

2c

2d

3a

3b

3c

4a

4b

5

6a

Crosby

PLATE 58

1 Blackpoll Warbler,
   (a) female in breeding
      plumage
   (b) male in breeding
      plumage
   (c) autumn immature

2 Bay-breasted Warbler,
   (a) male in breeding
      plumage
   (b) male in autumn
      plumage
   (c) female in breeding
      plumage
   (d) autumn female

3 Blackburnian Warbler,
   (a) autumn
   (b) male in breeding
      plumage
   (c) female in breeding
      plumage

4 Chestnut-sided Warbler,
   (a) autumn immature
   (b) male in breeding
      plumage

5 Yellow-throated Warbler,
   male in breeding
   plumage

6 Pine Warbler,
   (a) female
   (b) adult male

Range. Holarctic. Breeds from north-central Alaska and across much of Canada (*see* Range in Canada) south to central Mexico and western Florida; also across Eurasia from near the northern edge of the tree belt south to northern Africa, Egypt, Asia Minor, northwestern India, and northern China. New World populations winter in South America.

Range in Canada. Summer resident, breeding from southern Yukon (Whitehorse, perhaps Burwash Landing), western Mackenzie (Fort Norman, Great Slave Lake), northwestern and central-eastern Saskatchewan (Lake Athabasca, Cumberland House), central Manitoba (also an isolated breeding record near Churchill), western and central Ontario (Malachi, Sioux Lookout, Hearst, South Porcupine, probably Moose Factory), southern Quebec (La Ferme, Lake St. John, Anticosti Island; possibly Lake Waswanipi), and southern Newfoundland (Codroy Valley, Shoal Harbour), south through British Columbia (including Queen Charlotte and Vancouver islands, but not known in the Peace River parklands), Alberta (but scarce in the Peace River District), southern Saskatchewan, southern Manitoba, southern Ontario, southern Quebec (including Magdalen Islands), New Brunswick, Prince Edward Island, and Nova Scotia.

Rare on north shore of the Gulf of St. Lawrence. Casual in southern Keewatin (Eskimo Point: 25 miles south), northern Manitoba (Churchill), and southern Labrador (Hopedale, St. Mary's River). Accidental on Victoria Island (Cambridge Bay) and Mansel Island, N.W.T.

Subspecies. *Hirundo rustica erythrogaster* Boddaert is the breeding subspecies over all of Canada. The Asiatic race, *H. r. gutturalis* Scopoli, is accidental 90 mi. west of Tasu Sound, Queen Charlotte Is., B.C., where an emaciated specimen was captured on July 15, 1960.

CLIFF SWALLOW
L'Hirondelle à front blanc
Petrochelidon pyrrhonota (Vieillot)
Plate 46. L. 5 to 6 in.

Tail relatively short, almost square or very slightly forked. *Adults:* Forehead pale buff to whitish; crown dark glossy blue, the back similar but streaked with white; collar around back of neck greyish; rump cinnamon buff; throat and sides of head, rich chestnut with small patch of black on lower throat; breast, sides, and flanks, pale greyish brown; belly white or whitish. *Young:* Resemble adults somewhat but upper parts mostly dark brown; throat and sides of head dusky, sometimes mixed with dull chestnut. The buffy rump patch distinguishes both adults and young from other swallows.

Measurements (*P. p. pyrrhonota*). *Adult male:* wing, 105.5–111.5 (109.4); tail, 47.0–51.0 (48.8); exposed culmen, 6.4–7.3 (6.8); tarsus, 12–13 (12.3). *Adult female:* wing, 105–112 (108.8) mm.

Field Marks. Most like Barn Swallow in general coloration but chunkier, with much shorter *squarish* tail, a *buffy rump patch*, and a whitish forehead patch. *Voice:* Rather soft but tends to be more squeaky than that of other swallows.

Habitat. Forages over water, marshes, and open land. In breeding season the vicinity of suitable nesting places (*see* Nesting), ideally within cruising distance of open water for drinking and foraging, and mud for nesting material.

Nesting. Highly colonial, sometimes in hundreds and rarely in thousands, usually in much smaller numbers. Nest is made of pellets of mud gathered by the birds. It is usually roofed over and often has a more or less downward protruding neck forming the entrance. Nest chamber is scantily lined with grass and feathers. Nests are close together and are plastered to the vertical walls of cliffs and canyons; but especially in the East this swallow, adopting man-made structures, has placed its nest on buildings, particularly under the eaves, on concrete bridges, and under culverts. *Eggs,* usually 4 or 5; white to creamy, variously dotted and spotted with light and dark browns. Incubation period 12 to 14 days (reported by various authors). House Sparrows frequently destroy the eggs and occupy the nests of this swallow.

Range. Breeds from central Alaska and Canada south through the United States (except South Carolina, Florida, and the eastern Gulf states) to southern Mexico. Winters in South America.

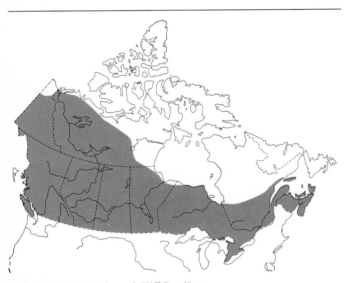

Breeding Distribution of Cliff Swallow

Range in Canada. Summer resident, breeding from northern Yukon (Old Crow), northern Mackenzie (Mackenzie Delta, Lockhart and Anderson rivers, Coppermine and Kendall rivers), Keewatin (Nueltin Lake, perhaps Back River below Macdougall Lake), northern Manitoba, northern Ontario (Fort Severn), and southern Quebec (Lac Simard, Seven Islands, Anticosti Island) south through southern British Columbia (but not recorded from Queen Charlotte Islands), southern Alberta, southern Saskatchewan, southern Manitoba, southern Ontario, southwestern and central-southern Quebec (Montreal, Hatley, Gaspé Peninsula), New Brunswick, Prince Edward Island, and Nova Scotia (including Cape Breton Island). Numbers of this swallow have declined in many areas in recent years.

Subspecies. (1) *Petrochelidon pyrrhonota pyrrhonota* (Vieillot): Man. (except southwestern part) eastward; also extreme sw. B.C. (2) *P. p. hypopolia* Oberholser (paler less rusty breast, usually paler rump patch, average larger size): Yukon, Mack., B.C. (except extreme southwest, but west at least to Okanagan Valley), Alta., Sask., and extreme sw. Man. (Whitewater Lake).

PURPLE MARTIN

L'Hirondelle pourprée. *Progne subis* (Linnaeus)
Plate 46. L. 7.3 to 8.5 in.

Tail distinctly, but not deeply, forked; upper mandible slightly hooked at tip. Our largest swallow. *Adult male:* Above and below dark glossy purplish blue; wings and tail dull blackish. *Adult female and young in first spring:* Upper parts mixed dark blue and grey, often with grey collar across back of neck and greyish forehead; throat, breast, sides, and flanks greyish brown, the feathers with grey margins, paling to whitish on belly and under tail coverts but with dark shaft streaks. Young males resemble adult females during the first year.

Measurements. *Adult male:* wing, 145.0–152.5 (149.5); tail, 71.5–78.5 (75.1); exposed culmen, 10.3–12.5 (11.4); tarsus, 14.5–15.5 (15.1). *Adult female:* wing, 141.0–152 (144.0) mm.

Field Marks. Our largest swallow. The adult male, uniformly *dark above and below* (looks black in some lights) is unlike any other swallow. At a distance in gliding flight, the Starling might be confused with it, but the slender bill of the Starling is usually apparent. Females and young have grey throats and breasts, whitish bellies. *Voice* is a good means of identification when learned. It is rather loud and pleasing and contains characteristic chirruping notes and gurgles that are easily recognized.

Habitat. The vicinity of suitable nesting boxes in open places on country farms, in towns and cities. In uninhabited areas, open parts of woodland, woodland openings and edges, and burntlands with hollow dead trees for nesting. Forages both high and low over open water, marshes, and open terrain. Tends to be locally distributed, and many apparently suitable areas are not inhabited by this swallow.

Nesting. Varies from single pairs to large communities. Today most nest in man-provided bird houses of various sizes from singles to ornate many-compartment houses placed on tall poles (15 to 20 feet) in open places. Occasionally openings or cavities in buildings are used. Formerly nested in hollow trees, woodpecker holes, and cavities in cliffs before man provided nesting boxes, and does so today in remoter and uninhabited country. Nest is loosely made of grasses, twigs, feathers, and often fresh leaves and a little mud. *Eggs,* usually 4 or 5; dull white. Incubation usually 15 to 17 days (Allen and Nice), mainly, if not entirely, by the female.

Range. Breeds (locally, absent from extensive areas) from southern Canada south to Baja California and central Mexico, the Gulf of Mexico coast, and southern Florida. Winters in South America.

Range in Canada. Summer resident, breeding locally in extreme southwestern and central-eastern British Columbia (in two widely separated areas: southern Vancouver Island,

Breeding Distribution of Purple Martin

smaller than crows and are often brightly coloured. Many jays are crested and have long tails. Instead of walking on the ground, they hop.

Birds of this family are of uncertain economic status. They are valuable as scavengers and destroyers of insects, but, on the other hand, they eat cultivated fruits and grains and sometimes destroy the eggs and young of other birds.

GRAY JAY (Canada Jay)
Le Geai gris. *Perisoreus canadensis* (Linnaeus)
Plate 47. L. 10.8 to 12.2 in.

Plumage loose and fluffy. Head without a crest. Bill rather short. Extent and depth of greys varies somewhat geographically but not enough to cause confusion as to species. *Adults* (*P. c. canadensis*): Head white with blackish slate cap on hind crown and nape, this dark colour extending narrowly forward to encircle eyes; back, wings, and tail slaty, the flight feathers and tail feathers tipped with white; abdomen, sides, and flanks, plain grey (paler than black) paling to whitish near tail; bill and legs black. *Juvenal:* All blackish grey above and below, darkest on top of head, palest on lower abdomen toward tail; tips of wing and tail feathers, brownish white; bill partially light-coloured (*see* Subspecies).

Measurements (*P. c. canadensis*). *Adult male:* wing, 138.0–148.5 (143.2); tail, 142.0–150.5 (144.4); exposed culmen, 20.6–21.8 (21.3); tarsus, 33.0–37.0 (35.6). *Adult female:* wing, 136.5–146.5 (139.5) mm.

Field Marks. A grey crestless jay, typically of coniferous forests, with fluffy plumage, short bill, and longish tail. The dark hind-neck, eye, and bill are conspicuous against the otherwise white head. It is very curious, often very bold. It frequently visits backwoods camps and picnic grounds for scraps. Young in juvenal plumage (first summer) are uniformly dark (in molting, white areas of the adults often show, especially as white moustache marks); usually they are accompanied by adults. *Voice:* Extremely varied consisting of harsh chatter, whistles (frequently *quee-oo*, dropping rapidly in pitch), soft chuckles, and many other notes, and including the mimicking of other birds. Said to have a soft, prolonged, warbling song.

Habitat. Coniferous and mixedwood forests, forest openings, and bogs.

Nesting. Nest, in a tree, usually (not always) a conifer, and most often between 4 and 15 feet above the ground. Nest is made of twigs, bark, leaves, grass, moss, and caterpillar cocoons with a substantial lining of hair, feathers, fine grass, and sometimes pine needles. Its foundation of coarse twigs makes it rather bulky. *Eggs,* 2 to 6, usually 3 to 4; greyish, quite evenly dotted and fine-spotted with olive-buff. Incubation 16 to 18 days, by the female (O. B. Warren).

Range. Breeds from near treeline in north-central Alaska and across Canada, and south to northern California, central Arizona, northern New Mexico, South Dakota (locally: Black Hills), northern Minnesota, northern Michigan, south-central Ontario, northeastern New York, northern parts of Vermont and New Hampshire, and Maine. Winters mostly in breeding range.

Vancouver; Peace River parklands), Alberta (Sylvan Lake and Penhold eastward and north to Fort McMurray and the Peace River District: Dixonville), north-central and southern Saskatchewan (Kazan Lake, Cumberland House, Moose Mountain; perhaps absent from southwestern corner), southern Manitoba (The Pas southward), western and southern Ontario (Minaki, Kenora, Port Arthur; and from about Sault Ste. Marie, Mattawa, and Ottawa southward), southern Quebec (Montreal, Quebec, Ste. Anne de la Pocatière, Trois Pistoles, Sherbrooke), southern New Brunswick (Pointe du Chêne, Hampton, Fredericton), Nova Scotia (Amherst; formerly Windsor, Truro, Oxford), and perhaps Prince Edward Island. In recent years there has been a decline in its numbers in the Maritimes.

Subspecies. *Progne subis subis* (Linnaeus).

Remarks. By erecting suitable nesting houses, we can induce these fine swallows to spend the summer in our gardens. Their graceful flight, pleasant voices, gentle ways, and economically beneficial food habits make them a real asset to have about. Starlings and House Sparrows compete with them for nesting sites, and that is why Martin houses should be taken down in the autumn and not be put up until the Martins return in the spring.

The food of the Purple Martin is almost entirely insects, which it catches on the wing.

Family **Corvidae** – Jays, Magpies, and Crows

Number of Species in North America 18; in Canada 8

A large family of conspicuous birds, which is found in much of the world but not in New Zealand. Size medium to large, including the largest of passerine birds. Bill is stout, tapering, usually about as long as the head. Nostrils are covered with stiff, bristle-like feathers. Tarsi are scutellate in front, plain behind. Primaries ten. The crows are black, black and white, or dull-coloured; the wings longer than the tails; and on the ground, instead of hopping, they walk. Jays are usually

Range in Canada. Permanent resident, breeding (north to about treeline) from northern Yukon (Old Crow), northern Mackenzie (wooded parts of Mackenzie Delta, Anderson River, lower Horton River, Thelon River), southwestern Keewatin (probably Windy River), northern Manitoba (Sandhill Lake, Churchill), northern Ontario, northern

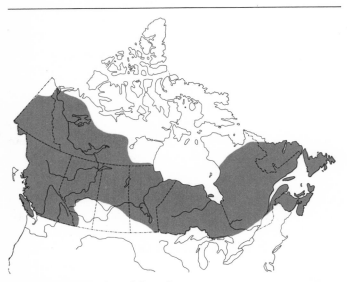

Breeding Distribution of Gray Jay

Quebec (Chimo, Whale River, George River), northern Labrador (wooded parts), and Newfoundland south through British Columbia (including Vancouver Island, but absent from Queen Charlotte Islands), central and southwestern Alberta (south in the mountains and foothills to Waterton Lakes Park, and east of the mountains south to the edge of heavy woods: Pigeon and Battle lakes, and formerly, at least, to wooded country near Red Deer, Penhold, and Innisfail; absent from the southern and southeastern plains), central Saskatchewan (Prince Albert, Nipawin), southern Manitoba (except southwestern corner), south-central Ontario (Round Lake in Renfrew County; Algonquin Park; Lake Nipissing), southern Quebec (La Vérendrye Park, Laurentide Park, Rimouski, Gaspé Peninsula), New Brunswick, Prince Edward Island, and Nova Scotia (including Cape Breton Island).

Winters mostly within breeding range, north to northwestern Mackenzie (Mackenzie Delta) and northern Quebec (Chimo). Also wanders somewhat south of the breeding range in winter, some years in considerable numbers.

Subspecies. The following sketch of the subspecies is tentative pending further study with more adequate material: (1) *P. c. pacificus* (Gmelin): Yukon, nw. Mack., n. and c. B.C., sw. Alta. (Banff, Jasper); (2)*P. c. canadensis*(Linnaeus): n. Man., Ont., s. Que. (Lake Mistassini, Anticosti Island), N.B.; (3) *P. c. nigricapillus* Ridgway: n. Que., Lab.; (4) *P. c. sanfordi* Oberholser: Nfld., N.S., P.E.I., e. N.B.; (5) *P. c. albescens* Peters: Alta. (east of the mts.), Sask., w. Man., s. Mack.; (6) *P. c. bicolor* Miller: interior s. B.C., extreme sw. Alta. (Waterton Lakes Park); (7) *P. c. arcus* Miller: Rainbow Mts., B.C.; (8) *P. c. griseus* Ridgway: s. coastal B.C., n. to Kimsquit.

272

BLUE JAY

Le Geai bleu. *Cyanocitta cristata* (Linnaeus)
Plate 47. L. 11 to 12.5 in.

(*See* Field Marks.) Unmistakable.

Measurements. *Adult male:* wing, 133.5–143.0 (137.9); tail, 127.0–143.5 (134.2); exposed culmen, 23.8–28.4 (26.6); tarsus, 34.5–36.5 (35.6). *Adult female:* wing, 127.0–136.0 (130.8) mm.

Field Marks. A crested bird, slightly longer than a Robin, with blue upper parts, grey-white under parts with a black necklace, and white spots in wings and tail. The only bird likely to be confused with it is Steller's Jay (of the western mountains), which also has a crest but differs in having all-blue under parts (black in young) and in showing no white in wing or tail. Bluebirds are very much smaller birds without any crest. *Voice:* Extremely varied. A loud *jay, jay* call and a whistled *too-wheedle, too-wheedle,* are familiar to most people. It has a variety of other notes including a scream like a Red-shouldered Hawk, various chattering and conversational notes, and a soft pleasing but infrequently heard song.

Habitat. Mixed and deciduous woodland of various types, especially where beech and oak are present; shade trees about towns and cities.

Nesting. In a tree, most often coniferous, and usually 8 to 20 feet up. Nest is rather bulky and is made of sticks, moss, and lichens, grasses, wool, paper, and various soft items, and lined with grass, rootlets, and feathers. *Eggs,* usually 4 to 6; buffy to greenish or bluish with small spots and blotches of brown or olive. Incubation period 17 to 18 days (Arnold *in* Bent).

Breeding Distribution of Blue Jay

Range. Southern Canada (Alberta eastward) south to southeastern Texas, the Gulf of Mexico coast, and southern Florida.

Range in Canada. Permanent resident breeding in central Alberta (east of the mountains: Peace River District and Fort McMurray south to about Red Deer), central Saskatchewan (Kazan Lake, Yorkton), south-central and southern Manitoba (Thicket Portage, Clear Lake, Whitemouth), central and southern Ontario (Sioux Lookout, Kenora, Port Arthur, and Kapuskasing southward; probably north to Lake Nipigon and Lake Abitibi), southern Quebec (La Vérendrye Park, Lake St. John, Gaspé Peninsula southward including Magdalen Islands), Newfoundland, New Brunswick, Prince Edward Island, and Nova Scotia.

Occasionally wanders south on the prairies to southern Alberta (Craigmyle, Brooks) and southern Saskatchewan (Ravenscrag, Regina).

Subspecies. *Cyanocitta cristata bromia* Oberholser. Recently the Nfld. population has been described as *C. c. burleighi* Bond, but the writer has not examined any Nfld. specimens and therefore can offer no comment on the validity of this proposed new subspecies.

Remarks. The Blue Jay is handsome, noisy, mischievous, and inquisitive. It adds life to the woodlands at any time of the year, especially in winter when so many other birds have moved to warmer climates. Its raucous calls are heard at all times of the year, but it is often noisiest in the quiet of autumn when most birds are silently hurrying south. It is practically omnivorous, eating fruits, insects, grains, acorns, and, unfortunately, sometimes the eggs and nestlings of other birds. Although economically of dubious value, it is surely one of the most beautiful and interesting of birds.

STELLER'S JAY
Le Geai de Steller. *Cyanocitta stelleri* (Gmelin)
Plate 47. L. 12 to 13.4 in.

Head crested. *Adults:* Head, neck, upper back, and upper breast blackish, the forehead usually streaked with blue, the throat more or less streaked with grey; wings, tail, lower back, rump, and under parts (posterior to upper breast) deep blue, the wings and tail usually with some black bars. Interior birds (*annectens*) often have a whitish spot above the eye. *Young:* Have blue wings and tail, but back, rump, and the under parts are blackish.

Measurements (*C. s. stelleri*). *Adult male:* wing, 144.0–150.0 (147.7); tail, 137.0–149.5 (141.4); culmen, 29.3–32.3 (30.3); tarsus, 42.0–47.5 (45.5). *Adult female:* wing, 139.0–150.0 (143.3) mm.

Field Marks. A dark blue and black prominently crested bird somewhat larger than a Robin. A much darker jay than the Blue Jay and *with dark under parts. Voice:* A harsh *shack-shack-shack, wek-wek-wek,* and various other calls, even a warbled song.

Habitat. Coniferous and mixedwood forests, either extensive or broken; also many other types of treed places, often including orchards and gardens.

Nesting. Most frequently in a conifer (often Douglas fir). Nest is a rather bulky but well-made structure of twigs, frequently plastered with mud, and lined with rootlets, grass, pine needles, or other soft material. *Eggs,* 3 to 5; greenish or bluish, fairly evenly dotted or spotted with browns or olive.

Range. Resident from southern Alaska, western and southern British Columbia, and southwestern Alberta south

through southern California and Mexico to El Salvador and the highlands of Nicaragua; east to southwestern Texas.

Range in Canada. Permanent resident in western and southeastern British Columbia (Stikine River, Poison Mountain about 60 miles north of Hazelton, and Yellowhead Pass southward including Queen Charlotte and Vancouver islands) and southwestern Alberta (Jasper and Waterton parks).

Individuals occasionally wander eastward in Alberta (Glenevis, Whitecourt, Swan Hills, Cochrane). Casual in eastern Saskatchewan (Indian Head, Saltcoats). Accidental in Quebec (Cap Rouge, November 8, 1926; subspecies: *annectens*).

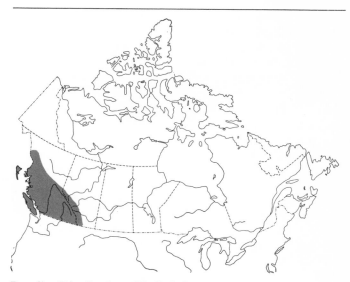

Breeding Distribution of Steller's Jay

Subspecies. (1) *Cyanocitta stelleri stelleri* (Gmelin): coastal B.C. (lower Stikine R., Vancouver I.). (2) *C. s. carlottae* Osgood, a darker race averaging somewhat larger: Queen Charlotte Islands, B.C. (3) *C. s. annectens* (Baird), with paler coloration than *stelleri,* much paler than *carlottae,* and often with a whitish area above the eye: sw. Alta., and interior B.C. Possibly, as some authors assert, its breeding range in the Skeena R. region extends to the coast (Porcher I.) interrupting that of *stelleri,* but material known to be breeding is needed to establish this. (4) *C. s. paralia* Oberholser: extreme sw. mainland of B.C. w. of the Cascades (Munro and Cowan, 1947; Aldrich *in* Jewett, *et al.,* 1953. On the other hand, this population is included in the nominate race in the A.O.U. Check-list, 1957).

BLACK-BILLED MAGPIE
La Pie bavarde. *Pica pica* (Linnaeus)
Plate 47. L. 18 to 22 in.

Tail very long (making up more than half the bird's total length), graduated. Head, neck, back, tail coverts, throat, and breast, black; scapulars, belly, sides, and flanks, white; inner webs of primaries largely white; wings glossy greenish blue; tail glossy green with more or less purple or bronze toward tip; upper rump greyish white; bill and legs black.

273

Measurements. *Adult male:* wing, 196.0–223.5 (207.5); tail, 242.0–343.5 (280.8); exposed culmen, 32.2–35.9 (33.5); tarsus, 46.0–50.5 (48.3). *Adult female:* wing, 187.0–202.0 (195.4) mm.

Field Marks. Unmistakable. A largish black-and-white bird with very long tail and flashing white patches in the wing tips when flying. *Voice:* A harsh rapid *yak yak yak yak yak;* often a querulous *yak* or two.

Habitat. Thickets and scattered trees in open places rather than heavy forest; shrubbery and trees along coulees, shelter belts on the prairies; streamside and canyon shrubbery, tree patches, edges and openings of woodland.

Nesting. Nest, in a tall bush or tree, is a domed-over mass of sticks, often thorny ones, with one or more entrances in the side leading to an inside cup of mud which is lined with rootlets, fine grass, and hair. *Eggs,* usually 6 to 9; greenish grey heavily blotched with browns. Incubation 16 to 18 days (C. E. Bendire), by the female.

Range. Both New and Old Worlds. In North America, from southern and central coastal Alaska and western Canada south to central-eastern California, Nevada, Kansas, Nebraska, and South Dakota. Also across Eurasia and in northwestern Africa.

Range in Canada. Permanent resident, breeding in southern Yukon (Canyon, Carcross; probably Fortymile), interior British Columbia (Chilkat Pass, Williams Lake, Okanagan Valley, Roosville), Alberta (north at least to Peace River District), Saskatchewan (north at least to Beaver River, Carlton, and Nipawin), and western Manitoba (north to Pikwitonei, Mile 213 Hudson Bay Railway).

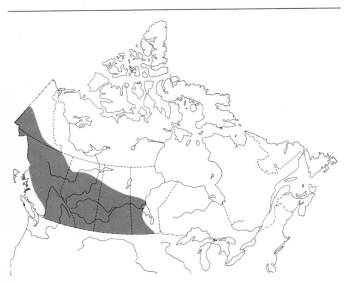

Breeding Distribution of Black-billed Magpie

Winters mainly within the breeding range, but there is an apparently regular movement north and east of it. Wanders north to southern Mackenzie (Wrigley, Dubawnt River, Fort Resolution, Fort Smith), southern Keewatin (Windy River), northern Saskatchewan (Lake Athabasca, Reindeer Lake), northern Manitoba (Churchill), western Ontario (Sioux Lookout, Kenora), and coastal British Columbia; rarely to eastern Ontario (western James Bay, Timmins,

Point Pelee, Odessa). Casual in western Quebec (Eastmain). Hypothetical in Labrador (Davis Inlet, where one was reported to L. M. Tuck, in litt., as having been shot on September 2, 1957, but not preserved).

Its breeding range has expanded eastward and northward within the past half century, and reports indicate more regular winter occurrence eastward and northward of the breeding range.

Subspecies. *Pica pica hudsonia* (Sabine).

COMMON RAVEN
Le Grand Corbeau, *Corvus corax* Linnaeus
Plate 47. L. 22 to 26.5 in.

Somewhat similar to Common Crow but much larger and with much heavier bill; feathers of throat elongated and pointed (Fig. 62); tail somewhat wedge-shaped. *Adults* (sexes similar): All black with purplish or violet lustre. *Young in juvenal plumage* (worn only a short time after leaving nest): Similar to adults but head and body dull brownish black and feathers of throat not elongated or pointed.

Fig. 62 Common Raven showing elongated, pointed throat feathers

Measurements (*C. c. principalis*). *Adult male:* wing, 417.0–445.0 (427.9); tail, 228.0–258.5 (244.5); exposed culmen, 72.0–78.0 (74.4); tarsus, 62.0–67.5 (64.9). *Adult female:* wing, 398.0–437.0 (421.4) mm.

Field Marks. In Canada, likely to be confused only with the Common Crow. Although much larger than the Crow, size is often deceptive in the field, unless the two are seen together. The Raven shows a definitely rounded or wedge-shaped spread tail (easily noted in flight overhead); on take-off from the ground the Raven often takes two or three hops to become air-borne, whereas the crow jumps directly into the air; in flight the Raven's longer neck and bill extend farther ahead of the wings. Ravens glide and soar more frequently, and often do barrel-rolls, dives, and tumbles. *Voice* is one of the best distinctions. The Raven's commonest call is a hoarse, far-carrying, rather wooden croak or *kwawk* (very different from the Crow's *caw*). It has a variety of other notes including a bell-like one. Young Ravens are often very noisy, with higher pitched, more prolonged calls than adults, which are easily distinguishable from those of young crows.

Habitat. Most often mountainous and wilder hill country and sea-coasts in both arctic and forested regions. Breeding distribution in the Arctic is governed by presence of cliffs for nesting, often those used by seabird colonies. In wooded regions trees are frequently used as nesting sites permitting nesting in flatter lowlands. Largely a scavenger, it forages over a wide variety of terrain but is partial to shores of lakes, rivers, and the sea; and in settled country, roadsides and town garbage dumps. Assertions that it shuns civilization are not necessarily true, for it prospers in numerous well-settled parts of the Maritimes (notably the heavily farmed Annapolis Valley) and visits regularly subarctic towns and villages within its breeding range in the north country, perching on buildings and scavenging at garbage dumps, often becoming quite tame where not persecuted. Its preferred habitat and that of man do not overlap to a great extent.

Nesting. In single pairs on cliff ledges and cavities and in trees (mostly conifers). Nest, a large mass of sticks lined with various soft materials, depending on availability, such as moss, grass, seaweed, and hair. *Eggs*, usually 3 to 5; similar to those of Common Crow but usually larger. Incubation 20 to 21 days (*in* Witherby, *et al.*) in the British Isles; 20 days (R. C. Harlow) in Pennsylvania.

Range. Both New and Old Worlds. In the New World from subarctic Alaska, arctic Canada, and Greenland, south through western United States and Mexico to Nicaragua and in eastern North America south to Minnesota, northern Michigan, Maine and, in the Appalachian Mountains, south to northern Georgia. In the Eastern Hemisphere from northern Eurasia south to northern Africa, Asia Minor, northwest India, and Japan.

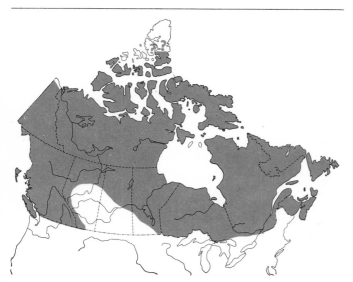

Breeding Distribution of Common Raven

Range in Canada. Permanent resident, breeding from high arctic islands (locally, depending on cliffs for nesting: Prince Patrick Island, southern Ellesmere Island) south through Yukon, Mackenzie, Keewatin, and southern Baffin Island

to southern British Columbia (including coastal islands), northern Alberta (south perhaps to Lesser Slave Lake and possibly farther south in the mountains), central Saskatchewan (Flotten Lake, Nipawin), central-western and southern Manitoba (northwestern Lake Winnipegosis, Rennie), western and south-central Ontario (Wonderland Lake, Gordon Lake, Algonquin Park), southern Quebec (near Aylmer, Lake Lyster, Rivière du Loup, Percé, Magdalen Islands), Labrador, Newfoundland, New Brunswick, Prince Edward Island, and Nova Scotia. Wanders north to northern Ellesmere Island, but evidence of breeding is lacking.

Winters mainly within breeding range north at least to Melville Island and northern Baffin Islands, N.W.T.; also somewhat south of the breeding range in Alberta, Saskatchewan, and rarely extreme southern Ontario.

Subspecies. (1) *Corvus corax principalis* Ridgway: all Canada except s. interior B.C. (2) *C. c. sinuatus* Wagler, characterized by average smaller size and slightly longer tarsus: s. interior B.C.: specimens examined from Okanagan Valley, Horsefly River, Yahk, Revelstoke.

COMMON CROW

La Corneille américaine. *Corvus brachyrhynchos* Brehm
Plate 47. L. 17 to 21 in.

Similar to Common Raven but much smaller; feathers of throat not elongated or pointed; tail not wedge-shaped. *Adults:* All black with violet or greenish blue gloss strongest on back, wings, and tail. *Juvenal plumage* (worn only a short time after leaving nest): Dull brownish black, only wings and tail glossy.

Measurements (*C. b. brachyrhynchos*). *Adult male:* wing, 303.0–328.0 (316.9); tail, 170.0–200.0 (183.3); exposed culmen, 46.0–52.0 (48.5); tarsus, 58.0–63.0 (60.5). *Adult female:* wing, 300.0–321.5 (310.4) mm.

Field Marks. Large size, all black coloration, and familiar *caw*. Its longish bill separates it from black hawks. *See* Common Raven and, on the Pacific Coast, Northwestern Crow, both similar to the Common Crow.

Habitat. Highly adaptable and resourceful, and with an appetite for a vast range of vegetable and animal foods, the crow is capable of occupying a correspondingly great variety of habitats. It prefers open places for foraging and wooded areas for nesting, resting, and roosting. Agricultural areas with their woodlots and broad cultivated fields are ideal for its requirements, and greatest populations are found in such habitats. Obviously the Crow is one of the minority of species that have profited most from extensive land use by man. It flourishes also in coastal areas. Extensive heavy forest has smaller populations, and these are mainly in the vicinity of lakes, rivers, marshes, meadows, and bogs. Winter populations in deep-snow regions usually concentrate about garbage dumps of towns and cities. Tidal shores support large winter flocks even in deep-snow areas. In many places winter flocks have greatly declined with the passing of the old slaughter houses.

Nesting. Usually in trees, both coniferous and deciduous, and at various heights, sometimes in low bushes or on the ground. Nest is a durable structure of sticks, lined mainly

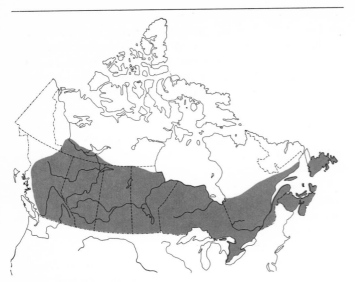

Breeding Distribution of Common Crow

with various soft materials such as grass, moss, leaves, bark, rootlets, hair, or rags. *Eggs*, usually 4 to 6; greenish, variously blotched and spotted with browns. Incubation 17 to 20 days, by both sexes (O. W. Knight).

Range. Breeds across southern Canada (except the West Coast) and south to northern Baja California, central Arizona, central Texas, the Gulf of Mexico, and southern Florida. Winters from parts of southern Canada southward.

Range in Canada. Breeds from north-central interior British Columbia (east of the coast: Hazelton, Fort Connolly, Babine Lake, and Peace River District), southwestern Mackenzie (Fort Simpson, Hay River, Fort Smith), northern Alberta, northern Saskatchewan (Lake Athabasca), northern Manitoba (Churchill), northern Ontario, central Quebec (Lake Mistassini, Havre St. Pierre, Cross River near Harrington Harbour), and Newfoundland (except the northern peninsula) south through southern British Columbia (east of the coast), Alberta, Saskatchewan, Manitoba, Ontario, Quebec (including Anticosti and Magdalen islands), New Brunswick, Prince Edward Island, and Nova Scotia.

Winters in southern British Columbia (Okanagan Valley, Nulki Lake), southern Saskatchewan (Regina), southern Ontario, southern Quebec (Hull, Montreal, Quebec, Arvida, Isle Verte, Gaspé Peninsula), southern Newfoundland, New Brunswick, Prince Edward Island, and Nova Scotia.

Casual in eastern Keewatin (Eskimo Point).

Subspecies. (1) *Corvus brachyrhynchos brachyrhynchos* Brehm: sw. Mack., n. Alta., n. Sask., Man., Ont., Que., Nfld., N.B., P.E.I., and N.S. (2) *C. b. hesperis* Ridgway, averaging smaller and with relatively smaller and more slender bill: interior B.C., c. and s. Alta., s. Sask.

Remarks. It has been said that if the average person were asked to name four birds, one of them would probably be the Crow. Although it is familiar to everyone, very few have much good to say for it. It is omnivorous and eats practically anything edible. It is destructive to crops, particularly corn, and it often takes the eggs and young of more desirable birds. On the other hand, it destroys large numbers of insects.

It is generally conceded, however, that the harm it does outweighs the good. Consequently no laws protect it. Despite constant persecution, the Crow is an extremely resourceful bird, well able to look after itself and maintain its numbers. Probably it has actually profited and increased as a result of its contacts with man and his agriculture.

NORTHWESTERN CROW

La Corneille du Nord-Ouest. *Corvus caurinus* Baird
Plate 47. L. 16.5 to 17.5 in.

Like Common Crow but smaller with relatively smaller feet.

Measurements. *Adult male:* wing, 274.5–292.5 (283.5); tail, 152.0–170.5 (163.0); exposed culmen, 43.5–49.0 (47.0); tarsus, 46.0–53.0 (51.0). *Adult female:* wing, 256.5–284.5 (272.0); tail, 144.5–162.5 (153.0); exposed culmen, 41.5–47.5 (45.0); tarsus, 45.0–51.0 (48.0) mm (Ridgway).

Field Marks. Its voice is the best distinction in the field from the Common Crow, the *caw* of the Northwestern being a higher pitched, more nasal, and rather flat *kaah*. In flight, wing beats noticeably more rapid.

Habitat. Usually not far from salt water. Primarily a beachcomber, foraging on coastal shores, beaches, and tide flats; also agricultural areas. Coastal woodlands for nesting and roosting.

Nesting. Nest, a mass of sticks and twigs lined with softer materials like grass, hair, and bark fibre. Usually in a coniferous tree but sometimes on the ground under bushes, windfalls, or boulders. *Eggs*, usually 4 or 5; similar to those of Common Crow but slightly smaller.

Range. Coasts and islands from southern Alaska south to Washington.

Breeding Distribution of Northwestern Crow

Range in Canada. Permanent resident on the coast and islands of British Columbia (including Queen Charlotte and Vancouver islands and inland at least to Chilliwack).

Remarks. Additional studies are needed to ascertain beyond doubt whether this crow is really a separate species or merely a subspecies of the Common Crow.

276

CLARK'S NUTCRACKER

Le Casse-noix américain. *Nucifraga columbiana* (Wilson)
Plate 47. L. 12 to 13 in.

Adults (sexes alike): Head, neck, and body, pale smoky grey, whitish on forehead, throat, and about eye; wings black, the secondaries with broadly white ends; tail mostly white, the central feathers black; under tail coverts white; bill and feet black. *Young:* Similar to adults but paler and duller.

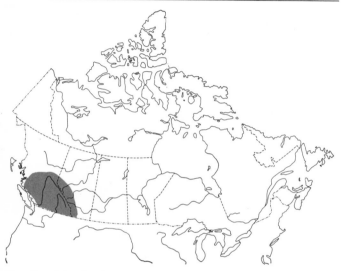

Breeding Distribution of Clark's Nutcracker

Measurements. *Adult male:* wing, 186–198 (191.1); tail, 109–122 (113.4); exposed culmen, 33.4–48.5 (39.8); tarsus, 34–37.5 (35.7). *Adult female:* wing, 177.5–194 (185.5) mm.

Field Marks. A stout grey bird with longish pointed black bill, black wings with a white patch, and white outer tail feathers. Usually found in the western mountains. Reminds one of a cross between a crestless jay and a woodpecker. The Gray Jay shows no contrasting blacks and whites in wing or tail and has a shorter bill and a longer tail. The Shrike is smaller, shows a black patch through the eye, and has a shorter blunter bill. Nutcrackers are usually noisy with harsh grating calls like *char-r-r* or *kra-a-a*, repeated two or three times.

Habitat. Typically, open or broken coniferous woods, clearings, edges, and burntlands at higher altitudes of the western mountains, descending to valleys in winter. Although largely dependent on conifer seeds for food, it eats many other foods and may forage in various situations. In winter it may visit camps or farmyards for scraps.

Nesting. In coniferous trees at various distances from the ground. Nest is of twigs lined with dry grass, shredded bark, conifer needles, and hair. *Eggs,* usually 2 to 4; pale greenish with small spots of pale brown or olive. Incubation probably 16 or 17 days (C. E. Bendire), by both sexes.

Range. Breeds from about central British Columbia, southwestern Alberta, central and western Montana, and western and southeastern Wyoming south through the mountains to northern Baja California, eastern Arizona, and western New Mexico.

Range in Canada. Permanent resident, breeding in southern and central British Columbia (east of the coast but west to Alta Lake) and in the mountains of southwestern Alberta.

Wanders west to Vancouver and Queen Charlotte islands, British Columbia; north to southern Yukon (Robinson, Rancheria River), and east of the mountains in Alberta (Porcupine Hills, Beaverlodge, Belvedere), southern Saskatchewan (Cypress Hills), and southern Manitoba (Winnipeg, Margaret).

Family **Paridae** – Titmice, Verdins, Bushtits

Number of Species in North America 14; in Canada 7

Small birds of woods and thickets with short but usually quite robust bills; nostrils hidden by tufts of stiff feathers; short rounded wings, and soft fluffy plumage. Except in the nesting season they are usually seen in small companies and are often accompanied by kinglets, nuthatches, and woodpeckers.

BLACK-CAPPED CHICKADEE

La Mésange à tête noire. *Parus atricapillus* Linnaeus
Plate 48. L. 4.8 to 5.7 in.

Plumage soft and loose. *Adults* (sexes similar): Crown and back of neck, black; back olive-grey (more or less mixed with buffy, especially in winter); wings and tail blackish slate, the secondaries and greater wing coverts edged with greyish white, the tail feathers edged with grey or white; chin and throat, black; sides of head, sides of neck, and under body, white; sides and flanks tinged with buff; bill black; legs dark bluish grey. *Young in juvenal plumage* are similar to adults but duller.

Measurements (*P. a. atricapillus*). *Adult male:* wing, 64.6–68.6 (66.1); tail, 58.0–73.0 (63.4); exposed culmen, 8.8–9.7 (9.1); tarsus, 15.9–16.8 (16.4). *Adult female:* wing, 60.0–65.4 (62.7) mm.

Field Marks. Familiar to almost everyone, and one of the easiest of birds to attract to the backyard feeding shelf. A fluffy, confiding, unstreaked little bird with a black cap and bib which contrast with the white on sides of head. Usually in small loose companies often associating with other woodland birds. *Voice:* Its clearly pronounced *chicka-dee-dee-dee* is frequently given at all times of the year. Its sweet whistled *fee-bee* (first part higher) is most often heard in late winter and spring. In Canada the only other chickadee with a jet-black cap is the Mountain Chickadee of the West which has a white eyebrow line.

Habitat. Forages in dry or wet deciduous or mixed woodlands of various age and extent, woodland openings and edges, tall thickets such as willow and alder, woodlots and wood patches, ornamental shrubbery and trees about houses, occasionally on weeds in open fields (*see also* 'Nesting').

Nesting. In a cavity, usually low, in a soft decaying stump, generally excavated by the birds, taking turns; sometimes in an old woodpecker hole, a natural cavity, or a bird box. Soft materials such as moss, vegetable fibres, hair, and feathers are carried inside the cavity to form the nest. *Eggs,* usually 6 to 8; dull white, spotted with reddish brown. Incubation about 13 days, by both parents (E. P. Odum).

Range. Central Alaska and southern Canada, south to northwestern California, central Utah, northern New Mexico, northeastern Oklahoma, central Missouri, southern Ohio, eastern Tennessee, western North Carolina, western Maryland, and northern New Jersey.

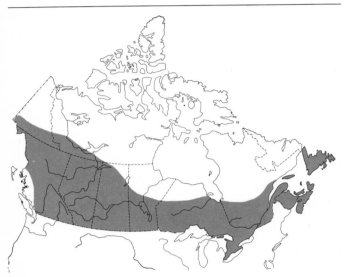

Breeding Distribution of Black-capped Chickadee

Range in Canada. Permanent resident (but apparently there is some withdrawal in winter from northernmost localities), breeding from southern Yukon (Burwash Landing, Carcross, Dezadeash Lake; probably Lapie River), southwestern Mackenzie (Fort Simpson, Fort Resolution), northern Saskatchewan (Lake Athabasca, Black Lake region), north-central Manitoba (Thicket Portage), north-central Ontario (Favourable Lake, Fort Albany), southern Quebec (La Ferme near Amos, Lake St. John, Matamek, Anticosti Island), and Newfoundland south through southern British Columbia (except coastal islands and north coast), Alberta, Saskatchewan, Manitoba, Ontario, Quebec (including Magdalen Islands), New Brunswick, Prince Edward Island, and Nova Scotia (including Cape Breton Island).

Subspecies. (1) *Parus atricapillus atricapillus* Linnaeus: e. Canada (except Newfoundland) west to w. Ont. and se. Man. (Winnipeg). (2) *P. a. bartletti* (Aldrich and Nutt), darker and browner than (1): Nfld. (3) *P. a. septentrionalis* Harris, paler than (1) with longer tail and wing: s. Yukon, sw. Mack., n. B.C. (south to Vanderhoof and Hazelton), Alta., Sask., w. and c. Man. (The Pas, Thicket Portage, Oak Lake). (4) *P. a. fortuitus* (Dawson and Bowles), very similar to (1) but slightly paler: s. B.C. (north at least to Lillooet and

Revelstoke, east to Flathead Valley). (5) *P. a. occidentalis* Baird, darker and browner even than (2): extreme sw. mainland B.C. (Vancouver, Chilliwack).

Remarks. Whoever saw a dejected Chickadee? Even on the greyest day of midwinter, when the thermometer remains below zero and the snow lies deep over the land, the Chickadee is the personification of cheerfulness and good nature. Chickadees rove through the woods in small loose companies, constantly pausing to scrutinize the leafless branches for the insect eggs they relish so much. Indeed, insects make up the greater part of their food throughout the year, these including some of the worst crop and orchard pests. Seeds and small wild fruit also are eaten.

This chickadee is one of the easiest of birds to attract to a backyard feeding shelf. Even nothing more than a piece of suet attached to the bark of a tree will provide a winter-long attraction for a small company.

MOUNTAIN CHICKADEE (Gambel's Chickadee)
La Mésange de Gambel. *Parus gambeli* Ridgway
Plate 48. L. 5 to 5.7 in.

Similar to Black-capped Chickadee but with a white eyebrow stripe, the sides and flanks much less buffy.

Measurements. *Adult male:* wing, 66.4–69.9 (68.6); tail, 59–63 (60.9); exposed culmen, 9.5–11.6 (10.2); tarsus, 16.5–18.5 (17.5). *Adult female:* wing, 63.6–67.5 (65.4) mm.

Breeding Distribution of Mountain Chickadee

Field Marks. The *black* cap distinguishes it from all other Canadian chickadees except the Black-capped. A white eyebrow line separates it from all others including the Black-capped. *Voice:* The *chickadee* call is harsher than that of the Black-capped and more variable, thus *chickadeer-deer, cha-dee-dee-dee,* and so on. The whistled call is *fee-bee-bee* (usually three or four syllables but occasionally only two; first note always highest). It also has lisping *sssp* calls like those of the Black-capped.

Habitat. Coniferous forests, up to near timberline in western mountains, especially more open types but foraging often includes deciduous woods and thickets. It forages in tree crowns to a much greater extent than the Black-capped.

Nesting. In a natural cavity or woodpecker hole in a tree, occasionally in a bird box. Moss, grass, plant fibres, fur, feathers, and almost any other available soft material make up the nest. *Eggs*, 6 to 12; dull white sometimes immaculate but usually spotted with reddish brown in various extents. Incubation 14 days (I. G. Wheelock).

Range. Mountains of western North America from northern British Columbia and southwestern Alberta south to northern Baja California, Arizona, New Mexico, and southwestern Texas.

Range in Canada. Permanent resident, breeding in the mountains of northwestern, central, and southern interior British Columbia (Atlin, Topley, Vanderhoof, Lillooet, Okanagan Landing, Cranbrook, Waldo) and southwestern Alberta (Jasper, Banff, and Waterton Lakes parks).

It has been recorded west in British Columbia to Stuie (in August) and the Alta Lake region (in October) and has wandered north to southwestern Yukon (Dezadeash Lake) and east in Alberta to Edmonton and near Calgary.

Subspecies. *Parus gambeli grinnelli* (van Rossem).

GRAY-HEADED CHICKADEE (Alaskan Chickadee)
La Mésange à plastron. *Parus cinctus* Boddaert
Plate 48. L. 5.4 to 5.8 in.

Somewhat similar to Boreal Chickadee but general coloration much paler and greyer; crown and back much greyer (less brownish), sides and flanks pale brownish buff (instead of rich cinnamon brown), wing tertials broadly edged with whitish, sides of neck white (instead of clear grey), size somewhat larger.

Measurements. *Adult male:* wing, 69–70 (69.8); tail, 65.5–68 (66.5); exposed culmen, 9–11 (10.1); tarsus, 15.5–16.5 (15.7). *Adult female:* wing, 65.5–69.5 (67.6); tail, 63–69 (67.3); exposed culmen, 9–10.6 (9.8); tarsus, 16–16 (16) mm.

Field Marks. Distinguishable from Boreal Chickadee by white (instead of clear grey) sides of neck, pale buff (instead

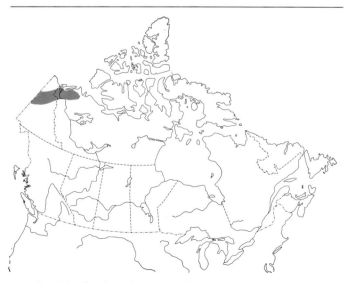

Breeding Distribution of Gray-headed Chickadee

of reddish brown) sides and flanks, and whitish margins of tertials. The colour of flanks and the whitish edgings of tertials suggest the Black-capped Chickadee but the greyish brown crown characterizes the Gray-headed. *Voice:* A complaining *dee-deer*, *chee-ee*, or *pee-vee* (O. Murie); slightly hoarser than that of the Boreal (S. D. MacDonald).

Habitat. Broken coniferous or aspen woods and willow thickets near the northern edges of tree limit.

Nesting. A cavity in a tree stump. Nest of mammal hair and moss. *Eggs*, 6 to 9; white, finely spotted with reddish brown.

Range. From northern Norway eastward across northern Eurasia and in Alaska, northern Yukon, and northwestern Mackenzie.

Range in Canada. Permanent resident in the northern limits of woodland in northern Yukon (Old Crow) and northwestern Mackenzie (Aklavik, Fort Anderson).

Subspecies. *Parus cinctus lathami* Stephens.

BOREAL CHICKADEE (Hudsonian or
Brown-headed Chickadee)
La Mésange à tête brune. *Parus hudsonicus* Forster
Plate 48. L. 5 to 5.5 in.

Adults: Crown and hind-neck brown; back, brownish olive to hair-brown; wings and tail, dark slate with paler grey edges; cheeks whitish merging into pale grey on auricular region and becoming dark grey on sides of neck; chin and throat, black; medial under parts white, slightly greyish on sides of chest; sides and flanks between cinnamon-brown and russet.

Measurements (*P. h. hudsonicus*). *Adult male:* wing, 63.2–66.2 (65.8); tail, 59–65.9 (63.2); exposed culmen, 7.6–9.8 (8.9); tarsus, 16–17.5 (16.9). *Adult female:* wing, 58.7–64.1 (62.8) mm.

Field Marks. The brown cap, reddish (instead of pale buffy) flanks, and more brownish (less greyish) general coloration distinguish it from the Black-capped Chickadee. It resembles the Chestnut-backed Chickadee of the West but lacks the red back of that species (*see also* Gray-headed Chickadee). *Voice:* Commonly *sickaday-day*, slower and a little more highly pitched than the *chickadee* of the Black-capped; easily recognizable.

Habitat. Primarily coniferous and mixed woodland but forages to some extent also in deciduous trees and thickets.

Nesting. In a natural cavity, woodpecker hole, or a cavity excavated by the chickadees in a tree or stump not often over ten feet above ground. Nest is of moss, shreds of bark, and mammal hair. *Eggs*, usually 5 to 7; white, sparingly fine-spotted with reddish brown.

Range. Resident in the coniferous forest belt from the northern limit of trees in continental Alaska and across Canada south to central-northern Washington, northwestern Montana, northeastern Minnesota, northeastern New York, northern Vermont, northern New Hampshire, and Maine.

Range in Canada. Permanent resident in the coniferous belt from northern Yukon (Old Crow), northwestern and western Mackenzie (Mackenzie Valley north to the Delta,

Great Bear Lake, Great Slave Lake), northern Saskatchewan (Lake Athabasca, Newnham Lake), northern Manitoba (Cochrane River, Churchill), northern Ontario (Severn River), northern Quebec (Fort Chimo, George River), Labrador (Okak southward), and Newfoundland south through southern British Columbia (east of the Coast Ranges), southwestern and central Alberta (Banff, Astotin Lake), central Saskatchewan (Flotten Lake, Prince Albert, Nipawin), southern Manitoba (Clear Lake, Spruce Woods Forest Reserve, Sprague; absent from extreme southwestern corner), south-central Ontario (Atikokan, Maclennan, Algonquin Park), southern Quebec (Lake Temiskaming, Lake Monroe, Lavaltrie, Baldwin Mills, St. Aubert, Percé, Anticosti and Magdalen islands; absent or very local in most of extreme southwestern corner), New Brunswick, Prince Edward Island, and Nova Scotia.

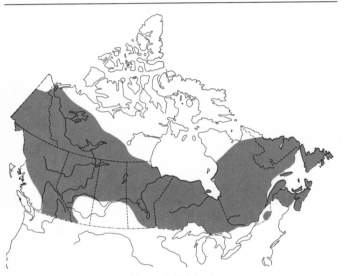

Breeding Distribution of Boreal Chickadee

Recorded west to Stuie, B.C. Winters mainly within breeding range north to northwestern Mackenzie (Mackenzie Delta), northern Saskatchewan (Stony Rapids), southwestern Keewatin (Windy River), and northern Quebec (George River). There is a more or less regular movement of individuals to areas somewhat south of the breeding range and apparently sometimes even northward as in southwestern Keewatin (Mowat and Lawrie, 1955: 111). Irregularly, irruptive autumn movements take large numbers to extreme southern Ontario and beyond.

Subspecies. (1) *Parus hudsonicus hudsonicus* Forster: e. Man. (Churchill, East Braintree), Ont., n. and c. Que. (south to about Lake St. John, the north shore of the Gulf of St. Lawrence, Anticosti I.), Lab., Nfld. (2) *P. h. littoralis* Bryant, averaging slightly smaller and browner than *hudsonicus*: s. Que., N.B., P.E.I., N.S. (3) *P. h. farleyi* Godfrey, a pale, brown-backed race with grey on sides of neck pale and restricted: Alta. (except mts.), s. Mack. (probably Fort Simpson, Fort Reliance), Sask., w. Man. (The Pas, Clear Lake). (4) *P. h. evura* Coues, a pale grey or olivaceous-backed bird with grey sides of neck often nearly as pale as in *farleyi*: n. Yukon (Old Crow), nw. Mack. (Mack. Delta).

(5) *P. h. columbianus* Rhoads, darker and less brownish than *hudsonicus*, much darker than *evura* or *farleyi*: B.C. and sw. Alta. *P. h. cascadensis* Miller is not considered separable.

CHESTNUT-BACKED CHICKADEE
La Mésange à dos marron. *Parus rufescens* Townsend
Plate 48. L. 4.5 to 5 in.

Crown and back of neck, dark brown; throat brownish black; cheeks and sides of neck, white; back and rump, chestnut; breast and median under parts, white; sides and flanks chestnut.

Measurements. *Adult male:* wing, 60.1–64.3 (61.9); tail, 48–52.5 (49.9); exposed culmen, 8.9–9.6 (9.3); tarsus, 14.5–16.5 (15.9). *Adult female:* wing, 56.5–66.8 (59.9) mm.

Field Marks. A chickadee of the West. Because of its brown head and chestnut sides it is likely to be confused mostly with the Boreal Chickadee. The Chestnut-back has a rich chestnut back, the white of face extends backwards onto sides of neck (instead of becoming grey), and the flanks are of a deeper red like the back. *Voice: tsick-a-dee-dee*, shriller and more rapid than in other chickadees; also various high-pitched lisping notes suggesting those of a Brown Creeper or Golden-crowned Kinglet.

Habitat. Mostly coniferous woods but also deciduous trees and thickets, even burntlands. Forages well up in trees as well as at lower levels.

Nesting. In a cavity in a dead tree or dead part of a living tree, either excavated by the chickadees or in a woodpecker hole or natural cavity. Nest is of various soft materials like hair or feathers with a moss foundation. *Eggs*, commonly 6 or 7; white, sparingly and lightly dotted with browns.

Range. Pacific Coast and islands from central-southern Alaska south to central California and for various distances inland in the mountains of British Columbia, Washington, Idaho, and northwestern Montana.

Range in Canada. Permanent resident, breeding commonly in western British Columbia (coastal slopes and islands

Breeding Distribution of Chestnut-backed Chickadee

280

including Vancouver, the Queen Charlottes, and other islands; in Skeena River Valley east to Hazelton; frequently recorded in the southern interior probably breeding locally in Glacier and Revelstoke parks; probably breeds also in Klehini Valley in the extreme northwest near the Alaskan boundary).

Subspecies. *Parus rufescens rufescens* Townsend.

TUFTED TITMOUSE
La Mésange huppée. *Parus bicolor* Linnaeus
Plate 48. L. 6 to 6.5 in.

A large crested chickadee *without* a black bib. Upper parts plain slate grey, the forehead blackish; under parts whitish with pale rusty flanks. Bill rather heavy, black.

Measurements. *Adult male:* wing, 130–157 (146.2); tail, 65–75 (68.5); exposed culmen, 11–13 (12.1); tarsus, 19.5–22 (20.4). *Adult female:* wing, 72–79.5 (76.7); tail, 61.5–71 (66.8); exposed culmen, 11–13 (12); tarsus, 19–21.5 (20.2) mm (Ridgway).

Field Marks. A crested small bird with plain bluish-grey upper parts, rusty flanks, and blackish forehead. The dark eye is conspicuous in the greyish white face. Other crested birds are very different (*see* Blue Jay, Waxwings). *Voice:* A whistled *péto* repeated several times; a hoarse *dee dee dee*.

Habitat. Deciduous and mixed woodland and patches in rural areas; and in residential areas where there is adequate tree growth as in parks and cemeteries. Visits feeding trays about houses.

Nesting. In a natural cavity in a tree, or in an abandoned woodpecker hole, or in a bird box at various heights. Leaves, bark, moss, and grass are used to fill up excess cavity space, and the nest cup is made of various soft materials like hair, rags, and string. Often the nest contains a cast snake skin. *Eggs*, most often 5 or 6; white, finely spotted with browns. Incubation period 12 days (Dickey *in* Bent).

Range. Permanent resident from southeastern Nebraska, southern Wisconsin, southern Ontario, southern New York, and southwestern Connecticut south to eastern Texas, the Gulf coast of United States, and central Florida. Has spread northward in recent years.

Range in Canada. Scarce permanent resident in southern Ontario. Known to have bred at Hamilton, Sarnia, and Lorne Park near Toronto. It has been recorded north to southern Georgian Bay and east to Kingston. A recent arrival, it was first observed at Point Pelee on May 2, 1914. Increase in numbers has been very slow since.

COMMON BUSHTIT
La Mésange buissonnière
Psaltriparus minimus (Townsend)
Plate 48. L. 4 to 4.5 in.

Bill deeper than broad, its depth at base more than half the length of exposed culmen. Tail slender, longish (longer than wing), and somewhat graduated. Top of head brown; back and rump brownish grey; under parts brownish white, darkening to brown on sides and flanks. No wing bars or other conspicuous marks.

Measurements. *Adult male:* wing, 46.5–47 (46.7); tail, 51–54 (52.6); exposed culmen, 7.5–8.1 (7.9); tarsus, 16–16 (16.0). *Adult female:* wing, 47.3–48.4 (47.9) mm.

Field Marks. A tiny nondescript brownish grey bird of southwestern British Columbia with stubby bill and rather long tail. Moves actively about exploring the branches in all positions, often upside down, with frequent high-pitched call-notes. Lack of any definite markings, such as wing bars, eye-ring, and eyebrow line, as well as its longer tail, distinguishes it from kinglets. *Voice:* Frequent high-pitched *tsit-tsit*'s, lisping notes, and a shrill quavering trill.

Habitat. Deciduous and mixed more open woodland and edges; thickets and patches of deciduous shrubbery in both rural and residential areas; logged-over areas growing up in bushes.

Nesting. Nest is amazingly large and intricately woven for such a tiny bird: a bag-like structure, 7 to 10 inches long and 3 or 4 inches wide, suspended from a branch and beautifully woven of mosses, lichens, spider webs, plant down, and insect cocoons. The entrance is at the side and usually near the top. *Eggs*, usually 5 to 7; dull white. Incubation about 12 days (A. B. Addicott), by both sexes.

Range. Southwestern British Columbia, southeastern Oregon, southwestern Wyoming, and western Colorado south to southern Baja California, Sonora, and western and central Texas.

Range in Canada. Permanent resident in extreme southwestern British Columbia (Vancouver region; and Vancouver Island: Victoria, Parksville, Comox). It is a recent arrival on Vancouver Island. The first nest for the island was found near Victoria, where now common, in 1945.

Subspecies. *Psaltriparus minimus minimus* (Townsend).

Family **Sittidae** – Nuthatches

Number of Species in North America 4; in Canada 3

Nuthatches forage on the trunk and branches of trees and characteristically work down the trunk head-first. They are small birds with straight, slender, tapering bills; rather long and pointed wings; short tails; and rather long toes, three in front, one behind, and all with laterally compressed claws. The name 'nuthatch' comes from the habit of inserting nuts in bark crevices and hammering them with the bill until the shell is broken.

WHITE-BREASTED NUTHATCH
La Sittelle à poitrine blanche. *Sitta carolinensis* Latham
Plate 48. L. 5.2 to 6.2 in.

Bill straight or slightly uptilted, slender, pointed; tail short, as in other nuthatches. Top of head and back of neck, black (in females, black of crown usually more or less mixed with grey); back and rump, pale bluish grey; two central tail feathers plain bluish grey, others black with much white toward tips; sides of head (to above eye), sides of neck, and under parts, white; with chestnut on thighs and on under tail coverts.

Measurements (*S. c. cookei*). *Adult male:* wing, 88.4–94.1 (90.6); tail, 44.5–50 (47.3); exposed culmen, 18.1–20 (19.1); tarsus, 17.5–19.5 (18.6). *Adult female:* wing, 88.5–90.4 (89.5) mm.

Field Marks. A short-tailed small bird working down a tree trunk upside-down is a nuthatch. The White-breasted Nuthatch, our largest species, forages on tree trunks and larger branches. Its plain white face (no black line through the eye) is the best distinction from the Red-breasted, for the latter's rusty breast is difficult to see in some individuals. Its black crown readily separates it from the little Pygmy Nuthatch of the West. *Voice:* Commonly a nasal *yank yank yank;* frequently soft notes that sound like *hit hit;* song, a hollow whistled *tew tew tew tew.*

Habitat. In the East, primarily maturer deciduous woodlands and mixedwoods, woodlots, orchards, shade trees of residential areas. In British Columbia, ponderosa pines are favoured.

Nesting. In a hole in a tree at various heights, a natural cavity, woodpecker hole, a cavity excavated by the nuthatches themselves, or in a bird box. Bark shreds, twigs, grass, and leaves are used as cavity fillers, and there is a lining of fur and feathers. *Eggs,* 5 to 9, white, rather evenly spotted with various browns and often a little lavender. Incubation 12 days (A. A. Allen).

Range. Resident from southern Canada south to southern Mexico (Oaxaca) and central Florida. Absent from much of the Great Plains.

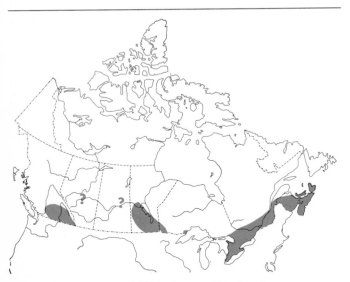

Breeding Distribution of White-breasted Nuthatch

Range in Canada. Permanent resident, breeding in interior southern British Columbia (Lillooet, Okanagan Valley, Canal Flats, Waldo), southern Manitoba (Swan River, Lake St. Martin, Winnipeg, Hillside Beach), western Ontario (Rainy River; probably Fort William), southern Ontario (Parry Sound District, North Bay, Ottawa southward), southwestern Quebec (Blue Sea Lake, Quebec, Montreal, Hatley; recorded in April north to Arvida without evidence of breeding), New Brunswick (St. Leonard, Saint John), Prince Edward Island (Harmony Junction), and

Nova Scotia (including Cape Breton Island). Probably breeds also in central-eastern Saskatchewan (Nipawin and perhaps Prince Albert).

Status in Alberta uncertain (specimen: St. Albert, December 30, 1958, and several sight records elsewhere). Casual on Vancouver Island (Comox).

Subspecies. (1) *Sitta carolinensis cookei* Oberholser: e. Canada westward to Sask. A St. Albert, Alta., winter specimen is referable to this race. (2) *Sitta carolinensis tenuissima* Grinnell, with longer, slenderer bill and darker grey upper parts: interior s. B.C. (3) *Sitta carolinensis aculeata* Cassin, smaller and paler above than *tenuissima*, less purely white below; casual in sw. B.C. according to the A.O.U. Check-list. The writer has seen no Canadian specimens of *aculeata*.

RED-BREASTED NUTHATCH

La Sittelle à poitrine rousse. *Sitta canadensis* Linnaeus
Plate 48. L. 4.1 to 4.8 in.

Adult male: Top of head and back of neck black; face white with black line through eye, creating a long white eyebrow line; back, rump, and wing coverts, greyish blue or bluish grey; central tail feathers bluish grey, others black with considerable white toward tips; chin, whitish passing into buff or ochraceous buff of under parts. *Adult female:* Similar to male but black of crown replaced by dark greyish blue and under parts paler. *Young* resemble adults of their respective sexes but are paler.

Measurements. *Adult male:* wing, 65.8–68.8 (67.3); tail, 34.5–42.5 (37.7); exposed culmen, 13.5–14.4 (13.9); tarsus, 15–16.5 (15.7). *Adult female:* wing, 63.8–67.9 (65.7) mm.

Field Marks. Smaller than the White-breasted Nuthatch. Our only nuthatch with a white eyebrow stripe. The reddish under parts are diagnostic when well developed, but some individuals show very little buffy underneath. *Voice:* A nasal *nyak nyak nyak*, higher in pitch than that of the White-breasted; also similar *hit* notes.

Habitat. Coniferous and mixedwood forests are preferred, but foraging is done also in deciduous trees to some extent.

Nesting. In a cavity usually excavated by the birds in the soft wood of a decaying tree, stump, or post, and at various heights usually among or near coniferous trees (occasionally 200 yards from coniferous trees). The cavity entrance is smeared with pitch, but the function of this is not understood satisfactorily. Nest is composed of materials such as shredded bark, grasses, and rootlets, often lined with hair. Sometimes the eggs are laid on wood chips on the cavity floor. *Eggs,* 4 to 7; white, variously spotted or dotted with reddish browns. Incubation 12 days (F. L. Burns).

Range. Breeds in coniferous forests from southeastern Alaska east to Newfoundland and south in the mountains to southern California, southeastern Arizona, Wyoming, and South Dakota, also to central Minnesota and northern Michigan, and in the Appalachians to eastern Tennessee and western North Carolina, southern New York, and Massachusetts. Winters within breeding range and somewhat south of it.

Range in Canada. Permanent resident in most of breeding

range, breeding from southern Yukon (Fort Selkirk, Kathleen River), southwestern Mackenzie (Fort Simpson, Tazin River), northwestern Saskatchewan (Lake Athabasca), central Manitoba (Reader Lake), north-central Ontario (Lac Seul, Lake Nipigon, Moose Factory), south-central Quebec (Lake Mistassini, Anticosti Island, north shore Gulf of St. Lawrence: Lac Allard, probably St. Augustin; recorded in two summers at Lourdes de Blanc Sablon), Labrador (Goose Bay, Makkovik), and Newfoundland (throughout) south to southern British Columbia (including Queen Charlotte and Vancouver islands), Alberta (but very locally in the southeast), southwestern and south-central Saskatchewan (Cypress Hills, Nipawin), southern Manitoba, southern Ontario (Wasaga Beach, Erindale, Kemptville), southern Quebec (Aylmer, Hatley, Gaspé Peninsula, Magdalen Islands), New Brunswick, Prince Edward Island, and Nova Scotia.

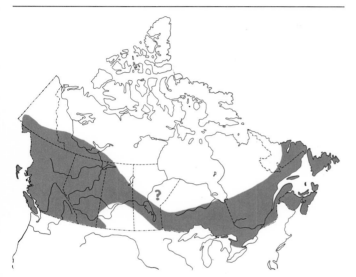

Breeding Distribution of Red-breasted Nuthatch

Casual north to northern Manitoba (Churchill) and central-eastern James Bay (Paint Hills Islands).

Winters mostly within breeding range, but many individuals move somewhat farther south in irregular numbers.

PYGMY NUTHATCH
La Petite Sittelle. *Sitta pygmaea* Vigors
Plate 48. L. 3.7 to 4.5 in.

Top of head greyish brown; on nape usually a vague area of whitish; rest of upper parts mostly bluish grey; two central tail feathers bluish grey with basal half white, rest of tail feathers blackish with considerable white toward tips; under parts and cheeks (to below eye), pale buffy; the flanks more or less bluish grey.

Measurements. *Adult male:* wing, 59.5–64.1 (62.2); tail, 30–35 (31.9); exposed culmen, 12.9–14.4 (13.9); tarsus, 14–15 (14.5). *Adult female:* wing, 58.7–65 (61.5) mm.

Field Marks. Our smallest nuthatch. A western species distinguished from our other nuthatches by its greyish brown crown. At closer range a whitish area on the nape is

often discernible. *Voice:* Utterly unlike our other two nuthatches, a very high-pitched, not nasal *te-dee, te-dee*, more like certain notes of the Goldfinch than a nuthatch's; various cheeping notes. Members of the flocks call frequently.

Habitat. Mainly open ponderosa pine woodlands.

Nesting. In a cavity in a dead tree, usually excavated by the nuthatches themselves, but sometimes in an old woodpecker hole. *Eggs,* most often 6 to 8; white flecked with reddish browns.

Breeding Distribution of Pygmy Nuthatch

Range. Resident in the mountains from southern British Columbia, western Montana, and southwestern South Dakota south to northern Baja California, Arizona, and the central plateau of Mexico south to Morelos and Puebla.

Range in Canada. Permanent resident in southern interior British Columbia (Okanagan Valley, Grand Forks, Newgate). Casual on Vancouver Island (near Comox, October 1931).

Subspecies. *Sitta pygmaea melanotis* van Rossem.

Family **Certhiidae** – Creepers

Number of Species in North America 1; in Canada 1

Most species of creepers are found in the Old World. The one North American species forages on the trunks of trees, advancing up the bark by jerky hitches. It has a stiff, slender, graduated tail, the feather tips of which are sharply pointed. The toenails are relatively large, curved, and sharp, that of the hind toe as long as the toe itself. Its food is mainly insects.

BROWN CREEPER
Le Grimpereau brun. *Certhia familiaris* Linnaeus
Plate 49. L. 5 to 5.75 in.

Bill slender, downcurved, sharp-pointed. Tail rather longish, graduated, the feathers stiffened and sharp-pointed. *Adults*

283

PLATE 59

(sexes similar): Upper parts, deep brown streaked with greyish white, becoming tawny on rump and upper tail coverts; wings mainly dark brown with a patch of pale buff across middle of primaries and secondaries; outer webs of tail feathers pale brown, inner webs dusky; sides of head brown with whitish eyebrow line; under parts white, the flanks and under tail coverts tinged buffy.

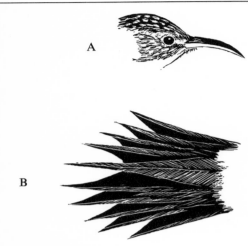

Fig. 63 Brown Creeper
(A) head   (B) tail

Measurements (*C. f. americana*). *Adult male:* wing, 62.4–67.6 (65.0); tail, 49–67.3 (60.6); exposed culmen, 13.3–15.9 (14.4); tarsus, 14.5–15 (14.8). *Adult female:* wing, 61.6–66.5 (63.3) mm.

Field Marks. A small bird with brown white-streaked upper parts, usually seen creeping up a tree trunk with longish tail pressed against the bark. When it reaches the top of a tree, it flies to the bottom of another, the wings showing a pale buffy patch in flight. At close range the downcurved bill can be seen. *Voice:* At all seasons a very high-pitched *seep*, the pitch similar to that of Golden-crowned Kinglet's *seet seet seet* but only one syllable, more prolonged, and less emphatic. Song, heard in spring, a short wiry warbler-like song: usually about three high-pitched rolling warbles preceded by a slightly longer, shriller note. It is similar to one of the songs of the Blackburnian Warbler.

Habitat. Primarily mature woodland either coniferous or deciduous but forages, especially in winter, in various situations including shade trees in residential areas and has even been seen on the wall of a tall building in the heart of a large city.

Nesting. Usually the nest is under a piece of loose bark of a tree but is reported occasionally in a natural cavity or old woodpecker hole. When built under loose bark, the nest is a crescent-shaped structure of twigs, bark shreds, moss, spider webs, and feathers. *Eggs*, 4 to 8, usually 5 or 6; white, sparsely marked with dots of reddish brown.

Range. Widely distributed in the Northern Hemisphere of both the New and Old Worlds. In North America from southeastern Alaska east to Newfoundland and south through the western mountains and through Mexico to

1 Palm Warbler
  (nominate race),
  (a) male in breeding
      plumage
  (b) young male in
      autumn

2 Prairie Warbler, male in
  breeding plumage

3 Wilson's Warbler,
  (a) adult male
  (b) female

4 Yellow-breasted Chat

5 Hooded Warbler,
  (a) adult female
  (b) adult male

6 Ovenbird

7 Louisiana Waterthrush

8 Northern Waterthrush

284

1a

1b

2

3a

3b

4

5a

5b

6

7

8

Crosby/62

1a 1b 2 3a 3b 3c 4 5a 5b 6a 6b 7a 7b 7c

Crosby '62

PLATE 60

1 Connecticut Warbler,
  (a) male in breeding
      plumage
  (b) autumn immature

2 MacGillivray's Warbler,
  male in breeding
  plumage

3 Mourning Warbler,
  (a) male in breeding
      plumage
  (b) female in breeding
      plumage
  (c) autumn immature

4 Kentucky Warbler, male
  in breeding plumage

5 Common Yellowthroat,
  (a) male in breeding
      plumage
  (b) female

6 Canada Warbler,
  (a) male in breeding
      plumage
  (b) autumn immature

7 American Redstart,
  (a) adult male
  (b) first-spring
      immature male
  (c) adult female

Breeding Distribution of Brown Creeper

Nicaragua; in eastern United States to southern Wisconsin and Massachusetts and in the Appalachians to eastern Tennessee and western North Carolina.

Range in Canada. Breeds in British Columbia (Queen Charlotte Islands, Stikine River, Dease Lake, Tetana Lake, Indianpoint Lake southward, including Vancouver Island), central and southwestern Alberta (Athabasca, Glenevis, Lac la Nonne, Pigeon Lake, Jasper, Banff), central Saskatchewan (Flotten Lake, Big River, Nipawin; probably Kazan Lake), central and southern Manitoba (The Pas, High Portage, Otter Falls), central and southern Ontario (Favourable Lake, Lake Nipigon, Kapuskasing, Lake Abitibi, probably north to southern James Bay; south to Middlesex, Welland, and Essex counties), southern Quebec (Lake Mistassini, Moisie Bay, Natashquan, Anticosti Island southward), Newfoundland, New Brunswick, Prince Edward Island, and Nova Scotia.

Summer sight records for southern Yukon (Dezadeash Lake, Tagish Lake).

Winters mainly within breeding range with some withdrawal probably from higher latitudes. Some move south to and through southern Alberta and southern Saskatchewan (areas in which it is not known to breed).

Subspecies. (1) *Certhia familiaris americana* Bonaparte: e. Canada w. to Man. (2) *C. f. montana* Ridgway, less buffy, with purer whites and average slightly larger size than *americana*: Sask., Alta., interior B.C. (east of Cascade and Coast ranges). (3) *C. f. occidentalis* Ridgway, brownest of the races: coasts and coastal islands of B.C.

Family **Cinclidae**–Dippers

Number of Species in North America 1; in Canada 1

Compactly built aquatic birds that dive and swim well, can walk on water bottom, but have unwebbed toes. Plumage dense; bill straight, short, laterally compressed; tail square or slightly rounded; wings short.

285

AMERICAN DIPPER

Le Cincle américain. *Cinclus mexicanus* Swainson
Plate 49. L. 7 to 8.5 in.

Bill laterally compressed (deeper than wide), tail short, plumage compact and dense. Whole body slaty grey, the head and neck tinged with brown, top of head darkest; narrow white mark on upper and lower eyelids.

Measurements. *Adult male:* wing, 83.1–94.6 (91.1); tail, 42.5–52 (49.1); exposed culmen, 18.5–20.1 (18.9); tarsus, 27.5–31 (29.1). *Adult female:* wing, 83.3–93.9 (87.4) mm.

Field Marks. Unmistakable. A chunky short-tailed all-grey bird, smaller than a robin, found about western mountain streams. When standing, it has a habit of rapidly raising and lowering its body by bending the legs; hence the name 'dipper.' Feeds in and under water at all seasons. Flight is buzzy, usually follows the stream, not far above the water; shows no distinctive markings in wings or tail. *Voice:* A clear melodious song is given at all seasons and in all kinds of weather. Alarm note *tzeet,* often repeated.

Habitat. Mountain streams at various elevations up to timberline; usually fast-moving streams that remain open in winter but sometimes mountain ponds or lakeshores.

Nesting. On a ledge, rocky niche, or crossbeam under a bridge or similar support along a stream, sometimes near or behind a waterfall. Nest, a bulky dome-shaped structure with an outer shell of moss and some grass. There is an entrance hole on the side leading to an inner bowl of grass. *Eggs,* usually 4 or 5; white. Incubation by the female only, about 16 days (H. W. Hann; G. J. Bakus).

Breeding Distribution of American Dipper

Range. From the Aleutian Islands and north-central Alaska, north-central Yukon, southwestern Alberta, north-central Montana, and southwestern South Dakota (Black Hills) south to southern California and through the highlands of Mexico and Central America to western Panama.

Range in Canada. Permanent resident along mountain streams in central and southern Yukon (Coal Creek, Ogilvie Range, Canyon Lake, Rose River. Perhaps north to

the Old Crow region where reported in April), throughout British Columbia (including Queen Charlotte and Vancouver islands), and southwestern Alberta (Jasper, Banff, and Waterton Lakes parks). Winters within most of breeding range including Yukon.

Casual in southern Mackenzie (Buffalo River near Great Slave Lake) and in southwestern Saskatchewan (Cypress Hills).

Subspecies. *Cinclus mexicanus unicolor* Bonaparte.

Family **Troglodytidae** – Wrens

Number of Species in North America 10; in Canada 8

Canadian species are small mostly brownish birds, often barred or spotted on wings, tail, and flanks. Wings short, rounded, with ten primaries. Bill slender, slightly downcurved. They are energetic and inquisitive, rarely still a moment. Usually they carry the tail high, often cocked up over the back. Habitat varies, depending on species, from woodland thickets to marshes, arid canyons, and rock piles. They feed mainly on insects.

HOUSE WREN

Le Troglodyte familier. *Troglodytes aedon* Vieillot
Plate 49. L. 4.5 to 5.3 in.

Tail short, bill slightly downcurved and pointed, as is typical of wrens. *Adults* (sexes similar): Upper parts dull greyish brown, the rump brighter and often with a few dusky bars and with concealed white spotting; tail brownish, narrowly barred with blackish; sides of head pale grey or buffy with a barely perceptible light eyebrow line; under parts dingy, more whitish medially, the breast tinged with buffy grey, the sides and flanks pale brown, more or less faintly barred with dusky.

Measurements (*T. a. parkmanii*). *Adult male:* wing, 49.6–53.3 (51.7); tail, 40–46.5 (43.6); exposed culmen, 12–13 (12.4); tarsus, 16.5–18.5 (17.5). *Adult female:* wing, 47.6–51.4 (49.9) mm.

Field Marks. Small size, brown upper parts, and stubby, often cocked-up tail indicate a wren. The House Wren is recognizable by its lack of definite markings, even the eyebrow stripe is usually invisible. Lacks the usually definite eyebrow stripe and heavily barred side of the smaller Winter Wren and has a less stubby tail; lacks the eyebrow line and white tail spots of Bewick's Wren. Usually habitat separates it from the two marsh wrens; but the Carolina, Cañon, and Rock wrens all have distinctive markings. *Voice:* Sings with great frequency, over long periods of the day, a rapid, chattering, rather unmusical, but pleasant song which rises in pitch at the beginning and falls off toward the end. It is easily recognized when heard a few times. Also a scolding, grating chatter.

Habitat. Deciduous thickets and shrubbery in various situations in woodland openings and open woodland, along prairie coulees and shelter belts, in mountain valleys, burntlands, and especially near human habitations on farmland and in residential areas. In breeding season a cavity suitable for nesting must be in the vicinity.

Nesting. In cavities of extremely varied types but usually a hole in a tree or a bird box. It is extremely adaptable, however, and has been known to use various objects—such as pockets in clothing, an old shoe, even a cow skull—left hanging on trees, posts, or in sheds; cavities in houses and in farm machinery or old automobiles, and behind the loose bark of a dead tree. The nest is a mass of twigs, and rubbish as cavity filler, with a lining of soft materials like hair or feathers. *Eggs,* most often 6 to 8; pinkish white, thickly dotted with reddish brown. Incubation 13 to 14 days (Baldwin and Kendeigh), chiefly by the female.

Range. Breeds from southern Canada south to northern Baja California, southeastern Arizona, northern Texas, northern Arkansas, Tennessee, and northern Georgia. Winters from the southern part of the breeding range south to southern Mexico, the Gulf coast, and southern Florida.

Breeding Distribution of House Wren

Range in Canada. Summer resident, breeding across southern, and in central-eastern, British Columbia (Comox, Kamloops, Okanagan Valley, Cranbrook; also Peace River parklands. Recorded in spring at Clearwater); northern, central, and southern Alberta (Keg River and Murdock Creek southward, but scarce in the southwestern mountainous corner); central and southern Saskatchewan (Dorintosh, Emma Lake, Nipawin, Cypress Hills, Regina. Recorded in summer at Kazan Lake); southern Manitoba (The Pas, Brandon, Lake St. Martin, Emerson, Sprague); central and southern Ontario (Malachi, Sioux Lookout, Lake Nipigon, Lake Abitibi southward); southwestern Quebec (Amos, Kenogami, Rivière du Loup, Hull, Montreal, Hatley); and New Brunswick (Fredericton, Grand Falls).

Scarce visitor to Nova Scotia (Gaspereau, Wolfville, Bridgetown, Sable Island) and Prince Edward Island, but breeding evidence lacking. Casual at Hazelton, B.C., and Churchill, Man.

Subspecies. (1) *Troglodytes aedon aedon* Vieillot: N.B., possibly extreme c.-s. Que. (Hatley). (2) *T. a. baldwini* Ober-

holser, allegedly somewhat darker and less rufescent than *aedon* but poorly marked: Que., s. Ont. (n. to Bigwood, Lake Nipissing, Algonquin Park). (3) *T. a. parkmanii* Audubon, paler and greyer, slightly larger than *baldwini*: B.C., Alta., Sask., Man., w. and c. Ont. (Malachi, Sioux Lookout, Lake Abitibi). Areas of intergradation of the respective races in the East require refinement because of lack of adequate material from critical areas.

Remarks. As its name implies, the House Wren often summers near houses where the grounds provide suitable bushy cover and a nesting cavity. A bird box with a seven-eighths-inch entrance is often accepted. House Wrens seem to be forever fussing and scolding over nothing at all. The male sings tirelessly from dawn to dusk, and in the lazy quiet of the noonday heat its energy is completely anomalous. Insects make up most of its menu.

As mentioned above, under 'Nesting,' this wren utilizes a wide variety of cavities for nesting. Sometimes these are unwisely chosen. Once a House Wren attempted for some days to fill the bottomless space between the roof and fly of the writer's tent. It deposited over a peck of sticks on the ground below, before it abandoned the attempt. Another pair nested in the door of an old discarded automobile. On sunny afternoons the heat within the metal door was intolerable, and the female remained inside for less than a minute at a time, emerging panting with open bill. Eventually the nest was abandoned, and the eggs were found to be baked hard.

Two broods, sometimes three, are raised in a season. House Wrens do not remain mated permanently or even throughout a whole year. In fact, they change mates between two nesting periods in the same season, and there is evidence that males sometimes practice polygamy.

WINTER WREN
Le Troglodyte des forêts
Troglodytes troglodytes (Linnaeus)
Plate 49. L. 4 to 4.5 in.

Smaller than the House Wren; tail much shorter. *Adults* (*T. t. hiemalis*): Upper parts reddish brown; the back, scapulars, and rump lightly barred with dusky; rump with concealed white spots; wings and tail mostly brown, barred with dusky; narrow buffy line over eye; under parts pale brownish, the abdomen and flanks darker and more or less barred and speckled with dusky. *Young* darker below, the eyebrow stripe indistinct.

Measurements (*T. t. hiemalis*). *Adult male:* wing, 45.5–49.1 (47.4); tail, 26.5–30.5 (29.5); exposed culmen, 11.3–12.3 (11.9); tarsus, 17.5–18.5 (18.1). *Adult female:* wing, 41.6–50 (45.0) mm.

Field Marks. A tiny wren, with reddish brown upper parts and very stubby cocked-up tail, usually seen in woodlands and woodland tangles. Smaller and darker than the House Wren and with distinctly barred flanks, usually an eyebrow line (but often not perceptible in young), and shorter tail. Has a habit of bobbing. *Voice:* Very different from that of the House Wren. Song an amazing performance for such a small bird, a sustained (up to eight or nine seconds), loud, and extremely varied procession of rapid notes, occasionally interspersed with a trill or a slight pause, after which the song goes on again, the notes tumbling over one another. Alarm note, a double *kip-kip* (but often only one *kip*), suggests a little the Song Sparrow's *chimp* (which is usually single) but is sharper.

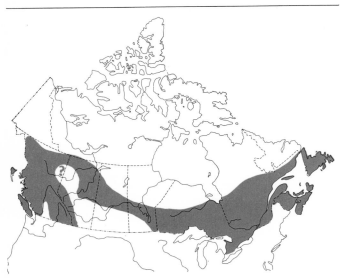

Breeding Distribution of Winter Wren

Habitat. In the nesting season mostly maturer coniferous woodland, typically in shadowy moist forests where the floor is strewn with brushy tangles and fallen trees, especially along streams and lakes; also brush and slashing in smaller forest openings. Forages in the low forest stratum, but much of the singing is done also in the tops of tall conifers. In migration both coniferous and deciduous woodlands are frequented, especially those with brush-strewn floors.

Nesting. Very often in a cavity in the earthy roots of an upturned tree, in and under old stumps and brush piles, in mossy banks and in other less common situations. The nest is rather bulky and is made of twigs, moss, and grasses with an entrance on the side leading to the interior, which is lined with feathers or fur. *Eggs*, most often 5 or 6; white, dotted usually sparingly with reddish brown.

Range. Northern Hemisphere of both the New and Old Worlds. In North America from the Aleutians and southeastern Alaska eastward to Newfoundland, and south to central California, central Idaho, the Great Lakes, western and central Massachusetts, and in the Appalachians to northern Georgia. Also in Iceland and much of Eurasia. In winter retreats from the colder more northern parts of its range in Canada.

Range in Canada. Breeds in British Columbia (commonly on the coast and coastal islands and north to Stikine River and Dease Lake, perhaps to Haines Road near the Alaska border; locally in the interior: Driftwood River, Likely, Okanagan Landing, Rocher Déboulé, Revelstoke National Park, probably Tupper Creek; apparently absent from much of the drier more sparsely wooded southern parts), northern and northwestern Alberta (south to Athabasca and in the

mountains: Jasper, Banff, Waterton Lakes parks), central Saskatchewan (probably Big River; Amyot and Crean lakes), Manitoba (Overflowing River, Hillside Beach), central and southern Ontario (Favourable Lake, Moose Factory; Middlesex, Waterloo, and Prince Edward counties), southern Quebec (Lake Mistassini, Lac Ste. Anne, Natashquan, St. Augustin, Belles Amours Bay, Anticosti Island; Aylmer, Montreal, Percé, Magdalen Islands), southern Labrador (L'Anse au Loup), Newfoundland, New Brunswick, Prince Edward Island, and Nova Scotia.

Winters in small numbers in British Columbia, southern Ontario, southwestern Quebec, New Brunswick, Nova Scotia, and rarely Newfoundland.

Recorded in summer in southern Yukon (Sheldon Lake, August 1944) and in southern Mackenzie (upper Buffalo River).

Subspecies. (1) *Troglodytes troglodytes hiemalis* Vieillot: c.-e. B.C. (Peace R. parklands) and Alta. except the Rocky Mts.) eastward through Sask., Man., Ont., Que., Nfld., N.B., P.E.I., and N.S. (2) *T. t. pacificus* Baird, darker with less distinctly barred upper parts: B.C. (except Peace R. parklands) and the mts. of sw. Alta.

BEWICK'S WREN
Le Troglodyte de Bewick. *Thryomanes bewickii* (Audubon) Plate 49. L. 5 to 5.5 in.

Adults: Upper parts brown, with a conspicuous whitish line over eye; flight feathers with more or less dusky barring; central two tail feathers brown barred with dusky, outer ones blackish brown, their outer web with white markings and broadly tipped with greyish white; under parts greyish white, the sides and flanks tinged with brown, under tail coverts barred with blackish.

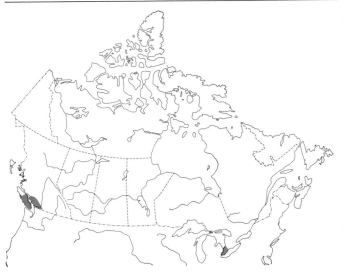

Breeding Distribution of Bewick's Wren

Measurements (*T. b. calophonus*). *Adult male:* wing, 51.5–56.5 (54.2); tail, 51–57 (52.7); exposed culmen, 14.6–17.2 (15.9); tarsus, 19.5–20.5 (20.1). *Adult female:* wing, 48.8–52.1 (50.9) mm.

Field Marks. Its conspicuous whitish eyebrow streak distinguishes it from the House Wren. Its *less reddish* brown upper parts, greyish (no buffy or rusty wash) breast and belly, and slenderer build separate it from the Carolina Wren. When the white edge of the tail can be seen, this distinguishes it from both. Its tail is noticeably longer too. *Voice:* Song is variable and far-carrying, often a little like that of a Song Sparrow. Also has a buzzing scold note.

Habitat. Thickets and brushy places in farming country, urban areas, or open woods.

Nesting. In various kinds of cavities about the habitations of man, including bird boxes. Also in old woodpecker holes, in knotholes in fallen trees, and even in dense brush piles. Sticks, leaves, straw, and other debris are used as nest cavity fillers, and this is lined with feathers or similar soft material.

Range. Southwestern British Columbia, central Washington, southern Utah, southern Nebraska, southern Michigan, extreme southern Ontario, central Pennsylvania, and Virginia, south to southern Baja California and southern Mexico (Oaxaca) and to northern parts of the Gulf states.

Range in Canada. Permanent resident in southwestern British Columbia (Victoria, Comox, Vancouver, Chilliwack, Howe Sound) and in extreme southern Ontario (Point Pelee; recorded in summer north to York and Grey counties. A recent arrival in Ontario, first recorded in 1898; first nest found 1950).

Subspecies. (1) *Thryomanes bewickii calophonus* Oberholser: sw. B.C. (2) *T. b. altus* Aldrich: s. Ont.

CAROLINA WREN

Le Troglodyte de Caroline
Thryothorus ludovicianus (Latham)
Plate 49. L. 5.2 to 6 in.

Adults: Upper parts reddish brown, with broad whitish eyebrow stripe, rump with concealed white spots; wings and tail, duller brown than back and barred with dusky; under parts mostly buffy, palest on throat (whitish), darkest on breast, sides, and flanks; under tail coverts barred with black.

Measurements. *Adult male:* wing, 54.5–64 (60.4); tail, 45.5–55.5 (50.6); exposed culmen, 15–18 (16.6); tarsus, 20–22.5 (21.5). *Adult female:* wing, 55–59.5 (56.9) mm (Ridgway).

Field Marks. A large reddish-brown wren with a conspicuous whitish eyebrow stripe and buffy under parts, especially the flanks and breast. *Song:* A loud rich whistled *tea-kéttle, tea-kéttle, tea-kéttle.* It sings in all seasons.

Habitat. Thickets and tangles in open woodland, often along streams, either in the country or in residential areas.

Nesting. In various kinds of cavities and crannies either in woodlands or about human habitations. Nest is of twigs, leaves, moss, bark fibres and is lined with softer materials such as feathers, hair, fine rootlets, and fine grass. *Eggs,* usually 4 to 6; white or buff, usually heavily spotted with browns. Incubation said to be 12 to 14 days (Bent), chiefly by the female.

Range. Resident from southeastern Nebraska east to southeastern Massachusetts and south through central and

coastal Texas to northeastern Mexico, the Gulf coast, and southern Florida.

Range in Canada. Permanent resident in southern Ontario (breeding from Point Pelee to Toronto and Canton. Nesting was first recorded in Ontario in 1905 at Point Pelee). Rare non-breeding wanderer north to Ottawa. Casual in southwestern Quebec (Fort Chambly) and southern Manitoba (Delta, October 20, 1938; Winnipeg, August 31, 1925).

Breeding Distribution of Carolina Wren

Subspecies. *Thryothorus ludovicianus ludovicianus* (Latham).

LONG-BILLED MARSH WREN

Le Troglodyte des marais
Telmatodytes palustris (Wilson)
Plate 49. L. 4.1 to 5.5 in.

Adults: Top of head plain blackish brown; on back a triangular blackish-brown patch streaked with white; rest of upper parts mostly brown, the tail barred dusky; white stripe over eye; under parts whitish, the sides and flanks plain buffy brown, the breast often lightly tinged with same.

Measurements (*T. p. dissaëptus*). *Adult male:* wing, 49–55.8 (51.1); tail, 35.5–43 (40.5); exposed culmen, 14.1–15.5 (14.6); tarsus, 20.5–21.5 (21.3). *Adult female:* wing, 47.2–51.6 (49.1) mm.

Field Marks. Any wren deep in a wet cattail marsh is probably this one. Both species of marsh wrens show white streaks on the back. The Long-billed is larger, has no streaks on the dark crown, shows a *well-defined* white line over the eye, and occurs in wetter marshy places than the Short-billed. *Voice:* Song is rather low-pitched but vigorous, bubbly, and staccato.

Habitat. Cattail, tule, and bulrush shallow-water marshes.

Nesting. In cattail, tule, and bulrush marshes. The nest is a largish ball of marsh vegetation with side entrance and is attached to upright marsh plants. The exterior is of long, coarse vegetation, and the inner lining is of soft materials such as cattail down and feathers. In addition to the nest used to house the eggs and young, which is built by the female, there are also several incomplete extra nests built by the male. The males of most wrens make such dummy nests, the function of which is not satisfactorily known. *Eggs*, most frequently 5 or 6, are dull brown (thus different from other wrens), finely dotted or spotted with darker browns. Incubation 13 days (W. A. Welter), by the female.

Range. Breeds from southern Canada south to northern Baja California, central New Mexico, the Gulf coast (Texas to Florida) and to central Florida on the Atlantic Coast.

Breeding Distribution of Long-billed Marsh Wren

Range in Canada. Breeds in suitable marshes in central and southern British Columbia (Vanderhoof region, Kleena Kleene, Duncan, Vancouver, Okanagan Valley, Columbia River), Alberta (Lake Athabasca southward to Red Deer and locally at Lake Newell. Not known in the mountains of the southwest), central Saskatchewan (Kazan Lake, Emma Lake, Nipawin, Devil's Lake, Regina), southern Manitoba (Riding Mountain, Lake St. Martin, Whitemouth), western Ontario (Indian Bay, Wabigoon, Sibley Park), southern Ontario (north at least to Killaloe, Lake Doré, and Ottawa; probably Manitoulin Island and Lake Nipissing), southwestern Quebec (Buckingham, Montreal, Magog, Sorel), and southern New Brunswick (Midgic).

Winters in southern British Columbia; rarely in southern Ontario (Point Pelee). Scarce migrant or casual visitant in Nova Scotia (Port Joli Harbour, Wallace, Wolfville).

Subspecies. (1) *Telmatodytes palustris dissaëptus* (Bangs): Breeds in s. Ont., sw. Que., and N.B. (2) *T. p. iliacus* Ridgway (paler and more brownish than *dissaëptus*): w. Ont. (Indian Bay) and Man. (3) *T. p. laingi* Harper (much paler and buffier than *iliacus*): Alta. (east of the Rockies), Sask. (4) *T. p. plesius* (Oberholser) (much less rufescent than *laingi*): c. and s. interior B.C. (5) *T. p. paludicola* (Baird), compared with *plesius*, darker and less greyish: sw. B.C. (Duncan, Vancouver, Huntingdon).

Also (6) *T. p. palustris* (Wilson) of the U.S. coast (Rhode I. to Virginia) is a casual visitant to N.S. (Port Joli Harbour), and (7) *T. p. waynei* Dingle and Sprunt, of the U.S. coast

(se. Virginia and N. Carolina) is accidental in N.B. (Grand Manan, Fairville).

SHORT-BILLED MARSH WREN
Le Troglodyte à bec court
Cistothorus platensis (Latham)
Plate 49. L. 4 to 4.5 in.

A very small wren with streaks on top of head and on back. *Adults:* Upper parts brown streaked with blackish and white; rump, upper tail coverts, and tail, barred with dusky; sides of head buffy with usually a faint narrow dusky line through eye and without any *distinct* light eyebrow stripe; under parts white with buffy wash across breast, and on sides, flanks, and under tail coverts.

Measurements. *Adult male:* wing, 43.4–46.2 (44.6); tail, 32.5–41 (37.9); exposed culmen, 10.3–11.6 (10.9); tarsus, 15.5–17 (16.3). *Adult female:* wing, 41.5–45.1 (43.5) mm.

Field Marks. The streaked back makes it one of the marsh wrens. Short-billed, compared with Long-billed, has top of head streaked (instead of plain blackish brown) and a scarcely visible buffy eyebrow stripe (Long-billed has a well-marked white one). Habitat often helps to distinguish the two; the Short-billed inhabits marsh grass rather than cattails. *Voice:* Song, an unmusical effort, begins with two or more dry *tsips* (like the sound produced by hitting two small stones together), followed by rapid unmusical notes on a descending scale and often a little trill at the end.

Habitat. Moist grass and sedge marshes, bogs, and damp meadows, often with a scattering of low bushes and often bordering willows or alders. It does not ordinarily inhabit cattails.

Nesting. In grassy marshes. Nest, a ball of grass well hidden in the upright grass or sedge to which it is attached and with an entrance at the side. Usually several dummy nests are made in the vicinity. *Eggs*, 4 to 8, usually 7; white. Incubation 12 to 14 days (L. H. Walkinshaw).

Range. Breeds from southeastern Saskatchewan east to eastern New Brunswick and south to Arkansas and south-

Breeding Distribution of Short-billed Marsh Wren

290

eastern Virginia; also from southern Mexico south through Central America and south to southern South America.

Range in Canada. Breeds in southeastern Saskatchewan (Nipawin, Quill lakes, Yorkton District), southern Manitoba (The Pas, Norway House, Aweme, Lake St. Martin, Sprague), western Ontario (Indian Bay, Wabigoon, Kenora, Thunder Bay region), southern Ontario (north to Sault Ste. Marie, Lake Nipissing, Ottawa), extreme southwestern Quebec (Perkins Mills, Lanoraie bog, Hatley, Sorel, Quebec), and southern New Brunswick (Midgic).

Scarce straggler to Alberta (Camrose, September 19, 1927. Also there are a few sight records.)

Subspecies. *Cistothorus platensis stellaris* (Naumann).

CAÑON WREN
Le Troglodyte des cañons
Catherpes mexicanus (Swainson)
L. 5.2 to 5.7 in.

Bill relatively long and slender. *Adults:* Top of head, nape, and upper back greyish brown changing to chestnut on lower back and rump, the upper parts dotted with black and white; tail rusty, narrowly barred with black; throat and upper breast white, rest of under parts chestnut, barred or dotted with black and flecked with white.

Measurements. *Adult male:* wing, 56.5–61.5 (59.7); tail, 51–54 (52.4); exposed culmen, 19–22.5 (20.5); tarsus, 17.5–18.5 (18.1). *Adult female:* wing, 55–60.5 (57.2) mm (Ridgway).

Field Marks. In Canada to be expected only in interior southern British Columbia. The plain white throat and upper breast contrasting with chestnut abdomen make it easy to identify. *Voice:* Song is an impressive whistle on a descending scale varying in speed and duration: *dée-ah dée-ah dée-ah dah-dah-dah.* Also *check.*

Habitat. Canyon walls (especially along water), cliff faces, and rockslides.

Nesting. In crevices of rocks or caves. *Eggs,* usually 5 or 6; white with sparse dots of reddish brown.

Range. Resident from interior southern British Columbia, northern Idaho, southeastern Montana, and southwestern South Dakota south through western United States and Mexico to the Isthmus of Tehuantepec and southern Baja California.

Range in Canada. Very local permanent resident in southern interior British Columbia (southern Okanagan Valley from Osoyoos north to Penticton, perhaps to Naramata).

Subspecies. *Catherpes mexicanus conspersus* Ridgway.

ROCK WREN
Le Troglodyte des rochers. *Salpinctes obsoletus* (Say)
Plate 49. L. 5.2 to 6.2 in.

Adults: Upper parts greyish brown or brownish grey, finely speckled with black and whitish; rump cinnamon; tail with two central feathers greyish brown barred with dusky, the others broadly tipped with cinnamon-buff and crossed by a subterminal band of black; under parts whitish tinged with pinkish buff on sides and flanks, throat and upper breast more or less finely streaked with dusky. *Young:* Similar to adults but upper parts only faintly dotted with black (white flecks lacking); under parts without streaking of any kind.

Measurements. *Adult male:* wing, 65.3–73.7 (70.3); tail, 49–55 (51.9); exposed culmen, 16.2–19 (17.1); tarsus, 20–22 (21.2). *Adult female:* wing, 66.4–69.3 (68.2) mm.

Field Marks. A large pale greyish brown wren of rocky places in the West (*see* Habitat). Spread tail shows buffy tips and subterminal black bar on all but two middle feathers. Adults show dusky throat streaks (absent in young) on otherwise plain whitish under parts (*see* Cañon Wren, which also inhabits rocky places). *Voice:* Song is variable but with many couplets, often a contralto *tra-lee tra-lee tra-lee tra-lee;* also frequent trills.

Habitat. Rocky outcrops, broken cliff faces, talus slopes, canyons, even hard earth banks, often in dry hot situations in mountains and on the western plains.

Nesting. In crevices and crannies in and among rocks (*see* Habitat). Entrance to nest is often paved with small flat stones. Nest is made of grass, weeds, and rootlets; lined with fine grass, hair, and feathers. *Eggs,* 4 to 8, usually 5 or 6; white sparingly fine-spotted with reddish browns.

Range. Breeds from interior southern British Columbia, southern Alberta, southern Saskatchewan, and northwestern North Dakota south to southern Baja California and through the highlands and deserts of Mexico and Central America to Costa Rica. Winters from Oregon, Montana, and Wyoming southward.

Breeding Distribution of Rock Wren

Range in Canada. Summer resident, breeding in southern interior British Columbia (Cache Creek, Kamloops, Okanagan Valley, Elko; species has been recorded without evidence of breeding north to Hanceville and Indianpoint Lake); southern Alberta (Jasper, Frank, Red Deer River, Milk River), and southern Saskatchewan (Cypress Hills, Pilot Butte).

In migration west rarely to Vancouver Island (Victoria, Comox).

There are three extraordinary but convincing summer sight records: near Stanton, northwestern Mackenzie (E. O. Höhn); Fort Chipewyan, northern Alberta (Francis Harper); and Churchill, Manitoba (J. A. Crosby and Eva Beckett).

Subspecies. *Salpinctes obsoletus obsoletus* (Say).

Family **Mimidae** – Mockingbirds and Thrashers

Number of Species in North America 11; in Canada 4

This family, which is restricted to the Western Hemisphere, is in many ways intermediate between the wrens and the thrushes. Compared with wrens, thrashers are larger, have longer tails, and possess rictal bristles. They have longer tails than thrushes, somewhat downcurved bills, and scutellate tarsi. They are delightful singers, and several species are famous for their ability as mimics.

NORTHERN MOCKINGBIRD

Le Moqueur polyglotte. *Mimus polyglottos* (Linnaeus)
Plate 50. L. 9 to 11 in.

Adult male: Upper parts brownish grey; wings and tail blackish slate edged with greyish; greater and middle wing coverts tipped white, forming two white wing bars; conspicuous patch of white at base of primaries; tail with three outermost feathers mainly white; under parts pale grey; legs and bill blackish; eye pale yellowish.

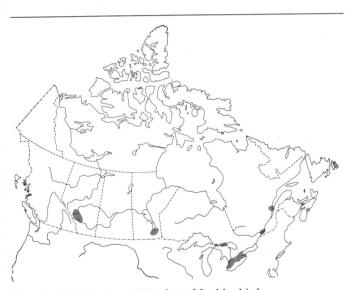

Breeding Distribution of Northern Mockingbird

Measurements. *Adult male:* wing, 106–120 (111.4); tail, 110–134 (119.9); exposed culmen, 17–18.5 (17.9); tarsus, 29.5–34 (32.5). *Adult female:* wing, 100–111.5 (104.8) mm (Ridgway).

Field Marks. A slender, long-tailed bird, grey above, greyish white below; with two white wing bars, a white patch in the wings (conspicuous in flight), and mainly white outer tail feathers. The Shrike is similar but has a black face

292

mask. Townsend's Solitaire, of the West, also is similar but has a whitish eye-ring, dark grey under parts (not much paler than upper parts), and usually much buff in the wing patch. *Voice:* The Mockingbird's song is long, loud, usually very melodious, but includes various harsh sounds and imitations of other bird songs. A distinctive feature is that a phrase is often repeated *three* or more times before a new one is taken up (Brown Thrasher frequently uses paired phrases).

Habitat. Shrubbery and tangles, hedgerows, various kinds of ornamental shrubbery about buildings.

Nesting. Usually between 4 and 20 feet up in a shrub, tree, or vine. Nest is rather bulky, a loosely woven but durable cup of twigs, moss, bark strips, grass, leaves, and trash, lined with rootlets and dried grass. *Eggs,* usually 4 or 5; pale bluish or greenish blotched and spotted with browns. Incubation approximately 12 days, by the female (Amelia Laskey).

Range. Resident from northern and north-central United States and parts of southern Canada (very locally), south to southern Mexico (Isthmus of Tehuantepec), Jamaica, and the Virgin Islands.

Range in Canada. Very local permanent resident, spreading northward into Canada slowly and recently. It is known to have nested in southern Alberta (Didsbury), southern Ontario (Amherstburg, Toronto, Manitoulin Island), southwestern Quebec (Como, Tadoussac), Nova Scotia (Halifax, probably Debert), Newfoundland (St. John's), and probably Manitoba (Delta: juvenal with natal down adhering to head and nape).

Rare or casual in southern British Columbia (Duncan, Springhouse, Wells Gray Park), Saskatchewan (Cypress Hills region, Regina), New Brunswick (Grand Manan, Fredericton), and Prince Edward Island (Deroche Pond, Souris); also the northern Gulf of St. Lawrence region (Seven Islands, Anticosti Island, Bonaventure Island), central and northern Ontario (Port Arthur, Fort William, Moosonee). Accidental in southern Keewatin (McConnell River: June 20, 1960, specimen).

Subspecies. (1) *Mimus polyglottos polyglottos* (Linnaeus): Breeding birds of e. Canada west through Man.; the Duncan, B.C., specimen has been referred to this race but has not been seen by the writer. (2) *Mimus polyglottos leucopterus* (Vigors) averages slightly larger with relatively shorter tail, upper parts slightly paler grey, more buffy above and below, white in wings a little more extensive: Sask. to B.C. presumably, but no western breeding material is available for examination.

CATBIRD

Le Moqueur-chat. *Dumetella carolinensis* (Linnaeus)
Plate 50. L. 8.4 to 9.4 in.

Mostly dull slate grey, slightly paler underneath; top of head blackish; under tail coverts mostly chestnut; tail blackish.

Measurements. *Adult male:* wing, 88–96.1 (91.6); tail, 90–101.5 (96.1); exposed culmen, 15.1–18 (16.8); tarsus, 26–28 (27.4). *Adult female:* 85.7–94.4 (89.7) mm.

Field Marks. A slate-grey bird of thickets, smaller and

longer-tailed than a Robin, and with blackish cap and chestnut under tail coverts. Frequently flicks its longish black tail. *Voice:* A complaining cat-like mewing is a common and unmistakable call; also an explosive stony *kak kak kak*. Song is sustained and made up of various phrases punctuated by short pauses, some phrases very musical, others discordant, and often including imitations of other bird songs and sounds. Although the song is similar to that of the Brown Thrasher and the Mockingbird, the Catbird does not ordinarily repeat its phrases; thus it is easy to distinguish Catbird songs from those of its two near relatives.

Breeding Distribution of Catbird

Habitat. Low, dense deciduous thickets (occasionally coniferous) along streams, ponds, roadsides, woodland edges, and prairie coulees; also commonly in bushes and shrubbery of gardens.

Nesting. In thick shrubbery, usually between 3 and 8 feet above ground. The nest, rather bulky, is made of twigs, weed stems, grass, and leaves with a neat inner cup of fine rootlets and shreds of bark. *Eggs*, usually 3 to 5; glossy deep greenish blue, unmarked. Incubation probably 12 to 13 days.

Range. Southern Canada (interior British Columbia east to Cape Breton Island) south to eastern Oregon, central Arizona, Texas, central parts of the Gulf states, and southern Florida. Winters mainly from southeastern United States and eastern Mexico through Central America to Panama and on islands in the Caribbean Sea.

Range in Canada. Summer resident, breeding in southern British Columbia (Bella Coola, Huntingdon, Lillooet, Williams Lake, Cranbrook. Breeding unknown on Vancouver Island), central and southern Alberta (north at least to Athabasca region; recorded in summer without breeding evidence to Lesser Slave Lake), central and southern Saskatchewan (north at least to Meadow Lake and Nipawin), southern Manitoba (Overflowing River, Oak Lake, Lake St. Martin, Sprague), south-central and southern Ontario (north to about Shoal Lake, Kenora, Sault Ste. Marie, Lake Nipissing), southwestern Quebec (Blue Sea Lake, Montreal, Baldwin Mills, Quebec, Ile aux Coudres, Rivière du Loup),

New Brunswick (scarce in northern parts), and Nova Scotia (including rarely Cape Breton Island).

Casual on Vancouver Island (Comox); Arvida and Seven Islands, Quebec.

BROWN THRASHER
Le Moqueur roux. *Toxostoma rufum* (Linnaeus)
Plate 50. L. 10.5 to 12 in.

Upper parts reddish brown; two white wing bars (buffy in autumn); under parts buffy white (palest on throat and abdomen), the breast, sides, and flanks heavily streaked with dark brown; eye yellow.

Measurements (*T. r. rufum*). *Adult male:* wing, 98.1–110.4 (103.6); tail, 119.5–138.5 (127.6); exposed culmen, 23.8–27.6 (25.9); tarsus, 33–35 (34.1). *Adult female:* wing, 100.4–105.5 (102.7) mm.

Field Marks. Slightly larger and much longer-tailed than a Robin. Its bright reddish-brown upper parts and heavily streaked under parts perhaps suggest a thrush, but the Brown Thrasher's long tail, yellow eye, conspicuous white wing bars, and larger size should eliminate confusion. *Voice:* Song is loud and musical and is made up of a long procession of phrases punctuated by slight pauses. Many of the phrases are repeated and are thus given in pairs: *Drop it—drop it; cover it up—cover it up; pull it up—pull it up.* The paired phrases are an easy way to distinguish the song from that of the Catbird, which is otherwise similar. Also a powerful throaty *chip*.

Habitat. Deciduous thickets, bushy fields, woodland edges, and young second growth.

Breeding Distribution of Brown Thrasher

Nesting. In thickets and shrubbery, especially thorny types; sometimes on the ground. Nest is rather loosely constructed of twigs, sticks, weed stems, and strips of bark, and is lined with rootlets. *Eggs*, usually 4 or 5; pale bluish white, rather uniformly covered with small brown spots. Incubation 11 to 14 days (W. G. Erwin), by both sexes.

Range. Breeds from southern Canada (southeastern

293

Alberta east to southwestern Quebec) and southwestern Maine south to eastern Colorado, northern and eastern Texas, the Gulf states, and southern Florida. Most individuals withdraw from the northern part of the range for the winter.

Range in Canada. Summer resident, breeding in southeastern Alberta (Hardisty, Calgary, Medicine Hat, Milk River. Species reported north to Cold Lake), southern Saskatchewan (Prince Albert, Cypress Hills, Regina), southern Manitoba (Dauphin, Brandon, Shoal Lake, Winnipeg, Sprague), western Ontario (Emo, Kenora), southern Ontario (north to about Bigwood and Lake Nipissing; species reported north to Gogama), and southwestern Quebec (Aylmer, Montreal, probably Blue Sea Lake; recorded in the breeding season in the Lake St. John basin). Winters rarely in southern Ontario (Point Pelee, Toronto), casually elsewhere in Canada.

Casual in eastern Gaspé Peninsula (Sandy Lake) and on lower Moisie River (Specimen: June 15, 1952), in New Brunswick (Chatham, St. Andrews, Grand Manan), and Nova Scotia (Brier Island; also sight records by several competent observers). Accidental in southeastern Hudson Bay (Belcher Islands), and Newfoundland (Cappahayden).

Subspecies. (1) *Toxostoma rufum rufum* (Linnaeus); s. Ont., s. Que. (2) *T. r. longicauda* (Baird), averaging very slightly larger: w. Ont. (Kenora), s. Man., s. Sask., se. Alta.

SAGE THRASHER
Le Moqueur des armoises
Oreoscoptes montanus (Townsend)
Plate 50. L. 8 to 9 in.

Bill rather thrush-like; tail short for a thrasher. Upper parts greyish brown, the crown and back faintly streaked with dusky shade; a poorly defined pale eyebrow line; two narrow pale wing bars; outer tail feathers tipped white; under parts buffy white, more or less heavily streaked with brown; eye yellow.

Measurements. *Adult male:* wing, 95–103 (98.7); tail, 87–95 (90.8); exposed culmen, 14.5–17.5 (16.4); tarsus, 28.5–31.5 (30.4). *Adult female:* wing, 94–100 (96.2) mm (Ridgway).

Field Marks. A bird of semi-arid sagebrush plains, slightly smaller than a Robin, with brownish grey upper parts, heavily streaked under parts, white tips to the outer tail feathers, two narrow white wing bars. *Voice:* Song is sustained (has been timed up to 2½ minutes), energetic, and pleasing. It contains the usual thrasher repetition of phrases, but, unlike the song of the Brown Thrasher, there are no well-marked pauses between phrases. There is a little suggestion of the Catbird, but without the pauses.

Habitat. Dry sagebrush plains and thickets on arid hillsides.

Nesting. Usually in sagebrush or other bushes, sometimes on the ground. Nest is rather bulky, often partly arched over. It is made of coarse twigs and lined with grass and rootlets. *Eggs*, 4 or 5; greenish blue, spotted and blotched with reddish browns.

Range. Breeds from southern interior British Columbia, central Montana, and southwestern Saskatchewan south in the interior to central-southern California, northern New Mexico, northwestern Texas, and western Oklahoma. Winters from southern parts of the breeding range south to southern Baja California and in northern mainland Mexico.

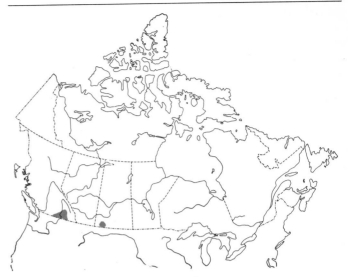

Breeding Distribution of Sage Thrasher

Range in Canada. Very local summer resident, breeding in southern British Columbia (Osoyoos, White Lake, Similkameen Valley near International Boundary) and southwestern Saskatchewan (Eastend). Rare straggler to Alberta (Calgary, Walsh, Orion).

Family **Turdidae** – Thrushes, Solitaires, and Bluebirds

Number of Species in North America 18; in Canada 13

The thrushes are a very large family, widely distributed in most parts of the world. There is a good deal of variation in the appearance of the many species, but the young in juvenal plumage (and the adults of many species as well) have spotted breasts and undivided tarsi, and the outermost of the ten primaries is small or spurious in most species. The family contains some of the world's finest singers including the Nightingale of Europe and the Hermit Thrush of North America.

AMERICAN ROBIN
Le Merle américain. *Turdus migratorius* Linnaeus
Plate 52. L. 9 to 10.8 in.

Adult male (T. m. migratorius): Top of head, sides of head, and nape, black but with small white areas about the eye; rest of upper parts mostly dark grey, becoming blackish on wings and tail; outer tail feathers tipped white; throat streaked black and white; breast, sides, flanks, and upper abdomen, cinnamon-rufous; lower abdomen and under tail coverts white; eye brown; bill yellow. *Adult female:* Similar to adult male but paler; black of head duller and more restricted; breast paler, many feathers edged with white. *Juvenal:* Somewhat like adults but feathers of back with white or buffy mesial streaks and black tips; wing coverts with white or buffy streaks; throat white; breast, upper abdomen, sides, and flanks, reddish brown (often mainly whitish on breast) conspicuously spotted with black.

Measurements (*T. m. migratorius*). *Adult male:* wing, 126–133 (129.9); tail, 95–105 (101.2); exposed culmen, 19–22.1 (20.9); tarsus, 32–35 (34.1). *Adult female:* wing, 120–132.5 (126.9) mm.

Field Marks. Familiar to almost everyone. Size, brick-red breast, dark grey back, and yellow bill are a combination that distinguishes adults. Young have black spots on the breast (showing relationship to the thrush family) and pale streaks on the back, but they otherwise look much like the adults that usually accompany them. *Voice:* Song a procession of two- or three-syllable phrases that suggest *cheer-up* or *cheerily* with variations in pitch and often continued for long periods through spring and summer. There also are various alarm and scold notes as well as a very high-pitched lisping whistle of alarm.

Habitat. About farms, woodlots and thickets provide cover and nesting places, and open fields furnish ideal foraging; and in residential areas ornamental trees and shrubbery, together with grassy lawns, provide equally well for the Robin's needs. It also favours open and broken woodlands, second growth of cut-over forest areas and burntlands, forest openings and edges. In general it is much less common in heavily forested areas than in areas inhabited by man, and doubtless the Robin is one of the minority of species that have benefited by the coming of the white man.

Nesting. Usually in trees or bushes (either coniferous or deciduous), most frequently 5 to 15 feet up but often much higher and occasionally on the ground. Often in recesses and nooks of building exteriors, sometimes inside buildings. Nest, a substantial structure of twigs, weed stems, and grass with base and walls of mud, lined with fine grasses and similar soft material. *Eggs*, usually 4 (in Newfoundland usually 3); plain blue. Incubation usually 12 to 13 days, by the female.

Range. Breeds from the limit of trees in Alaska and across Canada south to southern Mexico and the Gulf coast of the United States. Winters from southern Canada southward to Guatemala and southern Florida.

Range in Canada. Breeds from the limit of trees, or slightly north of it, in northern Yukon (Old Crow, Lapierre House), northern Mackenzie (Kittagazuit, Fort Anderson, Coppermine, Thelon River), southern Keewatin (Windy River, Angikuni Lake), northern Manitoba (Churchill), northern Ontario (Fort Severn), northern Quebec (Fort Chimo, Indian House Lake; probably Gregory Lake and George River), Labrador, and Newfoundland south through southern Canada from Vancouver Island, B.C., to Cape Breton Island, N.S.

Winters in southwestern and southern British Columbia, southern Ontario (north rarely to Fort Frances, Port Arthur, and Ottawa), southwestern Quebec (Montreal, Quebec; north rarely to Arvida and Pointe des Monts),

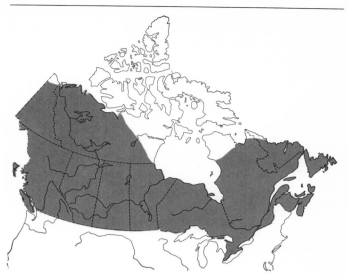

Breeding Distribution of American Robin

New Brunswick (Saint John, Fredericton), Prince Edward Island (Souris), Nova Scotia (Wolfville, Pictou), and southern Newfoundland (regularly on Avalon Peninsula); also rarely and precariously in southern Alberta, southern Saskatchewan (Regina), and southern Manitoba (Winnipeg).

Casual on Herschel Island, Yukon; and at Frobisher Bay, Baffin Island.

Subspecies. (1) *Turdus migratorius migratorius* Linnaeus: Yukon, Mack., Keewatin, n. and c. B.C. (Atlin, François Lake, Tupper Creek), n. and c. Alta., Sask. (except sw. corner), Man., Ont., s. Que. (Blue Sea Lake, Quebec, Lake St. John, Gaspé Pen.), N.B., P.E.I., N.S. (2) *T. m. nigrideus* Aldrich and Nutt, adult males with black of head and nape extending to upper back, averaging darker generally than *migratorius:* n. and c. Que. (south to Moar and Paul bays, Lake Mistassini, and the outer north shore of the Gulf of St. Lawrence), Lab., Nfld. (3) *T. m. propinquus* Ridgway, averaging paler and slightly larger than *migratorius*, white tip of outer tail feathers absent or much reduced: s. interior B.C. (Indianpoint Lake, Lillooet, Wardner), s. Alta. (Banff, Red Deer River), and sw. Sask. (Cypress Hills, possibly somewhat farther east but no material available for examination). (4) *T. m. caurinus* (Grinnell), darker and slightly smaller than *propinquus;* lacks decided white spots on tips of outer tail feathers: coastal B.C. (Queen Charlotte and Vancouver islands; Vancouver).

Remarks. The American Robin is probably familiar to more people in Canada than any other bird. Its vast distribution, its pleasing song and personality, and its fondness for the trees and lawns about our dwellings make it a bird that is not likely to be overlooked. It arrives in most parts of the country early in the spring when the first patches of bare ground are beginning to show through the snow, and it is unquestionably our favourite harbinger of spring.

Our robin was given its name by the early settlers who noted its reddish breast which reminded them of the famous Robin Redbreast of the Old World. However, our bird is very much larger, and aside from the colour of its breast it is not similar to the Old World bird.

The American Robin has a varied menu, but insects, worms, and fruits make up the bulk of it. Indeed its fondness for fruits occasionally gets it into trouble with growers of small cultivated fruits. On open grassy areas, such as lawns, it eagerly seeks earthworms.

FIELDFARE
La Grive litorne. *Turdus pilaris* Linnaeus
L. 9.5 to 10.5 in.

Head, neck, and rump, bluish grey; back mostly brown; tail blackish; throat and breast, buffy brown streaked with black; sides and flanks, heavily marked with blackish or blackish brown; rest of under parts white.

Status in Canada. Accidental. One record: Jens Munk Island, Foxe Basin, off Baffin Island, a rough skin found by Graham W. Rowley in possession of an Eskimo in 1939.

Range. Northern Eurasia (Scandinavia east to south-central Siberia). In 1937 a small colony became self-established in southern Greenland (Julianehaab District).

VARIED THRUSH
Le Merle à collier. *Ixoreus naevius* (Gmelin)
Plate 52. L. 9 to 10 in.

Adult male: Upper parts slate grey; side of face blackish; over eye and back to neck, an orange-brown line; tail with small white tip to outermost feathers; two wing bars, much edging of flight feathers, and much of the under parts, orange-brown; a broad black band across breast; spread wing shows a white band across inner webs of flight feathers.
Adult female: Similar in pattern to adult male, but much paler and duller, upper parts brownish olive, breast band similar to back or paler.

Measurements (*I. n. meruloides*). *Adult male:* wing, 122–129 (125.8); tail, 86–94.5 (90.1); exposed culmen, 19.8–21 (20.6); tarsus, 29.5–32.5 (31.7). *Adult female:* wing, 120.5–130 (125.6) mm.

Field Marks. Resembles American Robin in size, shape, and orange-brown breast, but broad black band (grey in female) across breast, orange-buff line above and behind eye, orange-brown wing bars and wing patches readily distinguish Varied Thrush. *Voice:* Song is an eerie resonant whistle in various pitches, often in a minor key, and is like the echo of a bell, prolonged at the same pitch and dying away.

Habitat. In breeding season, forests and woodland from coastal to subalpine, shady damp forests preferred. Forages in lower stratum, especially on the forest floor.

Nesting. Usually 5 to 15 feet above ground in a tree. Nest is made of twigs, grass, weed stems, and moss, more or less reinforced with mud and lined with grass. *Eggs,* usually 3 or 4; blue (somewhat paler than the Robin's), sparsely marked with small spots of brown.

Range. Breeds from north-central Alaska, northern Yukon, and northwestern Mackenzie south to north-western California, northern Idaho, and northwestern Montana. Winters from southern British Columbia to northern Baja California.

Range in Canada. Breeds in Yukon (north to Old Crow), northwestern and western Mackenzie (Mackenzie Delta, Fort Norman, Fort Franklin, Wrigley), British Columbia (throughout, including Queen Charlotte and Vancouver islands), and southwestern Alberta (Jasper, Banff, and Waterton Lakes parks).

Winters in western and southern British Columbia (Departure Bay, Vancouver, Queen Charlotte Islands, Okanagan Landing).

In migration it wanders occasionally east of the mountains in Alberta (Belvedere, Edmonton, Castor, Rosebud, Camrose, Sullivan Lake, Red Deer). Casual in southern Saskatchewan (Burnham, September 17, 1949; sight record Regina, September 9, 1958). Accidental in Quebec (Manicouagan, August 28, 1890), New Brunswick (Stanley: March 25, 1960—had wintered there), and Ontario (Maple and Norland).

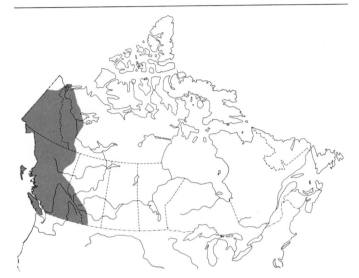

Breeding Distribution of Varied Thrush

Subspecies. (1) *Ixoreus naevius naevius* (Gmelin): coastal islands and west slope of the Coast and Cascade ranges in B.C. (2) *I. n. meruloides* (Swainson), adult female greyer and paler than *naevius*: Mack., Yukon, n. interior B.C. (Like Dickinson, 1953, I find little consistent difference between coastal and southern interior B.C. material. However, the limited Mackenzie material I examined is more greyish above, and I am reluctant to draw conclusions at present on the validity of *meruloides*.)

WOOD THRUSH
La Grive des bois. *Hylocichla mustelina* (Gmelin)
Plate 51. L. 7.5 to 8.5 in.

A large brown-backed thrush. Upper parts mostly brown, the crown and hind-neck russet or cinnamon brown, the upper tail coverts and tail tinged with greyish olive; eye-ring white; ear coverts streaked with white and dusky; under parts mostly white, with buffy suffusion across breast, and with large black or dark brown spots on breast, sides, and flanks.

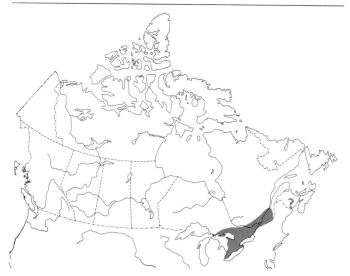

Breeding Distribution of Wood Thrush

Measurements. *Adult male:* wing, 104.5–113 (109.0); tail, 67–77.5 (71.5); exposed culmen, 16–19 (17.1); tarsus, 30–33 (31.6). *Adult female:* wing, 103–109.5 (105.6) mm.

Field Marks. A large brown-backed thrush with back of neck *more tawny than the back*, the heavy round spotting of under parts *extending to sides and flanks. Voice:* A clear unhurried beautiful song, often with bell-like qualities and typically in three syllables, the first high, the second lower, the third a high trill, thus *cedar-lee*. Shorter than the songs of our other *Hylocichla* thrushes. Alarm note *quirt* or a sharp *pit pit*.

Habitat. The lower stratum of maturer deciduous woodland.

Nesting. In a tree or sapling, usually 5 to 15 feet up. Nest is of grasses, weed stems, and trash, with a middle layer of mud, a few dead leaves in the bottom, and a lining of rootlets. *Eggs*, greenish blue, slightly smaller than those of a Robin and a bit more pointed. Incubation 13 to 14 days, by the female (Weaver *in* Bent).

Range. Breeds from southeastern South Dakota, central Wisconsin, southern Ontario, southwestern Quebec, southwestern Maine and probably southwestern New Brunswick south to southeastern Texas, the Gulf coast of United States, and northern Florida. Winters mainly from northern Mexico to Panama.

Range in Canada. Breeds in southern Ontario (north to Iron Bridge, Lake Nipissing, Eau Claire), southwestern Quebec (Gatineau Park, Lac Tremblant, Château-Richer, Cap Tourmente), and probably southwestern New Brunswick (probably St. Stephen, St. Andrews, Woodstock). Casual in Nova Scotia (West Middle Sable, October 30, 1963).

HERMIT THRUSH

La Grive solitaire. *Hylocichla guttata* (Pallas)
Plate 51. L. 6.3 to 7.6 in.

Reddish brown tail contrasts with olive-brown back, distinguishing it from similar thrushes. *Adults (H. g. faxoni):*

Upper parts, olive brown becoming reddish brown on rump and tail; eye-ring whitish; under parts whitish with pale buff suffusion across breast, the breast with large wedge-shaped spots of blackish brown; sides of throat with narrow streaks of blackish brown; sides and flanks pale brownish grey.

Measurements (*H. g. faxoni*). *Adult male:* wing, 89.3–95 (92.2); tail, 67–73.5 (69.6); exposed culmen, 13–15.2 (14.1); tarsus, 28–31 (29.8). *Adult female:* wing, 82–96 (87.6) mm.

Field Marks. A brown-backed thrush with a well-spotted breast and a distinctive *reddish tail*. Often slowly raises the tail after alighting or when disturbed, and frequently flicks wings. Beginners might confuse it with the Fox Sparrow because of the red tail, but the Fox Sparrow has a conical stubby bill. *Voice:* Many consider it the finest singer in North America. A clear, ethereal, bell-like song made up of phrases with considerable pauses between. The phrases are similar in form but in various pitches. The lower phrases are extremely beautiful. The first note of each phrase is lower and longer than the rest of the notes. Also a soft *chuck* and several other calls.

Habitat. Mixed deciduous-coniferous or pure coniferous woodlands varying from wooded bogs and swamps to dry sandy and sparse jack pine; second growth of burntlands and logged-over clearings with standing dead trees which are favoured as singing perches. Inhabits forest floor and lower stratum of woodlands.

Nesting. Usually on the ground; rarely in a low brush or sapling. Nest usually composed of twigs, bark fibre, ferns, and moss, lined with rootlets and pine needles. *Eggs*, 3 to 6, usually 3 or 4; plain greenish blue (rarely with a few spots). Incubation 12 days (Gross *in* Bent), mainly, if not entirely, by the female.

Breeding Distribution of Hermit Thrush

Range. Breeds from central Alaska eastward across much of forested Canada to Newfoundland and south to southern California, northern New Mexico, central Minnesota, central Pennsylvania, and western Maryland. Winters from southern parts of the breeding range south to Baja California, Guatemala, and southern Florida.

297

Range in Canada. Breeds from southern Yukon (Little Salmon River, Donjek River, Haines Junction, Nisutlin River), southern Mackenzie (Fort Simpson, Hay River, Buffalo River, Soulier Lake), northern Saskatchewan (Lake Athabasca), northern Manitoba (Herchmer, Bird), northern Ontario (Favourable Lake, Lake Attawapiskat), central Quebec (Moar Bay; Lake Mistassini; 90 miles south of Knob Lake), southern Labrador (Goose Bay, Cartwright), and Newfoundland south to southern British Columbia (including coastal islands), central and southwestern Alberta (Lac la Nonne, Athabasca, Jasper, Banff, Waterton Lakes parks; perhaps rarely Red Deer), central Saskatchewan (Prince Albert, Nipawin), southern Manitoba (Garland, Hillside Beach, Whitemouth), southern Ontario (Mount Forest; Madoc; Junetown in Leeds County), southern Quebec (Kingsmere, Montreal, Hatley, Magdalen Islands), and throughout New Brunswick, Prince Edward Island, and Nova Scotia.

Winters in small numbers in south coastal British Columbia (Comox, Victoria) and occasionally in southern Ontario (Toronto, Hamilton, Queenston).

Accidental in Southampton Island, Northwest Territories, October 4, 1929.

Subspecies. Much disagreement exists among authors concerning the number of valid subspecies and the allocation of names. Until adequate material is available to clarify the matter, the A.O.U. Check-list (1957) may be followed. (1) *Hylocichla guttata guttata* (Pallas): sw. Yukon south to s.-c. interior B.C. (but not ne. part). (2) *Hylocichla guttata nanus* (Audubon): coast and coastal islands of B.C. (3) *Hylocichla guttata auduboni* (Baird): s. interior B.C. (4) *Hylocichla guttata faxoni* Bangs and Penard: c. Yukon, ne. B.C., Mack., Alta., Sask., Man., Ont., c. and s. Que., N.B., P.E.I., N.S. (5) *Hylocichla guttata crymophila* Burleigh and Peters: Nfld.

Remarks. The Hermit Thrush is considered by many to be the finest singer of all North American birds. Its ethereal music, with its clear bell-like tones, is especially effective in the quiet of a north woods on a summer evening.

SWAINSON'S THRUSH (Olive-backed Thrush)

La Grive à dos olive. *Hylocichla ustulata* (Nuttall)
Plate 51. L. 6.4 to 7.7 in.

Adults: Upper parts olive brown or olive grey; eye-ring and line from eye to base of bill, buff; cheeks, buffy streaked with dusky; breast and sides of throat spotted with dusky; sides suffused with olive brown; rest of under parts white.

Measurements (*H. u. swainsoni*). *Adult male:* wing, 94.1–101.8 (99.1); tail, 65.5–76 (70.4); exposed culmen, 12.7–15 (13.5); tarsus, 27–30 (28.4). *Adult female:* wing, 89.5–98.4 (93.8) mm.

Field Marks. Breast is much more heavily spotted than that of Veery; lacks reddish-brown tail of Hermit Thrush; buffy eye-ring and face distinguish it from the Gray-cheeked Thrush. *Voice:* Song less impressive than that of the Hermit or Wood Thrush, but still very musical and pleasing. Each phrase rises higher than the preceding one, rolling upward. Calls include a *wick* and a high-pitched *queep*.

Habitat. Deciduous tall shrubbery; also coniferous woods, often with an admixture of thickets of alder, willow, or other tall shrubs; and second growth of burntlands and logged-over areas.

Nesting. Usually in a low evergreen tree or bush, sometimes a deciduous one. Nest of various materials including twigs, grass, weed stems, leaves, moss, and lichens. *Eggs,* usually 3 or 4; blue, rather evenly marked with pale browns. Incubation period about 12 days, by the female.

Range. Breeds from central Alaska eastward across forested Canada to Newfoundland and south to California, Colorado, southern Ontario, central New Hampshire, and Maine; farther south in the Appalachian Mountains. Winters from Mexico south to Peru, northern Paraguay, western Brazil, and British Guiana.

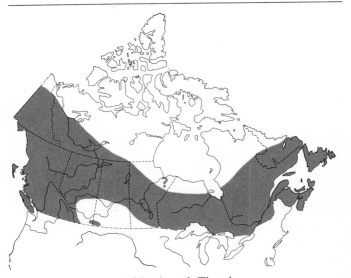

Breeding Distribution of Swainson's Thrush

Range in Canada. Breeds from northern Yukon (Old Crow, Lapierre House), western Mackenzie (Fort Norman, Fort Simpson, Fort Resolution), northern Saskatchewan (Lake Athabasca), central Manitoba (Thicket Portage, probably York Factory), northern Ontario, central Quebec (Fort George, Knob Lake region), southern Labrador (upper Hamilton River, Goose Bay, Cartwright), and Newfoundland south to southern British Columbia (including coastal islands), southern Alberta (but locally in south: Cypress Hills and through the Rocky Mountains), southwestern and central Saskatchewan (Cypress Hills, Nipawin), southern Manitoba (Riding Mountain, Whitemouth, Rennie), southern Ontario (southern Georgian Bay, Haliburton, Robindale, Cumberland), southern Quebec (Gatineau Park, Montreal, Magog, Gaspé Peninsula, Anticosti Island, Magdalen Islands), New Brunswick, Prince Edward Island, and Nova Scotia.

Accidental on Meighen Island, N.W.T.

Subspecies. (1) *Hylocichla ustulata swainsoni* (Tschudi): s.-c. and ne. Alta. (Lac la Nonne, Wood Buffalo Park), Sask., Man., Ont., Que., Lab., Nfld., N.B., P.E.I., N.S. (2) *H. u. incana* Godfrey (averages even greyer than *almae*): Yukon, w. Mack. (Fort Norman, Fort Simpson), n. B.C.

Dease Lake, Summit Lake on Alaska Highway), n.-c. Alta. (Grimshaw, Joussard). (3) *H. u. almae* Oberholser (averages somewhat greyer than *swainsoni*): s. and c. interior B.C. (4) *H. u. ustulata* (Nuttall), with brownish upper parts: coastal B.C.

GRAY-CHEEKED THRUSH

La Grive à joues grises. *Hylocichla minima* (Lafresnaye) Plate 51. L. 6.5 to 8 in.

Adults: Upper parts (including tail) uniform greyish olive (or greyish), eye-ring greyish white; cheek olive, narrowly streaked with greyish white; under parts mostly white, the breast faintly buffy and spotted with blackish, this spotting running narrowly up sides of throat; sides and flanks pale greyish olive.

Measurements (*H. m. aliciae*). *Adult male:* wing, 92.3–106.4 (100.9); tail, 65.5–73 (69.5); exposed culmen, 12.6–15 (14.1); tarsus, 29–32 (30.0). *Adult female:* wing, 95.5–105 (99.9) mm.

Field Marks. Distinguished from the Veery by heavy instead of very light breast spots and by much greyer (not tawny) general coloration; from Hermit Thrush by dull olive, instead of reddish tail; from Wood Thrush by uniform dark grey upper parts (no tawny on back of neck) and much less heavy and more restricted spotting of under parts; and from Swainson's Thrush by greyish (instead of buffy) eye-ring and cheeks. *Voice:* Song suggests that of the Veery but usually rises in pitch near the end. Alarm note *whee-u* suggesting a similar call of the Veery.

Habitat. In breeding season prefers coniferous woods, denser stands near treeline, dense stunted spruce on coastal islands and near timberline of mountains. In migration, various types of woodland and roadside shrubbery.

Nesting. Low in trees (up to 25 feet) or bushes or on the ground. *Eggs*, usually 3 to 5; greenish blue dotted (sometimes faintly) with browns. Incubation 13 to 14 days (G. J. Wallace) by the female; 12 days (J. K. Jehl and D. J. T. Hussell).

Range. Breeds from northeastern Siberia, northern Alaska, and from near treeline across Canada south to northwestern British Columbia, north-central Saskatchewan, southeastern New York, and northwestern Massachusetts. Winters from southern Mexico and the West Indies south to Peru, northwestern Brazil, and British Guiana.

Range in Canada. Breeds from northern Yukon (Old Crow), northern Mackenzie (Mackenzie Delta, Horton River, Bathurst Inlet), southwestern Keewatin (Angikuni Lake, Tha-Anne River), northern Quebec (Fort Chimo, George River), Labrador (Okak, Peter Lake, Nain, Cartwright), and Newfoundland south to northwestern British Columbia (Haines Road: Mile 85; recorded in the breeding season from Driftwood Mountains and Bulkley Lake east of Telegraph Creek), southern Mackenzie (Great Slave Lake; probably Hill Island Lake), northeastern Saskatchewan (Hasbala Lake), northern Manitoba (Sandhill Lake, Churchill, Herchmer, York Factory), northwestern Ontario (Fort Severn), central-western and southeastern Quebec

(Kinglet Lake; 90 miles south of Knob Lake; north shore of the Gulf of St. Lawrence westward at least to Natashquan; Shickshock Mountains; Percé; probably the Magdalen Islands), and Nova Scotia (Seal and Mud islands; probably French Mountain on Cape Breton Island).

Transient in all of extreme southern Canada west to western Alberta.

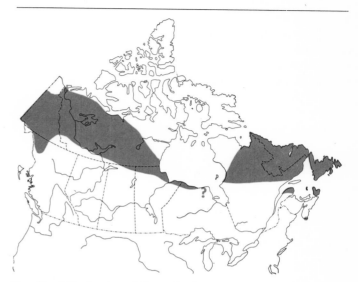

Breeding Distribution of Gray-cheeked Thrush

Subspecies. (1) *Hylocichla minima minima* (Lafresnaye): Nfld., Gaspé Pen. (2) *H. minima bicknelli* Ridgway (resembles *minima* in more brownish coloration but is smaller): N.S. (3) *H. m. aliciae* (Baird), more greyish or olivaceous than the two other subspecies, averages larger than *bicknelli*): all of the North American mainland west and north of the north shore of the Gulf of St. Lawrence. (*Note:* Racial affiliations of populations inhabiting the north shore of the Gulf of St. Lawrence, P.Q., are unknown.)

VEERY

La Grive fauve. *Hylocichla fuscescens* (Stephens) Plate 51. L. 6.5 to 7.7 in.

Decidedly tawny upper parts and very light and sparse spotting on breast distinguish it from other similar thrushes. *Adults:* Upper parts tawny brown; no obvious eye-ring; breast strongly suffused with buff and only lightly spotted with tawny brown, this spotting running up along sides of throat; sides and flanks are suffused with paler greyish brown; rest of under parts white.

Measurements (*H. f. fuscescens*). *Adult male:* wing, 98.5–104.6 (99.9); tail, 69.1–77.5 (73.7); exposed culmen, 12.4–14.6 (13.4); tarsus, 27–31.9 (29.2). *Adult female:* wing, 92.6–100.8 (96.5) mm.

Field Marks. The faintly and sparsely spotted breast and tawny upper parts distinguish it from other similar thrushes. Song, too, is easily recognized. *Voice:* Song a rolling *whée-u, whée-u, ré-a, ré-a* on a descending scale. Call *phew* or *whée-u*, downslurred.

Habitat. Deciduous or deciduous-coniferous woodland,

PLATE 61

especially where more open with an understory of deciduous shrubbery; second growth, willow or alder shrubbery along lakes, streams, and coulees.

Nesting. On or near the ground. Nest is of twigs, grass, weeds, and is lined with fine grass, dry leaves, rootlets, and hairs. *Eggs*, 3 to 5, usually 4; greenish blue. Incubation 11 to 12 days (O. Annan), by the female.

Range. Breeds from interior British Columbia east to Newfoundland and south to northeastern Arizona, northeastern South Dakota, southeastern Minnesota and in the Alleghenies south to Georgia and on the Atlantic Coast south to Washington, D.C. Winters from Central America south to Colombia and central and northeastern Brazil.

Breeding Distribution of Veery

Range in Canada. Summer resident, breeding in interior British Columbia (Kimsquit, Kleena Kleene, Lac la Hache, Williams Lake Indian Reserve No. 13, Okanagan Landing, Trail), central and southern Alberta (Edmonton, Athabasca, Waterton Lakes Park, Cypress Hills), central and southern Saskatchewan (Meadow Lake, Prince Albert, Nipawin, Cypress Hills, Moose Mountain), southern Manitoba (Swan River, Lake St. Martin, Hillside Beach southward), western Ontario (Malachi, Kenora, Sioux Lookout, Port Arthur, perhaps Rossport), southern Ontario (Sault Ste. Marie, Lake Nipissing, New Liskeard southward), southern Quebec (Dorval in central La Vérendrye Park, Lake St. John, Hatley, Quebec, Lac Trois Saumons, Anse St. Denis, Lac Baker, Lac Rimouski, Biencourt, Matapedia, Magdalen Islands), southwestern Newfoundland (Codroy and Humber river valleys), New Brunswick, and central and southern Nova Scotia (Annapolis Valley, Stewiake, Yarmouth). Reports of breeding on Anticosti Island and extreme eastern Gaspé Peninsula require confirmation.

Subspecies. (1) *Hylocichla fuscescens fuscescens* (Stephens): N.S., N.B., sw. Que. (but not Magdalen Is.), s. Ont. (intergrading with *salicicola* in northern part of its Ont. range, Rossport east to Lake Nipissing). (2) *H. f. salicicola* Ridgway (duller, less tawny, more olivaceous than *fuscescens*): B.C., Alta., Sask., Man., w. Ont. (east to Rossport, inter-

1 Western Tanager,
    (a) male in breeding
       plumage
    (b) female

2 Summer Tanager,
    (a) male in breeding
       plumage
    (b) female

3 Scarlet Tanager,
    (a) male in breeding
       plumage
    (b) female

4 Orchard Oriole,
    (a) male in breeding
       plumage
    (b) first-spring
       immature male
    (c) female

5 Baltimore Oriole,
    (a) male in breeding
       plumage
    (b) female

6 Bullock's Oriole,
    (a) male in breeding
       plumage
    (b) female

7 Eastern Meadowlark

8 Western Meadowlark

9 Bobolink,
    (a) male in breeding
       plumage
    (b) female

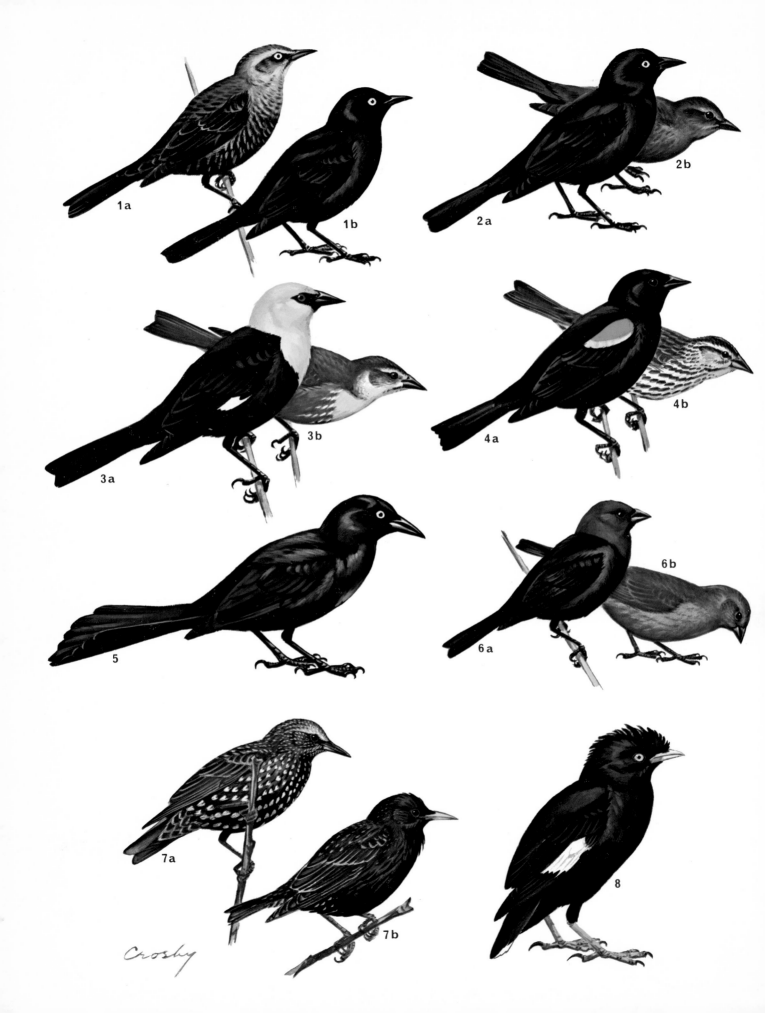

1a

1b

2a

2b

3a

3b

4a

4b

5

6a

6b

7a

7b

8

Crosby

grading in northern periphery of range east to Lake Nipissing with *fuscescens*). (3) *H. f. fuliginosa* Howe (a poorly-characterized race, browner than *salicicola*, darker than *fuscescens*, but many individuals are not separable): Nfld., Magdalen Is., P.Q.

EASTERN BLUEBIRD

Le Merle bleu à poitrine rouge. *Sialia sialis* (Linnaeus)
Plate 52. L. 6.5 to 7.7 in.

Adult male: Bright deep blue above, including sides of head and most of wings and tail; throat, breast, sides, and flanks, reddish brown; belly and under tail coverts, white. *Adult female:* Similar to adult male but very much duller above and below. *Juvenal:* Crown and back brownish grey, the back spotted with white; flight feathers and tail mostly blue but duller than the adults; under parts soiled white, streaked and spotted with brown.

Measurements. *Adult male:* wing, 93.7–101.9 (97.8); tail, 57–67 (62.8); exposed culmen, 12–14 (13.1); tarsus, 19–21 (20.0). *Adult female:* wing, 93.6–96.8 (94.9) mm.

Field Marks. The bright blue upper parts, combined with reddish brown breast, distinguish it from other eastern birds. Blue Jay and Indigo Bunting have much blue in the plumage but are otherwise very different. The Mountain Bluebird of the Prairies and western mountains has a blue breast. The Western Bluebird, of southern British Columbia, closely resembles the Eastern Bluebird, except that the adult male Western has an all-blue throat and the female a bluish grey one. *Voice:* Pleasant, low, short warbles.

Habitat. Open and sparse woods, woods edges, burntland with old standing trees, orchards, farmland; in the nesting season a suitable nesting cavity must be in the vicinity.

Nesting. In tree cavities, old woodpecker holes, and bird boxes at heights from 3 to 30 feet. Nest is of grass often with an admixture of leaves, twigs, rootlets, feathers, and hair. *Eggs,* 3 to 7, usually 4 to 6; pale blue, rarely white. Incubation period about 16 days (Amelia R. Laskey), the male assisting the female.

Breeding Distribution of Eastern Bluebird

Range. Breeds from southeastern Arizona and southern Canada (Saskatchewan east to Nova Scotia) south through Mexico to Nicaragua, the United States Gulf coast, and southern Florida. Winters mainly from north-central United States southward.

Range in Canada. Breeds in southern Saskatchewan (Cypress Hills, Moose Mountain, Regina; reports of breeding near Prince Albert require confirmation), southern Manitoba (Oak Lake, Riding Mountain, Lake St. Martin, Sprague), central and southern Ontario (north to about Malachi, Wabigoon, Sioux Lookout, Hearst, Lake Abitibi; probably north to Favourable Lake and near Moose Factory), southern Quebec (Blue Sea Lake, Montreal, Quebec, Lac Trois Saumons, Rivière du Loup, Godbout; recorded in summer, perhaps breeding, Senneterre, St. Félicien, Tadoussac, and on Gaspé Peninsula), New Brunswick, and Nova Scotia (locally: Loch Broom, Gaspereau; not known on Cape Breton Island). Rare visitor to Prince Edward Island (near Charlottetown), but evidence of breeding is wanting. Casual at Havre St. Pierre, Anticosti Island, and Knob Lake, Quebec.

Winters occasionally in southern Ontario (Point Pelee, Toronto, Port Hope).

Subspecies. *Sialia sialis sialis* (Linnaeus).

WESTERN BLUEBIRD
Le Merle bleu à dos marron. *Sialia mexicana* Swainson
Plate 52. L. 6.5 to 7.5 in.

Adult male: Upper parts bright blue (deeper than in Eastern Bluebird), sides of head and entire throat duller blue; often more or less chestnut on back and scapulars; breast, sides, and flanks, reddish brown; abdomen and under tail coverts,

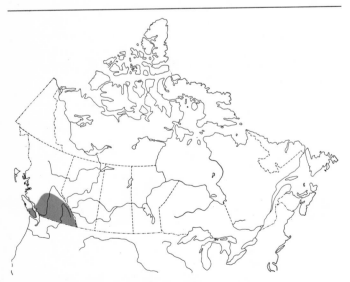

Breeding Distribution of Western Bluebird

pale bluish grey. *Adult female:* Similar to male but very much duller, the back often brownish but not chestnut; throat greyish with bluish tinge. *Juvenal:* Similar to that of Eastern Bluebird but blue of wings and tail deeper.

Measurements. *Adult male:* wing, 100.9–107.9 (104.5);

tail, 62–68 (65); exposed culmen, 12–14 (13.2); tarsus, 20–22.5 (20.8). *Adult female:* wing, 97–103.1 (100.5) mm.

Field Marks. A little larger than the House Sparrow. Similar to the Eastern Bluebird but with a blue throat in the male (sometimes chestnut on the back also can be discerned), a grey throat in the female. When reddish back patch is present, this is diagnostic. Its reddish brown breast and darker blue upper parts separate it from the Mountain Bluebird. Male Lazuli Bunting is similarly coloured but is smaller, with a stubby sparrow bill and two white wing bars which bluebirds never have.

Habitat. Sparse woodland, burntland, and logged areas where there are dead trees and stubs to provide nesting cavities and lookout posts; sometimes orchards.

Nesting. Nesting similar to Eastern Bluebird. *Eggs,* usually 4 to 6; pale blue.

Range. Southern British Columbia and central Montana south through the mountains to Baja California, Michoacan, Puebla, and Veracruz, southern Mexico.

Range in Canada. Breeds in southern British Columbia (Vancouver Island, Alta Lake, Huntingdon, Lac la Hache, Okanagan Valley, Fort Steele, Newgate).

Winters in small numbers in southern British Columbia (Victoria, Comox, Chilliwack, Okanagan Valley).

Subspecies. *Sialia mexicana occidentalis* Townsend.

MOUNTAIN BLUEBIRD
Le Merle bleu des montagnes
Sialia currucoides (Bechstein)
Plate 52. L. 6.5 to 7.75 in.

Adult male: Upper parts bright cerulean blue (paler than in Eastern or Western bluebird); sides of head, throat, breast, and sides, blue but duller and paler than on upper parts; abdomen and under tail coverts white. *Adult female:* Upper parts smoky grey, often tinged with blue; rump, tail, and much of wings, pale bluish; under parts pale brownish or buffy grey, becoming white on abdomen and under tail coverts. *Juvenal:* Similar to that of Eastern and Western bluebird, but distinguishable from both by paler blue on wings, tail, and rump.

Measurements. *Adult male:* wing, 108.8–120.2 (113.8); tail, 67.5–76.5 (71.9); exposed culmen, 12.2–15 (13.9); tarsus, 21.5–23 (22.3). *Adult female:* wing, 105.6–112.6 (109.8) mm.

Field Marks. Male, an all-blue bird a bit larger than a House Sparrow. The lack of any reddish brown on the breast distinguishes it from other male bluebirds. The adult female is greyish brown, but enough blue can usually be seen in wings, rump, and tail to distinguish it as a bluebird. The blue is paler than in other female bluebirds. Other birds with blue coloration are easily distinguishable: Blue and Steller's jays (conspicuous crests, much larger size), and Indigo Bunting (much smaller than a bluebird and with a stubby sparrow bill). The Mountain Bluebird has a habit of hovering frequently. *Voice:* a low *turr*. Song a short warble.

Habitat. Open country with well-spaced trees; woodland openings and edges; burntlands, lumbered areas; farmland.

Nesting. In natural cavities in trees, in abandoned woodpecker holes, on buildings, in bird boxes, or in rock crevices. *Eggs*, usually 5 or 6; pale blue, very rarely white.

Range. Breeds from central Alaska and western Canada south to California, Nevada, Arizona, southern New Mexico, Colorado, South Dakota (Black Hills), and northeastern North Dakota. Winters from southern British Columbia (rarely) and Montana south to Mexico and southern Texas.

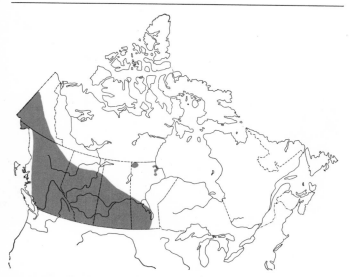

Breeding Distribution of Mountain Bluebird

Range in Canada. Breeds in southern Yukon (Dawson, Lapie River, Canyon), British Columbia (Atlin, Muncho Lake south through the interior; also on the south coast: Horseshoe Lake, Coquitlam), north-central and southern Alberta (Grimshaw and Fort McMurray southward), central and southern Saskatchewan (Kazan Lake, Nipawin southward), and Manitoba (Garland, Spruce Woods Forest Reserve; also in the extreme northern part: Kasmere Lake, *see* Mowat and Lawrie, 1955; and probably Churchill, *see* Taverner and Sutton, 1934).

Recorded in Mackenzie (Fort Resolution, Fort Franklin, Hawk Rapids on upper Back River). Casual on Queen Charlotte Islands, B.C.

Winters rarely or casually in southern British Columbia (Comox, Okanagan Landing).

WHEATEAR

Le Traquet motteux. *Oenanthe oenanthe* (Linnaeus)
Plate 51. L. 5.5 to 6 in.

Adult male: Upper parts grey, becoming white on forehead and abruptly white on upper tail coverts; wings mostly black; tail with middle two feathers blackish, the rest with basal two-thirds white and terminal third black; across face a black patch passing under eye and with a whitish line above; throat and breast buffy; rest of under parts white, more or less tinged buffy. *Adult female:* Similar to adult male but upper parts more brownish, no black patch across face. *Young (first autumn):* Similar to adult female but much browner above; under parts pinkish buff darkening to cinnamon buff on breast.

Measurements (*O. o. leucorhoa*). *Adult male:* wing, 100.5–106.5 (103.8); tail, 54.5–60.5 (58.3); exposed culmen, 13–15 (13.9); tarsus, 27–30.5 (28.9). *Adult female:* wing, 97–103.5 (99) mm (Ridgway).

Field Marks. A restless ground bird, which in all plumages shows a distinctive white rump patch and a black-and-white tail pattern (two centre feathers black, rest with basal two-thirds white, terminal third black). Adult male has black patch across face. Wheatears frequently bob, spread the tail, and move it up and down. *Voice:* A strong *chack-chack*. Song a short pleasant warble in which melodious notes are mixed with harsher ones.

Habitat. Open terrain. Stony tundra, shrub tundra, and other wastelands of the Arctic; rocky slopes, scree, and alpine meadows above timberline in the mountains.

Nesting. In crevices in rocks, cliffs, buildings, holes in the ground or under stones. Nest rather loosely made of grasses and sometimes moss; lined with grass, hair, feathers, and woolly material. *Eggs*, usually 5 to 7; pale blue. Incubation 13 to 14 days (Hantzsch).

Range. In North America breeds in eastern arctic Canada, Labrador, and Greenland; also in Alaska, Yukon, and western Mackenzie. In the Old World breeds in Iceland, Jan Mayen, Spitsbergen, the British Isles, northern Norway, Finland, northern Russia, and northern Siberia, south to northern Africa, Asia Minor, and central Asia. New World populations winter in the Old World.

Range in Canada. Breeds in Yukon (King Point, Old Crow, Ogilvie Mountains, Tepee Lake) and northwestern Mackenzie (Richardson Mountains on western edge of Mackenzie Delta); also in northeastern Canada from Ellesmere Island (near Slidre Fiord) south to White Island (Cape Frigid—N. G. Smith), northern Quebec (Erik Cove, Port Burwell), and along the coast of Labrador (south at least to Gready Island—L. M. Tuck). Has been recorded without evidence of breeding on Boothia Peninsula (Felix Harbour, May 2, 1830).

Breeding Distribution of Wheatear

Winters in the Old World, but occasional individuals occur in migration seasons in southern Ontario (Fort William, Albany River, Beaumarais, Chatham; sight records at Hainsville, Prescott, Manotick); southern Quebec (Godbout, lower Moisie River; sight records at Natashquan Anticosti Island).

Subspecies. (1) *Oenanthe oenanthe oenanthe* (Linnaeus): Yukon, sw. Mack. (2) *O. o. leucorhoa* (Gmelin) (averages larger, with more strongly buffy under parts in autumn plumage): e. Canada.

TOWNSEND'S SOLITAIRE
Le Solitaire de Townsend
Myadestes townsendi (Audubon)
Plate 51. L. 8 to 9.5 in.

Bill rather short, broad and flattened at base; tail rather long, its feathers somewhat tapered. *Adults:* Brownish grey above and below, but under parts decidedly paler; eye-ring dull white; wings with tawny patch (partly hidden by wing coverts); outermost two or three feathers of tail tipped white, the outer margin of outermost feathers white. *Young:* Wings (except coverts) and tail as in adults, but head and body feathers and wing coverts spotted with pale buff or whitish and margined with blackish.

Measurements. *Adult male:* wing, 109.1–119.7 (114.8); tail, 96.5–106.5 (100.8); exposed culmen, 11.2–13.0 (12.3); tarsus, 20.5–22 (21.3). *Adult female:* wing, 105.6–115.5 (112.1) mm.

Field Marks. A slim brownish-grey bird with short bill, longish tail, white eye-ring, and in flight a buffy wing patch and white outer edge of tail. Young have similar wings and tails to those of adults, but the head and body have pale spots. From female bluebirds, the Solitaire's longer tail and lack of any blue in wings or tail distinguish it. Its white eye-ring, buff wing patch, and darker grey under parts separate it from the Mockingbird. *Voice:* Song is sustained and delightful, parts suggesting that of the Purple Finch. A monotonous metallic *pink*.

Habitat. Open and broken forests, spaced trees, and burntlands on slopes and rougher mountain country.

Nesting. On or near the ground (often protected by an overhang for shelter or concealment); often in cutbanks along roads and trails; in cavities at the base of trees, under overhanging banks or tree roots (including roots of an upturned tree), and under rocks. *Eggs,* 3 to 5, usually 4; entirely different from those of other thrushes: dull white, more or less uniformly spotted and finely blotched with various browns; sometimes spots are restricted, forming a loose ring.

Range. Breeds from central-eastern Alaska, southern Yukon, southwestern Mackenzie, southwestern Alberta, and southwestern South Dakota south in the western mountains to southern California and northern Mexico (Durango). Winters at lower altitudes north to southern British Columbia.

Range in Canada. Breeds from southern Yukon (Dawson, Carcross, Lapie River; recorded in summer north to Bern Creek) and southwestern and central-western Mackenzie

(mouth of Nahanni River; probably Carcajou River near Canol Road—juvenal specimen August 6, 1958), south through British Columbia (mostly east of the coast: Chilkat Pass, Telegraph Creek, Nulki Lake, Chilliwack, Wardner) and in northwestern Alberta (mountains and foothills: Jasper, Banff, and Waterton Lakes parks; Gorge Creek).

Winters in southern British Columbia (Victoria, Okanagan Valley, Moyie Valley).

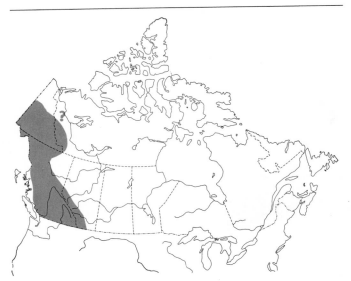

Breeding Distribution of Townsend's Solitaire

Wanders east of the breeding range in migration in Alberta (Clyde, Elk Island Park, Camrose, Sullivan Lake, Rosebud, Benyon, Brooks) and more rarely to Saskatchewan (Eastend, Burnham, Lake Johnstone, Regina, Yorkton, Nipawin; one wintered in Regina 1960–61). Casual in Manitoba (Stonewall). Accidental in Ontario (Point Pelee, March 8, 1962) and in New Brunswick (Woodstock, January 15 to April 6, 1952).

Subspecies. *Myadestes townsendi townsendi* (Audubon).

Family **Sylviidae**–Old World Warblers, Gnatcatchers, and Kinglets

Number of Species in North America 7; in Canada 4

A very large family, most species of which are confined to the Old World. It is represented in Canada by two kinglets and a gnatcatcher. The kinglets are tiny arboreal birds and, next to hummingbirds, our smallest species.

ARCTIC WARBLER
Le Pouillot boréal. *Phylloscopus borealis* (Blasius)
L. ca. 4.8 in.

Suggests a small vireo but bill tip sharp, never slightly hooked. Much duller than autumn Tennessee Warbler, decidedly less yellowish below, larger with decidedly heavier bill. *Adults:* Upper parts greyish olive; line over eye pale yellowish or whitish; very narrow whitish wing bar obscure in worn plumage); under parts plain whitish tinged with yellow, the sides and flanks tinged with greyish olive.

Status in Canada. Accidental on Prince Patrick Island (Mould Bay, July 21, 1949), N.W.T. The specimen, too large for the Alaska race *kennicotti*, is referred to *P. borealis borealis* (Blasius).

BLUE-GRAY GNATCATCHER

Le Gobe-mouches gris bleu. *Polioptila caerulea* (Linnaeus) Plate 53. L. 4 to 5 in.

Bill slender, tail rather long (nearly same length as wing), outermost primary very small. *Adult male:* Upper parts mainly greyish blue; across forehead a narrow line of black, this extending backward over eye; wings slaty, tertials margined whitish; tail mainly black, the outermost feather white, the next mainly white, and the third (from outside) tipped with white; sides of head, pale grey; under parts white, the breast and sides with a bluish grey wash. *Adult female:* Similar to adult male but upper parts less decidedly bluish and without the black lines on forehead and sides of crown.

Measurements. *Adult male:* wing, 49–54.5 (52.1); tail, 48–54 (50.3); exposed culmen, 9–11 (9.9); tarsus, 16.5–18 (17.2). *Adult female:* wing, 50–52 (50.9) mm.

Field Marks. A slender tiny bird with greyish blue upper parts, white eye-ring, longish black tail with white outer borders. Often cocks and flits tail. Common call, a high-pitched, thin complaining *chee*.

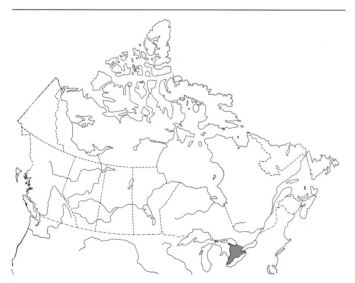

Breeding Distribution of Blue-gray Gnatcatcher

Habitat. Open mature woodland, tall shade trees, brushy thickets with scattered trees. Although it is found most often well up in mature trees, it may be found also in low thickets and small growth.

Nesting. Usually in tall trees, infrequently in a sapling, anywhere from 10 to 60 feet above ground but usually high. Nest is saddled on a limb or placed in the fork of a branch. It is compact and similar to a hummingbird's, being made of

various soft plant materials held together with spider web and ornamented on the outside with lichens. *Eggs*, usually 4 or 5; pale blue to whitish with small spots of different browns. Incubation about 13 days (Bent).

Range. Northern California, Utah, eastern Nebraska, southern Wisconsin, extreme southern Ontario, central-western New York, and southern New Jersey, south through Mexico to Guatemala, the Gulf coast of United States, and the Bahama Islands. Winters from southern United States southward.

Range in Canada. Breeds in southern Ontario (Tobermory: 12 miles south; London; Point Pelee; Turkey Point; Port Colborne).

Casual in migration east to Kingston and Ottawa, Ontario; New Brunswick (Grand Manan); and probably also southwestern Quebec (sight records only: Quebec City, Lennoxville).

Subspecies. *Polioptila caerulea caerulea* (Linnaeus).

GOLDEN-CROWNED KINGLET

Le Roitelet à couronne dorée. *Regulus satrapa* Lichtenstein Plate 53. L. 3.5 to 4 in.

A very small bird with fine-pointed bill. *Adult male:* Centre of crown orange with outer border yellow, this in turn bordered (on forehead and sides of crown) by black; line over eye dull white; back of neck, greyish changing to greenish olive on back (brightening on rump); wings and tail dusky, the feathers edged with yellowish; two whitish wing bars; under parts whitish tinged with buffy olive. *Adult female:* Similar to adult male, but centre of crown all yellow (no orange). *Young* for a short time after leaving nest lack the crown patch, texture of body plumage is looser, coloration is more brownish olive. White eyebrow line distinguishes them from Ruby-crowned Kinglet.

Measurements (*R. s. satrapa*). *Adult male:* wing, 54.3–58.8 (57.1); tail, 41.5–45 (43.3); exposed culmen, 6.3–8.5 (7.7); tarsus, 16.5–17.5 (17.2). *Adult female:* wing, 52.7–56 (54.8) mm.

Field Marks. Kinglets are tiny olive green and grey birds, smaller and shorter-tailed than warblers. Both species are very active in the tree branches and have a characteristic and frequent habit of flicking the wings. The yellow crown with black border and the white eyebrow stripe distinguish this species from the Ruby-crowned Kinglet. The voices of the two are very different. *Voice:* A call frequently given at all times of the year is a hurried high-pitched lisping *tsee-tsee-tsee;* also a single *tsee*, similar to the call of the Brown Creeper but less prolonged. Song very high-pitched, the first parts like the call-notes and ending in an unmusical twitter.

Habitat. Coniferous forests and groves, mixedwoods with a preponderance of conifers. Also in migration and winter, deciduous trees or bushes.

Nesting. Usually well up in a coniferous tree (but sometimes low). Nest of green mosses, lichens, strips of bark, rootlets; lined with feathers. Nest is spherical with the opening at the top. It is usually suspended or partly so from twigs but sometimes is placed on a limb. *Eggs*, 5 to 10, usually 8 or 9; whitish or creamy with pale brown dots or spots.

Range. In coniferous woodland from southeastern Alaska east across southern Canada to Newfoundland and south to southern California and Arizona (also the highlands of southern Mexico and Guatemala), central Minnesota, northern Michigan, southern Ontario, northern New York, southern Maine, and in the mountains south to Tennessee and western South Carolina. Winters north to southern Canada.

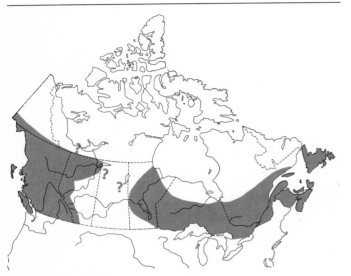

Breeding Distribution of Golden-crowned Kinglet

Range in Canada. Breeds in coniferous woodland in southern Yukon (probably Kathleen River), throughout British Columbia (including coastal islands), northern and southwestern Alberta (Mile 110 Mackenzie Highway, Wood Buffalo Park, Fort Chipewyan, Swan Hills, and the Rocky Mountains of the southwest), northern, central, and southeastern Manitoba (Churchill, Overflowing River, Duck Mountain, Julius), central and southern Ontario (Malachi, Lac Seul, Moose Factory, Lake Abitibi; south rarely to York County, formerly to London), southern Quebec (Lake Mistassini, Lac Méchant, Gaspé Peninsula, Anticosti Island southward, perhaps east to Little Mecatina River), Newfoundland, New Brunswick, Prince Edward Island, and Nova Scotia,

Winters in southern and coastal British Columbia, southern Alberta, southern Saskatchewan (Nipawin), southern Manitoba, southern Ontario, southern Quebec, the Maritime Provinces, and Newfoundland.

Subspecies. (1) *Regulus satrapa satrapa* Lichtenstein: e. Canada and west to ne. Alta. (2) *R. s. amoenus* van Rossem (upper parts brighter and less greyish than in *satrapa*): interior B.C. and mts. of Alta. (3) *R. s. olivaceus* Baird (darker, more brownish above than *amoenus*, under parts average more dusky): coastal B.C., west of the Cascades.

Remarks. It seems surprising to find these feathered mites happily wintering in Canada when many larger species have gone south to warmer climates. In dim coniferous trees that shelter them from the wind, they flit about so actively that it is often hard to see them clearly. They feed almost entirely on insects (including the spruce bud moth) and spiders. They glean insects, their eggs and hidden larvae, from branches and bark and also are skilful flycatchers.

RUBY-CROWNED KINGLET
Le Roitelet à couronne rubis. *Regulus calendula* (Linnaeus) Plate 53. L. 3.7 to 4.5 in.

Similar in form and colour to Golden-crowned Kinglet but differs in head markings. *Adult male:* Top of head with a patch of vermilion; rest of upper parts greyish olive, brightening on rump and edges of flight feathers (flight feathers dusky); two whitish wing bars; edges of tertials whitish; sides of head plain greyish, except whitish eye-ring; under parts plain pale-buffy grey, the flanks more yellowish. *Adult female:* Similar to adult male but without crown patch. *Young* (for a short time after leaving nest) lack a crown patch in both sexes but can be distinguished from young Golden-crowned Kinglets by lack of a pale eyebrow stripe.

Measurements (*R. c. calendula*). *Adult male:* wing, 55.9–61.1 (57.8); tail, 42–46.5 (43.5); exposed culmen, 7.7–9.4 (8.7); tarsus, 18.5–19.5 (19.0). *Adult female:* wing, 53.4–57.6 (55.7) mm.

Field Marks. Kinglets are olive green above and grey below, tiny active birds of tree branches, smaller than warblers, and with a characteristic habit of nervously flicking the wings. The Ruby-crowned Kinglet's whitish eye-ring and complete lack of any stripes over the eye easily separate it from the Golden-crowned Kinglet. The ruby crown patch of the male is often hard to see. *Voice:* Song, the last parts of which are surprisingly loud for so small a bird, is variable but usually in three parts: *tee tee tee, chur chur chur, teedadeé teedadeé teedadeé.* Scold notes: *churr* or *cheater.* Also a husky *did-it* (sometimes only a single note) which readily distinguishes the species.

Habitat. In nesting season, coniferous forests, woodlands, muskegs, also mixedwoods. In migration, all kinds of woodland; also thickets of tall shrubbery such as alder and willow.

Nesting. In coniferous trees at almost any height but most often well up. Nest and *eggs*, usually 5 to 11 to a clutch, are very similar to those of the Golden-crowned Kinglet.

Range. Breeds in coniferous woodland from northwestern Alaska east across Canada to southern Labrador and Newfoundland and south to Guadaloupe Island off Baja California, central Arizona, central New Mexico, central Saskatchewan, northern Michigan, southern Ontario, northern Maine, and Nova Scotia. Winters from southern British Columbia and northern interior United States south to Guatemala, the Gulf coast of United States, and Florida.

Range in Canada. Breeds in Yukon (widely in the south; recorded in late May north to Old Crow), Mackenzie (Aklavik, Norman Wells, Nahanni Mountains, Fort Simpson, upper Grandin River, northern Wood Buffalo Park), northern Saskatchewan (Lake Athabasca, Stony Rapids, Reindeer Lake), northern Manitoba (Churchill, Herchmer), northern Ontario, northern Quebec (Richmond Gulf, Chimo,

George River, Indian House Lake), central Labrador (Attikamagen Lake, Goose Bay, Cartwright; perhaps north to Okak), and Newfoundland south through British Columbia; northern, central, and southwestern Alberta (south to edge of the parklands and through the mountains of the southwest; only a migrant on the prairies); central Saskatchewan (Waskesiu, Nipawin), southern Manitoba (Duck Mountain, Lake St. Martin, Whitemouth, Julius; but only a migrant in extreme southwest corner), southern Ontario (south very locally to Guelph), southern Quebec (Lac Bâtiment, Lac Fraser, Woburn, Biencourt, Gaspé Peninsula, Magdalen Islands), New Brunswick, Prince Edward Island, and Nova Scotia.

Winters in southwestern British Columbia.

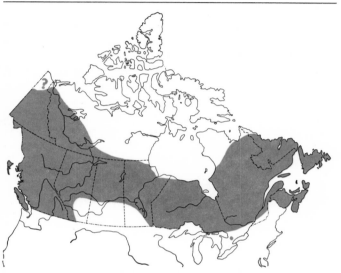

Breeding Distribution of Ruby-crowned Kinglet

Subspecies. (1) *Regulus calendula calendula* (Linnaeus): Yukon, n. B.C., Alta. (except sw. mts.), Sask., Man., Ont., Que., Lab., Nfld., N.B., P.E.I., N.S. (2) *R. c. cineraceus* Grinnell (greyer and paler than *calendula*): interior s. and s.-c. B.C., sw. Alta. (Waterton Lakes and Banff parks). (3) *R. c. grinnelli* Palmer (darker than the preceding two subspecies): B.C. coast and coastal islands.

Family **Motacillidae** – Wagtails and Pipits

Number of Species in North America 7; in Canada 3

Terrestrial birds of open country with longish tails; slender bills; wings with nine primaries and with the inner secondaries elongated, often as long as the longest primaries; hind toe longish with long hind toenail. Instead of hopping on the ground they habitually walk and have a habit of wagging the tail up and down.

[White Wagtail. La Bergeronnette grise. *Motacilla alba* Linnaeus. Hypothetical: Turner's (1885, *Proc. U.S. Nat. Mus.* 8:236) report of four (supposedly two parents and two young of the year) on August 29, 1883, near Fort Chimo, Quebec, is only a sight record, a second-hand one at

that, for the observation was made by two employees of the Hudson's Bay Company and later reported to Turner. The only other reported occurrence in Canada is of one that travelled on a ship from Ireland to the coast of Labrador in 1939 (Martin, 1939, *Can. Field-Nat.* 53: 121).]

YELLOW WAGTAIL
La Bergeronnette flavéole. *Motacilla flava* Linnaeus
Plate 69. L. ca. 6.5 in.

Bill slender, sharp pointed; tail long; hind toenail elongated. *Adults* (breeding season): Top of head, nape, and face dark ashy grey; whitish line over eye; back olive green, often somewhat shaded with brown and brightening on rump; wings brown, the tertials edged with greenish white, the wing coverts margined with same, thus forming two yellowish white wing bars; middle tail feathers blackish brown, outermost mainly white; under parts greenish yellow. *Young:* Wing and tail similar to adults but upper parts brown, under parts plain dingy brownish white or buffy white, the throat white with blackish border.

Measurements (*M. f. tschutschensis*). *Adult male:* wing, 74–82 (77.4); tail, 65–71 (67.5); exposed culmen, 11–12 (11.7); tarsus, 23–26.5 (24.5). *Adult female:* wing, 73–77 (74.6) mm (Ridgway).

Field Marks. A slender greenish-yellow bird with light eyebrow line, and a longish tail (which it flirts up and down and sideways). Outer tail feathers white. Adults have greenish-yellow under parts. Young are brown above and buffy white below with a whitish throat bordered by blackish blotches. Young somewhat resemble Water Pipit but lack stripes on the under parts.

Range. Eurasia and western Alaska.

Status in Canada. Found in summer in northern Yukon (near mouth of Firth River); probably breeds.

Subspecies. *Motacilla flava tschutschensis* Gmelin.

WATER PIPIT (American Pipit)
Le Pipit commun. *Anthus spinoletta* (Linnaeus)
Plate 50. L. 6 to 7 in.

Bill slender, short, pointed; hind toenail elongated. *Adults* (breeding plumage): Upper parts greyish brown, the top of head and the back streaked with dusky; buffy white line over eye; wings dusky brown with buffy edging; tail mainly dusky brown, the outermost feather on each side largely white, with less white on the next, and on only the tip, if any white is present, of third from outside; under parts pinkish buff, the upper breast, sides, and flanks narrowly streaked with dusky. Legs blackish brown. *Adults and young* (autumn): Upper parts much browner and more olive; breast, sides, and flanks more heavily streaked with dusky. Legs blackish brown.

Measurements (*A. s. rubescens*). *Adult male:* wing, 76.9–86.2 (82.8); tail, 61–66 (63.3); exposed culmen, 12.3–13.5 (12.8); tarsus, 21–23 (21.7). *Adult female:* wing, 75.5–84 (79.3) mm.

Field Marks. A sparrow-sized, brownish, thin-billed bird with dark breast streaks. Feeds on the ground often in flocks, walks instead of hopping; frequently wags tail. In flight shows white outer tail feathers. Although the Vesper Sparrow and some longspurs show white in the outer tail feathers, the slim bill of the Water Pipit separates it from them and other sparrows. It most closely resembles Sprague's Pipit of the prairies, but the Water Pipit's blackish (instead of flesh-coloured) legs distinguish it. *Voice:* At any time of year a sharp *tsip-tsip* (usually given in twos) or *tsip it*, especially when flushing or in flight. This note is much sharper than a similar one given by the Horned Lark. On the breeding grounds a tinkling flight song is common.

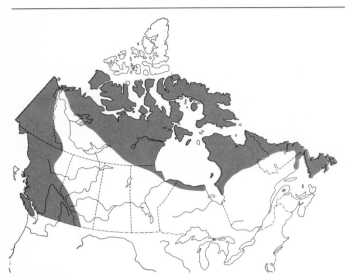

Breeding Distribution of Water Pipit

Habitat. For nesting in the Arctic, vegetated, usually sloping, rocky ground; in the mountains, rocky situations and alpine meadows mostly above timberline. In migration, open areas with low or no vegetation; shores, beaches, mud flats, moist fields, gravel pits, sand dunes.

Nesting. On the ground. Under or near a rock, under low vegetation, on a mossy hummock, or in a cavity in a rock pile. Nest mainly of grasses and twigs. *Eggs*, 4 to 7, usually 4 or 5; greyish or buffy white, thickly spotted with various browns, often so thickly that the background colour is nearly or quite obscured. Incubation probably close to that of the Old World nominate race, about 14 days.

Range. Breeds in Eurasian and North American tundra and mountains. In North America from northern Alaska east to western Greenland and south in the western mountains to Oregon, Utah, northern Arizona, and northern New Mexico; also south locally to Maine (Mount Katahdin). Canadian populations winter mainly in the United States and south to Guatemala.

Range in Canada. Breeds in suitable arctic barrens, alpine treeless areas, and similar situations from northern Banks Island (Mahogany Point), Bylot Island, and northern Baffin Island south through Yukon (including Herschel Island) to southern British Columbia and southwestern Alberta (Rocky Mountains), south-central and southeastern Mackenzie (Manitou Island on Great Bear Lake, Dubawnt River), southern Keewatin (Nueltin Lake), northern Manitoba (Churchill), northern Ontario (Little Cape, Cape

Henrietta Maria), southern Quebec (Moar Bay, Knob Lake, Blanc Sablon, Wapitagun; locally Mount Albert on Gaspé Peninsula), southern Labrador, and Newfoundland.

Migrates through all southern Canada. Small numbers winter in southern British Columbia (Victoria, Lulu Island).

Subspecies. (1) *Anthus spinoletta rubescens* (Tunstall) is the breeding bird of all Canada except B.C. and sw. Alta. (2) *A. s. pacificus* Todd (paler coloration): B.C. (north at least to Dease Lake), sw. Alta. No breeding material for sw. Yukon examined.

SPRAGUE'S PIPIT

Le Pipit des prairies. *Anthus spragueii* (Audubon)
Plate 50. L. 6 to 6.9 in.

Hind toenail longer than that of Water Pipit; crown and upper parts decidedly streaked, feathers margined with buffy; legs pale. *Adults:* Crown and upper parts decidedly streaked buffy and dusky; tail dusky, the two outer tail feathers largely white; cheeks and under parts buffy white, the breast sharply (but not profusely) streaked with dusky; legs pale brown, flesh, or pale yellowish brown.

Measurements. *Adult male:* wing, 78.5–84.9 (82.0); tail, 53–60 (56.7); exposed culmen, 12–13.8 (12.7); tarsus, 21–23 (22.2). *Adult female:* wing, 77.2–83.5 (78.6) mm.

Breeding Distribution of Sprague's Pipit

Field Marks. A buffy brown, slender-billed sparrow-sized bird of the western prairies; shows white outer tail feathers in flight. Its slender bill separates it from the sparrows (including the longspurs), lack of black areas on head or upper breast from the Horned Lark. Resembles Water Pipit but has pale legs, buff-striped upper parts, and generally paler coloration. *Voice:* Song is given in series of seven or eight tinkling double notes on a descending scale, usually as the bird circles high in the air: *seweé, seweé, seweé.*

Habitat. Prairie grasslands and short-grass plains, preferably unplowed and unburned.

Nesting. On the ground and often overarched with grass. Nest is mainly of grasses with some weed stems and coarser grasses in the outer bowl. *Eggs*, 4 to 7; greyish white, spotted with olive brown or purplish brown.

Range. Breeds from the prairies of Canada south to Montana, North Dakota, and northwestern Minnesota. Winters from southern Arizona, Texas, southern Louisiana, and northwestern Mississippi to southwestern Mexico.

Range in Canada. Breeds in suitable grassland in north-central, central, and southern Alberta (from Dixonville in Peace River District and Athabasca south to the International Boundary, and west to the foothills, e.g., Yaha Tinda prairies just east of Banff National Park), central and southern Saskatchewan (Prince Albert region, Nipawin southward), and central-western and southern Manitoba (The Pas, Lake St. Martin, Aweme, Hillside Beach southward).

Family **Bombycillidae** – Waxwings

Number of Species in North America 2; in Canada 2

Crested arboreal birds, their short bills broad at the base and slightly hooked at the tip; wings, rather long, pointed, have ten primaries (outermost much reduced); the tips of some of the secondaries often have small, red, waxlike appendages (Fig. 64), but these are not always present, and their presence is not correlated with age, sex, or season. Tail moderate, tail coverts long. Plumage sleek. Fruits and berries make up the bulk of their food, but insects also are taken, often flycatcher-fashion.

Fig. 64 Secondary feather from wing of Bohemian Waxwing showing waxlike appendage at tip

BOHEMIAN WAXWING

Le Jaseur de Bohême. *Bombycilla garrulus* (Linnaeus)
Plate 53. L. 7.5 to 8.7 in.

Head crested, bill short, flattened toward base; plumage sleek. *Adults:* Soft brownish grey generally, brownest (cinnamon) on head, greyish on rump and abdomen; narrow mask through eye and patch on throat, black; secondaries with white tips to outer webs and with bright red (rarely yellow) sealingwax-like appendages, sometimes absent; primaries and primary coverts blackish, the coverts tipped white, the primaries with tips of yellow and/or white; tail becoming blackish near end and with broad yellow tip; under tail coverts, chestnut. *Young in juvenal plumage* (worn only a short time): Similar to adults but much duller, crest smaller, red appendages to secondaries fewer or absent; under parts, dark olive grey streaked with white, middle of abdomen whitish; no black bib.

Measurements. *Adult male:* wing, 109.6–118.9 (113.9);

tail, 64.5–69 (66.1); exposed culmen, 12.1–14 (12.9); tarsus, 19.5–21 (20.2). *Adult female:* wing, 108.7–117.5 (112.7) mm.

Field Marks. Crest, brownish coloration, black patch through eye, and yellow tail tip make it a waxwing. Usually seen in flocks. Tiny red appendages on secondaries are often absent, and when present they are difficult to see. Similar to Cedar Waxwing but larger, *with chestnut instead of whitish under tail coverts*, small white patches in wing. Young birds are duller with smaller crest, no black on throat, and the olive brown under parts are streaked with white. Chestnut under tail coverts and wing pattern (white and yellow patches) distinguish them from Cedar Waxwing of similar age. *Voice:* Similar to that of Cedar Waxwing but lower in pitch, more buzzy.

Habitat. In breeding season coniferous (sometimes mixed-wood) woodlands and muskegs; also burntlands. In winter various types of berry- and fruit-producing trees and shrubs, often about dwellings.

Nesting. On a branch 4 to 50 feet up in a coniferous tree. Nest of twigs, grass, *Usnea* lichen, and lined with fine grass, plant fibres, or conifer needles. *Eggs*, 4 to 6; pale blue and well marked with blackish dots and often a few fine lines.

Range. Breeds widely in Eurasia and in northwestern North America. In North America from western Alaska east to Manitoba and south to central Washington, northern Idaho, northwestern Montana, and southern Alberta.

Breeding Distribution of Bohemian Waxwing

Range in Canada. Breeds in Yukon (Old Crow, Fortymile, Burwash Landing, Carcross), Mackenzie (Mackenzie Delta, Anderson River, Great Bear Lake, Fort Reliance, Fort Smith), interior British Columbia (Atlin, Telegraph Creek, Pouce Coupé, Carpenter Mountain in the Cariboo, Moose River in Yellowhead Pass region, Alta Lake), northern and western Alberta (south to about Athabasca River and for an undetermined distance in the mountains), northern Saskatchewan (Lake Athabasca, Kazan Lake), and northern Manitoba (Churchill, Cochrane River, Thicket Portage).

Winters from central British Columbia Puntchesakut Lake, François Lake), southwestern Mackenzie (Fort Liard) central Alberta (Edmonton, Elk Island National Park), central Saskatchewan (Prince Albert National Park), and southern Manitoba (Lake St. Martin) southward; irregularly in southern Ontario (Sault Ste. Marie, Lake Nipissing, Cochrane, Ottawa southward), and southwestern Quebec (Hull, Montreal, Quebec; rarely Arvida); very rarely in New Brunswick (Grand Manan, Saint John, Fredericton), and Nova Scotia (Halifax, Pictou); probably Prince Edward Island.

Subspecies. *Bombycilla garrulus pallidiceps* Reichenow.

CEDAR WAXWING
Le Jaseur des cèdres. *Bombycilla cedrorum* Vieillot
Plate 53. L. 6.5 to 8 in.

Similar to Bohemian Waxwing but smaller; lacks white or yellow on the wing and has no chestnut on under tail coverts. *Adults:* Narrow band across forehead and back over eyes, black; chin blackish passing into brown on throat; rest of head, neck, breast, and back cinnamon brown passing into grey on rump and blackish toward end of tail (which has a broad yellow tip); wings slaty grey, the secondaries with tiny red appendages like sealing wax (but sometimes lacking); abdomen, sides, and flanks, pale greenish yellow; under tail coverts whitish. *Young in juvenal plumage:* Similar to adults but much greyer; crest shorter; no black behind eye or on throat; breast and sides, olive brown streaked with white; middle of abdomen whitish; red appendages to secondaries either lacking or poorly developed.

Measurements. *Adult male:* wing, 90.6–98 (95.4); tail 57.5–63.5 (59.5); exposed culmen, 10.1–11.3 (10.6); tarsus, 15.5–16.5 (15.9). *Adult female:* wing, 89.5–96.9 (94.1) mm.

Field Marks. A crested brownish bird with a yellow-tipped tail is a waxwing. Sits erect, usually is seen in flocks or companies. Similar only to the Bohemian Waxwing, from which the following points separate it: under tail coverts white (never chestnut); no white or yellow patches in wings; abdomen, sides, and flanks pale yellowish (instead of soft grey). *Voice:* A high-pitched whistled hiss, similar to that of the Bohemian Waxwing but higher-pitched and less buzzy.

Habitat. Extremely varied, open and sparse woodlands, either deciduous or coniferous, sparse second growths, trees and shrubbery about dwellings, orchards, edges of dams, lakes, rivers, marshes, bogs, and burntlands where standing dead trees provide lookout perches; the vicinity of berry and small-fruit-bearing trees and bushes.

Nesting. In the horizontal branches of trees or tall shrubs, either deciduous or coniferous, 4 to 40 feet up. Nest is bulky, made of twigs, bark strips, plant fibres, fine rootlets, *Usnea*, paper, rags, or twine; lined with fine similar materials. *Eggs,* 3 to 5; pale bluish grey or greenish blue, with usually well-spaced small spots or dots of black or blackish brown. Incubation period averages 11.7 days (R. B. Lea), by the female.

Range. Breeds from extreme southeastern Alaska east to Newfoundland and south to northern California, northern Utah, northwestern Oklahoma, southern Illinois, northern Alabama, and northern Georgia. Winters from northern United States (and locally southern Canada) south to Panama.

Range in Canada. Breeds across southern Canada north to north-central British Columbia (Skeena River valley, Tetana Lake, Tupper Creek), northern Alberta (Lake Athabasca, Peace River District), northern Saskatchewan (Stony Rapids), central Manitoba (Thicket Portage), northern Ontario (Moose Factory), south-central Quebec (Lake Mistassini, inner north shore of the Gulf of St. Lawrence: Matamek, Natashquan; recorded in summer in August east to 22 miles inland from St. Augustin—specimen), New Brunswick, Prince Edward Island, Nova Scotia, and Newfoundland.

Casual in southwestern Mackenzie (Fort Simpson, June 18, 1958—specimen) and northeastern Manitoba (Churchill). Scarce migrant on Queen Charlotte Islands.

Winters in southern British Columbia (Victoria, Vancouver, Okanagan Landing), southern Ontario (Fort William, Huntsville, Ottawa southward), southwestern Quebec (Montreal, Quebec), southern New Brunswick, southern Nova Scotia, and irregularly elsewhere (north occasionally to Saskatoon, Saskatchewan).

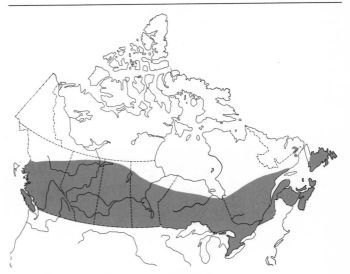

Breeding Distribution of Cedar Waxwing

Remarks. The Cedar Waxwing is attired in soft, harmonious colours. Its silky plumage seemingly never has a feather out of place. It has a friendly nature and generally is seen in flocks. The bulk of its food is made up of small fruits, mostly wild kinds. About orchards of ripe cherries, however, it can be destructive. It devours quite a variety of insects also, often catching them flycatcher-fashion.

Family **Laniidae** – Shrikes

Number of Species in North America 2; in Canada 2

Medium-sized birds with robust, strongly hooked bills, the upper mandibles with a notch and a toothlike projection near the tip (Fig. 65). The feet are suitable for perching but are not fitted for grasping or holding prey. Perhaps because the feet are relatively weak, prey is impaled on thorns or barbed wire to hold it. The family is a large one that originated in the Old World and reaches its best development there. Shrikes subsist on animal food, such as insects, small birds, and small mammals.

Fig. 65 Head of Loggerhead Shrike

NORTHERN SHRIKE

La Pie-grièche boréale. *Lanius excubitor* Linnaeus
Plate 53. L. 9 to 10.7 in.

Upper mandible hooked. Adults (female often duller with less white in wings and tail): Crown, nape, and back, light bluish grey paling to white on rump, with ends of scapulars, the lower forehead, and a line back over eyes, white also; black mask from base of bill to ear coverts; wings mostly black with a white patch at base of primaries; secondaries and tertials narrowly tipped white; tail mostly black but outer feather on either side mainly white with rapidly diminishing extent of white on each more inward feather; under parts white with more or less fine wavy dusky barring (but sometimes nearly or quite absent). *Young (first year):* Resemble adults but grey areas very much browner; face patch confined to behind eye, brownish and veiled; under parts more brownish and much more heavily barred with dusky.

Measurements (*L. e. borealis*). *Adult male:* wing, 108.4–116.3 (112.9); tail, 104–115 (110.0); exposed culmen, 18.3–19 (18.7); tarsus, 25.5–28 (26.3). *Adult female:* wing, 109.8–113.2 (111.9) mm.

Field Marks. A grey-and-black robin-sized bird with a *black mask* through the eye and a hooked bill is a shrike. Flight is undulating, and the white patch in the wing flashes conspicuously. When perched, it flicks its tail frequently. The Northern Shrike closely resembles the Loggerhead Shrike, but in settled parts of southern Canada only the Loggerhead is likely to be encountered in summer and only the Northern in winter. The Northern Shrike is a larger bird, usually shows more or less barring on the breast, lacks any black on the forehead, often shows a pale area at the base of the bill. Young of the year are more easily confused, but those of the Northern are more brownish above and below than young Loggerheads and have much more heavily barred under parts. *Voice:* Song a disjointed but musical medley of warbled notes, whistles, imitations of other bird songs, interspersed with various harsh notes. The performance is usually given from a treetop and is often of long duration. Alarm note is a harsh *sheck sheck*.

Habitat. On the breeding grounds, open sparse woods, thickets, bogs; also low growth near or above timberline of mountains. In winter, various types of more open situations where trees, hedges, wood patches, shade trees, or telephone poles provide lookout perches (habitat often similar to that occupied in summer by the Loggerhead Shrike).

Nesting. In a branch of a tree or bush. Nest is bulky, made of twigs and lined with rootlets, wool, hair, lichens, and feathers. *Eggs*, usually 4 to 7, sometimes up to 9. Eggs greyish white, spotted and blotched with olive brown or dull olive and usually some spots of purplish grey.

Range. Eurasia, northern Africa, and northern North America. In North America breeds from Alaska across the northern mainland of Canada to Labrador; winters south to northern California, central Arizona, central Missouri, central Ohio, and Maryland.

Breeding Distribution of Northern Shrike

Range in Canada. Breeds from Yukon (Fortymile; Ogilvie Range; possibly north to Old Crow where recorded in spring), northern Mackenzie (Mackenzie Delta, Fort Anderson, Great Slave Lake), southwestern Keewatin (probably Windy River), northern Quebec (Fort Chimo, Indian House Lake), and northern Labrador (Okak), south to northern British Columbia (Atlin, Mile 80 Haines Road, Dease Lake), northern Alberta (Lake Athabasca), northern Manitoba (Churchill, York Factory), central Quebec (Great Whale River, Knob Lake region), and southern Labrador (Sandwich Bay).

In migration and winter all across settled southern Canada: southern British Columbia (including Vancouver Island), Alberta, Saskatchewan, Manitoba, Ontario, southern Quebec, Newfoundland, New Brunswick, Prince Edward Island, and Nova Scotia.

Subspecies. (1) *Lanius excubitor borealis* Vieillot: e. Canada. (2) *L. e. invictus* Grinnell (paler and larger): Man. (Churchill, York Factory) westward.

Remarks. From some vantage point like a treetop, post, or wire, the Northern Shrike patiently watches for its prey. It eats mice, small birds, and, when available, large insects. It often impales its prey on a torn or fence-wire barb, or wedges it into a fork in a branch. Although a predator, it is a songbird with weak untaloned feet. Its heavy hooked beak serves as a weapon to deliver a blow, to hold and shake its prey, or to tear off pieces of flesh for eating. Never abundant, it has no great effect on its prey species.

LOGGERHEAD SHRIKE (Migrant Shrike)

La Pie-grièche migratrice. *Lanius ludovicianus* Linnaeus
Plate 53. L. 8.6 to 9.2 in.

Similar to Northern Shrike but smaller; *adults* with darker grey upper parts, unbarred (or nearly so) under parts, black face bar more extensive, reaching narrowly across lower forehead. *Young* Loggerhead Shrikes in juvenal plumage, however, have no black on the forehead and show fine barring on breast and sides, but this barring is much finer and less conspicuous than in the Northern Shrike.

Measurements (*L. l. migrans*). *Adult male:* wing, 94.8–100.9 (97.9); tail, 88.5–100 (95.3); exposed culmen, 14.8–16.6 (15.5); tarsus, 25.5–28.5 (26.4). *Adult female:* wing, 90.5–98.1 (95.1) mm.

Field Marks. A grey-and-black robin-sized bird with a black bar through the eye is a shrike. The Loggerhead, though very similar to the Northern, is smaller. Adults have unbarred under parts and the black of face bar extends narrowly across the lower forehead. Young Loggerheads are very lightly barred with dusky on breast and sides but are more greyish (not brownish). A shrike found in settled southern Canada in summer is probably a Loggerhead, in winter probably a Northern (*see* Mockingbird). *Song:* A mixture of pleasing and harsh notes; usually of shorter duration than the song of the Northern.

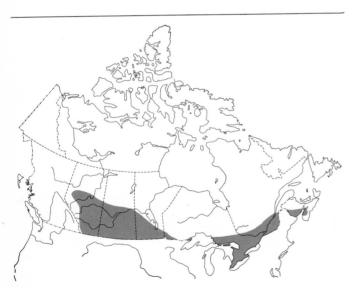

Breeding Distribution of Loggerhead Shrike

Habitat. Open country with hedgerows, copses, scattered trees or tall shrubs, telephone poles and wires, and fence posts where adequate lookout posts and nesting sites are present.

Nesting. From 5 to 20 feet up in a tree or shrub (especially a thorny one). Nest is rather bulky and is made of twigs lined with rootlets, plant fibres, soft cottony or woolly materials, hair, feathers, rags, or paper. *Eggs*, 4 to 6; greyish white, spotted and blotched with greys and browns. Incubation period 13 to 16 days (O. W. Knight).

Range. Breeds from southern Canada (Alberta east to Nova Scotia) south through the United States to southern Mexico, the Gulf coast of United States, and southern Florida. Winters mainly from north-central United States southward.

Range in Canada. Breeds in north-central, central, and southern Alberta (east of the mountains, from Fairview and Lesser Slave Lake southward), central and southern Saskatchewan (Meadow Lake, Nipawin southward), southern Manitoba (Swan River, Lake St. Martin, Deer Lodge), western Ontario (Emo), southern Ontario (Fort William, Sault Ste. Marie, Lake Nipissing, Ottawa southward), southwestern Quebec (Hull, Montreal, Hatley, Quebec, St. Pacôme, Kamouraska), New Brunswick (Upper Woodstock, Sussex, Fairville), and rarely Nova Scotia (Chipman Corner).

Rare visitor to southern British Columbia (Chilliwack, Osoyoos, Edgewood, Okanagan Landing). Casual in northern Manitoba (Churchill).

Subspecies. (1) *Lanius ludovicianus migrans* Palmer: se. Man. (intergrading westward with *excubitorides* in the Lake St. Martin region), s. Ont., s. Que., N.B., N.S. (2) *L. l. excubitorides* Swainson (averages paler, upper tail coverts and edges of scapulars more extensively whitish): c. and s. Alta., c. and s. Sask., sw. Man. (Swan River, Douglas). (3) *L. l. gambeli* Ridgway: the southern B.C. visitants have been referred to this form.

Family **Sturnidae**–Starlings

Number of Species in North America 2; in Canada 2

A large Old World family, two species of which have been introduced by man into North America. One species, the Common Starling, has flourished and spread rapidly across the continent. The other, the Crested Myna, has remained confined mostly to the vicinity of Vancouver, B.C., where it was introduced early in the century.

COMMON STARLING

LÉ'tourneau sansonnet. *Sturnus vulgaris* Linnaeus
Plate 62. L. 7.5 to 8.5 in.

Bill almost as long as head, tapering to a point. Tail short, square. Feathers of breast in adults with pointed tips, long and attenuated in adult males. *Adult male* (breeding plumage: midwinter, spring, early summer): Glossy blackish with purple and green reflections; wings and tail, blackish edged with buff; some buffy spots on back usually retained from winter plumage; bill mainly yellow, but base of lower mandible dark grey or bluish, iris brown, legs reddish brown. *Adult male* (winter plumage: late summer–early winter): Similar to adult male in breeding plumage but upper parts with numerous buffy spots, under parts with many white spots; bill mainly dusky. *Adult female:* Similar to respective plumages of adult male but feathers of breast with shorter, less attenuated tips, iris with a yellowish outer edge; in breeding plumage the base of the lower mandible is creamy or pinkish (instead of dark grey or bluish). *Young* (*juvenal plumage*): Upper parts dark greyish brown; wings and tail with buffy edges; throat whitish; rest of under parts greyish brown, the middle of abdomen streaked whitish.

Measurements. *Adult male:* wing, 121.5–130.5 (127.2); tail, 61–64 (62.6); exposed culmen, 25.9–29.1 (27.7); tarsus, 27–30 (29.3). *Adult female:* wing, 120–126.5 (122.9) mm.

Field Marks. Looks black, thus resembles a blackbird but with short stubby tail. From midwinter to midsummer its yellow bill separates it from any Canadian blackbird. When in late summer the bill turns dusky, the plumage becomes white-spotted, unlike any of our blackbirds. In flight it has a characteristic short-tailed triangular outline, and at a distance the under side of the spread wings looks brownish against the black body. Ordinary flight, swift and direct. Usually seen in flocks, often very large. As it frequents buildings of cities, towns, and farms, it is familiar to most people who live in southern Canada. Although the young are mouse-brown, they have the same stubby tail and characteristic outline as the adults. *Voice:* Song, a rambling procession of whistles, warbles, squeaks, chirps, clicks, gurgles, and often imitations of other bird voices. Calls include various whistles and other notes. Flocks gathered for roosting keep up a continuous twittering chorus.

Habitat. Extremely variable. Frequents city, town, country. For nesting, it requires cavities in trees, building crevices, and similar situations; for roosting, trees, bushes, cattail marshes, buildings, and cliffs; for feeding, open places such as pastures, fields, gardens, lawns, garbage dumps, marshes, and shores.

Nesting. In woodpecker holes and natural cavities in trees; in cavities about buildings or cliffs; and in bird boxes; often in country mail boxes. Sticks, straw, weed stems, grass, and trash are used to fill the cavity, and there is a lining of finer grasses and feathers. *Eggs*, usually 4 or 5, often 6; rarely more. They are pale bluish or greenish white, rarely white. Incubation 11 to 14 days (various authors), by the female assisted by the male.

Range. Iceland, northern Norway, northern Finland, northern Russia, and southern Siberia (east to about Lake Baikal) south to the Canary Islands, Palestine, Iraq, Iran, central India, and northeastern China.

Introduced into North America (New York City, 1890) and now breeding all across southern Canada and in much of the United States. More northern populations partly migratory.

Range in Canada. Introduced; range still expanding. In 1964 its breeding range was approximately as follows: north-central, central, and southern British Columbia (Kitwanga, Kispiox, Peace River District, Hazelton, Victoria, Brisco), southern Mackenzie (Fort Smith, Lookout Point on Thelon River), Alberta (Peace River District, Fort Chipewyan, Jasper, Beynon, Brooks), central and southern Saskatchewan (Duck Lake, Prince Albert, Nipawin, Cypress Hills, Regina), Manitoba (Churchill, Brandon,

Winnipeg, Sprague), Ontario (Favourable Lake, Sioux Lookout, Attawapiskat River, Moosonee southward), Quebec (Taschereau, Amos; Lake St. John; and north shore of the Gulf of St. Lawrence: Natashquan, Blanc Sablon southward including Magdalen Islands; apparently also casually in northern part: Fort McKenzie—Bleakney, *Can. Field-Nat.* 67: 44–45), southern Labrador (Goose Bay), Newfoundland, New Brunswick, Prince Edward Island, and Nova Scotia (including Cape Breton Island).

Winters in more or less diminished numbers within much of the breeding range; also in north coastal British Columbia (Bella Coola, Prince Rupert, Queen Charlotte Islands).

This Old World species has spread into Canada from the United States where it was first introduced at New York City in 1890. It was first recorded in the provinces of Canada approximately as follows: Ontario: Niagara Falls, autumn, 1914; Nova Scotia: Halifax, December 1, 1915; Quebec: Betchouane, April 1917; New Brunswick: Grand Manan, autumn, 1924; Prince Edward Island: Tignish, late 1930 or early 1931; Manitoba: York Factory, May 11, 1931; Alberta: Camrose, late 1934; Saskatchewan: Tregarva, spring, 1937; Newfoundland: Tompkins, June 9, 1943; British Columbia: Williams Lake, winter, 1945–46.

Breeding Distribution of Common Starling

Subspecies. *Sturnus vulgaris vulgaris* Linnaeus.

Remarks. The unfortunate introduction of the Starling into North America is an example of the inevitable blunders inherent in tampering with the delicate balance of nature by persons equipped with little more than good intentions. The modest numbers of Starlings liberated in New York City in 1890 have now grown to millions that have spread and are still spreading over the greater part of the United States and southern Canada.

The Starling's food habits are mainly beneficial, for insects make up the bulk of its menu. It has an appetite for small fruits, however, and sometimes does serious damage in the cherry orchard.

Much more serious is its habit of usurping the nesting cavities used by many of our native birds. Doubtless it is a major factor in the recent widespread decline of the beautiful Red-headed Woodpecker and probably the Bluebird also. Its nesting and roosting in large numbers on buildings poses another serious problem involving many thousands of dollars' worth of damage annually.

CRESTED MYNA

L'Étourneau huppé. *Acridotheres cristatellus* (Linnaeus)
Plate 62. L. 9 to 10.5 in.

Nasal plumes, erect and well developed, form a low crest over base of bill. *Adults* (sexes similar but female with smaller nasal crest): Plumage mainly blackish, the under parts washed with grey; wings black, the base of the primaries and outer secondaries white, forming a large white wing patch; tail and under tail coverts black, tipped with white; eye, orange to yellow; bill pale yellowish, rose-coloured at base; legs orange-yellow. *Young:* Resemble adults but plumage is dark brown, crest lacking, and there are no white tips to tail or under tail coverts.

Measurements. *Adult male:* wing, 129–141 (134); tail, 71–84 (77.9); exposed culmen, 21.1–26.7 (24.2); tarsus, 38.5–40 (39.4). *Adult female:* wing, 129–132.5 (130.8) mm.

Field Marks. A black, chunky, short-tailed, robin-sized bird with yellowish bill and a peculiar crest (much less-developed in females than in adult males) at the base of the bill covering the nostrils. A white patch in the wing is very conspicuous in flight and can sometimes be partly seen when the bird is perched. Young for a short time after leaving the nest are much browner than adults, and the crest is not developed; but their silhouette otherwise resembles that of the adults, and they show a light bill and a white patch in the spread wing.

Habitat. Forages in open agricultural areas: fields, gardens, orchards, pastures with the cattle; and in garbage dumps. Roosts usually in flocks on city buildings and in trees.

Nesting. In woodpecker holes and other cavities in trees; in crevices, cavities, holes, and pipes of buildings; and in bird boxes. The nest cavity is filled with trash, like grass, weeds, paper, feathers, rootlets, and cast snake skins. *Eggs,* 4 to 7, usually 4 or 5; greenish blue. Incubation 14 days (Mackay and Hughes).

Range. East Pakistan, northern Burma, and southern China south to southern Burma, French Indochina, Hainan, and Formosa. Introduced in the Philippines, Japan, and British Columbia.

Range in Canada. Introduced into Vancouver, British Columbia in the 1890's. Common (but numbers fluctuate) in the Vancouver region including Lulu Island and western parts of the Fraser Delta; also small numbers locally on southern Vancouver Island (Nanaimo; has been observed from Courtenay south to Victoria).

Subspecies. *Acridotheres cristatellus cristatellus* (Linnaeus).

Remarks. Unlike the Common Starling, the Crested Myna has not spread significantly in the more than 65 years since it was introduced. Mackay and Hughes (1963, *Can. Field-Nat.* 77: 154–162) place its numbers in the Vancouver area at between 2,000 and 3,000, a decline in the past 35 years.

Family **Vireonidae** – Vireos

Number of Species in North America 12; in Canada 8

Small plain woodland birds without conspicuous patterns, usually dull greenish olive above, white below. Bill rather short, rather thick, slightly hooked. Wings with ten primaries, the outermost very short or vestigial. These birds are arboreal and resemble some of the duller-coloured warblers, but usually the heavier bill and more sluggish movements of the vireos will distinguish them. Economically they are very beneficial, since they consume large numbers of insects including both hairy and hairless caterpillars. The family is confined exclusively to the Western Hemisphere. The name *vireo*, derived from Latin, indicates green coloration and refers to the colour of the upper parts.

WHITE-EYED VIREO

Le Viréo aux yeux blancs. *Vireo griseus* (Boddaert)
Plate 54. L. 4.5 to 5.5 in.

A small vireo with rather heavy bill. Upper parts olive green, the neck more greyish; broad yellow streak from base of bill back over and almost around the eye; wings and tail, dusky brown edged with olive green; wings with two yellowish white wing bars; under parts mostly white, the sides and flanks yellow, this colour extending to the shorter under tail coverts; iris white; legs greyish blue.

Measurements. *Adult male:* wing, 60–65 (61.4); tail, 46–54 (49.0); exposed culmen, 9.5–11 (10.1); tarsus, 18–20 (19.5). *Adult female:* wing, 57–63 (60.5) mm (Ridgway).

Field Marks. A small vireo with two wing bars, yellow eye-ring, and yellow bar from base of bill back to eye; whitish throat and breast. The white eye is diagnostic but usually cannot be seen in the field. The Yellow-throated is another vireo with yellow eye-ring, but it has a yellow throat and breast. The Solitary Vireo has a light eye-ring and bar in front of eye, but these are white, not yellow. *Song:* Unlike that of other vireos. It usually contains five to seven notes beginning and ending with a *chick* or *tick*.

Habitat. Thickets, especially on moist ground.

Range. Eastern Nebraska, southern Wisconsin, central Ohio, and Massachusetts (probably) south to central Mexico, the Gulf coast of United States, and southern Florida; also Bermuda.

Status in Canada. Casual in Ontario: Listowel, Woodstock, Point Pelee, Erie Beach, Toronto, Ottawa.

Subspecies. *Vireo griseus noveboracensis* (Gmelin).

HUTTON'S VIREO

Le Viréo de Hutton. *Vireo huttoni* Cassin
Plate 54. L. 4.3 to 4.7 in.

A very small nondescript vireo with white wing bars. Upper parts dull olive, becoming greenish olive on rump; incomplete eye-ring and poorly defined streak from base of bill to eye, whitish; wings and tail dusky with olive edging, the wings with two white bars; under parts dull buffy olive becoming whitish on abdomen.

Measurements. *Adult male:* wing, 59.5–63 (60.9); tail, 47–50 (48.6); exposed culmen, 8.5–9 (8.7); tarsus, 18.5–20 (19.0). *Adult female:* wing, 59–62 (60.2) mm (Ridgway).

Field Marks. A small nondescript vireo of the south coast of British Columbia with two white wing bars, a whitish incomplete eye-ring, and whitish stripe from base of bill to eye. In general, its colour somewhat resembles the Ruby-crowned Kinglet, but the bill is thicker and the head larger. *Song: Cheé-ah* or *cheé-wee* frequently repeated, the accent may be either on first or second syllable.

Habitat. Deciduous, and mixed woodland and shrubbery.

Nesting. Nest is suspended from a fork in a branch of a tree (deciduous or coniferous) or tall shrub. *Eggs*, 3 to 5, usually 4; white with scattered small spots and dots of browns, mostly near the larger end.

Range. Permanent resident from southwestern British Columbia south along the Pacific Coast to southern Baja California and from central Arizona, southwestern New Mexico, and western Texas south to Guatemala.

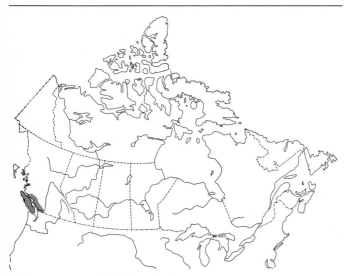

Breeding Distribution of Hutton's Vireo

Range in Canada. Permanent resident in southwestern British Columbia (Vancouver Island north to Cape Scott; and the southwest coast of the mainland north at least to Kingcome Inlet).

Subspecies. (1) *Vireo huttoni huttoni* Cassin: mainland of sw. B.C. (2) *V. h. insularis* Rhoads (darker in colour): Vancouver Island.

[**Bell's Vireo.** *Vireo bellii* Audubon. Hypothetical. There are several sight reports allegedly of this species for extreme southern Ontario, but no specimen has been taken in Canada.]

YELLOW-THROATED VIREO
Le Viréo à gorge jaune. *Vireo flavifrons* Vieillot
Plate 54. L. 5 to 6 in.

Bill rather stout. Our only vireo combining white wing bars with a *bright yellow throat* and breast. *Adults:* Top and sides of head, back of neck, and upper back, yellowish olive; eye-ring and lores, yellow; lower back and rump, slaty grey; wings with two prominent white bars; tail blackish with greyish white edging; throat and breast, bright yellow; rest of under body chiefly white, becoming greyish on flanks; iris brown; legs bluish grey.

Measurements. *Adult male:* wing, 74–80 (77.1); tail, 47.5–52 (49.2); exposed culmen, 10.5–12 (11.5); tarsus, 18–20 (19.3). *Adult female:* wing, 72–78 (75) mm (Ridgway).

Field Marks. No other Canadian vireo has a combination of two white wing bars and a bright yellow throat and breast. It might be confused with the Pine Warbler, but the vireo has a thicker, blunter bill and lacks the Pine Warbler's white tail patches. The Philadelphia Vireo has a yellowish breast but no wing bars. *Song:* Similar to the Red-eyed Vireo's but lower pitched, more deliberate, more musical.

Habitat. Chiefly open stands of mature deciduous trees, often in residential areas, foraging in the upper stratum.

Nesting. Nest is suspended from a fork in a tree branch. Much spider web is used in the construction of the deep, well-made nest, which is beautifully decorated with lichens and egg cases of spiders. *Eggs*, 3 to 5, usually 4; white, well spotted on the larger end with various browns; usually somewhat more heavily marked than in other vireos.

Range. Breeds from southern Manitoba, central Wisconsin, central Michigan, southern Ontario, southwestern Quebec, northern New Hampshire, and southwestern Maine (locally) south to central and eastern Texas, the Gulf coast of United States, and central Florida. Winters mainly from southern Mexico south to Panama.

Breeding Distribution of Yellow-throated Vireo

Range in Canada. Breeds in southern Manitoba (Winnipeg, Fort Garry; probably Emerson), southern Ontario (Peterborough and Ottawa southward), southwestern Quebec (Hull, Montreal, Hatley; probably Sherbrooke).

Recorded rarely, without evidence of breeding, in Saskatchewan (Madge Lake, Nipawin), and western Ontario (Shoal Lake, Kenora). Sight records only for New Brunswick. Casual in Nova Scotia (Indian Harbour, April 9, 1958).

SOLITARY VIREO (Blue-headed Vireo)

Le Vireo à tête bleue. *Vireo solitarius* (Wilson)
Plate 54. L. 5 to 6 in.

Top and sides of head and hind-neck, dark slaty grey; eye-ring and lores, white; back, rump, and upper tail coverts, olive green; two white or yellowish wing bars; tail blackish with olive green edging except the outermost feather on each side which has narrow white edging; under parts mostly white, the sides and flanks yellow mixed with olive green; under tail coverts usually with yellowish suffusion; iris brown; legs blue-grey.

Measurements (*V. s. solitarius*). *Adult male:* wing, 69.6–74.8 (72.7); tail, 50.5–54.0 (52.2); exposed culmen, 9.6–11.6 (10.7); tarsus, 17–19 (18.0). *Adult female:* wing, 72.2–74.6 (73.2) mm.

Field Marks. A vireo with two whitish wing bars, dark grey sides of head (contrasting with white throat), white eye-ring and lores. *Voice:* Song a series of spaced short phrases similar to those of the Red-eyed Vireo but with longer pauses between and, especially in the western mountains, shriller. Sometimes the phrases are run together producing a continuous rich warble. Nasal scolding notes.

Habitat. More open mixed coniferous and deciduous woods.

Nesting. In a tree, usually a conifer, and ordinarily not more than 15 feet above the ground (although much higher nests are quite often seen). *Eggs,* 3 to 5, usually 4; white, spotted and dotted sparsely (mostly near the large end) with light and dark browns.

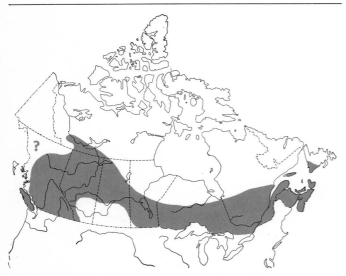

Breeding Distribution of Solitary Vireo

Range. Southern Canada south in the mountains to southern Baja California, Guatemala, and El Salvador; and to North Dakota (locally), central Minnesota, central Michigan, southern Ontario, and northern New Jersey; in the mountains to northern Georgia. Winters from southern United States southward to Nicaragua and Cuba.

Range in Canada. Breeds in British Columbia (across the southern part including Vancouver Island and north on the

PLATE 63

1 Cardinal,
   (a) adult male
   (b) adult female

2 Black-headed Grosbeak,
   (a) adult female
   (b) adult male

3 Indigo Bunting,
   (a) female
   (b) male in breeding
      plumage

4 Rose-breasted Grosbeak,
   (a) male in breeding
      plumage
   (b) female

5 Lazuli Bunting,
   (a) female
   (b) male in breeding
      plumage

6 Dickcissel,
   (a) adult female
   (b) male in breeding
      plumage

7 House Sparrow,
   (a) female
   (b) male in breeding
      plumage

1a

1b

1c

2b

2a

3

5a

5b

6

Crosby
63

PLATE 64

mainland at least to the Vanderhoof region and Peace River parklands; perhaps north to Dease Lake: specimen taken June 22, 1962), southwestern Mackenzie (Fort Smith probably to Fort Simpson), northern and central Alberta (Grimshaw, Wood Buffalo Park, Athabasca, Glenevis), northwestern and central Saskatchewan (Lake Athabasca, Prince Albert, Nipawin), central and southern Manitoba (Thicket Portage, Duck Mountain, Clandeboye Bay on southern Lake Manitoba, Rennie), central Ontario (Favourable Lake, Moose Factory, Port Sydney, Algonquin Park, Combermere), southwestern Quebec (Mount Plamondon, Waswanipi – Bell River area, Lake St. John, Grande Grève southward; probably southern Lake Mistassini; status on Magdalen Islands uncertain), southwestern Newfoundland (Doyles), New Brunswick, Prince Edward Island, and Nova Scotia.

Subspecies. (1) *Vireo solitarius solitarius* (Wilson): ne. B.C. (Peace River parklands), sw. Mack., n. and c. Alta., Sask., Man., Ont., Que., Nfld., N.B., P.E.I., N.S. (2) *V. s. cassinii* Xantus (duller coloration): s. B.C. (Indianpoint Lake, Nulki Lake, Comox, Waldo); migrant in sw. Alta. (Canmore, May 27, 1891) but not known to breed there.

YELLOW-GREEN VIREO
Le Viréo jaune-verdâtre. *Vireo flavoviridis* (Cassin)
L. 5.5 to 6.5 in.

Very similar to Red-eyed Vireo but more yellowish below; the wing linings, axillars, and under tail coverts, clear sulphur yellow; the sides and flanks, bright olive green; markings on sides of head less distinct.

Status in Canada. Accidental in Quebec (Godbout, May 13, 1883). The specimen has been referred to *V. f. flavoviridis* (Cassin). Normal range of species is from Mexico south to Colombia, Ecuador, Peru, northern Bolivia, and western Brazil.

RED-EYED VIREO
Le Viréo aux yeux rouges. *Vireo olivaceus* (Linnaeus)
Plate 54. L. 5.3 to 6.5 in.

Our only vireo with a red eye. The largest of our vireos lacking white wing bars. *Adults:* Crown mouse-grey, bordered on either side by a narrow dusky line; rest of upper parts dull olive green; over eye a broad greyish white stripe and a dusky stripe through the eye; wings and tail dusky with yellowish green edging; no wing bars; under parts white, the flanks tinged with yellowish olive, the wing linings pale sulphur yellow, and the under tail coverts with a yellowish suffusion; eye red; legs bluish grey.

Measurements. *Adult male:* wing, 79.2–82.7 (80.5); tail, 53–57 (55.2); exposed culmen, 12–14.4 (13.2); tarsus, 17–18.5 (17.5). *Adult female:* wing, 76.8–79.7 (77.9) mm.

Field Marks. Lacks white wing bars, therefore most likely to be confused with Warbling and Philadelphia vireos. Its white eyebrow stripe, bordered above and below by a black line, is decidedly more definite than that of the other two. Its grey crown contrasts more strongly with its green back. Its breast is white, that of the Philadelphia yellowish. Its

317

larger size is not always apparent, and its red eye is hard to see in the field. Its song is completely different from that of the Warbling Vireo. *Voice:* Short, similar phrases with slightly rising inflection and delivered tirelessly for long periods of the day in the breeding season. Alarm note, a complaining nasal *quee*.

Habitat. Primarily deciduous trees and tall shrubbery: parklands; shade trees; more open woodland; shrubbery, such as alder and willow, along streams and lakes; second growth of burntlands and logged areas; open mixedwoods.

Nesting. In a tree or bush most often 5 to 10 feet above ground, but varying from 3 to 55 feet, usually in a deciduous tree, occasionally in a conifer. Nest, a well-made cup, suspended by its rim from the fork of a branch. The outside of the nest is made of bits and strips of bark, paper from wasp nests, moss, lichens, leaves, plant fibres, bound together with spider webs. It is lined with grasses, rootlets, pine needles, sometimes hair. *Eggs*, usually 3 or 4; dull white marked mostly near the large end with dots or small spots of reddish brown, dark brown, or blackish. Incubation period 12 to 14 days, by the female (L. de K. Lawrence).

Range. Breeds from southern Canada (*see* Range in Canada) south to northern Oregon, northern Idaho, Wyoming, eastern Colorado, western Oklahoma, central Texas, the United States Gulf coast, and central Florida. Winters from Colombia and Venezuela to eastern Peru and western Brazil.

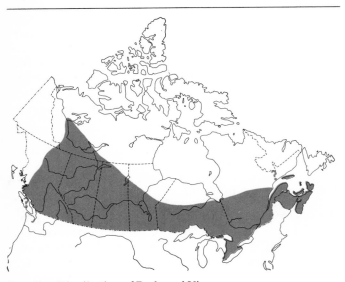

Breeding Distribution of Red-eyed Vireo

Range in Canada. Breeds in southwestern Mackenzie (forts Norman, Simpson, Resolution); eastern and southwestern British Columbia (Lower Liard Crossing, Trutch, Peace River parklands, Vanderhoof area, Hagensborg, Chilliwack, Hope, Okanagan Landing, Cranbrook; although recorded rarely in nesting season on Vancouver Island, breeding data are lacking); north, central, and southern Alberta; northwestern, central, and southern Saskatchewan (Lake Athabasca, Dead Lake on Churchill River southward); central and southern Manitoba (Thicket Portage southward); north-central and southern Ontario (Favour-

able Lake, southern James Bay southward); south-central and southwestern Quebec (Mistassini Post, Lake St. John, Ilets Jérémie, Tadoussac, Anticosti Island, Aylmer, Montreal, Hatley, Gaspé Peninsula, Magdalen Islands); New Brunswick; Prince Edward Island; and Nova Scotia (including Cape Breton Island).

Casual in Newfoundland (Cape Anguille) and on lower Moisie River, Quebec.

Remarks. All through the warm summer days, the Red-eyed Vireo's song goes on and on as the bird searches leisurely among the leafy branches for its insect food. Its songs are short phrases punctuated with pauses. Many have a rising inflection that sounds as though the bird were asking questions and answering them itself. Vast numbers of insects are destroyed by vireos, and some berries are eaten also.

PHILADELPHIA VIREO

Le Viréo de Philadelphie. *Vireo philadelphicus* (Cassin)
Plate 54. L. 4.5 to 5 in.

Crown grey (in autumn often tinged with olive); rest of upper parts greyish olive green; over eye a dull greyish white stripe and through eye a dusky streak (head markings similar to Red-eyed Vireo but much less distinct); wings and tail, dark greyish brown with olive green edging; no wing bars; breast and sides pale yellow, usually becoming whitish on throat and abdomen; eyes brown; legs bluish grey.

Measurements. *Adult male:* wing, 65.4–70 (68.2); tail, 45–52 (48.9); exposed culmen, 9–11 (10.2); tarsus, 16–17 (16.9). *Adult female:* wing, 63.7–68.8 (66) mm.

Field Marks. No wing bars and no eye-ring, thus differing from all vireos of regular occurrence in Canada except the Red-eyed and Warbling. It is smaller with less distinct head markings than the Red-eyed. Its pale yellow (instead of white) breast distinguishes it from both the Red-eyed and Warbling vireos. Lack of white wing bars separates it from the Yellow-throated. Resembles Tennessee and Orange-crowned warblers, but the vireo's thicker, blunter bill is very different from the slender, pointed warbler bill. *Voice:* Song similar to that of the Red-eyed Vireo but higher-pitched and with longer pauses between phrases.

Habitat. Open mixed and deciduous woodland, woods edges, aspen parklands, second growth on burntlands and logged areas, thickets of alder and willow.

Nesting. In a deciduous tree or tall shrub, 10 to 45 feet up. Nest suspended in usual vireo fashion. Bark strips, plant down, and *Usnea* lichen are likely to be part of the nest exterior, and there is a lining of grasses, pine needles, and sometimes animal hair. *Eggs*, 3 to 5; white, sparsely spotted (near the large end mostly) with browns. Incubation 14 days or a little less, by both sexes (H. F. Lewis).

Range. Breeds mainly in Canada (*see* Range in Canada) but also south to central-northern North Dakota, northern New Hampshire, and central Maine. Winters from Guatemala south to Panama and northwestern Colombia.

Range in Canada. Breeds in central-eastern British Columbia (Peace River parklands); northern, central, and south-central Alberta (Fort Chipewyan, Athabasca, Sundre); northwestern and central Saskatchewan (Fond du Lac, Kazan Lake, Flotten Lake, Somme; reports of breeding in extreme southeast are not completely satisfactory); central and southern Manitoba (Thicket Portage, Swan River, Duck Mountain, Whitemouth); north-central, central, and southern Ontario (Favourable Lake, southern James Bay south to Rainy River, Bruce Peninsula, Washago, Buckshot Lake);

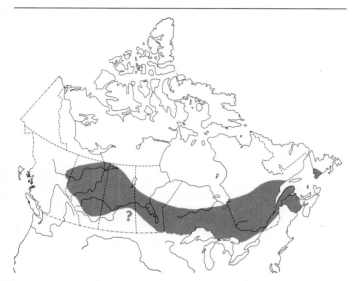

Breeding Distribution of Philadelphia Vireo

south-central and southwestern Quebec (Eastmain, Mistassini Post, Lake St. John, Moisie Bay, Quebec City, Gaspé Peninsula); New Brunswick (Tabusintac, probably Edmundston and Anagance); and probably southwestern Newfoundland (female with brood patch at Tompkins, July 12, 1943). Rare or casual in Nova Scotia (Norwood. No breeding evidence).

WARBLING VIREO
Le Viréo mélodieux. *Vireo gilvus* (Vieillot)
Plate 54. L. 5 to 6 in.

Top of head and back of neck smoke grey, the back and rump similar but tinged with olive green; white stripe over eye less distinct than in Red-eyed or Philadelphia vireos; wings and tail, brownish grey with pale edges; no wing bars; under parts mostly white, the sides and flanks, lightly tinged with pale yellow or pale buff; eye brown; legs bluish grey.

Measurements (*V. g. gilvus*). *Adult male:* wing, 67.1–74.8 (70.1); tail, 50–57 (51.9); exposed culmen, 10.2–12.5 (11.1); tarsus, 17–18.5 (17.9). *Adult female:* wing, 64.6–71.1 (68.0) mm.

Field Marks. It has no white wing bars and no eye-ring; thus it is similar to the Red-eyed and Philadelphia vireos. Its white (not yellowish) breast separates it from the Philadelphia Vireo. Smaller size and much less distinct head markings distinguish it from the Red-eyed. Its song is entirely different from that of our other vireos. Its heavier bill and more leisurely motions distinguish it from warblers. *Voice:* Its song is not broken up into disconnected phrases as in our other common vireos. It is a continued musical warble, usually gradually rising in pitch and intensity; similar to the song of the Purple Finch but much less energetic and less loud.

Habitat. Mature deciduous trees, usually well up in the leafy canopy. Open woodland both deciduous and mixed, woodland edges, shade trees in towns and cities, orchards, parks, prairie groves, alder and willow thickets.

Nesting. Usually high in a deciduous tree. Nest is a well-made cup, suspended by its rim from a fork of a twig, frequently near the end of the branch. *Eggs*, 3 to 5; dull white sparsely dotted with browns, mostly near the large end. Incubation reported to be 12 to 14 days (O. W. Knight), by both sexes.

Range. Breeds from southern Canada, south to Baja California and central-northern Mexico, central Texas, southern Louisiana, northern Alabama, western North Carolina, and Virginia. Winters from Mexico to Guatemala and El Salvador.

Range in Canada. Breeds in central-western and southwestern Mackenzie (Fort Norman, Fort Simpson, Fort Smith), British Columbia (all across south including Vancouver Island and northward on the mainland to Atlin, Trutch, and Lower Liard Crossing), Alberta (throughout, but scarce in southeast), central and southern Saskatchewan (southern Prince Albert National Park, Codette, Regina, Yorkton), southern Manitoba (Duck Mountain, Dauphin, Fairford, St. Vital, Whitemouth), western Ontario (Kenora), southern Ontario (Manitoulin Island, North Bay, Ottawa southward), southwestern Quebec (Gatineau Park, Montreal, Hatley, Quebec City; possibly slightly farther east as a single singing individual has been taken at Lac Trois Saumons, and a single singing individual recorded from Cacouna). Although reported from New Brunswick and Nova Scotia, no specimen has been taken.

Breeding Distribution of Warbling Vireo

Subspecies. (1) *Vireo gilvus gilvus* (Vieillot): se. Alta. (east of the mts.), Sask., Man., Ont., Que. (2) *V. g. swainsonii* Baird (coloration darker than in *gilvus*, size smaller): B.C., sw. Mack.; n. and sw. Alta.

319

Family **Parulidae** – Wood Warblers

Number of Species in North America 57; in Canada 42

The wood warblers are confined to the Western Hemisphere and are well represented during the summer months in Canada. They are small and frequently brightly coloured. Most have slender sharp-pointed bills, wings with nine primaries, and rather even tails. The adult males and females in breeding plumage are often coloured differently, while in autumn the adults may be very different again; the autumn immatures and juvenals just out of the nest are still different. These various plumages in the same species, combined with the fact that warblers are among the most active of birds, often foraging high in the leafy treetops, make field identification of the many species an intriguing challenge. The beginner would probably be well advised to confine himself at first to the adult males in spring.

Although called warblers, they do not warble. Many of the songs are not particularly musical, but they are energetic, pleasing, and distinctive enough to be useful aids in identification. The food of our warblers is mostly insects, but occasionally a few seeds or a little fruit is eaten. They are numerous in summer and collectively destroy vast numbers of insects.

BLACK-AND-WHITE WARBLER

La Fauvette noire et blanche. *Mniotilta varia* (Linnaeus)
Plate 55. L. 4.5 to 5.5 in.

Culmen somewhat convex. *Adult male:* Boldly striped black-and-white above and below, except belly, which is plain white; a broad white stripe down centre of otherwise black crown; two white wing bars; outer tail feathers with white areas on inner webs. *Adult female:* Similar to adult male but duller, the whites tinged with buff; under parts more extensively white, the dusky stripes confined mainly to sides and flanks.

Measurements. *Adult male:* wing, 67.2–71.5 (68.6); tail, 45.5–54 (49.6); exposed culmen, 10.4–12.1 (11.7); tarsus, 16.5–17 (16.8). *Adult female:* wing, 64.5–67.8 (66.4) mm.

Field Marks. A black-and-white striped warbler with a white stripe down middle of crown. Other black-and-white warblers (Black-throated Gray and Blackpoll) have no white stripe through middle of crown. Its distinct white eyebrow stripe also separates it from the Blackpoll. The Black-and-white has a distinctive habit of creeping along the branches and trunks of trees. *Song:* High pitched and rolling, usually made up of a number of double syllables, thus *weetsy weetsy weetsy weetsy weetsy weetsy.*

Habitat. Deciduous and mixed woodlands of various types, especially in moister situations. Forages in lower or middle branches, also in willow or alder shrubbery on edges of coniferous woodland.

Nesting. On the ground in a slight depression, often at the base of a tree, shrub, or stump, or beside a log or stone. Occasionally in a low stump or in the roots of an overturned tree. Nest is of grass, bark strips, leaves, moss, and rootlets; lined with hair. *Eggs,* 4 or 5, rarely 6; white, speckled or blotched with reddish browns and often some purplish grey. Incubation 13 days (Hatch *in* Forbush), by the female.

Range. Breeds from Canada south to eastern Montana, central Texas, southeastern Louisiana, central Alabama, central Georgia, and southeastern North Carolina. Winters from northern Mexico, southern Texas, central Florida, and the Bahamas south through the West Indies and Central America to Ecuador, Colombia, and northern Venezuela.

Breeding Distribution of Black-and-white Warbler

Range in Canada. Summer resident breeding in central-western and southwestern Mackenzie (Fort Norman, Fort Simpson, Fort Smith), central-eastern British Columbia (Peace River parklands), Alberta (Peace River District, Wood Buffalo Park, south at least to Belvedere and Camrose; possibly Cypress Hills where presence in July is recorded); central Saskatchewan (Kazan Lake, Nipawin, probably Madge Lake), central and southern Manitoba (Thicket Portage, The Pas, Riding Mountain, Portage la Prairie, Shoal Lake, Hillside Beach, Rennie), north-central and southern Ontario (Favourable Lake, Lake Attawapiskat, Moose Factory southward), southern Quebec (Val d'Or, Lake St. John, Mingan, Anticosti Island, Aylmer, Hatley, Montreal, Gaspé Peninsula, Magdalen Islands; species recorded east to St. Augustin), Newfoundland, New Brunswick, Prince Edward Island, and Nova Scotia (including Cape Breton Island).

PROTHONOTARY WARBLER

La Fauvette orangée. *Protonotaria citrea* (Boddaert)
Plate 55. L. 5.3 to 5.8 in.

Bill longish, sharp-pointed. *Adult male:* Head, neck, and under parts (except white under tail coverts) bright orange-yellow; back, yellowish olive green; rump and wing coverts bluish grey; no wing bars; tail blackish except that most of the inner webs of all but innermost feathers are white with black tips; bill blackish; legs dark bluish. *Adult female:* Similar to adult male but duller, the yellowish olive green of back extending over back of neck to top of head.

Measurements. *Adult male:* wing, 71.1–74.2 (72.9); tail, 46.2–49.8 (48); exposed culmen, 12.9–13.7 (13.2); tarsus, 18.3–19.8 (19). *Adult female:* wing, 65.5–69.1 (67.3) mm (Ridgway).

Field Marks. A golden-yellow warbler with plain bluish grey wings (no wing bars) and white areas in tail. Separable from the Yellow Warbler by dark (instead of yellow) wings, and white (instead of yellow) areas in tail. It lacks the Blue-winged Warbler's white wing bars and black line through eye. *Song:* A loud ringing *tweet tweet tweet tweet tweet*.

Habitat. Usually the vicinity of flooded or swampy woodlands.

Nesting. Usually in a woodpecker hole or natural cavity in a tree, rarely more than 15 feet up. Sometimes on man-made buildings, bridges, or in bird boxes. *Eggs,* usually 4 to 6; boldly spotted and blotched with browns and purplish greys. Incubation period 12 to 14 days (L. H. Walkinshaw).

Range. Breeds from southern Minnesota, southern Michigan, southern Ontario, central New York, and New Jersey south to eastern Texas, the Gulf coast of United States, and central Florida. Winters from southern Mexico south through Central America to Colombia and northern Venezuela.

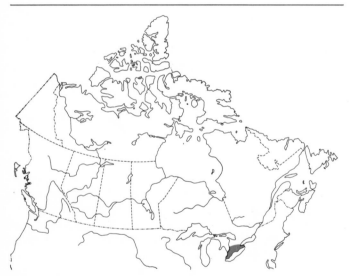

Breeding Distribution of Prothonotary Warbler

Range in Canada. Local summer resident, breeding only in extreme southern Ontario (Rondeau Park, Port Rowan, Turkey Point, Point Abino, Hamilton).

Casual in New Brunswick (Milltown, October 31, 1862), and Nova Scotia (Cape Sable, September 20, 1962).

WORM-EATING WARBLER
La Fauvette vermivore. *Helmitheros vermivorus* (Gmelin)
Plate 55. L. 5 to 5.75 in.

Bill rather large for a warbler. Sexes similar. Head buffy with broad black stripe on either side of crown and a narrower one through the eye; rest of upper parts greyish olive green; no wing bars or patches in the tail; under parts plain buffy; bill and legs brownish.

Measurements. *Adult male:* wing, 66.3–72.9 (69.3); tail, 47.7–51 (49.3); exposed culmen, 12.9–14.5 (13.7); tarsus, 17.3–18.3 (18.0). *Adult female:* wing, 64.8–67.1 (65.8) mm (Ridgway).

Range. Breeds from northeastern Kansas, central Ohio, and southeastern Massachusetts south to northeastern Texas, central-southern Louisiana, northern Georgia, and northeastern North Carolina. Winters from Mexico south to Panama and in the West Indies.

Status in Canada. Casual in southern Ontario (London, May 28, 1908; Long Point, May 4, 1960; also, individuals were banded at Bradley's Marsh and Long Point, spring, 1961).

GOLDEN-WINGED WARBLER
La Fauvette à ailes dorées
Vermivora chrysoptera (Linnaeus)
Plate 55. L. 4.9 to 5.3 in.

Adult male: Top of head, lemon yellow; rest of upper parts bluish grey; sides of head, whitish with broad black patch from base of bill to ear coverts; middle and greater wing coverts yellow, producing a conspicuous yellow patch on the wing; outer three tail feathers on each side with much white toward tips; throat patch black; rest of under parts whitish becoming greyish on sides of breast, sides, and flanks; bill blackish; eyes brownish. *Adult female:* Similar to adult male but duller; the black of throat and sides of head replaced by grey.

Measurements. *Adult male:* wing, 59.7–65 (62.2); tail, 43.2–47.5 (46.2); exposed culmen, 10.4–11.4 (10.7); tarsus, 17–18 (17.5). *Adult female:* wing, 57.7–63.5 (59.9) mm (Ridgway).

Field Marks. Male is a black-throated warbler with a yellow wing patch. Female similar but blacks replaced by grey. *Song:* A buzzy *zee bz bz bz*, the first syllable highest.

Habitat. Shrubby wastes, old bushy pastures, bushy edges and openings in deciduous woodland, shrubby borders of streams.

Nesting. On the ground, or very near it. Nest, usually on dead leaves or in ferns or weed stalks, is rather bulky and is made of strips of bark, grass, and leaves and lined with finer grass and shreds of bark. *Eggs,* 4 to 7; white, variously marked with browns and purplish grey.

Range. Breeds from southern Manitoba, central-eastern Minnesota, northern Michigan, southern Ontario, and eastern Massachusetts south to southeastern Iowa, northern Indiana, southern Ohio, northern Georgia, northwestern South Carolina, and southeastern Pennsylvania. Winters from Guatemala and Nicaragua south to central Colombia and northern Venezuela.

Range in Canada. Local summer resident, breeding in southern Manitoba (Vivian) and in extreme southern Ontario (northward as far as Mac Station, northwest of Barrie; Buckthorn Lake, Peterborough County; and Canoe Lake, north of Kingston).

Wanders north rarely to Manitoulin Island and Ottawa,

Ontario; in Manitoba has been noted also in Winnipeg, Portage la Prairie, Aweme, Ponemah Beach, and Whitemouth. Accidental in Nova Scotia (Bon Portage Island, May 17, 1961).

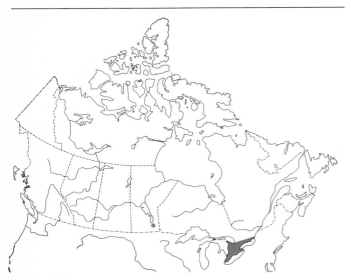

Breeding Distribution of Golden-winged Warbler

Hybrids. In areas where both Golden-winged and Blue-winged warblers breed, the two sometimes hybridize. Hybridization produces two main phenotypes which were thought to be separate species and were called, respectively, Brewster's Warbler (Plate 55) and Lawrence's Warbler. Lawrence's, the rarer of the two, is not illustrated but has yellow under parts, black throat, and black patch on side of head. A male of the Brewster type was collected near London, Ontario, on May 14, 1956. There are various sight records in southern Ontario of Brewster's, but only two of Lawrence's. In 1956, a female Golden-winged paired with a male Blue-winged at Milton Heights, Ontario, and raised a brood of four young. For a discussion of the genetics of Brewster's and Lawrence's warblers, *see* K. C. Parkes 1951, *Wilson Bulletin* 63: 5–15.

BLUE-WINGED WARBLER
La Fauvette à ailes bleues. *Vermivora pinus* (Linnaeus)
Plate 55. L. 4.5 to 5 in.

Adult male: Top of head and under parts, lemon-yellow except whitish under tail coverts; narrow black stripe through eye; back, scapulars, rump, and upper tail coverts, olive green; wings mostly dusky, but bluish grey coverts and edging give them a bluish look when folded; two white or yellowish white wing bars; tail, bluish grey, the inner webs of outer feathers with much white; bill, blackish in spring, paler in autumn. *Adult female:* Similar to adult male but duller, the olive green more extensive, covering most of top of head.

Measurements. *Adult male:* wing, 57.7–63.2 (60.2); tail, 43.4–48.3 (46); exposed culmen, 10.4–11.4 (10.7); tarsus, 17–18 (17.3). *Adult female:* wing, 56.1–59.2 (57.7) mm (Ridgway).

Field Marks. A yellow warbler with very narrow blackish stripe through the eye, two white wing bars. *Song:* Commonly an unhurried buzzy two syllable *zee-bee*, the second syllable usually (not always) lower, a little suggestive of a sigh.

Habitat. Brushy neglected fields and pastures, woodland openings and edges, thickets along streams and swamps.

Nesting. On or very near the ground, usually among vegetation. *Eggs*, 4 to 7, usually 5 or 6; white, sparsely spotted or speckled with browns and purplish grey.

Range. Breeds from eastern Nebraska, southeastern Minnesota, southern Michigan, northern Ohio, extreme southern Ontario (rarely), southern New York, and southwestern Massachusetts, south to northwestern Arkansas, southern Illinois, northern Alabama, northern Georgia, North Carolina, and Delaware. Winters from southern Mexico south to Nicaragua and Panama.

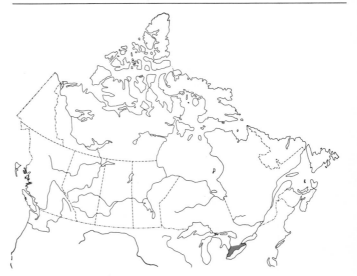

Breeding Distribution of Blue-winged Warbler

Range in Canada. Breeds rarely in extreme southern Ontario (Ancaster, Milton Heights, Sulphur Springs).

It has wandered north, rarely, to Wasaga Beach and Kingston, Ontario. Accidental in Saskatchewan (Regina, November 9, 1965).

TENNESSEE WARBLER
La Fauvette obscure. *Vermivora peregrina* (Wilson)
Plate 56. L. 4.5 to 5 in.

Male in breeding plumage: Top of head and hind-neck, bluish grey; line over eye whitish; narrow line through eye dusky; back, scapulars, wing coverts, and rump, olive green; wings and tail with olive-green edging; no wing bars; outer tail feathers usually with an inconspicuous small greyish white patch; under parts plain greyish white; legs dark bluish grey or brownish grey. *Female (breeding plumage):* Similar to adult male but grey of head mixed with olive green; the pale line over eye and on under parts tinged with yellow. *Adult male (autumn):* Crown mixed with olive green; under parts more greenish than in breeding plumage. *Adult female (autumn):* No grey on head; upper parts all olive green, under parts washed with yellow. *Young (first autumn):* No grey on crown; upper parts all olive green; line over eye and under parts yellow, becoming more whitish on belly and under tail coverts (which sometimes are decidedly yellowish, however); some show a poorly defined light wing bar.

Measurements. *Adult male:* wing, 62.6–67.5 (64.9); tail, 41–45 (42.6); exposed culmen, 10–11.5 (10.5); tarsus, 16.2–17.4 (16.7). *Adult female:* wing, 56.3–63.3 (60.5) mm.

Field Marks. Spring adults with grey top of head, white line over eye, and dark line through eye. Beginners might confuse it with Philadelphia, Red-eyed, or Warbling Vireo, but the warbler's slender sharp-pointed bill and quicker actions should eliminate confusion. The autumn Tennessee resembles the Orange-crowned Warbler, but the under parts of the Tennessee are never streaked; its eye stripes are more definite; it usually has white under tail coverts, but the Orange-crowned always has yellow ones. However, many Tennessee Warblers also have yellowish under tail coverts. Their song is suggestive of that of the Nashville Warbler but is louder, more staccato, and usually in three instead of two parts.

Habitat. Coniferous, mixed, and deciduous woodlands, bogs, alder and willow thickets, burntlands, more open deciduous second growth. In migration all types of woodland.

Nesting. On the ground often in bogs but sometimes on dry hillsides. Nest often in sphagnum and sometimes arched-over by moss or grass. The nest is of grasses. *Eggs,* 4 to 7; white, dotted or spotted with reddish browns.

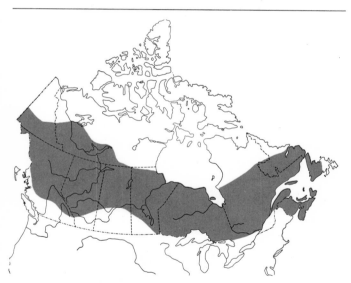

Breeding Distribution of Tennessee Warbler

Range. Breeds widely in forested Canada (*see* Range in Canada) and south to northwestern Montana, northern Minnesota, northern Wisconsin, northern Michigan, northeastern New York, southern Vermont, central New Hampshire, and southern Maine. Winters from southern Mexico and Guatemala south to Colombia and Venezuela.

Range in Canada. Summer resident, breeding from southern Yukon (Pine Creek, Kathleen Lake, Hutchi Lakes, Watson Lake), central-western and southern Mackenzie (Brackett Lake, Norman Wells, Fort Rae, Fort Reliance), northern Saskatchewan (Lake Athabasca), northern Manitoba (Churchill), northern Ontario, north-central Quebec (Knob Lake), southern Labrador (Goose Bay, Cartwright, Sawbill), and western Newfoundland (Gaff Topsail, Doyles) south to southern British Columbia (mainland only: Kimsquit, Chezacut, Indianpoint Lake, probably 158 Mile House and Kootenay National Park), southwestern and south-central Alberta (Banff Park, Red Deer, Camrose), south-central Saskatchewan (Cochin, Prince Albert, Nipawin, Somme), southern Manitoba (Duck Mountain, Hillside Beach, Whitemouth), south-central Ontario (North Bay, Algonquin Park), southern Quebec (Amos, Stoneham, Rivière du Loup, Gaspé Peninsula, inner north shore of the Gulf of St. Lawrence, Anticosti Island, and probably Magdalen Islands), New Brunswick, Prince Edward Island, and Nova Scotia (Wolfville, Albany; Cape Breton Island).

ORANGE-CROWNED WARBLER
La Fauvette verdâtre. *Vermivora celata* (Say)
Plate 56. L. 4.8 to 5.3 in.

Adult male: Upper parts dusky olive green, brightening on rump; a partly concealed crown patch of dull orange; eyelids and line over eye, yellowish; a narrow, poorly defined streak of dusky through eye; wings and tail without white patches; under parts including under tail coverts and wing linings greenish yellow, the breast and sometimes the throat indistinctly streaked with olive green; bill dark grey; legs olive grey. *Adult female:* Very similar to adult male, sometimes indistinguishable, but usually duller and more greyish in colour, the orange crown patch more restricted or absent. *Young in autumn:* Similar to adults but duskier, the crown patch either very small or wanting.

Measurements (*V. c. celata*). *Adult male:* wing, 56.9–62.5 (59.8); tail, 46–51.5 (48.6); exposed culmen, 10–11.2 (10.6); tarsus, 16.5–18.5 (17.5). *Adult female:* wing, 55–59.2 (56.8) mm.

Field Marks. A dingy greenish yellow warbler with no distinct markings, the crown patch rarely visible. Its vaguely streaked and usually more extensively yellow under parts distinguish it from autumn Tennessees. The Nashville Warbler also has a reddish crown patch but shows a white eye-ring against more greyish sides of the head; it has brighter yellow unstreaked under parts. *Song:* A colourless trill, dropping slightly in pitch near the middle, and weakening near the end.

Habitat: Brushy and open deciduous woods, the deciduous elements of mixedwoods, second growths in clearings or burntlands, various brushy thickets and stands of tall shrubbery.

Nesting. On the ground, sometimes in a low bush. Nest, of grass, shreds of bark, and moss, lined with fine grass, hair, and feathers. *Eggs,* 4 to 6; white, finely dotted around the larger end with reddish browns and often a little purplish grey.

Range. Breeds in central Alaska and much of forested Canada (*see* Range in Canada) and south to Baja California, southern Arizona, and western Texas. Winters from southern United States south to Guatemala and southern Florida.

Range in Canada. Summer resident, breeding in Yukon (Old Crow southward), western and central-southern Mackenzie (Mackenzie Delta; forts Anderson, Norman, Simpson; Hill Island Lake), British Columbia (throughout, including coastal islands), Alberta (throughout north, centre, and in mountains of southwest; local in southeast: Red Deer River, Cypress Hills), Saskatchewan (Lake Athabasca, Flotten Lake, Prince Albert National Park, Nipawin; locally in the south: Cypress Hills, Qu'Appelle Valley), Manitoba (Lynn Lake, Churchill, Duck Mountain, Aweme), northern and central Ontario (Fort Severn, Favourable Lake, Lake Attawapiskat, Big Piskwanish, Lake Nipigon, Kapuskasing, Genier), central Quebec (Kinglet Lake, Paul and Moar bays, Lake Albanel, Moisie Bay), and southern Labrador (Goose Bay).

Uncommon migrant south of the breeding range in southern Ontario, and a scarce migrant in southwestern Quebec (Montreal, Quebec City, Hatley). Casual in Nova Scotia (Halifax) and at Hope Point and Bernard Harbour on Dolphin and Union Strait, N.W.T.

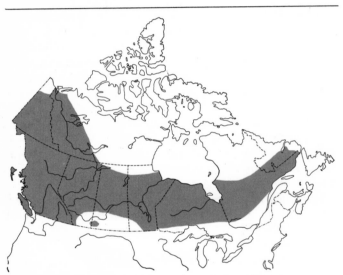

Breeding Distribution of Orange-crowned Warbler

Subspecies. (1) *Vermivora celata celata* (Say) (palest and greyest race): n., c., se. Yukon, Mack., n. and c. Alta. (except mts. and Cypress Hills), n. and c. Sask. (except Cypress Hills), Man., Ont., Que. (2) *V. c. orestera* Oberholser (similar to *celata* but larger, more yellowish): sw. Yukon (Kluane Lake, Carcross), interior B.C. (east of the coast), s. Alta. (sw. mts., Cypress Hills), sw. Sask. (Cypress Hills). (3) *V. c. lutescens* (Ridgway) (brighter yellow in colour than either *celata* or *orestera*, smaller than the latter): B.C. coast and islands.

NASHVILLE WARBLER
La Fauvette à joues grises. *Vermivora ruficapilla* (Wilson) Plate 56. L. 4.5 to 5 in.

Adult male: Top of head, cheeks, hind-neck, and sides of neck, bluish grey; chestnut patch on top of head, but usually somewhat obscured by grey; eye-ring white; narrow streak from base of bill to eye, greyish white; rest of upper parts olive green; wings and tail with no white bars or patches; under parts, including under tail coverts, bright yellow becoming whitish on lower belly. *Adult female:* Similar to adult male but duller in colour and with chestnut crown patch smaller or absent. *Young (first autumn):* Duller than adults, the grey of head more brownish, crown patch of male smaller or absent, almost always absent in female.

Measurements (*V. r. ruficapilla*). *Adult male:* wing, 56–61.7 (59.2); tail, 40–47 (44.2); exposed culmen, 9.3–10.9 (10.1); tarsus, 16–17 (16.6). *Adult female:* wing, 53.3–57.6 (56.3) mm.

Field Marks. Bright plain yellow under parts and grey head, white eye-ring. The grey which extends down low on cheeks and sides of neck is sharply cut off from bright yellow throat. No white wing bars or tail patches. In autumn the grey of head is more brownish, but yellow of throat is still sharply cut off from it. *Song:* Resembles somewhat that of Tennessee Warbler but has less carrying power and is in two instead of three (usually) parts: *see it, see it, see it, ti-ti-ti-ti-ti,* the second part lower than the first and more rapid.

Habitat. Sparse immature deciduous or mixed woods, especially where aspen or birch are a component, with low bushes, on either dry or moist land: second growths on old clearings, burntlands, sparsely treed bogs.

Nesting. On the ground, usually well concealed by shrubs or in a mossy hummock; nest of moss, grass, bark strips, leaves; lined with fine grass or hair. *Eggs,* 4 or 5; white, speckled with reddish browns usually mainly about the large end. Incubation mostly, if not entirely, by the female.

Breeding Distribution of Nashville Warbler

Range. Breeds from southern Canada south to central California, northern Utah, southern Minnesota, southern Michigan, northeastern West Virginia, and western Maryland. Winters from northern Mexico, southern Texas, and southern Florida south to Guatemala.

Range in Canada. Summer resident, breeding in southern

British Columbia (Pemberton, Lillooet, Clearwater, Revelstoke, Pitt Lake, Trail), central and southern Manitoba (Moose and Cedar lakes, Duck Mountain, Hillside Beach, Rennie), central and southern Ontario (Favourable Lake, Lake Nipigon, and probably Moose Factory southward, but very local in extreme south, reportedly to Middlesex County), southern Quebec (Taschereau, Amos, Lake St. John, Lake Ste. Anne on Toulnustouc River, perhaps Mingan, Piashte Bay, and Anticosti Island, southward including Magdalen Islands), New Brunswick, Prince Edward Island, and Nova Scotia (including Cape Breton Island). Probably breeds also in central Saskatchewan (Prince Albert National Park). Summer sight records for southwestern Newfoundland.

Subspecies. (1) *Vermivora ruficapilla ruficapilla* (Wilson): Man., Ont., Que., N.B., P.E.I., N.S., probably Sask. (2) *V. r. ridgwayi* van Rossem (rump brighter, more yellowish, lower abdomen more extensively whitish): s. B.C.

VIRGINIA'S WARBLER

La Fauvette de Virginia. *Vermivora virginiae* (Baird)
L. 4.3 to 4.7 in.

Adults: Upper parts grey except chestnut patch on crown and bright olive green rump and upper tail coverts; eyering white; no wing bars or tail patch; under parts, greyish white with yellow patch on middle of breast (sometimes extending to throat), and bright yellow under tail coverts.

Status in Canada. Accidental in southern Ontario (Point Pelee National Park, May 16, 1958). (Its breeding range is in southwestern United States from central Nevada, southeastern Idaho, northeastern Utah, and central northern Colorado southward.)

PARULA WARBLER

La Fauvette parula. *Parula americana* (Linnaeus)
Plate 55. L. 4.3 to 4.9 in.

Adult male: Upper parts mainly greyish blue, this extending down over face and sides of breast; upper and lower eyelids partly white; in middle of back, a large patch of greenish yellow; two prominent white wing bars; two or three outermost tail feathers on each side with large white patch near tip; throat and much of breast, yellow; yellow of throat separated from that of breast by a blackish band and behind that band some spots of reddish brown; sides usually tinged with chestnut; abdomen and under tail coverts white. *Adult female:* Resembles adult male but is duller, band across breast either absent or very much restricted, but often there are a few brownish feather tips on upper breast. *Young in autumn:* Blue of upper parts much obscured by greenish; breast band lacking or only faintly indicated.

Measurements. *Adult male:* wing, 58.1–64.7 (61.1); tail, 41–45.5 (43.5); exposed culmen, 9.9–11 (10.4); tarsus, 16–17 (16.5). *Adult female:* wing, 53.7–59 (56.2) mm.

Field Marks. This and the Canada Warbler are our only two bluish-backed warblers with yellow under parts. The Parula's two white wing bars and tail patches, greenish yellow patch on the back, different face pattern, and (when present) different breast band readily separate it from the Canada. The Parula's greenish yellow back patch separates it from other warblers, and the breast of the male is very distinctive. *Song:* Although there are variations, the usual pattern is a buzzy rising trill ending in an abrupt emphatic *zip* or *wip*.

Habitat. Either deciduous or coniferous woods and openings, particularly in moister places where the lichen *Usnea* (old man's beard moss) grows. Forages most often at medium heights and up to upper branches. In migration various types of woodland and tall shrubbery.

Nesting. Nest is hollowed out in a hanging bunch of *Usnea* lichen, often without lining or with only a few pieces of grass or other plant material or a few horse hairs. Where *Usnea* is scarce, a hanging cluster of hemlock or spruce may be used and some *Usnea* added. *Eggs*, usually 4 or 5; white, speckled and spotted with browns and drab. Incubation 12 to 14 days, by the female (R. and J. Graber).

Range. Breeds from southeastern Manitoba east to Nova Scotia and south to the Gulf coast from eastern Texas to central Florida. Winters from Mexico south through Central America to Nicaragua and from Florida south through the Greater and Lesser Antilles to Barbados.

Breeding Distribution of Parula Warbler

Range in Canada. Summer resident, breeding locally in southeastern Manitoba (Waugh), central and southern Ontario (Off Lake, Lake Abitibi, Long Point), southern Quebec (Lake Waswanipi, Blue Sea Lake, Quebec City, Lac Rimouski, Percé, Hatley, Lac Trois Saumons), New Brunswick, Prince Edward Island, Nova Scotia (including Cape Breton Island).

Occurs in summer north to Lake St. John and Anticosti Island, Quebec. Scarce visitor to Saskatchewan (Emma Lake, Fort Qu'Appelle, Moose Mountain, McLean, Sovereign). Casual in Alberta (Turner Valley: 15 miles west).

Remarks. This is one of the smallest and prettiest of the wood warblers. It often forages high in the treetops where it may best be located by its song. It is widely but unevenly distributed in summer, its numbers being influenced by the availability of the lichen *Usnea*, which it prefers as a nesting site. The name 'parula' which means little titmouse, refers to its occasional tendency to cling upside-down to a branch or cluster in chickadee-fashion.

YELLOW WARBLER

La Fauvette jaune. *Dendroica petechia* (Linnaeus)
Plate 55. L. 4.75 to 5.25 in.

Inner webs of tail with large *yellow* patches, thus differing from other Canadian warblers of generally yellow coloration. *Adult male:* Upper parts mostly yellowish olive green, becoming yellow, sometimes with an orange tinge, on crown; wings dark with yellow edging; tail with large patches of *yellow on inner webs;* sides of head and the under parts rich yellow, the breast, sides, and flanks striped with chestnut. *Adult female:* Similar to adult male but duller, slightly more greenish above, paler yellow below and with few or no chestnut stripes. *Young (first autumn):* Similar to adult female but less yellow above; under parts unstreaked pale dusky yellow; yellow patches in tail smaller and paler.

Measurements (*D. p. aestiva*). *Adult male:* wing, 59.2–64.3 (62.1); tail, 43–47 (45.2); exposed culmen, 9.1–11 (10.2); tarsus, 17.5–18.5 (18.1). *Adult female:* wing, 56.7–63.2 (59.0) mm.

Field Marks. The common yellow warbler in much of Canada, often nesting in ornamental shrubbery in gardens. Adult male's reddish breast-streaks are readily seen at close range, but in females and young the streaks are faint or absent. In any plumage the *yellow* patches in the tail are diagnostic. Female Wilson's Warbler closely resembles female and young Yellow Warbler, but it has no light patches in the tail. The eastern race of the Palm Warbler has reddish streaks on a yellow breast, but the Palm Warbler constantly wags its tail (which has white instead of yellow patches). The Yellow Warbler and the Goldfinch are both sometimes called 'yellow bird,' but the slender bill and yellowish instead of black wings easily distinguish the warbler. *Song:* Lively, cheerful, but variable. Many songs sound like *tzee tzee tzee tzee sétta wee see.* Many people confuse it with that of the Chestnut-sided Warbler.

Habitat. Thickets, especially those of alder and willow, in moister areas like the edges of streams, lakes, bogs, marshes; garden shrubbery is almost equally popular.

Nesting. In bush or tree, most often 3 to 8 feet up but rarely as high as 40 feet. Nest is firmly fastened to a fork of a branch and is composed of plant fibres, grasses, shredded bark, sometimes twine or cotton wool. Although often bulky externally, the cup is neat and is lined with fine grasses, hairs, and plant down. *Eggs*, usually 4 or 5; white to bluish white, spotted mostly around the large end, with various browns and purplish greys. Incubation, mostly if not entirely by the female, is reported to average 11 days (F. G. Schrantz).

Range. Breeds from north-central Alaska, and from near treeline across Canada south to southern Baja California, central Peru, coastal Venezuela, Trinidad, the Antilles, Bahamas, and Florida Keys. Winters from Mexico and the Bahamas south to Peru and Brazil.

Range in Canada. Summer resident, breeding from northern Yukon (Old Crow, Lapierre House), northwestern and central Mackenzie (Mackenzie Delta, Richards Island, Fort Anderson, Fort Reliance), northern Saskatchewan (Lake Athabasca, Black Lake area, Reindeer Lake), northern Manitoba (Lynn Lake, Churchill), northern Ontario (Fort Severn, James Bay), central Quebec (Richmond Gulf, mouth of Great Whale River, Lake Mistassini, north shore of the Gulf of St. Lawrence; recorded in summer north to headwaters of Swampy Bay River), southern Labrador (Grand Falls, Holton Harbour, Goose Bay), and Newfoundland south to southern coastal and interior British Columbia, and to southern parts of Alberta, Saskatchewan, Manitoba, Ontario, Quebec (including Magdalen Islands), New Brunswick, Prince Edward Island, and Nova Scotia (including Cape Breton Island).

Accidental on Southampton Island, N.W.T. (August 1951).

Breeding Distribution of Yellow Warbler

Subspecies. (1) *D. p. aestiva* (Gmelin) (the palest Canadian race): se. Alta., s. Sask., extreme s. Man., s. Ont. (Off Lake, North Bay), s. Que. (Que., Gaspé Pen.), N.B., P.E.I., and N.S. (but on Cape Breton I. intergrading with and closer to *amnicola*). (2) *D. p. amnicola* Batchelder (darker, more olivaceous above than *aestiva*): Yukon, Mack., ne. B.C. (Peace River District), n. and c. Alta., n. and c. Sask., n. and c. Man., n. and c. Ont., c. Que. (Lake St. John, Anticosti I., north shore Gulf of St. Lawrence; also Magdalen Islands), s. Lab., and Nfld. (3) *D. p. rubiginosa* (Pallas) (darker above than *amnicola*, the forehead more extensively olivaceous): w. B.C. (Atlin, Hazelton, Victoria). (4) *D. p. morcomi* Coale: interior s. B.C. (Okanagan Landing, Newgate). The subspecies of the Yellow Warbler are in need of study.

Remarks. Because the Yellow Warbler, more often than most warblers, frequents the ornamental shrubbery about our dwellings all across the country, it is probably seen more often by the average person than any other warbler. Many know it as 'yellow bird.' Its spritely, if not particularly melodious, song is rendered with enthusiasm, especially in May and June. One male has been credited with 3,240 songs in a day at the height of the singing season. Insects are its main food.

MAGNOLIA WARBLER
La Fauvette à tête cendrée
Dendroica magnolia (Wilson)
Plate 56. L. 4.4 to 5.1 in.

Broad white band on tail separates it in all plumages from other Canadian warblers. *Adult male (breeding plumage):* Top of head and nape bluish grey; line back from eye white; sides of head black; back and scapulars black; rump patch yellow; tail mostly black, with a broad white band across its middle (but not across two centre feathers); wings with two white wing bars; under parts mostly bright yellow, the breast, sides, and flanks heavily streaked with black, the under tail coverts white. *Adult female (breeding plumage):* Similar to adult male but top of head duller; back, olive green with black spots; white wing bars narrower; black streaks on under parts narrower and duller. *Young and adults in autumn:* Resemble adult females in breeding plumage, but top and sides of head greyish; back olive green, sometimes spotted with black (adult male); under parts mostly plain yellow, more or less faintly streaked on sides and flanks.

Measurements. *Adult male:* wing, 58.7–61.5 (60.5); tail, 47–51.5 (49.1); exposed culmen, 9.1–11 (9.8); tarsus, 17.5–18.5 (17.9). *Adult female:* wing, 54.1–59.8 (57.1) mm.

Field Marks. A yellow-breasted, yellow-rumped warbler with distinctive tail markings. In any plumage the tail from below appears white at the base with a very broad black band across the end (*see* Cape May Warbler). *Song: Wisha wisha wisha witsy,* rising slightly. Also a distinctive call-note, *tlep.*

Habitat. On breeding grounds, mostly young or low coniferous woods or open mixedwood and edges. In migration, various types of woodland and thickets.

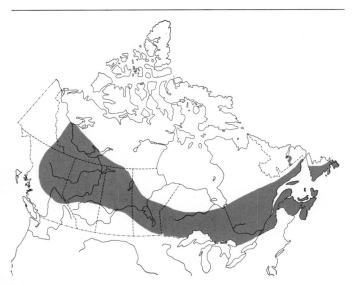
Breeding Distribution of Magnolia Warbler

Nesting. Usually (not always) low in a small conifer. Nest is of grass and weeds, lined with hair and fine rootlets. *Eggs,* 3 to 5, usually 4; white variably marked with reddish browns and purplish grey, especially on larger end. Incubation 11 to 13 days, apparently by the female (A. C. Bent).

Range. Breeds in Canada (*see* Range in Canada) and south in the United States to northeastern Minnesota, central Wisconsin, central Michigan, and locally to central West Virginia, western Virginia, northeastern Pennsylvania, northwestern New Jersey, and northern Massachusetts. Winters from central Mexico through Central America to Costa Rica and the West Indies.

Range in Canada. Summer resident, breeding in central-western and southwestern Mackenzie (Fort Norman, western Great Slave Lake), northeastern, central, and south-central British Columbia (Trutch, Liard Crossing, Driftwood Valley, Little River P.O., Hazelton, Quesnel, Indianpoint Lake), northern and central Alberta (south to about Jasper, Edson, Edmonton), northwestern and central Saskatchewan (Lake Athabasca, Meadow Lake, Nipawin), central and southern Manitoba (Thicket Portage, Oxford House, Riding Mountain, Hillside Beach), central and southern Ontario (Favourable and Attawapiskat lakes, Moose Factory, Off Lake, Port Arthur, Wasaga Beach, Sharbot Lake), south-central and southern Quebec (Eastmain, Lake Mistassini, north shore of the Gulf of St. Lawrence east at least to St. Augustin, Anticosti Island, Low, Hatley, Gaspé Peninsula, Magdalen Islands), southern Newfoundland, New Brunswick, Prince Edward Island, and Nova Scotia (including Cape Breton Island); probably Labrador (Hamilton River).

CAPE MAY WARBLER
La Fauvette tigrée. *Dendroica tigrina* (Gmelin)
Plate 56. L. 4.7 to 5.6 in.

Adult male (breeding plumage): Top of head and narrow line through eye, black or blackish; patch of chestnut on sides of face sometimes interrupting yellow above eye; sides of neck yellow; back and scapulars, yellowish green spotted or streaked with black; rump yellow; tail blackish with large white patches on outer feathers near tip (decreasing extent of white inward); patch of white on wing coverts; under parts, yellow fading to white on lower abdomen; throat, breast, sides, and flanks, streaked with black often with a tinge of chestnut on throat. *Adult female (breeding plumage):* Much duller than adult male, the top of head olive streaked dusky; sides of head, pale yellow with olive ear coverts; rump patch and sides of neck, yellowish; two faint white wing bars; under parts whitish, the whitish more or less tinged with yellow; throat, breast, and sides streaked with dusky. *Adult male (autumn):* Similar to adult male in spring but upper parts tinged with grey, under parts lightly frosted with white. *Adult female (autumn):* Similar to female in breeding plumage but a bit more decidedly yellow on breast and rump, streaks of under parts veiled by white. *Young (autumn):* Resemble adults, in autumn, of their respective sexes, but white of tail more restricted; male with no chestnut on face and no black cap; female with less or no yellow on under parts, but with a faint tinge of yellow always present on sides of neck.

Measurements. *Adult male:* wing, 65.4–71.3 (67.2); tail, 45.5–50.5 (47.9); exposed culmen, 9.9–11 (10.5); tarsus, 17–18.5 (17.8). *Adult female:* wing, 61.3–67 (63.4) mm.

Field Marks. Adult male's chestnut cheeks, white patch on wing coverts, and yellow black-streaked under parts are a combination that is unmistakable. Female lacks chestnut cheeks and is of much duller general coloration but shows a yellow rump and a yellowish area on sides of neck. Young female in autumn is extremely dull coloured (Plate 56) but has a yellowish rump and a small yellowish patch on sides of neck. This yellowish neck patch, although sometimes obscure, is characteristic of the Cape May, regardless of how dull the bird may be otherwise, and distinguishes it from other similar warblers such as the Myrtle and the Audubon's (which have a more definite yellow rump patch) (*see also* Magnolia and Palm warblers). *Song:* A high-pitched sibilant *seep seep seep seep*, four or more times in the same high pitch.

Habitat. On breeding grounds, coniferous woods and mixedwoods, especially more open types and edges. Sings and nests mainly in the upper branches. In migration various kinds of woods and thickets.

Nesting. Usually near the top of a conifer, 30 to 60 feet up. Nest of moss, grass, small twigs, and plant down, lined with fine grass, hair, and feathers. *Eggs,* 4 to 9; white, spotted, mostly near the large end, with reddish browns and a little purplish grey.

Range. Breeds in Canada (Alberta east to Nova Scotia) and south in the United States to northeastern North Dakota, northern and central-eastern Minnesota, northern Wisconsin, northern Michigan, northeastern New York, central-eastern Vermont, and southern Maine. Winters in the West Indies.

Range in Canada. Summer resident breeding in south-western and central-southern Mackenzie (Fort Simpson, Slave River), central-eastern British Columbia (probably: Peace River parklands), northern and central Alberta (Grimshaw, Wood Buffalo Park, Fort Assiniboine), central Saskatchewan (Kazan Lake, Prince Albert National Park), central and southeastern Manitoba (Thicket Portage, Duck Mountain, Julius), north-central and central Ontario (Lac Seul; Favourable and Nipigon lakes; Moose Factory; Dorcas Bay in Bruce County; Algonquin Park), southern Quebec (Eastmain, Lake St. John, St. Margaret River, Lac Trois Saumons, Gaspé Peninsula, Blue Sea Lake, Ulverton), New Brunswick, Prince Edward Island, and Nova Scotia (rather rare but including Cape Breton Island).

Recorded without evidence of breeding on Anticosti Island and at mouth of Natashquan River, Quebec.

Casual in Newfoundland (St. Andrews, August 25, 1959).

BLACK-THROATED BLUE WARBLER
La Fauvette bleue à gorge noire
Dendroica caerulescens (Gmelin)
Plate 57. L. 4.8 to 5.5 in.

Adult male: Upper parts mainly dark greyish blue, occasionally with some black spots on back; a small white patch at the base of the primaries; no wing bars; outer feathers of tail with large white patches reaching to near ends; sides of head, throat, upper breast, and sides, black; rest of under parts white. *Adult female:* Very different from male. Upper parts and cheeks uniform dull olive or olive green, often with a trace of blue on crown, upper tail coverts, and edging of tail; at base of primaries a small whitish spot, smaller than that of adult male and sometimes concealed; no wing bars; whitish stripe over eye; lower eyelid partly white; outer tail feathers with or without inconspicuous greyish patches; under parts plain pale greenish yellow. *Young (autumn):* Like adult of their respective sexes; male with blue of upper parts duller and somewhat mixed with olive; black below with grey feather tips; and posterior white under parts tinged with yellow.

Measurements. *Adult male:* wing, 64–67.1 (64.9); tail, 50–53 (51.2); exposed culmen, 9.2–11 (10.1); tarsus, 18–18.5 (18.3). *Adult female:* wing, 57.6–62.8 (60.7) mm.

Field Marks. The male with blue upper parts, black face, throat, and sides, and a small white spot near base of primaries is unmistakable. Females are plain, unstreaked, olive green and look like several other warblers, especially female Tennessees. Usually the small white wing spot at the base of the primaries, which marks the Black-throated Blue, can be seen. When this mark cannot be discerned, the solidly dark cheeks separate it from the Tennessee, and the lack of wing bars from the female Cerulean. *Song:* Very distinctive. A lazy *zwée-a zwée-a zwée-a zwee*, the last upslurred. A Junco-like chip.

Habitat. In the breeding season, deciduous and mixed woodland where there is an understory of shrubs or saplings; often old clearings and logged-over areas.

Nesting. From a few inches to 3 feet above ground in a sapling, shrub, or small tree. Nest rather bulky, composed of bark shreds, leaves, rotten wood and lined with rootlets, fine grasses, or hair. *Eggs,* 3 to 5, usually 4; spotted, blotched, or clouded with browns. Incubation 12 days, by the female (Louise de K. Lawrence).

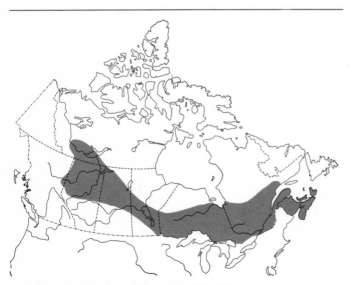

Breeding Distribution of Cape May Warbler

Range. Breeds from southeastern Canada (western Ontario east to Nova Scotia) south to central-eastern Minnesota, northern Wisconsin, central Michigan, western and northeastern Pennsylvania, southeastern New York, Rhode Island, and Massachusetts and in the Appalachian Mountains to northeastern Georgia. Winters mainly in the West Indies.

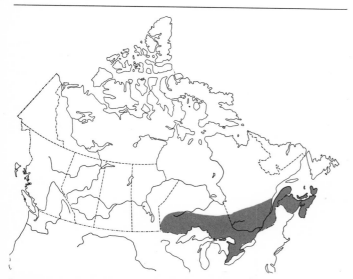

Breeding Distribution of Black-throated Blue Warbler

Range in Canada. Summer resident, breeding in central and southern Ontario (Lac Seul, Kapuskasing, Lake Abitibi; Bruce, Simcoe, and Prince Edward counties), southern Quebec (La Vérendrye Park, Mount Plamondon, Lake St. John, Tadoussac, Gaspé Peninsula, Chelsea, Hatley, Lac Trois Saumons), New Brunswick, Prince Edward Island, and Nova Scotia (including Cape Breton Island). Recorded in summer at Mingan, Anticosti Island, and Magdalen Islands, Quebec; Indian Bay, southeastern Manitoba; and Emma Lake, central Saskatchewan. Recorded in migration seasons in western Manitoba (Treesbank); southern Saskatchewan (Percival, Moose Jaw, Regina). Casual in Alberta (Edmonton, Tofield, Rosebud, and near Nordegg).

Subspecies. *Dendroica caerulescens caerulescens* (Gmelin).

MYRTLE WARBLER
La Fauvette à croupion jaune
Dendroica coronata (Linnaeus)
Plate 57. L. 5 to 6 in.

Adult male (breeding plumage): Upper parts mostly bluish grey, streaked with black and with a patch of bright yellow on crown and another on rump; streak over eye and small spot on upper and lower eyelid white; across face a broad black patch; three outer tail feathers with a white patch on inner web; two white wing bars; under parts mainly white, the breast, sides, and flanks heavily streaked with black, and with a yellow patch on either side of breast. *Adult female (breeding plumage)*: Similar to adult male but duller; more brownish above, black streaking narrower below, cheek patch duller. *Young and adults in autumn:*

Upper parts and sides of head mainly brownish, the back and scapulars streaked with black, crown patch partly or quite concealed by brown feather tips; conspicuous yellow rump patch; under parts mostly dingy white; the breast, sides, and flanks streaked with dusky, and with a faint yellow patch usually on either side of breast but sometimes absent in young females (*see* Audubon's Warbler).

Measurements (*D. c. coronata*). *Adult male:* wing, 70.2–74.3 (72.7); tail, 55–58.5 (57.0); exposed culmen, 10–10.9 (10.4); tarsus, 18–19.5 (18.5). *Adult female:* wing, 67.7–72 (69.7) mm.

Field Marks. Although other warblers like the Cape May, Magnolia, and Palm have a yellowish rump patch, it is not so bright nor so well marked as that of the Myrtle. This, in combination with a yellow patch on either side of the breast, distinguishes the Myrtle from other warblers except Audubon's of the West. Myrtle has a white throat, Audubon adults a yellow one. *Song:* A tinkling trill like the rattle of a small chain, either rising or falling near the end. The ordinary call-note *chep* is distinctive in the East but is very similar to that of Audubon's Warbler of the West.

Habitat. Coniferous and mixed woodlands, especially in more open situations. In migration, various types of woods, thickets, roadside trees, gardens.

Nesting. Usually in a coniferous tree (infrequently deciduous), 1 to 50 feet above ground, most often about 10 to 15 feet, very rarely on the ground. Nest, rather loose and bulky, is made of twigs, grass, rootlets, and moss and is lined with hair and often feathers. *Eggs*, generally 4 or 5; white, spotted and blotched with various browns and often some underlying grey. Incubation 12 to 13 days (O. W. Knight), by the female mainly.

Range. Breeds from north-central Alaska and across Canada (*see* Range in Canada) south to northern British Columbia, central Alberta, northern Minnesota, central Michigan, eastern New York, eastern Pennsylvania, and Massachusetts. Winters mainly from northern and north-central United States south to central Panama and the Greater Antilles.

Range in Canada. Breeds from northern Yukon (Old Crow, Lapierre House), northwestern and central Mackenzie (Mackenzie Delta, Fort Anderson, southeastern Great Bear Lake, Fort Reliance), southwestern Keewatin (probably: Windy River), northern Manitoba (Sandhill Lake, probably Churchill), northern Ontario (Fort Severn, Moose Factory), northern Quebec (Richmond Gulf, Kinglet Lake, Lake Bienville, Indian House Lake), north-central Labrador (Tikkoatokak Bay, Angutausugevik), and Newfoundland south to northern and north-central British Columbia (Atlin, Dease Lake, Peace River District), central and southwestern Alberta (Jasper Park, Bow Valley, perhaps Battle River region), central and southeastern Saskatchewan (Flotten Lake, Prince Albert, Nipawin, Fort Qu'Appelle), southern Manitoba (Duck Mountain, Spruce Forest Reserve, Hillside Beach), southern Ontario (Bruce, Simcoe, Frontenac, and Leeds counties), southern Quebec (Gatineau Park, Hatley, Gaspé Peninsula, Anticosti and Magdalen islands, north shore of Gulf of St. Lawrence), New Brunswick, Prince Edward Island, and Nova Scotia (including

Cape Breton Island). Migrates throughout southern Canada including southern British Columbia and Vancouver Island.

Winters in southern Nova Scotia (very locally in small numbers: Wolfville, Yarmouth, Port Mouton).

Casual on King William Island, Baker Lake, Chesterfield Inlet, and Southampton Island, N.W.T.

Breeding Distribution of Myrtle Warbler

Subspecies. (1) *Dendroica coronata coronata* (Linnaeus): n.-c. Alta. (Grimshaw, Lesser Slave Lake), Sask., Man., Ont., Que., Lab., Nfld., N.B., P.E.I., N.S. (2) *D. c. hooveri* McGregor (slightly larger than *coronata* and with slightly less solidly black breast): Yukon, Mack., nw. B.C.

Remarks. This species might well be the most numerous of the wood warblers in Canada. It breeds over vast parts of the country, and its numbers, especially in autumn migration, are often most impressive. Although primarily an insect eater, the Myrtle is one of few warblers that can subsist on berries and seeds over protracted periods. I have several times seen Myrtle Warblers wintering in Nova Scotia despite the cold and deep snow, usually in the vicinity of bayberry bushes, the berries of which they were eating eagerly. Checks later on showed that they wintered successfully.

AUDUBON'S WARBLER
La Fauvette d'Audubon
Dendroica auduboni (Townsend)
Plate 57. L. 5.2 to 6.2 in.

Very similar to Myrtle Warbler, differing as follows. *Adults in breeding plumage:* Throat bright yellow instead of white, but yellow is less extensive in females; cheeks mostly bluish grey, not solid black; white areas in tail usually more extensive and present on four or five (instead of two or three) outermost feathers; and in the adult male the white of the wing bars is more extensive, often forming a wing patch. *Adults in autumn:* Similar to Myrtle Warbler but throat yellow or yellowish, white in tail more extensive. *Young in autumn:* Very similar to young of Myrtle Warbler. Some show more or less yellow on the throat which distinguishes

them from the Myrtle. Often, however, there is no yellow on the throat, in which case the larger amount of white in the Audubon's tail (usually on four or five outer feathers; usually only two or three in the Myrtle Warblers) separates them.

Measurements (*D. a. memorabilis*). *Adult male:* wing, 73.5–80 (76.1); tail, 56–63.5 (59.0); exposed culmen, 10.1–11.4 (10.7); tarsus, 18–20 (19.2). *Adult female:* wing, 70.2–75.2 (72.6) mm.

Field Marks. Like the Myrtle Warbler but distinguishable by yellow throat (Myrtle has a white one). Some immature Audubon's in autumn have no yellow on throat and cannot safely be distinguished from Myrtles. *Voice:* Similar to that of the Myrtle Warbler.

Habitat. For nesting, coniferous and mixed woodland, especially more open types; in the mountains up to near timberline. In migration various types of trees and thickets.

Nesting. In coniferous (sometimes deciduous) trees at various heights. Nest is made of twigs, grass, and rootlets; lined with fine grass, rootlets, hair, and feathers. *Eggs,* 3 to 5; whitish, spotted and blotched with browns and some grey.

Range. Breeds from central British Columbia, southern Alberta, and southwestern Saskatchewan, south through the mountains to northern Mexico (northern Baja California, Durango). Winters from southwestern British Columbia, southwestern Utah, central New Mexico, and southern Texas to Costa Rica.

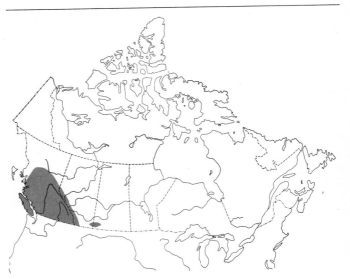

Breeding Distribution of Audubon's Warbler

Range in Canada. Breeds in central and southern British Columbia (Hazelton; Summit Lake north of Prince George; Victoria; Vancouver; Okanagan Landing; Cranbrook), southwestern and extreme southeastern Alberta (Jasper, Banff, Waterton Lakes parks; locally in southeast: Cypress Hills), and extreme southwestern Saskatchewan (Cypress Hills).

In migration, recorded on the plains of southern Alberta (Calgary, Rosebud, Camrose, Clyde, Egremont) and in southeastern Saskatchewan (Regina, Indian Head).

Winters sparingly in southwestern British Columbia (Victoria, Vancouver).

Subspecies. (1) *Dendroica auduboni auduboni* (Townsend): Coastal B.C. (2) *D. a. memorabilis* Oberholser (averages slightly larger): se. B.C., s. Alta., sw. Sask.

BLACK-THROATED GRAY WARBLER
La Fauvette grise à gorge noire
Dendroica nigrescens (Townsend)
Plate 57. L. 4.6 to 5.2 in.

Adult male (breeding plumage): Crown and sides of head black; small narrow yellow spot between bill and eye and a white line back from eye to side of nape; back, bluish grey streaked with black; outer three tail feathers with inner webs largely white; two white wing bars; throat black, separated from black of cheek by a broad white stripe; sides and flanks streaked with black; rest of under parts white. Bill and legs black. *Adult female (breeding plumage):* Similar to adult male but much duller, crown greyish, throat mainly white, more or less blackish on lower throat or upper breast, streaks on sides more greyish black. *Young and adults in autumn:* Resemble adults in spring but upper parts largely brownish, streaks on back vague or lacking; under parts whitish with brownish tinge, the throat and sides with more or less blackish or dusky.

Measurements. *Adult male:* wing, 58.7–63.4 (61.3); tail, 47–52 (49.3); exposed culmen, 9.3–10.8 (10.2); tarsus, 17–18 (17.5). *Adult female:* wing, (4 only) 58.1–59 (58.6) mm.

Field Marks. Usually found in southwestern British Columbia. Adult male is a black-throated warbler with grey upper parts and white under parts, the only yellow a narrow spot between eye and bill (often hard to see). Its solid black cheeks and black-streaked sides distinguish it from chickadees. Females and young lack a black throat patch but have solid dark cheeks which distinguish them from Black-and-White and Blackpoll warblers, with which they might otherwise be confused. The Blackpoll has pale brown legs; the Black-throated Gray, black legs. *Song:* Low

Breeding Distribution of Black-throated Gray Warbler

lisping *weezy weezy weezy wee-zee*, the end accented and slurred up or down.

Habitat. More open coniferous and mixedwoods, especially with bushy undergrowth; openings and edges.

Nesting. In coniferous or deciduous trees or shrubbery generally at lower elevations but sometimes quite high. Nest is of plant fibre, grass, small weed stalks, and is lined with hair and feathers. *Eggs,* 3 to 5, usually 4; white, speckled with reddish browns and some underlying purple, mostly on large end.

Range. Breeds from southwestern British Columbia and northwestern and central Colorado south in the mountains to northern Baja California, Arizona, and New Mexico. Winters from central California and southern Arizona to southern Mexico.

Range in Canada. Local summer resident, breeding in southwestern British Columbia (Stuie and Hagensborg in Bella Coola valley southward, and east as far as Lillooet. Scarce transient on Vancouver Island).

Accidental in Saskatchewan (Regina, May 3, 1965) and in southern Ontario (Toronto, December 1952; May 1962).

TOWNSEND'S WARBLER
La Fauvette de Townsend
Dendroica townsendi (Townsend)
Plate 57. L. 4.5 to 5 in.

Adult male (breeding plumage): Crown, cheeks, and throat, black; broad stripe over eye, small patch under eye, broad stripe between cheeks and throat, and the sides of the neck, yellow; back, scapulars, and rump, olive green spotted or streaked with black; outer two tail feathers with inner webs mainly white, the next with less white; two white wing bars; breast yellow (but black of throat extends to upper breast); sides yellowish streaked with black; belly and under tail coverts white. *Adult female (breeding plumage):* Similar to adult male in breeding plumage but crown with much olive; cheeks olive instead of black; throat mostly yellow, breast striped with black. *Young and adults in autumn:* Similar to adult female in breeding plumage but upper parts with little or no streaking; the throat and breast yellow, the sides lightly streaked with dusky.

Measurements. *Adult male:* wing, 63.1–69.9 (66.5); tail, 47.1–54 (51.5); exposed culmen, 9.9–10.8 (10.2); tarsus, 18.1–19 (18.5). *Adult female:* wing, 59.4–64.8 (62.5) mm.

Field Marks. Yellow on head and breast combined with black throat, crown, and face patch in male; olive face patch in female and young. It differs from other extreme western warblers so much that little confusion is likely. Resembles Black-throated Green Warbler but has a definite cheek patch. *Song:* Lazy and buzzy, the quality suggestive of that of the Black-throated Green Warbler but usually more sibilant or lisping at the end.

Habitat. In breeding season, coniferous forest, often foraging and singing high in the treetops. In migration various kinds of woodland and shrubbery.

Nesting. In a coniferous tree. *Eggs,* 3 to 5; white, speckled and spotted with browns.

Range. Breeds from southern Alaska and southern

PLATE 65

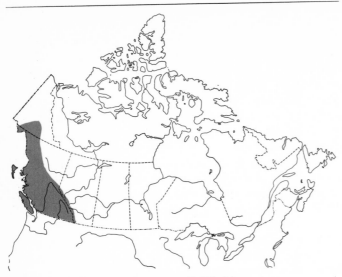

Breeding Distribution of Townsend's Warbler

Yukon south on the coast and islands to northwestern Washington and in the interior to central Oregon, northern Idaho, central-southern Montana, and northwestern Wyoming. Winters in west-central and southern California and from central Mexico south to Nicaragua.

Range in Canada. Breeds from southern Yukon (Rose and Lapie rivers; probably Marsh Lake), British Columbia (including Queen Charlotte and Vancouver islands, but apparently absent from northeastern corner), and southwestern Alberta (Rocky Mountains).

Wanders east of the Rocky Mountains rarely: in southern Alberta (Rosebud).

BLACK-THROATED GREEN WARBLER

La Fauvette verte à gorge noire. *Dendroica virens* (Gmelin)
Plate 57. L. 4.4 to 5.3 in.

Adult male (spring plumage): Upper parts yellowish olive green, the back with or without small spots of black; often a small yellow area in centre of forehead; sides of head and sides of neck, yellow with narrow dusky streak through eye; two white wing bars; two outermost tail feathers mainly white, the third and often others with tip of inner web white; throat and breast black; belly and under tail coverts white (often tinged with yellow); sides streaked with black. *Adult female (breeding plumage)*: Similar to adult male but duller generally, with less white in tail; chin and throat yellow, the upper breast blackish with white feather tips. *Adult male (autumn)*: Like adult male in breeding plumage but has black throat and breast feathers with whitish tips. *Young male and females in autumn:* Similar to adult male in autumn but throat and breast yellowish, often with some black on upper breast.

Measurements. *Adult male:* wing, 60.5–65.5 (63.4); tail, 47–52.5 (50.1); exposed culmen, 10–10.9 (10.4); tarsus, 17–18.5 (17.7). *Adult female:* wing, 59.3–63.8 (61.0) mm.

Field Marks. The yellow sides of the head with the black throat and upper breast of the adult male and the blackish upper breast of the adult female easily distinguish it.

PLATE 66

1 Lark Sparrow, adult

2 Harris's Sparrow,
   (a) autumn immature
   (b) adult in breeding
      plumage

3 Lark Bunting,
   (a) male in breeding
      plumage
   (b) female

4 Ipswich Sparrow

5 Savannah Sparrow

6 Vesper Sparrow

7 Rufous-sided Towhee,
   (a) adult male
      (western races)
   (b) female
      (eastern race)
   (c) adult male
      (eastern race)

Young often show no black on the upper breast or throat, but the yellow cheeks separate it from otherwise similar warblers. Its range does not overlap that of the Townsend's Warbler (which has a dark cheek patch). *Song* is a pleasing, lazy *zee zee zee zoo zee* on an even pitch, except that the second syllable from the last is lowest.

Habitat. In breeding season, more open coniferous and mixedwoods. Conifers with an admixture of birch or aspen are ideal; edges and second growths. In migration, various kinds of woodland and thickets.

Nesting. Usually (not always) in conifers, both small and large and at various heights. Nest is of grasses and shredded bark, lined with fine vegetable material, hair, and feathers. *Eggs*, usually 4 or 5; white, speckled and spotted with reddish browns, and some underlying purplish grey. Incubation from 12 (C. J. Stanwood) to 13 (L. de K. Lawrence) days, mainly, if not entirely, by the female.

Range. Breeds from Alberta east to Newfoundland and in the United States south to central-eastern Minnesota, central Michigan, eastern Ohio, Pennsylvania (locally), and northern New Jersey, and in the mountains south to Alabama and northern Georgia. Winters from southern Texas and southern Florida south to the Greater Antilles and Panama.

Breeding Distribution of Black-throated Green Warbler

Range in Canada. Breeds in northern and central Alberta (Chenal des Quatre Fourches, Peace River District, Athabasca, Belvedere, Glenevis), central Saskatchewan (Kazan Lake, Emma Lake), central and southern Manitoba (Moose and Cedar lakes, Duck Mountain, Julius), central and southern Ontario (Favourable and Attawapiskat lakes, lower Moose River; Long Point, Toronto), south-central and southern Quebec (Mistassini Post; north shore of Gulf of St. Lawrence east at least to St. Augustin: 22 miles north; Anticosti Island; Gatineau Park; Hatley; Gaspé Peninsula; Magdalen Islands), southern Labrador (Goose Bay), Newfoundland, New Brunswick, Prince Edward Island, and Nova Scotia (including Cape Breton Island).

Probably breeds in central-eastern British Columbia

(Chetwynd – Moberly Lakes region).

Scarce migrant in southern Alberta and southern Saskatchewan.

Subspecies. *Dendroica virens virens* (Gmelin).

Remarks. The unhurried song of the Black-throated Green Warbler has pleasant connotations with the scent and shade of evergreen woodlands on warm summer days. This bird is more often heard than seen, for much of its foraging is done in the medium to higher levels of the trees. It is rather tame, however; and especially when feeding in the lower branches it is an easy bird to observe. It is a persistent singer, and its song is both pleasing and easy to recognize. Insects, gleaned from the branches and foliage of trees, make up the bulk of its diet.

CERULEAN WARBLER

La Fauvette azurée. *Dendroica cerulea* (Wilson)
Plate 57. L. 4 to 5 in.

Adult male: Upper parts and cheeks bright blue, the back streaked with black; tail with small white patch on inner web of all feathers except middle pair; two white wing bars; under parts mainly white with a narrow blue-black band across upper breast; sides and flanks streaked with blue-black. *Adult female:* Upper parts pale bluish to olive greenish, unmarked; sides of head whitish with narrow dusky streak through eye, pale stripe above eye; wings and tail similar to those of adult male; under parts whitish more or less tinged yellowish; sides and flanks usually with suggestion of streaking. *Young (first autumn):* Resemble adult female but more greenish above, more yellowish below.

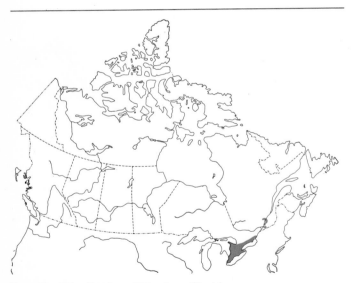

Breeding Distribution of Cerulean Warbler

Measurements. *Adult male:* wing, 62–67.6 (65.5); tail, 43.2–47.7 (45); exposed culmen, 9.4–10.2 (9.9); tarsus, 15.7–17 (16.5). *Adult female:* wing, 58.2–62.7 (61.2) mm (Ridgway).

Field Marks. Adult male with blue upper parts, white under parts, narrow blackish band across upper breast, and two white wing bars is easily recognized. Females and young are much more obscure. Presence of wing bars and lack of a small white spot at base of primaries separate them from the female Black-throated Blue. From young Blackpoll Warblers they can be distinguished by paler (less deep yellow) under parts and by lack of any streaks or spots on the back. *Song:* It resembles the buzzy song of the Parula, but the last syllable is prolonged and rising in pitch.

Habitat. In nesting season usually mature deciduous woodland, foraging and singing high in the trees. Sometimes coniferous trees.

Nesting. In a branch of a deciduous or, less often, coniferous tree usually 25 to 60 feet up. Nest is rather shallow but is neatly made of bark shreds, grass, or small weed stalks and is lined with hair and rootlets. *Eggs*, 3 to 5, usually 4; white or whitish, speckled or blotched with browns.

Range. Breeds from southeastern Nebraska east through extreme southern Ontario to southeastern New York and south to eastern Texas, southeastern Louisiana, central Alabama, and North Carolina. Winters in South America (Colombia and Venezuela to Peru and Bolivia).

Range in Canada. Breeds in southern Ontario (Walkerton, Bruce County; Toronto; Kingston southward). Sight records only for southwestern Quebec (Senneville, Philipsburg, Mount St. Hilaire. Probably breeds at Mount St. Hilaire where observed on several occasions in June 1961 and 1962 by David E. Sergeant).

Casual in southwestern Manitoba (Whitewater Lake, June 2, 1924).

BLACKBURNIAN WARBLER

La Fauvette à gorge orangée. *Dendroica fusca* (Müller)
Plate 58. L. 4.5 to 5.5 in.

Adult male: Above, mostly black, a narrow yellow patch on crown and two whitish stripes down back; line over eye, sides of neck, throat, and breast, bright orange; cheeks black; large white patch on wing coverts; inner webs of outer two to four tail feathers with much white; under parts behind orange breast, whitish tinged with orange; sides and flanks streaked with black. *Adult female:* Resembles adult male but yellow replaces orange; upper parts, olive green streaked with black and a little whitish; cheek patch olive; two white wing bars. *Young (autumn):* Closely resembles adult female but even duller, yellows paler; centre patch of crown much obscured.

Measurements. *Adult male:* wing, 65.5–69.3 (67.8); tail, 46–49.5 (48.1); exposed culmen, 10.4–11.3 (10.7); tarsus, 16.5–18 (17.3). *Adult female:* wing, 61.9–66.4 (64.1) mm.

Field Marks. Adult male with bright orange breast and black upper parts is unmistakable. In females and young, yellows replace the orange of the adult male, and dark olive green replaces the blacks; however, the dark cheek patch is clearly outlined against the yellow of eyebrow and throat. *Song:* Very high-pitched and wiry, often ending in a readily recognizable high buzz, *zip zip zip zip zeeeeee;* also a rolling high-pitched *chickety chickety chickety chick.*

Habitat. In nesting season, coniferous and mixed woodland, both mature and well-developed second growth, foraging most often among higher branches. In migration various types of woods and thickets.

Nesting. Usually in a branch of a coniferous tree, 5 to 85 feet up. Nest is of small twigs, dry grasses, soft plant down or *Usnea* lichen, lined with rootlets, hair, and fine grass. *Eggs*, usually 4 or 5; white, spotted and blotched with reddish browns and often some underlying purplish greys. Incubation 12 to 13 days, by the female (Louise de K. Lawrence).

Range. Breeds from central Saskatchewan east to Gaspé Peninsula and Nova Scotia, and south to central Minnesota, central Wisconsin, central Michigan, northeastern Ohio, Massachusetts, and in the Appalachian Mountains to northern Georgia and South Carolina. Winters from Guatemala south to central Peru and Venezuela.

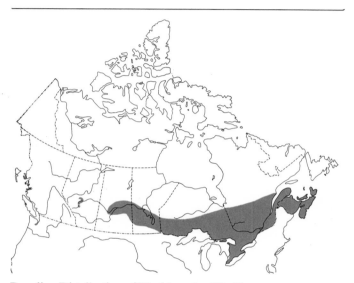

Breeding Distribution of Blackburnian Warbler

Range in Canada. Summer resident, breeding in central Saskatchewan (Crean and Emma lakes, Prince Albert, Cumberland House, Candle Lake), central and southern Manitoba (Overflowing River, Riding and Duck mountains, Hillside Beach, Rennie), central and southern Ontario (northern limits uncertain but north at least to Lac Seul, Lake Nipigon, and Lake Abitibi, and southward to near Long Point, Toronto, and Leeds County), southern Quebec (Waswanipi—Bell River area, Lake St. John, Pointe des Monts, Lac Ste. Anne on Toulnustouc River; Gatineau Park, Hatley, Lac Rimouski, Gaspé Peninsula), New Brunswick, Prince Edward Island, and Nova Scotia (including Cape Breton Island).

Perhaps breeds locally in central Alberta (singing males reported in June at Glenevis; specimens taken in Edmonton, 1917, and at High River, June 17, 1931). Recorded without evidence of breeding north to Trout Lake and Severn House, Ontario; and to Lake Albanel and Natashquan, Quebec.

Remarks. In full sunlight, against a background of dark coniferous trees, the flame-coloured breast of the Blackburnian Warbler is most impressive. The male is one of our most brilliant warblers, but his wiry little song is rather unmusical. Like other warblers this one is mainly insectivorous, its diet high in forest insects that are destructive to trees.

YELLOW-THROATED WARBLER
La Fauvette à gorge jaune. *Dendroica dominica* (Linnaeus)
Plate 58. L. 4.75 to 5.75 in.

Adults (sexes similar but female usually has less black on top of head and sides of throat and neck): Upper parts bluish grey, the forehead and sides of crown, black; white line over eye (may be either yellow or white in front of eye) joining white patch on side of neck; a tiny white spot on mid-forehead and another under eye; broad black patch on sides of head, extending down side of neck and breaking up on sides of breast to form black streaks along sides and flanks; throat and breast lemon yellow, abdomen and under tail coverts white; two white wing bars; two or three outermost tail feathers with large white patches. *Young in autumn:* Similar to adults but more brownish above and below.

Field Marks. To be identified in Canada with caution. A grey-backed warbler with lemon-yellow throat and upper breast, white stripe above eye (may be yellow in front of eye) and white patch on side of neck; two white wing bars. Perhaps female or young Blackburnian Warblers might be mistaken for it. The Blackburnian has a similar dark cheek patch, but its eyebrow stripe and patch on side of neck are yellow. The Yellow-throated Warbler creeps along the branches.

Range. Breeds from Nebraska east to southeastern New York and southwestern Connecticut and south to eastern Texas, the United States Gulf coast, central Florida, and the northern Bahamas.

Status in Canada. Accidental in Newfoundland (St. John's, November 11, 1953). This specimen is referable to *D. d. albilora* Ridgway. There are sight records for southern Ontario (Niagara Falls, Manotick).

CHESTNUT-SIDED WARBLER
La Fauvette à flancs marron
Dendroica pensylvanica (Linnaeus)
Plate 58. L. 4.5 to 5.3 in.

Adult male (breeding plumage): Crown, bright greenish yellow bordered by black; back and scapulars streaked black and greenish yellow; region in front of eye black, this extending in a broad narrowing patch down to jaw and also joining black stripe above eye; ear region and sides of neck white; two yellowish wing bars; three outer tail feathers with white patch; under parts plain white, except broad chestnut stripe extending from near black jaw patch backward along sides and flanks. *Adult female (breeding plumage):* Similar to adult male but black and chestnut areas reduced; yellow crown duller, more greenish. *Adult male (autumn):* Upper parts mainly bright greenish yellow, sparsely streaked or spotted with dusky on back and rump; sides of head plain grey without black; under parts plain white with well-marked chestnut stripe along sides. *Adult female and young in autumn:* Similar to adult male in autumn but with very little or no chestnut on flanks.

Measurements. *Adult male:* wing, 61.6–65.8 (63.8); tail, 47–51 (49.7); exposed culmen, 9.9–10.6 (10.2); tarsus, 17–18 (17.6). *Adult female:* wing, 58.6–61.5 (60.1) mm.

Field Marks. *Breeding plumage:* Easily recognized by the chestnut sides, yellow crown, yellow wing bars, and plain white under parts. *Autumn plumages:* Plain grey face (no black), greenish yellow upper parts, yellow wing bars; adults usually with more or less chestnut on sides, young lack it. The Bay-breasted, the only other warbler with chestnut sides, is in breeding plumage so different otherwise that there is little chance of confusion. Sometimes the Bay-breast also shows chestnut on the sides in autumn, but the Chestnut-sided Warbler's plain grey face (sharply cut off from the yellow top of head), lack of a dusky eye streak, and decidedly white under parts mark it. *Song:* Rather loud and emphatic. Has two common songs, one of which suggests that of the Yellow Warbler but has a distinctive ending, the next-to-last syllable strongly accented. To some it sounds like *very, very pleased to meetcha.*

Breeding Distribution of Chestnut-sided Warbler

Habitat. Open bushy second growth and thickets, deciduous or mainly so, on both dry and moist ground.

Nesting. In a sapling, low bush, or vine, usually 1 to 3 feet up. Nest is constructed of shredded bark, grass, fine weed stalks, and frequently some plant down and is lined with fine grass and often some hair. *Eggs,* 3 to 5, generally 4; white—spotted, speckled, or blotched with browns and some greys. Incubation 12 to 12½ days, by the female (Louise de K. Lawrence).

Range. Breeds from central-eastern Alberta east to Nova Scotia and south to eastern Nebraska, southern Wisconsin, northern Ohio, central New Jersey, and in the Appalachians to northern Georgia and northwestern South Carolina. Winters from southern Nicaragua to Panama.

Range in Canada. Summer resident, breeding in central-eastern Alberta (Boyle), central Saskatchewan (Carlton, Emma Lake, Candle Lake, Nipawin; probably Flotten Lake), central and southern Manitoba (The Pas, Riding Mountain, Portage la Prairie, Hillside Beach, Indian Bay),

central and southern Ontario (Malachi, Lake Nipigon, Lake Abitibi, south to Lake Erie), southern Quebec (Lake Chicobi; Amos region, Lake St. John, Tadoussac, Lac Rimouski; Hull, Montreal, Hatley, Baker Lake; recorded rarely on Gaspé Peninsula, but evidence of breeding is lacking), New Brunswick (throughout western side but not known in northeastern part), Prince Edward Island, and Nova Scotia (but no record for Cape Breton Island).

Hypothetical in Newfoundland (sight records only).

BAY-BREASTED WARBLER

La Fauvette à poitrine baie. *Dendroica castanea* (Wilson) Plate 58. L. 5 to 6 in.

Adult male (breeding plumage): Crown chestnut; forehead and sides of head black; patch on sides of neck buffy; back and rump, grey streaked with black; two white wing bars; two or three outer tail feathers with a white patch; throat, upper breast, sides, and flanks, rich chestnut but chin often blackish; rest of under parts white with slight buffy tinge. *Adult male (autumn):* Very different. Upper parts mostly olive green with some black streaks; usually traces of chestnut on crown; wing bars with slightly yellowish tinge; under parts yellowish or greenish on throat, pale buffy on abdomen and under tail coverts; more or less chestnut on sides. *Adult female (breeding plumage):* Essentially like adult male in breeding plumage but chestnut of crown sparse and streaked with black; black of cheeks mixed with grey; chestnut of throat and sides sparse, patchy, paler. *Young and adult female (autumn):* Similar to adult male in autumn but usually without (or just a trace of) chestnut on sides.

Breeding Distribution of Bay-breasted Warbler

Measurements. *Adult male:* wing, 71.7–74.9 (73.1); tail, 51–54 (52.7); exposed culmen, 10–11.1 (10.7); tarsus, 18.5–19 (18.9). *Adult female:* wing, 69.4–71.9 (70.5) mm.

Distinctions. Autumn specimens closely resemble corresponding plumages of Blackpoll Warbler. When traces of chestnut are present on the sides, this eliminates the Blackpoll Warbler (but *see* Chestnut-sided Warbler). When no chestnut is present on the sides, such Bay-breasts are separable from Blackpolls by their pale buffy (instead of white) under tail coverts and usually unstreaked (instead of faintly but definitely streaked), less greenish yellow under parts, and usually darker legs.

Field Marks. Adults in breeding plumage, with chestnut on throat and sides and a buffy patch on sides of neck, are readily identified. In autumn, adults and young are very different from breeding adults, being olive green above, buffy white below; thus they closely resemble autumn Blackpoll Warblers. Some individuals of the Bay-breast have traces of chestnut on the sides, which quickly eliminates the Blackpoll (but *see* Chestnut-sided Warbler, autumn). Bay-breasts with no chestnut on the sides can usually be distinguished from autumn Blackpolls by their buffish under tail coverts (pure white in Blackpoll), usually unstreaked and less greenish under parts, and usually darker legs (Plate 58). The buffish under tail coverts and streaked back distinguish them in autumn from duller-coloured individuals of the Pine Warbler. *Song:* Very high and sibilant: *zée-a, zée-a, zée-a, zee* in much the same pitch.

Habitat. In breeding season, coniferous woods, often with an admixture of deciduous trees; wood edges and openings; second growths.

Nesting. Usually 5 to 20 feet up in a coniferous tree. Nest is of fine twigs and grass, lined with rootlets and hair. *Eggs,* 4 to 7, most often 5; white, spotted and blotched with browns and underlying spots of grey. Incubation slightly over 12 days (H. L. Mendall), by the female.

Range. Breeds from Alberta east to Nova Scotia and south in the United States to northeastern Minnesota, northern Wisconsin, northeastern New York, and southern Maine. Winters from Panama to northern Colombia and western Venezuela.

Range in Canada. Summer resident, breeding in southwestern Mackenzie (probably Wrigley, Fort Simpson), northeastern and central-eastern British Columbia (probably Peace River District, perhaps Lower Liard Crossing; recorded in breeding season once at Indianpoint Lake, Tetana Lake), northern Alberta (Lesser Slave Lake, Athabasca River northward, probably to Wood Buffalo Park), central Saskatchewan (Flotten Lake; probably Kazan Lake and Cumberland House), central and southern Manitoba (The Pas, Oxford House, Riding Mountain, Indian Bay), central and southern Ontario (Lake Attawapiskat, Moose Factory; Off Lake, Dorcas Bay in Bruce County, Algonquin Park), south-central and southern Quebec (Mistassini Post, Lake St. John, St. Margaree River; Blue Sea Lake, Hatley, Gaspé Peninsula, Anticosti and Magdalen islands), New Brunswick, Prince Edward Island, and Nova Scotia (including Cape Breton Island).

Recorded in June on the inner north shore of the Gulf of St. Lawrence (Matamek, Johan Beetz Bay, mouth of Big Natashquan River). There are several convincing summer sight records for Newfoundland.

Remarks. In many parts of the country the Bay-breasted Warbler is uncommon and handsome enough to elicit a second look from most observers. It is one of the later arrivals in spring migration and it often passes through quickly, but occasionally good numbers remain about for a few days. It is at once the wonder and the despair of many how this and the Blackpoll Warbler can look so different in spring plumage and yet so much alike in autumn dress.

BLACKPOLL WARBLER
La Fauvette rayée. *Dendroica striata* (Forster)
Plate 58. L. 5 to 5.75 in.

Adult male (spring): Top of head down to eyes, black; sides of head, white; back, scapulars, and rump, grey or olive grey streaked with black; two white (or yellowish) wing bars; outer two or three tail feathers with a white spot on inner web; under parts white; sides of throat, sides of breast, and sides of body, streaked with black; legs pale brown. *Adult male (autumn):* Very different from spring. Upper parts olive green (no black cap), streaked with dusky; sides of head olive yellow with faint pale line over eye; under parts yellowish, very much less profusely streaked than in spring; under tail coverts white. *Adult female (spring):* Upper parts greenish grey streaked with black; wings and tail, similar to adult male in spring but wing bars more yellowish; pale stripe over eye; under parts whitish suffused with yellow and finely streaked with black on sides of throat, sides of breast, and sides of body. *Young and adult female in autumn:* Similar to adult male in autumn but more faintly streaked below.

Measurements. *Adult male:* wing, 70.1–75.3 (73.2); tail, 48–53 (50.8); exposed culmen, 10.1–11 (10.5); tarsus, 18.5–20 (19.2). *Adult female:* wing, 66.5–72.8 (69.2) mm.

Distinctions (*see* Bay-breasted and Pine Warbler).

Field Marks. Male in spring and early summer, a black-capped warbler with plain *white cheeks* which distinguish it from the Black-and-white and the Black-throated Grey warblers. Lack of a black bib separates it from the Black-capped Chickadee. In autumn it is very much like autumn Bay-breasted Warbler, but under tail coverts are always white (*see* Bay-breasted Warbler). Autumn birds may be confused with some Pine Warblers, but the Blackpoll has light brown legs (instead of blackish) and some streaking on the upper parts (the Pine has plain upper parts). *Song:* An extremely high-pitched *tsit tsit tsit tsit tsit* in the same pitch, rising in volume toward the middle, falling off toward the end; thus easy to recognize.

Habitat. Coniferous woods, especially spruce, frequently stunted, also mixedwood edges, logged and burned areas, alder thickets, frequently on moist ground. In migration both deciduous and coniferous trees.

Nesting. Usually low in a spruce, rarely on the ground. Nest is of grasses, lichens, fine mosses, and twigs; lined with feathers, hairs, and fine grasses. *Eggs,* generally 4 or 5; white, speckled and blotched with browns and some greys.

Range. Breeds across Canada in northern coniferous forests (*see* Range in Canada) and south in northeastern United States to eastern New York, northwestern Massachusetts, central New Hampshire, and southern Maine; also in Alaska. Winters in South America from Colombia to eastern Peru, western Brazil, and Chile.

Range in Canada. Summer resident, breeding from near tree limit in northern Yukon (Old Crow), northern Mackenzie (northern Mackenzie Delta, Fort Anderson, Artillery Lake, Thelon River), southern Keewatin (Nueltin Lake, Tha-Anne River), northern Manitoba (Churchill), northern Ontario (Fort Severn), northern Quebec (Richmond Gulf, Fort Chimo, George River, Indian House Lake), northern Labrador (Port Manvers, Nain), and Newfoundland south to south-central interior British Columbia (Mosher Creek,

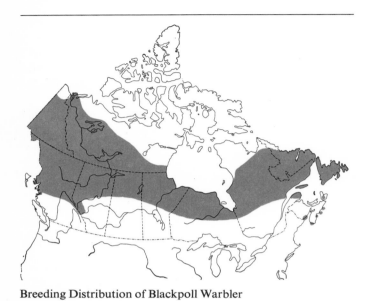

Breeding Distribution of Blackpoll Warbler

Indianpoint Lake), central and southwestern Alberta (Athabasca and south in the mountains and foothills to Banff and Bragg Creek), north-central Saskatchewan (Kazan Lake), central Manitoba (The Pas, Thicket Portage), north-central Ontario (Favourable Lake, Lake Attawapiskat), southern Quebec (Mistassini Post, Anticosti Island, eastern Gaspé Peninsula, Magdalen Islands), coastal New Brunswick (Kent Island), and Nova Scotia (Cape Fourchu, islands off the south shore, Cape Breton Island).

PINE WARBLER

La Fauvette des pins. *Dendroica pinus* (Wilson)
Plate 58. L. 5 to 5.75 in.

Adult male: Upper parts unstreaked yellowish olive green; cheeks similar to upper parts; obscure yellowish line over eye; two white wing bars; two outer tail feathers on each side with large white patches; throat, breast, and upper abdomen, yellow usually faintly streaked with olive; lower abdomen and under tail coverts, white. *Adult female:* Similar to but much duller than male; upper parts tinged brownish, nape often greyish; cheeks greyish; under parts dingy white, more or less yellowish on breast; flanks tinged brownish. *Young female in autumn:* Upper parts still browner than adult female in autumn, often without decided green above or yellow below.

Measurements. *Adult male:* wing, 68.9–72.8 (70.9); tail, 52.9–56 (54.1); exposed culmen, 9.9–11.6 (10.7); tarsus, 17.2–18.7 (18.0). *Adult female:* wing, 66.6–70.5 (68.4) mm.

Field Marks. Males have a decidedly yellow breast, often faintly streaked; two white wing bars; large white patches in outer tail feathers, and no other conspicuous markings. Females and young in autumn are extremely nondescript, brownish or greyish above, dingy white below often with a buffy or yellowish tinge to the breast, white wing bars, white under tail coverts. The Pine Warbler's dark legs usually distinguish it from autumn Blackpolls, its white under tail coverts from autumn Bay-breasts, its plain unstreaked back from both. The Pine Warbler's creeping habits, frequent association with pine trees, and song also assist in identifying it. *Song:* Very much like the trill of a Chipping Sparrow but usually a little more musical and often somewhat slower. Speed is variable, however.

Habitat. In nesting season, usually pine woodlands. In migration various kinds of trees are used for foraging.

Nesting. In the branches of a pine tree (various species) from 10 feet upwards from the ground. Nest is made of weed stalks, shreds of bark, pine needles, and lined with hair, feathers, and pine needles. *Eggs*, 3 to 5, usually 4; white, speckled and blotched with browns and some greys.

Range. Breeds in pine woodland from southern Manitoba east to southern Quebec and south to the Gulf Coast of the United States, southern Florida, the Bahamas, and Hispaniola. Winters mainly from Arkansas, Tennessee, and South Carolina southward in the breeding range.

Range in Canada. Summer resident, breeding in southern Manitoba (Julius, Sprague), western Ontario (Off Lake, Malachi), central and southern Ontario (upper Michipicoten River, Washagami, and Ottawa southward locally to the southern border), and locally in southwestern Quebec (Hull, Chambly).

Breeding Distribution of Pine Warbler

Occurs in Alberta rarely but status uncertain (Castor, June 5, 1924; Athabasca: sight records of singing males in July). Casual in southern New Brunswick (Saint John, Grand Manan), Nova Scotia (Gaspereau, Sable River), and Saskatchewan (Regina).

Subspecies. *Dendroica pinus pinus* (Wilson).

Remarks. This warbler is well named, for it prefers to live in pine trees of various species. It has a habit of creeping about the branches or even on the trunks of trees. Insects are its favourite food, but it eats many pine seeds, wild fruits, and berries if insects are not available.

KIRTLAND'S WARBLER
La Fauvette de Kirtland. *Dendroica kirtlandii* (Baird)
Plate 56. L. ca. 5.75 in.

A large warbler. *Adult male:* Upper parts, bluish grey with black stripes (coarse on back, fine on top of head); cheeks blackish with spot of white on upper and lower eyelids; outer two tail feathers on each side with white patch on inner web; under parts pale yellow; the sides of breast lightly streaked with black, the sides of body heavily so; under tail coverts, white. *Adult female:* Resembles adult male but is duller, nape and rump more brownish grey; cheeks grey; yellow of under parts paler, the breast more extensively speckled with black.

Measurements. *Adult male:* wing, 67.4–71.8 (70.2); tail, 58–62 (60.2); exposed culmen, 10–11.3 (10.8); tarsus, 20–22 (20.9). *Adult female:* wing, 64–71 (66.7) mm.

Field Marks. A large tail-wagging warbler, bluish grey above, yellow below. Might be confused with Canada Warbler, but the Kirtland's black-streaked sides, black-streaked back, dark legs, and habit of pumping the tail up and down should distinguish it. The young Magnolia Warbler looks a little like the Kirtland's but has a yellow rump patch, a distinctive tail pattern, and lacks the tail-wagging habit. In nesting season (not known to nest in Canada) it is confined to immature jack pine woodlands.

Range. Breeds in central Michigan. Winters in the Bahama Islands.

Status in Canada. Rare migrant in Ontario (Toronto, Point Pelee, Hamilton, Pointe au Baril. Has been recorded in June in Ontario, but there is no evidence of breeding).

PRAIRIE WARBLER
La Fauvette des prés. *Dendroica discolor* (Vieillot)
Plate 59. L. 4.3 to 5.2 in.

A small warbler. *Adult male:* Upper parts yellowish olive green, the back with chestnut spots (partly concealed in autumn); two yellowish wing bars; three outer tail feathers on each side with very large white areas, the outermost mainly white on both webs; sides of head yellow with narrow black line through eye and a broader black patch down over jaw; under parts bright yellow, the sides of breast and sides of body broadly streaked black; legs dark olive brown. *Adult female:* Similar to adult male but usually duller, the chestnut spots on back faint or absent, the blacks on sides of head replaced by grey; black streaks on sides of body more obscure. *Young females:* Upper parts plain greyish olive green, cheeks grey, wing bars obsolete; streaks on sides faint.

Measurements. *Adult male:* wing, 54.4–58.2 (56.5); tail, 47.5–50.5 (49.0); exposed culmen, 9–10.2 (9.7); tarsus, 17–19 (18.2). *Adult female:* wing, 51–57 (53.8) mm.

Field Marks. A small tail-wagging warbler with bright yellow under parts, black streaks confined to sides of head and body, the males with *two distinct face stripes*, and chestnut spots on back (the last often hard to see). Females and young are duller with black of head replaced by greenish grey. *Song:* Easily recognizable once learned. A series of distinct notes rising gradually higher in pitch to the end.

Habitat. Not grassy prairies as its name erroneously suggests. Instead, dry scrubby areas, brushy second growths, and, in sand dune country, pine and ground juniper.

Nesting. In bushes or saplings usually 2 to 5 feet above ground, sometimes considerably higher. Its compact nest is made of plant down, grass, and leaves and lined with rootlets, hair, feathers, and cottony plant materials. Incubation 12 to 13 days (L. H. Walkinshaw), by the female.

Range. Breeds from southeastern South Dakota east to southern New Hampshire and south to eastern Oklahoma, southern Louisiana, northern Mississippi, southeastern Alabama, and the Florida Keys. Winters from central Florida south through the West Indies and in islands off Mexico and Central America.

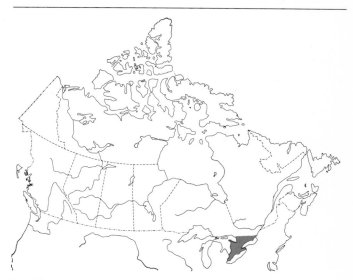

Breeding Distribution of Prairie Warbler

Range in Canada. Breeds locally in southern Ontario (Lambton County up the shore of Lake Huron and southern Georgian Bay; Cross Lake, Frontenac County; and between Westport and Kingston). Recorded in June rarely north to Lake Nipissing, and in migration at Ottawa, Eganville, and Lake Doré, Ontario. Casual in southern New Brunswick (Machias Seal Island).

Subspecies. *Dendroica discolor discolor* (Vieillot).

PALM WARBLER
La Fauvette à couronne rousse
Dendroica palmarum (Gmelin)
Plate 59. L. 5 to 5.75 in.

There are two subspecies, one eastern, one western, different enough to be recognizable in the field.

D. p. palmarum: Adults (*sexes similar*) in *breeding plum-*

age: Crown chestnut with narrow yellowish line in middle of forehead; back and scapulars greyish olive brown, narrowly streaked darker; lower rump and upper tail coverts, yellowish olive; two indistinct buffy wing bars; two outer tail feathers on each side with white patch at end of inner web, occasionally a small white spot on third; yellow stripe over eye; cheeks and sides of neck, greyish brown; throat, breast, and under tail coverts bright yellow, the sides of throat, breast, and sides of body narrowly streaked with brown; abdomen whitish or faintly yellowish; legs olive brown. *Adults in autumn:* Similar to breeding adults but crown with little or no chestnut, stripe over eye white, under parts whitish (except yellow under tail coverts), only faintly tinged with yellow and streaked with dusky. *Young in autumn:* Like adults in autumn but browner above, buffy white below, the breast and sides lightly streaked with brownish, under tail coverts yellow.

D. p. hypochrysea (eastern Ontario eastward): Similar to above but entire under parts yellow, even in autumn and immature plumages; streaks on under parts more chestnut than brown; upper parts more olive; size averages slightly larger.

Measurements (*D. p. hypochrysea*). *Adult male:* wing, 61.7–68.8 (65.2); tail, 48–56.5 (53.0); exposed culmen, 9.6–10.5 (10.1); tarsus, 19–21 (19.9), *Adult female:* wing, 59.4–64.5 (61.5) mm.

Field Marks. A tail-wagging warbler which even in dullest plumages has bright yellow under tail coverts, greenish yellow rump (noticeably paler than back). In breeding plumages a dull red cap is diagnostic. The eastern race (eastern Ontario eastward) has the entire under parts yellow in breeding plumage, yellowish in autumn. The western race has less extensively yellow under parts in breeding plumage (Plate 59) and in autumn young buffy white under parts (except yellow under tail coverts). Kirtland's and Prairie warblers also are tail-waggers. *Song:* A simple, flat-toned trill, a little like that of the Chipping Sparrow but less energetic.

Habitat. In nesting season, bogs or barrens or similar situations on either dry or wet ground where trees are scattered and where there is ground shrubbery.

Nesting. On or near the ground, often concealed by shrubby vegetation or under a seedling; occasionally in a low conifer sapling. Nest is of weed stalks, grass, shreds of bark, and moss, and is lined with fine grass, rootlets, and feathers. *Eggs,* 4 or 5; white, speckled with browns and sometimes a little lavender, mostly around the large end. Incubation 12 days (F.L. Burns).

Range. Breeds in Canada from northern Alberta and western Mackenzie east to Newfoundland and in northern United States south to northeastern Minnesota, central Michigan, central New Hampshire, northern and eastern Maine. Winters from Louisiana east to North Carolina and south to the Yucatan Peninsula, northern Honduras, the Greater Antilles, the Bahamas, and Bermuda.

Range in Canada. Breeds from central-western Mackenzie (Kelly Lake; forts Norman, Providence, and Resolution), northwestern Saskatchewan (Lake Athabasca), northern Manitoba (Bird, probably Herchmer), northern Ontario (Fort Severn, Attawapiskat River mouth, Moosonee), south-

central Quebec (Mistassini Post, Seven Islands, Mingan), southern Labrador (Goose Bay), and Newfoundland south to northeastern British Columbia (Trutch), central Alberta (Glenevis, Elk Island Park), central Saskatchewan (Roddick, probably Nipawin), southern Manitoba (Overflowing River, Indian Bay), central and southern Ontario (Lake of the Woods, Ottawa), southern Quebec (Lanoraie; Matane County), New Brunswick, Prince Edward Island, and Nova Scotia (including Cape Breton Island).

Accidental at Bernard Harbour, Dolphin and Union Strait, Mackenzie, N.W.T., September 28, 1915. Casual at Vancouver, British Columbia.

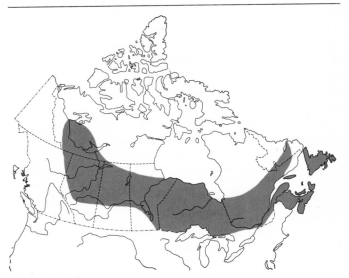

Breeding Distribution of Palm Warbler

Subspecies (described above): (1) *Dendroica palmarum palmarum* (Gmelin): w. and c. Canada east to Moosonee and Kapuskasing, Ont. (2) *D.p. hypochrysea* Ridgway: e. Canada west to Lake Mistassini, P.Q., and Ottawa, Ont.

OVENBIRD

La Fauvette couronnée. *Seiurus aurocapillus* (Linnaeus)
Plate 59. L. 5.5 to 6.5 in.

Adults (sexes similar): Top of head with two blackish stripes extending backward from forehead to nape, these stripes bordering an area of brownish orange; rest of upper parts, sides of head, and sides of neck plain olive green; eye-ring whitish; wings and tail with no white markings; under parts white, spotted or streaked with blackish on breast and sides and with a line of same on either side of throat; legs flesh colour.

Measurements (*S. a. aurocapillus*). *Adult male:* wing, 72.8–77.4 (75.5); tail, 53–56 (54.1); exposed culmen, 11.4–12.4 (12.0); tarsus, 21–22.5 (21.9). *Adult female:* wing, 69.8–76.1 (72.8) mm.

Field Marks. A large warbler with unmarked olive green upper parts, wings, and tail; white under parts heavily streaked with black on breast and sides; whitish eye-ring, and a dull orange crown bordered by two black stripes. Usually seen *walking* on the ground or on a low branch in deciduous woodland. Waterthrushes are somewhat similar but have a pale line over the eye and an unmarked crown. Beginners might confuse the Ovenbird with small thrushes, but the black marks in its under parts are stripes rather than spots, especially on the sides. *Song:* Unmistakable. Sounds like *teacher* repeated five to fifteen times, each repetition becoming louder.

Habitat. Deciduous closed-canopy woodlands, preferably with not too much underbrush and a good carpet of leaf litter; occasionally mixedwoods. Sometimes open jack pine woodland or rarely even white spruce forest (Amos, P.Q., region).

Nesting. On the ground, usually in more open parts of the forest floor. Nest is arched over, often by leaf litter, like a Dutch oven (hence the name Ovenbird). Nest is of grass, weed stems, rootlets, leaves, and moss, with a lining of fine grasses and hair. *Eggs,* 3 to 6; white, spotted with reddish browns and some purplish grey, generally forming a wreath around the large end. Incubation 11 days and 12 hours to 14 days, averaging 12 days, 5.6 hours (H. W. Hann), by the female.

Range. Breeds from southern Mackenzie east to Newfoundland and in the United States south to eastern Colorado, southeastern Oklahoma, northern Alabama, and northern Georgia. Winters from the Gulf of Mexico coast and southern South Carolina south to Panama, northern Colombia, northern Venezuela, and the Lesser Antilles.

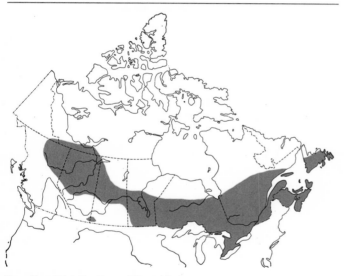

Breeding Distribution of Ovenbird

Range in Canada. Summer resident, breeding in northeastern British Columbia (Liard Hot Springs, Fort Nelson, Muskwa, Peace River parklands), southern Mackenzie (Fort Resolution), northern and central Alberta (south to about Edmonton; also locally in extreme southeast: Cypress Hills); central and, very locally, southwestern Saskatchewan (Kazan Lake, Prince Albert, Cumberland House, Nipawin; locally Cypress Hills), central and southern Manitoba (The Pas, Thicket Portage, Norway House, Riding Mountain, Aweme, Rennie), central and southern Ontario (Favourable Lake, Moosonee southward), south-central and southern Quebec (Mistassini Post, Mingan, Anticosti Island

southward, including Magdalen Islands), Newfoundland, New Brunswick, Prince Edward Island, and Nova Scotia (including Cape Breton Island).

Subspecies. (1) *Seiurus aurocapillus aurocapillus* (Linnaeus): Most of the Canadian part of the breeding range except Nfld. and extreme se. Alta. and sw. Sask. (Cypress Hills). However, limited material available from n. Alta. tends toward *cinereus* and perhaps should be referred to that race. (2) *S. a. cinereus* Miller (averages paler and more greyish above than *aurocapillus*): extreme se. Alta. and sw. Sask. (Cypress Hills). (3) *S. a. furvior* Batchelder (darker above with more brownish-orange crown patch, heavier crown stripes): Nfld.

NORTHERN WATERTHRUSH
La Fauvette des ruisseaux
Seiurus noveboracensis (Gmelin)
Plate 59. L. 5 to 6 in.

Adults and young: Above uniform olive (varying among individuals between brownish and greyish olive); buffy line over eye; sides of head dusky olive; wings and tail without any conspicuous light areas; under parts pale yellow to white, the throat dotted, the breast and sides liberally streaked with sooty olive; legs brownish flesh.

Measurements (*S. n. notabilis*). *Adult male:* wing, 72.7–76.9 (75.3); tail, 51.5–55.5 (53.1); exposed culmen, 12.6–13.9 (13.3); tarsus, 20.5–22.5 (21.5). *Adult female:* wing, 70–74 (72.2) mm.

Field Marks. This thrush-like warbler, heavily streaked below, has a prominent buffy eyebrow stripe and a habit of constantly teetering its body like a Spotted Sandpiper. Its small size, teetering motions, and streaked (instead of spotted) under parts separate it from real thrushes. Extremely similar to Louisiana Waterthrush (rare in Canada), but the Northern's more yellowish under parts, buffy instead of white eyebrow stripe, and, best of all, its spotted throat (immaculate in Louisiana Waterthrush) will mark it. *Song:* Loud, spirited, almost staccato, usually ending in a characteristic *chew chew chew*.

Habitat. Shrubby thickets, notably alder and willow, near water along streams, ponds, and lakes, swamps, bogs, and wet parts of woodlands with shallow pools of water.

Nesting. In the roots of an upturned tree, or in a cavity of a bank or stump. Nest is of mosses, leaves, grasses, and twigs and is lined with hair and blossom stalks of mosses. *Eggs,* generally 4 or 5; white, blotched and spotted with browns and often some purplish greys. They are usually more heavily marked than those of the Ovenbird. Incubation 12 days, by the female (S. W. Eaton).

Range. Breeds from north-central Alaska east across Canada to Newfoundland and south to northern Idaho, western Montana, northern North Dakota, northern Wisconsin, northern Michigan, northeastern Ohio, northern Pennsylvania, and Massachusetts. Winters from Mexico, Cuba, and the Bahamas south to Ecuador, northeastern Peru, southern Venezuela, and the Guianas.

Range in Canada. Summer resident, breeding from northern Yukon (Old Crow), northwestern Mackenzie

(Mackenzie Delta, McTavish Arm), northern Saskatchewan (Lake Athabasca, Black Lake region, Cochrane River), northern Manitoba (Churchill), northern Ontario (Severn House, Moose Factory), northern Quebec (Richmond Gulf, Indian House Lake, probably Fort Chimo), central Labrador (Davis Inlet southward; has been recorded without evidence of breeding north to Angutausugevik), and Newfoundland south to south-central and southeastern British Columbia (Stuie, Horse Lake, Flathead Valley), Alberta (south to the Edmonton region and in the southwestern mountains to Waterton Lakes Park), central Saskatchewan (Flotten Lake, Nipawin, Cumberland House), southern Manitoba (Dauphin, Indian Bay), southern Ontario (Toronto), southern Quebec (Gatineau Park, Hatley, Lac Rimouski, Percé), and throughout New Brunswick, Prince Edward Island, and Nova Scotia. Recorded in summer in southwestern Keewatin (Windy Bay).

Accidental in Franklin (Banks Island, September 11, 1914).

Breeding Distribution of Northern Waterthrush

Subspecies. (1) *Seiurus noveboracensis noveboracensis* (Gmelin): e. Que. (Knob Lake, Moisie Bay, Rivière du Loup), Lab., Nfld., N.B., P.E.I., N.S. (2) *S. n. notabilis* Ridgway, more greyish, less greenish upper parts; less yellowish under parts; Yukon, Mack., n. B.C. (Atlin, Fort Nelson), Alta., Sask., Man., Ont., w. Que. (Mistassini Post, Lake St. John, Gatineau Park). (3) *S. n. limnaeus* McCabe and Miller, with darker upper parts than *notabilis*, under parts intermediate in yellow between *noveboracensis* and *notabilis*, size (except tarsus) small: c. and se. B.C.

Remarks. Waterthrushes are really wood warblers, not thrushes. The name 'water warbler' would be a more suitable one, for they do prefer the vicinity of water. Like the Ovenbird, they walk instead of hopping; but unlike it, they have a habit of almost constantly teetering the body like a Spotted Sandpiper. They spend most of their time on or near the ground, but not infrequently a male will select a perch high in a tree for singing purposes. The Northern Waterthrush eats insects and other small animal material.

LOUISIANA WATERTHRUSH
La Fauvette hoche-queue. *Seiurus motacilla* (Vieillot)
Plate 59. L. 5.9 to 6.3 in.

Very similar to Northern Waterthrush but averages larger, especially bill; under parts usually much whiter; line over eye, white; throat, virtually unspotted. *Adults and young:* Upper parts uniform greyish olive; broad *white* stripe over eye; no white patches in wings or tail; under parts white, heavily streaked with brownish, except throat, which is immaculate or at most with mere flecks of brown; a narrow line on either side of throat; legs flesh-coloured.

Measurements. *Adult male:* wing, 75.7–84.3 (80.3); tail, 49.5–55.4 (51.8); exposed culmen, 12.4–13.5 (13.2); tarsus, 21.6–22.9 (22.3). *Adult female:* wing, 79.9–81 (78.7); exposed culmen, 12.9–14.2 (13.5) mm (Ridgway).

Field Marks. Extremely similar in appearance and habits to Northern Waterthrush but has a white (instead of buffy or yellowish) eyebrow stripe, lacks any yellowish in the white of under parts; has an *unspotted* throat. *Song:* Similar to that of Northern Waterthrush but the last part more variable, lacking the *chew chew chew* ending, which is so frequent in the Northern's song.

Habitat. Wooded ravines with running streams, woodland swamps.

Nesting. Similar to Northern Waterthrush. *Eggs*, 4 to 6; white, speckled and blotched with browns and greys. Incubation 12 to 14 days, by the female (S. W. Eaton).

Range. Breeds from eastern Nebraska, southern Michigan, southern Ontario, central New York, and Rhode Island south to eastern Texas, the United States Gulf coast, and South Carolina. Winters from northern Mexico, Cuba, and the Bahamas south to northern South America.

Range in Canada. Breeds locally in extreme southern Ontario (London, Webster's Falls).

KENTUCKY WARBLER
La Fauvette de Kentucky. *Oporornis formosus* (Wilson)
Plate 60. L. 5 to 5.8 in.

Adult male: Crown black, some feathers tipped with grey; line over eye and almost encircling eye, yellow; cheek patch and band down sides of neck, black; rest of upper parts, wings, and tail, plain olive green; under parts including under tail coverts, bright yellow. *Adult female:* Similar to adult male but duller, the blacks of head replaced by dusky are more restricted.

Measurements. *Adult male:* wing, 65–74.7 (70.1); tail, 49–52.3 (51); exposed culmen, 11.4–12.7 (11.9); tarsus, 20.8–23.4 (22.3). *Adult female:* wing, 62.7–66.8 (65) mm (Ridgway).

Distinctions. Canada Warbler also has a yellow eye-ring and eyebrow line but differs in its blue-grey upper parts, markings on breast, and white (instead of yellow) under tail coverts. The Hooded Warbler shows some white in the tail.

Range. Breeds from southeastern Nebraska, central Indiana, southern Pennsylvania, and southwestern Connecticut south to central Texas, southern Mississippi, and central Georgia.

Status in Canada. Casual visitor to southern Ontario (Point Pelee, Strathroy, Bryanston, Bradford, Rondeau Provincial Park). Accidental in Nova Scotia (Sable Island, September 1, 1902). Reported occurrence in Quebec (Quebec City) unsatisfactory.

CONNECTICUT WARBLER

La Fauvette à gorge grise. *Oporornis agilis* (Wilson)
Plate 60. L. 5.2 to 6 in.

Wing longer than in Mourning Warbler. *Adult male:* Head, throat, and upper breast, slaty grey, palest on throat; complete white eye-ring; rest of upper parts, wings, and tail, plain olive green; abdomen and under tail coverts, yellow; sides and flanks, pale olive green; legs, brownish flesh colour. In autumn the top of head is brown. *Adult female:* Similar to adult male but duller and more brownish; the slate of head, neck, and breast is replaced by brownish olive or greyish olive; throat, brownish buff or buffy white. *Young:* Similar to adult female but breast darker and more olivaceous; eye-ring slightly buffy.

Measurements. *Adult male:* wing, 68.8–73.5 (71.2); tail, 47.5–52.5 (49.5); exposed culmen, 11.7–12.9 (12.2); tarsus, 20–22.5 (21.3). *Adult female:* wing, 67.5–71.8 (69.3) mm.

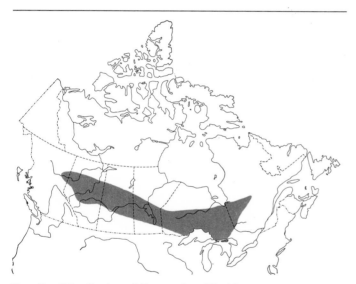

Breeding Distribution of Connecticut Warbler

Field Marks. Adult male most closely resembles male of Mourning and MacGillivray's warblers but has a complete white eye-ring (incomplete in MacGillivray's, absent in Mourning) and lacks any black on the throat or breast. Adult females and young in autumn have the breast more brownish, a complete and more conspicuous eye-ring, and longer under tail coverts than corresponding plumages of Mourning and MacGillivray's (both of which have usually incomplete eye-rings). However, many young in autumn are difficult to distinguish. Novices often mistake the Nashville Warbler for the Connecticut, but the Nashville is much smaller and has a yellow throat which is sharply marked off from the grey cheeks. *Song: Chuckety chuckety chuckety chuck* and various similar renditions of repeated syllables.

Habitat. For nesting, frequently spruce and tamarack bogs; also, especially in central Alberta, dry ridges, knolls with open poplar woods. In the Amos, P.Q., region uses open immature jack pine.

Nesting. On the ground often at the base of a small sapling or weed. Nest is of grasses, plant fibres, sometimes a few leaves. *Eggs*, 4 or 5; white, variously marked with browns.

Range. Breeds from central-eastern British Columbia east to north-central Ontario and central-western Quebec and south to northern Minnesota, northern Wisconsin, northern Michigan, and south-central Ontario. Winters from northern Venezuela to central Brazil.

Range in Canada. Breeds in central-eastern British Columbia (Tupper Creek), north-central and central Alberta (Peace River District, Fort McMurray, Belvedere), central Saskatchewan (Kazan Lake, Prince Albert, and near Roddick), central and southern Manitoba (The Pas, Riding Mountain, Whitemouth), north-central to south-central Ontario (Favourable Lake, southern James Bay, Hearst, Cochrane, Sault Ste. Marie: 20 miles north), and central-western Quebec (Rupert House; Amos region; probably east to Lake Mistassini).

Hypothetical in Nova Scotia (one reportedly found dead on Sable Island apparently was not examined by an authority; also sight records at Bon Portage Island).

MOURNING WARBLER

La Fauvette triste. *Oporornis philadelphia* (Wilson)
Plate 60. L. 5 to 5.75 in.

Wing decidedly shorter than that of Connecticut Warbler; under parts brighter yellow. *Adult male:* Head and neck slate grey, eye-ring absent, the feathers of upper breast mostly black, those of throat mostly black with grey tips; rest of upper parts olive green; no wing bars or tail spot; under parts from lower breast to under tail coverts bright yellow, darkening on sides and flanks to olive green. In autumn, the black of upper breast is much veiled with grey. *Adult female:* Similar to adult male but entire hood grey without black on upper breast or throat and in autumn with a faint whitish eye-ring. *Immatures in autumn:* Faint eye-ring present. Upper parts uniform dark olive green. Under parts mostly yellow, usually including throat, the upper breast usually tinged with olive, grey, and often some buff; and in young males often a few concealed black feathers are present.

Measurements. *Adult male:* wing, 58.6–64.4 (61.5); tail, 45.5–53 (49.3); exposed culmen, 11–12.6 (11.6); tarsus, 20–21.5 (20.4). *Adult female:* wing, 55.4–60.4 (58.1) mm.

Field Marks. Adult male is separable from that of Connecticut Warbler by black of upper breast and by lack of a white eye-ring; from adult male of MacGillivray's by lack of white on eyelids. Adult female has hood and upper breast grey (brownish in Connecticut). The autumn immature Mourning Warbler has a pale eye-ring but usually a yellowish throat (autumn immature of Connecticut has a brownish upper breast without yellow on throat). In all these plumages the Mourning Warbler has much brighter yellow under parts. The autumn Mourning Warbler also resembles the female Common Yellowthroat, but the uniformly yellow under parts of the former (belly whitish or buffy in Yellowthroat) distinguish it. *Song:* A rolling *churry churry churra churra* with variations.

Habitat. Shrubbery and bushes of young second growth on burntlands and clearings; woodland edges and sunny openings; margins of bogs and marshes.

Nesting. Usually on the ground, often in tangles of briery shrubs or other low vegetation; occasionally in a low bush. Nest rather bulky and made of dead leaves and grasses, lined with rootlets, hair, and fine grasses. *Eggs,* 3 to 5; white, spotted and blotched mostly at large end with reddish browns and some purplish grey. Incubation by the female (G. W. Cox).

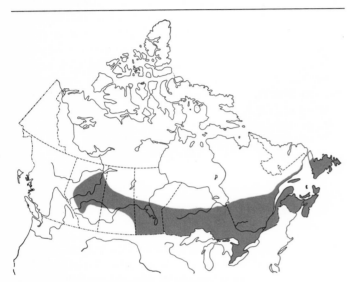

Breeding Distribution of Mourning Warbler

Range. Breeds from central Alberta east to Newfoundland and south to northeastern South Dakota, northeastern Illinois, northern Ohio, southeastern New York, and Massachusetts; and in the Appalachian Mountains to West Virginia and northwestern Virginia. Winters from southern Nicaragua and Costa Rica south to northern Ecuador, central Colombia, and western Venezuela.

Range in Canada. Breeds in Alberta (east of the Mountains and foothills: Lesser Slave Lake, Chipewyan south to Red Deer), central Saskatchewan (Kazan Lake, Emma Lake, Roddick, Cumberland House, Nipawin), central and southern Manitoba (Cormorant and Cross lakes southward), central and southern Ontario (Favourable Lake, southern James Bay southward), south-central Quebec (Eastmain, Mistassini Post, Anticosti Island, and probably east to mouth of Little Mecatina River, and southward including Magdalen Islands), Newfoundland, New Brunswick, Prince Edward Island, and Nova Scotia (including Cape Breton Island).

Remarks. When Alexander Wilson first discovered this bird, he named it Mourning Warbler because of the black areas on its breast. Wilson never saw more than one specimen. Had he known the bird better, he doubtless would have

given it a more suitable name. There is nothing about its behaviour or loud cheerful song to suggest mourning.

MacGILLIVRAY'S WARBLER
La Fauvette des buissons
Oporornis tolmiei (Townsend)
Plate 60. L. 4.8 to 5.5 in.

Wing shorter, under parts brighter yellow than Connecticut Warbler. *Adult male (breeding plumage):* Top and sides of head and sides of neck bluish slate deepening to blackish in front of eye and with a white spot on both upper and lower eyelid; rest of upper parts plain olive green; no wing bars or tail patches; throat and upper breast blackish, the feathers tipped with grey. *Adult female (breeding plumage):* Similar to adult male but throat and breast without any black, the throat sometimes almost whitish; head paler grey without any black in front of eye; white spots on upper and lower eyelids present but usually less prominent.

Measurements. *Adult male:* wing, 57.6–62.2 (59.6); tail, 50.5–54.5 (52.3); exposed culmen, 10.5–12.1 (11.3); tarsus, 20–22 (20.9). *Adult female:* wing, 53.2–60.2 (56.6) mm.

Field Marks. (*See* Connecticut and Mourning Warblers, both of which are more eastern in distribution.) However, autumn immatures of MacGillivray's Warbler are not safely separable in the field from those of the Mourning Warbler. Autumn birds somewhat resemble female and autumn Common Yellowthroats but have a more uniformly yellow abdomen and often a suggestion of a hood showing down to the upper breast. *Song:* Three or four quick notes in the same pitch, followed by several lower notes: *See it, see it, see it, peachy, peachy.*

Breeding Distribution of MacGillivray's Warbler

Habitat. Brush and thickets on logged-over areas, forest edges and openings, bushy mountainsides, and similar tall shrubbery on either moist or dry ground.

Nesting. Usually in a bush or weed not over two feet from the ground, rarely up to six feet. Nest of weed stalks and grasses, lined with fine grasses, rootlets, and hair. *Eggs,* usually 3 to 5; white, spotted and blotched with browns and some grey.

Range. Breeds from southeastern Alaska, northern British Columbia, southern Alberta, and southwestern Saskatchewan south to central California, central Arizona, and central New Mexico. Winters from northern Mexico south to Panama.

Range in Canada. Breeds in extreme southwestern Yukon (Haines Road: Miles 98 and 113), British Columbia (Haines Road: Mile 45, Dease Lake, Lower Liard Crossing, and Tupper Creek southward including Vancouver Island), southern Alberta (Jasper and Waterton Lakes parks, Coleman; and very locally east of the southwestern mountains: Red Deer River valley, Cypress Hills), and extreme southwestern Saskatchewan (Cypress Hills). Recorded eastward in Saskatchewan to Wood Mountain (specimen: June 11, 1895).

Subspecies. *Oporornis tolmiei tolmiei* (Townsend).

COMMON YELLOWTHROAT (Maryland Yellow-throat)
La Fauvette masquée. *Geothlypis trichas* (Linnaeus)
Plate 60. L. 4.5 to 5.7 in.

Wings rather short, rounded; tail only slightly shorter than folded wing; tarsus over one-third as long as wing. *Adult male (breeding plumage):* Forehead and sides of head black, forming a mask which is margined narrowly above and behind by greyish; rest of upper parts, wings, and tail, olive green; no wing bars or tail patches; throat and breast, yellow; abdomen whitish to pale buff; sides and flanks, brownish olive. In autumn, the black mask feathers are tipped with grey. *Adult female:* Differs from adult male in having no black mask; crown and sides of head greyish olive, the forehead often tinged with brown; pale eyebrow line and inconspicuous pale eye-ring. *Young in autumn:* Resemble adults in autumn but are duller and browner, the male with black mask only partly developed and lacking its grey border.

Measurements (*G. t. brachidactyla*). *Adult male:* wing, 52–58.4 (55.0); tail, 48.5–53.5 (50.9); exposed culmen, 10.6–11.6 (11.0); tarsus, 19.5–21.5 (20.1). *Adult female:* wing, 49.3–57.9 (52.6) mm.

Field Marks. A warbler of low shrubbery and with wren-like motions. The adult male, with broad black mask and yellow throat, is unmistakable. Young males in autumn often show enough of the tell-tale black mask to identify them. Females have no mask but usually (not always) show some yellowish on throat, and in any case the throat is pale and is sharply cut off from the dark cheeks. Might be confused with Connecticut, Mourning, or MacGillivray's in autumn plumages, but the Yellowthroat has a whitish or dull buffy abdomen; in the other three it is yellow. *Voice:* Song is distinct, sounding like *witchery witchery witchery*, but is variable both individually and geographically. Its *chip* has a peculiar husky quality that identifies it.

Habitat. Low bushes and thickets bordering streams, ponds, roadsides, and wood edges; bushy pastures and old fields; cattails and bulrushes of marshes and similar situations, most frequently on moist ground but often in dry bushy places as well.

Nesting. On or very near the ground among low vegetation. Nest of weed stalks, grasses, and leaves is rather bulky and has a lining of fine grasses and often hair. *Eggs,* 3 to 5, usually 4; white, marked mostly at the large end with browns, some black, and often underlying grey. Incubation 12 days, by the female (P. B. Hofslund).

Range. Breeds from southeastern Alaska east to Labrador and Newfoundland and south to southern Mexico, the Gulf coast of United States, and southern Florida. Winters from southern United States south to Panama and Puerto Rico.

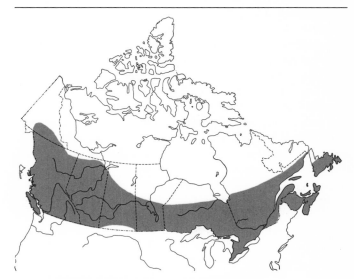

Breeding Distribution of Common Yellowthroat

Range in Canada. Breeds in southern Yukon (Hutshi Lake, Pelly River at Canol Road), British Columbia (Atlin, Lower Liard Crossing southward including Vancouver Island), Alberta (southern Wood Buffalo Park and Peace River District southward), central and southern Saskatchewan (Kazan Lake, Cumberland House southward), central and southern Manitoba (Cormorant Lake, Cross Lake southward), north-central and southern Ontario (Lac Seul, southern James Bay southward), south-central and southern Quebec (lakes Mistassini and Albanel, outer north shore of the Gulf of St. Lawrence southward including Anticosti and Magdalen islands), Newfoundland, New Brunswick, Prince Edward Island, and Nova Scotia.

Subspecies. (1) *Geothlypis trichas brachidactyla* (Swainson): e. Canada from e. Ont. (Amyot, Fort Albany) east to Nfld. and N.S. (2) *G. t. campicola* Behle and Aldrich (similar to *brachidactyla* but upper parts lighter, yellow of under parts richer and more extensive): w. Ont. (Lac Seul), Man., Sask., Alta., and s. and c. B.C. (east of the coast). (3) *G. t. yukonicola* Godfrey (similar to *campicola* but upper parts distinctly greyer): s. Yukon, nw. B.C. (Dease Lake). (4) *G. t. arizela* Oberholser (very similar to *campicola* but upper parts more yellow-green, less greyish): coastal B.C. (Vancouver Island, Chilliwack).

Remarks. The male, with his bright yellow throat and jet black mask, is one of the easiest of birds to recognize. Most vegetation tangles, especially those near moist places, have at least one pair of these interesting warblers. They are very active birds, peering and posturing with wrenlike energy when intruders enter their domain. They seem more irritated than alarmed, however, and repeatedly utter a characteristically husky *tscick* of disapproval.

YELLOW-BREASTED CHAT

La Fauvette polyglotte. *Icteria virens* (Linnaeus)
Plate 59. L. 6.75 to 7.5 in.

Size very large for a warbler. Bill shorter than head, stout, its ridge decidedly convex. Wings and tail nearly equal in length (the tail often a trifle longer) and both somewhat rounded. *Adult male:* Upper parts, including wings and tail, greyish olive green (often quite greyish in worn plumage); no wing bars or tail patches; stripe from bill back over eye, spot under eye, and stripe from base of bill back over jaw, white; rest of sides of head, greyish green becoming slaty or blackish in front of eye; throat, breast, and under wing coverts, bright yellow; rest of under parts white, tinged on sides and under tail coverts with buffy grey. *Adult female:* Similar to adult male but usually duller in colour, the yellows less bright, the dark area in front of eye more greyish. *Autumn adults and young:* Similar to summer adults but upper parts more decidedly green, flanks more buffy.

Measurements (*I. v. auricollis*). *Adult male:* wing, 75.5–83.9 (79.3); tail, 74–88 (81.1); exposed culmen, 13.1–16.7 (14.8); tarsus, 25.5–28 (26.6). *Adult female:* wing, 73–80 (77.6).

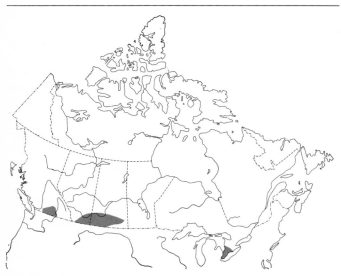

Breeding Distribution of Yellow-breasted Chat

Field Marks. Large size, bright yellow breast, two white stripes on side of head, no wing bars, and longish tail make good field marks. Habitat and song also are helpful. *Song:* Very varied, a series of disjointed noises: *cuks*, *quits*, and harsh nasal laughing notes, often interspersed with a series of whistles somewhat suggesting a man whistling to a dog.

Habitat. Thickets and tangles of tall shrubbery beside streams or ponds, in old overgrown bushy clearings and in similar situations where it can keep out of sight.

Nesting. In a small tree, sapling, or bushy tangle usually 2 to 5 feet above ground. Nest is bulky and is composed of coarse materials like leaves, shreds of bark, coarse straws, and weed stalks, and lined with fine grasses. *Eggs,* 3 to 5; white, spotted usually over the entire egg with browns and purplish grey. Incubation 11 days by the female (Petrides).

Range. Breeds from southern Canada (very locally) and northern United States south to north-central Mexico, the United States Gulf coast, and northern Florida. Winters from Mexico and southern Texas south to western Panama.

Range in Canada. Breeds in southern British Columbia (Okanagan and Similkameen valleys), southeastern Alberta (Steveville, Empress, Milk River valley), southern Saskatchewan (Frenchman River valley, Maple Creek, Fort San, near Tregarva), and southern Ontario (Perth County, Port Burwell, Point Pelee).

Casual in New Brunswick (Grand Manan, Machias Seal Island, St. Andrews), Nova Scotia (Brier Island, Port Mouton), and Newfoundland (Cappahayden, St. John's). Most of these east coast records are for autumn or winter.

Subspecies. (1) *Icteria virens virens* (Linnaeus): s. Ont. (2) *I. v. auricollis* (Deppe) (more greyish upper parts, white of malar region more extended, yellow of under parts deeper): B.C., Alta., Sask.

HOODED WARBLER

La Fauvette à capuchon. *Wilsonia citrina* (Boddaert)
Plate 59. L. 5 to 5.75 in.

Adult male: Forehead and sides of head, bright yellow; rest of head, neck, throat, and upper breast, black; remainder of upper parts, yellowish olive green; no wing bars; two outer tail feathers on each side with inner webs extensively white, the next with a white patch; under parts from black of hood to tail, bright yellow. *Adult female:* Similar to adult male but with either mere traces of black suggesting part of the male's hood, or no black at all. The white in the tail distinguishes it from similar mostly-yellow warblers without white wing bars.

Measurements. *Adult male:* wing, 65.5–69.1 (67.6); tail, 55.4–59.7 (57.7); exposed culmen, 9.9–11.2 (10.7); tarsus, 19–20.1 (19.7). *Adult female:* wing, 60.2–66.8 (63.0) mm (Ridgway).

Field Marks. Adult male, with its black hood and yellow mask, is unmistakable. Adult females and young females in autumn are olive green above, yellow below, and show only traces, if any, of the male's black hood. The white in the tail of the Hooded distinguishes it from similar yellow warblers without white wing bars, e.g., Wilson's Warbler. *Song: Weeta-weeta-wee-tee-o* suggests that of the Magnolia Warbler but is much louder.

Habitat. Favours mature deciduous forest, particularly along stream bottoms and ravine edges and where saplings and shrubbery grow on the forest floor. Inhabits the lower forest stratum.

Nesting. Nest site averages about 26 inches above ground in the fork of a seedling, bush, or grape tangle. Nest is of dead leaves and bark strips, held together by spider silk and lined with fine shreds of bark and grasses. *Eggs,* usually 3 or 4; white, speckled or blotched with browns, mostly around the large end. Incubation 12 days; young remain in nest about eight days after hatching (A. B. Williams).

Range. Breeds from northeastern Nebraska east to Rhode Island and south to southeastern Texas, the United States Gulf coast, and northern Florida. Winters from southeastern Mexico south to Costa Rica and rarely Panama.

Range in Canada. Breeds only in extreme southern Ontario (Orwell, Tillsonburg).

Wanders somewhat farther north in Ontario (to Toronto and Kingston). Casual in Nova Scotia (Cape Sable, September 30, 1962) and accidental in northern Manitoba (Churchill, June 10, 1952). Hypothetical (sight records only) in southern Quebec and southern New Brunswick.

WILSON'S WARBLER

La Fauvette à calotte noire. *Wilsonia pusilla* (Wilson)
Plate 59. L. 4.25 to 5.1 in.

Bill short, rather wide at base; bristles about mouth extending forward beyond nostrils. *Adult male:* Crown black; forehead and stripe over eye, yellow; rest of upper parts olive green, this extending forward over ear coverts; rest of sides of head yellow; no wing bars or white patches in tail; under parts lemon yellow including under tail coverts, the sides and flanks tinged with olive green. *Adult female:* Similar to adult male but black cap usually restricted and much hidden by olive. *Young in first autumn:* Similar to adults but males with cap more broadly tipped with olive, females with cap concealed or absent.

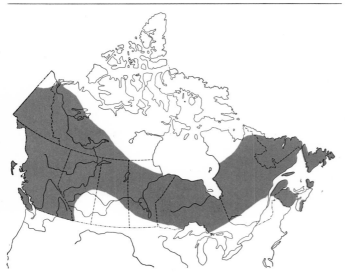

Breeding Distribution of Wilson's Warbler

Measurements (*W. p. pusilla*). *Adult male:* wing, 52–56.6 (54.3); tail, 46.5–50 (49.0); exposed culmen, 8.4–9.2 (8.8); tarsus, 17–18 (17.4). *Adult female:* wing, 49.8–53.4 (51.8) mm.

Field Marks. A yellow warbler without wing bars or pale patches in the tail. Adults with a black cap (smaller in female), a bright yellow stripe over eye. The dark eye stands out on an otherwise featureless face. Young Yellow Warblers

have yellow wing bars and yellow patches in the tail. Female and young Hooded Warblers show white in the tail. Male Goldfinch is a yellow bird with a black cap, but its thick sparrow-like bill and black wings quickly distinguish it. *Song:* A series of rapid, almost staccato, chattering notes, dropping in pitch toward the end.

Habitat. In nesting season frequents shrubbery, such as alder, willow, and dwarf birch in moist open places especially along streams, ponds, and bogs; and at various elevations in the mountains in shrubbery of valley bottoms, mountainsides, and alpine meadows.

Nesting. On the ground, often at the base of a shrub or small tree or in a grass hummock. Nest is bulky and is made of grasses, small leaves, and mosses, and is lined with grasses and hair. *Eggs*, 4 to 6, usually 5; white, finely spotted and speckled with reddish browns.

Range. Breeds from northern Alaska east to Labrador and Newfoundland, and south to southern California, central Nevada, northern Utah, and northern New Mexico, northern Minnesota, northern Vermont, and central Maine. Winters from northern Mexico and southern Texas south to Costa Rica and western Panama.

Range in Canada. Summer resident, breeding from northern Yukon (Old Crow), northwestern and central-eastern Mackenzie (Mackenzie Delta, Fort Anderson, Artillery Lake), northwestern Saskatchewan (Lake Athabasca), northern Manitoba (Herchmer, York Factory), northern Ontario (Fort Severn, Fort Albany), northern Quebec (Richmond Gulf, Indian House Lake; perhaps George River Post), central Labrador (Makkovik, Cartwright) and Newfoundland south through British Columbia (including Vancouver Island), southwestern and central-eastern Alberta (Banff and Waterton Lakes parks; Nevis), central Saskatchewan (Kazan Lake, Nipawin), southern Manitoba (Lake St. Martin), south-central Ontario (Sudbury), southern Quebec (Amos, Mistassini Post, Lake St. John, north shore of the Gulf of St. Lawrence; Anticosti Island; Matane County; Gaspé), New Brunswick (locally, Tabusintac), and locally in Nova Scotia (Deerfield, Harrigan Cove; probably Cape Breton Island). Migrant in Prince Edward Island, but possibly breeds rarely. Accidental in northern Baffin Island (Arctic Bay, July 1954).

Subspecies. (1) *Wilsonia pusilla pusilla* (Wilson): Mack. (Fort Anderson, Artillery Lake), n. and e. Alta. (north and east of mts. and foothills), Sask., Man., Ont., Que., Lab., Nfld., N.B., N.S. (2) *W. p. pileolata* (Pallas) (coloration above and below brighter than in *pusilla*): s. Yukon (no northern material examined, but Old Crow specimens are referred to *pusilla* by Irving, 1960), B.C. (interior), and nw. Alta. (mts. and foothills). (3) *W. p. chryseola* Ridgway (brighter above and below than *pileolata*): sw. coastal B.C. (Victoria, Vancouver).

Remarks. This bright little bundle of animation goes about its daily chore of securing food with zest and excitement. It darts after flying insects and takes them with an audible snap of its bill. It has a habit of nervously twitching its tail. Even on migration, preference for bushy moist places like those on its nesting grounds is still marked, but it is then much more tolerant of other types, including dry ones.

CANADA WARBLER

La Fauvette du Canada. *Wilsonia canadensis* (Linnaeus)
Plate 60. L. 5 to 5.75 in.

Mouth bristles well developed. Wings rather long and pointed. *Adult male:* Forehead and much of crown black, the feathers much edged with grey, and sometimes a pale narrow line in mid-forehead; rest of upper parts, bluish grey; no wing bars or tail patches; narrow streak from base of bill to eye and eye-ring, yellow; area in front of eye extending back under eye to side of neck, black; under parts bright yellow except a necklace of black spots and white under tail coverts. *Adult female:* Similar to adult male but duller. Forehead with little or no black, crown often tinged yellow-olive; black of face replaced by olive grey; spotting across breast sparser, spots dusky or olive instead of black. *Young in autumn:* Similar to adult female, but breast markings are still fainter, and the upper parts are often lightly washed with olive brown.

Measurements. *Adult male:* wing, 61.9–67.8 (64.8); tail, 53.5–58.5 (56.2); exposed culmen, 10–11.4 (10.7); tarsus, 18–19.5 (18.9). *Adult female:* wing, 60.1–62.6 (61.6) mm.

Field Marks. A black necklace (but faint and greyish in females and young) on otherwise unmarked bright yellow under parts. Plain grey upper parts, yellowish eye-ring and thin line from bill to eye, white under tail coverts. *Song:* Is preceded by a single *chip* (sometimes two) and a very slight pause, then the quick slightly staccato song which often contains characteristic *ditchety* phrases.

Breeding Distribution of Canada Warbler

Habitat. Shrubbery undergrowths of woodlands, tall shrubbery such as alder and willow along streams, swamps, and similar moist places.

Nesting. On or near the ground under a sapling, in a mossy hummock, on a mossy stump or log, in a bank cavity, or among the roots of an overturned tree. Nest rather bulky and made of weeds, grasses, leaves, and bark shreds, and lined with fine plant fibres, rootlets, and often hair. *Eggs,* 3 to 5; white, well speckled with chestnut.

348

PLATE 67

1 Oregon Junco,
   (a) autumn immature
   (b) adult male

2 Slate-colored Junco,
   (a) autumn immature
   (b) adult male

3 Field Sparrow

4 Tree Sparrow

5 Clay-colored Sparrow,
   (a) adult
   (b) autumn immature

6 Brewer's Sparrow

7 Chipping Sparrow,
   (a) adult
   (b) autumn immature

1a

1b

2a

2b

3

4

5a

5b

6

7a

7b

Crosby

Crosby

PLATE 68

1 White-crowned Sparrow,
  (a) adult
      (*gambelii* race)
  (b) adult
      (*leucophrys* race)
  (c) autumn immature
      (*leucophrys* race)

2 Golden-crowned
  Sparrow,
  (a) adult
  (b) autumn immature

3 White-throated Sparrow,
  (a) adult
  (b) autumn immature

4 Swamp Sparrow
  (a) adult
  (b) autumn immature

5 Lincoln's Sparrow, adult

6 Fox Sparrow,
  (a) adult (eastern race)
  (b) adult
      (*townsendi* race)

7 Song Sparrow, adult
  (eastern race)

Range. Breeds in Canada from Alberta east to Nova Scotia and south in the United States to central Minnesota, central Michigan, northern Ohio, and in the Appalachians to eastern Tennessee, northwestern Georgia, western North Carolina, and to northern New Jersey. Winters from Colombia and Venezuela south to central Peru.

Range in Canada. Summer resident, breeding in northern and central Alberta (Fort McMurray south to Beaver River south of Cold Lake; and west to Belvedere and Joussard; probably Grimshaw), central Saskatchewan (Flotten Lake, Carlton, Cumberland House, Nipawin), central and south-western Manitoba (The Pas, Moose and Cedar lakes, Lake St. Martin), north-central and southern Ontario (Favourable Lake, Moose Factory, Abitibi Lake; south, at least formerly, to Middlesex County); south-central and southern Quebec (Mistassini Post, Matamek, Anticosti Island; Montreal, Hatley, Gaspé Peninsula), New Brunswick, Prince Edward Island, and Nova Scotia (including Cape Breton Island).

AMERICAN REDSTART
La Fauvette flamboyante. *Setophaga ruticilla* (Linnaeus)
Plate 60. L. 4.7 to 5.7 in.

Bill broad at base for a warbler. Wings rather long and pointed. *Adult male:* Head, neck, back, throat, and upper breast, black; central tail feathers black, the others orange or salmon pink with a broad terminal band of black; wings black with substantial orange patch at the base of the flight feathers; sides of breast and under wing coverts, orange; belly white, the sides tinged with orange. *Adult female:* Crown, hind-neck, and sides of head grey, passing into olive on back and rump; wings and tail patterned as in adult male but patches yellow instead of orange; throat and breast dull greyish white; rest of under parts white with patch of yellow on either side of breast; mid-breast and sides and flanks often tinged yellowish. *Young (first autumn):* Similar to adult female. *Young male (first spring):* Similar to adult female but with irregular black markings appearing about head and on under plumage.

Measurements (*S. r. tricolora*). *Adult male:* wing, 61.7–65.5 (63.5); tail, 55–58.5 (56.8); exposed culmen, 8–9.1 (8.7); tarsus, 17–18.5 (17.5). *Adult female:* wing, 57.1–62.4 (59.4) mm.

Field Marks. A distinctively marked warbler with a habit of frequently drooping its wings and spreading its tail. The adult male with its black and orange pattern is unmistakable. The adult female and young, although grey above, have wing, tail, and breast pattern like that of the adult male, but the patches are yellow instead of orange. *Song:* High-pitched, lisping, but variable: *tsee tsee tsee tsee-o* (slurred downward at end) or *teetsy teetsy teetsy* and other songs.

Habitat. More open parts of deciduous and mixed woodlands, second growths, woodlots, tall shrubbery.

Nesting. Usually in a deciduous (rarely coniferous) tree or tall shrub generally 6 to 25 feet up. Nest is often in a crotch or group of upright branches. It is neatly and firmly made of grasses, plant down, and shreds of bark and is lined with hair, grass, rootlets, or feathers. *Eggs*, 3 to 5, usually 4; white, spotted and speckled with browns and a little purplish grey. Incubation 12 days, by the female (A. C. Bent).

Range. Breeds from southeastern Alaska east to southern Labrador and Newfoundland, and south to eastern Oregon, northern Utah, northern Colorado, southeastern Oklahoma, southeastern Louisiana, and central Georgia. Winters from Mexico, Cuba, and Puerto Rico south to Ecuador and northern Brazil.

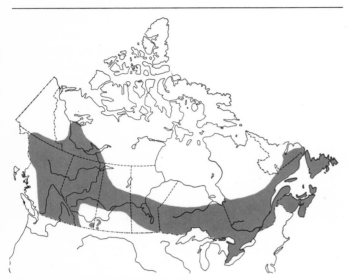

Breeding Distribution of American Redstart

Range in Canada. Summer resident, breeding from northern British Columbia (Atlin, Liard Crossing), central-western and central-southern Mackenzie (Fort Norman, Fort Resolution), north-central Saskatchewan (Kazan Lake, Cumberland House), north-central Manitoba (Cormorant Lake, Thicket Portage), north-central Ontario (Favourable Lake, Moose Factory), central Quebec (Eastmain, Mistassini Post; north shore of the Gulf of St. Lawrence; St. Augustin River: 22 miles inland; Anticosti Island), southern Labrador (Goose Bay), and Newfoundland south through southern interior British Columbia (Pemberton eastward), southern Alberta (but in extreme southeast only locally: Cypress Hills), south-central Saskatchewan (apparently only a migrant in most of the southern prairies; probably Cypress Hills), southern Manitoba, southern Ontario, southern Quebec (including Magdalen Islands), New Brunswick, Prince Edward Island, and Nova Scotia (including Cape Breton Island). Summer sight records for extreme central-southern Yukon (Watson Lake, Morley River).

Accidental on Banks Island, N.W.T. (Sachs Harbour, September 19, 1952) and at Port Burwell, N.W.T.

Subspecies. (1) *Setophaga ruticilla tricolora* (Müller): All of Canada except extreme s. Ont. (2) *S. r. ruticilla* (Linnaeus) (adult females and immature males slightly darker above): extreme s. Ont. (Hamilton southward).

Remarks. This is one of the handsomest and most active of our warblers. Rarely still a moment, it flits from branch to branch, darts after flying insects, or snatches up insect larvae from twigs and foliage. It has a characteristic habit of drooping its wings and fanning its tail, thus displaying the contrasty orange patches located there. It is a common summer resident in much of its extensive range.

Family **Ploceidae**–Weaver Finches

Number of Species in North America 2; in Canada 1

There are no native American species of this Old World family. One species, the House Sparrow, has been introduced into Canada and now flourishes in most of southern Canada and the United States.

HOUSE SPARROW (English Sparrow)
Le Moineau domestique. *Passer domesticus* (Linnaeus)
Plate 63. L. 5.8 to 6.7 in.

More robust generally than our native sparrows with relatively heavy strong bill. *Adult male (breeding plumage):* Top of head, nape, and rump, grey; chestnut patch from eye to nape and broadening over side of neck; small white spot behind eye; patch between eye and base of bill, black; back streaked with black, buff, and chestnut; wing with white bar; tail all dark brown with narrow buffy edging; throat and middle of breast, black; ear coverts grey; jaw and sides of neck, whitish; rest of under parts greyish white, the sides and flanks grey or buffy grey; under tail coverts tinged with buffy brown; bill black; legs brownish. *Adult male (autumn and winter):* Similar to adult male in breeding plumage but more brownish generally, the black of throat and breast partly hidden by grey feather tips; bill dark brown, pale toward base. *Adult female:* Upper parts dull brown, the back streaked as in the male but lacking chestnut patch behind eye and with little or no chestnut on wing coverts, no black on throat or breast; a pale buffy line from above eye back to nape; dingy wing bar present; under parts dingy grey with buffy tinge; bill as in winter male. *Young (first autumn):* Resemble adults in autumn, but the young males have black of throat and breast even more concealed by pale feather tips.

Measurements. *Adult male:* wing, 73.9–79 (76.4); tail, 54.5–60 (57.9); exposed culmen, 12.1–13.9 (12.8); tarsus, 18.5–20 (19.3). *Adult female:* wing, 72.4–77.5 (74.7) mm.

Field Marks. The common sparrow about the buildings of cities and farms, thus familiar to everyone. Male with black bib (partly hidden in fall and winter), chestnut patch back from eye, and white wing bar. Females, dull brown above, with a faint buffy stripe back from eye, dingy grey under parts, and a heavier bill than that of the native sparrows. The call is diagnostic. *Voice:* A monotonous *chirp* or *chisseck*, repeated over and over *ad nauseum* and all too familiar to any city dweller; also a harsh chatter.

Habitat. The vicinity of human buildings and cultivated land: cities, farms, fields, yards, garbage dumps, streets, and roadsides.

Nesting. In cavities about buildings, dense growths of vines on buildings, bird boxes, natural and woodpecker cavities in trees, tree branches; sometimes drives Cliff Swallows from their mud nests and occasionally uses cavities in banks excavated by Bank Swallows. Cavities are filled with coarse materials such as straw, feathers, and assorted trash. When nest is built in tree branches, it is an untidy domed structure with an entrance hole in the side. *Eggs*, 3 to 7, most often 5; variable in colour, white to pale greenish or bluish, finely and rather uniformly spotted with greys and browns. Incubation 12 to 13, or even 14 days, mostly by the female but with assistance from the male (Jourdain, *in* Witherby); usually 12 days (R. L. Weaver).

Range. Native to Eurasia and northern Africa. It has been introduced by man in many parts of the world, including North and South America. In North America from Canada south to southern United States and south-central Mexico (Guerrero).

Range in Canada. Introduced and widely established (first introduced into North America in 1850 at Brooklyn, New York, and somewhat later in Quebec City and Halifax, Canada). Permanent resident breeding from central and northeastern British Columbia (Porcher Island, Fort Nelson), southwestern Mackenzie (Fort Simpson, Fort Smith), northwestern and central Saskatchewan (Lake Athabasca, Emma Lake), northern Manitoba (Churchill), northern Ontario (Fort Severn, Fort Albany, Moose Factory), southwestern Quebec (La Ferme, Chibougamau, Lake St. John, Godbout, Seven Islands, Anticosti Island, Gaspé Peninsula; recorded without evidence of breeding at Havre St. Pierre), and northern Newfoundland (St. Anthony) southward all across southern Canada including Vancouver Island, British Columbia; the Maritime Provinces; and Magdalen Islands, Quebec.

Subspecies. *Passer domesticus domesticus* (Linnaeus).

Remarks. The introduction of the House Sparrow into North America was a mistake. It flourished and has spread to most settled parts of Canada and the United States. It is a pugnacious ruffian, driving away our native birds and usurping their nesting cavities. Its all too successful competition with Tree Swallows and other native cavity-nesting birds is well known to all who provide and maintain nesting boxes for our native species, and it is doubtless a major factor in the recent serious decline in the Cliff Swallow's numbers. The name 'House Sparrow' is a misnomer, as the species belongs to the weaver finch family and is not really a sparrow. However, its name has been so universally accepted that attempts now to correct it would probably prove futile.

Family **Icteridae**–Meadowlarks, Blackbirds, and Orioles

Number of Species in North America 22; in Canada 12

This interesting family is confined to the Western Hemisphere. Its species vary greatly in colour from plain black (often with striking iridescence) through yellows, browns, reds, and oranges. As in the Fringillidae, the cutting edge of the lower mandible angles abruptly downward near its base, but in most icterids the bill is longer, slenderer, and

less conical than in fringillids; and the culmen is usually extended backward onto the forehead. The wings have nine primaries. The tail is variable in length and is often rounded.

BOBOLINK
Le Goglu. *Dolichonyx oryzivorus* (Linnaeus)
Plate 61. L. 6.5 to 8 in.

Bill, short and sparrow-like; wings longish, the two outermost feathers longest; tail, rather stiff and with sharp-pointed tips (Fig. 66); hind toenail much elongated. *Adult male (breeding plumage)*: Head and under parts black, some of the feathers of flanks, abdomen, and under tail coverts edged with buff; large buff patch on back of neck; upper back, black streaked with buffy; rest of back, rump, upper tail coverts, and scapulars, pale grey to whitish; wing and tail, black with yellowish edging; bill black; legs brown. *Adult male (winter plumage)*: Similar to adult female, but often a few black feathers are still not molted by the time it departs from Canada in autumn. *Adult female:* Upper parts, buffy olive streaked with black; top of head with central pale streak, bordered on either side by a broad blackish or brownish stripe; sides of head yellowish olive with narrow blackish streak extending backward from eye; wing and tail dusky, edged with yellowish olive; under parts plain yellowish olive, the sides, flanks, and under tail coverts streaked with black; bill brown, darkest near tip; legs brown. *Young in autumn plumage:* Similar to adult female but often more decidedly yellowish on under parts.

Fig. 66 Pointed tail feathers of Bobolink

Measurements. *Adult male:* wing, 92.8–99.8 (95.8); tail, 63.5–70.5 (66.6); exposed culmen, 14.5–15.8 (15.2); tarsus, 26–28 (27.0). *Adult female:* wing, 83–88.4 (85.9) mm.

Distinctions. Adult females, autumn adults of both sexes, and young in autumn, with striped upper parts and sparrow-like bills, closely resemble sparrows. The long hind toenail of the Bobolink suggests one of the longspurs, but the Bobolink's sharp-pointed tail feathers are different from those of longspurs. Some sparrows have sharp-pointed tail feathers, but those particular species are smaller than the Bobolink, and their hind toenails are not elongated.

Field Marks. Adult male in spring and summer, with black under parts, whitish scapulars, greyish white rump, and large buff patch on back of neck, is one of the easiest birds to recognize. In the West, the male Lark Bunting also has black under parts, but white areas are confined to patches in the wings. Females and autumn young very closely resemble sparrows but are somewhat larger and more yellowish, and they have distinctive call-notes. *Voice:* Song is a delightful, loud, bubbling performance made up of short banjo-like notes, sung as the male flies, on rapidly but shallowly beating wings, or when he is perching; also a characteristic call-note of late summer and autumn which sounds like *pink* and helps identify the sparrow-like females and young.

Habitat. Fields and meadows of tall grass, clover, alfalfa, or grain. Also, in autumn, marshes and other open places.

Nesting. On the ground in tall grass or similar vegetation in open places. Nest is flimsily made of grasses and weed stalks with a sparse lining of fine grasses. *Eggs,* 4 to 7, usually 5 or 6; pale grey to pale brownish, irregularly blotched and spotted with various browns and purplish greys. Incubation variously reported 10 to 13 days, by the female.

Range. Breeds from southeastern British Columbia east to Nova Scotia and south to northeastern California, northern Utah, central Colorado, northeastern Kansas, central Illinois, northwestern Ohio, northern West Virginia, Pennsylvania, and central New Jersey. Winters in eastern Bolivia, western Brazil, Paraguay, and northern Argentina.

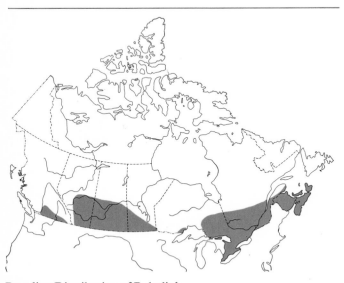

Breeding Distribution of Bobolink

Range in Canada. Summer resident, breeding in southern interior British Columbia (Penticton, Waldo; north locally to 150 Mile House), southern Alberta (Heinsberg, Camrose, Calgary), central and southern Saskatchewan (Saskatoon, Nipawin, Eastend, Yorkton, Regina), southern Manitoba (Garland, St. Laurent, Whitemouth), central and southern Ontario (Port Arthur, Chapleau southward;

reported in summer, and probably breeds, north to Sioux Lookout, Kapuskasing, Missanabie, Strickland, Cochrane, and Matheson), southwestern Quebec (Taschereau, Amos, Lake St. John, Percé southward, but status on Magdalen Islands uncertain), New Brunswick, Nova Scotia (including Cape Breton Island), and Prince Edward Island (Bideford, Ellerslie). It has only recently colonized Prince Edward Island.

Casual in northern Ontario (Moose Factory), Newfoundland (Cape Broyle, June 9, 1956), southern Labrador (Gready, September 12, 1927), and southeastern Quebec (Bradore Bay, summer 1924).

Remarks. In Canada, we know the Bobolink in summer when the male is handsomely attired in black, white, and buff. He delivers his ecstatic, banjo-like song either while perched or in slow flight with rapid shallow wing strokes. We associate him with broad fields of tall grass redolent with clover and speckled with buttercups and daisies.

In late summer, shortly before leaving Canada, the male assumes a dull sparrow-like plumage similar to that of the female, and the famous song is heard no more. Bobolinks then rove about in flocks, and the usual call becomes a metallic *pink*. In migration through southern United States they are called 'rice birds' because they are sometimes destructive of grain. While in Canada, however, Bobolinks are highly insectivorous, but they eat some weed seeds as well.

EASTERN MEADOWLARK
La Sturnelle des prés. *Sturnella magna* (Linnaeus)
Plate 61. L. 8.5 to 11 in.

Bill tapering, nearly straight, pointed in side view, but in dorsal view the tip is somewhat rounded; ridge of bill extends well back on forehead; wings short; tail rather short, its feathers somewhat pointed; feet large, especially hind toe. *Adult male (breeding plumage):* Crown with median buffy stripe, bordered on each side by a broader blackish stripe; rest of upper parts streaked with buff, black, and browns; tertials and secondaries heavily barred with black but with light brown edges; bend of wing yellow; tail feathers brownish grey barred with black, but the outer feathers chiefly white; pale stripe from nostril back over eye is yellow in front of eye, buff behind eye; narrow blackish line extending back from eye; rest of sides of head greyish white, usually with fine streaks on ear coverts; throat, much of breast, and abdomen lemon-yellow; broad black crescent on breast, its ends extending to sides of neck; sides, flanks, and under tail coverts, buffy white streaked with black. *Adult female (breeding plumage):* Similar to adult male but obviously smaller, coloration somewhat duller, the dark stripes on crown streaked with brown; black crescent on breast smaller. *Adults and young in autumn:* Similar to adults in spring but much more brownish above and below, with buffy feather tips obscuring the black crescent and dulling the yellow parts.

Measurements. *Adult male:* wing, 116.7–125 (119.7); tail, 71–82.5 (78.1); exposed culmen, 27.5–34.6 (32.7); tarsus, 38.5–41.5 (40.3). *Adult female:* wing, 104–113.8 (107.4) mm.

Distinctions (*see* Western Meadowlark).

Field Marks. A short-tailed robin-sized bird with a black crescent on its bright yellow breast. Flies with rapid beats of the short wings alternating with very short glides and showing white outer feathers in the short tail. The flicker also has a black crescent on the breast but shows a white rump patch and no white in the tail. The Western Meadowlark is the only bird with which the Eastern is likely to be confused (*see* Western Meadowlark). *Voice:* Song, a clear, high-pitched, far-carrying whistle, often rendered as *spring o' the year*, is entirely different from that of the Western Meadowlark. A harsh chatter of alarm.

Habitat. Open fields and similar places with adequate grassy cover. In autumn, grain stubbles are popular.

Nesting. On the ground in open grassy areas. Nest is concealed in grass and usually has dome-shaped roof. Nest is made of grasses and weed stalks and is lined with fine grasses. *Eggs*, 3 to 7, most frequently 5; white—speckled, spotted, and blotched with browns and bluish grey. Incubation 13 to 15 days, usually 14, by the female (G. B. Saunders, *in* Bent).

Range. Southern Ontario east to New Brunswick and south through central and eastern United States to Arizona, New Mexico, Texas, the Gulf coast, Cuba, and through Mexico and Central America south to Colombia, Venezuela, British Guiana, and Brazil.

Breeding Distribution of Eastern Meadowlark

Range in Canada. Breeds in southern Ontario (Sault Ste. Marie, North Bay, Ottawa, southward), southwestern Quebec (Blue Sea Lake, Stoneham, Rivière du Loup, Biencourt), southern New Brunswick (Sussex), and Nova Scotia (Windsor, but rare in summer). Reports of breeding on Magdalen Islands, P.Q., need confirmation.

Recorded without evidence of breeding north to central Ontario (Gogama, Cochrane, Englehart); Lake St. John, Pointe des Monts, Seven Islands, and Percé, Quebec; and Prince Edward Island. Accidental in central-western Quebec (Eastmain, November 17, 1946) and Newfoundland (St. Shotts, January 4, 1938).

Winters in extreme southern Ontario (Point Pelee,

London, Toronto, Hamilton, Kingston, casually north to Ottawa); rarely Nova Scotia (most that attempt to do so do not survive).

Subspecies. *Sturnella magna magna* (Linnaeus).

WESTERN MEADOWLARK

La Sturnelle de l'Ouest. *Sturnella neglecta* Audubon
Plate 61. L. 8.5 to 11 in.

Extremely similar to Eastern Meadowlark but *yellow of throat more extensive* (Fig. 67), reaching up to lower cheeks (malar region), upper parts paler and more greyish, the feather edges paler and wider, wings and tail more sharply barred (bars not so confluent or run together as in Eastern); sides and flanks more spotted than streaked.

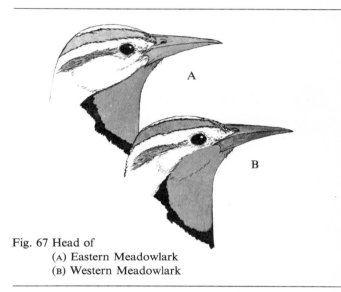

Fig. 67 Head of
(A) Eastern Meadowlark
(B) Western Meadowlark

Measurements (*S. n. neglecta*). *Adult male:* wing, 121–132 (125.6); tail, 72–79 (76.0); exposed culmen, 29.9–35.8 (32.7); tarsus, 36.5–40.5 (38.0). *Adult female:* wing, 105.5–118.5 (109.9) mm.

Field Marks. Not ordinarily separable in the field by sight from the Eastern Meadowlark. Voice, however, is very different. *Voice:* The rich bubbling song is completely different from the thin high-pitched whistle of the Eastern Meadowlark. A throaty *chuck* also is unlike any utterance of the Eastern.

Habitat. Open grassy areas similar to the habitat preferences of the Eastern Meadowlark.

Nesting. Similar to that of Eastern Meadowlark.

Range. Breeds from British Columbia east to southern Ontario and south to northern Mexico, central Texas, and Louisiana.

Range in Canada. Breeds in central and southern British Columbia (François Lake, Lonesome Lake southward including Vancouver Island), north-central and southern Alberta (Peace River southward), central and southern Saskatchewan (Meadow Lake, Amyot Lake, Nipawin southward), southern Manitoba (Swan River, Garland, Lake St. Martin, Sprague), western Ontario (Emo, Dryden, Port Arthur), southern Ontario (rarely and locally: Sault Ste.

Marie, Rutherglen, Hamilton, Bradford), and very rarely southwestern Quebec (Quebec City: paired with *magna*).

Winters in southern British Columbia, and occasionally in southern Alberta, southern Saskatchewan, and southern Manitoba.

Casual in southern Mackenzie (Fort Simpson and 30 miles below Fort Simpson), northern Manitoba (Churchill), and central-eastern Ontario (Moose Factory, Moosonee).

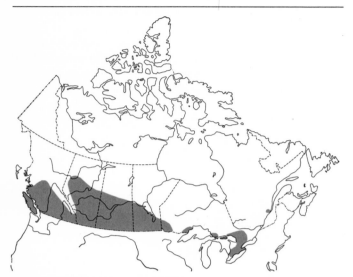

Breeding Distribution of Western Meadowlark

Subspecies. (1) *Sturnella neglecta neglecta* Audubon: Alta., Sask., Man., Ont., Que. (2) *S. n. confluenta* Rathbun (darker, more extensively blackish upper parts than in *neglecta*): throughout s. B.C. (east at least to Elko).

Remarks. Meadowlarks are not larks at all. They are brightly coloured members of the blackbird family. There are two species of meadowlarks in Canada, the Eastern and the Western. It amazes most people how two species can sound so different yet look so much alike.

YELLOW-HEADED BLACKBIRD
Le Carouge à tête jaune
Xanthocephalus xanthocephalus (Bonaparte)
Plate 62. L. 8.5 to 11 in. (female much shorter than male).

Adult male: Head, neck, and most of breast, rich yellow to nearly orange, also often a few yellow feathers near vent; patch about eyes and narrow margin around base of bill, black; patch on wing (primary coverts and part of greater wing coverts) white; rest of plumage black. *Adult female:* Mostly dusky brown, the wings without a white patch; stripe over eye, cheeks, and throat vary from whitish to yellowish usually becoming yellow on upper breast but sometimes mostly white also; lower breast streaked with white. *Young male (first autumn):* Similar to adult female but larger, the yellows darker and richer; the primary coverts tipped with white, thus faintly suggesting a white wing patch. *Young male (first spring):* Similar to young male in autumn but yellows purer, the top of head more blackish. *Young female in autumn:* Similar to adult female.

Measurements. *Adult male:* wing, 135–143.5 (139.9); tail, 95–107.5 (101.9); exposed culmen, 21.4–25.8 (23.2); tarsus, 33–35.5 (34.3). *Adult female:* wing, 112–116.5 (113.8) mm.

Field Marks. Adult male is unmistakable. Adult female and young with yellowish or whitish areas about head and breast can scarcely be mistaken for anything else. The song is a yodeling often-discordant *kleep-kloop-a-áh-oo*. Call, *chuck.*

Habitat. For nesting, deeper sloughs, wet marshes, and lake edges where there is adequate emergent vegetation. Forages also on grainfields, freshly plowed ground, barnyards, and similar places.

Nesting. In emergent vegetation usually over water, the nest attached to growing marsh plants. It is a basket-like structure, woven from dead, water-soaked vegetation. *Eggs*, 3 to 5, usually 4; whitish, quite thickly speckled over all with browns and greys. Incubation 12 to 13 days, by the female (R. W. Fautin).

Range. Breeds from central-interior British Columbia east to extreme western Ontario and northwestern Ohio, south to southern California, northeastern Baja California, southern New Mexico, northern Texas, Missouri, and northwestern Indiana. Winters from southwestern central California, east to southern Louisiana and south to south-central Mexico.

Breeding Distribution of Yellow-headed Blackbird

Range in Canada. Breeds in interior-central and southern British Columbia (Ootsa Lake, Tachick Lake, Kleena Kleene, Okanagan Valley, Wardner), Alberta (Athabasca Delta and Peace River District southward, but locally in south), north-central and southern Saskatchewan (Kazan Lake, Churchill River southward), central and southern Manitoba (Cedar and Moose lakes, La Rivière, Victoria Beach), and extreme western Ontario (Rainy River, Saganagons Lake). Recorded in summer east to Quibell and Lake Nipigon, Ontario.

Casual in extreme southwestern British Columbia (Denman Island Spit), southern Mackenzie (Fort Simpson, Hay River), northern Manitoba (Churchill), and southern Ontario (Toronto, London, Stamford Centre). Accidental in Quebec (Rupert House, Godbout, Ste. Anne de la Pocatière, Montreal).

Hypothetical (sight records) in Nova Scotia (Sable Island, Bon Portage Island, Cape Sable).

RED-WINGED BLACKBIRD

Le Carouge à épaulettes. *Agelaius phoeniceus* (Linnaeus)
Plate 62. L. 7.5 to 10 in.

Adult male: Completely black except red lesser wing coverts and buffy whitish middle wing coverts (forming a conspicuous red patch at bend of wing with buffy whitish border). *Young male (first autumn):* Dull black, much obscured and margined with buff and reddish brown above and with pale buff to whitish below; usually a buffy streak over eye; wing patch, orange spotted with black (some individuals with little or no orange). *Young male (first spring):* Dull black with some pale feather edges; wing patch, orange spotted with black. *Adult female:* Very different from adult male. Upper parts, brownish black streaked and edged with buffs, greyish, and rusty; light streak through middle of crown and another over eye; lesser wing coverts (near bend of wing) often more or less reddish or orange; under parts, streaked whitish and blackish; chin and throat, less heavily marked or immaculate and often pinkish, buffy, or greenish yellow.

Measurements (*A. p. phoeniceus*). *Adult male:* wing, 115–124.5 (120.3); tail, 88–97.5 (91.2); exposed culmen, 21.7–24.7 (22.7); tarsus, 26.5–29.5 (28.6). *Adult female:* wing, 96–102.5 (98.0) mm.

Field Marks. The male is usually unmistakable, but when perched the red shoulder patch is often concealed. However, at least the buffy white border of the red patch can be seen. The female has the *entire* breast, abdomen, and sides streaked black-and-white. *Voice:* Song is a gurgling, cheerful *konk-ke-ree*, the first syllable lowest in pitch, the third syllable highest, prolonged, and usually trilled. Common call, *chuck*. When alarmed, a down-slurred *tee-err*.

Habitat. For nesting, freshwater marshes and water edges which have thick growths of cattails, bulrushes, sedges, and similar vegetation; bushes and small trees on water margins; occasionally dry upland fields. Forages mostly in fields and grain stubbles, ploughed land, and various open places. After nesting, flocks scatter over the countryside during the day and converge at dusk on marshes to roost.

Nesting (*see* Habitat). Nest, a loosely woven structure of coarse marsh vegetation lined with finer grasses. Most often it is woven into and supported by living marsh vegetation and less often in bushes and small trees on water edges; sometimes in weeds of dry upland fields; rarely in a larger tree. *Eggs*, 3 to 5, usually 4; pale bluish green, blotched, spotted, and streaked with browns, black, grey, and purple. Incubation, 10 to 12 days, usually 11, is entirely by the female (A. A. Allen).

Range. Northwestern British Columbia east to southwestern Newfoundland and south to Costa Rica, the northern Bahamas, Cuba, and Isle of Pines.

Range in Canada. Breeds from southern Yukon (Von

Wilczek Lakes), central-western and central-southern Mackenzie (Fort Norman, eastern Great Bear Lake, Fort Simpson, Slave River delta), northwestern and central Saskatchewan (Lake Athabasca, Cumberland House), central Manitoba (The Pas, Thicket Portage, Oxford House), north-central Ontario (Lake Attawapiskat, Moosonee), southwestern Quebec (Lake St. John, Grandes Bergeronnes, Gaspé Bay), and southwestern Newfoundland (Stephenville Crossing, Doyles) and southward through all extreme southern Canada (but not Queen Charlotte Islands, British Columbia).

Winters in southern British Columbia (Vancouver Island, Okanagan Valley) and extreme southern Ontario (in small numbers: Point Pelee, Toronto, Chatham; rarely north to Ottawa).

Casual in northern Manitoba (Churchill) and at Johan Beetz Bay, Quebec. Accidental on Victoria Island (Cambridge Bay), N.W.T.

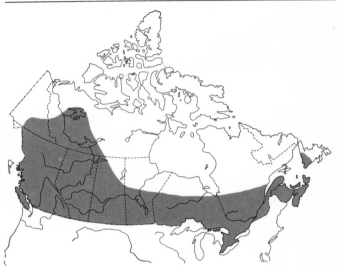

Breeding Distribution of Red-winged Blackbird

Subspecies. (1) *Agelaius phoeniceus phoeniceus* (Linnaeus): c. and s. Ont. (Sault Ste. Marie, Lake Abitibi), s. Que., sw. Nfld., N.B., P.E.I., N.S. (2) *A. p. arctolegus* Oberholser (similar to *phoeniceus* but larger): s. Yukon, Mack., n. and s.-c. B.C. (Williams Lake, 100-Mile House), Alta., Sask., Man., w. and nw. Ont. (Sioux Lookout, Moosonee). (3) *A. p. nevadensis* Grinnell (bill slenderer, females average a little greyer than *arctolegus*): interior s. B.C. (Okanagan Landing, Kamloops, Newgate). (4) *A. p. caurinus* Ridgway (averages smaller than *nevadensis;* females more richly coloured): sw. B.C. (Vancouver Island, Vancouver).

Remarks. The male Red-winged Blackbird effervesces with energy and personality. His bright red epaulettes flash in the sun as he flits from one perch to another, and the marshes ring with his cheerful *conqueree* song. The males arrive early in the spring, often when most of the marshes are still icebound. The modestly attired females come a little later. In spring and autumn, the seeds of weeds and cereal crops make up about 90 per cent of its food. During June and July, however, insects and other animal food comprise from 70 to 100 per cent of it, the young being fed entirely on animal food. Unduly large late-summer and autumn flocks are often destructive of grains.

ORCHARD ORIOLE

L'Oriole des vergers. *Icterus spurius* (Linnaeus)
Plate 61. L. 6 to 7.25 in.

Bill tapering, pointed, very slightly downcurved; tail shorter than folded wing, rounded. *Adult male:* Head, neck, back, scapulars, upper breast, and tail, black; wings mainly black with greater coverts and flight feathers edged with whitish or pale chestnut, lesser and middle coverts chestnut; lower back, tail coverts, and all under parts posterior to upper breast, rich chestnut. *Adult female:* Upper parts yellowish olive becoming greyish and duller on back and scapulars; wings greyish dusky with pale edging and two white wing bars; under parts olive yellowish. *Young (first autumn):* Similar to adult female but male larger with more brownish back. *Young male (first spring):* Similar to adult female but with black chin and throat and often with traces of black and chestnut elsewhere.

Measurements. *Adult male:* wing, 75.6–80 (77.8); tail, 67.4–71.9 (69.5); exposed culmen, 15–16.9 (15.9); tarsus, 20–22.1 (21.1). *Adult female:* wing, average 74.7 mm.

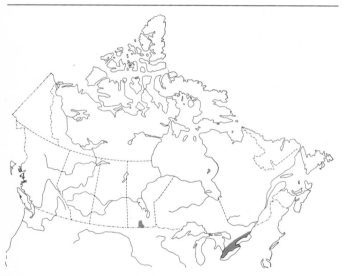

Breeding Distribution of Orchard Oriole

Field Marks. The adult male with its chestnut and black coloration is easy to recognize. First-year male in spring resembles the female but has a black bib (Baltimore Oriole with black throat has more orange colouring on breast). Female resembles female Baltimore Oriole but is smaller and has more uniform greenish yellow under parts with no orange tinge. Somewhat similar to female Scarlet Tanager but bill much slenderer and more sharply pointed. *Song:* Less loud than that of Baltimore Oriole and quite different, more Robin-like; short, ending with slurred, falling, harsher notes.

Habitat. Scattered trees about gardens, orchards, shade trees along roadsides. Avoids heavily forested regions.

Nesting. Nest is a pouch woven of grasses and suspended from a fork in a branch of a tree or shrub 7 to 20 feet up. It is not so deeply pouched as that of the Baltimore Oriole. *Eggs,* 3 to 7, usually 4 or 5; whitish, spotted and scrawled with browns and purplish grey, heaviest around large end. Incubation variable, reportedly 11 to 14 days, by the female.

Range. Breeds from southern Manitoba, southern Ontario, and Massachusetts south to northern Mexico, southern Texas, the Gulf Coast of United States, and northern Florida, and west to central Nebraska and northeastern Colorado. Winters from southern Mexico to Colombia and Venezuela.

Range in Canada. Breeds locally in southern Manitoba (Cypress River) and southern Ontario (Point Pelee, Chatham, Toronto; Prince Edward County; Gananoque).

Casual in south-central Manitoba (Lake St. Martin), southern New Brunswick (Kent Island), and Nova Scotia (Three Fathom Harbour; Sable Island).

Hypothetical in Quebec (sight records only: Lacolle, Bonaventure Island).

BALTIMORE ORIOLE

L'Oriole de Baltimore. *Icterus galbula* (Linnaeus)
Plate 61. L. 7 to 8.2 in.

Form similar to that of Orchard Oriole but larger and differently coloured. *Adult male:* Head, neck, back, scapulars, and narrow extension onto upper breast, black; rest of under parts, rump, and upper tail coverts, bright rich orange-yellow; wings mainly black, the flight feathers edged narrowly with white, tertials and greater wing coverts broadly edged with same, lesser and middle wing coverts yellow; tail with two middle feathers black (except concealed yellow bases), rest of tail feathers yellow at tips, the extent of yellow increasing outwardly. *Adult female:* Yellow olive above, variably spotted with black; rump dull yellow olive to dull orange; tail similar but duller; wings dusky with two white bars and narrow whitish edging; under parts dull orange, frequently (not always) with some black on throat and occasionally elsewhere. *Young (first autumn):* Resemble adult female but paler and without black on throat.

Measurements. *Adult male:* wing, 89.2–98.9 (93.7); tail, 70–76.5 (73.7); exposed culmen, 17.6–19.7 (19.0); tarsus, 22–24 (23.0). *Adult female:* wing, 85–92.1 (88.9) mm.

Field Marks. Adult male, with bright flashing orange and black plumage, will be confused only with Bullock's Oriole, but the all-black head of the Baltimore distinguishes it. Female is very similar to female Bullock's Oriole, but the Baltimore's under parts are usually more uniformly yellowish (Bullock's abdomen and sides are usually whitish or greyish) (*see also* female Orchard Oriole). *Voice:* Song is a series of loud, clear, varied whistles with irregular pauses between. Also a grating chatter of anxiety. A common call-note is a low whistled *tewly.*

Habitat. Scattered tall trees, particularly elms; also more open deciduous woodland.

Nesting. Nest is a curious bag-like structure up to six or more inches deep, suspended from a tree branch, often well up. The entrance is usually at the top. The nest is skilfully woven of plant fibres, hair, and twine. It is durable and may remain intact for several years. When the leaves have fallen, it is quite conspicuous in the bare branches. *Eggs,* 4 to 6; greyish white, with streaks, blotches, and irregular scrawls of browns, black, and a little purplish grey. Incubation period, variously reported 12 to 15 days.

Range. Breeds from central Alberta east to central Nova Scotia and south to west-central Oklahoma, northeastern Texas, southeastern Louisiana, north-central Georgia, western South Carolina, central Virginia, and Delaware. Winters mainly from southern Mexico south to Colombia and Venezuela.

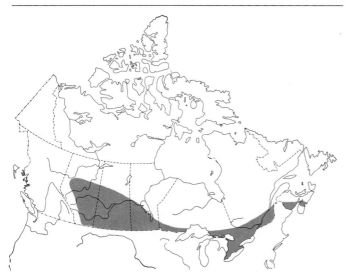

Breeding Distribution of Baltimore Oriole

Range in Canada. Breeds in central and southeastern Alberta (Shaftsbury, Lesser Slave Lake, Cold Lake southward, east of the Rockies and foothills, to Milk River), central and southern Saskatchewan (Kazan Lake, Emma Lake, Nipawin, Eastend, Regina), southern Manitoba (Dawson Bay on northern Lake Winnipegosis, Lake St. Martin, Indian Bay), western Ontario (Malachi, Kenora, Port Arthur), southern Ontario (Iron Bridge, Lake Nipissing southward), southwestern Quebec (Blue Sea Lake, Quebec City, Montmagny, Montreal, Hatley), southern New Brunswick (Fredericton, Sussex), and Nova Scotia (Berwick, Gaspereau, Mill Village). Rare in Prince Edward Island (near Charlottetown) and evidence of breeding is lacking.

Casual in south-central Ontario (Chapleau) and at Seven Islands, Quebec. Accidental in British Columbia (Chilliwack; Okanagan Valley), northern Manitoba (York Factory), and Newfoundland (Ramea; Newfoundland banks). Occasional late autumn and winter visitant to Nova Scotia.

Remarks. On a day in early May, when the buds are bursting and dandelions brighten the green new grass, a series of loud piping whistles announces that the Baltimore Oriole is back for the summer. The song is neither rhythmical nor musical, but it does seem to signify that another turning point in the year is reached, with summer near at

hand. The male sings often as he searches the branches for insects, but by early July his song frequency has rapidly tapered off. This oriole eats insects, including vast numbers of caterpillars, and some small fruits.

BULLOCK'S ORIOLE
L'Oriole à ailes blanches. *Icterus bullockii* (Swainson)
Plate 61. L. 7.3 to 8.3 in.

Adult male: Top of head, back of neck, back, stripe down middle of throat, and line through eye, black; wings mostly black, much of middle and greater coverts white, forming large white wing patch, flight feathers edged in white; middle tail feathers black (except hidden yellow bases), outer tail feathers mostly yellow and tipped blackish; rump and upper tail coverts yellow; stripe over eye, cheeks, and under parts (except black of throat), orange-yellow. *Adult female:* Crown and hind-neck yellowish olive; back and rump olive greyish; upper tail coverts and tail, olive yellow; two white wing bars; sides of head, vague stripe over eye, sides of neck, and breast, dull orange-yellow; throat usually more whitish, sometimes blotched with black; abdomen and sides dull buffy white; under tail coverts yellowish or yellow. *Young in autumn:* Resemble adult female but duller and with no trace of black on throat. *Young male in spring:* Resembles adult female, but chin, broad stripe down throat, and patch in front of eye, black.

Measurements. *Adult male:* wing, 98.7–102.7 (101.3); tail, 77.5–81.5 (80.1); exposed culmen, 17.8–20 (18.9); tarsus, 24–26.5 (24.6). *Adult female:* wing, 91.2–98.6 (94.0) mm.

Breeding Distribution of Bullock's Oriole

Field Marks. Adult male with orange cheeks, black crown, black line through eye, and very *large* white wing patch is easily identified. Females closely resemble female Baltimore Orioles but are a little more greyish above with more whitish abdomen and sides, and they have a tendency to show a faint yellowish eyebrow stripe. *Song:* Clear, whistled, spaced notes, somewhat similar to those of the Baltimore Oriole but less varied.

Habitat. Deciduous woodlands, trees along streams, river valleys, farmland, and other open areas.

Nesting. A woven bag-like structure similar to that of the Baltimore Oriole. Usually hangs from a tree branch but sometimes is anchored also at the sides to upright twigs. The three to six *eggs* are greyish white with markings similar to those of the Baltimore Oriole but usually finer, the irregular black lines and scrawls running around the larger end. Incubation about 14 days (C. E. Bendire), by the female.

Range. Breeds from southern interior British Columbia east to southwestern Saskatchewan and southwestern North Dakota, western Nebraska, and western Oklahoma, and central Texas south to interior southern California, southern Nevada, southern Arizona, northern Mexico, and southern Texas. Winters from western Mexico to northwestern Costa Rica.

Range in Canada. Breeds in southern interior British Columbia (Alkali Lake, Okanagan Valley, Creston), southern Alberta (Medicine Hat, probably Walsh), and southwestern Saskatchewan (Eastend). Casual in southeastern Saskatchewan (Yorkton).

Subspecies. *Icterus bullockii bullockii* (Swainson).

RUSTY BLACKBIRD

Le Mainate rouilleux. *Euphagus carolinus* (Müller)
Plate 62. L. 8.5 to 9.8 in.

Adult male (*breeding plumage*): All black with faint bluish green gloss on body and slight violet gloss on head and neck; bill and legs black; eye yellowish white. *Adult male* (*winter plumage*): Similar, but black partly veiled by rusty brown feather tips on upper parts, and by paler brown feather tips on sides of head and under parts. *Adult female* (*breeding plumage*): Plain dull slate, the upper parts darker and slightly glossy; bill and legs, black; eye, pale yellow. *Adult female* (*winter plumage*): Similar to breeding plumage but washed and overlaid with rusty brown, the under parts tipped with paler brown or buff; stripe over eye buff. *Young in autumn:* Similar to adults in autumn.

Measurements. *Adult male:* wing, 110.5–117.4 (114.6); tail, 85–94.5 (88.9); exposed culmen, 19–21.9 (20.5); tarsus, 29.5–33 (31.4). *Adult female:* wing, 103.1–112.4 (107.3) mm.

Field Marks. Eyes yellow in both sexes. Very similar to Brewer's Blackbird but male in breeding plumage much less glossy, the head and neck not strongly purplish. Females in breeding plumage are dull slate in colour like female Brewer's in comparable plumage but have yellowish (not brown) eyes. Autumn Rusties are much more heavily blotched with rusty brown and pale brown than are Brewer's. Grackles are much larger and (at close range) glossier. Cowbirds have stout, sparrow-like bills and brown eyes. *Voice:* Song is short and ends in a high note that sounds like a squeaky hinge.

Habitat. Wet woods and tall shrubbery where pools of water stand on the ground; bogs, partly flooded lake and stream edges, beaver dams.

Nesting. In a low conifer or, less often, a deciduous bush, at heights usually less than 10 feet, generally (not always) near water. Nest is a bulky and strongly made structure of

twigs, grass, moss, and rotting vegetation (which dries very hard) and is lined with fine grasses. *Eggs*, 4 or 5; pale bluish green, well spotted and blotched (but rarely scrawled) with various browns and a little grey. Incubation about 14 days, by the female (A. C. Bent).

Range. Breeds from northern Alaska east to Labrador and Newfoundland and south to central British Columbia, central Manitoba, northeastern New York, northern New Hampshire, central Maine, and Nova Scotia.

Breeding Distribution of Rusty Blackbird

Range in Canada. Breeds from northern Yukon (Old Crow), northern Mackenzie (Mackenzie Delta, Fort Anderson, Dease Arm), southern Keewatin (Nueltin Lake), northern Manitoba (Churchill), northern Ontario (Fort Severn, James Bay), northern Quebec (Richmond Gulf, Fort Chimo), central Labrador (Nain), and Newfoundland south to south-central interior British Columbia (east of Coast Ranges: Likely), south-central and southwestern Alberta (Jasper, Okotoks, Red Deer region), central Saskatchewan (Prince Albert, Nipawin), central Manitoba (Riding Mountain National Park), western and south-central Ontario (Savanne, Durham, Algonquin Park), southern Quebec (La Vérendrye Park, Petite Rivière, St. François, St. Fabien de Panet, Ste. Anne des Monts, Anticosti and Magdalen islands), New Brunswick, Prince Edward Island, and Nova Scotia.

Winters in small numbers in southern Ontario (Kitchener, Reaboro, Toronto, Kingston) and casually elsewhere in other southern parts of the country.

Subspecies. (1) *Euphagus carolinus carolinus* (Müller): Breeds in all of Canada except that occupied by the following race. (2) *E. c. nigrans* Burleigh and Peters (rusty feather edges in autumn average darker): Nfld., Magdalen Is., and N.S. (possibly also eastern N.B.).

Remarks. Before the ice is gone from the lakes and while woodland pools formed by the melting snow still abound, the Rusty Blackbird returns in the spring. Its straw-coloured eyes search out favoured food morsels along shallow water edges or in moist leaf litter. If disturbed, the birds fly up and alight in the leafless branches of nearby trees, and soon the flock breaks into a squeaky cacophony of blackbird music. In most thickly settled parts of the country the Rusty Blackbird is only a spring and autumn transient.

BREWER'S BLACKBIRD
Le Mainate à tête pourprée
Euphagus cyanocephalus (Wagler)
Plate 62. L. 8 to 10.3 in.

Adult male: Black, the head and neck strongly glossed with purple, the rest of plumage faintly glossed with bluish green; bill and legs black; eye, pale yellowish or straw. *Young male in autumn:* Similar to adult male but feathers of head, neck, back, breast, and sides faintly tipped with greyish brown or buff. *Adult female (breeding plumage):* Head, neck, and under parts brownish grey, very faintly glossed with greenish on under parts and with purplish on head; back, wings, and tail, darker and glossier; bill and legs black; eye, light brown. *Females in autumn:* Similar to female in breeding plumage but head, neck, and breast paler and more buffy grey.

Measurements. *Adult male:* wing, 121–133 (128.4); tail, 95–102.5 (99.8); exposed culmen, 20.4–24 (21.7); tarsus, 29.5–33.5 (31.7). *Adult female:* wing, 115–121 (117.4) mm.

Field Marks. Adult male, with pale yellowish eyes, resembles that of the Rusty Blackbird, but the head and neck of the Brewer's are much more purplish. It is much smaller than the Common Grackle. The adult female looks much like a female Rusty, but the female Brewer's has brownish (instead of yellowish) eyes. Autumn Brewer's are much less rusty.

Breeding Distribution of Brewer's Blackbird

Habitat. More open areas with bushy tangles near by; hedges, roadside shrubbery, and bushy growths along streams and irrigation ditches; and on farmlands. Forages extensively in fields, pastures (often associates with cattle and sheep), golf courses, and lawns. It doubtlessly has profited by man's clearing of forests, irrigation projects, and cultivated crops.

Nesting. Often in loose colonies. Nest may be on the ground, in low bushes, or in trees. It is composed of coarse twigs and grasses, often mixed with mud and lined with fine rootlets, hair, and fine grasses. *Eggs,* most often 5 or 6; pale greenish grey, spotted and blotched with browns, sometimes so heavily marked that the grey ground colour is hidden. Incubation reportedly 12 to 14 days, by the female.

Range. Breeds from British Columbia east to western Ontario and south to Baja California, central Arizona, New Mexico, northern Texas, Oklahoma, northern Iowa, and southwestern Michigan. Winters from southwestern Canada, Montana, Kansas, and Alabama south to southern Mexico and the Gulf coast.

Range in Canada. Breeds in central and southern British Columbia (Smithers on Bulkley River, Comox, Columbia Lake), north-central and southern Alberta (Meikle River north of Peace River and Calling Lake north of Athabasca, southward), central and southern Saskatchewan (Ile-à-la-Crosse, Prince Albert, Nipawin southward), southern Manitoba (Swan River, Dauphin, Lake St. Martin, Rennie), western and south-central Ontario (Fort Frances, Port Arthur, Sault Ste. Marie, McKerrow, Rutter). A recent arrival in eastern Ontario, it is extending its range eastward.

Recorded in autumn in Queen Charlotte Islands, British Columbia. Casual in southwestern Mackenzie (Fort Simpson, June 15, 1958) and north-central Ontario (Lake Attawapiskat, June 5, 1939). Accidental in Keewatin (Baker Lake, November 1923).

Winters in southern British Columbia (Vancouver Island, Vancouver, Kelowna) and rarely in south-central Alberta (Camrose).

COMMON GRACKLE (Bronzed Grackle)
Le Mainate bronzé. *Quiscalus quiscula* (Linnaeus)
Plate 62. L. 11 to 13.5 in.

Much larger than the Rusty or Brewer's blackbirds; tail decidedly graduated, the middle feathers longest. *Adult male:* Head, neck, and upper breast highly iridescent greenish blue or purple; rest of plumage, uniform shiny bronze with more or less purplish reflection on wings and tail; bill and legs black; eye yellowish white. *Adult female:* Similar to adult male but smaller; coloration duller. *Young in juvenal plumage* (worn a short time after leaving nest): Dull sooty brown with a suggestion of purplish sheen on wings and tail; eye brown. *Young in autumn plumage:* Like adults.

Measurements (*Q. q. versicolor*). *Adult male:* wing, 141–153 (145.1); tail, 126.5–143 (133.1); exposed culmen, 28.8–31.9 (30.4); tarsus, 35–38 (36.8). *Adult female:* wing, 128–132 (130.2) mm.

Field Marks. Our largest blackbird (longer than a Robin). At close range it is decidedly glossy with the bluish and purplish of head and neck sharply cut off from the shiny bronze remainder of the plumage; whitish eyes prominent. At a distance it looks all black. Tail is long and wedge-shaped. Flight is steadier and more level than that of most other blackbirds. Especially in spring, the spread tail is keel-shaped, turned up at the sides in a V-shape, this most apparent in flight. *Voice:* Song is short, discordant, and squeaky but is readily recognizable. Common call is a lusty *chuck*.

Habitat. Forages on the ground, especially where wet, in open places such as fields, pastures, lawns, golf courses, shores, marshes, or in wet alders and willows or open wet woodlands. Perches and nests in open woods, parks, groves, and shade trees.

Nesting. Frequently in small colonies. Usually in trees, preferably conifers; occasionally in bushes, cavities in trees; even rarely on the ground or inside buildings. Nest is a bulky but sturdy structure of sticks, weeds, and grass, these usually plastered together with mud and lined with grasses and rootlets. *Eggs*, usually 4 to 6; pale bluish or greenish and boldly blotched, scrawled, and spotted with browns or black. Incubation 14 days, by the female (A.O. Gross, *in* Bent), usually 11 to 12 days (Petersen and Young).

Range. Breeds from southern Canada (Alberta east to southwestern Newfoundland) and southward, east of the Rockies, to central Colorado, central and southern Texas, the Gulf coast of United States, and southern Florida. Withdraws in winter from most breeding areas in Canada.

Breeding Distribution of Common Grackle

Range in Canada. Breeds in southern Mackenzie (Fort Resolution); central-eastern British Columbia (probably Tupper Creek); Alberta (east of the Rockies but local in northern forested areas and on the prairies); northwestern, central, and southern Saskatchewan (Lake Athabasca, Churchill River; local on southern prairies); northern, central, and southern Manitoba (Churchill southward); central and southern Ontario (Favourable Lake, Rossport, Amyot, Lake Abitibi, possibly Moose Factory southward); southern Quebec (Lake Abitibi, Amos, Lake St. John, Havre St. Pierre southward including Anticosti and Magdalen islands; found in summer at St. Augustin); southwestern Newfoundland; New Brunswick; Prince Edward Island; and Nova Scotia (including Cape Breton Island). Wanders rarely to forts Simpson and Reliance, Mackenzie; Jasper and Banff, Alberta; and to northern and eastern Newfoundland (St. Anthony, Bay Bulls).

Small numbers winter in southern Ontario and rarely in southern Quebec, southern New Brunswick, Prince Edward Island, and Nova Scotia.

Subspecies. (1) *Quiscalus quiscula versicolor* Vieillot is the only subspecies of regular occurrence in Canada. (2) *Q. q. stonei* Chapman (body plumage less uniform, the back and scapulars more or less barred with metallic blue, green, purple, and bronze): Accidental visitor to N.B. (Kent Island, November 20, 1931).

Remarks. Even while the snow is still deep in shaded places, the Common Grackles make their early spring appearance. Their squeaky songs sound like unoiled wheelbarrows and, though certainly not musical, are not altogether unpleasant. Grackles are gregarious and usually are seen in flocks, often including other blackbirds. They look black at a distance but at close range are really quite handsome. They have bright yellow eyes, and the surprisingly iridescent colours of their plumage flash in the sun as the birds swagger about. Their diet includes many insects, grains, seeds, fruits, garbage, and not infrequently the eggs and young of other birds.

BROWN-HEADED COWBIRD

(Eastern or Nevada Cowbird)
Le Vacher. *Molothrus ater* (Boddaert)
Plate 62. L. 7 to 8.25 in.

Bill short for a blackbird, stout and sparrow-like; tail shorter than folded wing, square at tip. *Adult male:* Head and neck brown; rest of plumage black with greenish and purplish gloss; bill and legs black; eye brown. *Adult female:* Greyish brown above, slightly glossy, the feathers with darker centres; under parts brownish grey with fine dark streaking; throat much paler and with little or no streaking; bill and legs blackish brown; eye brown. *Juvenal plumage:* Similar to adult female but feathers of upper parts margined with grey; under parts buffy or whitish streaked with greyish brown, throat paler and much less heavily streaked. Young in first winter plumage are very similar to adults.

Measurements (*M. a. ater*). *Adult male:* wing, 107–114.6 (109.1); tail, 69.5–80.5 (75.2); exposed culmen, 16.6–18.8 (17.7); tarsus, 25–27 (25.9). *Adult female:* wing, 94–100.5 (97.9) mm.

Field Marks. A small brown-eyed blackbird with short sparrow-like bill. Male, with brown head and glossy black body (bird looks all black at a distance), is easy to recognize. Females are brownish grey, nondescript blackbirds, but the sparrow-like bill distinguishes it from female Rusties and Brewer's. *Voice:* Its song is a couple of low gurgles followed by a squeak: *glug – glug – ge-leek*. A common call is a high-pitched almost hissing whistle followed by two short lower notes: *wheeeee-tse-tse;* also a *chuck*.

Habitat. Forages in open areas such as pastures, grainfields, and other cultivated places. Often associates with cattle, horses, and other large mammals for the insects they stir up or attract. Perches in trees and bushes in various situations.

Nesting. It is parasitic, building no nest of its own. The female lays its eggs in the nests of other small birds, particularly warblers, vireos, finches, flycatchers, and thrushes. Ordinarily the individual Cowbird lays only one of its eggs in a given nest, but sometimes more than one Cowbird lays in the same nest. Sometimes the host throws the Cowbird egg from the nest or builds a new floor over the offending egg. In most cases the parasite's egg is incubated and the young Cowbird raised, often at the expense of some or all of the host's own young. The *eggs* are whitish, speckled and blotched with various browns over most of the egg's surface. The incubation period is 11 to 12 days (M. M. Nice; H. W. Hann).

Range. British Columbia east to Nova Scotia and south to northern Mexico, Louisiana, southern Mississippi, and South Carolina. Winters south to southern Mexico.

Breeding Distribution of Brown-headed Cowbird

Range in Canada. Breeds in central and southern British Columbia (Calvert Island, Nulki Lake, François Lake, Swan Lake in Peace River District southward including Vancouver Island); southern Mackenzie (Fort Simpson, Fort Resolution); northern, central, and southern Alberta; north-central and southern Saskatchewan (Kazan Lake, Cumberland House southward); southern Manitoba (The Pas, Lake St. Martin, Hillside Beach, Sprague); south-central and southern Ontario (Malachi, Kenora, Port Arthur, Rossport, Biscotasing, and Ottawa southward); southern Quebec (Amos, La Malbaie, Tadoussac, Havre St. Pierre southward, but breeding status on Anticosti and Magdalen islands is uncertain; an isolated breeding record at Great Whale River (Todd, 1963)); New Brunswick; Nova Scotia (Halifax, Wolfville, Wedgeport; a recent arrival in the province; first definite nesting 1929; breeding on Cape Breton Island is uncertain, but species has occurred at Port Hood and Sydney); Prince Edward Island (breeding first recorded in 1953 at Stanhope); and recently in Newfoundland.

Recorded without definite evidence of breeding in northern British Columbia (Queen Charlotte Islands, Atlin, Dease Lake, Fort Nelson), central-western Mackenzie

(Fort Norman, Norman Wells), northwestern Saskatchewan (Lake Athabasca), northern Manitoba (Churchill), north-central Ontario (Trout Lake, Lake Attawapiskat, Moosonee), southeastern Quebec (Harrington Harbour), southern Labrador (Capstan Island).

Winters sparingly in southern Ontario (north rarely to Ottawa) and, in recent years, regularly in southern Nova Scotia and southern New Brunswick. Rarely elsewhere in southern Canada.

Subspecies. (1) *Molothrus ater ater* (Boddaert): e. Ont. (Rossport eastward), s. Que., N.B., P.E.I., N.S. (2) *M. a. artemisiae* Grinnell (averages larger, with longer, relatively slenderer bill, and paler more brownish coloration in females): B.C., Mack., Alta., Sask., Man., w. Ont. (intergrades with *ater*).

Remarks. The Cowbird gets its name from its common habit of associating with cattle and other large mammals that attract and stir up insects. Indeed a very large part of the Cowbird's diet is made up of insects, including many destructive ones. Its food habits therefore are highly beneficial. The good it does, however, is doubtless more than nullified by its parasitic nesting habits (*see* Nesting), which certainly cause the destruction of large numbers of young insectivorous and seed-eating small birds.

Family **Thraupidae**–Tanagers

Number of Species in North America 4; in Canada 3

This large, varied, and often brightly coloured group is confined to the Western Hemisphere, but most of the species are tropical and only three range northward as far as Canada. Tanagers are most closely related to the finches and, like them, have nine primaries. The cutting edge of the lower mandible is usually less abruptly angular at the base than in the finches, and in most species the bill is notched near the tip. Although some kinds in the tropics are extremely similar to finches, the three Canadian species are readily separable from them by the more elongated bill. The Scarlet and Western tanagers have the cutting edge of the upper mandible slightly 'toothed.' Our tanagers are forest birds. They feed on insects and some fruit.

WESTERN TANAGER
Le Tangara à tête rouge. *Piranga ludoviciana* (Wilson)
Plate 61. L. 7 to 7.75 in.

Bill stout but somewhat elongated, shorter than head, its ridge downcurved; upper mandible slightly toothed near middle of cutting edge. *Adult male (breeding plumage):* Head red, palest on throat; rest of under parts, neck, rump, and upper tail coverts, yellow; back, wings, and tail, mostly black; two pale yellow wing bars. *Adult male (autumn):* Similar, but head mostly greenish olive with some red on forehead and chin. *Immature male (first spring):* Similar to adult male in spring but duller, the flight feathers more brownish. *Adult female:* Crown, cheeks, hind-neck, rump, and upper tail coverts, greenish olive; back, olive grey; wings and tail, greyish brown; two whitish or pale yellow wing bars; under parts yellow. *Young in first autumn:* Similar to adult female but males have yellow of under parts brighter, the females duller.

Measurements. *Adult male:* wing, 91–97.9 (94.8); tail, 67–75.5 (70.0); exposed culmen, 13.9–16 (14.9); tarsus, 19–21.4 (20.1). *Adult female:* wing, 88.3–94.9 (92.3) mm.

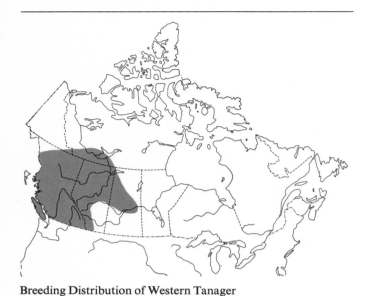

Breeding Distribution of Western Tanager

Field Marks. The only Canadian tanager with yellow or whitish wing bars. Females somewhat resemble female orioles but have stouter, less sharply pointed bills; greener, less orange plumage; and the tanager is usually decidedly more sluggish. *Voice:* Song somewhat suggests that of a Robin but is so much hoarser and lower that it is easily recognizable. It is very similar to the Scarlet Tanager's song. Common call-note, a querulous *purty*.

Habitat. Open coniferous and mixed woodland.

Nesting. In a branch of a coniferous (less often deciduous) tree at various heights. Nest is rather loosely constructed of twigs, rootlets, and grasses and is lined with hair and fine rootlets. *Eggs,* usually 3 to 5; pale blue, speckled and spotted with browns over most of their surface. Incubation, by the female, is of 13 days' duration (I. G. Wheelock).

Range. Breeds from southern Alaska, northern British Columbia, central-southern Mackenzie, northeastern Alberta, and central Saskatchewan south to northern Baja California, northern Sonora, southwestern New Mexico, and western Texas. Winters from Baja California and central Mexico through Guatemala and El Salvador to Costa Rica.

Range in Canada. Summer resident, breeding in northern, central, and southern British Columbia (Upper Stikine River, Peace River District, and southward including Vancouver Island but not Queen Charlotte Islands), southern Mackenzie (Fort Liard, Fort Smith; perhaps Fort Simpson where several times recorded in summer), northern, central, and southwestern Alberta (Wood Buffalo Park; Peace River region; Jasper, Banff, and Waterton Lakes parks; Elk Island

Park), and central Saskatchewan (Kazan Lake, Big River, Nipawin).

Recorded in summer in southern Yukon (Kluane; Rancheria River; between Morley River and Teslin).

Accidental in Ontario (Cooksville; several sight records elsewhere), southern Quebec (Kamouraska, June 10, 1938), and Nova Scotia (Digby, November 20, 1957).

SCARLET TANAGER

Le Tangara écarlate. *Piranga olivacea* (Gmelin)
Plate 61. L. 6.5 to 7.6 in.

Bill shape similar to that of Western Tanager. *Adult male (breeding plumage):* Bright scarlet with all-black wings and tail. *Adult male (autumn and winter):* Yellowish olive green except black wings and tail. *Immature male (first spring):* Similar to adult male in breeding plumage but red usually duller, the primaries and secondaries brownish instead of black. *Adult female:* Upper parts olive greenish; wings and tail, dark greyish brown (not black), edged with olive green; under parts, dull pale yellow, becoming brighter on under tail coverts. *Young (first autumn):* Similar to adult female, but young males have some of the wing coverts and scapulars black.

Measurements. *Adult male:* wing, 91–97.9 (95.0); tail, 62.7–70 (67.1); exposed culmen, 13.3–16.1 (14.8); tarsus, 18.5–20.1 (19.2). *Adult female:* wing, 88.8–96 (91.3) mm.

Breeding Distribution of Scarlet Tanager

Field Marks. The male in breeding plumage, a scarlet bird with black wings and tail, is not likely to cause any recognition difficulty. The male Summer Tanager has the reds duller and no black on wings or tail. Always lacks prominent wing bars shown by Western Tanager and orioles. Female is more greenish, less yellowish, below than female Summer Tanager. *Voice:* Song resembles that of the Robin but with a hoarse quality that readily identifies it. Common call-note is a raspy *chip-kurr*.

Habitat. Prefers mature deciduous woodland but often frequents mixedwoods and pine woods.

Nesting. Well out on a horizontal branch of a tree, 10 to 50 feet up. Nest is a rather shallow and loosely built structure of twigs, rootlets, and grasses with a lining of grasses and rootlets. *Eggs*, 3 or 5, usually 4; bluish or greenish, spotted or speckled with browns. Incubation period 13 to 14 days, by the female (L. S. Kohler).

Range. Breeds from southeastern Manitoba east to New Brunswick and south to eastern Oklahoma, central Alabama, and northern Georgia. Winters in South America from Colombia to Bolivia.

Range in Canada. Summer resident, breeding in southeastern Manitoba (Whitemouth, Indian Bay), western Ontario (Malachi, Port Arthur, perhaps Lac Seul), southern Ontario (Hawk Junction, Goulais Bay north of Sault Ste. Marie, Lake Nipissing southward), southwestern Quebec (Lake Timiskaming, Rivière du Loup, Old Chelsea, Montreal, Hatley), and New Brunswick (sparingly: Fredericton; Loch Lomond Road, St. John County).

Casual in Nova Scotia (Wolfville, Pictou, Seal Island, Westport, Yarmouth, Halifax), Newfoundland (Ferryland, Colinet Island in Placentia Bay, Funk Island), and probably southeastern Saskatchewan (several sight records). Accidental in British Columbia (Comox, November 14, 1926).

SUMMER TANAGER

Le Tangara vermillon. *Piranga rubra* (Linnaeus)
Plate 61. L. 7 to 7.8 in.

Bill similar to that of Scarlet Tanager but somewhat larger and with 'tooth' obsolete. *Adult male (summer and winter):* Plain dull red all over but somewhat paler below; flight feathers brown, edged with dull red; no wing bars. *Adult female:* Upper parts plain yellowish olive green; flight feathers brownish, edged with yellowish olive green; no wing bars; a vague yellowish eye-ring and obscure yellowish streak from base of bill to eye; under parts dull yellow, brighter on under tail coverts. *Young in first autumn:* Resemble adult female, but the young male is more richly coloured.

Measurements (*P. r. rubra*). *Adult male:* wing, 92.5–99.6 (95.5); tail, 71.1–74.7 (72.4); exposed culmen, 16.8–19.3 (17.5); tarsus, 18.3–19.8 (19.3). *Adult female:* wing, 88.9–95.8 (91.9) mm (Ridgway).

Field Marks. Adult male is all rose-red without black on wings or tail, thus differing from Scarlet Tanager. Female is more yellowish, especially below, than female Scarlet. Lack of pronounced wing bars always separates it from the Western Tanager.

Range. Breeds from southeastern California, New Mexico, Nebraska, Iowa, central Ohio, Maryland, and Delaware south to northern Mexico and southern Florida. Winters from northern Mexico south to Bolivia and Brazil.

Status in Canada. Casual visitant to southern Ontario (Toronto, Hamilton, Point Pelee, London), southern New Brunswick (Grand Manan), and Nova Scotia (Yarmouth, Annapolis Royal, Wolfville, Halifax, West Middle Sable). Hypothetical in southwestern Quebec (Montreal). Accidental in Manitoba (The Pas, May 25, 1966).

Subspecies. *Piranga rubra rubra* (Linnaeus).

Family **Fringillidae** – Grosbeaks, Finches, Sparrows, and Buntings

Number of Species in North America 89; in Canada 56

This is the largest of our bird families. It is widely distributed through most of the world but is not represented in the Australian region. Wing and tail shape are variable; the wing has nine primaries. The bill is stout, conical, and hard; the cutting edge of the lower mandible in most species turns down at a sharp angle near the base of the bill. It is therefore ideal for crushing seeds, which make up a large part of the diet of most species. Although mainly seed eaters, many species eat insects also. Young in the nest are fed on insects almost exclusively.

Song quality in the various species varies from the sublime to the ridiculous, but songs of most species are pleasing, and some are very beautiful.

CARDINAL

Le Cardinal. *Richmondena cardinalis* (Linnaeus)
Plate 63. L. 7.5 to 9.3 in.

Head crested; bill heavy and grosbeak-like; wings short, rounded; tail rather long. *Adult male:* Mainly vermilion red, the back and rump darkest and with greyish feather edges; bib and narrow area around base of bill, black; bill red or orange-red. *Adult female:* Wings and tail dull red, the feathers broadly edged with greyish olive; crest also dull red, tipped and mixed with greyish olive; rest of upper parts greyish olive; under parts tawny or buffy, the breast often with a little red; bill reddish or pinkish.

Measurements (*R. c. cardinalis*). *Adult male:* wing, 91–98.2 (94.1); tail, 96–108.7 (102.2); total culmen, 18.3–20 (19.2); tarsus, 23.9–26 (24.6). *Adult female:* wing, 88.1–96 (90.9) mm.

Field Marks. A Catbird-sized bird with prominent crest and heavy reddish bill, the male red with black on throat and base of bill; the female brownish with dull red wings, tail, crest, and bill. *Voice:* Various clear whistled notes, often *hurry, hurry, hurry.* Call-note a thin *tsip*, rather weak for the size of the bird.

Habitat. Deciduous or coniferous thickets, bushy tangles, and hedges on woodland edges, borders of old fields, clearings, streamside shrubbery, and bushy areas about dwellings.

Nesting. In tall shrubbery or small trees, usually 5 to 8 feet up. Nest is loosely constructed of twigs, shredded bark, weed stems, rootlets, and grasses and is lined with grasses, rootlets, or hair. *Eggs*, 3 or 4; white to greyish or greenish white and variously spotted and blotched with browns. Incubation about 12 to 13 days, by the female (Amelia Laskey).

Range. Permanent resident from southeastern South Dakota east through extreme southern Ontario to Connecticut and south to the Gulf of Mexico coast and southern Florida; and from southeastern California, central Arizona, southern New Mexico, and northern Texas south to southern Mexico and. British Honduras.

Range in Canada. Breeds and resides throughout the year in southern Ontario (north to Owen Sound, Orillia, and Tweed) and occasionally in southern Manitoba (Winnipeg). It has greatly expanded its range northward in the past half century, First Canadian nesting was reported from Point Pelee, Ontario, in 1901.

Breeding Distribution of Cardinal

Wanders occasionally farther north in Ontario (rarely to Port Arthur, Sault Ste. Marie, Gogama, Kirkland Lake, Lake Nipissing, Ottawa).

Casual in southern Saskatchewan (Craven; also sight records elsewhere), southwestern Quebec (Hudson Heights, Montreal, Quebec City), and Nova Scotia (Digby, Halifax).

Subspecies. *Richmondena cardinalis cardinalis* (Linnaeus).

ROSE-BREASTED GROSBEAK
Le Gros-bec à poitrine rose
Pheucticus ludovicianus (Linnaeus)
Plate 63. L. 7 to 8.5 in.

Bill heavy and large, the ridge of upper mandible curved. *Adult male* (*breeding plumage*): Head, neck, throat, most of back, and most of wings, black; middle wing coverts, tips of secondaries and tertials, and base of primaries, white; tail feathers black, the outer three on each side with large white areas on inner webs; wing linings, breast, and narrow extension down centre of breast, carmine red; rest of under parts white. *Adult male* (*autumn and winter*): Wings and tail similar to adult male in breeding plumage; head, neck, back, and scapulars, brown streaked with black; stripe down middle of crown, another over eye, and one on cheek, buffy white; under parts including throat, mostly whitish, the breast with traces of red and washed with buffy; breast and sides streaked with dusky; wing linings reddish. *Immature male* (*first breeding plumage*): Similar to adult male in breeding plumage but flight feathers brown instead of black, and red of breast usually paler. *Young male* (*first autumn*): Similar to adult male in winter but wings and tail greyish brown, wings with two white

364

PLATE 69

1 Gray-crowned Rosy Finch,
  (a) adult male (*littoralis* race)
  (b) adult male (*tephrocotis* race)

2 Yellow Wagtail, male in summer

3 Smith's Longspur,
  (a) male in breeding plumage
  (b) female

4 Chestnut-sided Longspur,
  (a) female
  (b) male in breeding plumage

5 McCown's Longspur,
  (a) female
  (b) male in breeding plumage

6 Lapland Longspur,
  (a) male in winter
  (b) female in breeding plumage
  (c) male in breeding plumage

7 Snow Bunting,
  (a) winter plumage
  (b) male in breeding plumage

1a

1b

2

3a

3b

4a

4b

5a

5b

6a

6b

6c

7a

7b

Crosby

or buffy bars and with no (or very little) white in tail; on breast a flash of pink which is veiled by buff; wing linings pink. *Adult female:* Similar to young male in first autumn but no pink on breast; wing linings yellow; wing bars always white. (*Note:* In all above plumages, males have pink wing linings, females yellow.)

Measurements. *Adult male:* wing, 99–109.8 (104.4); tail, 70.1–78.5 (74.6); exposed culmen, 15.4–18.2 (16.9); tarsus, 22–24 (22.5). *Adult female:* wing, 99.1–105 (102.5) mm.

Field Marks. The contrasting black and white, the flashing white-spotted wings, and the red breast patch of the adult male in breeding plumage are easily recognized. Females and young look a little like the female Purple Finch but are obviously much larger. In the West, the female is easily confused with that of the Black-headed Grosbeak but is more whitish underneath (less brownish), and the breast is more heavily streaked. *Immature males* have reddish wing linings (which are diagnostic when they can be discerned); the Black-headed always have yellow ones. *Voice:* Song suggests that of the Robin, but it is more energetic and richer and is more rapidly delivered. Although its song is also similar to that of the Scarlet Tanager, it is much more energetic and completely lacks the characteristic harshness of the Tanager's song. Alarm note, a high-pitched *tick*. The voice distinguishes it from all but the Black-headed Grosbeak.

Habitat. Deciduous and mixed woodlands, ideally where larger trees grow not too far from tall shrubbery, such as along streams, lakes, ponds, and marsh edges; often second growths.

Breeding Distribution of Rose-breasted Grosbeak

Nesting. In tall shrubbery or a tree, usually 5 to 15 feet above ground. Nest is a fragile flattish structure, loosely made of twigs, strips of bark, rootlets, fine grasses, and sometimes conifer needles. *Eggs*, 3 to 5; variable, pale greenish, bluish, or greyish, spotted and blotched with reddish brown, dark brown, and purplish. Incubation 12 to 13 days (H. R. Ivor), by both sexes.

Range. Breeds from northeastern British Columbia east-ward across southern Canada to Nova Scotia and south to south-central Alberta, northern North Dakota, eastern Kansas, southwestern Missouri, eastern Tennessee, northern Georgia, western North Carolina, and central New Jersey. Winters from southeastern and southern Mexico south through Central America to Ecuador, Colombia, and Venezuela.

Range in Canada. Summer resident, breeding in northeastern British Columbia (Tupper Creek; probably Fort Nelson and Liard rivers), southwestern and central-southern Mackenzie (Fort Simpson, Buffalo River), northern, central, and southeast central Alberta (south, east of the mountains, to Battle River region and Red Deer), central and southeastern Saskatchewan (Kazan Lake, Cumberland House, Yorkton, possibly Regina), southern Manitoba (The Pas, Lake St. Martin, Aweme, St. Vital), western Ontario (Malachi, Sioux Lookout, Port Arthur), southern Ontario (Sault Ste. Marie, Washagami, Lake Nipissing southward; recorded in summer north to Lake Nipigon and Lake Abitibi but without evidence of breeding), southwestern Quebec (southern La Vérendrye Park, Lake St. John, Lac Trois Saumons southward), New Brunswick (St. Leonard, McAdam, Waterford), Prince Edward Island, and Nova Scotia (including Cape Breton Island, where scarce).

Casual in southwestern Alberta (Banff), south-central Quebec (Moisie River, Anticosti Island, Grande Grève) and Newfoundland (Doyles, Tompkins, St. John's).

BLACK-HEADED GROSBEAK
Le Gros-bec à tête noire
Pheucticus melanocephalus (Swainson)
Plate 63. L. 7 to 8.5 in.

Bill shaped as in Rose-breasted Grosbeak. *Adult male (breeding plumage):* Head, neck, chin, back, wings, and tail, mostly black; band across back of neck, rump, streaks on back (and often stripe behind eye and median crown stripe), cinnamon brown; wings with two white bars, base of primaries white, forming a white patch; large white patch on outermost three tail feathers; under parts cinnamon brown, becoming yellow in middle of belly and on under wing coverts; lower mid-abdomen whitish. *Adult male (autumn and winter):* Similar to above but upper parts more cinnamon or buffy. *Adult female:* Upper parts dark brown streaked with buffy or white, especially the middle of crown and on back; wings and tail greyish brown, the white areas on wings much restricted, those on tail absent or nearly so; wing linings yellow as in male; stripe over eye, chin, and sides of throat, whitish; breast mostly cinnamon-buff; abdomen pale yellow or white; sides and flanks streaked with dusky but streaks sparse or absent on breast (decidedly fewer than on breast of Rose-breasted Grosbeak). *Young (first autumn):* Similar to adult female but under parts paler, with little or no yellow; upper parts more spotted, head stripes more whitish, better defined; wing lining, yellow in both sexes. *Immature male (first breeding plumage):* Similar to adult male in breeding plumage but duller and with brown (instead of black) flight feathers. (*Note:* Female Rose-breasted Grosbeaks have saffron yellow wing linings, while those of the Black-headed Grosbeak are paler (lemon yellow).)

Measurements (*P. m. maculatus*). *Adult male:* wing, 97.4–103.5 (99.4); tail, 73.5–82.1 (77.8); exposed culmen, 15.4–17 (16.4); tarsus, 22–23.8 (23.1). *Adult female:* wing, 97–101 (99.0) mm.

Field Marks. Adult male with black head, white-patched black wings, cinnamon breast, sides, and rump, and heavy bill is easily recognized. Female is extremely similar to female Rose-breasted Grosbeak, but the Blackhead's more buffy (less whitish) and almost unstreaked breast is a help. *Voice:* Similar to that of Rose-breasted Grosbeak.

Habitat. More open woodlands (deciduous or mixed-wood), especially where there is an admixture of tall shrubbery as along streams, ponds, and lake edges, woodland openings and margins; open second growths and bushy places.

Nesting. In tall bushes or in trees (usually deciduous) often near water, 4 to 20 feet above ground. Nest is loosely constructed of twigs, weed stems, rootlets, and grass. Sometimes it is very flimsily made. *Eggs,* 2 to 5, usually 3 or 4; pale greenish or bluish, spotted and blotched with browns. Incubation 12 days (H. G. Weston, Jr.), by both sexes. As is true with the Rose-breasted Grosbeak, the male sometimes sings while incubating the eggs.

Range. Breeds from southern British Columbia, southern Alberta, and central Nebraska south to southern Mexico. Winters in Mexico.

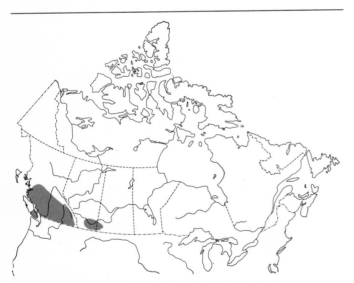

Breeding Distribution of Black-headed Grosbeak

Range in Canada. Summer resident, breeding in southern British Columbia (Hagensborg, Horseshoe Lake, Lower Quinsam Lake, Victoria, Chilliwack, Grand Forks, Newgate. Species recorded in migration at Lower Arrow Lake and Shuswap Falls), southern Alberta (Taber, Medicine Hat; occurred formerly north to High River), and southwestern Saskatchewan (Maple Creek).

Wanders occasionally farther east in Saskatchewan (Lake Johnstone, Regina, Estevan, and near Armley). Casual in southern Manitoba (near Delta; Treesbank).

Subspecies. (1) *Pheucticus melanocephalus maculatus* (Audubon): coastal sw. B.C. (Victoria, Chilliwack). (2) *P. m. melanocephalus* (Swainson), which averages slightly larger in size: interior s. B.C., s. Alta., sw. Sask.

BLUE GROSBEAK
Le Gros-bec bleu. *Guiraca caerulea* (Linnaeus)
L. 6.5 to 7.5 in.

Bill heavy, conical. *Adult male:* Mainly rich purplish blue; wings with two chestnut bars; under tail coverts, more or less tipped white. *Adult female:* Upper parts olive brown, more or less tinged with tawny, the back and scapulars vaguely streaked; wings and tail dusky brown, the wings with brown edgings and two tawny bars, the tail edged with greyish blue; under parts brownish buff, palest on throat and abdomen; head, rump, and wing coverts with more or less bluish. *Young (first autumn):* Resemble female.

Measurements. *Adult male:* wing, 82–90 (86.4); tail, 63.5–67 (66.0); exposed culmen, 14.7–17.5 (16.3); tarsus, 19.8–20.8 (20.5). *Adult female:* wing, 78–84 (81.5) mm.

Field Marks. Much larger size, heavier bill, and chestnut wing bars separate it from the male Indigo Bunting. It is much larger with relatively massive bill compared with female Indigo and Lazuli buntings.

Range. Breeds from central California, central South Dakota, southern Ohio, and southeastern Pennsylvania south to the Gulf States and through Mexico and Central America to Costa Rica.

Status in Canada. Casual visitant to southern Ontario (Long Point; also various sight records: Chatham, Bowmanville, Toronto, Cliff Lake), New Brunswick (Grand Manan), and Nova Scotia (Sable River, Halifax; also various sight records especially in spring, 1961, when observed at West Middle Sable, Waverley, Prince's Lodge, Lydgate). Sight records only for Quebec (Mille Vaches, Lac Simon).

Subspecies. *Guiraca caerulea caerulea* (Linnaeus).

INDIGO BUNTING
Le Bruant indigo. *Passerina cyanea* (Linnaeus)
Plate 63. L. 5.25 to 5.75 in.

Bill conical, its ridge convex. *Adult male (breeding plumage):* Blue all over, the head more purplish; wings and tail, dusky edged with blue. No wing bars. *Adult male (winter plumage):* Somewhat like adult female, the blue colour concealed by brown feather edges but showing on primaries, tail, rump, and wing coverts. *Adult female:* Upper parts olive brownish, the back sometimes lightly streaked, the rump sometimes with a greenish grey tinge; wings and tail dusky, narrowly edged with greenish; greater wing coverts and tertials edged with cinnamon-buff; under parts dull buffy whitish with some olive-buff on breast and sides, the breast faintly streaked with dusky greyish brown. Some individuals have a few blue feathers in the plumage. *Young in first autumn:* Resemble adult female. *Immature male (first breeding plumage):* Similar to adult male in breeding plumage but blues lighter, less pure; wing coverts with some brown.

Measurements. *Adult male:* wing, 66.7–69.5 (68.0); tail,

50.9–53.6 (52.1); exposed culmen, 9.9–11.5 (10.6); tarsus, 16.9–18.3 (17.5). *Adult female:* wing, 62.7–66.5 (63.7).

Field Marks. Adult male obviously smaller, with much less robust bill, than the rare Blue Grosbeak, lacks the Grosbeak's chestnut wing bars. Female is a brown finch, characterized by its lack of stripes, spots, or well-marked wing bars. Upper mandible is seen to be decidedly convex at close range. It resembles female Lazuli Bunting of the West but has less obvious wing bars. *Voice:* Song, a bit goldfinch-like but much more leisurely, the notes well spaced: *zwee zwee zwee, zorry zorry, tsu tsu*, finishing *diminuendo*. Alarm note a sharp *chip*.

Breeding Distribution of Indigo Bunting

Habitat. Likes a combination of bushy ground cover for nesting, and trees for singing: woodland edges and openings, old clearings, second growths, abandoned farms and old pastures, shrubby roadsides, streamsides, lake edges. Sings commonly high in a tall tree.

Nesting. In a shrub or bush not far above the ground. Nest, a cup-shaped structure of twigs, weeds, grass, bark shreds, and often a few leaves; lined with fine grasses and often hair. *Eggs*, 3 or 4; bluish white. Incubation 12 days (F. L. Burns), mainly by the female.

Range. Breeds from South Dakota and southern Manitoba east to Maine and south to southwestern Oklahoma, southeastern Texas, the Gulf coast of United States, and northern Florida. Winters mainly from central Mexico, Cuba, and the Bahamas south to central Panama.

Range in Canada. Summer resident, breeding in southern Manitoba (Portage la Prairie, Grand Beach, Hillside Beach), central and southern Ontario (Wabigoon, Port Arthur, Cochrane southward), southwestern Quebec (southern La Vérendrye Park, Quebec City, Gatineau Park, Montreal, Hatley; recorded in summer at St. Joseph de la Rive). Possibly breeds rarely in southern New Brunswick, but evidence not satisfactory.

Casual in Alberta (Lac la Nonne, Turner Valley, Elkwater Lake); Saskatchewan (Saskatoon, near Armley, Good Spirit Lake, Estevan); Pointe des Monts, Quebec;

New Brunswick (Grand Manan, Rothesay, and several other localities); Nova Scotia (numerous records mostly for southern peninsula, mainly April and May, one in June; recorded also from Sable Island); and Newfoundland (South Island, La Poile, Calvert, Portugal Cove).

Hypothetical (sight records only) for British Columbia (Trail) and Prince Edward Island (Marshfield).

LAZULI BUNTING

Le Bruant azuré. *Passerina amoena* (Say)
Plate 63. L. 5 to 5.75 in.

Adult male: Head, neck, throat, and rump, light cerulean blue; back and scapulars darker blue; wings and tail, blackish edged with bluish; two white wing bars; breast cinnamon, this colour extending to sides; abdomen and under tail coverts, white. *Adult female:* Upper parts greyish brown, the rump greyish blue; back often indistinctly streaked with dusky; wings and tail, dusky edged with greenish blue; two dull buffy or whitish wing bars; throat, breast, and sides, buffy (breast darkest); abdomen and under tail coverts, dingy white. *Young (first autumn):* Similar to adult female but without bluish tinge on rump and usually with fine dusky streaks on breast. *Immature male (first breeding plumage):* Like adult male but blue of upper parts is usually mixed with brown.

Measurements. *Adult male:* wing, 70.5–74 (72.2); tail, 52.9–57.9 (56.2); exposed culmen, 9–10 (9.7); tarsus, 15.9–17.9 (16.9). *Adult female:* wing, 66.2–72.4 (68.7) mm.

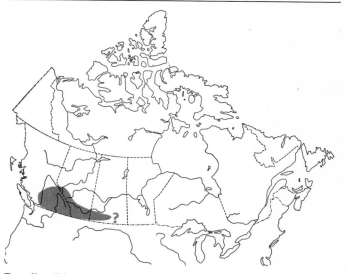

Breeding Distribution of Lazuli Bunting

Field Marks. About the size of a Chipping or Clay-colored Sparrow. The adult male, with bright blue upper parts and throat, cinnamon breast, and two white wing bars, is easily recognized. The female is a small plain brownish sparrow with a ruddy breast and a suggestion of blue on wings, rump, and tail edging; it has somewhat more definite wing bars than the female Indigo Bunting. Bluebirds are coloured somewhat similar to Lazuli Bunting, but the bunting's stubby bill is entirely different from the slender bluebird bill.

367

Voice: Song, which is variable but quite loud and strident, is a little suggestive of the Indigo Bunting's. It is made up of two to four groups of notes in different pitches, e.g., *swip swip swip, zu zu ee, see see, sip see see.* Call-note *tsip.*

Habitat. Bushy country, burntlands, and clearings.

Nesting. In a bush or coarse weed. Nest is a cup constructed of grass, plant fibres, and weed stems and is lined with fine grass and hair. *Eggs,* 3 or 4; bluish white (occasionally with small dark spots). Incubation period 12 days (F. L. Burns).

Range. Breeds from southern British Columbia east to southern Saskatchewan and northeastern South Dakota, south to northwestern Baja California, southern Nevada, central Arizona, and western Oklahoma. Winters from southern Baja California and southern Arizona south to south-central Mexico.

Range in Canada. Breeds in southern British Columbia (Lillooet, Williams Lake Indian Reserve No. 1, Okanagan Landing, Elko), southern Alberta (Jasper, Banff, and Waterton Lakes parks, Gorge Creek and east locally to Castor, Beynon, and Brooks), and southern Saskatchewan (Shaunavon, Moose Jaw, perhaps rarely Regina where a pair summered).

Casual in coastal British Columbia (Vancouver Island north to Shushartie). Accidental in southern Mackenzie (Fort Providence, July 4, 1903).

DICKCISSEL

Le Dickcissel. *Spiza americana* (Gmelin)
Plate 63. L. 6 to 7 in.

Middle tail feathers narrow and pointed. *Adult male:* Crown, hind-neck, and ear region, grey; stripe over eye, pale yellowish; back and scapulars, greyish brown striped with black; rump paler than back, unstreaked; wing coverts chestnut; bend of wing, yellow; no wing bars; lower throat with black bib (obscure or absent in autumn); upper throat white; breast bright yellow, often extending down middle of abdomen; rest of under parts white; bill bluish with dusky sides; legs greyish brown. *Adult female:* Somewhat similar to adult male but much duller; crown and ear patch, grey; crown and rump, narrowly streaked with dusky; stripe over eye, whitish; chestnut on wing coverts reduced or absent; throat, white without black bib but margined on either side by a narrow dusky streak; breast tinged with yellow and narrowly streaked with dusky; flanks streaked somewhat with dusky; rest of under parts whitish. *Young in autumn:* Similar to adult female but much tinged with buffy, the male with rich chestnut wing coverts, yellowish eyebrow stripe.

Measurements. *Adult male:* wing, 79–84.8 (81.1); tail, 54.2–61 (58.9); exposed culmen, 13.2–15 (14.3); tarsus, 22.6–24.5 (23.3). *Adult female:* wing, 74.7–77.5 (75.7) mm.

Field Marks. The adult male in breeding plumage (black bib on yellow breast) might suggest a tiny Meadowlark, but it is only half as large as a Meadowlark and its stubby bill is entirely different. The female resembles a female House Sparrow but usually shows a trace of yellow on the breast and has a more distinct eyebrow stripe and paler general

coloration. Female also resembles female Bobolink, but the general coloration is much greyer (less yellowish) and the Dickcissel has no pale median crown stripe or heavy line back from eye. *Voice:* Song has good volume, a somewhat staccato *chup-chup-klip-klip-klip* or *dick, dick, dickcissel.*

Habitat. Open situations such as grassy, clover, alfalfa, weedy, and brushy fields, meadows, and prairies.

Nesting. On or near the ground, sometimes in shrubs or in a tree. Nest, a rather bulky cup made of grass, weed stalks, and leaves, lined with grass and rootlets. *Eggs,* 3 to 5; pale blue.

Range. Breeds from eastern Montana, southern Saskatchewan, and southern Ontario south to central Colorado, central-southern Texas, southern Louisiana, and central Georgia; formerly, now sporadically, east to the Atlantic Coast and north to Massachusetts. Winters from south-central Mexico to Colombia, Venezuela, and the Guianas.

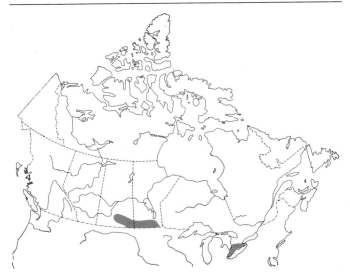

Breeding Distribution of Dickcissel

Range in Canada. Breeding is sporadic in most of its Canadian breeding range. Breeds in southern Saskatchewan (formerly at least: Regina; probably Lake Johnstone), southern Manitoba (Whitewater Lake, Oak Lake, Winnipeg), southern Ontario (formerly at least: Point Pelee, Lake St. Clair, London).

Casual in southern British Columbia (Vaseaux Lake, Victoria), southern Alberta (Walsh), eastern Ontario (Ottawa), southern Quebec (Moisie Bay, Johan Beetz Bay, Anticosti Island, Cape Gaspé), Prince Edward Island, Nova Scotia (Halifax, mouth of Bay of Fundy, Brier Island, Stewiake; also numerous sight records mostly in autumn), and Newfoundland (Terra Nova, Burgeo; sight record: St. Anthony). Several sight records for southern New Brunswick. Almost all of the many east coast records are for autumn.

Remarks. This bird appears often as a stray on the southeastern coast of Canada, sometimes north to Newfoundland and the north shore of the Gulf of St. Lawrence. In one small clearing on lower Moisie River, Quebec, it was recorded during three successive autumns, 1950 to 1952.

EVENING GROSBEAK

Le Gros-bec errant. *Hesperiphona vespertina* (Cooper)
Plate 64. L. 7 to 8.5 in.

Bill extremely heavy, cone-shaped, the culmen very broad without a ridge. Plumage somewhat variable. *Adult male:* Forehead and stripe over eye yellow; top of head black; rest of head, also neck and upper back, dark brownish olive passing into yellow on scapulars and lower back and on posterior under parts; upper tail coverts, tail, and most of wings black, but tertials white, forming a large wing patch; bill pale yellowish green; legs brownish or dark flesh colour. *Adult female:* Upper parts mostly grey, darkest on top of head, palest on rump; back of neck tinged greenish yellow; cheeks grey, similar to top of head; throat, abdomen, and under tail coverts whitish, with a dusky streak down each side of throat; breast, sides, and flanks, buffy greyish more or less mixed with yellow; wings dull black, the tertials grey-edged or tipped with whitish; primaries (except three outermost), white at base forming a small white patch; tail black, the inner webs broadly tipped white. *Young (first winter):* Resemble adults but young males may be separated from adult males by blackish inner margins of the white tertials.

Measurements (*H. v. vespertina*). *Adult male:* wing, 105.4–115.3 (110.9); tail, 60–69.6 (65.2); exposed culmen, 16.2–20 (18.6); tarsus, 19.8–21.9 (20.6). *Adult female:* wing, 104.7–111.4 (108.5) mm.

Field Marks. Usually in companies or flocks. Very large conical *yellowish-white* bill, black wings with large white patches. Males have much yellow in the plumage, the females mostly grey. *Voice:* Call, a *cleep* somewhat similar to the *cheep* of a House Sparrow but louder and more strident. Song, a rather short, jerky warble.

Habitat. In breeding season mixed and coniferous woodland including second growths, occasionally even nesting in a town shade tree. In winter and migration, various types of woods, wood patches, parks, and shade trees about towns. It is particularly partial to the seeds of the Manitoba maple or box elder, *Acer negundo*, and is readily attracted to backyard feeding shelves where sunflower seeds are favourites. Salted gravel piles attract it at any time of the year.

Nesting. In either a coniferous or deciduous tree, 15 to 60 feet up. Nest is a loosely made shallow structure of twigs, rootlets, and bark shreds and is lined with rootlets and fine twigs. *Eggs*, 3 to 5; bluish green marked with browns and greys. Much information is needed on the breeding cycle.

Range. Breeds in a rather narrow strip across Canada (British Columbia to Nova Scotia) and south in the mountains to central California and southern Mexico; in the East to northeastern Minnesota, northern New York, and Massachusetts. Winters from southern Canada southward irregularly to southern United States.

Range in Canada. Breeds locally (breeding range based largely on summer occurrences, as definite breeding data are relatively few) in north-central and southern British Columbia (Bear Lake, situated 50 miles north of Takla Lake, and south through Alta Lake, Okanagan Valley, Wardner, probably Vancouver Island, but not recorded from Queen Charlotte Islands); northern, central, and southwestern Alberta (Athabasca Delta, Dunvegan, Lesser Slave Lake, Swan Hills, Glenevis, Belvedere, Jasper, Banff); central Saskatchewan (Somme, Nipawin); southern Manitoba (Overflowing River, Selkirk, Indian Bay); central and southern Ontario (Minaki, Kenora, Elsas, Hawk Junction, Algonquin Park, Muskoka; unconfirmed report at Brockville); southern Quebec (Amos, Mount Plamondon, Lake St. John, Anticosti Island, Lac Rimouski, Quebec City region, Kingsmere, Coaticook, Ste. Anne des Monts; reported in summer at Godbout and Ilets Jérémie); New Brunswick (St. Leonard, Grand Lake, Nashwaak, Hampton, Riley Brook); and Nova Scotia (Ingonish Beach). Recorded once in summer in extreme central-southern Mackenzie (Buffalo River).

Winters within much of the breeding range and southward and eastward to Prince Edward Island and Newfoundland (east to St. John's).

Formerly this was primarily a western species, but in recent times it has rapidly pushed its breeding range eastward. In Ontario it was first known to nest at Lake of the Woods in 1920, first in Muskoka District in 1927, and first in Algonquin Park in 1932. It now breeds east to Cape Breton Island, Nova Scotia.

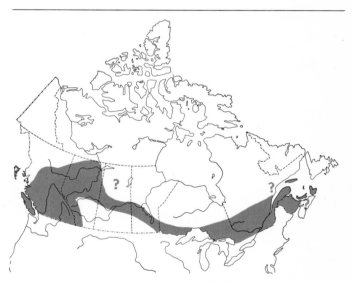

Breeding Distribution of Evening Grosbeak

Subspecies. (1) *Hesperiphona vespertina vespertina* (Cooper): All of the breeding range in Canada east of the Rockies. (2) *H. v. brooksi* Grinnell (averages darker in colour, especially females): B.C. and sw. Alta. (Rocky Mts.).

PURPLE FINCH

Le Roselin pourpré. *Carpodacus purpureus* (Gmelin)
Plate 65. L. 5.5 to 6.3 in.

Bill heavy, short, conical; tail shorter than wing and slightly forked. *Adult male:* Upper parts, head, neck, breast, and sides, variable red (duller in autumn and winter), the crown crimson to purplish red, the rump more pinkish, the back and scapulars streaked with brown; eye and ear region and patch on side of jaw often brownish; small area in front of eye, greyish white; wings and tail, dark brown narrowly edged with pale reddish or brownish; two faint narrow wing bars of brownish red; middle of abdomen and under tail coverts, white. *Immature male (first breeding plumage)*: Similar to adult female. *Adult female:* Upper parts, olive greyish streaked with dusky and also a little whitish; white line back from eye; eye and ear regions, olive; wings and tail dusky, narrowly edged with pale olive; two pale wing bars; under parts white, heavily streaked with olive except middle of abdomen, the under tail coverts usually unstreaked (sometimes longer ones are lightly streaked). Occasional females show traces of red in the plumage. *Young in first winter plumage:* Similar to adult female.

Measurements (*C. p. purpureus*). *Adult male:* wing, 78.4–85 (82.3); tail, 51.5–61.5 (58.4); exposed culmen, 10.2–12 (11.3); tarsus, 17.5–18.4 (17.9). *Adult female:* wing, 74.81.8 (78.3) mm.

Field Marks. Size of House Sparrow. The red (not purple) adult male is much smaller than the (Robin-sized) red male Pine Grosbeak. Uncrossed mandibles distinguish it from crossbills. Females and young are heavily streaked, with a dusky patch on sides of head and a white line back from eye; the heavy bill distinguishes them from other streaked sparrows of the East. In the West *see* Cassin's and House finches. *Voice:* Song is a rich, rapid, and spirited warble, very reminiscent of that of the Warbling Vireo but much more energetic. Call, a metallic *pink*, which is quite distinctive.

Habitat. More open mixed and coniferous woodland, openings and edges, farm woodlots, even orchards. In winter various kinds of trees and tall shrubbery, orchards, parks, and gardens.

Nesting. Five to sixty feet up in a tree (usually coniferous but more rarely in an apple or other deciduous tree or very rarely in a hedge). Nest, which is of twigs, grasses, and rootlets, is lined with fine grasses and hair. *Eggs,* 4 to 6; blue, with fine dark brown or blackish spots chiefly about the large end. Incubation period about 13 days (O. W. Knight).

Range. Breeds across wooded parts of Canada from British Columbia (except interior southern part) east to Newfoundland and south along the Pacific Coast to northern Baja California, and to North Dakota, central Wisconsin, northeastern Ohio, southeastern West Virginia, and southeastern New York. Winters from southern Canada (locally) south to southern United States.

Range in Canada. Breeds in southwestern Mackenzie (Fort Simpson); northern, central, and southwestern British Columbia (Atlin and at points along the Alaska Highway, south on the coast to Vancouver Island and in the interior to Big Bar Lake and southern Wells Gray Park); northern, central, and southwestern Alberta (Wood Buffalo Park south to Jasper and Banff in the mountains and to Edmonton, Elk Island National Park, and probably Battle River); central Saskatchewan (Kazan Lake, Prince Albert, Nipawin); south-central and southern Manitoba (The Pas, Norway House southward); central and southern Ontario

(Favourable Lake, Lake Attawapiskat, Moose Factory south to Lake of the Woods, London, St. Thomas, Kingston), south-central and southern Quebec (Eastmain, Lake Mistassini, Matamek, St. Augustin southward including Anticosti Island and probably Magdalen Islands); central and southern Newfoundland; New Brunswick; Prince Edward Island; and Nova Scotia (including Cape Breton Island). Recorded in summer in southern Yukon (Whitehorse, Rancheria River; probably Canyon).

Winters in southern British Columbia, southern Manitoba (Brandon, Winnipeg), southern Ontario (north at least to Port Arthur, Manitoulin Island, North Bay, Ottawa), southwestern Quebec (Hull, Montreal, Quebec), southern New Brunswick (Scotch Lake, Fredericton, St. John), Prince Edward Island, and Nova Scotia (Wolfville, Pictou, Antigonish, Halifax), and southern Newfoundland (St. John's).

Casual in southern Labrador (Cartwright). Accidental in eastern Franklin (off Resolution Island, September 1, 1877).

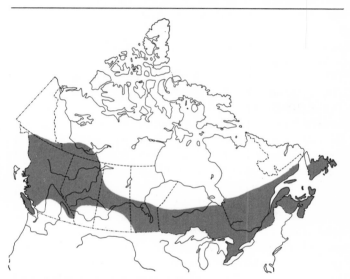

Breeding Distribution of Purple Finch

Subspecies. (1) *Carpodacus purpureus purpureus* (Gmelin): e. Man. (Selkirk, Rennie), Ont., Que., N.B., P.E.I., N.S., and Nfld. (2) *C. p. taverneri* Rand (paler coloration especially in adult male): sw. Mack., n. and c. B.C., Alta., Sask., w. Man. (Riding Mountain, The Pas). (3) *C. p. californicus* Baird (darker, with dorsal streaking in adult male more obscure): sw. B.C. (Comox, Kimsquit, Lillooet).

CASSIN'S FINCH
Le Roselin de Cassin. *Carpodacus cassinii* Baird
Plate 65. L. 6 to 6.8 in.

Similar to Purple Finch but larger with relatively less stubby bill and differing in colour as follows. *Adult male* with reds paler, the red of crown brighter, forming a definite cap which contrasts with the more brownish remainder of upper parts; throat and breast paler, more pinkish; under tail coverts usually conspicuously streaked with dusky. *Females and immatures* are more greyish (less olive) than in Purple

Finch, the streaks on under parts finer and sharper, *the under tail coverts usually conspicuously streaked with dusky.*

Measurements. *Adult male:* wing, 90.4–96.8 (93.4); tail, 61.8–66 (64.3); exposed culmen, 12–12.9 (12.5); tarsus, 18–19.1 (18.6). *Adult female:* wing, 86.3–92.6 (88.3) mm.

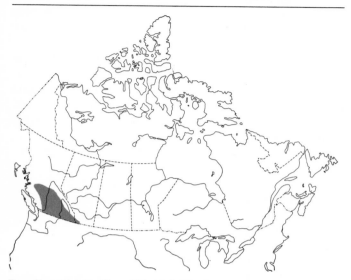

Breeding Distribution of Cassin's Finch

Field Marks. To be expected in southern interior British Columbia and extreme southwestern Alberta. It is separable, with difficulty, in the field from the Purple Finch by characters given above. It also resembles the smaller, more stubby-billed House Finch. The adult male Cassin's Finch, however, has the reds paler and less, if any, dusky streaking on the belly and sides than the male House Finch. Females and young Cassin's Finch have longer bills (with straighter culmen), darker coloration above and below, and sharper, finer, darker streaks on the under parts than the House Finch in corresponding plumages. *Song:* Similar to that of Purple Finch but call-note quite different, a two or three syllable *kee-up*, the second syllable lower.

Habitat. Open coniferous forests in the western mountains ranging up to considerable altitudes.

Nesting. In a coniferous tree at various heights above ground. Nest is of twigs, rootlets, and grasses, lined with fine grass. *Eggs*, usually 4 or 5; greenish blue, sparingly spotted with browns and purplish grey.

Range. Breeds from southern interior British Columbia, extreme southwestern Alberta, central Montana, northern Wyoming south in the interior mountains to northwestern California, northern Baja California, northern Arizona, and northern New Mexico. Winters within much of breeding range and south to northern Mexico.

Range in Canada. Breeds in southern interior British Columbia (Stuie, Clinton, Mile 85 Cariboo Road, Arrow Lakes, Okanagan, Wardner) and in extreme southwestern Alberta (Waterton Lakes Park).

Winters occasionally in southern British Columbia (Okanagan Landing).

Remarks. Cassin's Finch is very closely related to the much more widely distributed Purple Finch. The two look and seem to act very much alike, but the call-note of Cassin's Finch sounds like *kee-up* (first syllable high-pitched) and differs from the metallic *pink* of the Purple Finch.

HOUSE FINCH
Le Roselin familier. *Carpodacus mexicanus* (Müller)
Plate 65. L. 5 to 5.75 in.

Bill stubby, culmen much more downcurved than in Purple or Cassin's finches. *Adult male:* Forehead, stripe over eye, and rump, red, rosy pink, or scarlet; rest of upper parts brownish grey, obscurely streaked with darker brown and often washed with reddish; wings and tail, dusky with pale greyish edging and two obscure pale wing bars; throat and upper breast, reddish; lower breast, abdomen, sides, flanks, and under tail coverts whitish, thickly streaked with greyish brown. *Adult female:* Like adult male but without any red, that of the upper parts replaced by brown, that of throat and upper breast by whitish and striped with greyish brown as in the rest of the under parts; face lacks definite patterns shown in Purple and Cassin's finches. *Young:* Resemble adult female.

Measurements (*C. m. frontalis*). *Adult male:* wing, 74.5–83.2 (78.6); tail, 57–65 (61.7); exposed culmen, 9.3–11 (10.0); tarsus, 16–18.2 (17.2). *Adult female:* wing, 74.3–78 (75.9) mm.

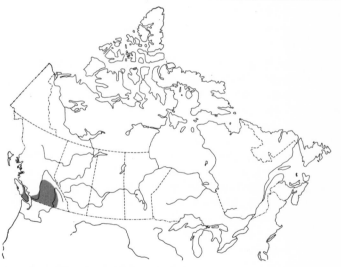

Breeding Distribution of House Finch

Field Marks. Gregarious. Resembles Purple and Cassin's finches but is smaller, and the stubbier bill has a more downcurved culmen. Adult male has the red coloration more restricted and the whole lower breast, abdomen, and sides thickly streaked with greyish brown. Females and young are paler above than Purple and Cassin's finches and have no definite face patterns. Its frequent habitat in western towns, which is similar to that of House Sparrows, tends to eliminate its two near relatives. *Voice:* A spirited warbling song somewhat suggesting a cross between a Purple Finch and a Vesper Sparrow. Some of its calls sound like the chirps of the House Sparrow.

371

Habitat. Sunny drier areas are preferred (but with at least some water available); farmlands with thin shrubbery, trees, orchards, and buildings; towns. In many ways similar to the requirements of the House Sparrow in cultivated and urban areas.

Nesting. Various situations such as crannies on building exteriors, vines about houses, bird boxes, tree cavities, clumps of shrubs, and even in old nests of other bird species like the Cliff Swallow, the Robin, and the Oriole. Nest is made of various soft materials depending upon availability, such as grass, twigs, rootlets, cotton wool, string. *Eggs*, usually 4 or 5; bluish, sparingly spotted with blackish. Incubation period averages 14 days (Bergtold).

Range. Southwestern and central-southern British Columbia, Idaho, Wyoming, and western Nebraska south to southern Mexico.

Range in Canada. Breeds in southwestern and central southern British Columbia: Vancouver Island (Victoria and north along the east coast to near Campbell River), Vancouver, Abbotsford, Chilliwack, Hope, Princeton, near Lillooet, the entire Okanagan Valley, Grindrod, Kamloops, and north to Williams Lake.

Winters in much of the breeding range in British Columbia. Casual in southwestern Alberta (Jasper Park, May 29, 1944).

Subspecies. *Carpodacus mexicanus frontalis* (Say).

PINE GROSBEAK

Le Gros-bec des pins. *Pinicola enucleator* (Linnaeus)
Plate 64. L. 9 to 9.75 in.

Bill stubby, heavy, the culmen decidedly downcurved, the upper mandible slightly hooked; nasal tufts long, concealing nostrils; tail slightly forked. *Adult male:* General coloration dull red (dull pinkish red in winter, light poppy red in summer), the feathers with grey bases, the grey showing through in many places; nasal tufts and narrow line in front of eye, blackish; back with dusky feather centres; scapulars mostly greyish; wings and tail dusky, the tertials and some secondaries edged with white; two white wing bars (often tinged reddish); abdomen, much of sides and flanks, grey; under tail coverts greyish centrally with whitish margins; bill blackish, often paler at base of lower mandible; legs black. *Immature male:* Similar to adult female, but some have crowns and rumps reddish instead of yellowish olive. *Adult female:* General colour plain grey, the crown and rump yellowish olive to russet; hind-neck, back, and under parts more or less washed with olive; wings and tail similar to those of adult male. *Young females:* Similar to adult females.

Measurements (*P. e. eschatosa*). *Adult male:* wing, 102.5–115.9 (110.8); tail, 85.1–95.1 (89.3); exposed culmen, 13.8–15.9 (14.6); tarsus, 19–23.1 (21.9). *Adult female:* wing, 105–110.9 (107.1) mm.

Field Marks. A large (Robin-sized) finch with heavy blackish bill. In migration and winter, frequently in small flocks. Usually tame. Motions are rather deliberate. Male Purple and Cassin's finches also are largely reddish but are much smaller and lack conspicuous white wing bars.

Females and young Pine Grosbeaks are large, plain grey finches with yellowish crown and rump and two white wing bars. The *dark* bill and lack of conspicuous white wing *patches* (other than bars) distinguish them from the Evening Grosbeak. *Voice:* Common call at all times of the year, two or three high-pitched musical whistles on a descending scale, somewhat suggesting that of the Greater Yellowlegs but less strident. The pleasing warbled song suggests that of the Purple Finch but is less energetic and usually shorter.

Habitat. In the breeding season more open coniferous forest (or less often, mixedwoods), openings and edges. In migration and winter, deciduous trees are much favoured (especially white ash, mountain ash, flowering crab), also shade trees about towns, apple orchards, and tall shrubbery.

Nesting. In a coniferous tree usually not more than 10 or 15 feet above ground but rarely up to 30. Nest is rather flimsily made of twigs, rootlets, grass, and moss. It is lined with such materials as fine rootlets, grasses, and hair. *Eggs*, usually 4 or 5; greenish blue with spots and dots of browns and purplish grey, mainly at the large end.

Range. Holarctic. In North America breeds in northern forests from northern Alaska eastward across Canada to Newfoundland and south to central California, northern New Mexico, central Manitoba, central Ontario, northern New Hampshire, central Maine, and Nova Scotia; also in northern woodlands of Eurasia from Scandinavia east to northeastern Siberia, Kamchatka, and northern Japan. Winters within much of the breeding range and irregularly considerably farther south.

Breeding Distribution of Pine Grosbeak

Range in Canada. Breeds from northern Yukon (Old Crow), northwestern and central Mackenzie (Mackenzie Delta, Great Bear Lake, Fort Reliance), northern Manitoba (Churchill, probably Sandhill Lake), northern Ontario (50 miles south of Winisk), northern Quebec (Richmond Gulf, Fort Chimo, Indian House Lake), north-central Labrador (Okak), and Newfoundland south to southern British Columbia (including Queen Charlotte and Vancouver islands), northern Alberta (probably Wood Buffalo Park), southwestern Alberta (mountains only: Banff and Jasper national parks), northern Saskatchewan (Tazin Lake, probably south to central parts), north-central Manitoba (Ilford and probably farther south), central and south-central Ontario (Timagami Forest Reserve, rarely south to Sundridge, and probably Combermere), southeastern and central-southern Quebec (locally: Mistassini Post, Biencourt, Lac Rimouski, Percé; Anticosti and Magdalen islands), New Brunswick, and Nova Scotia (including Cape Breton Island). Sight records in southwestern Keewatin (Windy River).

Winters within much of breeding range, north at least to northwestern Mackenzie (Mackenzie Delta), northwestern Saskatchewan (Lake Athabasca), south-central Quebec (Lake Mistassini), and southern Labrador; winters also in areas outside the breeding range: central and southern Alberta, southern Saskatchewan, southern Manitoba, southern Ontario, southwestern Quebec, and Prince Edward Island, as well as in all southern parts of the breeding range. Winter movements are irregular, and the species may be common or abundant in a given area one winter and absent the next.

Subspecies. (1) *Pinicola enucleator leucura* (Müller): c. Mack. (Great Bear Lake, Fort Reliance), n. and c. Man., n. and c. Ont., n. Que., Lab. (2) *P. e. eschatosa* Oberholser (smaller and darker than *leucura*): s. Que. (including Mistassini Post where intergrading with *leucura*), Nfld., N.B., N.S. (3) *P. e. alascensis* Ridgway (larger size, except bill, and paler coloration than *leucura*): Yukon, w. Mack. (Mackenzie Delta, Fort Simpson), ne. B.C. (4) *P. e. flammula* Homeyer (bill larger than in *leucura*, dusky centres of back feathers less distinct): nw. B.C. (Telegraph Creek, Dease Lake, Tetana Lake). (5) *P. e. carlottae* Brooks (small, especially tail, coloration dark): Queen Charlotte and Vancouver islands, and along the mainland coast of B.C. (6) *P. e. montana* Ridgway: s. interior B.C. (Punchesakut Lake, Indianpoint Lake southward) and sw. Alta. (Jasper and Banff parks).

GRAY-CROWNED ROSY FINCH

Le Roselin brun. *Leucosticte tephrocotis* (Swainson)
Plate 69. L. 5.8 to 6.8 in.

Adult male (*breeding plumage*): Nasal tufts white; crown black, bordered behind by grey which extends down over the cheeks often to throat in one of our two subspecies (*littoralis*), grey much more restricted in the other race (*L. t. tephrocotis*) and not extending onto cheeks; body mostly brown above and below, the back streaked with dusky; wings, rump, upper and lower tail coverts, and belly, more or less tinged with pink; bill black. *Adult male* (*winter*): Similar to breeding plumage but black on crown much restricted, the brown feathers of body margined with white or buffy; bill yellowish with blackish tip. *Adult female:* Similar to adult male but somewhat duller and paler. *Young:* Somewhat like adults but mostly greyish brown without pink on the body or grey on head.

Measurements (*L. t. littoralis*). *Adult male:* wing, 102.7–108.9 (104.9); tail, 62–73 (68.6); exposed culmen, 11–12.1 (11.5); tarsus, 18.9–20.9 (19.9). *Adult female:* wing, 101–104 (102.5) mm.

Field Marks. Sparrow-sized ground birds of the West, usually in groups or flocks. General coloration, dark brown with pink suffusion on rump, wings, and belly; black cap on grey top of head, the grey extending down over cheeks and ear region in the race *littoralis*, but in *tephrocotis* the cheeks and ear region are brown like the body. *Voice:* Common call-notes suggest those of the House Sparrow. Song a rich goldfinch-like warble.

Habitat. In summer, for nesting, it inhabits rocks and cliffs among the glaciers and permanent snow above timberline on mountain summits. In autumn it descends to lowlands in mountain valleys, the west coast, and foothills where it favours fields and open places, roadsides, straw stacks, farmyards, even invading the streets of towns and visiting feeding shelves.

Nesting. In crevices in cliffs or under rocks on mountain summits. The rather bulky nest is made of grass stems and rootlets and lined with grassy fibres, fine rootlets, plant down, or a few feathers. *Eggs*, 4 or 5; pure white.

Range. Islands of Bering Sea, the Aleutians, central Alaska, central Yukon, and southwestern Alberta south in the western mountains to central-eastern California, eastern Oregon, and northwestern Montana.

Breeding Distribution of Gray-crowned Rosy Finch

Range in Canada. Breeds on mountain summits from central Yukon (Ogilvie Range) south through southern British Columbia and southwestern Alberta (Jasper, Banff, and Waterton Lakes parks).

Winters in lowlands of southern and central British Columbia (north at least to Quesnel and Peace River District) and in southern and central Alberta (valleys and foothills of the southwestern Mountains and irregularly farther east to Elk Island Park and Brooks); also southwestern Saskatchewan (Eastend). Rarely elsewhere in Saskatchewan (east to Regina and Indian Head, north to the Carlton area and Torch River). Casually east to Manitoba

(Birtle). Sight record only for Ontario (near Fort William, March 1963).

Subspecies. (1) *Leucosticte tephrocotis littoralis* Baird (grey of head extends down over cheeks and ear region): sw. Yukon (Tepee Lake), w. B.C. (Dease Lake, Tenquille Lake, Déboulé Mountain, Vancouver Island). (2) *L. t. tephrocotis* (Swainson) (cheeks and ear region, brown like body): c. Yukon, south to se. B.C., and sw. Alta.

[**European Goldfinch.** Le Chardonneret élégant. *Carduelis carduelis* (Linnaeus). Hypothetical. L. 4.8 in. Adults, with red face, forehead, and chin; black hind crown; and black wings with very large yellow patch are a combination not shown by any native bird. The species has been introduced into parts of United States and is established in Long Island, New York. A specimen collected in Toronto, Ontario, May 21, 1887, and a recent sight record in New Brunswick may represent strays from the Long Island colony, but the possibility that they were escaped cage birds cannot be excluded.]

HOARY REDPOLL

Le Sizerin blanchâtre. *Acanthis hornemanni* (Holboell)
Plate 64. L. 4.5 to 6.1 in.

Similar to Common Redpoll but general coloration decidedly paler, the rump (except in worn breeding plumage) white or pinkish with little or no streaking, thus contrasting with the back. The subspecies *A. h. exilipes* is similar in size to *A. flammea flammea*, but *exilipes* (Hoary Redpoll) has a shorter more obtuse bill, a slightly longer tail, and the under tail coverts of *exilipes* are much more lightly streaked or immaculate.

Measurements (*A. h. exilipes*). *Adult male:* wing, 70.9–75.8 (74.1); tail, 56–63.7 (59.9); exposed culmen, 7–8.7 (7.9); tarsus, 13.8–15.9 (14.7). *Adult female:* wing, 68.1–72.4 (71.2) mm.

Field Marks. A very pale edition of the Common Redpoll, but rump white, contrasting with the back and tail.

Habitat. Usually similar to that of the Common Redpoll. In the high Arctic, ravines and rocky slopes with some shrubby ground cover.

Nesting. In bushes or crevices in rocks. Nest is of grass stems and weeds and is lined with feathers. Nest may be used more than one year (V.C. Wynne-Edwards). *Eggs,* usually 5 or 6; blue, spotted and dotted with light brown. Incubation is by the female.

Range. Breeds across the Arctic of both the New and Old Worlds. In North America from Alaska east across arctic Canada to Greenland; in winter south to southern British Columbia, eastern Montana, South Dakota, Minnesota, Indiana, Ohio, and Maryland.

Range in Canada. Breeds (locally, but range poorly known) in northern Yukon (Old Crow), northern and central-eastern Mackenzie (Mackenzie Delta, Anderson River, Bathurst Inlet, Thelon River), southern Victoria Island (Cambridge Bay), Keewatin (Adelaide Peninsula, Baker Lake, Windy River), northern Manitoba (Churchill); and from northern Ellesmere Island (Alert, Fosheim Peninsula) south through Bylot Island and Baffin Island (Clyde Inlet, Cumberland Peninsula) south to Southampton Island and northern Quebec (Fort Chimo). Reported breeding in

northern Labrador (Nachvak) requires confirmation. Summer sight records for Prince Patrick and Ellef Ringnes islands.

Winters within much of the breeding range (north at least to northern Yukon, northwestern Mackenzie, Southampton Island, and southern Baffin Island (Pangnirtung Fiord) and southward, locally and irregularly, to southern British Columbia (not reported from Vancouver Island) and other southern parts of the country including Alberta, Saskatchewan, Manitoba, Ontario, and Quebec. Definite records in the Maritime Provinces for only Nova Scotia (Gaspereau). Sight records only for Newfoundland.

Breeding Distribution of Hoary Redpoll

Subspecies. (1) *Acanthis hornemanni hornemanni* (Holboell), the largest and palest of the Redpolls: Northeastern Franklin (Ellesmere I., Bylot I., and at least n. Baffin I. —no breeding material from s. Baffin examined). (2) *A. h. exilipes* (Coues), smaller and slightly darker than *hornemanni*, the under tail coverts more often streaked: Yukon, Mack., s. Victoria Island, Keewatin, Man., and Que.

COMMON REDPOLL

Le Sizerin à tête rouge. *Acanthis flammea* (Linnaeus)
Plate 64. L. 4.5 to 6 in.

Similar to Hoary Redpoll but much darker, the rump not plain white but heavily streaked with dusky; under tail coverts with heavier dusky streaks; proportions also differ, depending somewhat on races concerned. *Adult male (breeding plumage):* Cap bright red; rest of upper parts, dark greyish brown with indistinct dark streaks and some of greyish white; rump, greyish white (often pinkish) heavily streaked with dusky; wings and tail, dark greyish brown; two narrow white wing bars; chin blackish; cheeks, breast, and sides often tinged with red or pink; rest of under parts white, the sides and under tail coverts streaked with dusky. *Adult male (winter):* Similar to breeding plumage but very much paler and more buffy, rump more whitish (often pinkish) but always decidedly streaked with dusky; wing bars more or less buffy; pink of breast paler. *Adult female:* Similar to adult male, including red cap, but without red or pink on under parts.

Measurements (*A. f. flammea*). *Adult male:* wing, 69.8–75.3 (72.7); tail, 50.4–60.2 (55.8); exposed culmen, 8.2–10.2 (9.0); tarsus, 13.6–15.8 (14.8). The northeastern race *rostrata* is much larger: wing, 75.6–83.9 (80.5). *Adult female* (*A. f. flammea*): wing, 68.3–74.8 (70.5) mm.

Field Marks. Redpolls are small stubby-billed finches with a bright red cap, blackish chin, dark streaks on sides, the adult males often showing a pinkish suffusion on the breast. In thickly settled southern parts of the country they are winter visitants and are usually seen in twittering flocks of various sizes, feeding either in weed patches on the ground or in trees. The Common Redpoll very closely resembles the Hoary, but the former's general coloration is noticeably darker; the rump is heavily streaked like the back (not decidedly white), and at close range the bill can often be seen to be slightly longer, less stubby than that of the Hoary. *Voice:* Flight call tends to be a double-noted *zit-zit.* Flocks maintain a constant twitter of metallic notes. Song, a trill accompanied by a twitter.

Habitat. Varies somewhat with latitude. In the high Arctic, ravines and rocky slopes with some shrubby ground cover. In the Subarctic and low Arctic, patches of spruce, dwarf birch, alder and willow thickets, mats of dwarf spruce, and other thick low shrubbery. In winter in southern localities, open woodland (either deciduous or coniferous), weed patches, fields, and bushy fence rows. It is especially fond of seeds of birch and alder.

Nesting. In dwarf trees and shrubs, on the ground on sedge tussocks, or in rock crevices. Nest is of grasses and twigs and is warmly lined with cottony plant down, feathers, sometimes fur or hair. *Eggs,* usually 5 or 6; blue, dotted and spotted with reddish brown. Incubation period 10 to 11 days (L. I. Grinnell) for *flammea;* 11 days (E. M. Nicholson) for *rostrata.*

Range. Circumpolar Arctic and Subarctic. In North America from Alaska eastward across northern Canada to Greenland. Winters from the southern breeding range south to northern California, Nevada, Colorado, Kansas, Ohio, West Virginia, and South Carolina.

Range in Canada. Breeds locally from northern Yukon (Herschel Island), northern Mackenzie (Mackenzie Delta, Franklin Bay, Coppermine), southern Victoria Island (Cambridge Bay), northern Keewatin (probably Perry River), northern Manitoba (Churchill), northern Ontario (Fort Severn, Little Cape, Cape Henrietta Maria), Baffin Island (Clyde Inlet, Cumberland Peninsula), northern Quebec (Sugluk, Fort Chimo), and northern Labrador (Nachvak), south to northwestern British Columbia (Atlin), southern Mackenzie (Fort Simpson, Fort Providence, Soulier Lake), northern Manitoba (Cochrane River, Herchmer, York Factory), northern Ontario (Lake Attawapiskat; summer records at Kenora, Port Arthur, Nakina), central and southeastern Quebec (Fort George, Knob Lake, Blanc Sablon; Magdalen Islands); southern Labrador (Cartwright), and Newfoundland (except southwestern corner). An amazing record of nesting in southern Saskatchewan (Mortlach) is reported by Lahrman and Nero (1961, *Blue Jay* 19 (3): 113–114).

Winters within southern parts of the breeding range and southward (but irregularly: common to abundant in some years, rare or absent in others in a given locality) in most parts of southern Canada including British Columbia (but rarely reported on the coastal islands), Alberta, Saskatchewan, Manitoba, Ontario, Quebec, New Brunswick, Prince Edward Island, Nova Scotia (including Cape Breton Island), and Newfoundland.

Breeding Distribution of Common Redpoll

Subspecies. (1) *Acanthis flammea flammea* (Linnaeus) is the breeding form of Yukon (except perhaps Herschel I., *see A. f. holboellii*), n. B.C., Mack., Victoria I., Keewatin, Man., Ont., Que., Lab., and Nfld. (2) *A. f. rostrata* (Coues), larger size with thicker bill, coloration somewhat darker and browner than in *flammea,* adult males with red of under parts less extensive and less intense: Baffin Island, N.W.T. (3) *A. f. holboellii* (Brehm), of doubtful validity but supposedly intermediate in size between *flammea* and *rostrata* with slenderer bill than the latter, colour similar to *flammea,* is alleged to be the breeding form of Herschel I., Yukon.

The common wintering form in southern Canada is *A. flammea flammea,* but *rostrata* is also a winter visitant in small numbers to southern parts of the East from Ont. to Nfld.

PINE SISKIN
Le Chardonneret des pins. *Spinus pinus* (Wilson)
Plate 64. L. 4.5 to 5.2 in.

Bill longer and more slender than that of redpolls and goldfinches. Tail slightly forked. Sexes similar in appearance. Upper parts, greyish brown streaked with dusky, paler on rump; wings and tail dusky with narrow yellowish or white edging; bases of wing and tail feathers yellow (often concealed), usually showing as a small wing patch; two whitish or buffy wing bars; under parts, dull white streaked (except on belly) with dusky.

Measurements. *Adult male:* wing, 68.3–76.2 (72.8); tail, 44.9–48.1 (46.5); exposed culmen, 9.8–11.1 (10.6); tarsus, 13.9–14.9 (14.3). *Adult female:* wing, 69–75.8 (71.5) mm.

Field Marks. A small heavily streaked finch with a touch of yellow on the wings and often at the base of the tail. Usually seen in groups or flocks. Its streaked breast distinguishes it from winter goldfinches. Its small yellow patch in the wings, heavily streaked breast, and longer, more pointed bill distinguish it from both species of redpolls. *Voice:* A frequently uttered call is a rather harsh *zwee-e-e-e-e-t*, rising in pitch. It is harsher than a similar call of the redpolls. Song is somewhat goldfinch-like but huskier and more buzzy. Has other goldfinch-like calls.

Habitat. Coniferous and mixed woods of various ages and densities, sometimes ornamental groves and shade trees about towns. Prefers conifers for nesting but forages in both conifers and deciduous trees as well as in shrubbery (especially alders) and at various heights.

Nesting. Usually in a conifer 6 to 40 feet above ground. Nest is of twigs, shredded bark, *Usnea* lichen, grass, and rootlets, and is lined with fine rootlets, hair, or moss. *Eggs,* 3 to 6; pale blue, spotted and speckled with browns and purplish, mainly about the large end. Incubation 13 days (Weaver and West), by the female only.

Range. Breeds in woodlands from southern Alaska east to Newfoundland and south to northern Baja California, and through the Mexican highlands to Guatemala, and in the central and southern United States south to Kansas, northern Pennsylvania, and Connecticut. Winters in the breeding range and south to southern Florida.

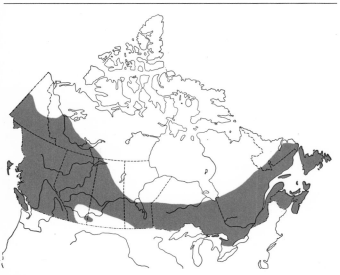

Breeding Distribution of Pine Siskin

Range in Canada. Breeds from central Yukon (Fortymile, Kluane Lake, Watson Lake), central-southern Mackenzie (near Fort Resolution, and northward along Mackenzie Valley to Fort Norman), northwestern and central-eastern Saskatchewan (Lake Athabasca, Nipawin), central-western and southern Manitoba (The Pas, Lake St. Martin), central Ontario (Casummit-Birch lakes, Favourable Lake, Kapuskasing; probably southern James Bay), central Quebec

(Lake Mistassini; Lac Ste. Anne on Toulnustouc River; St. Augustin; has been recorded in summer north rarely to Great Whale River and Knob Lake region), southern Labrador (Hamilton Inlet), and Newfoundland south through wooded parts of southern Canada in British Columbia (including Queen Charlotte and Vancouver islands), Alberta (except where suitable habitat is lacking on southeastern prairies), southern Saskatchewan (very locally: Cypress Hills, Indian Head), southern Manitoba (Spruce Woods Forest Reserve, Julius), southern Ontario (Guelph), southern Quebec (Gatineau Park, Hatley; and including Anticosti and Magdalen islands), New Brunswick, Prince Edward Island, and Nova Scotia (including Cape Breton Island).

Winters within most southern parts of its breeding range (but irregularly; common one year, perhaps absent the next in a given area) but is usually uncommon or rare in winter in Alberta and Saskatchewan.

Subspecies. *Spinus pinus pinus* (Wilson).

Remarks. The Pine Siskin is notable for its erratic comings and goings and unpredictable nesting times. It may be common and breeding in a given locality one year, completely absent the next. Togetherness is strong in their social structure, for they are almost always in flocks of various sizes, even at nesting times. They eat seeds of conifers, birch, and alder; small leaves, buds, and insects.

AMERICAN GOLDFINCH
Le Chardonneret jaune. *Spinus tristis* (Linnaeus)
Plate 64. L. 4.5 to 5.5 in.

Adult male (summer): General colour, canary yellow; crown, forehead, space in front of eyes, and most of wings and tail, black; tail coverts, middle wing coverts, ends of greater coverts, and edging on some of the flight feathers, white; inner webs of the tail feathers whitish toward the tips; legs pale brown; bill, orange-yellow darkening toward the tip. *Adult female (summer):* Upper parts brownish olive tinged with yellowish, especially on rump and scapulars; no black cap; wings and tail similar to those of the adult male, but dusky instead of black and with no yellow on the lesser wing coverts; under parts, greenish yellow but under tail coverts white; bill yellow, darkening toward tip. *Adults in winter:* Yellow is mostly replaced by brownish olive, and the black cap of the male is missing, but the male is distinguishable from the female by more blackish wings, clearer whites in wings, and bright yellow lesser wing coverts. *Immatures in first autumn and first winter* are more brownish than adults; the whitish wing areas are more buffy, and the males throughout their first year lack the bright yellow lesser wing coverts of adult males.

Measurements (*S. t. tristis*). *Adult male:* wing, 69.8–74 (71.9); tail, 42.4–51.5 (48.2); exposed culmen, 9.6–11 (10.1); tarsus, 12.5–14.2 (13.5). *Adult female:* wing, 67.4–73.8 (70.5) mm.

Field Marks. The summer male is a small, bright yellow, stubby-billed bird with black cap, wings, and tail. The Yellow Warbler, another yellow bird, has no black in the plumage and possesses a much slimmer bill. The duller female goldfinch might be confused by beginners with vireos or some warblers, but the goldfinch's stubby bill is very different. Winter goldfinches are much less distinctive (male lacks black cap), but usually they show a suggestion of yellow on head and neck; the wings and tail are blackish with whitish or buffy markings. The stubby bill marks it as a finch, and the completely unstreaked plumage is very different from that of Pine Siskins, most sparrows, the redpolls, and female Purple Finches. At any time of the year it is usually seen in groups or flocks. *Voice:* As it flies (flight is conspicuously undulating), an unmistakable *per-chic-o-ree.* Song is a sustained energetic procession of short trills and twitters with frequent querulous interjections of *sweet* or *swee.*

Habitat. Weedy fields, cultivated lands, roadsides, and similar open weedy places not too far from wood edges or patches, second growths, tall shrubs, or orchards. In nesting season requires open deciduous woods or shrubs.

Nesting. In a tree or shrub, 1 to 20 feet above ground. Trees preferred are scattered ones, in open places, not in extensive forests. The cup-like nest is composed of shredded bark, plant stems, and grass, and is lined with thistledown or other plant downs. *Eggs,* 2 to 7, usually 4 or 6; pale bluish. Incubation period 12 to 14 days (L. H. Walkinshaw), by the female.

Range. Breeds across southern Canada (British Columbia east to southwestern Newfoundland) and south to northern Baja California, southern Colorado, northeastern Texas, northern Louisiana, central Alabama, and South Carolina. Winters from southern Canada and northern United States south to Mexico, the Gulf coast of United States, and southern Florida.

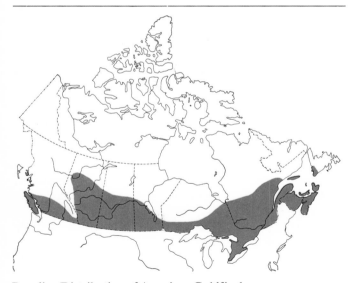

Breeding Distribution of American Goldfinch

Range in Canada. Breeds in southern British Columbia (Port Hardy, Alta Lake, Lytton, Williams Lake Indian Reserve No. 1, Okanagan Valley, Cranbrook, perhaps Alkali Lake), north-central and southern Alberta (Peace River, Athabasca southward), central and southern Saskatchewan (Kazan Lake, Cumberland House southward),

central-western and southern Manitoba (The Pas, Lake St. Martin, Hillside Beach southward), central and southern Ontario (Sioux Lookout, Lake Nipigon, Lake Abitibi, and probably Moose Factory southward), southern Quebec (Amos, Lake St. John, Lac Ste. Anne on Toulnustouc River, Anticosti Island, and Gaspé southward, but status on Magdalen Islands uncertain), and southwestern Newfoundland (Cape Anguille, Doyles), New Brunswick, Prince Edward Island, and Nova Scotia (including Cape Breton Island). Casual at Natashquan, Quebec, and southern Labrador (Cape Mugford).

Winters in southern British Columbia (Esquimalt, Vancouver, Chilliwack, Okanagan Valley), southern Ontario, southwestern Quebec (north to Quebec City region), New Brunswick, and Nova Scotia.

Subspecies. (1) *Spinus tristis tristis* (Linnaeus): Ont., Que., Nfld., N.B., N.S., P.E.I., intergrading with the following race in extreme western Ont. (Ingolf). (2) *S. t. pallidus* Mearns (adult females, winter males, and immatures in winter paler than *tristis,* size slightly larger): interior B.C., Alta., Sask., Man. (3) *S. t. jewetti* van Rossem (winter plumage darker and browner than in *pallidus*): s. coastal B.C. (Vancouver Island, Chilliwack).

Remarks. Everything the Goldfinch does seems to radiate good nature and the joy of living. Its song is lively, almost effervescent; its flight is bouncy and undulating. Many people call it 'wild canary' or 'thistle bird,' the latter because of its fondness for thistle seeds. It also relishes various other kinds of seeds, particularly those of dandelions, and takes some insects as well.

LESSER GOLDFINCH
(Arkansas Goldfinch; Green-backed Goldfinch)
Le Chardonneret mineur. *Spinus psaltria* (Say)
L. 3.8 to 4.5 in.

Form similar to that of American Goldfinch but measurements smaller. *Adult male:* Variable geographically: either with upper parts mostly black (*S. psaltria psaltria*) or with black crown and rest of upper parts dull greenish olive (*S. p. hesperophilus*); wings mostly black with white patch at base of primaries; greater wing coverts tipped white, and tertials margined with white; tail black, the inner webs of the outermost feathers white with black tips; under parts light yellow, paler on under tail coverts. *Adult female:* Olive green above (including rump); wings duller than in male and with white patch at base of primaries more restricted or absent; white in tail restricted to a small white spot on each outer feather or almost imperceptible.

Distinctions. Differs from American Goldfinch in smaller size. Adult male in summer with either black or dull olive upper parts, instead of canary yellow (retains black cap all year); white patch at base of primaries; different tail pattern. Adult female resembles American Goldfinch, but rump is olive like the back, instead of paler.

Range. Breeds from western Oregon, northern Nevada, northern Utah, northern Colorado, and central Texas south to northwestern Peru, Colombia, and northern Venezuela.

Status in Canada. Casual in British Columbia: Indian-point Lake and Huntingdon. Both specimens have been referred to the subspecies *S. p. hesperophilus* (Oberholser).

RED CROSSBILL

Le Bec-croisé rouge. *Loxia curvirostra* Linnaeus
Plate 65. L. 5.5 to 6.5 in.

Bill with tips somewhat elongated and crossed (Fig. 68), the tip of the upper mandible bent downward, the lower upward; tail somewhat notched. No white bars on wings (in North American populations). *Adult male:* General coloration above and below, dull red; brightest on rump, dullest on back where brown feather centres show through; wings and tail, blackish brown; no wing bars; middle of abdomen greyish; under tail coverts grey (the feathers with large dark centres), usually washed with reddish. *Adult female:* General coloration greyish olive, more or less striped and spotted darker, becoming yellow on rump and often on breast and sides; wings and tail, plain blackish brown with narrow pale edges. *Immature male:* Variable, some resembling adult female; many others have various mixtures of yellows, reds, and green. *Juvenals of both sexes:* When they leave the nest, both sexes are pale greyish, more or less tinged with olive or yellowish and conspicuously streaked on head and body with dusky; wings and tail similar to those of adult female.

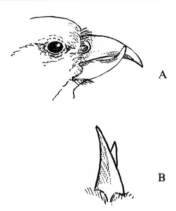

Fig. 68 Bill of Red Crossbill
(A) lateral view
(B) dorsal view

Measurements (*L. c. pusilla* from Newfoundland). *Adult male:* wing, 88.3–97.7 (91.7); tail, 53–59.4 (55.9); exposed culmen, 17–18.6 (17.7); tarsus, 16.3–17.8 (17.1). *Adult female:* wing, 87.2–92.3 (89.5) mm.

Field Marks. Large-headed, heavy-billed House-Sparrow-sized birds, usually seen in flocks in coniferous trees where they feed on the seeds of conifer cones, using both bill and feet like parrots, often hanging upside-down. Adult male reddish; female yellowish grey with yellowish rump. Often tame, sometimes allowing the crossed bill tips to be seen, which mark them as crossbills. The plain wings (no white bars) separate them from White-winged Crossbills. *Voice:* Calls *jip jip*, less harsh and more musical than calls of the White-winged Crossbill. Song loud, shorter than that of the

White-winged, consists of whistled notes, more or less interspersed with warbled phrases (L. de K. Lawrence).

Habitat. Usually coniferous trees, the bird's movements often guided by the abundance or scarcity of the cone crop. Feeds less often on seeds or fruits of deciduous trees and shrubs, e.g., elm, flowering crab, and alder.

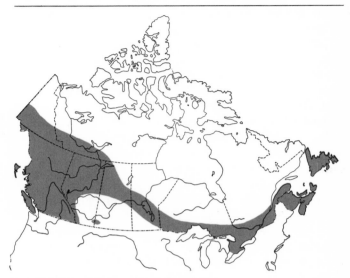

Breeding Distribution of Red Crossbill

Nesting. The nest, which is at various heights, usually in a coniferous tree and well out on a branch, is made of twigs, shreds of bark, weed stems, grass, and is lined with moss, plant down, fur, or feathers. *Eggs*, usually 3 or 4, sometimes 5; pale bluish green, spotted with browns and lavender, mostly at the larger end. Incubation, by the female, is between 12 and 15 days (Ross and Ross), but exact period is not known. Nesting time is erratic; it may breed any time of the year.

Range. Boreal coniferous forests across Eurasia and North America south to northern Spain, northern Africa, islands in the Mediterranean, northern India, southern China, Japan, and the northern Philippines. In North America from southeastern Alaska east to Newfoundland and south in the mountains to northern Baja California, northern Nicaragua, and in eastern United States south to northern Wisconsin, Tennessee, and North Carolina.

Range in Canada. Permanent resident but highly nomadic, its wanderings governed to a large extent by the availability of its staple food, conifer seeds. Nesting time is as erratic as its wanderings and may occur in any month of the year. The breeding range is not well known. Its presence in an area is no guarantee that it is breeding there. Its nesting in a given area is no indication that it will nest there next year or in the next decade, or that it nested there last year. Breeds in coniferous forests of southern Yukon (Kluane, Nisutlin River); southern Mackenzie (Fort Smith, Fort Simpson); British Columbia (throughout, including coastal islands); Alberta (but in the south confined to the Rockies and foothills and the Cypress Hills); northwestern, southwestern, probably central Saskatchewan (Lake Athabasca, Cypress Hills); southern Manitoba (recorded north to Echimamish

River but without evidence of breeding); central and southern Ontario (Lake Manitowick, northern Algoma District; Rutherglen; Algonquin Park; Pakenham; Toronto. Species recorded north to Fort Severn and Sutton River); southern Quebec (Tadoussac, Lac Grand; reportedly wanders to Great Whale River and Natashquan); New Brunswick (Grand Manan, Scotch Lake); Prince Edward Island; Nova Scotia (Wolfville, Halifax, Seabright); and Newfoundland.

Subspecies. (1) *Loxia curvirostra pusilla* Gloger (larger size, general coloration darker): Breeds in Nfld. Wanders, mainly in winter, to Ont., Que., N.B., and N.S. (2) *L. c. minor* (Brehm), smaller with slenderer bill and paler coloration than *pusilla*: Breeds in Ont., Que., N.B., P.E.I., and N.S.; wanders westward, probably breeding, to s. Man., c. and nw. Sask., s. Mack. (Fort Smith). (3) *L. c. bendirei* Ridgway (similar to *minor* but slightly larger, wing and bill longer; reds brighter, more scarlet; greys sootier): sw. Sask. (Cypress Hills), sw. and se. Alta. (Rocky Mts., Cypress Hills), interior B.C., s. Yukon. (4) *L. c. sitkensis* Grinnell, the smallest of our crossbills with stubby bill (culmen 13.5–15 mm): Resident in coastal B.C. but wanders sporadically sometimes in large numbers east as far as N.B. Perhaps has bred in the interior (*see* Griscom, 1937, *Proc. Boston Soc. Nat. Hist.* 41(5): 77–212, for a study of the subspecies of this crossbill.)

WHITE-WINGED CROSSBILL
Le Bec-croisé à ailes blanches. *Loxia leucoptera* Gmelin
Plate 65. L. 6 to 6.75 in.

Bill tips crossed as in Red Crossbill, but bill is thinner. Two white wing bars in all plumages. *Adult male:* General coloration variable red (bright scarlet or vermilion in summer, dull and pinkish in winter); scapulars, area across back, wings, and tail black, the tertials tipped with white; two conspicuous white wing bars; mid-abdomen and flanks greyish, the latter streaked with dusky; under tail coverts blackish with grey margins. *Adult female:* Wings and tail as in adult male: elsewhere mostly olive green or greyish streaked with dusky, the rump clear yellow; breast and sides, washed with yellow and streaked with dusky; rest of under parts, grey streaked with dusky. *Immature male (first winter):* Somewhat resembles adult male, but reds mostly replaced by yellow mixed with more or less red. *Juvenal plumage* (worn only a short time after leaving nest): General coloration, pale greyish or brownish streaked with dusky; wings blackish with two white bars.

Measurements. *Adult male:* wing, 86.2–90.4 (88.0); tail, 57.1–63.5 (60.9); exposed culmen, 15.9–16.9 (16.2); tarsus, 15.9–17 (15.6). *Adult female:* wing, 80.5–87.1 (83.9) mm.

Field Marks. When the crossed mandibles are visible, this species could be confused with only the Red Crossbill, but the conspicuous white wing bars distinguish the White-winged in all plumages. The white wing bars separate it also from the Purple Finch, the much smaller size from the Pine Grosbeak, and the crossed bill tips distinguish it from both. *Voice:* Call *cheet cheet*, much harsher and more strident than corresponding calls of the Red Crossbill and unlike any

other. When heard in chorus, as from a flying flock, it becomes a characteristic, easily recognized chatter. The song is delightful, vigorous, varied, and sustained, containing frequent canary-like trills, as well as harsh rattles and pleasing warbles. The volume changes frequently. The singer perches in the top of a coniferous tree or flies in circles on slowly flapping wings.

Habitat. Open coniferous or mixed woodlands, openings, edges, and groves. Primarily a bird of conifers, it is less inclined to feed in deciduous trees and shrubs than the Red Crossbill.

Nesting. May occur in any month of the year. Nest is placed in a coniferous tree at various heights above the ground. It is constructed of twigs, *Usnea* lichen, and bark shreds, and is lined with grasses, hair, or feathers. Incubation is by the female. Incubation period not known.

Range. Resident in boreal coniferous forests in Eurasia (Scandinavia east to Siberia); in northern North America; and there is an isolated resident population in Hispaniola. In North America breeds from central Alaska eastward across Canada to Labrador and Newfoundland and south in northern United States to northern Oregon, northern Minnesota, northern Michigan, northern New York, northern Vermont, New Hampshire, and Maine.

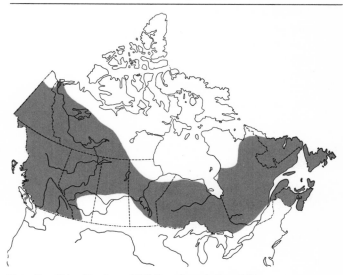

Breeding Distribution of White-winged Crossbill

Range in Canada. Resident in coniferous forests from northern Yukon (Old Crow), northern Mackenzie (Mackenzie Delta, Dease River, Thelon River); northern Saskatchewan (Lake Athabasca, Black Lake region); central Manitoba (The Pas, Grand Rapids); northern Ontario (Fort Severn, Fort Albany); northern Quebec (Great Whale River, Lower Seal Lake, Fort Chimo, Indian House Lake); north-central Labrador (Okak, Hopedale); and Newfoundland south through British Columbia (but scarce on Queen Charlotte and Vancouver islands where nesting is not known); southwestern and central-eastern Alberta; central Saskatchewan (Flotten Lake); southeastern Manitoba (Julius); southern Ontario (Michipicotin River, Head Lake); southern Quebec (La Vérendrye Park, Stoneham, Lac

Rimouski, Gaspé Peninsula; also Anticosti and Magdalen islands); New Brunswick; Prince Edward Island; and Nova Scotia. Winters within the areas included above and wanders somewhat farther south.

Casual in northern Manitoba (Churchill). Accidental in Franklin (southern Baffin Island: Lake Harbour).

Subspecies. *Loxia leucoptera leucoptera* Gmelin.

GREEN-TAILED TOWHEE

Le Tohi à queue verte. *Chlorura chlorura* (Audubon)
L. 6.5 to 7 in.

Bill conical but not heavy; tail quite long (longer than wing), the outer feathers shortest. *Adult male:* Top of head reddish brown; rest of upper parts olive grey; wings and tail mostly yellowish olive green; edge of wing near bend and the under wing coverts, yellow; no wing bars; throat white, forming a large white patch, which is sharply defined against deep grey of breast and sides of head; abdomen white; sides and flanks brownish grey; spot between eye and base of bill (supraloral region) white. *Adult female:* Usually slightly duller than adult male.

Measurements. *Adult male:* wing, 76.4–83.3 (80.0); tail, 79.5–87.2 (83.8); exposed culmen, 12.2–12.9 (12.7); tarsus, 22.6–25.4 (24.1). *Adult female:* wing, 71.1–78.7 (75.9) mm (Adapted from Ridgway).

Distinctions. A long-tailed greyish green bird with large reddish brown cap and large white throat patch, sharply defined against the deep-grey breast and sides of head.

Range. Breeds from central Oregon, southwestern Montana, and Wyoming south through the mountains to southern California, central Arizona, and southern New Mexico.

Status in Canada. Casual or accidental in Saskatchewan (Tregarva, June 6, 1929, and Dollard, May 18, 1944, are supported by specimens; also sight record: Tregarva, June 28, 1935); southern Quebec (St. Augustin west of Quebec City, October 31, 1957: specimen); and Nova Scotia (Cape Sable Island, May 14, 1955: specimen).

Hypothetical in Ontario (sight records only: Welland, London, Terra Cotta).

RUFOUS-SIDED TOWHEE

(Eastern, Red-eyed, and Spotted Towhee)
Le Tohi commun. *Pipilo erythrophthalmus* (Linnaeus)
Plate 66. L. 7.5 to 8.7 in.

Tail rather long (longer than wing); bill conical. Western populations have more white in wing coverts and back; females are much darker brown than in eastern populations. *Adult male* (*Pipilo e. erythrophthalmus* of eastern Canada): Head, neck, upper parts, and upper breast black, the black of upper breast sharply cut off from the white lower breast and abdomen; sides and flanks chestnut, this extending to the under tail coverts, where paler; wings black with a small white patch, formed by the white basal parts of the outer webs of the outermost four or five primaries; tertials with some white outer edges; tail black with large mass of white on terminal part of several outer feathers on each side. Eye

red. *Adult female:* Similar to adult male, but black is replaced by brown. *Young* (for a short time after leaving the nest) are streaked with dusky above and below.

Western races have the wing coverts, scapulars, and back spotted with white, but white is more restricted on the primaries; western females have the head, neck, and upper parts much darker than in the eastern nominate race (a very dark greyish brown or greyish black instead of the more cinnamon brown of eastern birds).

Measurements (*P. e. erythrophthalmus*). *Adult male:* wing, 82–90.5 (86.5); tail, 88–98.2 (93.4); exposed culmen, 12.5–14.2 (13.4); tarsus, 25.6–29 (27.7). *Adult female:* wing, 77.3–89.1 (81.9) mm.

Field Marks. Instantly recognizable. Catbird size with long tail and sparrow-type bill. Black (in male) or brown (in female) head and upper parts, strikingly reddish brown sides, white abdomen sharply cut off from dark breast, large amount of white in the ends of the outer tail feathers. Western populations with more white in back and in wing coverts than eastern birds, and the western females have much darker brown (almost blackish) heads and upper parts. In the East the common call is *to-whee*, second syllable higher; song is two notes followed by a trill and is often thought to sound like *drink your teeeeea*. Voice of western populations is somewhat different but includes a whining nasal alarm note and a song that ends in a buzzy trill (often at a distance only the trill is audible).

Breeding Distribution of Rufous-sided Towhee

Habitat. Bushy areas and thickets with an accumulation of leaf litter on the ground: brushy fields, willow-alder patches, woodland edges and openings. On the prairies, shrubbery along coulees and streams. In the mountains bushy shrubbery on mountainsides and valleys, and on the West Coast shrubby tangles.

Nesting. On the ground or near it in a low bush. Nest is rather loosely made of weed stalks, strips of bark, twigs, and grasses and is lined with fine grasses and rootlets. *Eggs,* 4 to 6; white, speckled with reddish brown and a little lavender. Incubation 12 to 13 days (C.E. Heil).

Range. Breeds from southern Canada (British Columbia east to southwestern Quebec), northern Vermont, central New Hampshire, and southwestern Maine south through Mexico to Guatemala, northern Oklahoma, central-southern Louisiana, the eastern Gulf coast of the United States, and southern Florida. Winters north to southern British Columbia and extreme southern Ontario.

Range in Canada. Breeds in southern British Columbia (Comox, Lillooet, Okanagan Landing, Elko), southern Alberta (east of the Mountains: Lethbridge, Calgary, Morrin, Rosebud; perhaps north to Coronation and Wainwright), southern Saskatchewan (Cypress Hills, Elbow, Carlton), southern Manitoba (Treesbank, Winnipeg), southern Ontario (north to Sudbury, North Bay, Ottawa), and extreme southwestern Quebec (Ormstown).

Casual in Quebec City, Isle aux Basques, and lower Moisie River, Quebec; New Brunswick (Irishtown, Fredericton, Gannet Rock); Nova Scotia (Northport, Greenfield); and Newfoundland (Corner Brook).

Subspecies. (1) *Pipilo erythrophthalmus erythrophthalmus* (Linnaeus), described above: Man., Ont., Que. (2) *P. e. arcticus* (Swainson) (resembles *erythrophthalmus* but wing coverts, scapulars, and back spotted with white; females with head and upper parts blackish brown): Alta., Sask. (3) *P. e. curtatus* Grinnell (similar to *arcticus* but blacks purer, less olivaceous): interior s. B.C. (Lillooet, Elko). (4) *P. e. oregonus* Bell (similar to *curtatus* but coloration darker): coastal sw. B.C. (Comox, Chilliwack).

LARK BUNTING
Le Pinson noir et blanc
Calamospiza melanocorys Stejneger
Plate 66. L. 6 to 7.5 in.

Bill quite large, deeper than broad at its base. *Adult male (summer):* Mostly plain black, the middle and greater wing coverts white, forming a contrasting patch; tertials edged with white; some white on tips of inner webs of some tail feathers; bill bluish grey. *Adult female:* Upper parts greyish brown streaked with dusky; wings and tail dusky, wing patch much smaller and more buffy than that of the male; white spot near tip of inner web of some tail feathers; sides of head with pale line over eye and brownish ear patch; under parts white, the breast and sides streaked with dusky and with a blackish line down either side of throat. *Adult male (winter):* Similar to adult female, but wing patch larger, with traces of black showing through, especially on breast or throat. *Juvenal* (shortly after leaving nest): Similar to adult female but feathers of upper parts more buffy and paler, the back more scaly, the under parts with finer streaks.

Measurements. *Adult male:* wing, 84.7–90.6 (87.9); tail, 64.8–68 (66.2); exposed culmen, 11.6–15 (13.5); tarsus, 22.9–26 (24.8). *Adult female:* wing, 81.8–85 (83.3) mm.

Field Marks. Adult male in summer, a black bird of the western prairies (slightly larger than the House Sparrow) with a conspicuous white patch in the wing. Could be confused only with the Bobolink, but the latter has white on the back but not in the wings. Females, young, and winter males are brown-and-white-streaked sparrows with a pale line over the eye. They look a little like the female Purple Finch but usually show a white or buff patch in the wing which distinguishes them from the Purple Finch and other similar birds. Habitat preferences, too, are very different from those of the Purple Finch. *Voice:* Song is delightful and varied, containing whistles, trills, and some repetitions of *wack wack wack*. It is given either when the singer is perched, or when the bird half-floats to the ground with peculiar slow flaps of fully extended wings.

Habitat. Drier treeless plains and prairies, especially where the grasses have a considerable admixture of sagebrush.

Nesting. On the ground, often under a small shrub or tuft of grass. Nest is rather loosely constructed of grass and rootlets. *Eggs*, 4 to 6; pale blue, usually unmarked.

Range. Breeds from southern Alberta, southern Saskatchewan, southwestern Manitoba, and southwestern Minnesota south (east of the Rockies) to southeastern New Mexico, western Oklahoma, and Kansas. Winters from southern California, central Arizona, and north-central Texas to central Mexico.

Breeding Distribution of Lark Bunting

Range in Canada. Breeds in southern Alberta (east of the Rockies: west to Calgary and Fort Macleod; north to about Sibbald, Castor, and Youngstown), southern Saskatchewan (Crane Lake, Regina, Indian Head, Kindersley), and southwestern Manitoba (Brandon). There is a tendency for the breeding range to expand temporarily during periods of dry summers.

Casual in southern British Columbia (Chilliwack, Okanagan Landing, Ootsa Lake, Kootenay National Park), central Saskatchewan (Carlton, Prince Albert, Nipawin), eastern Manitoba (Hillside Beach). Accidental in eastern Ontario (Lowbush, June 5, 1925; sight record Toronto, September 21, 1941), and New Brunswick (Nantucket Island, August 15, 1910).

Sight records only for Quebec (Seven Islands) and Nova Scotia (Brier Island, Lansdowne Station, Cape Sable Island, Lawrencetown Beach).

381

IPSWICH SPARROW

Le Pinson d'Ipswich. *Passerculus princeps* Maynard
Plate 66. L. 5.9 to 6.5 in.

A large, pale, greyish edition of the Savannah Sparrow. In autumn and winter the yellow coloration over eye and on bend of wing is very faint or absent.

Measurements. *Adult male:* wing, 72.4–82.5 (76.4); tail, 52.8–64.8 (56.1); exposed culmen, 10.4–10.9 (10.6); tarsus, 21.6–24.1 (22.9). *Adult female:* wing, 72.4–82.5 (76.9) mm (Adapted from Ridgway).

Field Marks. A very pale greyish sparrow, the general coloration superficially suggesting a Vesper Sparrow, but without any white in the tail. Similar to the Savannah Sparrow but larger, paler, more greyish; in autumn and winter with little or no yellow over eye. *Voice:* Song is similar to that of the Savannah Sparrow but keyed slightly lower and ending with more of a trill (Dwight), slightly more musical (J. J. Elliott).

Habitat. Coastal sand dunes and upper beaches.

Nesting. On the ground in a cup-shaped hollow, scratched out in the sand and usually under a shrub or tuft of grass. Nest is of grass and weed stalks lined with fine grasses. *Eggs*, usually 4 or 5; greyish white or bluish white, broadly marked or splashed with brown and often a little purplish.

Range. Breeds on Sable Island, Nova Scotia. Winters along the Atlantic Coast south to southern Georgia and north to the peninsula of Nova Scotia.

Range in Canada. Breeds only on Sable Island, off Nova Scotia. Small numbers winter in Nova Scotia (Sable Island, Wolfville, Martinique Beach).

Migrates in spring and autumn, in small numbers at least, through western Nova Scotia (Grand Pré Meadows, Summerville Beach, Martinique Beach) and in spring at least through southern New Brunswick (Grand Manan, Kent Island, Point Lepreau, Saint John).

Remarks. Throughout its lifetime, the Ipswich Sparrow is rarely far from the pounding surf. Its winters are spent in a narrow coastal strip of beaches and sand dunes between Nova Scotia and Georgia. In summer it is restricted to lonely Sable Island — a desolate, treeless stretch of shifting sand in the Atlantic Ocean, sixty miles off Nova Scotia. Thus it has the smallest breeding range of all Canadian birds.

Over the years, this unassuming sparrow has survived more perils than most land birds are called upon to face. Its spring migration to Sable Island, a tiny fog-shrouded dot in the stormy Atlantic Ocean, demands accurate navigation as well as the strong flying ability necessary to combat buffeting winds that would carry it off-target to its death.

Its small insular breeding grounds have been subjected to man's unwise introduction of rabbits, which depleted the sparse vegetation; of cats (thirty or more were introduced at one time), which depleted the rabbits; and of foxes, which in one season obliterated both the cats and the rabbits. The Ipswich Sparrow withstood the ravages of these introduced predators and lived to see their extirpation on Sable Island. Currently it seems to be maintaining its numbers satisfactorily.

Unfortunately the greatest peril of all is still ahead for the Ipswich Sparrow. Its summer home, sandy Sable Island, is gradually being washed away and within the next few hundred years will probably disappear altogether. Will the Ipswich Sparrow go with it? Its chances for long survival seem slim.

SAVANNAH SPARROW

Le Pinson des prés. *Passerculus sandwichensis* (Gmelin)
Plate 66. L. 5 to 5.8 in.

Bill conical but rather slender; culmen nearly straight; wings longer than tail; tail very slightly forked, tail feathers with more or less pointed tips (except when worn). *Adults (sexes similar):* Upper parts brown, the top of head and back streaked with whitish, buffy, and black; narrow median crown-streak, yellowish white; a yellow stripe over and in front of eye; cheeks brownish; wings and tail dusky with light brown edges but without any white areas; bend of wing, yellowish; under parts white, the sides of throat, breast, sides, and flanks streaked sharply with blackish brown and medium brown; a buffy or whitish stripe across jaw (malar region) bordered above and below by a blackish line; bill dusky, pale at base of lower mandible; legs flesh colour. *Young (first winter plumage):* Similar to adults but decidedly more buffy. *Juvenal plumage:* Resembles adults but much more strongly buffy or yellowish.

Measurements (*P. s. savanna*). *Adult male:* wing, 68.3–73.2 (70.5); tail, 49.9–54.8 (51.9); exposed culmen, 9.8–11.3 (10.6); tarsus, 20.1–21.8 (20.9). *Adult female:* wing, 62–68.1 (65.2) mm.

Field Marks. A streaked sparrow of open places, especially grassy fields. Resembles the Song Sparrow but has a yellowish line over the eye; a narrow yellowish white streak in centre of crown; a much shorter, slightly forked tail (Song Sparrow has a rounded tail); and more pinkish legs. In the Prairie Provinces *see* Baird's Sparrow. *Voice:* Song is a lisping *tsip tsip tsip tsip tse-wheeeeeeeeee-you* (the *wheeee* is trilled, the final *you* abrupt and much lower). Alarm note *tsip.*

Habitat. Open areas, especially moist grasslands such as hayfields and meadows; marshes (either fresh or salt), bogs, grassy sand dunes, and grassy streamsides. Areas with herbaceous plants or clumps of shrubbery are popular, but extensive tree cover is avoided.

Nesting. On the ground, in a hollow scratched out by the birds, usually sheltered by grass, a shrub, or a small tree. Nest is of grass and plant stems, occasionally some moss, and is lined with fine grasses. *Eggs*, usually 4 to 6; whitish, variously spotted and splashed with browns and often a little purplish. Sometimes the browns hide most of the ground colour. Incubation period 12 days (R. S. Palmer).

Range. Breeds from northern Alaska east to northern Labrador and Newfoundland and south to southern Baja California, southern Mexico, and Guatemala; and in eastern United States south to Missouri, Indiana, Ohio, West Virginia, western Maryland, and southeastern Pennsylvania.

Range in Canada. Breeds from northern Yukon (Herschel Island), northern Mackenzie (Richards Island, Coronation

Gulf, lower Perry River), northern Keewatin (Back River, Chesterfield Inlet), northern Manitoba (Churchill), northern Ontario (Fort Severn, Cape Henrietta Maria), islands in James Bay, northern Quebec (Sugluk, mouth of Koksoak River, George River), northern Labrador (Ramah southward), and Newfoundland south through southern British Columbia (including Vancouver Island), Alberta, Saskatchewan, Manitoba, Ontario, Quebec (including Anticosti and Magdalen islands), New Brunswick, Prince Edward Island, and Nova Scotia.

Winters in small numbers in southwestern British Columbia, extreme southern Ontario, and Nova Scotia.

Casual on Southampton Island and Pelly Bay, N.W.T. Accidental on Cornwallis Island (Resolute Bay, September 4, 1954), N.W.T.

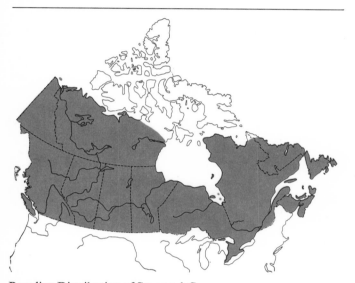

Breeding Distribution of Savannah Sparrow

Subspecies. (1) *Passerculus sandwichensis labradorius* Howe, coloration dark and brownish: Nfld., Lab., n. Que. (Ungava Bay south at least to s. James Bay, Lake St. John, and the north shore of the Gulf of St. Lawrence), n. Ont. (south to Biscotasing, North Bay). (2) *P. s. savanna* (Wilson), paler than either *labradorius* or *oblitus*, browner than *oblitus*: breeds in N.S., P.E.I., N.B., Magdalen Is. (3) *P. s. mediogriseus* Aldrich, darker and somewhat more brownish than *savanna*: s. Ont. (Bigwood southward), s. Que. (Eastern Townships, Gaspé Pen. (4) *P. s. oblitus* Peters and Griscom, coloration dark, more greyish (less brownish) than *savanna* and *labradorius*: Keewatin, Man., w. Ont. (5) *P. s. brooksi* Bishop, smallest of the races, intermediate in colour between *anthinus* and *nevadensis*: nw. coastal B.C. (Vancouver Island, Sumas, Rainbow Mts.). (6) *P. s. anthinus* Bonaparte, bill slenderer than in eastern races, somewhat more brownish than *oblitus*: n. Yukon, n. Mack. (east to Perry River, Thelon River) and south to interior s.-c. B.C. (149 Mile Cariboo Road, Nulki Lake). (7) *P. s. nevadensis* Grinnell, very pale and grey, bill slender: s. interior B.C. (where not typical), c.-e. B.C. (Peace River parklands), Alta., Sask., sw. and c.-w. Man. (The Pas, Lake St. Martin, Whitewater Lake). (8) *P. s. sandwichensis* (Gmelin), migrant and

winter visitor to sw. B.C. (Vancouver Island, Vancouver) from breeding grounds in Alaska.

Remarks. In hayfields all across the country this is often the commonest sparrow. It is primarily a ground bird. It feeds and nests on the ground, but it perches on fence posts, wires, bushes, and trees as well. Its flight is low, swift, slightly undulating, and it terminates typically with the bird dropping suddenly back into the grass. The weak insect-like song may be given at any daylight hour but is especially frequent in the dusk of a calm summer evening. The Savannah Sparrow devours large quantities of weed seeds and insects and is a valuable bird to have about the farm.

GRASSHOPPER SPARROW

Le Pinson sauterelle. *Ammodramus savannarum* (Gmelin) Plate 65. L. 4.8 to 5.4 in.

Bill relatively heavier than in Savannah Sparrow; lesser wing coverts greenish yellow, thus different from other Canadian sparrows; tail feathers somewhat pointed. *Adults (breeding plumage):* Top of head mostly blackish, finely streaked with buffish or greyish and with a broad median stripe of greyish buff; rest of upper parts mixed greyish, buffy, chestnut, and black, the black most apparent on back and scapulars; hind-neck greyish, streaked with chestnut; wings dusky, edged with buffy grey; lesser wing coverts greenish yellow; bend of wing bright yellow; tail dusky, edged with buffy grey, the outer tail feathers paler than the inner ones; sides of head buffy, yellowish in front of eye, with a narrow dark streak extending backward from eye; under parts buff, paling to whitish on abdomen; bill pale bluish with dusky ridge; legs flesh colour. *Adults (winter):* Similar to breeding adults but brighter, the upper parts with more chestnut and less black, the under parts more buffy, the breast sometimes lightly streaked with reddish brown. *Juvenal plumage:* Scapulars tipped with russet spots; under parts dull buffy white, the breast distinctly streaked with dusky; no yellow over eye or on edge of wing.

Measurements (*A. s. pratensis*). *Adult male:* wing, 60–63.4 (61.6); tail, 43–47 (44.7); exposed culmen, 11–12.4 (11.6); tarsus, 17.8–21 (19.3). *Adult female:* wing, 58.4–62.7 (60.2) mm.

Field Marks. A small, rather short-tailed grass sparrow, the adults with buffy unstreaked breasts and unstreaked sides. Other similar sparrows of open fields have definite streaks on sides. It has a peculiar flat-headed appearance. *Voice:* Two main songs: (1) a short (one to three seconds) insect-like buzz which is preceded by one or two *chips*. (2) a sustained song, a jumble of squeaky, wiry notes. Singing is most frequent in early morning and late evening.

Habitat. Old fields, hayfields, and prairies with clumps of grass and weeds (preferably with last year's grass still standing). Situations are usually drier than those chosen by Savannah Sparrow.

Nesting. On the ground, the nest well hidden in grass or other vegetation and often arched over. Nest is made of grass and lined with fine grasses and hairs. *Eggs,* usually 4 or 5; white, spotted with reddish brown mainly about the larger end.

Range. Southern Canada (interior southern British Columbia east to southwestern Quebec), northern Vermont, central New Hampshire, and Maine south of southern California, Arizona, Colorado, central Texas, Arkansas, central Gulf states, and Florida; also from southern Mexico to central Panama, western Colombia, and Ecuador, Jamaica, Puerto Rico, Curaçao, and Bonaire. Winters from southern United States southward.

Breeding Distribution of Grasshopper Sparrow

Range in Canada. Breeds in central-southern British Columbia (Okanagan Valley, formerly at least), southern Alberta (Lost River valley, Calgary), southern Saskatchewan (15 miles north of Maple Creek; Regina; Earl Grey), southern Manitoba (Whitewater Lake, West Shoal Lake, Winnipeg), southern Ontario (north to Manitoulin Island and Ottawa; perhaps Fort William) and southwestern Quebec (Hull, Chambly Basin, Huntingdon).

Casual near Quebec City, Quebec; New Brunswick (Grand Manan); Prince Edward Island (5 miles northeast of St. Peters); and Newfoundland (Rose Blanche, Cape Race).

Subspecies. (1) *Ammodramus savannarum pratensis* (Vieillot): s. Ont., sw. Que. (2) *A. s. perpallidus* (Coues), with paler coloration, wing and tail longer, bill smaller: s. B.C., s. Alta., s. Sask., s. Man.

BAIRD'S SPARROW

Le Pinson de Baird. *Ammodramus bairdii* (Audubon)
Plate 65. L. 5 to 5.8 in.

Adults (female somewhat duller than male): Head suffused with buffy or ochraceous, deepest on crown and nape, palest (often white) on throat; top of head streaked with black, mostly on sides of crown leaving a rich buffy median stripe (less obvious in female); sides of head with two narrow black lines, one across lower jaw, one on side of throat; rest of upper parts light brown with blackish spots and streaks and with much feather edging of buff and white; wings, greyish brown edged with buff or pale rufous; tail

mostly dark brown edged with pale buff, the outer feather on each side buffy white terminally (less extensive in female); under parts white with buffy wash across breast and often on throat, and with sharply defined but well-spaced streaks of black or dark brown on breast (forming a sparse necklace) and sides; bill flesh colour, dusky near tip; legs brownish flesh. *Juvenals* resemble adults, but the feathers of the back are margined with white giving a scaly appearance; streaks on breast less sharply defined.

Measurements. *Adult male:* wing, 70–73.4 (71.6); tail, 49–53.8 (50.7); exposed culmen, 10.6–12 (11.4); tarsus, 20.9–22.3 (21.6). *Adult female:* wing, 66.3–70.5 (68.3) mm.

Field Marks. A sparrow of the prairies, somewhat suggesting a pale Savannah Sparrow. The strong buffy coloration of crown and nape and much sparser breast streaks distinguish it from the Savannah. The outer tail feathers, especially those of the male, often look whitish, particularly in flight. *Voice:* Song is two, three, or more *zips* followed by a musical little trill on a lower pitch.

Habitat. Dry grassy areas where the grass is fairly long and often where scattered low shrubs are present for singing perches; weedy fields, wheat fields, and in dry years on the bottoms of dried-out sloughs.

Nesting. On the ground among grass, either under grass or a low shrub or without overhead protection. Nest is of grass lined with finer grasses and occasionally hairs or setae of mosses. *Eggs*, 4 to 6; white, spotted and blotched with reddish brown, mostly about the larger end. Incubation period 11 days, by the female (Cartwright, Shortt, and Harris).

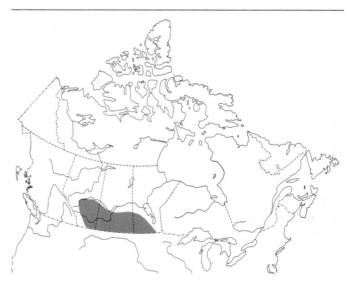

Breeding Distribution of Baird's Sparrow

Range. Breeds from southern Alberta east to southern Manitoba and south to Montana, central South Dakota, southeastern North Dakota, and central-western Minnesota. Winters from southern Arizona and New Mexico south to northern Mexico.

Range in Canada. Breeds in southeastern Alberta (north to Beaverhill Lake, west to Calgary), southern Saskatchewan (Maple Creek, Regina, Saskatoon, head of Last Mountain Lake; observed in summer north to Manito Lake, Redberry Lake, and Nipawin), and southern Manitoba (Swan River, Lake St. Martin, Winnipeg).

Casual at Grand Rapids, Manitoba.

LE CONTE'S SPARROW
Le Pinson de Le Conte
Passerherbulus caudacutus (Latham)
Plate 65. L. 4.5 to 5.3 in.

Bill rather slender; tail feathers narrow and sharply pointed. *Adults:* Top of head blackish and brown on either side, with a pale buff stripe down the middle of the crown; hind-neck striped with chestnut and buffy grey; back and scapulars, black mixed with brown, the feathers edged with pale buff, pale grey, or whitish; broad stripe over eye, buffy yellow; narrow line extending back from eye, blackish; ear patch greyish, malar region buffy yellow; no wing bars; no white in tail; bend of wing, white or whitish; breast, sides, and flanks buffy; sides and flanks (but not breast) streaked with blackish; bill bluish; legs dusky flesh colour. *Juvenal:* Similar to adults but more buffy yellowish, hind-neck with little or no chestnut, instead mostly yellowish; breast streaked with blackish.

Measurements. *Adult male:* wing, 50–55.3 (52.3); tail, 44.8–51 (48.1); exposed culmen, 9.6–11.5 (10.7); tarsus, 17–19.1 (18.0). *Adult female:* wing, 47.7–54.3 (50.8) mm.

Field Marks. A small short-tailed grass sparrow with very buffy eyebrow stripe; greyish ear region, plain buffy breast, but with the sides streaked with black. Most like the Sharp-tailed Sparrow but median crown stripe pale buff (instead of grey), hind-neck pinkish (instead of plain dark grey). Its sharply streaked sides and grey ear region (sometimes obscure and hard to see) separate it from the Grasshopper Sparrow. *Voice:* A short insect-like buzz: *tse bzzzzz*, about one second long.

Habitat. Moist grass and sedge meadows, damp thickly-matted grass and shrub tangles on edges of marshes and bogs, areas of tall rank grass either moist or dry.

Breeding Distribution of Le Conte's Sparrow

Nesting. On the ground or a few inches above it in a clump of dead grass and usually concealed by a tangle of vegetation. *Eggs,* 4 or 5; greenish white speckled with browns mainly at the larger end. Incubation period 13 days, by the female (L. H. Walkinshaw).

Range. Breeds from southern Mackenzie east to western Ontario and south to north-central Montana, North Dakota, Minnesota, northern Michigan, and southern Ontario. Winters south of the breeding range in central and southern United States.

Range in Canada. Breeds in southwestern and central-southern Mackenzie (Fort Simpson, Little Buffalo River), central-eastern British Columbia (Peace River parklands; probably in the Cariboo: 115 Mile House), Alberta (south to northeastern Waterton Lakes Park and Brooks, but local in the south), northwest-central, and very locally, in southern Saskatchewan (Lake Athabasca, Churchill River, Davidson, Indian Head), central and southern Manitoba (The Pas, Lake St. Martin, Hillside Beach southward), north-central to southern Ontario (Lakehead area, Attawapiskat Post, Big Piskwanish, East Point; Bradford, probably Toronto. Irregularly and locally in the south) and Quebec (Amos region; St. Fulgence, Saguenay River).

Recorded in migration at Beaupré, Quebec (May 21, 1935).

HENSLOW'S SPARROW
Le Pinson de Henslow
Passerherbulus henslowii (Audubon)
Plate 65. L. 4.7 to 5.3 in.

Bill rather stout; tail feathers narrow and pointed. *Adults:* Top of head, hind-neck, and sides of neck, pale olive greenish; two blackish stripes on crown on either side of a pale median crown stripe; back and scapulars chestnut and black, the feathers narrowly edged with white; rump chestnut brown with blackish feather centres; wings and tail tinged with chestnut brown and with blackish feather centres; bend of wing yellow; a narrow dark streak back from eye, another back from base of bill across jaw, and a narrow one on either side of throat; a dark area on ear region; under parts whitish, the breast, sides, and flanks decidedly buffy and streaked with blackish; bill brownish paling to flesh colour below; legs flesh.

Measurements (*P. h. henslowii*). *Adult male:* wing, 50.3–54.5 (52.9); tail, 46.1–51 (49.2); exposed culmen, 10.9–12.5 (11.6); tarsus, 16–17 (16.4). *Adult female:* wing, 49–55.4 (52.6) mm.

Field Marks. Another short-tailed flat-headed sparrow, this one frequenting upland fields. Its streaked breast, greenish hind-neck, and more chestnut wings distinguish it from the Grasshopper Sparrow. Its greenish hind-neck distinguishes it also from other similar sparrows such as Baird's, Le Conte's, and Sharp-tailed. Its song is the best means of recognizing it. *Voice:* Song, unlike that of any other Canadian bird, is ridiculously short and unmusical, a simple *tse-slick* with the accent on the second syllable. It sings most often at dusk; also regularly at night and on cloudy days; less often in the heat of sunny mid-day.

Habitat. Open fields and meadows in which the grass is interspersed with weeds (usually unmowed fields are preferred). Frequently the fields are damp and low-lying.

Nesting. Often in small loose colonies. Nest is most often on the ground, sheltered by a tuft of grass or a weed; occasionally 6 to 20 inches above ground in a weed or clump of grass. Nest is a loosely woven cup of grasses, often arched-over with grass. Incubation period 10 to 11 days, by the female (A. S. Hyde).

Range. Breeds locally from eastern South Dakota, central Minnesota, central Michigan, southern Ontario, southern Vermont, and New Hampshire south to eastern Kansas, southern Illinois, northern Kentucky, and North Carolina. Winters from southeastern Texas east to Florida and on the Atlantic coastal plain from South Carolina to central Florida.

Breeding Distribution of Henslow's Sparrow

Range in Canada. Breeds locally in southern Ontario (north to Ottawa, probably Manitoulin Island; east at least to Morrisburg). It has recently extended its breeding range north to Ottawa. Has been recorded in Quebec (Hull, Eccles Hill, Montreal).

Subspecies. *Passerherbulus henslowii henslowii* (Audubon).

SHARP-TAILED SPARROW
Le Pinson à queue aiguë. *Ammospiza caudacuta* (Gmelin) Plate 65. L. 5 to 5.8 in.

Bill slender for a sparrow; tail rather short (shorter than folded wings), its feathers narrow and sharply pointed. *Adults:* Top of head with broad median stripe of brownish grey, this bordered on either side by a blackish brown stripe; rest of upper parts olive grey, the back and scapulars conspicuously striped with blackish brown and a little white; sides of head rich buff with grey ear patch, a narrow blackish line back from the eye; no wing bars or tail patches; bend of wing yellow; under parts whitish but breast, sides, and flanks buffy and streaked with dusky; bill bluish dusky; legs pale brownish. *Juvenal:* General colour rich

buff, broadly streaked above with blackish and narrowly on sides and flanks, sometimes on breast.

Measurements (*A. c. subvirgata*). *Adult male:* wing, 57.8–60.4 (59.1); tail, 48.4–54.6 (50.3); exposed culmen, 11.7–12.3 (12.0); tarsus, 20.8–22.1 (21.6). *Adult female:* wing, 53.7–59 (56.0) mm.

Field Marks. A small, short-tailed sparrow with very buffy face, greyish ear patch, dark grey centre of crown, grey hind-neck, black and white stripes on back, buffy breast lightly striped (*see* Subspecies). The broad dark grey centre of crown and more contrastingly striped (with black and white) back distinguishes it from similar species like Henslow's, Grasshopper, Le Conte's, and Baird's sparrows. Also it frequents wetter habitats. Flight is buzzy and slow, the short wings beating rapidly. The Sharp-tailed Sparrow most closely resembles the Le Conte's but has a dark *grey* middle crown, *grey* hind-neck, and lightly streaked breast. *Voice:* Song is a short *te-sheeeeeeeeee;* the *sheee*-part highest-pitched, bubbly, and ending abruptly.

Habitat. On the coast, salt and brackish marshes (including wet *Spartina* areas), grassy meadows in the vicinity of salt water. In the western interior, margins of pools, lakes, and marshes, usually preferring a wetter habitat than that of the Le Conte's Sparrow.

Nesting. In loose colonies. On the ground in tall grass. Nest is made of grasses with a lining of finer grasses. *Eggs,* 4 to 6; pale greenish or bluish white, speckled thickly with browns. Incubation is by the female.

Breeding Distribution of Sharp-tailed Sparrow

Range. Breeds locally from southern Mackenzie and central Manitoba south to central Alberta, North Dakota, northeastern South Dakota, and northwestern Minnesota; also on southern James Bay; lower St. Lawrence River; and from northern New Brunswick south on the coast to North Carolina. Winters on the Atlantic Coast from New York south to southern Florida and on the Gulf of Mexico coast from southern Texas east to Florida.

Range in Canada. Summer resident, breeding (very locally) in southern Mackenzie (southwestern Great Slave

Lake), central-eastern British Columbia (Peace River parklands), northern and south-central Alberta (Dixonville, southern Slave River, and southward to about Red Deer but not in the mountains), central and southern Saskatchewan (Emma Lake, Cypress Lake, Davidson, probably Regina), central and southern Manitoba (The Pas, Riding Mountain, Carberry, Shelley, Caliento, Sprague), northern Ontario (coast of James Bay north to Cape Henrietta Maria), central-western and central-southern Quebec (in three widely disjunct areas. Coast of James Bay: north at least to Eastmain; lower St. Lawrence River: Ile aux Grues, St. Germain, L'Isle Verte; also Magdalen Islands), and along the coasts of New Brunswick, Prince Edward Island, and Nova Scotia (including Cape Breton Island).

Migrant in southern Ontario and southwestern Quebec (Lochaber).

Subspecies. (1) *Ammospiza caudacuta subvirgata* (Dwight): lower St. Lawrence R. and Magdalen Is., Que.; also N.B., P.E.I., and N.S. (2) *A. c. altera* Todd (much more richly coloured than *subvirgata* but less so than *nelsoni*; intermediate between the two): e. and w. coast of James Bay. (3) *A. c. nelsoni* (Allen) (more richly coloured than *altera*, buffs more intense, back more brownish, general coloration darker): s. Mack., c.-e. B.C., Alta., Sask., Man.

SEASIDE SPARROW

Le Pinson maritime. *Ammospiza maritima* (Wilson)
L. 5.2 to 6.5 in.

A salt-marsh sparrow. Form similar to that of the Sharp-tailed Sparrow but larger (especially bill), much duller and greyer (little or no buff anywhere); yellow line in front of eye and often extending back over it; pale streak across jaw; back not conspicuously streaked.

Status in Canada. Casual in Nova Scotia (West Lawrencetown, Halifax County; February 5, 1962, specimen collected by C. R. K. Allen and L. B. MacPherson). The subspecies of this specimen has not yet been determined.

Range. Atlantic coastal salt marshes from Massachusetts south to northern Florida and from central peninsular Florida along the Gulf of Mexico coast to southern Texas.

VESPER SPARROW

Le Pinson vespéral. *Pooecetes gramineus* (Gmelin)
Plate 66. L. 5.5 to 6.7 in.

Bill conical. *Adults* (slightly paler in breeding season than in winter): Upper parts greyish brown or brownish grey, streaked with dusky; eye-ring whitish; cheek patch brownish; lesser wing coverts reddish brown; two vague buffy wing bars; tail mostly dark brown, the outermost feather on each side and one feather, sometimes two, next to it with some white; under parts dull white; the side of throat, breast, sides, and flanks streaked with dusky, sometimes tinged with buffy; bill mostly dusky or brownish above, flesh colour below; legs flesh colour.

Measurements (*P. g. gramineus*). *Adult male:* wing, 79.6–83.1 (81.7); tail, 54.3–64.2 (60.9); exposed culmen, 11.1–12.1

(11.6); tarsus, 20.3–21.2 (20.7). *Adult female:* wing, 75.3–82.3 (78.5) mm.

Field Marks. A streaked brownish grey sparrow with *white outer tail feathers conspicuous in flight*. Face has a noticeable cheek patch and a narrow white eye-ring. The reddish brown lesser wing coverts (near bend of wing) are diagnostic when they can be seen. Juncos also have white outer tail feathers, but their dark slate upper parts distinguish them at a glance. Pipits, with similar tails, are slender-billed tail waggers, and they walk instead of hopping (*see also* longspurs). *Voice:* Song begins with two similar clear unhurried whistles, followed by higher ones and then by a descending jumble of twitters and trills.

Habitat. Grassy and weedy fields, pastures, prairies, clearings, roadsides, gravel pits, and similar open, weedy, fairly dry situations. Much activity is on or near the ground. Bushes, weeds, fence posts, and trees are used as singing posts and retreats.

Nesting. On the ground either hidden by a tuft of grass or a weed, or in the open. Nest is of grasses, rootlets, occasionally some weed stems, and is lined with fine grasses or horse hair. *Eggs*, usually 3 to 5; whitish, speckled and scrawled, sometimes thickly, with various browns and sometimes a little purplish grey. Incubation period 11 to 13 days (Knight, Burns), 13 to 14 days (Bryant).

Range. Breeds from interior British Columbia east to Nova Scotia and south to central-eastern California, central Arizona, central New Mexico, central Missouri, Tennessee, and North Carolina. Winters from southwestern United States, southern Illinois, West Virginia, southern Pennsylvania, and Connecticut south to southern Mexico, the Gulf of Mexico coast, and central Florida.

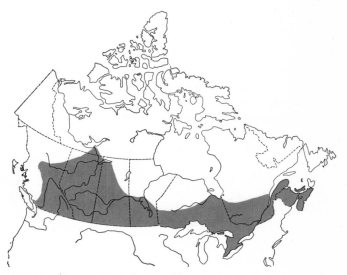

Breeding Distribution of Vesper Sparrow

Range in Canada. Summer resident, breeding in central and southern British Columbia (mostly east of the coast: François Lake, Peace River parklands southward); southern Mackenzie (probably Fort Smith, Fort Simpson); northern, central, and southern Alberta; central and southern Saskatchewan (Lake Athabasca, Nipawin southward); central and southern Manitoba (The Pas, Lake St. Martin, Hillside Beach southward); central and southern Ontario (Malachi, Sioux Lookout, Lake Nipigon, and Moose Factory southward); southern Quebec (La Sarre, Amos, Lake St. John, and Gaspé Peninsula southward but status on Magdalen Islands uncertain); New Brunswick; Prince Edward Island; and Nova Scotia (but occurrence on Cape Breton Island hypothetical).

In migration it is occasional in south coastal British Columbia (Alta Lake, Chilliwack).

Occasionally winters in Nova Scotia and extreme southern Ontario.

Casual on inner north shore of the Gulf of St. Lawrence (Lower Moisie River, Quebec, April 24, 1959).

Subspecies. (1) *Pooecetes gramineus gramineus* (Gmelin): e. Ont., Que., N.B. P.E.I., N.S. (2) *P. g. confinis* Baird (averages paler and greyer than *gramineus*): B.C., Alta., Mack., Sask., Man., w. Ont. (Wabigoon, Rainy River).

LARK SPARROW

Le Pinson à joues marron. *Chondestes grammacus* (Say)
Plate 66. L. 5.7 to 6.8 in.

Bill conical; wings longish, pointed; tail rounded, rather long but shorter than wing. *Adults (sexes similar):* Top of head chestnut, divided by a whitish median stripe, the chestnut becoming blackish on forehead; rest of upper parts greyish brown, the back and scapulars streaked with dark brown; sides of head white with a chestnut ear patch, a thin black line through the eye, a black line joining ear patch with base of bill and another along side of throat; two inconspicuous buffy wing bars; tail brownish to blackish, all feathers except the middle pair tipped with white, the white tips increasing in extent outwardly and with the outer web of the outermost feather white to the tail coverts; under parts plain white with black spot in centre of breast; breast and sides often lightly tinged with greyish brown; bill dull bluish dusky, paler below; legs flesh colour. *Juvenals* resemble adults, but crown and ear patch are greyish brown, the breast streaked or spotted with dusky.

Measurements (*C. g. strigatus*). *Adult male:* wing, 86.4–95.7 (91.4); tail, 69.5–76.7 (73.9); exposed culmen, 12–13.1 (12.7); tarsus, 19.1–21.9 (20.7). *Adult female:* wing, 81.9–87.4 (84.5) mm.

Field Marks. A little larger than a Song Sparrow. The chestnut, black, and white head markings, white-margined tail (white-tipped thus different from that of Vesper Sparrow), and plain white under parts with black breast spot make it unmistakable. *Voice:* Song is long, variable, and melodious, beginning with loud clear double notes followed by a series of short trills, runs, pauses, and *churs*. Also a weak *chip*.

Habitat. Open country with scattered trees or bushes; prairies, wood edges, roadsides, abandoned cultivated areas, and often about farms or villages. Badlands of Red Deer River south of Morrin, Alberta, are much favoured.

Nesting. On the ground, usually under a weed, or in a bush. Nest is of grass and weed stems with a lining of finer grasses, rootlets, and long hairs. *Eggs*, 3 to 5; white, spotted

and scrawled with blackish and often some purplish. They are quite distinctive. Incubation period 11 days (Ross Hardy).

Range. Breeds from southern interior British Columbia, southern parts of the Prairie Provinces, central Minnesota, southern Michigan, southern Ontario, western New York, and central Pennsylvania south to southern California, northern Mexico, Louisiana, central Alabama; rarely to Virginia and central North Carolina. Winters in southern United States and south to southern Florida, southern Mexico, and El Salvador.

Breeding Distribution of Lark Sparrow

Range in Canada. Summer resident, breeding in southern interior British Columbia (Okanagan and Similkameen valleys, north at least to Kamloops; possibly has nested west to Chilliwack), southeastern Alberta (Steveville, Medicine Hat, Milk and Lost rivers, Chin Coulee; recorded in summer north to Botha), southern Saskatchewan (Cypress Hills region, Swift Current, Regina, sporadically north to Nipawin and Battleford), southern Manitoba (Oak Lake, Winnipeg), and southern Ontario (Point Pelee, Walsingham, Toronto).

Occurrence records north to Puntchesakut Lake, British Columbia; Prince Albert, Saskatchewan; Lake St. Martin, Manitoba; Sault Ste. Marie and near Chapleau, Ontario.

Accidental in southeastern Quebec (lower Moisie River, May 25, 1955, a specimen of the western race *strigatus;* sight record at Aguanish, August 25, 1934), New Brunswick (Grand Manan: three specimens of *strigatus*, one of *grammacus*), and Nova Scotia (Sable Island, Upper Granville. Sight records for Grand Desert, West Middle Sable, Bon Portage Island, Brier Island. The Upper Granville specimen was identified by the writer as *grammacus*, the eastern race.).

Subspecies. (1) *Chondestes grammacus grammacus* (Say): Breeds in s. Ont. An accidental visitor to N.S. and N.B. (2) *C. g. strigatus* Swainson (upper parts paler, streaks on back narrower): Breeds in B.C., Alta., Sask., Man. Accidental visitor east to se. Que. (lower Moisie River) and s. N.B. (Grand Manan).

BACHMAN'S SPARROW

Le Pinson des pinières. *Aimophila aestivalis* (Lichtenstein)
L. about 5.75 in.

Wing short, rounded; tail equal to or longer than wing; tail decidedly graduated, the outer feathers much the shortest, tail feathers rather narrow with rounded tips. *Adults:* Upper parts grey or buffy grey, heavily streaked with chestnut brown (becoming mostly greyish on the rump); sides of head buffy grey with thin dark line extending backward from the eye; bend of wing pale yellow; no white in wings or tail; breast, sides, and flanks buffy, the flanks sometimes streaked with brown; belly greyish white.

Measurements (*A. a. bachmani*). *Adult male:* wing, 58.4–63.5 (61.2); tail, 60.9–66.5 (64.0); exposed culmen, 10.9–13.2 (12.2); tarsus, 18.3–20.3 (19.3). *Adult female:* wing, 57.9–60.4 (59.2) mm (adapted from Ridgway).

Field Marks. A brown-backed sparrow with buffy unstreaked breast. A little like the Field Sparrow but bill not pink.

Range. Breeds from southern Missouri, central Ohio, and central Maryland south to southeastern Texas, the Gulf coast of United States, and central Florida.

Status in Canada. Casual in southern Ontario (Point Pelee, April 16, 1917; Long Point, May 6, 1928; also sight records).

Subspecies. *Aimophila aestivalis bachmani* (Audubon).

BLACK-THROATED SPARROW (Desert Sparrow)

Le Pinson à gorge noire. *Amphispiza bilineata* (Cassin)
L. 4.75 to 5.25 in.

Adults: Plain grey above, the back tinged with brown; conspicuous line over eye and another on jaw, white; ear patch dark grey; area in front of eye, black; chin, throat, and middle of breast, jet black; rest of under parts, white becoming greyish on sides and flanks; no wing bars; tail blackish, the outermost feather on each side with white outer web and tipped white, and often the second and third feather from outside also white-tipped; bill bluish dusky, legs brownish black.

Measurements (*A. b. deserticola*). *Adult male:* wing, 64.0–70.6 (67.3); tail, 60.9–68.3 (64.3); exposed culmen, 9.9–10.7 (10.2); tarsus, 18.0–19.8 (19.1). *Adult female:* wing, 62.2–66.0 (64.5).

Field Marks. A grey, black-throated sparrow with a conspicuous white line over the eye and another along the jaw and some white in the outer tail feathers. Harris's Sparrow also has a black throat but is a much larger sparrow with very different face pattern and no conspicuous white in the tail.

Range. Breeds from northeastern California, southwestern Wyoming, northwestern Oklahoma, and central-northern Texas south to southern Baja California and north-central Mexico (Jalisco, Hidalgo). Winters from United States deserts southward.

Status in Canada. Accidental in British Columbia (Murtle Lake, Wells Gray Park, June 8, 1959).

Subspecies. *Amphispiza bilineata deserticola* Ridgway.

SAGE SPARROW

Le Pinson de Bell. *Amphispiza belli* (Cassin)
L. 5.2 to 6.2 in.

Adults: Upper parts and sides of head greyish brown or brownish grey, the back decidedly brown and usually more or less streaked with dusky; spot in front of eye and narrow eye-ring, white; sides of throat with a few fine dark streaks leaving a white malar stripe; rest of under parts white, usually with a dusky spot in middle of breast; the sides buffy and streaked with dusky; wings and tail blackish with pale brown edging; outer tail feathers with outer web and narrow tip, white; bill, pale greyish blue.

Measurements (*A. b. nevadensis*). *Adult male:* wing, 77.47–81.28 (79.25); tail, 70.61–78.49 (74.68); exposed culmen, 9.4–10.41 (10.16); tarsus, 20.83–22.61 (21.59). *Adult female:* wing, 72.39–80.01 (75.69) mm (Ridgway).

Field Marks. A greyish brown sparrow, white below with an inconspicuous dark spot in middle of breast, a few fine dark streaks on sides of throat, and a few streaks on the sides. The tail is often flicked upward when the bird is alarmed, and when spread it shows narrow white outer edges.

Range. Breeds from interior central Washington, southern Idaho, and northwestern Colorado south to central Baja California, southern Nevada, and northwestern New Mexico.

Status in Canada. Casual in southwestern British Columbia (Lulu Island, October 2, 1930).

Subspecies. *Amphispiza belli nevadensis* (Ridgway).

SLATE-COLORED JUNCO

Le Junco ardoisé. *Junco hyemalis* (Linnaeus)
Plate 67. L. 5.75 to 6.5 in.

Adult male: Head, neck, back, rump, wings, breast, sides, and flanks, plain dark slate colour, darkest (almost black) on head; lower breast, abdomen, and under tail coverts, plain white sharply cut off from slaty parts; central tail feathers slaty black, the two outermost tail feathers white, the third partly slate, partly white; bill pinkish or flesh colour, often tipped with dusky especially in fall and winter; legs brownish flesh colour. *Adult female:* Similar to adult male but paler grey and usually (not always) with some dusky in second from outermost tail feather. *Young in first autumn and winter:* Similar to adults, but males somewhat tinged with brown, the females decidedly so, the slaty areas washed with brown, the tertials edged with brown. *Juvenal:* Head, neck, back, rump, breast, sides, and flanks, greyish brown streaked with dusky; abdomen white; tail similar to that of adult.

Measurements (*J. h. hyemalis*). *Adult male:* wing, 76.4–79.8 (78.4); tail, 64.1–70.1 (67.2); exposed culmen, 10.2–11.5 (10.8); tarsus, 20.2–21.8 (20.9). *Adult female:* wing, 70.2–76 (73.4) mm.

Distinctions. Likely to be confused only with the Oregon Junco (*see* Field Marks). In general the Slate-colored has slate-coloured sides, the Oregon Junco brown sides. Some first-year female Slate-colored Juncos and many females of the western race *cismontanus* have brownish sides, but usually there is some indication of slate colour near the junction of the base of the hood with the sides. In the Oregon Junco the dark hood colour stops short of the sides.

Field Marks. About 'Song Sparrow' size. General unstreaked slate coloration, dark breast sharply cut off from the white abdomen, and white outer tail feathers conspicuous in flight, mark it as a junco. In Canada it is likely to be confused only with the Oregon Junco. The Slate-colored generally has slaty sides, the Oregon brown sides. Note the difference in shape of the hood (Plate 67), the slate colour of which extends down the sides in the Slate-colored and cuts off above the *brown* sides in the Oregon. First-year female Slate-colored Juncos often have brownish sides and brownish backs and sometimes are difficult to distinguish from the Oregon Junco in the field. *Voice:* Song is a trill somewhat like that of the Chipping Sparrow but more musical; also a soft rambling combination of twitters, warbles, and *chips*. Its alarm note, a *chip* with a characteristic snapping ring to it.

Habitat. In the nesting season, coniferous and mixed woodlands, especially openings and edges; burntlands, occasionally gardens. In winter and migration, various weedy places; fields, roadsides, gardens, and similar situations not too far from cover of trees or thickets.

Nesting. On or near the ground, the nest usually concealed under vegetation, behind tree roots or under a fallen tree; often in a cavity in a steep slope; sometimes in the roots of an upturned tree or in a crevice in a stump; exceptionally on the verandah of a house. Nest is a cup, outwardly constructed of rootlets, grass, and moss, and lined with fine grasses, rootlets, hairs, moss stems, rarely porcupine quills. *Eggs*, usually 4 or 5, rarely 6; whitish or pale bluish white, speckled (occasionally somewhat blotched) with reddish browns and often a little purplish grey. Incubation 11 to 12 days (F. L. Burns), by both sexes. Two broods annually.

Range. Breeds from northwestern Alaska east to Labrador and Newfoundland and much of forested Canada (*see* Range in Canada) and south in the United States to central Minnesota, Wisconsin, central Michigan, northeastern Ohio, northern and western Pennsylvania, New York, and Connecticut, and in the Appalachian Mountains to northern Georgia. Winters from southern Canada south to northern Mexico and southern United States.

Range in Canada. Breeds from northern Yukon (Old Crow), northwestern and central Mackenzie (Mackenzie Delta, Fort Anderson, Fort Reliance), southern Keewatin (Windy River), northern Manitoba (Churchill), northern Ontario (Shagamu River), southern James Bay (Charlton and Paint Hills islands, probably Akimiski Island), northern Quebec (Richmond Gulf, Indian House Lake; perhaps also Kopaluk and Chimo where recorded in August), Labrador (Nain, Makkovik, Goose Bay, Cartwright), and Newfoundland south to central-interior British Columbia (Hazelton, Sinkut Mountain, Peace River parklands), south-central Alberta (Nevis, Jasper), south-central Saskatchewan (Roddick, Nipawin), southern Manitoba (Riding Mountain, Winnipeg, Rennie), southern Ontario (locally south to Toronto, formerly at least to London), southern

Quebec (Gatineau Park, Hatley, Gaspé Peninsula, Anticosti and Magdalen islands), and throughout New Brunswick, Prince Edward Island, and Nova Scotia.

Winters in small numbers in southern British Columbia, southern Alberta (north to Edmonton), southern Saskatchewan (north to Nipawin), southern Manitoba (Winnipeg), southern Ontario (Huntsville, Ottawa southward), southwestern Quebec (Aylmer, Montreal, Quebec City), New Brunswick, Prince Edward Island, Nova Scotia, and Newfoundland (Avalon Peninsula, Tompkins, Ship Cove).

Casual on Banks Island (Sachs Harbour, May 23, 1953); Baillie Island; Bernard Harbour, Mackenzie, June 8, 1916; Repulse Bay; Southampton Island; and southern Baffin Island (Lake Harbour, June 2, 1931), N.W.T.

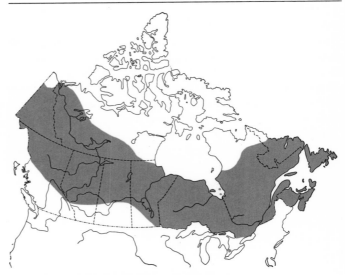

Breeding Distribution of Slate-colored Junco

Subspecies. (1) *Junco hyemalis hyemalis* (Linnaeus): Breeds in n. and c. Yukon, Mack., s. Keewatin, Alta. (except mts.), Sask., Man., Ont., Que., Lab., Nfld., N.B., P.E.I., and N.S. (2) *J. h. cismontanus* Dwight (similar to *hyemalis* but hood more blackish, often noticeably darker than back; back more brownish; females with sides more mixed with pinkish brown): sw. Yukon, n. and c. B.C. (northeast at least to Muncho and Summit lakes where intergrading with *hyemalis*), sw. Alta. (Jasper Park); hybridizes with *oreganus* where the ranges of the two overlap.

OREGON JUNCO

Le Junco à dos roux. *Junco oreganus* (Townsend)
Plate 67. L. 5.5 to 6.3 in.

Varies geographically in colour (*see* Subspecies). *J. o. oreganus* of coastal British Columbia, *adult male:* Head, neck, and upper breast black, thus forming a hood which is well defined both above and below, the black *not* extending onto sides; sides and flanks pinkish cinnamon; back and scapulars rich dark brown; rump slaty grey; abdomen white contrasting sharply with black breast; no wing bars; tail blackish, its outermost feathers white or nearly so, the

390

second mostly white, the third with a little white toward tip; bill pinkish flesh and often dusky at tip; legs pale brownish; *adult female:* Similar to adult male but head, neck, and breast, dull slate; top of head, hind-neck, and back, brown; sides and flanks duller and less pinkish; *juvenal:* Upper parts brown streaked with black; throat, breast, and sides, buffy streaked with black; otherwise similar to adults.

Measurements (*J. o. montanus*). *Adult male:* wing, 76.1–80.2 (77.6); tail, 67–73.4 (69.9); exposed culmen, 9.3–10.6 (9.9); tarsus, 19.5–21 (20.4). *Adult female:* wing, 69.8–74.5 (73.0) mm.

Distinctions (*see* Slate-colored Junco). Extremely puzzling hybrids often occur where the breeding ranges of this and the Slate-colored Junco overlap.

Field Marks. The plain black or grey hood (cut off sharply against the white abdomen) and white outer tail feathers identify it as a junco. In Canada it requires separation chiefly from the Slate-colored Junco. Adult males are usually easy to recognize, but some females are difficult. Note that the dark hood on the breast tends to turn up on the sides of breast and does not extend onto the sides; on the Slate-colored Junco this turns downward on the sides of the breast and onto the sides. Oregon Junco never has slate-coloured sides. However, some female Slate-colored Juncos that in winter plumage have pinkish sides are confusing. Numerous puzzling hybrids occur where the breeding areas of the two species overlap. *Voice:* Similar to that of Slate-colored Junco.

Habitat. Similar to Slate-colored Junco.

Nesting. Similar to Slate-colored Junco. Incubation period 12 days (S. D. MacDonald).

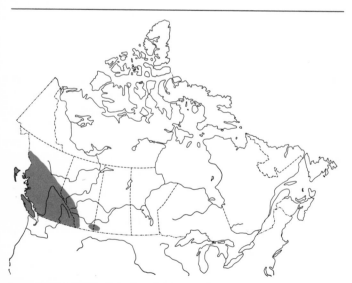

Breeding Distribution of Oregon Junco

Range. Breeds from southeastern Alaska, central British Columbia, southern Alberta, and southwestern Saskatchewan south to northern Baja California, western Nevada, southern Idaho, and northwestern Wyoming.

Range in Canada. Breeds in central and southern British Columbia (Queen Charlotte Islands, Stikine River, Dease

Lake, McGregor River southward including Vancouver Island. Recorded in summer north to Haines Road Mile 45); southwestern and southeastern Alberta (southwestern mountains: Jasper, Banff, and Waterton Lakes parks; also in the widely separated Cypress Hills); and extreme southwestern Saskatchewan (Cypress Hills).

Casual on Banks Island (Sachs Harbour, May 30, 1953), N.W.T.

Winters in British Columbia (coast north to Queen Charlotte Islands; southern interior), southwestern Alberta (Banff), and occasionally in small numbers east to southern Ontario and rarely southwestern Quebec with rare sight records east to Nova Scotia.

Subspecies. Many consider this and the Slate-colored Junco conspecific because of intergradation shown through *J. h. cismontanus,* and consequently group all the races under the species name *hyemalis.* This arrangement seems to have merit, but for the present the writer follows the A.O.U. Check-list in treating them as separate species. (1) *Junco oreganus oreganus* (Townsend), with very dark head, sides, and back; very ruddy back and sides: coastal B.C. (s. to Calvert I.). (2) *J. o. shufeldti* Coale with greyer, less reddish back, less blackish head, than *oreganus:* sw. B.C. (west slopes of the Coast Range, intergrading with *oreganus* on Vancouver Island). (3) *J. o. montanus* Ridgway, similar to *shufeldti* but wings and tail averaging shorter: c. and s. interior B.C., sw. Alta. (4) *J. o. mearnsi* Ridgway, paler grey hood, paler more pinkish sides than in any of the above-mentioned races: se. Alta., and sw. Sask. (Cypress Hills).

TREE SPARROW
Le Pinson hudsonien. *Spizella arborea* (Wilson)
Plate 67. L. 5.8 to 6.5 in.

Adults: Top of head, streak extending back from eye to small ear patch, and (usually) small streak across jaw, chestnut; rest of head and neck grey, hind-neck tinged with rusty; rest of under parts greyish white, unstreaked but with a dusky spot in centre of breast, a small chestnut patch on each side of breast, sides buffy brown; back and scapulars streaked with black, buffy, and brown; rump plain brown; wings with two conspicuous white bars; tail plain dusky with outer edge of outermost feather greyish white; upper mandible and tip of lower mandible dusky, rest of lower mandible yellow; legs pale brownish; feet blackish. *Juvenal plumage* (worn for a short time after leaving nest): Top of head brown with dusky streaks; breast and sides buffy with dusky streaks; otherwise similar to adults.

Measurements (*Spizella arborea arborea*). *Adult male:* wing, 72.1–76.8 (74.8); tail, 63.4–69 (66.7); exposed culmen, 9.5–11 (10.4); tarsus, 19.6–21.6 (20.7). *Adult female:* wing, 69.1–72.1 (70.4) mm.

Field Marks. In settled parts, a winter visitor or spring and autumn migrant. Has red cap, single dusky spot in middle of unstreaked breast, two white wing bars, and usually a little yellow on the lower mandible. The similar Field Sparrow differs in its pink bill and lack of breast spot. The Chipping Sparrow has a black line through the eye and no breast spot.

The Swamp Sparrow is darker and duller above and lacks conspicuous white wing bars (but sometimes has a small dusky breast spot). *Voice:* The spritely but modest song begins with two or more higher notes and ends in a warble. When feeding, a musical *teelit* or *teelwit*. Call-note *tseet*, different enough from the *chips* of other birds to be recognizable.

Habitat. In nesting season, open woody shrubbery such as willow, dwarf birch, and alder, sometimes scrub conifers along streams, in bogs, and above timberline in the western mountains, and on some of the low-arctic tundra. Also in winter and migration, weedy fields, gardens, and similar open places that provide weed seeds.

Nesting. On the ground or more rarely in a low shrub or tree (rarely up to five feet above ground) and usually under a woody shrub. Nest is a cup made externally of heavy grass and weed stalks, rootlets, bits of moss, lichen, or bark, and lined with feathers, hair, sometimes sporophytes of moss. *Eggs*, 4 to 6, usually 5; pale bluish to pale greenish, speckled with browns. Incubation 12 to 13 days, by the female (A. M. Baumgartner).

Range. Breeds in Alaska and across central Canada (Yukon east to Labrador). Winters from southern Canada south to northern California, central Arizona, central Texas, Arkansas, Tennessee, and North Carolina.

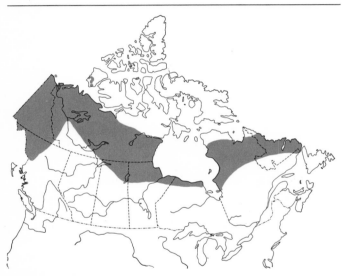

Breeding Distribution of Tree Sparrow

Range in Canada. Breeds from northern Yukon (Herschel Island, Firth River), northern Mackenzie (Mackenzie Delta, lower Anderson River, Coppermine, Bathurst Inlet, Thelon River), central-interior Keewatin (Beverly Lake), northern Manitoba (Churchill), northern Ontario (Fort Severn, Little Cape, Cape Henrietta Maria), southern James Bay (South Twin Island), northern Quebec (Povungnituk River, Leaf River, Fort Chimo), Labrador (Saglek Bay, Battle Harbour), south to northwestern British Columbia (Dease Lake), southeastern Yukon (Sheldon Lake), central-western and southeastern Mackenzie (Fort Franklin, Hill Island Lake), northern Saskatchewan (Reindeer Lake, perhaps Fond-du-Lac), northern Manitoba (Herchmer, Cape

Tatnam), northern Ontario, central Quebec (Paint Hills Islands, Knob Lake, Bradore). Possibly breeds on Banks Island, N.W.T. (May and June records at De Salis Bay, Cape Kellett, Sachs Harbour).

Winters in southern British Columbia, southern Alberta (in small numbers north to Camrose), southwestern Saskatchewan (Cypress Hills region), southern Ontario (North Bay, Ottawa southward), southwestern Quebec (Aylmer, Montreal, rarely north to Quebec City), New Brunswick, Prince Edward Island, and Nova Scotia.

Transient in Newfoundland but not known to breed or winter.

Subspecies. (1) *Spizella arborea arborea* (Wilson): Breeds from e. Mack. (Coppermine), Keewatin, and n. Sask., east to Lab., and e. Que. (2) *S. a. ochracea* Brewster (coloration paler, size slightly larger than in *arborea*): Breeds in Yukon, nw. B.C., and nw. Mack. (Mackenzie Delta, Anderson R., Fort Franklin).

Remarks. In the autumn, when the Tree Sparrows come down to southern Canada, we know that winter is near. In loose flocks they rustle about in the half-bare shrubbery, and their call-notes possess an icy tinkle. The Tree Sparrow is valuable as a destroyer of weed seeds.

CHIPPING SPARROW
Le Pinson familier. *Spizella passerina* (Bechstein)
Plate 67. L. 5 to 5.8 in.

Adult male: Crown chestnut, forehead grey and black; back and scapulars, light brown streaked with black; rump grey; broad stripe over eye, also chin and throat, whitish; through eye a narrow black stripe; rest of sides of head and remainder of under parts plain grey; wings with two inconspicuous whitish bars; tail dusky with no white patches; bill blackish in spring but with base of lower mandible paler, in autumn lower mandible mostly flesh colour; legs pale brown or flesh. *Adult female:* Similar to adult male but often duller and frequently with the crown more or less streaked with black. *Adults in autumn:* Colours duller, less contrasting, chestnut of crown usually partly hidden by buffy feather tips. *Young in first autumn:* Resemble adults but much duller, the top of head brown streaked with black; line over eye as well as wing bars, buffy; breast and sides of head strongly tinged buffy; bill dark brown above, flesh colour below. *Juvenal:* Similar above to autumn young but breast and sides with dusky streaks.

Measurements (*S. p. passerina*). *Adult male:* wing, 66.6–72.5 (70.1); tail, 55.6–60.2 (58.5); exposed culmen, 9–9.9 (9.4); tarsus, 16–17.8 (16.7). *Adult female:* wing, 66.2–70.5 (67.5) mm.

Field Marks. Spring and summer adults, with plain grey breast, red cap, black streak through eye and a broad white stripe over it, are not likely to be mistaken. Autumn birds, however, are very similar to autumn Clay-colored Sparrows. The cheek patch of the Clay-colored usually shows a dark margin which the Chipping Sparrow lacks. Under good conditions, the grey rump of the Chipping Sparrow distinguishes it from the Clay-colored (which has a buffy brown rump) (*see also* Brewer's Sparrow). *Voice:* Song a simple dry trill made up of a procession of rapidly uttered *chips*. A single *chip*.

Habitat. Openings and edges of woodlands; scattered trees; thickets and trees bordering open grassy places; orchards, gardens, shrubbery, and lawns about dwellings.

Nesting. In a deciduous or coniferous tree, bush, or vine, usually 3 to 10 feet up, but seldom up to 25 feet, or rarely on the ground. Nest is a cup, composed externally of grass stems and often some weed stems, and is lined with hair, fur, or rootlets. *Eggs*, 3 to 5; blue, spotted with dark brown, blackish, reddish brown, sometimes some lavender, mostly around the large end; rarely immaculate. Incubation, mostly by the female but occasionally assisted by the male, 11 days (L. H. Walkinshaw).

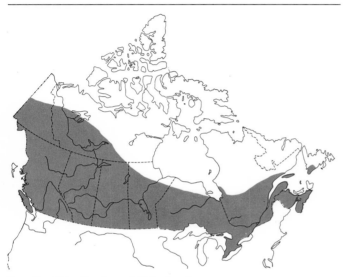

Breeding Distribution of Chipping Sparrow

Range. Breeds from Yukon and British Columbia east to Newfoundland and south to northern Baja California, Nicaragua, the United States Gulf coast, and northern Florida. Winters from southwestern and central United States southward.

Range in Canada. Breeds from central Yukon (Dawson), central Mackenzie (Fort Good Hope, Fort Reliance, Dickson Canyon), northern Alberta, northern Saskatchewan (Lake Athabasca, Reindeer Lake), northeastern Manitoba (Bird, Ilford), central Ontario (Moose Factory), southern Quebec (Fort George, Mistassini Post, Seven Islands, Mingan, Anticosti Island; recorded in summer at Natashquan), and southwestern Newfoundland (Codroy Valley) south throughout extreme southern Canada: southern British Columbia (but not on Queen Charlotte Islands), Alberta, Saskatchewan (local in south), Manitoba, Ontario, southwestern Quebec (also Magdalen Islands), New Brunswick, Prince Edward Island, and Nova Scotia (including Cape Breton Island).

Casual at Churchill, Manitoba, and northern Newfoundland (St. Anthony).

Occasional in winter in Nova Scotia (Gaspereau, Wolfville, Port Mouton) and southern Ontario (Toronto).

Subspecies. (1) *Spizella passerina passerina* (Bechstein):

s. and e. Ont., s. Que., sw. Nfld., N.B., P.E.I., N.S. (2) *S. p. boreophila* Oberholser (larger, more greyish than *passerina*): Yukon, Mack., B.C., Alta., Sask., Man., w. Ont. (west of the Great Lakes, perhaps east to the foot of James Bay).

CLAY-COLORED SPARROW
Le Pinson des plaines. *Spizella pallida* (Swainson)
Plate 67. L. 4.9 to 5.5 in.

Adults: Crown with buffy-grey median stripe, sides of crown brown streaked with black; hind-neck and sides of neck, greyish; back and scapulars buffy brown streaked with black; rump brownish or greyish brown; tail brown, narrowly edged with grey; two faint whitish or pale buffy wing bars; broad stripe over eye buffy white; ear patch buffy brown with narrow dark brown border above and below; under parts whitish, somewhat tinged with pale greyish buff on breast and sides; bill dusky above and at tip, otherwise flesh colour; legs brownish flesh. *Young (first autumn):* Similar to adults but much more buffy; the crown not much darker than the back, its median stripe less distinct than in adults; breast strongly tinged buffy. *Juvenal:* Quite similar to young in autumn but breast and sides with dusky streaks.

Measurements. *Adult male:* wing, 58.1–62.8 (60.7); tail, 57–61.7 (58.9); exposed culmen, 8.6–10 (9.5); tarsus, 16.7–18.5 (17.6). *Adult female:* wing, 56.4–63.5 (59.4) mm.

Breeding Distribution of Clay-colored Sparrow

Field Marks. A small sparrow with a plain breast, somewhat resembling a Chipping Sparrow, but adult Clay-color differs in having a grey hind-neck and a more distinct brown ear patch bordered above and below by a narrow dark brown line, and in lacking a definite black line through the eye. Autumn Chippies and Clay-colors both show a brown ear patch, but in the Chipping this patch is not bordered by a dark line above and below; also the Chipping has a grey rump (never brown), but the rump of the autumn Clay-colored is usually buffy brown (*see also* Brewer's Sparrow). *Voice:* Song is two to four insect-like buzzes and is readily recognizable. Also a weak *chip*.

393

Habitat. Woody shrub patches and thickets, such as willow, alder, wolfberry, and rose, along streams, edges of ponds, lakes, or swamps; tall shrubbery on meadows; areas where aspen groves are interspersed with woody shrubbery; brushy openings, edges, and burns of woodland (either deciduous or coniferous).

Nesting. One to 7 feet up in deciduous bushes or small conifers; occasionally on the ground. Nest is outwardly of grass and weed stems and is lined with fine grass and hair. *Eggs*, 3 to 5; greenish blue, spotted and speckled with various browns or black, mostly around the large end. Incubation period 11 to 11.5 days (L. H. Walkinshaw).

Range. Breeds from interior British Columbia east to southern Ontario and south to central Montana, southeastern Wyoming, southeastern Colorado, northern Texas (very locally), northern Iowa, southern Wisconsin, and central Michigan. Winters in southern Texas and Mexico.

Range in Canada. Breeds in interior British Columbia (Minaker River, Charlie Lake; sparsely farther west and farther south to Nulki Lake, Fifty-nine Mile House, Okanagan Landing); southern Mackenzie (Hay River, Fort Resolution; recorded in June at Fort Simpson but evidence of breeding lacking), northern, central, and southern Alberta; northwestern, central, and southern Saskatchewan (Lake Athabasca, Cumberland House southward), central-western and southern Manitoba (The Pas, Hillside Beach southward), western Ontario (Ingolf, Kenora, Wabigoon, Port Arthur), and southern Ontario (Sault Ste. Marie; very locally elsewhere: Craigleith, Camp Borden, Ayr, Trafalgar).

Recently an isolated nesting record at Ottawa (nest found by the writer June 4, 1966).

Casual in southwestern Quebec (near Amos, specimen taken July 5, 1965; sight records for Gatineau Park, Ste. Anne de Bellevue, Philipsburg, Ste. Catherine).

BREWER'S SPARROW

Le Pinson de Brewer. *Spizella breweri* Cassin
Plate 67. L. 5. to 5.4 in.

Adults: Upper parts pale greyish brown streaked with black, but rump only indistinctly streaked; two poorly defined buffy white wing bars; tail, dark brown narrowly edged with grey; inconspicuous greyish brown cheek patch has faint darker narrow line above and below it; poorly defined pale streak over eye; under parts dull white, the breast and sides lightly washed with greyish buff (sometimes very faintly streaked); bill dusky above, brownish flesh below; legs, brownish flesh. *Young in first autumn:* Similar to adults but more buffy above; wing bars buffy and more distinct. *Juvenal:* Similar to young in first autumn but breast and sides with dusky streaks.

Measurements (*S. b. breweri*). *Adult male:* wing, 59.6–64.5 (61.8); tail, 56.9–63.2 (59.7); exposed culmen, 8.7–10 (9.2); tarsus, 16.5–17.9 (17.4). *Adult female:* wing, 57.5–62.2 (60.2) mm.

Field Marks. A slender pale greyish sparrow with plain breast and streaked upper parts. Perhaps most likely to be confused with Clay-colored Sparrow but lacks the median crown stripe of the Clay-color, has the sides of head more

uniform, and is without conspicuous grey on the hind-neck *Voice:* Song is surprisingly varied and sustained with numerous abrupt changes in pitch and tempo, combining buzzes and canary-like trills. Various nervous *lisps* and *chips*.

Habitat. Open country with low bushy shrubbery on the plains, on mountain meadows above timberline, and in open parts of mountain valleys.

Nesting. In a sagebrush bush or other low shrub. Nest is a compact cup of grass and weed stems and is lined with hair and fine grasses. *Eggs*, 3 or 4; greenish blue speckled with reddish browns.

Range. Southwestern Yukon, central-western and southern Alberta, southwestern Saskatchewan, and southwestern North Dakota south to southern California, central Arizona, and northwestern New Mexico. Winters in southwestern United States and northwestern Mexico.

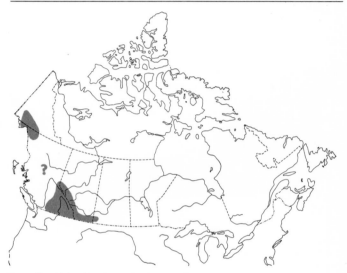

Breeding Distribution of Brewer's Sparrow

Range in Canada. Breeds in southwestern Yukon (Kluane region), interior British Columbia (Chilkat Pass, Atlin, Similkameen and Okanagan valleys, Midway, Elko), central-western and southern Alberta (Jasper, Banff, and Waterton Lakes parks; Milk River), and southwestern Saskatchewan (Cypress Hills region).

Has wandered farther east in Saskatchewan to Old Wives Lake (Lake Johnstone).

Subspecies. (1) *Spizella breweri breweri* Cassin: s. Alta. (east of the mts.), sw. Sask.; also c.-s. B.C. (White Lake, Midway). (2) *S. b. taverneri* Swarth and Brooks (darker above, slightly larger than *breweri*): sw. Yukon, nw., c., and se. B.C. (se. to Elko).

FIELD SPARROW

Le Pinson des champs. *Spizella pusilla* (Wilson)
Plate 67. L. 5.1 to 6 in.

Adults: Top of head, back, and scapulars, rusty brown, the back and scapulars streaked with blackish but head and neck not streaked; rump plain light brown; wings with two whitish bars; tail dark brown with narrow grey edging; sides of head grey with pale eye-ring and touches of rusty behind eye and on ear coverts; under parts whitish with buffy wash across breast and on sides and flanks; bill reddish or pink; legs brownish flesh colour. *Juvenal:* Similar to adults but duller, the crown brown instead of rusty, the breast and sides with light dusky streaks.

Measurements (*S. p. pusilla*). *Adult male:* wing, 62.7–67.8 (64.9); tail, 62–68.4 (65.9); exposed culmen, 8.7–9.8 (9.1); tarsus, 17.6–18.9 (18.3). *Adult female:* wing, 60–63.3 (62.9) mm.

Field Marks. Has rusty upper parts, white wing bars, and unstreaked breast, thus resembling the Tree Sparrow, but the present species has a pinkish bill and lacks a dusky spot on the breast. *Voice:* The pleasing song begins with two or more slow sweet whistles, then speeds up to a trill at the end. Call-note, *tsip.*

Habitat. Neglected brushy fields, old grown-up pastures, areas of thorn scrub, burntlands, wood edges, sparse second growths, and areas where small trees are interspersed with brambles and grasses.

Nesting. In a low bush or scrubby small tree or on the ground. Nest of grasses, weed stems, and rootlets is lined with fine grasses, hair, and sometimes bark fibre. *Eggs,* 2 to 5; greyish white to bluish, spotted and speckled with reddish browns. Incubation, 11 to 12 days (L. H. Walkinshaw), by the female.

Range. Breeds from southeastern Montana east across northern United States and through southern Ontario and southwestern Quebec to southern Maine and south to central Texas, Louisiana, and southern Georgia. Winters from Kansas east to Massachusetts and south to northeastern Mexico, southern Texas, the United States Gulf coast, and central Florida.

Breeding Distribution of Field Sparrow

Range in Canada. Breeds in southern Manitoba (rarely: near Winnipeg), southern Ontario (Wasaga Beach, Ottawa southward), and southwestern Quebec (Philipsburg, Frelighsburg; probably Sweetsburg and Gatineau).

Casual elsewhere in Quebec (lower Moisie River, April 24, 1959; Magdalen Islands, July 8, 1887); southern New Brunswick (Machias Seal Island; Grand Manan), and probably Nova Scotia (various sight records).

Casual in winter in southern Ontario (Toronto).

Subspecies. *Spizella pusilla pusilla* (Wilson).

HARRIS'S SPARROW

Le Pinson à face noire. *Zonotrichia querula* (Nuttall)
Plate 66. L. 7 to 7.75 in.

Adults (*spring and summer*): Top of head, nape, front of face, chin, and throat, black, which extends as streaks or spots to the mid-breast; sides of head behind eye mostly grey with small black patch just behind ear region; remainder of upper parts brown, the back and scapulars streaked with black; two white wing bars; tail greyish brown, its outer feathers often narrowly tipped with white; under parts (except black throat and mid-breast) white, the sides and flanks buffy, streaked with black and dusky; under tail coverts buffy with grey-brown centres; bill pinkish brown; legs pale brown. *Adults* (*autumn and winter*): Similar to adults in spring but cheeks and sides of neck buffy, spot behind ear region brown, blacks somewhat obscured. *Young* (*first autumn*): Similar to adults in autumn but throat white, bordered on either side by a narrow blackish stripe; crown feathers black centrally and much margined with greyish buff giving crown a scaly appearance; a necklace of blackish brown on upper breast. *Juvenal:* Greyish-buff above, streaked with dusky, heavily (almost blackish) on crown, but stripes on rump paler and sparser; sides of breast buffy finely streaked dusky; under parts whitish, the breast and sides streaked dusky; throat with dusky stripe on each side; wing bars buffy.

Measurements (breeding birds). *Adult male:* wing, 83–89.4 (85.7); tail, 79.1–86 (81.7); exposed culmen, 12–13.4 (12.9); tarsus, 23–25 (24.2). *Adult female:* wing, 78.9–83.5 (81.0) mm. (Specimens in fresh autumn plumage average slightly larger in wing and tail.)

Field Marks. A large sparrow. Adult in spring and summer with black throat, face, and crown; grey cheeks; pinkish bill; in autumn with buffy cheeks and the blacks somewhat obscured. First autumn immature has the throat white, a heavy necklace of blackish brown, and buffy cheeks. *Voice:* The song is whistled, begins with one to several notes on the same pitch in a minor key usually; these are followed by other notes which may be either higher or lower. Has a loud metallic *chip;* also musical twitters, often interspersed with harsh notes.

Habitat. In the nesting season patches of stunted trees and woody shrubbery in the ecotone between forest and tundra. In migration and winter, various thickets, edges of woodland, and hedgerows.

Nesting. On the ground in the shelter of a shrub or stunted tree. Nest is composed externally of twigs, weed stems, mosses, and lichens, and is well lined with fine grasses. *Eggs,* 3 to 5; pale greenish or greyish (variously blotched, often heavily) and speckled with reddish browns. Incubation period at least 13½ days (fourth egg did not hatch) according to J. R. Jehl and D. J. T. Hussell.

Range. Breeds in Mackenzie, Keewatin, and northern Manitoba. Winters from southern British Columbia, northern Utah, northern Nebraska, and central Iowa south to southern California, central Arizona, south-central Texas, and Tennessee.

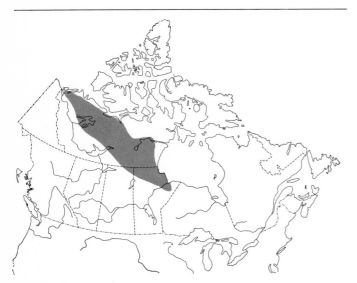

Breeding Distribution of Harris's Sparrow

Range in Canada. Breeds in Mackenzie (eastern Mackenzie Delta, head of Great Bear River, Bathurst Inlet, eastern Great Slave Lake, Thelon River); southern Keewatin (Nueltin Lake, Tha-Anne River); and northern Manitoba (Cochrane River, Churchill, Bird).

Common spring and autumn transient in Saskatchewan and Manitoba; scarce transient in British Columbia, Alberta, and western Ontario (Port Arthur).

Casual in southern and central Ontario (London, Strathroy, Etobicoke, Rossport, Kirkland Lake) and extreme southwestern Quebec (St. Laurent).

Winters sparingly in southern British Columbia (Victoria, Sumas, Lillooet).

WHITE-CROWNED SPARROW
Le Pinson à couronne blanche
Zonotrichia leucophrys (Forster)
Plate 68. L. 6.5 to 7.5 in.

Geographically variable (*see* Subspecies). *Adults* (*Z. l. leucophrys*): Top of head with two broad stripes of black, separated by a broad median stripe of white; black of crown reaches down to cover upper half of lores (but not in most western races; *see* Subspecies); a narrow black line extends from eye to back of nape with a broader band of white above it; rest of face, sides of neck, and breast, plain grey becoming whitish on throat and abdomen and becoming greyish buffy on sides and flanks; back and scapulars, light grey broadly streaked with brown; rump and upper tail coverts pale brownish; wings with two white bars; tail dark brown; bill reddish or pinkish brown (but *see* Subspecies); legs flesh colour to brown. *Young* (*first autumn*): Similar to adults but more brownish (less grey-

ish); the dark head stripes brown instead of black, the light head stripes buffy instead of whitish. *Juvenal:* Similar to young in first autumn but breast and sides profusely streaked with dusky; streaks of the back and scapulars, black instead of brown.

Measurements (*Z. l. leucophrys*). *Adult male:* wing, 76.8–83 (79.9); tail, 72–76.3 (74.1); exposed culmen, 10.9–12.2 (11.8); tarsus, 22.1–24 (23.2). *Adult female:* wing, 73.1–79 (75.4) mm.

Field Marks. The conspicuous black and white stripes on the otherwise grey head distinguish this largish sparrow from most others except the White-throated Sparrow. However, the White-crown's pinkish or yellowish (instead of mostly dusky) bill, lack of a yellow spot in front of eye, and absence of a sharply defined white throat patch are points that distinguish it. The White-crown's paler (pinkish or yellowish) bill and lack of any yellow on the crown distinguish it from the Golden-crowned Sparrow. Young White-crowns in their first autumn have reddish brown and buff head stripes but otherwise closely resemble the adults. The geographic races differ considerably and under good conditions can sometimes be distinguished in the field (*see* Subspecies). *Voice:* Song is rather short and a little melancholy. It begins with one or two leisurely whistles followed by quicker notes, ending in two or three rapidly descending notes. It is much less impressive than that of the White-throated Sparrow.

Habitat. Throughout its vast breeding range it is primarily a bird of woody shrubbery and thickets in more open situations: dwarf birch and dwarf willow patches on the tundra edge or along streams and depressions; in recumbent or stunted spruce on wind-swept coasts; also bushy edges of woodlands, openings, old burns, and mountainside shrubbery.

Nesting. On the ground or near the ground in a bush or stunted tree. Nest is rather bulky, composed externally of twigs, coarse grass, shreds of bark, often moss and lichen, and is lined with fine grasses and rootlets or hair. *Eggs*, usually 4 or 5; pale greyish white to pale greenish blue, thickly blotched and speckled with reddish browns. Incubation period averages 12 to 12½ days and up to 14 days (B. D. Blanchard), by the female.

Range. Breeds from northern Alaska eastward across much of the northern mainland of Canada to Labrador and northern Newfoundland and south in the United States to south-central California, Nevada, central Arizona, and northern New Mexico. Winters from southern British Columbia, southern Idaho, Kansas, Kentucky, and western North Carolina south to central Mexico, the Gulf coast of United States, and Cuba.

Range in Canada. Breeds from northern Yukon (Old Crow), northern Mackenzie (Mackenzie Delta, mouth of Anderson River, Coppermine, Bathurst Inlet), central Keewatin (Back River), northern Manitoba (Lynn Lake, Churchill), northern Ontario (Fort Severn), northern Quebec (Lake Maryland, Gregory Lake, Fort Chimo), Port Burwell, N.W.T., and northern Labrador south through southern British Columbia (including southern Vancouver Island but absent from the north coast and Queen Charlotte Islands, sparsely and locally in extreme southern interior mountains), northern, western, and southeastern Alberta (Peace River, Dixonville, Lake Athabasca; Jasper, Banff, and Waterton Lakes parks eastward to Nordegg and Calgary; also Cypress Hills), northern and extreme southwestern Saskatchewan (Lake Athabasca, Black Lake region; also in the widely-separated Cypress Hills), northern Manitoba (Brochet, Ilford), northern Ontario (Fort Albany, Moose Island), James Bay (Akimiski Island, Paint Hills Islands), south-central Quebec (Paul Bay, Knob Lake, Sawbill, the outer north shore of the Gulf of St. Lawrence from about Johan Beetz Bay eastward), and northern Newfoundland (Flower's Cove, St. Anthony).

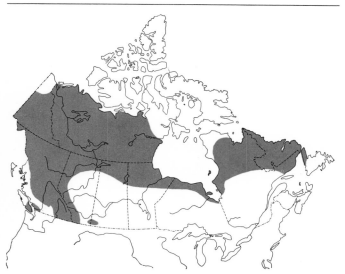

Breeding Distribution of White-crowned Sparrow

Spring and autumn transient through most of Canada south of the breeding range but uncommon in New Brunswick, rare and irregular in Nova Scotia and Prince Edward Island.

Casual in Franklin District: Banks Island (Sachs Harbour), Melville Peninsula (Elizabeth Point), and southern Baffin Island (Dorset, Taverner Bay, Lake Harbour). Accidental on Fletcher's Ice Island (lat. 82° 37′N., long. 99° 50′W.), June 16, 1957.

Subspecies. (1) *Zonotrichia leucophrys leucophrys* (Forster), white stripe above eye cut off in front by a black bar; bend of wing usually white; bill pinkish: Breeds in Ont. (intergrading with *gambellii* at Fort Severn), Que., Lab., Nfld. (2) *Z. l. gambellii* (Nuttall), resembles *leucophrys*, but white line over eye not cut off anteriorly but extends forward unbroken to base of bill; bill yellowish or pinkish brown: Yukon, Mack., Keewatin south to nw. and c.-s. B.C. (intergrading with *oriantha* at Elko), sw. Alta. (intergrades with *oriantha* from Banff southward), n. Sask., n. Man. (intergrading with *leucophrys*), and nw. Ont. (intergrades with *leucophrys* at Fort Severn). (3) *Z. l. oriantha* Oberholser (white stripe over eye interrupted by black bar, thus resembling *leucophrys* but back coloration paler): sw. and se. Alta. (Waterton Lakes Park, Cypress Hills), sw. Sask. (Cypress Hills), also se. B.C. (Elko). (4) *Z. l. pugetensis*

Grinnell (white stripe over eye not cut off in front of eye by a black bar, thus resembling *gambellii* but coloration above and below darker and duller, bend of wing consistently yellow, size slightly smaller): sw. B.C. (Vancouver Island, Vancouver).

GOLDEN-CROWNED SPARROW
Le Pinson à couronne dorée
Zonotrichia atricapilla (Gmelin)
Plate 68. L. 6 to 7.2 in.

Adults: Top of head black with a broad median stripe of yellow which becomes abruptly grey posteriorly; back and scapulars olive brown, broadly streaked with blackish brown; rump plain olive brown; two white wing bars; tail plain brown; sides of head, sides of neck, throat, and breast, greyish or brownish grey; sides and flanks brownish; abdomen whitish; bill brownish or dusky above, pale below; legs pinkish brown to greyish brown. *Young (first autumn):* Similar to adults but without the broad black crown stripes. Instead, the forehead is yellowish olive, the posterior part of crown greyish brown, both flecked or narrowly streaked with dusky. *Juvenal:* Resembles young in first autumn but yellowish olive is lacking on forehead; sides of throat, breast, sides, and flanks are streaked with dusky. Any trace of yellow in the crown separates the young from young White-crowns.

Measurements. *Adult male:* wing, 77.3–84 (81.1); tail, 76–81.3 (78.6); exposed culmen, 11.2–12.1 (11.9); tarsus, 23.1–25.2 (24.4). *Adult female:* wing, 75.2–79.5 (77.5) mm.

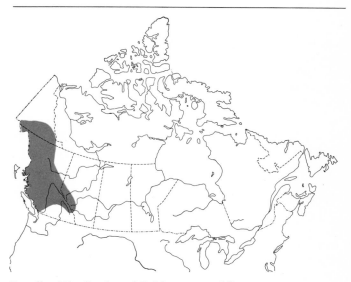

Breeding Distribution of Golden-crowned Sparrow

Field Marks. A large sparrow somewhat like the White-crowned, but adults lack white stripes on head. Instead, the Golden-crown has a broad yellow median crown stripe, bordered on each side by a broad black stripe, and has a mostly dark bill instead of a yellowish or pinkish one. Young in autumn might be confused with the White-crowned but lack the well-defined brown and buffy head stripes of the White-crown and usually show yellow on the forehead (which the White-crown never has). *Voice:* Song is usually three or four whistled notes on a descending scale and is usually in a minor key.

Habitat. In the nesting season, thickets of shrubbery, mostly above or at timberline in the western mountains, recumbent and dwarf conifers near timberline, shrubbery along streams. In migration and in winter it favours brushy situations similar to those inhabited by the White-crown.

Nesting. On the ground or low in a shrub or dwarfed tree. *Eggs*, usually 4 or 5; pale greenish or pale buffy speckled with browns.

Range. Breeds from western coastal Alaska and south-central Yukon south to southern British Columbia and southwestern Alberta. Winters from southern British Columbia southward (mostly west of the Cascades and Sierra Nevada) to northern Baja California.

Range in Canada. Breeds from south-central Yukon (Sheldon Lake) southward to southern British Columbia (Coast Ranges and eastward: Alta Lake, Tonquin Pass), and southwestern Alberta (Jasper and Banff National parks east to Mountain Park).

In migration southern British Columbia including Queen Charlotte and Vancouver islands. Winters in small numbers in southwestern British Columbia (Victoria, Vancouver, Okanagan Landing).

Casual east of the Rockies in Alberta (Red Deer) and Saskatchewan (Regina, Indian Head), and northwestern Mackenzie (Tuktoyaktuk).

WHITE-THROATED SPARROW

Le Pinson à gorge blanche. *Zonotrichia albicollis* (Gmelin)
Plate 68. L. 6.3 to 7.2 in.

Adults (Variable; *see* Lowther, 1961, *Can. J. Zool.* 39: 281–92): Top of head with two broad lateral stripes varying from all black to dark chestnut brown; median crown stripe varying from white to grey or tan; back and scapulars, chestnut brown striped with black; rump plain pale brown; two white wing bars; bend of wing, pale yellow; tail, dark brown narrowly edged with pale brown; broad pale stripe over eye, yellow in front, white to buffy behind eye; narrow line from eye to nape, black to brown; cheeks and upper breast, grey (often more or less streaked with dusky); throat patch white, sharply cut off from surrounding grey and framed on each side by a thin line of black; sides and flanks, grey mixed with brown; abdomen white; bill dark brown above, paler and more bluish grey below; legs pinkish flesh or pale brown. *Juvenal:* Upper parts mostly chestnut brown streaked with black; median crown stripe and stripe over eye, buffy grey; line extending from eye to nape, brown; wing bars buffy; sides of throat, breast, and sides, buff streaked with blackish brown; throat greyish white (but not sharply cut off in a patch); abdomen, dull white tinged with buff. Juvenals of the White-throat are readily distinguished from juvenal White-crowns by much more rusty coloration in the upper parts of the former.

Measurements. *Adult male:* wing, 72–77.8 (73.9); tail, 68–77 (73.2); exposed culmen, 10–12 (11.4); tarsus, 23–24.1 (23.6). *Adult female:* wing, 65.4–73.9 (69.3) mm.

Field Marks. A largish sparrow. Its striped head is most

like that of the White-crowned Sparrow, but the present species has a white throat patch well defined against the grey of breast, a yellow spot in front of eye, and a dark bill (instead of pinkish or yellowish). *Voice:* The plaintive whistled song begins with two clear leisurely notes, followed by a three-note phrase, repeated two or three times. Canadians often paraphrase it *I-love-Canada, Canada, Canada.* It also has a lisping call-note, *tseet.*

Habitat. Bushy openings in or edges of woodlands (mostly coniferous or mixedwood), burntlands, clearings cluttered with slashing, open young woodlands and thickets.

Nesting. Usually on the ground beneath a shrub or in a clump of grass. Nest is a cup composed externally of grass, twigs, chips of rotten wood, mosses, conifer needles and lined with fine grasses, rootlets, hair, sometimes pine needles. *Eggs*, 3 to 5, usually 4; greyish, bluish, or greenish white, variously blotched and speckled with browns and sometimes some purplish grey. Incubation period 11 to 14 days (J. K. Lowther).

Range. Breeds from wooded parts of Canada (southern Yukon and interior British Columbia east to Newfoundland) south in the United States to northern North Dakota, central Minnesota, central Michigan, northern Ohio, northern West Virginia, southeastern New York, and Massachusetts.

Breeding Distribution of White-throated Sparrow

Range in Canada. Breeds from southeastern Yukon (Watson Lake), central-western and southern Mackenzie (Norman Wells, central-northern Great Slave Lake), northern Saskatchewan (Stony Rapids, Black Lake), northern Manitoba (Bird, Herchmer, Fort Nelson; probably Churchill), northern Ontario (Shagamu River), north-central Quebec (Great Whale River, Knob Lake), southern Labrador (Goose Bay, Cartwright), and Newfoundland south to central-interior British Columbia (commonly in northeast; and westward sparingly to Kispiox Valley and Nulki Lake), central Alberta (south to about Red Deer and Nevis), central and southeastern Saskatchewan (Prince Albert, Sheho, probably Moose Mountain region) and through southern Manitoba, southern Ontario, southern Quebec (including Anticosti and Magdalen islands), New Brunswick, Prince Edward Island, and Nova Scotia.

In migration occurs sparingly south of the breeding range in southern British Columbia (rarely west to Vancouver Island), southern Alberta, and southern Saskatchewan.

Accidental in southern Baffin Island (West Foxe Islands, July 3, 1955).

Remarks. The unhurried, clearly whistled song of the White-throated Sparrow is one of the delightful summer sounds of the north woods. Except in the extreme West, this sparrow is numerous as a summer resident or as a spring and autumn migrant. It eats insects, weed seeds (including seeds of ragweed), and wild fruits.

FOX SPARROW

Le Pinson fauve. *Passerella iliaca* (Merrem)
Plate 68. L. 6.7 to 7.5 in.

Adults: A large, sturdily built sparrow, extremely variable geographically in colour, eastern populations mostly rusty red, west coast birds entirely different, mostly sooty brown (*see* Subspecies). *Adults (P. i. iliaca):* Rusty brown and grey in various proportions, the rusty brightest on wings, tail, and upper coverts, much mixed with grey on top of head and on back (but top of head and back often mostly grey); two inconspicuous whitish wing bars; under parts white with broad stripes, blotches, and arrow-shaped spots of rusty and chestnut on sides of throat, breast, sides, and flanks; bill dusky above, yellowish below; legs flesh to clay colour. *Juvenal:* Similar to adults but much duller above, white of under parts less pure, streaks on breast narrower (less blotched); plumage texture looser.

Measurements. *Adult male:* wing, 84.6–91.4 (87.8); tail, 69.2–75.6 (72.9); exposed culmen, 11.2–13.8 (12.4); tarsus, 23.8–24.9 (24.5). *Adult female:* wing, 80.8–86.4 (83.9) mm.

Field Marks. A large robust sparrow, its coloration varying greatly geographically (*see* Subspecies). East of the Rockies and in the northwest it is characterized by its fox reds (especially the tail); the under parts white, heavily blotched and arrow-marked with rusty or chestnut. In interior southern British Columbia it is dark grey above; and on the west coast it is a sooty brown colour. Much foraging is on the ground where the birds scratch noisily among the leaf litter. *Voice:* The delightful but short song begins with two or three somewhat slurred whistles and closes with more rapid notes which descend in pitch.

Habitat. Woodland thickets and edges, scrubby woods either coniferous or deciduous, stunted conifers on the coasts, burntlands, and cut-over land, streamside shrubbery.

Nesting. On the ground under a bush or tree or low in a tree or shrub. Nest is of grass, twigs, moss, and rootlets and is lined with grass, hair, and often wool or feathers. *Eggs,* usually 4 or 5; bluish white or greenish white, speckled and spotted with reddish browns.

Range. Breeds from northern Alaska east to Labrador and Newfoundland and south to northwestern Washington on the Pacific coast of United States and in the mountains to southern California and to central parts of Nevada, Utah, and Colorado. Winters from southern Canada (locally) and northern United States to southern United States.

Range in Canada. Breeds from northern Yukon (Old Crow, Lapierre House), northwestern and central-eastern Mackenzie (Mackenzie Delta, Anderson River, Artillery Lake), southwestern Keewatin (Nueltin Lake); northeastern Manitoba (Churchill), northern Ontario (Fort Severn, Moose Factory), northern Quebec (Richmond Gulf, Fort Chimo, Indian House Lake), and northern Labrador (perhaps north to Nachvak) south to southern British Columbia (including Queen Charlotte and Vancouver islands but locally in the interior, mostly near timberline), southwestern and central-eastern Alberta (Waterton Lakes Park, Red Deer), central Saskatchewan (Nipawin, probably Meadow Lake), central Manitoba (Ilford; an old report of breeding at Duck Mountain requires confirmation), northern Ontario (Moose Factory), southeastern and central-southern Quebec (Pilgrim and Basque islands; Anticosti and Magdalen islands), south coastal Nova Scotia (probably islands off Harrigan Cove), and southern Newfoundland.

Winters in southwestern British Columbia and rarely in southern Ontario, southwestern Quebec, New Brunswick, Nova Scotia, and southern Newfoundland.

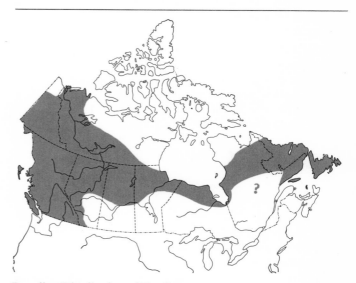

Breeding Distribution of Fox Sparrow

Subspecies. (1) *Passerella iliaca iliaca* (Merrem), (a rusty brown race): Breeds in n. Ont., Que., Lab., Nfld., and N.S. (2) *P. i. zaboria* Oberholser (similar to *iliaca* but averages darker and more greyish): Yukon, Mack., n. B.C. (south to Dease Lake, Peace River parklands), n. and c. Alta. (but not sw. mts.), n. Sask., n. Man. (3) *P. i. altivagans* Riley (similar to *zaboria* but browns less rufescent and upper parts more vaguely streaked): Breeds from interior c. and se. B.C. (Thutade Lake, Mount Revelstoke), and sw. Alta. (Jasper Park intergrading southward in Banff toward *schistacea*). (4) *P. i. schistacea* Baird (head and back dark grey, little streaked): extreme se. B.C. and sw. Alta. (Waterton Lakes Park). (5) *P. i. olivacea* Aldrich (averages slightly darker and more olivaceous than *schistacea*): sw. and s.-c.

interior B.C. (Mount McLean, Nelson). (6) *P. i. fuliginosa* Ridgway (the darkest and sootiest of the races): sw. B.C. (coast including Vancouver Island but not Queen Charlotte Is.). (7) *P. i. townsendi* (Audubon), similar to *fuliginosa* but somewhat brighter and less sooty): Queen Charlotte Is., B.C.

In addition, the following races that breed in Alaska winter in sw. B.C.: (8) *P. i. unalaschensis* (Gmelin); (9) *P. i. insularis* Ridgway; (10) *P. i. sinuosa* Grinnell; (11) *P. i. annectens* Ridgway.

LINCOLN'S SPARROW
Le Pinson de Lincoln. *Melospiza lincolnii* (Audubon)
Plate 68. L. 5.3 to 6 in.

Ninth (outermost) primary longer than fourth. *Adults:* Top of head, light brown streaked with black and divided by a median stripe of grey; back, scapulars, rump, and upper tail coverts, olive brown streaked with black, most heavily on the back; edges of flight feathers rusty brown; tail greyish brown, the two central feathers with a dusky median stripe; stripe over eye and sides of neck, greyish; cheek patch margined above and below by a narrow dark brown streak; malar region buffy; band across breast, sides, and flanks, buffy streaked with black; throat and abdomen white; bill dusky above, bluish below, also often a little yellowish; legs brownish flesh. *Young (first autumn):* Closely resemble adults. *Juvenals:* Similar to adults but colours more suffused, white of throat and abdomen much less pure, no pure grey median crown stripe, plumage texture looser. Juvenals very closely resemble those of the Swamp Sparrow but have the roof of the mouth greyish brown instead of yellow; and when the wing is well developed, the ninth (outermost) primary is longer than the fourth.

Measurements (*M. l. lincolnii*). *Adult male:* wing, 61.2–65.3 (63.5); tail, 54.1–60 (56.7); exposed culmen, 10.3–11.3 (10.8); tarsus, 19.9–22.6 (21.7). *Adult female:* wing, 54.6–63 (58.9) mm.

Field Marks. The broad, buffy, black-streaked band across the breast and down the sides distinguishes it from adults of other sparrows. Juvenal Song and Swamp sparrows are very similar to juvenal Lincoln's, being almost impossible to separate in the field. Adult Lincoln's, however, have whiter throat and abdomen and a characteristic sleekness that is very different from the loose texture of the plumage of juvenal Song and Swamp sparrows.

The Lincoln's Sparrow is a skulker, adept at keeping out of sight. On the breeding grounds it can often be recognized by its nervous, almost frenzied, rapid *chips* when an intruder appears. Meanwhile the bird is never still, bobbing, turning, flitting the wings and tail constantly with each *chip. Voice:* Song is easily recognizable, a pleasing but hurried melody with some of the bubbling qualities of the House Wren and some characteristics of the Purple Finch's song. The *chip* alarm note is variable even in the same individual.

Habitat. In the breeding season, bogs, moist meadows with patches of alder and willow or stunted conifers, and similar moist and bushy places are favoured. In migration various types of thickets, brush piles, hedges, roadsides, and often weedy or grassy open places near bushes or wood edges.

Nesting. On the ground. Nest is of coarse grasses lined with finer grasses and rootlets. *Eggs,* 4 or 5; whitish or greenish white, blotched and speckled with browns. Incubation period 13 days (J. M. Speirs and R. Andoff).

Range. Breeds from northwestern Alaska east to central Labrador and south in the western mountains to southern California and northern New Mexico, and in the east to northern Minnesota, northern Michigan, northern New York, and central Maine. Winters from southern United States south to Guatemala and El Salvador.

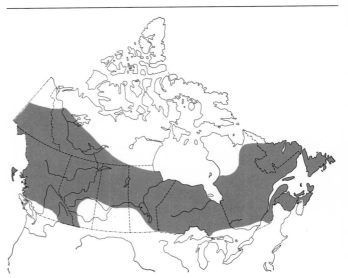

Breeding Distribution of Lincoln's Sparrow

Range in Canada. Breeds from central Yukon (Fortymile), central-western and southeastern Mackenzie (forts Good Hope, Simpson, and Resolution; Hill Island Lake), northern Saskatchewan (Lake Athabasca, Reindeer River), northern Manitoba (Churchill), northern Ontario, northern Quebec (Great Whale River, Fort Chimo, Indian House Lake), central Labrador (Hopedale), and Newfoundland south to southern British Columbia (including Queen Charlotte and probably Vancouver islands and on the mainland south at least to Chilcotin Lake, Clinton: 6 miles south, Carpenter Mountain), southwestern and south-central Alberta (Waterton Lakes Park, Red Deer, Camrose), central Saskatchewan (Prince Albert, Nipawin), southern Manitoba (Duck Mountain, Whitemouth, Julius), southern Ontario (Algonquin Park, very locally south to Wainfleet Marsh), southern Quebec (very locally: Lac des Loups, Baldwin Mills, Quebec City, Biencourt, Gaspé Peninsula, Anticosti and Magdalen islands), New Brunswick, Prince Edward Island, and Nova Scotia (locally, mostly in eastern localities).

Casual in northern Yukon (Old Crow).

Subspecies. (1) *Melospiza lincolnii lincolnii* (Audubon): Ont., Que., Lab., Nfld., N.B., P.E.I., N.S. (2) *M. l. gracilis* (Kittlitz): coastal B.C. (Queen Charlotte and Vancouver is.; Khutze Inlet). (3) *M. l. alticola* (Miller and McCabe): Yukon, Mack., B.C. (except coast), Alta., Sask., Man.

Remarks. In a low tree or bush on the nesting grounds, the Lincoln's Sparrow reveals its presence by its bubbling song. If an intruder approaches, the sparrow stops singing and slips away. A few minutes later it may sing again from shrubbery farther on. In migration it is usually silent, and because it is extremely adept at keeping out of sight, most of the population slips through unobserved.

SWAMP SPARROW

Le Pinson des marais. *Melospiza georgiana* (Latham)
Plate 68. L. 5 to 5.8 in.

Ninth (outermost) primary shorter than fourth. *Breeding plumage:* Top of head variable. Commonly, crown is chestnut, forehead black divided by a narrow grey line, but often top of head is dark brown streaked with black and with a grey median line from base of bill to nape; back and scapulars reddish brown, broadly streaked with black and narrowly with white; rump olive brown, upper tail coverts brown; most of exposed parts of closed wing, chestnut; tail, brown edged with rusty, the two centre feathers with a blackish median stripe; sides of head and sides of neck mostly grey, cheeks slightly brownish, bordered above by a narrow, dark postocular streak and below usually by another reaching back from gape; throat and abdomen whitish; a broad pale grey band across breast extending to sides where it joins the brown of sides and flanks; breast often finely streaked darker and often with a vague dusky spot; bill dusky above, paler below; legs pale brownish. *Adults in autumn and winter:* Resemble breeding birds but top of head often more heavily streaked with black and with more buffy general coloration. *Young in first autumn:* Like adults in autumn but eyebrow stripe buffy or even, rarely, yellow instead of pure grey, and as a rule more buffy generally. *Juvenal:* Very similar to juvenal Lincoln's Sparrow but usually darker above with darker chestnut wing edging. The usually (not always) yellowish inside of mouth distinguishes juvenals in the flesh from those of both the Lincoln's Sparrow and the Song Sparrow.

Measurements (*M. g. georgiana*). *Adult male:* wing, 58.9–62.7 (60.7); tail, 53–60 (56.1); exposed culmen, 9.9–12 (11.1); tarsus, 20.9–22.3 (21.6). *Adult female:* wing, 54.5–61.4 (57.6) mm.

Field Marks. A rather dark-backed sparrow of wetlands, for the most part showing chestnut on the wing edgings and a chestnut cap; a whitish throat and plain grey breast (often there is a vague dusky breast spot). Chipping and Tree sparrows also have red caps, but the Tree Sparrow, a winter bird in settled southern parts of Canada, has prominent white wing bars and a *well-defined* breast spot instead of a vague one, or none at all. The Chipping Sparrow is a slenderer bird with all-grey (instead of brownish) flanks; the dark line through the eye extends forward to the base of the bill, not just behind the eye; and it has very different habitat preferences. *Voice:* Song is a trill a little like that of the Chipping Sparrow but more musical, slower, and louder. Call-note, a metallic *chink*.

Habitat. In the breeding season, wetlands. Margins of ponds, lakes, and streams with tall emergent vegetation such as cattails, or woody shrubbery like alder and willow; freshwater marshes with tangles of vegetation. In migration it favours this type of habitat but frequents also weedy fields near water or even dry thickets on wood edges and openings.

Nesting. In a tussock of marsh vegetation or low in a bush. Nest is composed outwardly of coarse grasses or grass-like vegetation and is lined with fine grasses. *Eggs*, usually 4 or 5; variable in coloration but usually pale bluish green, blotched and speckled with various shades of brown. Incubation period about 13 days (O. W. Knight).

Range. Breeds from Mackenzie and northeastern British Columbia east to southern Labrador and Newfoundland and south in the United States to eastern Nebraska, northern Missouri, northern Indiana, central Ohio, south-central West Virginia, and Delaware. Winters from eastern Nebraska, Iowa, southern Wisconsin, and extreme southern parts of eastern Canada (locally and rarely) south to southern Texas, the Gulf coast of the United States, and southern Florida.

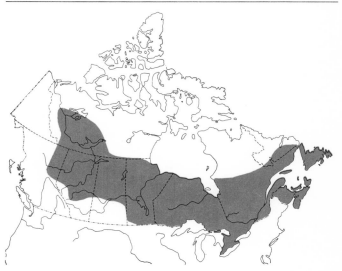

Breeding Distribution of Swamp Sparrow

Range in Canada. Breeds in central-western and southern Mackenzie (Norman Wells, Keith Arm, Hill Island Lake), northeastern and central-eastern British Columbia (Minaker River, Nulki Lake, Peace River parklands), northern to south-central Alberta (south to Battle River region and Red Deer), northern and central Saskatchewan (Lake Athabasca, Churchill River, Emma Lake, Nipawin); northern, central, and southern Manitoba; northern, central, and southern Ontario; central and southern Quebec (Paul Bay, Lake Mistassini, the north shore of the Gulf of St. Lawrence east to Blanc Sablon at least, and southward including Anticosti and Magdalen islands), southern Labrador (Goose Bay), Newfoundland, New Brunswick, Prince Edward Island, and Nova Scotia (including Cape Breton Island).

Scarce in migration in southern British Columbia (Yahk, Indianpoint Lake).

Casual in north-central Quebec (near Redmond Lake).

Occasional in winter in extreme southern Ontario, southwestern Quebec, New Brunswick, Prince Edward Island, and Nova Scotia.

Subspecies. (1) *Melospiza georgiana ericrypta* Oberholser: B.C., Alta., Sask., Man., n. Ont. (Rainy River Dist., Chapleau), c. and s. Que. (s. to Lake St. John, Gaspé Pen.), Lab., Nfld., extreme n. N.B. (2) *M. g. georgiana* (Latham), characterized by darker, duller upper parts: s. Ont. (Biscotasing, Eganville southward), sw. Que. (Kazabazua, Quebec City southward), c. and s. N.B., P.E.I., N.S.

SONG SPARROW

Le Pinson chanteur. *Melospiza melodia* (Wilson)
Plate 68. L. 6 to 7 in.

Wings short and rounded; ninth (outermost) primary shorter than or equal to fourth; tail longish and rounded at tip. The species is extremely variable geographically, west coast populations being darker than more eastern populations (*see* Subspecies). *Adults* (*M. m. melodia*): Top of head brown, narrowly streaked with black and with a narrow grey median stripe; back and scapulars, brown streaked with black and with a little greyish feather edging; rump, olive brown lightly streaked with dusky; upper tail coverts with a median streak of dark brown; two inconspicuous whitish wing bars; tail brown, the two central feathers with a dusky median line; broad whitish or greyish line over eye; sides of head buffy or greyish with three dark narrow stripes: one behind eye, one along lower edge of cheek, the third bordering sides of throat; sides of neck greyish, lightly streaked with brown; under parts white, the breast, sides, and flanks distinctly streaked with dark brown or black with usually a central breast spot; bill, dusky above, paler below; legs pale brownish. *Juvenal:* Resembles adult, but white and grey areas are replaced by yellowish white or buffy; breast streaks finer and usually not forming a breast spot; plumage texture looser. Very similar to juvenal Lincoln's and Swamp sparrows but (when wing fully developed) outermost (ninth) primary shorter than fourth in the Song, longer in Lincoln's. In the flesh, the juvenal Swamp Sparrow has the inside of mouth yellowish, thus separating it from juvenal Song Sparrow.

Measurements (*M. m. melodia*). *Adult male:* wing, 62.4–69.9 (65.8); tail, 63.1–71 (66.9); exposed culmen, 11.5–13.1 (12.2); tarsus, 20.9–22.3 (21.8). *Adult female:* wing, 60–64.5 (61.9) mm.

Field Marks. A common bird about garden shrubbery all across southern parts of the country. A brown-backed sparrow (in British Columbia very dark and sooty), its whitish under parts heavily streaked with brown and usually with a dark central breast spot. Flies with a pumping action of the longish tail. Several other sparrows have a conspicuously streaked breast, but the Song Sparrow lacks white outer tail feathers shown by the Vesper; it is smaller and much less heavily streaked below than the Fox Sparrow; it has a longer tail than the Savannah and never shows any yellow in front of the eye; adults lack the buffy suffusion on the breast shown by the Lincoln's. In addition, the Song Sparrow's frequently uttered call-note instantly separates it from any of these. *Voice:* The spritely sweet song is a characteristic spring and summer sound in most of southern Canada. It begins with two or three loud notes which sound like *sweet, sweet, sweet,* followed by a trill, then several short notes that run down to the end of the song. The common call-note is *chimp* with a peculiar quality unlike that of any similar sparrow.

Habitat. Bushy shrubbery along the margins of ponds, lakes, and streams; bushy openings and edges of woods; farmland thickets; shrubbery about buildings; hedgerows; bushy pastures. Not a bird of closed-canopy mature forest.

Nesting. Either on the ground or in a bush or small tree. Early nests are most often on the ground. Nest, composed externally of grasses, weeds, bark and leaves, is lined with finer grasses, roots, and hair. *Eggs*, 3 to 5; pale bluish to greyish green, speckled and blotched with browns and reddish browns. Incubation, by the female alone, requires slightly over 12 or 13 days, rarely 14 or 15 days (Margaret M. Nice).

Range. Breeds from southern Alaska (including the Aleutian Islands) eastward across much of southern Canada to Newfoundland, and south to Mexico, northern New Mexico, northern Arkansas, southeastern Tennessee, northern Georgia, and northwestern South Carolina. Winters from southern Alaska and parts of southern Canada south to southern United States and Mexico.

Breeding Distribution of Song Sparrow

Range in Canada. Breeds from central-southern Yukon (Squanga Lake), central-southern Mackenzie (southern Great Slave Lake; perhaps Fort Simpson), northern Saskatchewan (Lake Athabasca, Stony Rapids, Reindeer River), northern Manitoba (Herchmer), northern Ontario (Raft River, Moosonee), southern Quebec (Island Rapids on Bell River, Lake St. John, north shore of the Gulf of St. Lawrence east to Blanc Sablon), and southwestern Newfoundland (Parsons Pond, Codroy Valley), south through British Columbia (including Vancouver and Queen Charlotte islands but not known to nest in the northeastern corner beyond Peace River parklands), Alberta, Saskatchewan, Manitoba, Ontario, Quebec (including Anticosti and Magdalen islands), New Brunswick, Prince Edward Island, and Nova Scotia (including Cape Breton Island).

Winters in coastal and southern British Columbia, southern Ontario (north rarely to Barrie and Ottawa), and in small numbers in southwestern Quebec (Montreal, rarely to Quebec City), southern New Brunswick, Prince Edward Island, and Nova Scotia; rarely in Newfoundland (Mobile, St. John's).

Casual at Churchill, Manitoba, and in southeastern Keewatin (mouth of McConnell River). Accidental on Banks Island (DeSalis Bay), N.W.T.

Subspecies. (1) *Melospiza melodia melodia* (Wilson): se. Ont. (Muskoka Dist.), Que., Nfld., N.B., P.E.I., N.S. (2) *M. m. euphonia* Wetmore (upper parts duller than *melodia*): s. Ont. (Bruce County, Hamilton). (3) *M. m. juddi* Bishop (upper parts more greyish, the back feathers with more contrasting blackish centres): c.-e. B.C. (Peace River), Mack., Alta. (except sw. mts.), Sask., Man., and w. Ont. (e. to James Bay). (4) *M. m. merrilli* Brewster (much darker than *juddi* and more uniformly coloured above): s. interior B.C. (Alta Lake, Shuswap Falls, Newgate), extreme sw. Alta. (Waterton Lakes Park). (5) *M. m. morphna* Oberholser (very dark coloration): sw. B.C. (Vancouver Island, Chilliwack). (6) *M. m. rufina* (Bonaparte), even darker and sootier than *morphna*, averages larger: n. coastal B.C. (Queen Charlotte, Porcher, and Spider is.). (7) *M. m. inexspectata* Riley (very similar to *morphna* but more greyish or sooty, less rufescent): s. Yukon, interior n. and c. B.C. (Atlin se. through interior B.C. to about lat. 51°, but not Peace River parklands). (8) *M. m. caurina* Ridgway (similar to *rufina* but larger): Migrant on the coast of B.C.

Remarks. This sparrow is one of the commonest and most widely distributed in southern Canada. It is also one of the most desirable. Although absent from many parts of Canada during the winter, it is one of the very earliest to return in the spring. From the first day of its arrival until well after most birds have ceased singing in late summer, its sweet, pleasing song is heard all over the countryside. Weed seeds bulk large in its diet, although it eats insects also. P. A. Taverner estimated, conservatively, that in the southern cultivated parts of Ontario alone Song Sparrows destroy over eleven thousand tons of weed seeds annually.

McCOWN'S LONGSPUR
Le Bruant à collier gris
Rhynchophanes mccownii (Lawrence)
Plate 69. L. 5.5 to 6.3 in.

Bill rather stout; hind toenail long and slender. *Adult male (breeding plumage)*: Top of head black, becoming mixed with brownish grey on nape and grey on back of neck; back and scapulars, pale buffy brown broadly streaked with dusky; rump more greyish, less heavily streaked; wings with patch of chestnut formed by some of the lesser and middle coverts; tail with two dusky central feathers, the rest mostly white and tipped with brownish black (but black much reduced or absent on outermost); sides of head grey with broad white line over eye and a black one from base of bill backward across jaw; under parts mostly white with a broad black crescent

across breast; bill bluish black; eyes dark brown. *Adult male (autumn and winter)*: Similar but black areas obscured by brownish or buffy feather tips. *Adult female*: Upper parts, pale buffy brown streaked with dusky; middle wing coverts usually with a trace of chestnut; tail as in adult male; sides of head pale buff with a narrow dark brown line extending back from eye and one from base of bill backward across jaw; under parts whitish, the breast feathers tipped with buff and sometimes some grey.

Measurements. *Adult male:* wing, 87–95.9 (90.3); tail, 51.5–58.5 (54.8); exposed culmen, 10.9–12.5 (11.9); tarsus, 19–20.4 (19.7). *Adult female:* wing, 81.7–86.2 (84.5) mm.

Fig. 69 Tail of McCown's Longspur

Field Marks. Adult male in spring and summer is easily recognizable by the black crescent on the breast and black top of head (Horned Lark also has a black crescent on the breast, but its thin bill and face markings are quite different). Female McCown's Longspur is a brown sparrow with unstreaked breast. It is most like the female Chestnut-collared Longspur, but the McCown's unstreaked under parts and peculiar tail pattern (spread tail forms an inverted dark 'T' on an otherwise white background; Fig. 69)

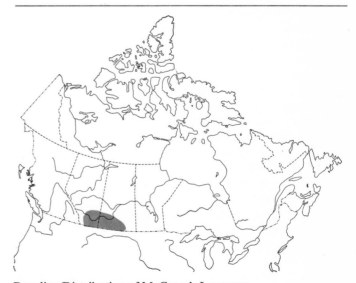

Breeding Distribution of McCown's Longspur

are helpful in separating the two (*see* Chestnut-collared Longspur). *Voice:* Song is an exuberant and pleasing series of warbles and twitters, usually given as the bird floats slowly downward to the ground with spread tail and wings.

Habitat. Short-grass plains; occasionally cultivated fields.

Nesting. In a small depression on the ground. Nest is mostly of coarse grasses and is lined with finer grasses. *Eggs*, 3 to 5, rarely 6; white to pale greenish, speckled, scrawled, and lined with browns and a little purplish grey. Incubation requires 12 days (F. W. Mickey), probably entirely by the female.

Range. Breeds from southern Alberta, southern Saskatchewan and central-northern North Dakota, south to southeastern Wyoming, northeastern Colorado, northwestern Nebraska, and central North Dakota. Winters from Arizona, Colorado, and Kansas south to northwestern Mexico and southeastern Texas.

Range in Canada. Breeds in southeastern Alberta (east of the mountains: north to Youngstown, west to Calgary) and southern Saskatchewan (Lucky Lake, Davidson, Regina). Recorded in migration in southwestern Manitoba (Whitewater Lake).

Casual in southern British Columbia (Chilliwack, Newgate).

LAPLAND LONGSPUR

Le Bruant lapon. *Calcarius lapponicus* (Linnaeus)
Plate 69. L. 6 to 7 in.

Hind toenail long, as long as or longer than hind toe. *Adult male (breeding plumage)*: Head and breast black, except a broad white or buffy stripe behind eye, this stripe extending downward on sides of neck and sides of breast; hind-neck chestnut; back and scapulars buffy, heavily striped with black; tail mostly blackish brown, the outermost feathers on each side largely white terminally, the next feather with only a little white near the tip; under parts, posterior to black breast, white, the sides and flanks streaked with black; bill yellow with dusky tip; legs blackish. *Adult female (breeding plumage)*: Somewhat like adult male but top of head brownish black streaked with buff; a broad buffy stripe over eye; ear patch brown, narrowly margined with black; variable amounts of black on lower throat and breast but mixed with white and buff (sometimes only narrowly streaked with black); hind-neck with chestnut paler, more restricted, and streaked with dusky. *Adults and young in autumn and winter*: Resemble adult females in breeding plumage but buffier above and below; males have more extensive chestnut patch on hind-neck but much obscured by buff feather tips. *Juvenal*: Upper parts yellowish buff and brown, heavily streaked with black; under parts yellowish white, the breast and sides tinged with yellowish buff and streaked with black; wings and tail of young similar to those of adults.

Measurements (*C. l. lapponicus*). *Adult male*: wing, 92–96.4 (93.7); tail, 61–69.4 (64.3); exposed culmen, 10.5–11.8 (11.2); tarsus, 19.9–21.9 (21.0). *Adult female*: wing, 84–87.6 (86.2) mm.

Distinctions. In all plumages shows less white in the tail than McCown's and Chestnut-collared longspurs (Fig. 70).

Field Marks. Adult males in breeding plumage are unmistakable by black crown, face, and breast and chestnut hind-neck. Females are more nondescript but usually are accom-

panied by males. Males (both old and young) in autumn and winter have no black on the head but show some evidence of chestnut hind-neck. Both males and females show broad buffy streaks on the back and less white in the spread tail than do other longspurs (Fig. 70). All longspurs spend much time on the ground and usually run instead of hopping. *Voice:* On the arctic breeding grounds, a short but lively, tinkling, warbling song is given in flight, usually as the bird descends slowly to the ground. Flight-call is of two or three syllables; the second and third notes run together and are slightly lower than the first.

Fig. 70 Tail of Lapland Longspur

Habitat. In the breeding season, arctic tundra, preferring wet hummocky areas, tussocky meadows, grass and shrub cover; also sedge tundra. In migration and winter, weedy and grassy fields, grain stubbles, airfields, and shores, usually in companies or flocks, often associated with Horned Larks, Snow Buntings, or Pipits.

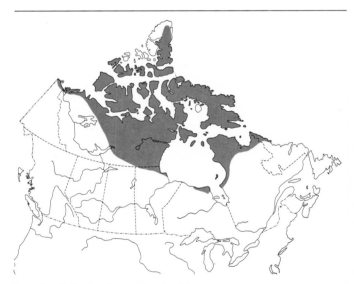

Breeding Distribution of Lapland Longspur

Nesting. In a depression in the ground, in a hummock or tussock, often under shrubs. Nest is of grasses lined with fine grasses, feathers, willow cotton, and sometimes hair. *Eggs*, usually 4 to 6; greenish grey to olive brown, blotched and speckled with browns and lined and spotted with black. Incubation 10½ to 13 days (W. H. Drury), by the female; 12 days (D. F. Parmelee).

Range. Circumpolar. Breeds in much of Alaska, northern

Canada, Greenland, and northern Eurasia. In North America winters from southern Canada south to northern California, northern Arizona, New Mexico, northeastern Texas, southern Louisiana, and Virginia.

Range in Canada. Breeds in the Arctic from Prince Patrick Island (Mould Bay), Melville Island (Winter Harbour), and northern Ellesmere Island (Lake Hazen) south to northern Yukon (Herschel Island), northern Mackenzie (Mackenzie Delta, Coppermine, Heuss Lake), southern Keewatin (Nueltin Lake), northeastern Manitoba (Churchill), northern Ontario (Little Cape, Cape Henrietta Maria), James Bay (Twin Islands), northern Quebec (Cape Jones, Payne Lake, mouth of Koksoak River, and northern Labrador south at least to Okak).

Migrates through most parts of southern Canada, being especially common in the Prairie Provinces but very rare in Newfoundland (sight record only: St. Anthony).

Winters in small numbers in southern British Columbia (Lulu Island, Okanagan Landing), southern Alberta (Milk River), southern Saskatchewan (Cypress Hills region), southern Ontario (north about to Ottawa), southwestern Quebec (Aylmer, Frelighsburg), New Brunswick, Prince Edward Island, and Nova Scotia.

Subspecies. (1) *Calcarius lapponicus lapponicus* (Linnaeus): Breeds in the Arctic Archipelago, e. Mack. (Coppermine), Keewatin, n. Man., n. Ont., n. Que., n. Lab. (2) *C. l. alascensis* Ridgway (upper parts paler than in *lapponicus*): Breeds in n. Yukon and nw. Mack. (Mackenzie Delta).

Remarks. In southern parts of Canada we know the Lapland Longspur as a spring and autumn migrant and winter resident. It is a ground bird, inhabiting open fields and shores in winter, often in association with Horned Larks and Snow Buntings. On the ground it ordinarily runs about, but it is capable of hopping also. In its summer home in the low Arctic, the male has a delightful song which he pours out while he gently floats down to the ground on set wings.

SMITH'S LONGSPUR
Le Bruant de Smith. *Calcarius pictus* (Swainson)
Plate 69. L. 5.7 to 6.5 in.

Hind toenail elongated. *Adult male* (*breeding plumage*): Top and sides of head black, bordered below by white and with a white line over eye and an elongated white spot on the ear region; back feathers and scapulars with blackish centres and broad buffy margins; back of neck and entire under parts, ochraceous buff; anterior lesser wing coverts black, posterior ones white, forming a broad white bar; tail brownish black centrally, the outermost feather on each side mainly white, that next to it with a long white stripe, the third from outside with traces of white on the basal part of outer web; bill dark brown above, paler below and often yellowish at base; legs brown. *Adult male* (*autumn and winter*): Similar to breeding male but black of head replaced by streaks of buff and dusky, the breast more or less lightly streaked with dusky. *Adult female:* Somewhat like winter male. *Young in autumn and winter:* Similar to adults in winter but anterior lesser wing coverts brown instead of black and with white wing bar very narrow.

Measurements. *Adult male:* wing, 90.5–95.5 (92.7); tail 60.5–68.3 (64.4); exposed culmen, 10–11.2 (10.7); tarsus, 19.2–20.8 (19.9). *Adult female:* wing, 84–91 (87.1) mm.

Field Marks. The adult male in breeding plumage, with black crown and cheeks and plain buffy under parts, is easily recognizable. Females and all autumn birds are more obscure, the head streaked buffy and dusky. The under parts are buffer than those of other longspurs, and the legs, especially of the young, are paler brown.

Habitat. In the nesting season, grassy and hummocky tundra. In migration, fields, prairies, airports, and similar grassy and weedy open places.

Nesting. On the ground, often on a mossy hummock or grassy tussock. Nest is of grasses lined with finer grasses, feathers, and down. *Eggs*, usually 4 to 6; pale greenish or pale bluish, speckled with browns and lined and spotted with black (only one set seen by the writer). Incubation period 11½ to 12 days (Jehl and Hussell).

Range. Breeds in northern Alaska and the low Arctic and Subarctic of northwestern mainland Canada east to northern Ontario. Winters from Kansas and Iowa south to Oklahoma, central Texas, northwestern Louisiana, Mississippi, and Alabama; rarely Tennessee.

Breeding Distribution of Smith's Longspur

Range in Canada. Breeds from northern Yukon (Herschel Island), northern Mackenzie (Caribou Hills west of Mackenzie Delta, Anderson River, Coppermine), south to extreme northwestern British Columbia (Kelsall Lake), central-eastern Mackenzie (Grassy Island), southern Keewatin (Windy River), northeastern Manitoba (Churchill), and northern Ontario (Fort Severn, Cape Henrietta Maria).

Migrates mainly through Manitoba, Saskatchewan, and Alberta. Rare in central and southern British Columbia (Dease Lake, Kispiox Valley, Swan Lake in Peace River District, Boundary Pass). Rare in southern Ontario (Port Arthur; sight records for Simcoe County).

Subspecies. Kemsies (1961, *Can. Field-Nat.* 75: 143–49) has recently proposed three subspecies: (1) *Calcarius pictus pictus* (Swainson): Breeds in Yukon, nw. B.C., Mack.,

Keewatin, n. Man.; (2) *C. p. mersi* Kemsies (upper parts with light and dark areas more in contrast, lower parts paler than in *pictus*): n. Ont.; (3) *C. p. roweorum* Kemsies, a dark race breeding in Alaska, has been recorded by Kemsies (loc. cit.) as a migrant in Mack., Alta., Sask., and Man. The validity of these races has not yet been decided upon by the A.O.U. Check-list Committee.

CHESTNUT-COLLARED LONGSPUR

Le Bruant à ventre noir. *Calcarius ornatus* (Townsend)
Plate 69. L. 5.2 to 6.5 in.

Hind toenail moderately elongated. *Adult male (breeding plumage)*: Top of head, stripe behind eye, stripe on lower ear coverts, black; stripe over eye and spot on nape, white; hind-neck deep chestnut; back and scapulars, buff and grey thickly striped with black; lesser wing coverts black; tail with two middle feathers mostly brown, the others white basally, the two or three outermost mainly white; cheeks and throat white, the cheeks tinged with buff (occasionally throat also); breast and most of anterior abdomen black (sometimes mixed with chestnut); posterior abdomen and under tail coverts, white; bill bluish grey, blackish at tip and along culmen; legs dark brown. *Adult male (autumn and winter)*: Similar to breeding plumage but black areas obscured or hidden by buffy feather tips. *Adult female:* Upper parts greyish buffy brown with dusky streaks; under parts greyish buff, breast and anterior abdomen darkest and usually faintly streaked with dusky; throat paler and often bordered on either side by a narrow dusky streak; legs more brownish than male's. *Young (first autumn and winter)*: Similar to adults in winter but lesser wing coverts brown and buff instead of black and white.

Measurements. *Adult male:* wing, 81.2–86.8 (84.4); tail, 55–60 (57); exposed culmen, 10–11.2 (10.7); tarsus, 18.9–20 (19.6). *Adult female:* wing, 75.9–80 (77.9) mm.

Fig. 71 Tail of Chestnut-collared Longspur

Field Marks. This and McCown's Longspur are summer residents of the prairies and are often found in the same area. In the nesting season the male Chestnut-collared has black under parts and a white or buffy face and throat, a combination that separates it from other longspurs. Females and autumn birds are more difficult to recognize, but in the Chestnut-collared the breast is faintly streaked (plain in Mc-Cown's) and the tail pattern, shown in flight, is different (Fig. 71). *Voice:* The spirited and pleasing song is usually given as the bird, with spread tail, glides to the ground after a short flight. Common call-note is *til-lip* (first syllable accented), also a staccato twitter, probably of alarm.

Habitat. Short-grass plains and prairies.

Nesting. On the ground, usually in a hollow and often concealed in grass or under shrubs. Nest is composed externally of grasses and weed stems and is lined with fine grasses and sometimes hair. *Eggs*, 4 to 6; greyish white to pale buff or greenish white, spotted, speckled, and lined with browns and lavender. The incubation period is 12½ days (A. D. DuBois), by the female.

Range. Breeds from southern Alberta east to southern Manitoba southeastward to northeastern Colorado, northern Nebraska, and southwestern Minnesota. Winters from northern Arizona, northeastern Colorado, and central Kansas south to northwestern Mexico, southern Texas, and northern Louisiana.

Breeding Distribution of Chestnut-collared Longspur

Range in Canada. Breeds in southern Alberta (west to Calgary, north to Bittern Lake), southern Saskatchewan (south of Biggar; Burke Lake, 15 miles east of Saskatoon; and Quill Lakes southward), and southwestern Manitoba (Brandon, Winnipeg).

Casual in British Columbia (Kispiox Valley, Newgate), northern Alberta (Fort MacMurray), and northern Manitoba (Churchill). Accidental in New Brunswick (Nantucket Island) and Nova Scotia (Cape Sable, May 28, 1964; also a sight record at Bon Portage Island).

SNOW BUNTING

Le Plectrophane des neiges
Plectrophenax nivalis (Linnaeus)
Plate 69. L. 6 to 7.4 in.

Bill rather small. Hind toenail rather long and slender. *Adult male (breeding plumage)*: Mostly pure white, but back, scapulars, alula, tertials, primaries, except basally, black (some individuals also have black primary coverts); four to six inner tail feathers black, the rest white; bill and legs black. *Adult male (winter)*: Similar to breeding male but upper parts, face, breast, and sides tinged with rusty brown, the blacks mostly concealed except in wing; bill yellow, tipped dusky. *Adult female (breeding plumage)*: Similar to adult male in breeding plumage but hind-neck usually with some dusky streaks, top of head and often other areas of body tinged with rusty; black of back and scapulars mixed with white and often extending farther down rump; primaries with less extensive white areas, the lesser and greater wing coverts blackish with whitish margins; bill and legs black. *Adult female (winter)*: Similar to breeding female, but upper parts, sides of head, breast, and sides of body tinged with rusty; bill yellow with dusky tip. *Juvenal*: Upper parts buffy grey, the back streaked vaguely with black, the rest very lightly streaked; throat pale grey, breast and sides buffy grey (paler than back) with faint dusky streaks; abdomen yellowish white.

Measurements. *Adult male:* wing, 103.8–110 (108.2); tail, 66–74 (68.9); exposed culmen, 9.8–11.4 (10.4); tarsus, 20.3–22 (21.5). *Adult female:* wing, 98–102.3 (99.9) mm.

Field Marks. A robust ground finch with much white in plumage. Usually runs instead of hopping. Flight undulating, flashing contrasting areas of black and white in the wing. In winter the white areas are heavily tinged with rusty, and the birds are usually in flocks. *Voice:* In flight it has a characteristic short, slightly rising, musical twitter, which often ends with an emphatic *chert*. On the breeding grounds it has a loud musical warbled song, which is given either on the ground or in flight.

Habitat. In the Arctic it favours terrain such as rocky shores and stony escarpments, mountain slopes, cliffs and their talus; hummocky moss tundra; also arctic human settlements. In migration and winter, open weedy and grassy fields, grain stubbles, shores, and roadsides.

Nesting. In crevices in rocks, cracks in cliffs (sometimes at considerable heights), under stones and rock piles, and in various other cavities and crannies. Nest is made of mosses and grasses and lined with grasses, feathers, and hair. *Eggs*, usually 4 to 7; greyish white to bluish white, blotched and speckled (often heavily) with various browns and often lavender. Incubation period 12½ to 13 days (Sutton and Parmelee), 12 days (Wynne-Edwards); by the female.

Range. Circumpolar arctic parts of the world and more locally in subarctic areas, migrating farther south in winter. In North America breeds in Alaska (including the Aleutian Islands), arctic Canada, and Greenland. Winters from central-western and southern Alaska and southern and south-central Canada south to Oregon, northern Utah, northern New Mexico, Kansas, Indiana, Ohio, and Virginia, and southward on the Pacific Coast casually to northwestern California and on the Atlantic Coast casually to Georgia.

Range in Canada. Breeds from the high Arctic, Prince Patrick Island (Mould Bay), Ellef Ringnes Island (Isachsen), Axel Heiberg Island, and northern Ellesmere Island (Alert) south to northern Yukon (Herschel Island), northwestern and central-eastern Mackenzie (Mackenzie Delta, Harrowby Bay, Clinton-Colden Lake), central and southeastern Keewatin (Beverly Lake, Chesterfield Inlet, Eskimo Point), Southampton Island, Hudson Bay (Belcher Is-

lands), northern Quebec (southern Ungava Bay), and northern Labrador (Okak, perhaps Nain).

Winters all across extreme southern Canada and north at least to northwestern British Columbia (Atlin), central Alberta, central Saskatchewan (Dorintosh, Cumberland

Breeding Distribution of Snow Bunting

House), southern Manitoba (Lake St. Martin), southern Ontario (Port Arthur, Lake Nipissing), southern Quebec (Aylmer, Lake St. John, Gaspé Peninsula), southern Labrador (Battle Harbour), Newfoundland, New Brunswick, Prince Edward Island, and Nova Scotia; in milder winters north to northwestern Mackenzie (Aklavik).

Subspecies. *Plectrophenax nivalis nivalis* (Linnaeus).

Remarks. In southern Canada the Snow Bunting is a sure harbinger of winter. It is well named, for it comes just prior to the first snow squalls of late autumn; it revels all winter in the snowy countryside; and it departs for the North while there is still snow in the southland.

In winter it is usually seen in flocks, sometimes large ones. It feeds on the seeds of weeds that project above the snow. When a flock alights on a weedy field, the birds lose no time in dispersing over the ground, running rapidly from one weed to another, occasionally jumping up to snatch seeds high on the bare stalks. As the flock works the field, those in the rear rise up from time to time and alight again ahead of the others. When the field has been worked over, they all take to the air. A large flock of Snow Buntings, their white and black patterns flashing, is a pretty sight as they wheel and swirl in the soft winter sunlight. Flight is somewhat undulating. As a long, loose flock flies low over a distant snowy field, the birds seem to appear and disappear alternately, depending on whether their dark or white areas are turned toward the observer. When heavy snows cover the weed tops, the birds become conspicuous at roadsides and farmyards.

For people living in the Arctic, the Snow Bunting becomes a harbinger of spring after leaving its winter range. On its northern nesting grounds it adds a delightful song to the already long list of its pleasing attributes.

407

Glossary

Abdomen. That part of the under surface of the body between the breast and the under tail coverts.

Acute. Sharp-pointed.

Adult. A bird that has assumed its final or definitive plumage type. (Birds wearing any immature plumage, even though breeding, are called subadult, immature, or juvenile.)

Albinism. Absence or partial absence of colour in parts of animals that are normally coloured. In complete albinism the animal is all white except the iris of the eye, which is pink (*see* melanism).

Altricial. Refers to species whose young, hatched blind and helpless, require considerable rearing before they can leave the nest (*see* precocial).

Allopatric. Refers to forms whose breeding ranges do not overlap (*see* sympatric).

Alula. Feathers attached to the 'thumb' part of the wing.

Anterior. More toward the front (*see* posterior).

Aquatic. Water-frequenting.

Arboreal. Tree-frequenting.

Asymmetrical. Not symmetrical.

Attenuated. As applied to feathers, tapering gradually; slender.

Avian. Pertaining to birds.

Auricular. Pertaining to the ear.

Auriculars. Feathers of the ear region.

Axillars. A group of feathers, usually more or less elongated, at the armpit between the wing and the body.

Bar. A long marking across the body or across a feather; a transverse marking (*see* stripe).

Belly. The under surface of the body between the breast and the under tail coverts. Here used interchangeably with 'abdomen.'

Belted. Having a band across breast or belly.

Bend of Wing. The most anterior part of the folded wing.

Booted. Refers to tarsus, not divided.

Cere. A covering, sometimes swollen, of the base of the upper mandible of the bill in some birds such as hawks, owls, and parrots.

Clutch. A complete set of eggs laid by an individual female at a single nesting.

Coalesce. To grow together or unite.

Commissural Line. Line of contact between upper and lower mandibles when closed.

Confluent. Running together.

Coniferous. Applied to trees: cone-bearing, mostly evergreens.

Conspecific. Belonging to one and the same species.

Contour Feathers. The vaned or webbed feathers of the bird that form its main outside covering and give it its characteristic outline or contour. They include the flight feathers, but not the down or hairlike filoplumes.

Coverts. Small feathers covering the base of the tail; also rows of small feathers on the wing, covering the base of the flight feathers and the wing surfaces; also short feathers covering the ear region.

Crepuscular. Pertaining to twilight.

Crest. Elongated feathers on top of head.

Crown. Top of the head.

Culmen. The ridge of the upper mandible (maxilla) of the bill.

Deciduous. Shed periodically. Applied to the broad-leafed trees that shed their leaves seasonally. The plumes of herons that are shed early are said to be 'deciduous' also.

Decurved. Down-curved.

Diurnal. Active in the daytime.

Dorsal. Pertaining to the back.

Ecotone. An area of transition between two major biotic communities.

Emarginate. As applied to the tail, slightly forked. As applied to a wing feather, abruptly narrowed as though cut away.

Erectile. Capable of being raised.

Ethology. The objective study of behaviour.

Exotic. Foreign.

Extensile. Capable of being thrust out, as the tongue.

Extinct. No longer living anywhere (*see* extirpated).

Extirpated. Eradicated from part of its range (*see* extinct).

Extralimital. Occurring normally beyond the geographic boundaries of the area being discussed.

Family. A taxonomic group composed of related genera. Family names end in 'idae.' It is lower in rank than the order, higher than the genus.

Feral. Wild. Here applied to domesticated animals that are living in the wild, independent of direct assistance from man.

Flanks. The hindmost part of the sides of the body.

Frontal. Pertaining to the forehead.

Form. A neutral term, applicable to any taxonomic unit, and without particular nomenclatural significance.

Genus (*plural genera*). A taxonomic group of species that are more closely related to one another than to other species.

Graduated. With reference to the tail: middle feathers longest, the rest becoming successively shorter.

Gregarious. In flocks.

Gular. Pertaining to the throat.

Hiatus. A gap or vacant area.
Holarctic. The northern parts of both the New and Old Worlds.
Hybrid. An individual whose parents are of two different species.

Immaculate. Without markings.
Indigenous. Native to a given part of the world.
Insectivorous. Insect-eating.
Iris (plural irides). The coloured part of the eye surrounding the black pupil.

Juvenal. Refers to that particular plumage succeeding the natal down (or succeeding in certain species the naked nestling stage without natal down). It is the first plumage of real contour feathers (*see* juvenile).
Juvenile. May be applied to any immature plumage or to an immature bird.

Lamellate. Equipped with fine plates (or lamellae) as in the sides of a duck's bill.
Lateral. Pertaining to the side.
Length. Of a bird, the distance in a straight line from the tip of the bill to the tip of the longest tail feather.
Loral. Pertaining to the lores.
Lores. The area between the eye and the base of the bill.

Mandibles. In plural, the two halves of the bill. In singular, the lower half of the bill (*see* maxilla).
Mantle. The plumage of the back and upper surface of the wings.
Maxilla. The upper half of the bill; also called upper mandible.
Median or Medial. Pertaining to the middle.
Melanism. An abnormally dark coloration caused by an excess of dark pigment (*see* albinism).
Mixedwood. In reference to woodlands, composed of both coniferous and deciduous trees.
Molt or Moult. Includes both the shedding and replacement of plumage.

Nail. A horny tip of the upper mandible (or maxilla) in ducks, geese, and swans.
Nape. That part of the hind-neck just below the base of the skull.
Nuchal. Pertaining to the nape or back of neck.
Nocturnal. Active at night.

Omnivorous. Eating a large variety of both animal and plant food.
Oology. The study of birds' eggs, especially the shell.
Order. A taxonomic group composed of related families.
Ornithology. The scientific study of birds.

Pectinate. Furnished with comb-like teeth as in the middle toe of herons.
Pectoral. Pertaining to the breast.
Pelagic. Frequenting the ocean, away from the coasts.
Pensile. As applied to nests, hanging suspended from a fork of a branch, or similar situation, and not supported below.
Periphery. An outer edge or boundary.
Phase. With reference to plumage, differences in colour not correlated with age, sex, race, or season.
Phenotype. The individual's expressed traits, of which the most readily apparent are its visible characters.
Piebald. Having contrastingly coloured patches, especially white and black.
Precocial. Refers to birds whose young hatch covered with down, able to run or swim shortly after hatching; e.g. ducks, sandpipers.

Primaries. The flight feathers attached to the hand (manus) of the wing. Primaries are counted from the inside outward.
Posterior. More toward the rear (*see* anterior).
Postocular. Behind the eye.
Pyriform. Pear-shaped.

Race. The same as subspecies.
Recurved. Curved upward.
Reticulate. With reference to the tarsus, marked so that it resembles a network.
Rump. That area of the upper parts between the back and the upper tail coverts.

Scapulars. A group of feathers growing from the shoulders (humeral feather tracts).
Scute. A horny plate or scale.
Scutellate. Referring to tarsus, covered with scutes or scales.
Secondaries. Those flight feathers attached to the forearm (ulna) of the wing. The innermost, when differently shaped and coloured, are often referred to as tertials but are really specialized secondaries.
Species. Popularly thought of as a 'kind' of animal or plant. A taxonomic group of similar individuals that interbreed freely among themselves (or are biologically capable of doing so) but do not normally breed with individuals of other such groups.
Speculum. A patch on the wing, usually rectangular, contrasting in colour with the rest of the wing and often brightly coloured and more or less iridescent. It is especially common in ducks.
Spicule. Applied here to small, hard, sharp-pointed bodies on the foot of the Osprey.
Sternum. The breastbone.
Stripe. Elongated marking running lengthwise of the bird (*see* bars).
Subapical. Near the tip.
Subspecies. Geographically limited subdivisions of the species that are taxonomically different from other such subdivisions of the same species.
Subterminal. Near the end.
Superciliary. Pertaining to the eyebrow.
Sympatric. Refers to two or more forms whose breeding ranges occupy the same ground or overlap more or less.

Tarsus. That part of the foot from the base of the toes to the heel. Although popularly thought of as the 'leg,' it is really only part of the foot, corresponding to the human instep but with the bones fused. It is properly the tarsometatarsus.
Taxonomy. The classification of plants and animals according to their natural relationships.
Terrestrial. Frequenting the ground.
Tertials. Often used as a name for the innermost secondaries when they differ in shape and colour (also, as in loons, in moult pattern) from the rest of the secondaries.
Truncate. Square-tipped.

Ulna. The stouter of the two bones of the forearm on which, in birds, grow the secondaries.

Vermiculated. Marked with fine irregularly wavy lines, suggesting the tracks of many small worms.
Ventral. Pertaining to the under side; opposite of dorsal.
Vernacular Name. The name of a taxonomic unit in one's own language.
Vinaceous. Wine-coloured.

Zygodactylous. Having two toes in front and two behind.

Selected References

Some Provincial Works on Birds

Where recent comprehensive works are available, these are listed first under each province; otherwise references are cited in the alphabetical order of authors' names.

Alberta

SALT, W. RAY, and A. L. WILK *1958*. The birds of Alberta. Department of Economic Affairs, Edmonton. 511 p.

BAKER, B. W., and L. H. WALKINSHAW *1946*. Bird notes from Fawcett, Alberta. Can. Field-Nat. 60: 5–10.

CLARKE, C. H. D., and I. MCT. COWAN *1945*. Birds of Banff National Park, Alberta, Can. Field-Nat. 59: 83–103.

COWAN, I. MCT. *1955*. Birds of Jasper National Park, Alberta, Canada. Can. Wildlife Serv., Wildlife Management Bull. Ser. 2, No. 8: 1–67.

FARLEY, FRANK L. *1932*. Birds of the Battle River region. Institute of Applied Art, Ltd., Edmonton. 85 p.

GODFREY, W. E. *1952*. Birds of the Lesser Slave Lake – Peace River areas, Alberta. Nat. Mus. Canada, Bull. 126: 142–175.

RAND, A. L. *1948*. Birds of southern Alberta. Nat. Mus. Canada, Bull. 111: 1–105.

RANDALL, T. E. *1933*. A list of the breeding birds of the Athabasca district, Alberta. Can. Field-Nat. 47: 1–6.

———— *1946*. Birds of the Eastern Irrigation District, Brooks, Alberta. Can. Field-Nat. 60: 123–131.

SOPER, J. D. *1942*. The birds of Wood Buffalo Park and vicinity, Northern Alberta and District of Mackenzie, N.W.T., Canada. Trans. Roy. Can. Inst. 24: 19–97.

———— *1949*. Notes on the fauna of the former Nemiskam National Park and vicinity, Alberta. Can. Field-Nat. 63: 167–182.

———— *1949*. Birds observed in the Grande Prairie – Peace River region of northwestern Alberta, Canada. The Auk 66: 233–257.

———— *1951*. The birds of Elk Island National Park, Alberta, Canada. Can. Wildlife Serv., Wildlife Management Bull., Ser. 2, No. 3: 1–60.

TAVERNER, P. A. *1919*. The birds of the Red Deer River, Alberta. The Auk 36: 1–21; 248–265.

British Columbia

MUNRO, J. A., and I. MCT. COWAN *1947*. A review of the bird fauna of British Columbia. B.C. Prov. Mus., Spec. Pub. No. 2: 1–285.

COWAN, I. MCT. *1939*. The vertebrate fauna of the Peace River District of British Columbia. B.C. Prov. Mus., Occas. Papers, No. 1: 1–102 (Birds, p. 11–66).

DICKINSON, J. C., JR. *1953*. Report on the McCabe Collection of British Columbian Birds. Bull. Mus. Comp. Zool. 109: 123–209.

MUNRO, J. A. *1949*. The birds and mammals of the Vanderhoof region, British Columbia. Am. Midl. Nat. 41: 1–138.

———— *1950*. The birds and mammals of the Creston region, British Columbia. B.C. Prov. Mus,. Occas. Papers, No. 8: 1–90.

PAUL, W. A. B. *1959*. The birds of Kleena Kleene, Chilcotin District, British Columbia, 1947–1958. Can. Field-Nat. 73: 83–93.

SWARTH, H. S. *1922*. Birds and mammals of the Stikine River region of northern British Columbia and southeastern Alaska. Univ. Calif. Pub. Zool. 24: 125–314.

———— *1924*. Birds and mammals of the Skeena River region of northern British Columbia. Univ. Calif. Pub. Zool. 24: 315–394.

———— *1926*. Report on a collection of birds and mammals from the Atlin region, Northern British Columbia. Univ. Calif. Pub. Zool. 30: 51–162.

WEEDEN, R. B. *1960*. The birds of Chilkat Pass, British Columbia Can. Field-Nat. 74: 119–129.

Franklin District

SNYDER, L. L. *1957*. Arctic birds of Canada. Univ. Toronto Press, Toronto. 310 p.

MACDONALD, S. D. *1954*. Report on biological investigations at Mould Bay, Prince Patrick Island, N.W.T. Nat. Mus. Canada, Bull. 132: 214–238.

MANNING, T. H., E. O. HÖHN, and A. H. MACPHERSON *1956*. The birds of Banks Island. Nat. Mus. Canada, Bull. 143: 1–144.

————, and A. H. MACPHERSON *1961*. A biological investigation of Prince of Wales Island, N.W.T. Trans. Roy. Can. Inst., 33 (pt. 2): 116–239.

PARMELEE, DAVID F., and S. D. MACDONALD *1960*. The birds of west-central Ellesmere Island and adjacent areas. Nat. Mus., Canada, Bull. 169: 1–103.

SHORTT, T. M., and H. S. PETERS *1942*. Some recent bird records from Canada's Eastern Arctic. Can. J. Research 20 (sec. D): 338–348.

SOPER, J. D. *1928*. A faunal investigation of southern Baffin Island. Nat. Mus. Canada, Bull. 53: 1–143.

———— *1946*. Ornithological results of the Baffin Island expeditions of 1928–1929 and 1930–1931, together with more recent records. The Auk 63: 1–24; 223–239; 418–427.

TODD, W. E. C. 1963. (*See* under Quebec)

TUCK, L. M., and LOUIS LEMIEUX 1959. The avifauna of Bylot Island. Dansk Ornithologisk Forenings Tidsskrift 53: 137–154.

WYNNE-EDWARDS, V. C. 1952. Zoology of the Baird Expedition (1950). 1. The birds observed in central and south-east Baffin Island. The Auk 69: 353–391.

Keewatin District

HARPER, FRANCIS 1953. Birds of the Nueltin Lake Expedition, Keewatin, 1947. Am. Midl. Nat. 49: 1–116.

MACPHERSON, A. H., and T. H. MANNING 1959. The birds and mammals of Adelaide Peninsula, N.W.T. Nat. Mus. Canada, Bull. 161: 1–63.

MANNING, T. H. 1948. Notes on the country, birds and mammals west of Hudson Bay between Reindeer and Baker lakes. Can. Field-Nat. 62: 1–28.

MOWAT, F. M., and A. H. LAWRIE 1955. Bird observations from southern Keewatin and the interior of northern Manitoba. Can. Field-Nat. 69: 93–116.

PREBLE, E. A. 1902. A biological investigation of the Hudson Bay region. N. Am. Fauna, No. 22: 1–140. U.S. Dept. of Agriculture, Washington, D.C.

SAVILE, D. B. O. 1951. Bird observations at Chesterfield Inlet, Keewatin, in 1950. Can. Field-Nat. 65: 145–157.

SUTTON, G. M. 1932. The birds of Southampton Island. Mem. Carnegie Mus., 12 (pt. 2. sec. 2): 1–275.

TODD, W. E. C. 1963. (*See* under Quebec)

Labrador

AUSTIN, OLIVER L., JR. 1932.The birds of Newfoundland Labrador. Mem. Nuttall Ornithological Club, No. 7: 1–229.

TODD, W. E. C. 1963. Birds of the Labrador Peninsula and adjacent areas. Univ. Toronto Press, Toronto, p. 1–819.

Mackenzie District

CLARKE, C. H. D. 1940. A biological investigation of the Thelon Game Sanctuary. Nat. Mus. Canada, Bull. 96: 1–135.

HANSON, H. C., PAUL QUENEAU, and PETER SCOTT 1956. The geography, birds, and mammals of the Perry River region. Arctic Inst. of North America, Spec. Pub., No. 3: 1–96.

HÖHN, E. O. 1959. Birds of the mouth of the Anderson River and Liverpool Bay, Northwest Territories. Can. Field-Nat. 73: 93–114.

MACFARLANE, R. 1908. List of birds and eggs observed and collected in the North-West Territories of Canada, between 1880 and 1894. *In* Through the Mackenzie Basin, by Charles Mair. William Briggs, Toronto. 494 p. (Birds, p. 287–447).

PORSILD, A. E. 1943. Birds of the Mackenzie Delta. Can. Field-Nat. 57: 19–35. (Some additional data published later by Cowan, 1948, Murrelet 29: 21–26; and by Höhn and Robinson, 1951, Can. Field-Nat. 65: 115–118.)

PREBLE, E. A. 1908. A biological investigation of the Athabaska-Mackenzie region. N. Am. Fauna 27: 1–574.

SOPER, J. D. 1942. (*See* under Alberta)

WILLIAMS, M. Y. 1922. Biological notes along fourteen hundred miles of the Mackenzie River system. Can. Field-Nat. 36: 61–66.

––––––––– 1933. Biological notes, covering parts of the Peace, Liard, Mackenzie and Great Bear River basins. Can. Field-Nat. 47: 23–31.

Manitoba

FLEMING, J. H. 1919. (*See* under Saskatchewan)

GODFREY, W. E. 1953. Notes on birds of the area of intergradation between Eastern Prairie and Forest in Canada. Nat. Mus. Canada, Bull. 128: 189–240.

ROGERS, F. J. 1937. A preliminary list of the birds of Hillside Beach, Lake Winnipeg, Manitoba. Can. Field-Nat. 51: 79–86.

SHORTT, T. M., and SAM WALLER 1937. The birds of the Lake St. Martin region, Manitoba. Contrib. Roy. Ont. Mus. Zool. No. 10: 1–51.

SOPER, J. D. 1953. The birds of Riding Mountain National Park, Manitoba, Canada. Can. Wildlife Serv., Wildlife Management Bull., Ser. 2, No. 6: 1–54.

TAVERNER, P. A. 1919. The birds of Shoal Lake, Manitoba. Ottawa Nat. 32: 137–144, 157–164; also 33: 12–20 (Supplementary data by E. S. Norman, 1920, Can. Field-Nat. 34: 154).

––––––––– , and G. M. SUTTON 1934. The birds of Churchill, Manitoba. Annals Carnegie Mus. 23: 1–83.

New Brunswick

SQUIRES, W. A. 1952. The birds of New Brunswick. The New Brunswick Mus., Monogr. Ser. No. 4. 164 p.

PETTINGILL, OLIN S., JR. 1939. The bird life of the Grand Manan Archipelago. Proc. Nova Scotian Inst. Sci. 19: 293–372.

Newfoundland

PETERS, HAROLD S., and THOMAS D. BURLEIGH 1951. The birds of Newfoundland. Newfoundland Dept. of Nat. Res., St. John's. 431 p. (Supplementary notes published by Godfrey, 1961. Nat. Mus. Canada, Bull. 172: 98–111).

Nova Scotia

TUFTS, ROBIE W. 1961 (=1962). The birds of Nova Scotia. Nova Scotia Mus., Halifax. 481 p.

GODFREY, W. E. 1958. Birds of Cape Breton Island, Nova Scotia. Can. Field-Nat. 72: 7–27.

Ontario

ALLIN, A. E. 1940. The vertebrate fauna of Darlington Township, Durham County, Ontario. Trans. Roy. Can. Inst. 23: 83–118.

BAILLIE, J. L., JR., and PAUL HARRINGTON 1936–37. The distribution of breeding birds in Ontario. Trans. Roy. Can. Inst. 21: 1–50, 199–283.

––––––––– , and C. E. HOPE 1943. The summer birds of the northeast shore of Lake Superior, Ontario. Contrib. Roy. Ont. Mus. Zool. 23: 1–27.

––––––––– 1947. The summer birds of Sudbury district, Ontario. Contrib. Roy. Ont. Mus. Zool. 28: 1–32.

BREMNER, R. M. 1949. Observations on the birds of the Casummit – Birch Lakes region of northwest Ontario. Can. Field-Nat. 63: 161–165.

BROOMAN, R. C. 1954. The birds of Elgin County. The Gilbert Press, St. Thomas.

BROWN, N. R. 1947. Observations on the birds of the Petawawa Military Reserve and surrounding district, Renfrew County, Ontario. Can. Field-Nat. 61: 47–55.

CALVERT, E. W. 1925. A preliminary list of the birds of the Lindsay district, Ontario. Can. Field-Nat. 39: 49–51, 72–74.

DEAR, L. S. 1940. Breeding birds of the region of Thunder Bay,

Lake Superior, Ontario. Trans. Roy. Can. Inst. 23: 119–143.

DENIS, KEITH *1961.* Birds of the Canadian Lakehead area. Thunder Bay Field Nat. Club, Suppl. 2: 1–8 (Mimeo.).

DEVITT, O. E. *1943–44.* The birds of Simcoe County, Ontario. Trans. Roy. Can. Inst. 24 (pt. 2): 241–314; 25 (pt. 1): 29–116. (Addenda published by same author in Can. Field-Nat. 64: 145–148; 76: 153–158.)

FLEMING, J. H. *1901.* A list of the birds of the Districts of Parry Sound and Muskoka, Ontario. The Auk 18: 33–45 (Corrections by same author, 1901, The Auk 18: 276–277).

_____ *1906–07.* Birds of Toronto, Ontario. The Auk 23: 437–453; 24: 71–89 (Additions by same author, 1913, The Auk 30: 225–228).

GOODWILL, J. E. V. *1942.* The summer birds of the Madsen Area, Patricia District, Ontario. Can. Field-Nat. 56: 131–133.

LLOYD, HOYES *1944.* The birds of Ottawa, 1944. Can. Field-Nat. 58: 143–175 (Addenda by same author and others have appeared more recently in same journal).

MACLULICH, D. A. *1938.* Birds of Algonquin Provincial Park, Ontario. Contrib. Roy. Ont. Mus. Zool. 13: 1–47.

MANNING, T. H. *1952.* Birds of the West James Bay and southern Hudson Bay coasts. Nat. Mus. Canada, Bull. 125: 1–114.

RICKER, W. E., and C. H. D. CLARKE *1939.* The birds of the vicinity of Lake Nipissing, Ontario. Contrib. Roy. Ont. Mus. Zool. 16: 1–25.

SAUNDERS, W. E., and E. M. S. DALE *1933.* History and list of birds of Middlesex County, Ontario. Trans. Roy. Can. Inst. 19: 161–248.

SMITH, W. JOHN *1957.* Birds of the Clay Belt of Northern Ontario and Quebec. Can. Field-Nat. 71: 163–181.

SHEPPARD, R. W. (n.d.) (=*1960*). Bird life of Canada's Niagara Frontier. Mimeo. 50 p.

SNYDER, L. L. *1928a.* The summer birds of Lake Nipigon. Trans. Roy. Can. Inst. 16: 251–277.

_____ *1928b.* A faunal investigation of the Lake Abitibi region, Ontario. Univ. Toronto Stud., Biol. Ser. 32: 1–34.

_____ *1930.* A faunal investigation of King Township, York County, Ontario. Trans. Roy. Can. Inst. 17: 183–202 (Additions by Ussher *1939.* Can. Field-Nat. 53: 101–110).

_____ *1931.* A faunal survey of Long Point and vicinity, Norfolk County, Ontario. Trans. Roy. Can. Inst. 18: 117–227.

_____ *1938.* A faunal investigation of western Rainy River district, Ontario. Trans. Roy. Can. Inst. 22: 157–213.

_____ *1941.* The birds of Prince Edward County, Ontario. Univ. Toronto Stud., Biol. Ser. 48: 25–92.

_____ *1942.* Summer birds of the Sault Ste. Marie region, Ontario. Trans. Roy. Can. Inst. 24: 121–153 (Addenda by Warburton, 1950, Can. Field-Nat. 64: 192–199).

_____ *1951.* Ontario birds. Clarke, Irwin and Co., Ltd., Toronto. 1–248 p.

_____ *1953.* Summer birds of Western Ontario. Trans. Roy. Can. Inst. 30: 47–95.

_____ *1957.* Changes in the avifauna of Ontario. *In* Changes in the Fauna of Ontario, edited by F. A. Urquhart. Univ. Toronto Press, p. 26–42.

SPIERS, D. H., and J. M. SPIERS *1947.* Birds of the vicinity of North Bay, Ontario. Can. Field-Nat. 61: 23–38.

TAVERNER, P. A., and B. H. SWALES *1907–08.* The birds of Point Pelee. Wilson Bull. 19: 37–54, 82–99, 133–153; and 20: 79–96, 107–129.

TODD, W. E. C. *1963.* (*See* under Quebec)

TONER, G. C., W. E. EDWARDS, and M. W. CURTIS *1942.* Birds of Leeds County, Ontario. Can. Field-Nat. 56: 8–12, 21–24, 34–44, 50–56.

WILLIAMS, M. Y. *1920.* Notes on the fauna of the Moose River and the Mattagami and Abitibi tributaries. Can. Field-Nat. 34: 121–126.

_____ *1921.* Notes on the fauna of Lower Pagwachuan, Lower Kenogami and Lower Albany rivers of Ontario. Can. Field-Nat. 35: 94–98.

_____ *1942.* Notes on the fauna of Bruce Peninsula, Manitoulin and adjacent islands. Can. Field-Nat. 56: 60–62, 70–81.

Prince Edward Island

GODFREY, W. E. *1954.* Birds of Prince Edward Island. Nat. Mus. Canada, Bull. 132: 155–213.

Quebec

TODD, W. E. C. *1963.* Birds of the Labrador Peninsula and Adjacent Areas. Univ. Toronto Press, Toronto. p. 1–819.

BALL, S. C. *1938.* Summer birds of the Forillon, Gaspé County, Quebec. Can. Field-Nat. 52: 95–103, 120–122 (Additions by same author, 1954. Can. Field-Nat. 68: 103–108).

_____ *1952.* Fall bird migration on the Gaspé Peninsula. Peabody Mus. Nat. Hist., Bull. 7: 1–211.

BRAUND, F. W., and E. P. MCCULLAGH *1940.* The birds of Anticosti Island, Quebec. Wilson Bull. 52: 96–123.

DIONNE, C. E. *1906.* Les oiseaux de la Province de Quebec. Dussault and Proulx, Quebec. 414 p.

EKLUND, CARL R. *1956.* Bird and mammal notes from the interior Ungava Peninsula. Can. Field-Nat. 70: 69–76.

GABRIELSON, I. N. *1938.* Summer notes from Blue Sea Lake. Can. Field-Nat. 52: 79–87 (Additions by same author, Can. Field-Nat., 1949, Vol. 63, p. 137–143; and 1962, Vol. 76, p. 192–199).

_____ *1952.* Notes on the birds of the north shore of the Gulf of St. Lawrence. Can. Field-Nat. 66: 44–59.

GABORIAULT, WILFRID *1961.* Les oiseaux aux Îles-de-la-Madeleine. Le Naturaliste Canadien 88: 166–224.

GODFREY, W. E. *1949.* Birds of Lake Mistassini and Lake Albanel, Quebec. Nat. Mus. Canada, Bull. 114: 1–43.

_____, and A. L. WILK *1948.* Birds of the Lake St. John Region, Quebec. Nat. Mus. Canada, Bull. 110: 1–32.

HARPER, FRANCIS *1958.* Birds of the Ungava Peninsula. University of Kansas, Misc. Pub. 17: 1–171.

HILDEBRAND, HENRY *1950.* Notes on the birds of the Ungava Bay District. Can. Field-Nat. 64: 55–67.

LEWIS, H. F. *1922–38.* Notes on Labrador Peninsula birds. The Auk 39: 507–516; 40: 135–137; 42: 74–86, 278–281; 44: 59–66; 45: 227–229; and Can. Field-Nat. 42: 191–194; 44: 109–111; 45: 113–114; 48: 98–102, 115–119; 51: 99–105, 119–123; 52: 47–51.

LLOYD, HOYES *1944.* (*See* under Ontario)

MANNING, T. H. *1946.* Bird and mammal notes from the east side of Hudson Bay. Can. Field-Nat. 60: 71–85.

_____ *1949.* The birds of north-western Ungava. *In* A summer on Hudson Bay, by Mrs. Tom Manning. Hodder and Stoughton, London, p. 155–224.

_____, and A. H. MACPHERSON *1952.* Birds of the East James Bay Coast between Long Point and Cape Jones. Can. Field-Nat. 66: 1–35.

MCNEIL, RAYMOND *1961.* Avifaune du Parc de la Vérendrye, Québec. Le Naturaliste Canadien 88: 97–129.

SAVILE, D. B. O. *1950.* Bird notes from Great Whale River, Que. Can. Field-Nat. 64: 95–99.

SMITH, W. J. *1957.* (*See* under Ontario)

TAVERNER, P. A. *1929*. Bird notes from the Canadian Labrador, 1928. Can. Field-Nat. 43: 74–79.

Saskatchewan

BELCHER, MARGARET *1961*. Birds of Regina. Saskatchewan Nat. Hist. Soc., Spec. Pub. 3: 1–76.

FLEMING, J. H. *1919*. Birds of northern Saskatchewan and northern Manitoba collected in 1914 by Capt. Angus Buchanan. Can. Field-Nat. 33: 109–113.

GODFREY, W. E. *1950*. Birds of the Cypress Hills and Flotten Lake regions, Saskatchewan. Nat. Mus. Canada, Bull. 120: 1–96.

HOUSTON, C. S. *1949*. The birds of the Yorkton District, Saskatchewan. Can. Field-Nat. 63: 215–241.

————, and M. G. STREET *1959*. The birds of the Saskatchewan River, Carlton to Cumberland. Saskatchewan Nat. Hist. Soc., Spec. Pub. 2: 1–205.

MITCHELL, H. H. *1924*. Birds of Saskatchewan. Can. Field-Nat. 38: 101–118.

MOWAT, F. M. *1947*. Notes on the birds of Emma Lake, Saskatchewan. Can. Field-Nat. 61: 105–115.

NERO, R. W. *1963*. Birds of the Lake Athabasca region, Saskatchewan. Saskatchewan Nat. Hist. Soc., Spec. Pub. 5: 1–143.

POTTER, L. B. *1943*. Bird notes from south-western Saskatchewan. Can. Field-Nat. 57: 69–72.

RANDALL, T. E. *1962*. Birds of the Kazan Lake region, Saskatchewan. Blue Jay 20: 60–72.

SCOTTER, G. W. *1961*. Summer observations of birds in northern Saskatchewan, 1960. Blue Jay 19: 70–74.

SOPER, J. D. *1952*. The birds of Prince Albert National Park, Saskatchewan. Can. Wildlife Serv., Wildlife Management Bull., Ser. 2, No. 4: 1–83.

TODD, W. E. C. *1947*. Notes on the birds of Southern Saskatchewan. Annals Carnegie Mus. 30: 383–421.

Yukon Territory

RAND, A. L. *1946*. List of Yukon birds and those of the Canol Road. Nat. Mus. Canada, Bull. 105: 1–76.

BANFIELD, A. W. F. *1953*. Notes on the birds of Kluane Game Sanctuary, Yukon Territory. Can. Field-Nat. 67: 177–179.

DRURY, W. H., JR. *1953*. Birds of the Saint Elias Quadrangle in the southwestern Yukon Territory. Can. Field-Nat. 67: 103–128.

GODFREY, W. E. *1951*. Notes on the birds of Southern Yukon Territory. Nat. Mus. Canada, Bull. 123: 88–115.

IRVING, LAURENCE *1960*. Birds of Anaktuvuk Pass, Kobuk, and Old Crow. United States Nat. Mus., Bull. 217: 1–409.

RAND, A. L. *1950*. H. B. Conover's work in Yukon. Can. Field-Nat. 64: 214–220.

SOPER, J. D. *1954*. Waterfowl and other ornithological investigations in Yukon Territory, Canada, 1950. Can. Wildlife Serv., Wildlife Management Bull., Ser. 2, No. 7: 1–55.

Birds of Some Contiguous Parts of the United States

EATON, E. H. *1910–14*. Birds of New York. 2 vols. New York State Museum, Memoir 12.

FORBUSH, E. H. *1925–29*. Birds of Massachusetts and other New England States, 3 vols. Commonwealth of Massachusetts, Boston.

GABRIELSON, I. N., and F. C. LINCOLN *1959*. The birds of Alaska. Wildlife Management Inst., Washington, D.C. 922 p.

JEWETT, S. G., W. P. TAYLOR, W. T. SHAW, and J. W. ALDRICH *1953*. Birds of Washington State. Univ. Washington Press, Seattle. 768 p.

PALMER, R. S. *1949*. Maine Birds. Bull. Mus. Comp. Zool. Vol. 102: 1–656.

ROBERTS, R. S. *1932*. The birds of Minnesota. 2 vols. Univ. Minnesota Press, Minneapolis.

SAUNDERS, A. A. *1921*. A distributional list of the birds of Montana. Pacific Coast Avifauna 14: 1–194.

TODD, W. E. C. *1940*. Birds of western Pennsylvania. Univ. Pittsburgh Press, Pittsburgh. 710 + p.

WOOD, NORMAN A. *1951*. The birds of Michigan. Misc. Pub., Mus. Zool., Univ. Michigan, No. 75: 1–559 (Much additional information was published later by Zimmerman and Van Tyne 1959, Occas. Pap. Mus. Zool., Univ. Michigan, No. 608: 1–63).

General Biology of Birds

MARSHALL, A. J. (*ed.*) *1960–61*. Biology and comparative physiology of birds. Academic Press, New York and London. Vol. 1: 479 p.; Vol. 2: 408 p.

PETTINGILL, OLIN S., JR. *1956*. A laboratory and field manual of ornithology. Third Edition. Burgess Publishing Co., Minneapolis. 379 p.

VAN TYNE, JOSSELYN, and A. J. BERGER *1959*. Fundamentals of ornithology. John Wiley and Sons, Inc., New York. 624 p.

WALLACE, GEORGE J. *1955*. An introduction to ornithology. Macmillan Co., New York. 443 p.

WELTY, JOEL C. *1962*. The life of birds. W. B. Saunders Co., Philadelphia and London. 546 p.

WOLFSON, ALBERT (*ed.*) *1955*. Recent studies in avian biology. Univ. Illinois Press, Urbana. 479 p.

Field Guides

PETERSON, ROGER T. *1947*. A field guide to the birds. Houghton Mifflin Co., Boston. 290 p. (North America east of the Rockies).

———— *1961*. A field guide to western birds. Houghton Mifflin Co., Boston. 366 p. (North America west of the 100th Meridian; also Hawaiian Islands).

POUGH, RICHARD H. *1951*. Aububon water bird guide. Water, game, and large land birds. Doubleday and Co., Garden City, N.Y. 352 p. (eastern and central North America).

———— *1953*. Audubon bird guide. Small land birds. Doubleday and Co., Garden City, N.Y. 312 p. (eastern and central North America).

Field Study of Birds

HICKEY, JOSEPH J. *1943*. A guide to bird watching. Oxford Univ. Press, London, New York, Toronto. 262 p. (Reprinted by Garden City Books, New York, in 1953). Contains much general information and suggests many projects for the amateur.

PETTINGILL, OLIN S., JR. *1956*. (*See* General Biology of Birds).

Bird Sounds

RECORDINGS

GUNN, W. W. H. Sounds of nature series: (1) Songs of Spring.

413

(2) A Day in Algonquin Park. (3) Birds of the Forest. (4) Warblers. (6) Finches. (7) Prairie Spring. (8) Thrushes, Wrens, and Mocking birds; and other albums of recordings. Federation of Ontario Naturalists, Don Mills, Ontario.

CORNELL UNIVERSITY LABORATORY OF ORNITHOLOGY. A field guide to bird songs; a field guide to western bird songs, and other albums of recordings. Houghton Mifflin. (Includes songs of many Canadian species.)

BOOKS

SAUNDERS, A. A. *1935*. A guide to bird songs. D. Appleton-Century Co., New York and London. 285 p.

Life Histories

BENT, A. C. *1919–58*. Life histories of North American birds. United States Nat. Mus., Bull. 107, 113, 121, 126, 130, 135, 142, 146, 162, 167, 170, 174, 176, 179, 191, 195, 196, 197, 203, and 211 (20 vols. to date). This monumental work brings together, from a vast number of scattered sources, information on courtship, nesting, eggs, young, immature plumages and molts, food, general behaviour, enemies, distribution, migration, and egg dates of all North American birds through the tanagers. Only the Fringillidae remain to be done. Although most of the volumes quickly went out of print, good reprints are being made available.

General Reference

PALMER, RALPH S. (*ed.*) *1962*. Handbook of North American birds. Vol. 1, Yale Univ. Press, New Haven and London. 567 p. The first volume is an encyclopedic treatment of the species, loons through flamingos. Other volumes are in preparation and will appear from time to time.

THOMSON, SIR A. LANDSBOROUGH (ed). *1964*. A New Dictionary of Birds. McGraw-Hill Book Company, New York, 928 p.

WITHERBY, H. F. (*ed.*) *1938–41*. The handbook of British birds. Vols. 1–5. H. F. and G. Witherby Ltd., London.

Descriptions and Measurements

RIDGWAY, ROBERT *1901–19*. The birds of North and Middle America. United States Nat. Mus. Bull. 50, Parts 1–8.

———, and HERBERT FRIEDMANN *1941–46*. The birds of North and Middle America. United States Nat. Mus. Bull. 50, Parts 9–10.

FRIEDMANN, HERBERT *1950*. The birds of North and Middle America. United States Nat. Mus. Bull. 50, Part 11.

Classification and Nomenclature

AMERICAN ORNITHOLOGISTS' UNION *1957*. Check-list of North American birds (Fifth Edition). 691 p. (The standard authority on scientific and English names of North American birds).

COMITÉ PERMANENT DES NOMS FRANÇAIS DES OISEAUX DU CANADA. *1962*. Noms des Oiseaux du Canada; Noms Français, Anglais, et Scientifiques. Second Edition. Can. Wildlife Service, Ottawa. 20 p. (The standard authority on French vernacular names of Canadian birds).

MAYR, ERNST *1942*. Systematics and the origin of species. Columbia Univ. Press, New York. 334 p.

———, E. G. LINSLEY, and R. L. USINGER *1953*. Methods and principles of systematic zoology. McGraw-Hill Book Co., New York, Toronto, London. 328 p.

Index

*The page numbers in **boldface type** indicate legend of Plate on which species appear.

421

French